W9-BKA-324

T. Ackman
237 Beam

Calculus and Analytic Geometry

Calculus and Analytic Geometry

Douglas F. Riddle
Utah State University

Wadsworth Publishing Company, Inc., Belmont, California

L. C. Cat. Card No.: 70-91734

Printed in the United States of America

---

4 5 6 7 8 9 10 74 73 72

Preface

In the preparation of this text, I have frequently been faced with direct opposition between what is mathematically proper and what is pedagogically proper. As a mathematician, I feel that we should use proper mathematics, but as a teacher, I feel that to say that one is teaching when no one is learning is like saying that one is selling when no one is buying. This conflict has led me to steer a middle course between the extremes of rigor and nonrigor.

The view that we must use proper mathematics at all costs is, I believe, responsible for the current wave of ultrarigorous texts that begin with an epsilon-delta definition of limits, introduce the mean-value theorem at an early stage, and give proofs of all theorems. The hoped-for results—students who really understand the underlying concepts of calculus—simply have not been attained with this level of sophistication.

Instead of beginning with an epsilon-delta definition of limits (when the student has little hope of understanding it), I begin with the problem of finding the slope of a graph at a given point and let this lead to an intuitive discussion of limits. This approach gives the student immediate results and indicates the importance of limits. Then, in Chapter 10, the student meets rigorous *geometric* definitions of limits and continuity. The epsilon-delta definitions are saved for Chapter 17—when the student is ready for a firm grasp of this central idea of calculus. Thus, the student first encounters these most basic concepts of limits and continuity without having to consider the algebraic manipulations that an epsilon-delta definition necessitates, and I think his insight is enhanced by the three separate exposures in the three different settings. The geometric definitions of limit and continuity are due to Professor R. L. Moore, who has used them successfully with his students for many years.

There are two other ways in which my treatment of limits and continuity differs from that usually found in beginning calculus texts. First, a limit point of the domain of a function is considered in connection with limits—so that the definition of a limit can be carried over directly to advanced calculus with *no* change. Second, independent definitions of limits and continuity allow them to be compared to show why limits are so easy to find when the function is continuous.

Since a proof of the mean-value theorem cannot be considered until limits and continuity are considered, this theorem is treated rather late in the text. This is proper, I think, because it is not an easy theorem to understand, prove, or use. Proofs of earlier theorems requiring the mean-value theorem are omitted in the text proper; however, they are supplied in Appendix B, and an instructor who wants to state the theorem early and prove the theorems based upon it will find it easy to do so. The logarithm is defined as the inverse of the exponential function, rather than in terms of an integral, because I feel the student lacks enough acquaintance with the integral to use it in defining functions.

Finally, curve sketching, especially without the use of the derivative, is considered in more detail than is common for integrated texts. A student who can sketch curves rapidly is well on his way toward setting up integrals. For most integrals, only a very rough sketch (without locating relative maxima, minima, or points of inflection) is needed. When curve sketching is considered only in conjunction with the derivative, the student often feels that he cannot sketch the curve without the time-consuming process of taking derivatives. He attempts to set up the integral by relying upon formulas rather than a sketch—often with disastrous results.

This book includes more analytic geometry than is customary in an integrated text. For those who want to omit or postpone some of it in order to take up differentiation as soon as possible, some of the less important sections of the first three chapters have been starred for that purpose.

The book, in a preliminary form, was thoroughly class tested in courses at Utah State University, and I thank my colleagues and students for their many helpful suggestions. Thanks are also due to Dr. Karl Stromberg of Kansas State University for his valuable criticisms and suggestions. I am grateful, also, to Professor Moore of the University of Texas for permission to use the definitions of limit and continuity on pages 215 and 229, respectively, and the Mathematical Association of America for permission to use the example given on page 349.

Douglas F. Riddle

Suggestions for Using This Text

The following table of prerequisites is given for those who may wish to vary the order of study of the chapters. Parentheses around chapter numbers indicate that the need for those chapters comes only in one or two sections of the chapters for which they are prerequisites. For example, all but the last two sections of Chapter 10 can be taken up without a knowledge of the derivative (Chapter 5). A chapter is listed as a prerequisite only when its material is used directly in the later chapter. In any case, when chapters are taken out of order, some care must be exercised in the selection of problems.

Chapter	*Prerequisite*	*Chapter*	*Prerequisite*
2	1	13	1–6, 11, (9, 12)
3	1, 2	14	1–6, 9, 11–13
4	—	15	4, 5, 8, 11, 12, (7)
5	1–4	16	1–6, 8, 9, 11–15
6	1–5	17	4, (5, 8, 10)
7	1–6	18	5, 11, 12, 17
8	1–5	19	4, 5, 8, 10–12, 15, 17, 18, (6)
9	1–3, (4–6)	20	1–3, 9, 13, (14)
10	4, (5)	21	1–5, 7, 13, 20
11	1–6, 8	22	1–7, 11–15, 20, 21
12	1–8	23	1–6, 8, 11, 12, 14–16, 20, 22

Contents

Appendix

Plane Analytic Geometry

1.1

The Cartesian Plane

Analytic geometry provides a bridge between algebra and geometry that makes it possible for geometric problems to be solved algebraically (or analytically). It also allows us to solve algebraic problems geometrically, but the former is far more important, especially when numbers are assigned to essentially geometric concepts. Consider, for instance, the length of a line segment or the angle between two lines. Even if the lines and points in question are accurately known, the number representing the length of a segment or the angle between two lines can be determined only approximately by measurement. Algebraic methods provide an exact determination of the number.

The association between the algebra and geometry is made by assigning numbers to points. Suppose we look at this assignment of numbers to the points on a line. First of all, we select a pair of points, O and P, on the line. The point O, which we call the origin, is assigned the number zero, and the point P is assigned the number one. Using OP as our unit of length, we assign numbers to all other points on the line in the following way: Q on the P side of the origin is assigned the positive number x if and only if its distance from the origin is x. A point Q on the opposite side of the origin is assigned the negative number $-x$ if and only if its distance from the origin is x. In this way every point on the line is assigned a real number and, for each real number, there corresponds a point on the line.

Thus a *scale* is established on the line, which we now call a *coordinate line*. The number representing a given point is called the *coordinate* of that point, and the point is called the *graph* of the number.

Just as points on a line (a one-dimensional space) are represented by single numbers, so points in a plane (a two-dimensional space) can be represented by pairs of numbers. Later we shall see that points in a three-dimensional space can be represented by triples of numbers.

In order to represent points in a plane by a pair of numbers, we select two intersecting lines and establish a scale on each line using the point of intersection as the origin. These two lines, called the axes, are distinguished by identifying symbols (usually by the letters x and y). For a given point P in the plane, there corresponds a point P_x on the x axis which is the point of intersection of the x axis and the line through P which is parallel to the y axis (if P is on the y axis, this line coincides with the y axis). Similarly, there exists a point P_y on the y axis which is the point of intersection of the y axis and the line through P which is parallel to (or is) the x axis. The coordinates of these two points on the axes are the *coordinates* of P. If a is the coordinate of P_x and b is the coordinate of P_y, then the point P is represented by (a, b). In this example, a is called the *x coordinate*, or *abscissa*, of P and b is the *y coordinate*, or *ordinate*, of P.

In a coordinate plane, the following conventions are normally followed:

(1) the axes are taken to be perpendicular to each other;
(2) the x axis is a horizontal line with the positive coordinates to the right of the origin, and the y axis is a vertical line with the positive coordinates above the origin;
(3) the same scale is used on both axes.

These are, of course, only conventions; they need not be followed when others are more convenient. One of these that we shall violate rather frequently is the third, because we shall sometimes consider figures that would be very difficult to sketch if we insisted upon using the same scale on both axes. In such cases, we shall feel free to use different scales, remembering that we have distorted the figure in the process. Unless a departure from convention is specifically stated or is obvious from the context, we shall always follow the other two conventions.

We can now identify the coordinates of the points in Figure 1.1. Note that all points on the x axis have the y coordinate zero, while those on the y axis have the x coordinate zero. The origin has both coordinates zero, since it is on both axes.

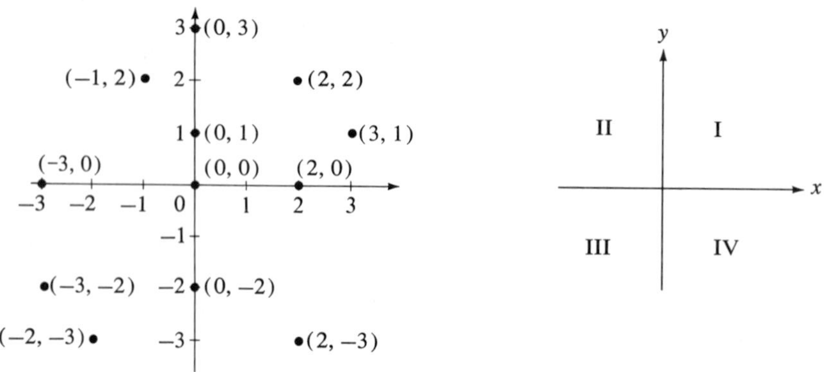

Figure 1.1

Figure 1.2

The axes separate the plane into four regions, called *quadrants*. It is convenient to identify them by the numbers shown in Figure 1.2. The points on the axes are not in any quadrant.

1.2

Distance Formula

Suppose we consider the distance between two points on a coordinate line. Let P_1 and P_2 be two points on a line, and let P_1 and P_2 have coordinates x_1 and x_2, respectively. If P_1 and P_2 are both to the right of the origin, with P_2 farther right than P_1(as in Figure 1.3(a)), then

$$P_1P_2 = OP_2 - OP_1 = x_2 - x_1.$$

Expressing the distance between two points is only slightly more complicated if one or both of the points are to the left of the origin. In Figure 1.3(b),

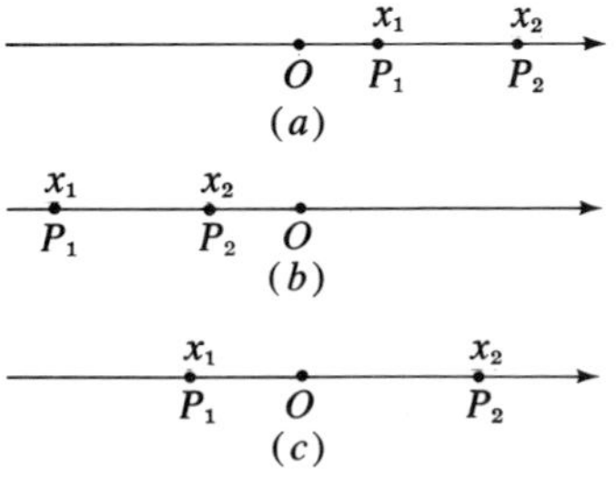

Figure 1.3

$$P_1P_2 = P_1O - P_2O = -x_1 - (-x_2) = x_2 - x_1,$$

and in Figure 1.3(c),

$$P_1P_2 = P_1O + OP_2 = -x_1 + x_2 = x_2 - x_1.$$

Thus, we see that $P_1P_2 = x_2 - x_1$ in all three of these cases in which P_2 is to the right of P_1. If P_2 were to the left of P_1, then

$$P_1P_2 = x_1 - x_2,$$

as you can easily verify. Thus P_1P_2 can always be represented as the larger coordinate minus the smaller. Since $x_2 - x_1$ and $x_1 - x_2$ differ only in that one is the negative of the other and since distance is always non-negative, we see that P_1P_2 is the one of these two that is positive. Thus,

$$P_1P_2 = |x_2 - x_1|.$$

This form is especially convenient when the relative positions of P_1 and P_2 are unknown. However, since absolute values are sometimes rather bothersome, they will be avoided whenever possible.

Let us now turn our attention to the more difficult problem of finding the distance between two points in the plane. Suppose we are interested in the distance between P_1: (x_1, y_1) and P_2: (x_2, y_2) (see Figure 1.4). If a vertical line is drawn through P_1 and a horizontal line through P_2, they intersect at a point Q: (x_1, y_2), and P_1P_2Q forms a right triangle (assuming P_1 and P_2 are not on the same horizontal or vertical

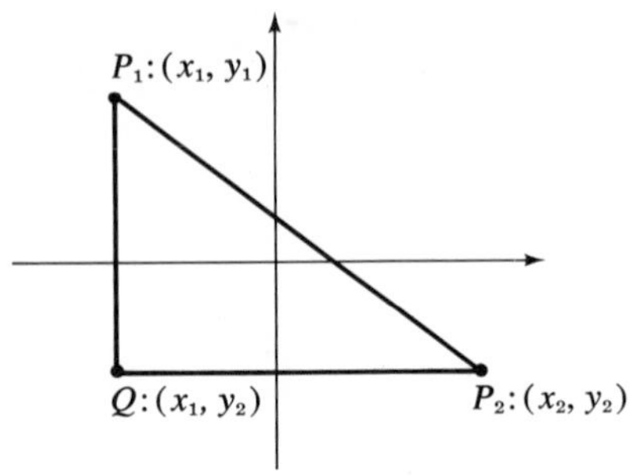

Figure 1.4

line) with the right angle at Q. Now we can use the theorem of Pythagoras to determine the length of P_1P_2. By the previous discussion,

$$QP_2 = |x_2 - x_1| \quad \text{and} \quad P_1Q = |y_2 - y_1|$$

(the absolute values are retained here, since we want the resulting formula to hold for *any* choice of P_1 and P_2, not merely for the one shown in Figure 1.4). Now by the Pythagorean theorem,

$$P_1P_2 = \sqrt{|x_2 - x_1|^2 + |y_2 - y_1|^2}.$$

But, since $|x_2 - x_1|^2 = (x_2 - x_1)^2 = (x_1 - x_2)^2$, the absolute values may be dropped at this stage and we have

$$P_1P_2 = \sqrt{(x_2 - x_1)^2 + (y_2 - y_1)^2}.$$

Thus we have proved the following theorem.

Theorem 1.1

The distance between two points P_1: (x_1, y_1) and P_2: (x_2, y_2) is

$$P_1P_2 = \sqrt{(x_2 - x_1)^2 + (y_2 - y_1)^2}.$$

In deriving this formula, we assumed that P_1 and P_2 are not on the same horizontal or vertical line; however, the above formula would hold even in these cases. For example, if P_1 and P_2 are on the same horizontal line, then $y_1 = y_2$ and $y_2 - y_1 = 0$. Thus,

$$P_1P_2 = \sqrt{(x_2 - x_1)^2} = |x_2 - x_1|.$$

Note that $\sqrt{(x_2 - x_1)^2}$ is *not always* $x_2 - x_1$. Since the symbol $\sqrt{\ }$ indicates the nonnegative square root, we see that if $x_2 - x_1$ is negative, then $\sqrt{(x_2 - x_1)^2}$ is not equal to $x_2 - x_1$ but, rather, equals $|x_2 - x_1|$.

Theorem 1.1 depends upon the convention that the axes are perpendicular. If this convention is not followed, Theorem 1.1 cannot be used. Another, more general formula, based upon the law of cosines can be derived; however, we shall not derive it here, since the convention of using perpendicular axes is so widely observed.

Example 1

Find the distance between P_1: (1, 4) and P_2: (−3, 2).

$$P_1P_2 = \sqrt{(-3-1)^2 + (2-4)^2} = 2\sqrt{5}.$$

Example 2

Determine whether or not A: (1, 7), B: (0, 3), and C: (−2, −5) are collinear.

$$AB = \sqrt{(0-1)^2 + (3-7)^2} = \sqrt{17},$$
$$BC = \sqrt{(-2-0)^2 + (-5-3)^2} = \sqrt{68} = 2\sqrt{17},$$
$$AC = \sqrt{(-2-1)^2 + (-5-7)^2} = \sqrt{153} = 3\sqrt{17}.$$

Since $AC = AB + BC$, the three points must be collinear (if they were not, they would form a triangle and any one side would be less than the sum of the other two).

Problems

In Problems 1–8, find the distance between the given points.

1. (1, −3), (2, 5).
2. (4, 13), (−1, 5).
3. (3, −2), (3, −4).
4. (−5, 1), (0, −10).
5. (1/2, 3/2), (−5/2, 2).
6. (2/3, 1/3), (−4/3, 4/3).
7. $(\sqrt{2}, 1), (2\sqrt{2}, 3)$.
8. $(\sqrt{3}, -\sqrt{2}), (-3\sqrt{3}, \sqrt{2})$.

In Problems 9–12, find the unknown quantity.

9. $P_1 = (1, 5), \quad P_2 = (x, 2), \quad P_1P_2 = 5.$
10. $P_1 = (-3, y), \quad P_2 = (9, 2), \quad P_1P_2 = 13.$
11. $P_1 = (x, x), \quad P_2 = (1, 4), \quad P_1P_2 = \sqrt{5}.$
12. $P_1 = (x, 2x), \quad P_2 = (2x, 1), \quad P_1P_2 = \sqrt{2}.$

In Problems 13–18, determine whether or not the three given points are collinear.

13. (2, 1), (4, 3), (−1, −2).
14. (3, 2), (4, 6), (0, −8).
15. (−2, 3), (7, −2), (2, 5).
16. $(1, \sqrt{2}), (4, 3\sqrt{2}), (10, 6\sqrt{2})$.
17. (−1/2, 2/3), (1/4, 3/5), (7/4, 7/15).
18. (3/4, 1/8), (2/3, 1/2), (1/6, 11/4).

In Problems 19–22, determine whether or not the three given points form a right triangle.

19. (0, 2), (−2, 4), (1, 3).
20. (−1, 3), (4, 6), (−3, 1).
21. $(\sqrt{3}-2, 2\sqrt{3}+1), (\sqrt{3}+2, -\sqrt{3}+1), (2\sqrt{3}-2, 2\sqrt{3}+2)$.
22. $(\sqrt{3}-3, 2\sqrt{3}+1), (\sqrt{3}-1, \sqrt{3}+1), (2\sqrt{3}-1, \sqrt{3}+2)$.
23. Show that (5, 2) is on the perpendicular bisector of the segment AB where $A = (1, 3)$ and $B = (4, -2)$.
24. Show that (−2, 4), (2, 0), (2, 8), and (6, 4) are the vertices of a square.
25. Show that (1, 1), (4, 1), (3, −2), and (0, −2) are the vertices of a parallelogram.
26. Show that (1, 2), (4, 7), (−6, 13), and (−9, 8) are the vertices of a rectangle.

27. Graph the circle with center $(-2, 3)$ and radius 5. For each of the following points, indicate whether it is inside, on, or outside the circle: $(1, 7)$, $(-3, 8)$, $(2, 0)$, $(-5, 7)$, $(0, -1)$, $(-5, -1)$, $(-6, 6)$, $(4, 2)$.
28. Find the center and radius of the circle circumscribed about the triangle with vertices $(5, 1)$, $(6, 0)$, and $(-1, -7)$.

1.3

Point-of-Division Formulas

Suppose we are presented with the problem of finding the point which is some fraction of the way from A to B. Is it possible to express the coordinates of the point we want in terms of the coordinates of A and B? Let A: (x_1, y_1) and B: (x_2, y_2) be given and let P: (x, y) be the point we are seeking. If we let

$$r = \frac{AP}{AB}$$

(see Figure 1.5), then P is 1/3 of the way from A to B when $r = 1/3$, and P is 4/5 of the way from A to B when $r = 4/5$, and so on. Thus we generalize the problem to one in which x and y are to be expressed in terms of x_1, y_1, x_2, y_2, and r. The problem can be simplified considerably by working with the x's and y's separately.

If A, B, and P are projected onto the x axis (see Figure 1.5) to give the points A_x, B_x, and P_x, respectively, we have, from elementary geometry,

$$r = \frac{AP}{AB} = \frac{A_x P_x}{A_x B_x} = \frac{x - x_1}{x_2 - x_1}.$$

Solving for x gives

$$x = x_1 + r(x_2 - x_1).$$

By projecting onto the y axis, we have

$$y = y_1 + r(y_2 - y_1).$$

These two results, known as point-of-division formulas, are stated in the following theorem.

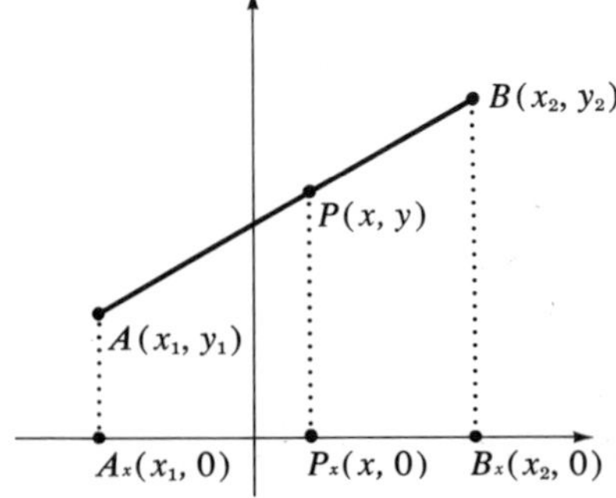

Figure 1.5

Theorem 1.2

If $A = (x_1, y_1)$, $B = (x_2, y_2)$, *and* P *is a point such that* $r = AP/AB$, *then the coordinates of* P *are*

$$x = x_1 + r(x_2 - x_1) \quad \textit{and} \quad y = y_1 + r(y_2 - y_1).$$

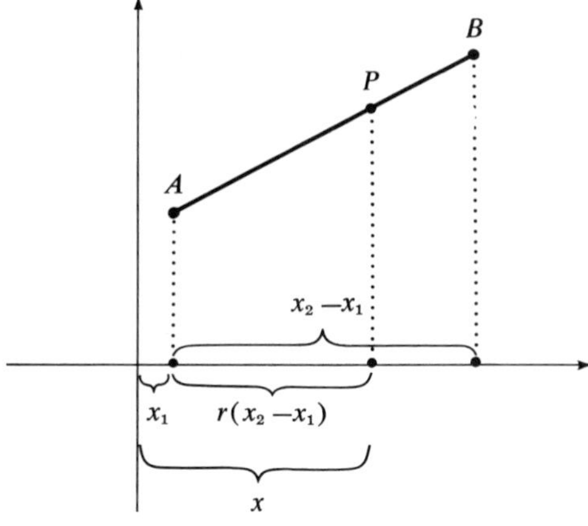

Figure 1.6

Figure 1.6 gives a geometric interpretation of the terms in the point-of-division formula for x. If you examine this figure carefully, it will help you to understand and remember the formulas. Note that if B is to the left of A, $x_2 - x_1$ is negative, but it has the same absolute value as the distance between the projections of A and B on the x axis. You might sketch this and compare your sketch with Figure 1.6. Of course, a similar figure can be used to interpret the y terms of the point-of-division formula.

Example 1

Find the point one-third of the way from A: (2, 5) to B: (8, −1).

$$r = \frac{AP}{AB} = \frac{1}{3}.$$

$$\begin{aligned} x &= x_1 + r(x_2 - x_1) & \qquad y &= y_1 + r(y_2 - y_1) \\ &= 2 + \frac{1}{3}(8 - 2) & &= 5 + \frac{1}{3}(-1 - 5) \\ &= 4; & &= 3. \end{aligned}$$

Thus the desired point is (4, 3).

So far we have tacitly assumed that r is between 0 and 1. If r is either 0 or 1, the point-of-division formulas would give us $P = A$ or $P = B$, respectively, a result that $r = AP/AB$ would lead us to expect. Similarly, if $r > 1$, then $r = AP/AB$ indicates $AP > AB$, which is exactly what the point-of-division formulas give. Thus if we wanted to extend the segment AB beyond B to a point P which is r times as far from A as B is, we could still use the point-of-division formulas.

Example 2

If the segment AB, where $A = (-3, 1)$ and $B = (2, 5)$, is extended beyond B to a point P twice as far from A as B is, find P.

$$r = \frac{AP}{AB} = 2.$$

$$\begin{aligned} x &= x_1 + r(x_2 - x_1) & \qquad y &= y_1 + r(y_2 - y_1) \\ &= -3 + 2[2 - (-3)] & &= 1 + 2(5 - 1) \\ &= 7; & &= 9. \end{aligned}$$

Thus $P = (7, 9)$.

While negative values of r do not make sense in $r = AP/AB$, we find that their use in the point-of-division formulas has the effect of extending the segment AB in the reverse direction—that is, from B through A to P. However, it is just as easy to use a positive value for r with the roles of A and B reversed.

Example 3

If the segment AB, where $A = (-3, 1)$ and $B = (2, 5)$, is extended beyond A to a point P twice as far from B as A is (see Figure 1.7), find P.

Using $r = -\dfrac{AP}{AB} = -1$, we get

$$\begin{aligned} x &= x_1 + r(x_2 - x_1) & \qquad y &= y_1 + r(y_2 - y_1) \\ &= -3 - 1[2 - (-3)] & &= 1 - 1(5 - 1) \\ &= -8; & &= -3. \end{aligned}$$

Thus $P = (-8, -3)$.

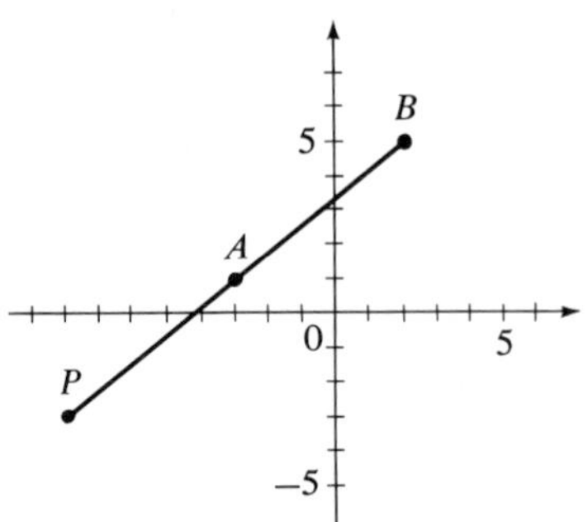

Figure 1.7

Reversing the roles of A and B, we have

$$r = \frac{BP}{BA} = 2, \quad B = (x_1, y_1) = (2, 5), \quad \text{and} \quad A = (x_2, y_2) = (-3, 1).$$

$$\begin{aligned} x &= x_1 + r(x_2 - x_1) & \qquad y &= y_1 + r(y_2 - y_1) \\ &= 2 + 2(-3 - 2) & &= 5 + 2(1 - 5) \\ &= -8; & &= -3; \end{aligned}$$

and $P = (-8, -3)$, as before.

One very important special case of the point-of-division formulas arises when $r = 1/2$, which gives the midpoint of the segment AB. Substituting into the point-of-division formulas, we have the following theorem.

Theorem 1.3

If P is the midpoint of AB, then the coordinates of P are:

$$x = \frac{x_1 + x_2}{2}, \qquad y = \frac{y_1 + y_2}{2}.$$

Thus, to find the midpoint of a segment AB, we merely average both the x and y coordinates of the given points. A moment of thought will reveal the reasonableness of this; the average of two grades is half-way between them, the average of two temperatures is half-way between them, and so forth.

Example 4

Find the midpoint of the segment AB, where $A = (1, 5)$ and $B = (-3, -1)$.

$$x = \frac{x_1 + x_2}{2} = \frac{1 - 3}{2} = -1; \qquad y = \frac{y_1 + y_2}{2} = \frac{5 - 1}{2} = 2.$$

Thus $P = (-1, 2)$.

Problems

In Problems 1–6, find the point P such that $AP/AB = r$.

1. $A = (3, 4)$, $B = (7, 0)$, $r = 1/4$.
2. $A = (4, -2)$, $B = (-2, -5)$, $r = 2/3$.
3. $A = (5, -1)$, $B = (-4, -5)$, $r = 1/5$.
4. $A = (2, 4)$, $B = (-5, 2)$, $r = 2/5$.
5. $A = (-4, 1)$, $B = (3, 8)$, $r = 3$.
6. $A = (-6, 2)$, $B = (4, 4)$, $r = 5/2$.

In Problems 7–10, find the midpoint of the segment AB.

7. $A = (5, -2)$, $B = (-1, 4)$.
8. $A = (-3, 3)$, $B = (1, 5)$.
9. $A = (4, -1)$, $B = (3, 3)$.
10. $A = (-1, 4)$, $B = (0, 2)$.
11. If $A = (3, 5)$, $P = (6, 2)$, and $AP/AB = 1/3$, find B.
12. If $P = (4, 7)$, $B = (2, -1)$, and $AP/AB = 2/5$, find A.
13. If $P = (2, -5)$, $B = (4, -3)$, and $AP/AB = 1/2$, find A.
14. If $A = (3, 3)$, $P = (5, 2)$, and $AP/AB = 3/5$, find B.

In Problems 15–18, find the point P between A and B such that AB is divided in the given ratio.

15. $A = (5, -3)$, $B = (-1, 6)$, $AP : PB = 1 : 2$.
16. $A = (-1, -3)$, $B = (-8, 11)$, $AP : PB = 3 : 4$.
17. $A = (2, -1)$, $B = (4, 5)$, $AP : PB = 2 : 3$.
18. $A = (5, 8)$, $B = (2, -1)$, $AP : PB = 5 : 1$.
19. If $P = (4, -1)$ is the midpoint of the segment AB, where $A = (2, 5)$, find B.
20. Find the point of intersection of the medians of the triangle with vertices $(5, 2)$, $(0, 4)$, and $(-1, -1)$.
21. Find the point of intersection of the diagonals of the parallelogram with vertices $(1, 1)$, $(4, 1)$, $(3, -2)$, and $(0, -2)$.

22. Find the center and radius of the circle circumscribed about the right triangle with vertices (1, 1), (1, 4), and (7, 4).
23. The point (1, 4) is at a distance 5 from the midpoint of the segment joining (3, −2) and $(x, 4)$. Find x.

Problems 24–28 ask you to prove certain theorems analytically. In doing so, remember that a plane does not come fully equipped with coordinate axes–the axes are artificially introduced to make the transition from geometry to algebra. Thus you may place them in *any* position you choose in relation to the given figure. Place them in a way which makes the coordinates of important points as simple as possible. For instance, one convenient placement of coordinate axes for dealing with theorems about triangles is shown in Figure 1.8(a). The placement of axes in Figure 1.8(a) makes the algebra simpler and the proof of a theorem no less general than the placement in Figure 1.8(b).

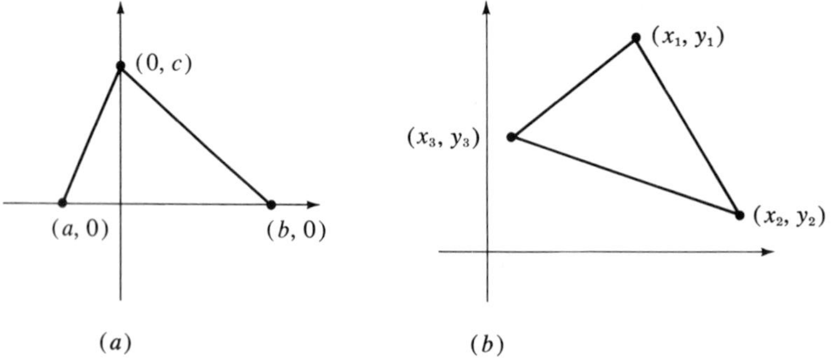

Figure 1.8

24. Prove analytically that the line through the midpoints of two sides of a triangle is parallel to and one-half of the length of the third side.
25. Prove analytically that the diagonals of a parallelogram bisect each other.
26. Prove analytically that the medians of a triangle are concurrent at a point two-thirds of the way from each vertex to the midpoint of the opposite side.
27. Prove analytically that the vertex and the midpoints of the three sides of an isosceles triangle are the vertices of a rhombus.
28. Prove analytically that the sum of the squares of the four sides of a parallelogram is equal to the sum of the squares of the two diagonals.

1.4

Inclination and Slope

An important concept in the description of a line and one that is used quite extensively throughout calculus has to do with the inclination of a line. First let us recall the convention from trigonometry which states that angles measured in the counterclockwise direction are positive, those measured in the clockwise direction are negative. Thus we have the following definition.

Definition

The ***inclination*** *of a line that intersects the x axis is the measure of the smallest non-negative angle which the line makes with the positive end of the x axis. The inclination of a line parallel to the x axis is* 0.

We shall use the symbol θ to represent an inclination. The inclination of a line is always less than 180°, or π radians, and every line has an inclination. Thus, for any line,

$$0^\circ \leq \theta < 180^\circ \quad \text{or} \quad 0 \leq \theta < \pi.$$

Figure 1.9 shows several lines with their inclinations. Note that the angular measure is given in both degrees and radians. Although there is no reason to show preference for one over the other at this time, we shall see when working with calculus that radian measure is the more natural way of representing an angle.

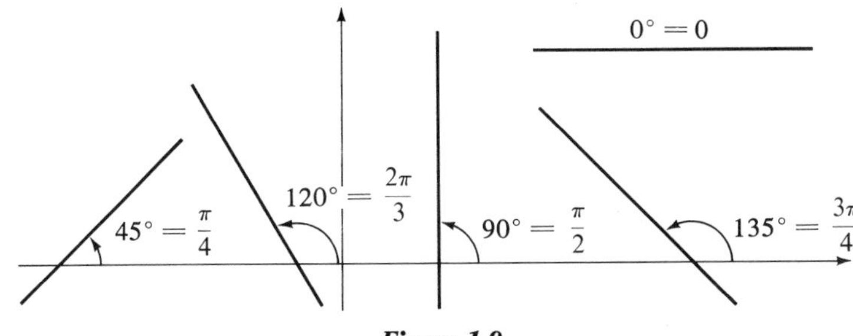

Figure 1.9

While the inclination of a line may seem like a simple representation, we cannot, in general, find a simple relationship between the inclination of a line and the coordinates of points on it without resorting to tables of trigonometric functions. Thus, we consider another expression related to the inclination—namely, the slope of a line.

Definition

The ***slope*** *m of a line is the tangent of the inclination; thus,*

$$m = \tan \theta.$$

While it is possible for two different angles to have the same tangent, it is not possible for lines having two different inclinations to have the same slope. The reason for this is the restriction on the inclination, $0^\circ \leq \theta < 180^\circ$. Nevertheless, one minor problem does arise from the use of slope: not every line has a slope, since not every angle has a tangent; however, the only possible angle of inclination which does not have a tangent is 90°. Thus vertical lines have inclination 90° but no slope. Do not confuse "no slope" with "zero slope." A horizontal line definitely has a slope and that slope is the number 0, but there is no number at all (not even 0) which is the slope of a vertical line. Some might object to this nonexistence of tan 90° by saying that it is "infinity," or "∞." However, infinity is not a number. Also, while the symbol ∞ is quite useful in calculus when dealing with limits, as you will see later, its use in algebra and an algebraic development of trigonometry leads to trouble.

While the nonexistence of the slope of certain lines is somewhat bothersome, it is more than counterbalanced by the simple relationship between the slope and the coordinates of a pair of points on the line. Recall that if θ is as shown in Figure 1.10

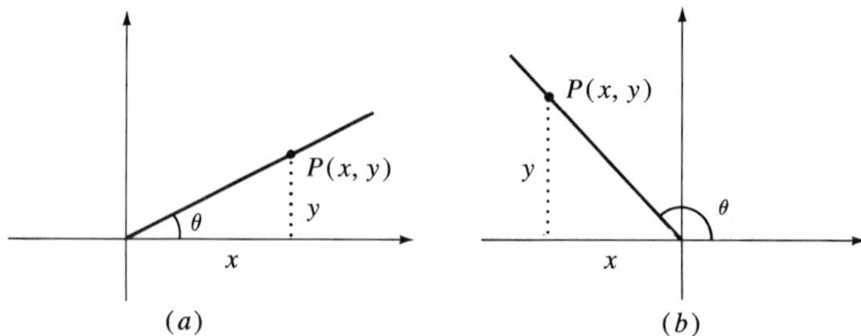

Figure 1.10

(in either of the two positions shown), then

$$\tan \theta = \frac{y}{x}.$$

Unfortunately, the lines with which we are dealing are not always so conveniently placed. Suppose we have a line with a pair of points, $P_1: (x_1, y_1)$ and $P_2: (x_2, y_2)$, on it (see Figure 1.11). If we place a pair of axes parallel to the old axes, with P_1 as the

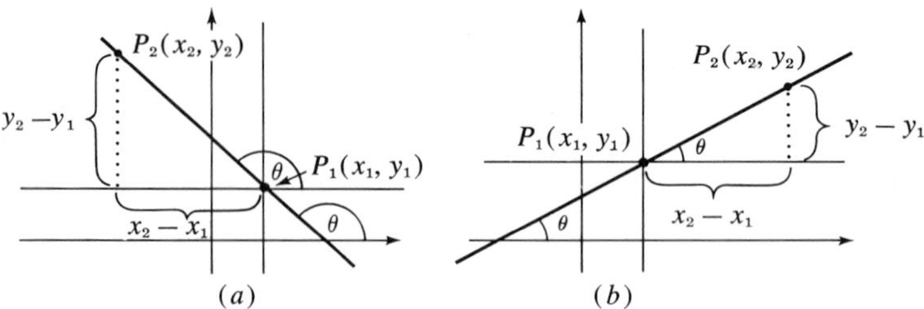

Figure 1.11

new origin, then the coordinates of P_2 with respect to this new coordinate system are $x = x_2 - x_1$ and $y = y_2 - y_1$. Now θ is situated in a position that allows us to use the definition of $\tan \theta$ and state the following theorem.

Theorem 1.4

A line through $P_1: (x_1, y_1)$ and $P_2: (x_2, y_2)$, where $x_1 \neq x_2$, has slope

$$m = \frac{y_2 - y_1}{x_2 - x_1} = \frac{y_1 - y_2}{x_1 - x_2}.$$

Example

Find the slope of the line containing $P_1: (1, 5)$ and $P_2: (7, -7)$.

$$m = \frac{y_2 - y_1}{x_2 - x_1} = \frac{-7 - 5}{7 - 1} = \frac{-12}{6} = -2.$$

Since a vertical line has no slope, Theorem 1.4 does not hold in that case; however, $x_1 = x_2$ for any pair of points on a vertical line, and the right-hand side of the slope formula is also nonexistent. Thus there is no slope when the right-hand side of the slope formula does not exist.

1.5

Parallel and Perpendicular Lines

If two nonvertical lines are parallel, they must have the same inclination and, thus, the same slope (see Figure 1.12). If two parallel lines are vertical, then neither one has slope. Similarly, if $m_1 = m_2$ or if neither line has slope, then the two lines are parallel. Thus, two lines are parallel if and only if $m_1 = m_2$ or neither line has slope.

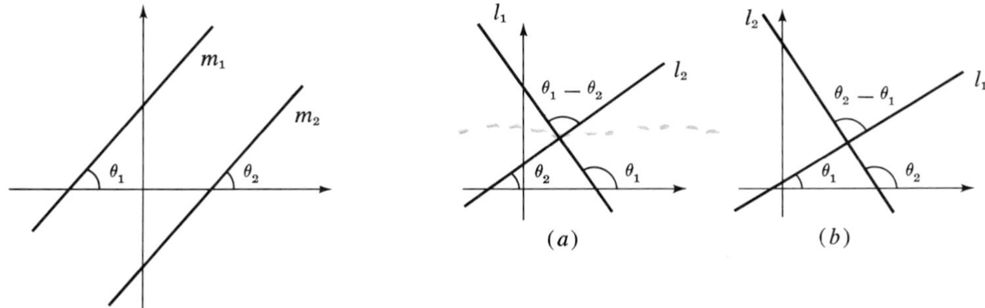

Figure 1.12

Figure 1.13

If lines l_1 and l_2 with inclinations θ_1 and θ_2, respectively, are perpendicular (see Figure 1.13), then

$$\theta_1 - \theta_2 = 90° \quad \text{or} \quad \theta_2 - \theta_1 = 90°,$$

and

$$\theta_1 = \theta_2 + 90° \quad \text{or} \quad \theta_1 = \theta_2 - 90°.$$

In either case (provided neither line is vertical),

$$\tan \theta_1 = -\cot \theta_2 = \frac{-1}{\tan \theta_2}$$

or

$$m_1 = \frac{-1}{m_2}.$$

Given $m_1 = -1/m_2$, the argument can be traced backward to prove that l_1 and l_2 are perpendicular. Thus if $m_1 = -1/m_2$, then l_1 and l_2 are perpendicular; and if l_1 and l_2 are perpendicular, then $m_1 = -1/m_2$ or one of the lines is horizontal and the other vertical.

Problems

In Problems 1–8, find the slope (if any) and the inclination of the line through the given points.

1. (2, 3), (5, 8).
2. (−1, 4), (4, 2).
3. (−2, −2), (4, 2).
4. (3, −5), (1, −1).
5. (−4, 2), (−4, 5).
6. (2, 3), (−4, 3).
7. (a, a), (b, b).
8. (a, a), $(-a, 2a)$.

In Problems 9–16, find the slopes of the lines through the two pairs of points; then determine whether the lines are parallel, coincident, perpendicular, or none of these.

9. (1, −2), (−2, −11); (2, 8), (0,2).
10. (1, 5), (−2, −7); (7, −1), (3, 0).
11. (1, 5), (−1, −1); (0, 3), (2, 7).
12. (1, 3), (−1, −1); (0, 2), (4, −2).
13. (1, 1), (4, −1); (−2, 3), (7, −3).
14. (1, −4), (6, 1); (2, 3), (−1, 6).
15. (1, 2), (3, 2); (4, 1), (4, −2).
16. (1, 5), (1, 1); (−2, 2), (−2, 4).
17. If the line through $(x, 5)$ and (4, 3) is parallel to a line with slope 3, find x.
18. If the line through $(x, 5)$ and (4, 3) is perpendicular to a line with slope 3, find x.
19. If the line through $(x, 1)$ and $(0, y)$ is coincident with the line through (1, 4) and (2, −3), find x and y.
20. If the line through (−2, 4) and $(1, y)$ is perpendicular to one through (−2, 4) and $(x, 2)$, find a relationship between x and y.
21. If the line through $(x, 4)$ and (3, 7) is parallel to one through $(x, -1)$ and (5, 1), find x.
22. Show by means of slopes that (1, 1), (4, 1), (3, −2), and (0, −2) are the vertices of a parallelogram.
23. Show by means of slopes that (−2, 4), (2, 0), (2, 8), and (6, 4) are the vertices of a square.
24. Prove analytically that the diagonals of a square intersect at right angles.
25. Prove analytically that the diagonals of a rhombus intersect at right angles.
26. Prove analytically that one median of an isosceles triangle is an altitude.
27. Prove analytically that the medians of an equilateral triangle are altitudes.

1.6

*Angle from One Line to Another**

If l_1 and l_2 are two intersecting lines, then an angle from l_1 to l_2 is any angle measured from l_1 to l_2. If the measurement is in the counterclockwise direction, then the angle is positive: if it is in the clockwise direction, the angle is negative. While there are many angles from l_1 to l_2, all are related (see Figure 1.14) in that, if α is one of them,

* An asterisk with a section heading signifies that the section may be omitted in classes that wish to move more quickly to the calculus.

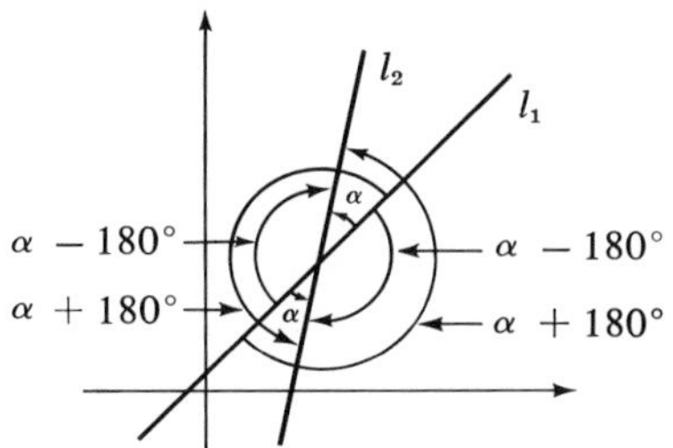

Figure 1.14

all can be expressed in the form

$$\alpha + n \cdot 180°,$$

where n is an integer (positive, negative, or zero). Since any two angles differ from each other by a multiple of 180°, they all have the same tangent.

Theorem 1.5

If l_1 and l_2 are nonperpendicular lines with slopes m_1 and m_2, respectively, and α is any angle from l_1 to l_2, then

$$\tan \alpha = \frac{m_2 - m_1}{1 + m_1 m_2}.$$

Proof

Figure 1.15 shows that

$$\alpha = \theta_2 - \theta_1$$

for one of the angles α from l_1 to l_2. Thus

$$\tan \alpha = \frac{\tan \theta_2 - \tan \theta_1}{1 + \tan \theta_1 \tan \theta_2}.$$

But, since $m_1 = \tan \theta_1$ and $m_2 = \tan \theta_2$, we have

$$\tan \alpha = \frac{m_2 - m_1}{1 + m_1 m_2}.$$

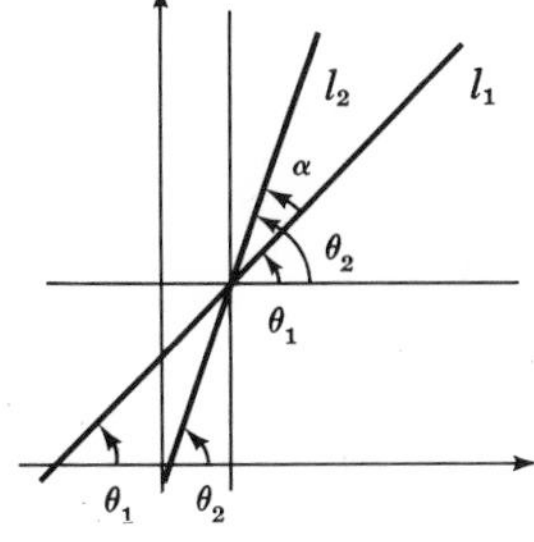

Figure 1.15

We have assumed in this argument that l_1 and l_2 intersect. If they do not, then $m_1 = m_2$. Using $m_1 = m_2$ in Theorem.1.5, we find that $\tan \alpha = 0$ and $\alpha = 0°$. Thus we shall use the convention that $\alpha = 0°$ if l_1 and l_2 are parallel. This is in agreement with the convention that $m = 0$ for horizontal lines.

The trigonometric identity used in this proof is, of course, true only when $\tan \alpha$ and $(m_2 - m_1)/(1 + m_1 m_2)$ both exist. Tan α does not exist if $\alpha = 90°$, but then $m_2 = -1/m_1$ and $1 + m_1 m_2 = 0$, which gives the one case in which $(m_2 - m_1)/(1 + m_1 m_2)$ does not exist. Thus Theorem 1.5 holds for all values of α except $\alpha = 90°$, for which case neither side of the equation exists.

Definition

***The angle** from l_1 to l_2 is the smallest nonnegative angle from l_1 to l_2.*

Example 1

If l_1 and l_2 have slopes $m_1 = 3$ and $m_2 = -2$, respectively, find the angle from l_1 to l_2.

$$\tan \alpha = \frac{m_2 - m_1}{1 + m_1 m_2} = \frac{-2 - 3}{1 + 3(-2)} = 1.$$

Thus, from trigonometric tables, $\alpha = 45°$.

Example 2

Find the slope of the line bisecting the angle from l_1, with slope 7, to l_2, with slope 1.

Let m be the slope of the desired line. Since $\alpha_1 = \alpha_2$ (see Figure 1.16), we have

$$\tan \alpha_1 = \tan \alpha_2$$

and

$$\frac{m - m_1}{1 + m_1 m} = \frac{m_2 - m}{1 + m_2 m},$$

$$\frac{m - 7}{1 + 7m} = \frac{1 - m}{1 + m},$$

$$(m - 7)(1 + m) = (1 + 7m)(1 - m),$$

$$8m^2 - 12m - 8 = 0;$$

$$m = -1/2 \quad \text{or} \quad m = 2.$$

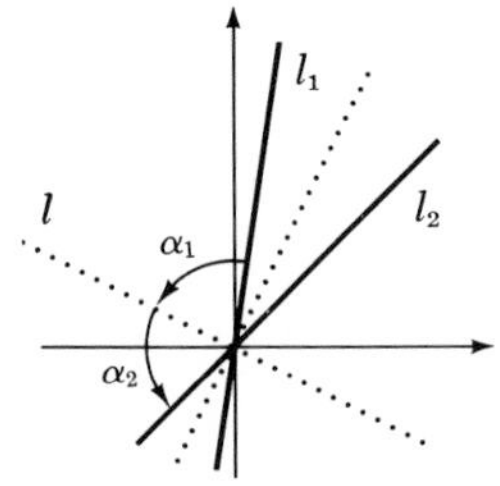

Figure 1.16

We have two answers, but obviously we want only one. Which one? Since one of them is the negative reciprocal of the other, they represent slopes of perpendicular lines, one of which is the bisector of the angle from l_1 to l_2, while the other bisects the angle from l_2 to l_1. An inspection of Figure 1.16 shows that the answer we want is $m = -1/2$.

Problems

In Problems 1–6, find the angle from l_1 to l_2 with slopes m_1 and m_2, respectively.

1. $m_1 = -2$, $m_2 = 3$.
2. $m_1 = 1$, $m_2 = 4$.
3. $m_1 = -3$, $m_2 = 2$.
4. $m_1 = 5$, $m_2 = -1$.
5. $m_1 = 10$, m_2 does not exist.
6. $m_1 = 0$, $m_2 = -1$.

In Problems 7–12, find the angle from l_1 to l_2, where l_1 and l_2 contain the points indicated.

7. l_1: (1, 4), (3, −1); l_2: (3, 2), (5, −1).
8. l_1: (2, 5), (−3, 10); l_2: (−1, −3), (3, 3).
9. l_1: (4, 5), (1, 1); l_2: (3, −3), (0, 4).
10. l_1: (1, 1), (0, 5); l_2: (4, 3), (−1, 2).
11. l_1: (2, 5), (4, 5); l_2: (1, 4), (3, −1).
12. l_1: (3, 4), (3, −1); l_2: (1, 5), (3, 5).

In Problems 13–18, find the slope of the line bisecting the angle from l_1 to l_2 with slope m_1 and m_2, respectively.

13. $m_1 = 3$, $m_2 = -2$.
14. $m_1 = 1$, $m_2 = -7$.
15. $m_1 = 2$, $m_2 = 3$.
16. $m_1 = -1$, $m_2 = 2$.
17. $m_1 = 10$, $m_2 = 13$.
18. $m_1 = 2$, $m_2 = 0$.

19. Find the interior angles of the triangle with vertices $A: (1, 5)$, $B: (3, -1)$, and $C: (-1, -1)$.
20. Find the interior angles of the triangle with vertices $A: (3, 2)$, $B: (4, 5)$, and $C: (-1, -1)$.
21. Find the slope of the line l_1 such that the angle from l_1 to l_2 is Arctan 2/3, where l_2 contains (2, 1) and (−4, −5).
22. Find the slope of the line l_1 such that the angle from l_1 to l_2 is 45°, where the slope of l_2 is −2.
23. Show by means of angles that $A: (1, 0)$, $B: (4, 4)$, and $C: (8, 1)$ are the vertices of an isosceles triangle.

1.7

Graphs and Points of Intersection

The graph of an equation in two variables x and y is simply the set of all points (x, y) in the plane whose coordinates satisfy the given equation. The determination of the graph of an equation is one of the principal problems of analytic geometry. Although we shall consider other methods in Chapter 6, we consider only point-by-point plotting here. To do this, we assign a value to either x or y, substitute the assigned value into the given equation, and solve for the other.

Example 1

Graph $x^2 + y^2 = 25$.

x	y
0	± 5
± 1	$\pm 2\sqrt{6}$
± 2	$\pm \sqrt{21}$
± 3	± 4
± 4	± 3
± 5	0

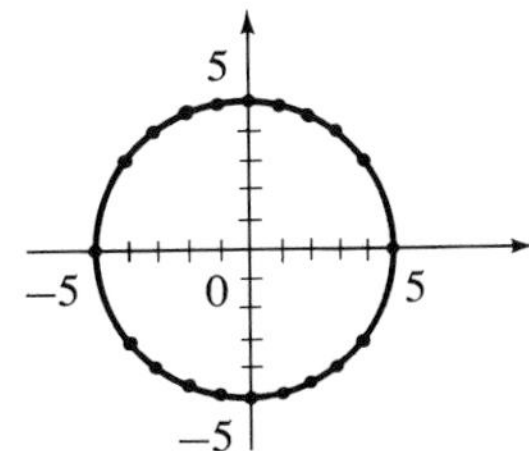

Figure 1.17

Example 2

Graph $y = |x| = \begin{cases} x, & \text{if } x \geq 0, \\ -x, & \text{if } x < 0. \end{cases}$

x	y
0	0
± 1	1
± 2	2
± 3	3
± 4	4

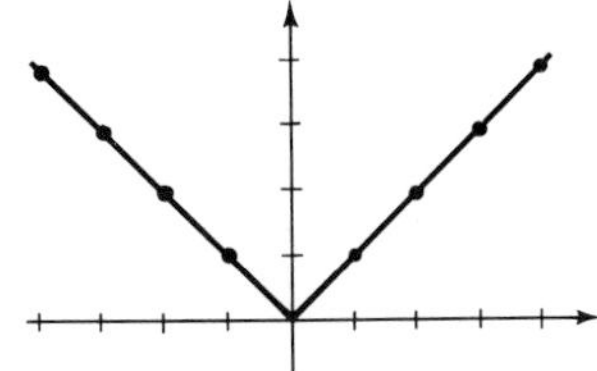

Figure 1.18

One obvious question that arises is, How many points must one plot before drawing the graph? There is no specific answer—just plot as many as are needed for a reasonable idea of what the graph looks like.

Since each point of a graph satisfies the given equation, a point of intersection of two graphs is simply a point that satisfies both equations. Thus, any such point can be found by solving the two equations simultaneously.

Example 3

Find all points of intersection of $x^2 + y^2 = 25$ and $x + y = 2$.

Solving the second equation for y and substituting into the first, we have

$$x^2 + (2 - x)^2 = 25,$$

$$2x^2 - 4x - 21 = 0,$$

$$x = \frac{4 \pm \sqrt{16 + 168}}{4} = \frac{2 \pm \sqrt{46}}{2} = 1 \pm \frac{1}{2}\sqrt{46},$$

$$y = 2 - x = 1 \mp \frac{1}{2}\sqrt{46}.$$

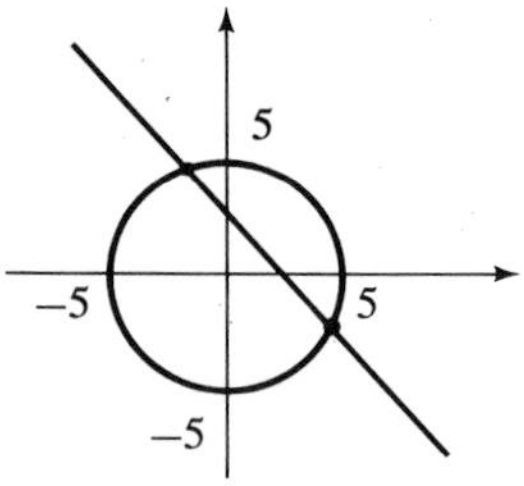

Figure 1.19

Thus, the two points of intersection are

$$\left(1 + \frac{1}{2}\sqrt{46}, 1 - \frac{1}{2}\sqrt{46}\right) \quad \text{and} \quad \left(1 - \frac{1}{2}\sqrt{46}, 1 + \frac{1}{2}\sqrt{46}\right).$$

Another interesting graph is represented by the equation $y = [x]$, where $[x]$ denotes the largest integer less than or equal to x. For instance, $[1] = 1$, $[3/2] = 1$, $[7/4] = 1$, $[-1/2] = -1$, and so on. The graph of $y = [x]$ is given in Figure 1.20. Note that each

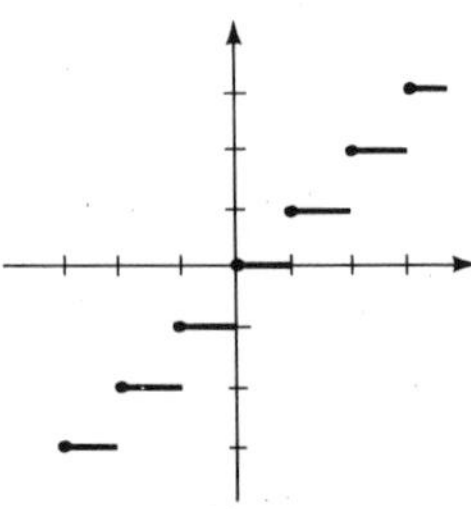

Figure 1.20

horizontal segment includes the left-hand end point but not the right-hand one. The relation between the weight of a letter and the amount of postage required is similar to this one.

Problems

Plot the graphs of the equations in Problems 1–28.

1. $3x - 5y = 2$.
2. $y = 4x - 5$.
3. $y = 2x + 1$.
4. $x - y = 2$.
5. $x^2 + y^2 = 1$.
6. $x^2 - y^2 = 1$.
7. $x^2 - y^2 = -1$.
8. $x^2 + y^2 = 0$.

9. $4x^2 + y^2 = 4.$
10. $4x^2 - y^2 = 4.$
11. $4x^2 - y^2 = -4.$
12. $x^3 = y^2.$
13. $y = |x| + 2.$
14. $y = |x + 2|.$
15. $y = |x| - 1.$
16. $y = |x - 1|.$
17. $|x| + |y| = 1.$
18. $|x + y| = 1.$
19. $y = [-x].$
20. $y = [x + 1].$
21. $y = [|x|].$
22. $y = |[x]|.$
23. $y = x + [x].$
24. $y = x - [x].$
25. $y = \sqrt{x}.$
26. $\sqrt{x} + \sqrt{y} = 1.$
27. $y = \dfrac{x}{x+1}.$
28. $y = \dfrac{x+1}{x}.$

In Problems 29–38, find the points of intersection and sketch the graphs of the equations.

29. $3x - 5y = 2$
    $4x + 2y = 1.$
30. $4x + y = 3$
    $x - y = 1.$
31. $x + y = 2$
    $x^2 + y^2 = 1.$
32. $x + y = 2$
    $x^2 + y^2 = 2.$
33. $2x + y = 2$
    $x^2 - y^2 = 1.$
34. $y = x^2 + 1$
    $x + y = 1.$
35. $x^2 + y^2 = 4$
    $(x - 2)^2 + y^2 = 4.$
36. $y = \sqrt{4 - (x - 2)^2}$
    $x = \sqrt{4 - y^2}.$
37. $x^2 - y^2 = 1$
    $x^2 + y^2 = 7.$
38. $x^2 - y^2 = 3$
    $4y^2 - x^2 = 9.$
39. Graph $y = x$, $y = -x$, $y = |x|$, $y = \sqrt{x^2}$. Compare.
40. Graph $y = x$, $y = x^3$, $y = x^5$, using the same axes.
41. Graph $y = x^2$, $y = x^4$, $y = x^6$, using the same axes.
42. Sketch the "postage stamp graph," giving the amount of postage in terms of the weight. What is its equation?
43. Sketch $y = \{x\}$, where $\{x\} = \min(x - [x], 1 - x + [x])$. Interpret the values of y geometrically. *Note*: $\min(x - [x], 1 - x + [x])$ means the smaller of the two numbers $x - [x]$ and $1 - x + [x]$.

The Line

2.1

Point-Slope and Two-Point Forms

The last section of Chapter 1 dealt with one of the two principal problems of analytic geometry, namely, sketching the graph of an equation. Now we shall begin considering the reverse problem—that is, given the description of a curve, find its equation. We shall restrict ourselves to lines at first.

The two simplest ways of determining a line are by a pair of points and by one point and the slope. Thus, if a line is described in either of these ways, we should be able to give an equation for it. We begin with a line described by its slope and a point on it.

Theorem 2.1

(Point-slope form of a line.) A line that has slope m and contains the point (x_1, y_1) *has equation*

$$y - y_1 = m(x - x_1).$$

Proof

Let (x, y) be any point different from (x_1, y_1) on the given line (see Figure 2.1). Since the line has slope, it is not vertical. Thus $x \neq x_1$, which gives

$$m = \frac{y - y_1}{x - x_1}$$

and

$$y - y_1 = m(x - x_1).$$

Although the formula was derived only for points on the line different from the given point (x_1, y_1), it is easily seen that (x_1, y_1) also satisfies the equation. Thus, every point on the line satisfies the equation. Suppose now that the point (x_2, y_2) satisfies the equation—that is,

$$y_2 - y_1 = m(x_2 - x_1).$$

If $x_2 = x_1$, then $y_2 - y_1 = 0$, or $y_2 = y_1$. In this case, $(x_2, y_2) = (x_1, y_1)$, which is on the line. If $x_2 \neq x_1$, then

$$\frac{y_2 - y_1}{x_2 - x_1} = m.$$

Thus, the slope of the line joining (x_1, y_1) and (x_2, y_2) is m, and this line has the point (x_1, y_1) in common with the given line. Thus, (x_2, y_2) is on the given line.

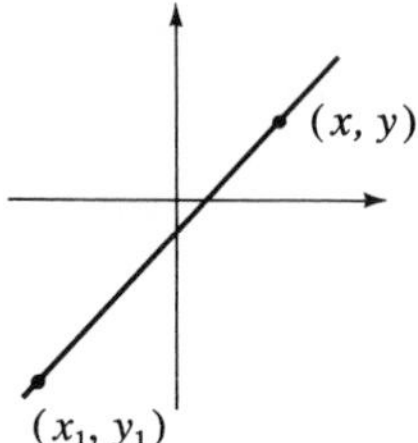

Figure 2.1

Example 1

Find an equation of the line through $(3, -2)$ with slope 4.

$$y - y_1 = m(x - x_1),$$
$$y - (-2) = 4(x - 3),$$
$$4x - y - 14 = 0.$$

Of course vertical lines cannot be represented by the point-slope form, since they have no slope. Again, remember that "no slope" does not mean "zero slope." A horizontal line has $m = 0$, and it can be represented by the point-slope form, which gives $y - y_1 = 0$. There is no x in the resulting equation! But the points on a horizontal line satisfy the condition that they all have the same y coordinate, no matter what the x coordinate is. Similarly, the points on a vertical line satisfy the condition that all have the same x coordinate. Thus, if (x_1, y_1) is one point on a vertical line, then $x = x_1$, or $x - x_1 = 0$ for every point (x, y) on it.

Example 2

Find an equation of the vertical line through $(5, -2)$.

Since the x coordinate of the given point is 5, all points on the line have x coordinates 5. Thus,

$$x = 5 \quad \text{or} \quad x - 5 = 0.$$

Theorem 2.2

(Two-point form of a line.) A line through (x_1, y_1) and (x_2, y_2), $x_1 \neq x_2$, has equation

$$y - y_1 = \frac{y_2 - y_1}{x_2 - x_1}(x - x_1).$$

It might be noted that this result is often stated in the form

$$\frac{y - y_1}{x - x_1} = \frac{y_2 - y_1}{x_2 - x_1}.$$

While the symmetry of this form is appealing, the form has one serious defect—the point (x_1, y_1) is on the desired line, but it does not satisfy this equation. It does satisfy the equation of Theorem 2.2.

The proof of Theorem 2.2 follows directly from Theorem 2.1, and the fact that $m = (y_2 - y_1)/(x_2 - x_1)$, provided $x_1 \neq x_2$. Actually this follows so easily from Theorem 2.1 that you may prefer to use the earlier theorem after finding the slope from the two given points. Of course, the designation of the two points as "point 1" and "point 2" is quite arbitrary.

Example 3

Find an equation of the line through (4, 1) and (−2, 3).

$$y - y_1 = \frac{y_2 - y_1}{x_2 - x_1}(x - x_1),$$

$$y - 1 = \frac{3 - 1}{-2 - 4}(x - 4),$$

$$x + 3y - 7 = 0.$$

Problems

In Problems 1–16, find an equation of the line indicated and sketch the graph.

1. Through $(2, -4)$; $m = -2$.
2. Through $(5, 3)$; $m = 4$.
3. Through $(2, 2)$; $m = 1$.
4. Through $(-4, 6)$; $m = 5$.
5. Through $(0, 0)$; $m = 1$.
6. Through $(0, 3)$; $m = 2$.
7. Through $(4, -2)$; $m = 0$.
8. Through $(2, 5)$; no slope.
9. Through (1, 4) and (3, 5).
10. Through (2, −1) and (4, 4).
11. Through (3, 3) and (1, 1).
12. Through (2, 1) and (−3, 3).
13. Through (0, 0) and (1, 5).
14. Through (0, 1) and (−2, 0).
15. Through (2, 3) and (5, 3).
16. Through (5, 1) and (5, 3).
17. Find equations of the three sides of the triangle with vertices (1, 4), (3, 0), and (−1, −2).
18. Find equations of the medians of the triangle of Problem 17.
19. Find equations of the altitudes of the triangle of Problem 17.
20. Find the vertices of the triangle with sides $x - 5y + 8 = 0$, $4x - y - 6 = 0$, and $3x + 4y + 5 = 0$.
21. Find equations of the medians of the triangle of Problem 20.
22. Find equations of the altitudes of the triangle of Problem 20.
23. Find an equation of the chord of the circle $x^2 + y^2 = 25$ which joins (−3, 4) and (5, 0). Sketch the circle and its chord.
24. Find an equation of the chord of the parabola $y = x^2$ which joins (−1, 1) and (2, 4). Sketch the curve and its chord.
25. Find an equation of the perpendicular bisector of the segment joining (4, 2) and (−2, 6).
26. Find an equation of the line through the points of intersection of the circles
$$x^2 + y^2 + 2x - 19 = 0 \quad \text{and} \quad x^2 + y^2 - 10x - 12y + 41 = 0.$$
Look over your work. Is there any easier way?
27. Repeat Problem 26 for the circles
$$x^2 + y^2 + 4x + 2y + 3 = 0 \quad \text{and} \quad x^2 + y^2 - 6x - 8y + 21 = 0.$$
What is wrong?
28. Find an equation of the line through the centers of the two circles of Problem 26.
29. What condition must the coordinates of a point satisfy in order that it be equidistant from (2, 5) and (4, −1)?

30. Find the center and radius of the circle through the points (1, 3), (4, −6), and (−3, 1).
31. Consider the triangle with vertices $A:(3, 1)$, $B:(0, 5)$ and $C:(7, 4)$. Find equations of the altitude and the median from A. What do your results tell us about the triangle?
32. The pressure within a partially evacuated container is being measured by means of an open end manometer. This gives the difference between the pressure in the container and atmospheric pressure. It is known that a difference of 0 mm of mercury corresponds to a pressure of 1 atmosphere and that if the pressure in the container were reduced to 0 atmospheres, a difference of 760 mm of mercury would be observed. Assuming that the difference D in mm of mercury and the pressure P in atmospheres are related by a linear relation, determine what such a relation is.
33. Knowing that water freezes at 0°C, or 32°F, that it boils at 100°C, or 212°F, and that the relation between the temperature in degrees centigrade C and in degrees fahrenheit F is linear, find that relation.
34. Show that a line through points (x_1, y_1) and (x_2, y_2) can be represented by

$$\begin{vmatrix} x & y & 1 \\ x_1 & y_1 & 1 \\ x_2 & y_2 & 1 \end{vmatrix} = 0.$$

35. Show that the points (x_1, y_1), (x_2, y_2), (x_3, y_3) are collinear if and only if

$$\begin{vmatrix} x_1 & y_1 & 1 \\ x_2 & y_2 & 1 \\ x_3 & y_3 & 1 \end{vmatrix} = 0.$$

36. Show that if no pair of the equations

$$A_1 x + B_1 y + C_1 = 0$$
$$A_2 x + B_2 y + C_2 = 0$$
$$A_3 x + B_3 y + C_3 = 0$$

represent parallel lines, then the lines are concurrent if and only if

$$\begin{vmatrix} A_1 & B_1 & C_1 \\ A_2 & B_2 & C_2 \\ A_3 & B_3 & C_3 \end{vmatrix} = 0.$$

37. A *Nagel line* of a triangle is a line containing a vertex and the point of the triangle which is half-way around the perimeter from that vertex. Prove that the three Nagel lines of a triangle are concurrent.
38. If ABC and $A'B'C'$, are two triangles (see Figure 2.2) such that the points of intersection of AB and $A'B'$, BC and $B'C'$, and CA and $C'A'$ are collinear, prove that the lines AA', BB', and CC' are concurrent.

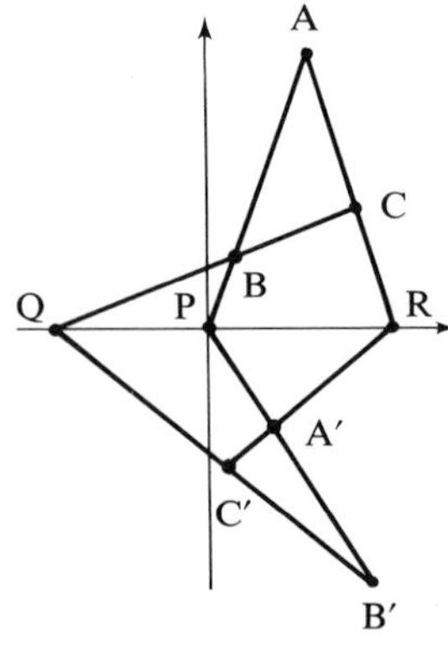

Figure 2.2

2.2

Slope-Intercept and Intercept Forms

The x and y intercepts of a line are the points at which the line crosses the x and y axes, respectively. These points are of the form $(a, 0)$ and $(0, b)$ (see Figure 2.3), but they are usually represented simply by a and b, since the 0's are understood by their position on the axes. We shall continue using the convention that the x and y intercepts of a line are represented by the symbols a and b, respectively. It might be noted that lines parallel to the x axis have no x intercept and those parallel to the y axis have no y intercept. While the x axis has infinitely many points in common with the x axis, we shall adopt the convention that it has no x intercept. Similarly, the y axis has no y intercept. Thus no horizontal line has an x intercept and no vertical line has a y intercept. One other special case is that of a line through the origin which is neither horizontal nor vertical; it has a single point (the origin) which is both its x and y intercept. In this case $a = b = 0$. With these special points defined, we now introduce two more forms of a line.

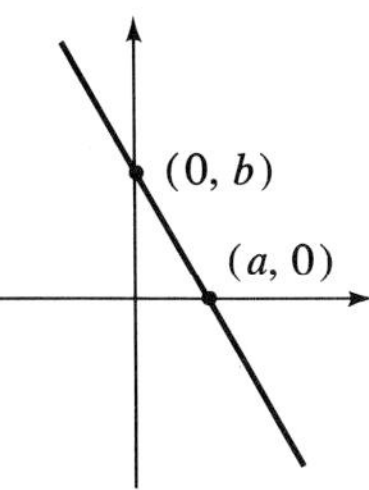

Figure 2.3

Theorem 2.3

(*Slope-intercept form of a line.*) *A line with slope m and y intercept b has equation*

$$y = mx + b.$$

Proof

Since the y intercept is really the point $(0, b)$, the use of the point-slope form gives

$$y - b = m(x - 0) \quad \text{or} \quad y = mx + b.$$

Theorem 2.4

(*Intercept form of a line.*) *A line with nonzero intercepts a and b has equation*

$$\frac{x}{a} + \frac{y}{b} = 1.$$

Proof

Since the intercepts are the points $(a, 0)$ and $(0, b)$, the line has slope

$$m = -\frac{b}{a}.$$

Using the slope intercept form, we have

$$y = -\frac{b}{a}x + b.$$

Dividing through by b gives

$$\frac{y}{b} = \frac{-x}{a} + 1, \quad \text{or} \quad \frac{x}{a} + \frac{y}{b} = 1.$$

It might be noted that these two forms are merely special cases of the point-slope and two-point forms; thus, the earlier forms may be used in place of these at any time. However, these forms, especially the slope-intercept form, are so convenient to use that it is well to remember them. We shall see an example of this shortly.

Example 1

Find an equation of the line with slope 2 and y intercept 5.

$$y = mx + b,$$
$$y = 2x + 5,$$
$$2x - y + 5 = 0.$$

There is no commonly used special form for a line with a given slope and x intercept. Although one can easily be derived, it has not proved as convenient as the slope-intercept form. If you know the slope and the x intercept, simply use the point-slope form, the point being $(a, 0)$.

Example 2

Find an equation of the line with x and y intercepts 5 and -2, respectively.

$$\frac{x}{a} + \frac{y}{b} = 1,$$
$$\frac{x}{5} + \frac{y}{-2} = 1,$$
$$-2x + 5y = -10,$$
$$2x - 5y - 10 = 0.$$

Just as it was true that vertical lines could not be represented by the point-slope form, we see that vertical lines cannot be represented by the slope-intercept form, since vertical lines have neither slope nor y intercept. The intercept form is even more restrictive. Neither horizontal nor vertical lines can be put into the intercept form, since horizontal lines have no x intercept and vertical lines have no y intercept. Furthermore, no line through the origin can be put into the intercept form, since (except for the horizontal or vertical ones) $a = b = 0$, giving 0's in the denominators.

In all of the examples we have considered so far, we used the special forms only as a starting point; the final form was always $Ax + By + C = 0$. The question arises, Can every equation representing a line be put into such a form and does every equation in such a form represent a line?

Theorem 2.5

(General form of a line.) Every line can be represented by an equation of the form

$$Ax + By + C = 0,$$

where A and B are not both zero, and any such equation represents a line.

Proof

Any line we consider is either vertical or can be put into slope-intercept form. Thus any line can be represented by either

$$x = k \quad \text{or} \quad y = mx + b.$$

Thus any line is in the form

$$x - k = 0 \quad \text{or} \quad mx - y + b = 0.$$

Both are special cases of $Ax + By + C = 0$.

Suppose we have an equation of the form $Ax + By + C = 0$, where A and B are not both 0. Let us consider two cases.

Case I: $B = 0$. Then

$$Ax + C = 0 \quad \text{and} \quad x = -\frac{C}{A}$$

(since $B = 0$ and A and B are not both 0, we know that $A \neq 0$ and we may divide by A). This represents an equation of a vertical line.

Case II: $B \neq 0$. Solving $Ax + By + C = 0$ for y, we have

$$y = -\frac{A}{B}x - \frac{C}{B}$$

(since $B \neq 0$, we may divide by B). This represents an equation of a line with slope $-A/B$ and y intercept $-C/B$.

Theorem 2.5 has the following implication for graphing: any equation of the form $Ax + By + C = 0$ represents a line, and its graph can be determined by two of its points. Since the intercepts are so easily found, finding the line through these two points (if there are two) is the quickest way of sketching a line. Of course, vertical or horizontal lines do not have two intercepts, but these are easily sketched. The only problem comes from lines through the origin. The origin is both the x and y intercept; so just find a second point in any convenient way.

Example 3

Sketch the line $2x - 3y - 6 = 0$.

When $y = 0$, $x = 3$, and when $x = 0$, $y = -2$. We did not put the equation into intercept form in order to determine the intercepts, although we might have done so; however, we can find the intercepts by inspection by setting y and x equal to zero in turn and solving for the other. Actually this represents a convenient way of putting the line into intercept form. Since $a = 3$ and $b = -2$, the intercept form of $2x - 3y - 6 = 0$ is

$$\frac{x}{3} + \frac{y}{-2} = 1.$$

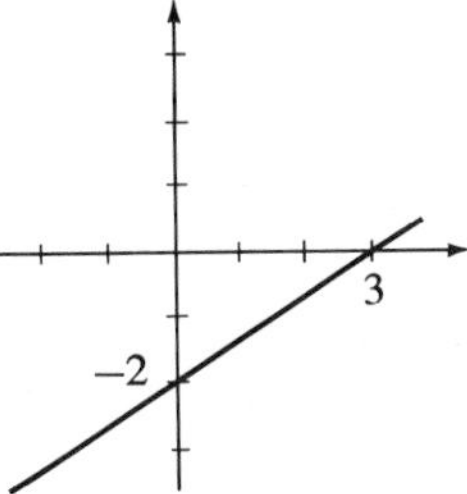

Figure 2.4

The graph of this equation is given in Figure 2.4.

Problems

In Problems 1–18, find an equation of the line described and express it in general form with integer coefficients. Sketch the line.

1. $m = 4$, $b = 2$.
2. $m = -1$, $b = 3$.
3. $m = 5$, $b = 1/2$.
4. $m = 2/3$, $b = -1/3$.

5. $m = 3/4$, $b = 2/3$.
6. $m = -1/6$, $b = -5/4$.
7. $m = 5$, $a = -2$.
8. $m = 6$, $a = 3$.
9. $a = 4$, $b = 2$.
10. $a = -1$, $b = 3$.
11. $a = 2$, $b = 1/2$.
12. $a = 1/2$, $b = 1/2$.
13. $a = 2/3$, $b = -2/5$.
14. $a = -3/4$, $b = 2/3$.
15. $a = b = 0$, through (2, 5).
16. $a = b = 0$, through (−2, −3).
17. $a = 4$, no b.
18. No a, $b = -3$.
19. Find an equation of the line parallel to $2x - 5y + 1 = 0$ and containing the point (2, 3).
20. Find an equation of the line parallel to $4x + y + 2 = 0$ with y intercept 3.
21. Find an equation of the line perpendicular to $x + 2y - 5 = 0$ and containing the point (4, 1).
22. Find an equation of the line perpendicular to $4x - y - 3 = 0$ with x intercept 4.
23. Find the center of the circle circumscribed about the triangle with vertices (1, 3), (4, −2), (−2, 1).
24. Find the center of the circle circumscribed about the triangle with sides $x + y = 2$, $x - y = 0$, $2x - y = 4$.
25. Find the orthocenter (points of concurrency of the altitudes) of the triangle with vertices (1, 4), (7, 3), (2, −3).
26. Prove analytically that the altitudes of a triangle are concurrent.
27. For what value(s) of m does the line $y = mx - 5$ have x intercept 2?
28. For what value(s) of m does the line $y = mx + 2$ contain the point (4, 5)?
29. For what value(s) of a does the line $(x/a) - (y/2) = 1$ have slope 2?
30. For what value(s) of b does the line $(x/3) + (y/b) = 1$ have slope −4?
31. Plot the graph of $x^2 - y^2 = 0$.
32. Plot the graph of $xy = 0$.
33. Plot the graph of $x^2 - 5x + 6 = 0$.
34. Plot the graph of $(x + y - 1)(3x - y + 2) = 0$.
35. The relationship between the vapor pressure p of a liquid and its absolute temperature T is given by the Clausius-Clapeyron equation

$$2.303 \log_{10} P = \frac{-\Delta H}{R} \cdot \frac{1}{T} + C,$$

where ΔH is the molar heat of vaporization of the liquid and R is the ideal gas constant, 1.987 calories degree^{-1} mole^{-1}. Measurements of the vapor pressure of a liquid were made at several temperatures and $\log_{10} P$ as ordinate was plotted against $1/T$ as abscissa. The resulting set of points determined a line with slope −0.0155. What is the molar heat of vaporization of the liquid?

36. The Freundlich equation for adsorption is

$$y = kC^{1/n},$$

where y represents the weight in grams of substance adsorbed, C the concentration in moles/liter of the solute. In logarithmic form, the equation is

$$\log_{10} y = \log_{10} k + \frac{1}{n} \log_{10} C.$$

Freundlich experimented with the adsorption of acetic acid from water solutions by charcoal and plotted $\log_{10} C$ as abscissa against $\log_{10} y$ as ordinate. He found that the points determined a line with slope 0.431 and "$\log_{10} y$" intercept −0.796. What are k and n?

37. Work Problem 34 of the previous section without expanding the determinant. (*Hint:* Use Theorem 2.5.)

2.3

*Distance From a Point to a Line**

Before considering the distance from a point to a line, let us recall some simple facts from the preceding section. $Ax + By + C_1 = 0$ and $Ax + By + C_2 = 0$ must be parallel, since they give

$$y = -\frac{A}{B}x - \frac{C_1}{B} \quad \text{and} \quad y = -\frac{A}{B}x - \frac{C_2}{B}$$

when $B \neq 0$, and they represent two vertical lines when $B = 0$. Moreover, if we are given the line $Ax + By + C = 0$ and the point (x_1, y_1), then the line through (x_1, y_1) and parallel to the given line is

$$Ax + By - (Ax_1 + By_1) = 0.$$

Also, $Ax + By + C_1 = 0$ and $Bx - Ay + C_2 = 0$ are perpendicular, since they give

$$y = -\frac{A}{B}x - \frac{C_1}{B} \quad \text{and} \quad y = \frac{B}{A}x + \frac{C_2}{A}$$

when neither A nor B is 0 and horizontal and vertical lines when either $A = 0$ or $B = 0$.

Theorem 2.6

The distance from the point (x_1, y_1) to the line $Ax + By + C = 0$ is

$$d = \frac{|Ax_1 + By_1 + C|}{\sqrt{A^2 + B^2}}.$$

Proof

Given the line

$$Ax + By + C = 0$$

and the point (x_1, y_1), then

$$Ax + By - (Ax_1 + By_1) = 0$$

is parallel to the given line and contains (x_1, y_1) (see Figure 2.5). Moreover, $Bx - Ay = 0$ is perpendicular to both of them. The distance we seek is the

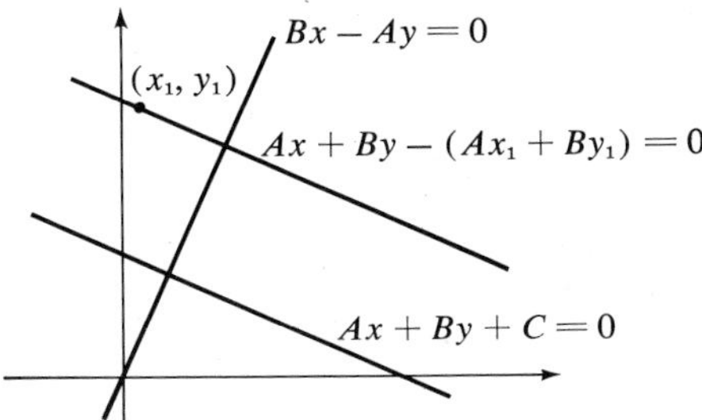

Figure 2.5

distance between the points at which the last equation intersects the preceding two equations. The point of intersection of $Bx - Ay = 0$ and $Ax + By + C = 0$ is

$$\left(\frac{-AC}{A^2+B^2}, \frac{-BC}{A^2+B^2}\right),$$

while the point of intersection of $Bx - Ay = 0$ and $Ax + By - (Ax_1 + By_1) = 0$ is

$$\left(\frac{A(Ax_1+By_1)}{A^2+B^2}, \quad \frac{B(Ax_1+By_1)}{A^2+B^2}\right).$$

Using the distance formula, we have

$$\begin{aligned} d &= \sqrt{\left(\frac{A(Ax_1+By_1)}{A^2+B^2} + \frac{AC}{A^2+B^2}\right)^2 + \left(\frac{B(Ax_1+By_1)}{A^2+B^2} + \frac{BC}{A^2+B^2}\right)^2} \\ &= \sqrt{\frac{(Ax_1+By_1+C)^2}{A^2+B^2}} \\ &= \frac{|Ax_1+By_1+C|}{\sqrt{A^2+B^2}}. \end{aligned}$$

Example 1

Find the distance from the point (1, 4) to the line $3x - 5y + 2 = 0$.

$$\begin{aligned} d &= \frac{|Ax_1+By_1+C|}{\sqrt{A^2+B^2}} \\ &= \frac{|3\cdot 1 - 5\cdot 4 + 2|}{\sqrt{3^2+(-5)^2}} \\ &= \frac{15}{\sqrt{34}}. \end{aligned}$$

The absolute value in the distance formula is sometimes very inconvenient in practice. We could get rid of it if we knew whether $Ax_1 + By_1 + C$ were positive or negative. The following theorem gives us a method of determining this.

Theorem 2.7

If $P(x_1, y_1)$ is a point not on the line $Ax + By + C = 0$ $(B \neq 0)$, then

(a) *B and $Ax_1 + By_1 + C$ agree in sign if P is above the line;*
(b) *B and $Ax_1 + By_1 + C$ have opposite signs if P is below the line.*

Proof

Case I: $B > 0$. Let Q be the point on the given line with abscissa x_1 (see Figure 2.6). If P is above the line, then $y_1 > y$. $By_1 > By$, since $B > 0$. Therefore,

$$Ax_1 + By_1 + C > Ax_1 + By + C.$$

Since (x_1, y) is on the line,

$$Ax_1 + By + C = 0 \quad \text{and} \quad Ax_1 + By_1 + C > 0.$$

If P is below the line, all of the above inequalities are reversed and

$$Ax_1 + By_1 + C < 0.$$

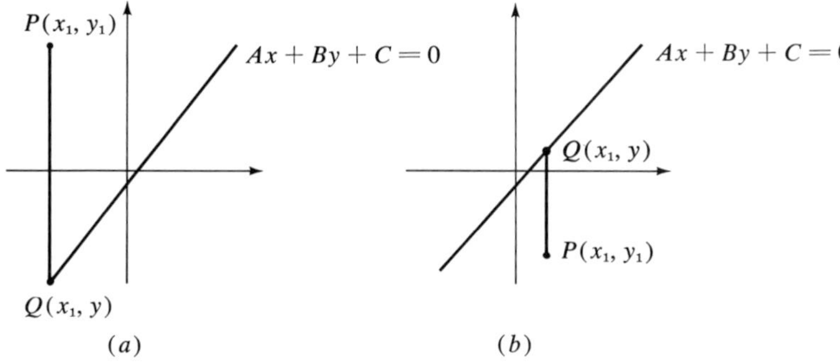

Figure 2.6

Case II: $B < 0$. If P is above the line, then $y_1 > y$. $By_1 < By$, since $B < 0$. Thus,

$$Ax_1 + By_1 + C < Ax_1 + By + C.$$

Again

$$Ax_1 + By + C = 0 \quad \text{and} \quad Ax_1 + By_1 + C < 0.$$

As with Case I, all of these inequalities are reversed if P is below the line, and

$$Ax_1 + By_1 + C > 0.$$

If $B = 0$, the line is vertical and there is no "above" nor "below." Theorem 2.7 does not apply to this case, but the distance from a point to a vertical line is easily found without using Theorem 2.6. Other methods of determining the sign of $Ax_1 + By_1 + C$ are given in Problems 32 and 33.

Example 2

Find an equation of the line bisecting the angle from $3x - 4y - 3 = 0$ to $5x + 12y + 1 = 0$.

If (x, y) is any point on the desired line (see Figure 2.7), then it is equidistant from the two given lines. By Theorem 2.6,

$$\frac{|5x + 12y + 1|}{\sqrt{5^2 + 12^2}} = \frac{|3x - 4y - 3|}{\sqrt{3^2 + (-4)^2}},$$

$$5\,|5x + 12y + 1| = 13\,|3x - 4y - 3|.$$

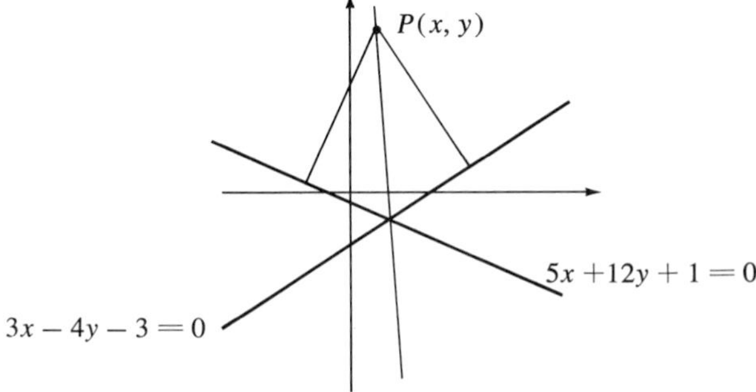

Figure 2.7

Now let us apply Theorem 2.7. Since P is above $5x + 12y + 1 = 0$ and the coefficient of y is positive, $5x + 12y + 1$ is also positive. Similarly, since P is above $3x - 4y - 3 = 0$ and B is negative,

$$3x - 4y - 3 < 0.$$

Thus

$$5(5x + 12y + 1) = -13(3x - 4y - 3) \quad \text{or} \quad 32x + 4y - 17 = 0.$$

Perhaps you object to the designation of P above both lines. Not every point on the bisector is above them. While this is true, the points on the bisector that are not above both are below both. Thus, we still have one expression positive and the other negative, and the result is the same.

It might be noted that we can avoid the use of Theorem 2.7 by considering both cases; that is, $5x + 12y + 1$ and $3x - 4y - 3$ either agree in signs or have opposite signs. We then get two answers, and Figure 2.7 indicates which is correct.

Problems

In Problems 1–10, find the distance from the given point to the given line.

1. $x + y - 5 = 0$, (2, 5).
2. $2x - 4y + 2 = 0$, (1, 3).
3. $4x + 5y - 3 = 0$, (−2, 4).
4. $x - 3y + 5 = 0$, (1, 2).
5. $3x + 4y - 5 = 0$, (1, 1).
6. $5x + 12y + 13 = 0$, (0, 2).
7. $2x - 5y = 3$, (3, −3).
8. $2x + y = 5$, (4, −1).
9. $3x + 4 = 0$, (2, 4).
10. $y = 3$, (1, 5).
11. Find the altitudes of the triangle with vertices (1, 2), (5, 5), (−1, 7).
12. Find the altitudes of the triangle with sides $x + y - 3 = 0$, $x - 2y + 4 = 0$, $2x + 3y = 5$.

In Problems 13–18, find an equation of the line bisecting the angle from the first line to the second.

13. $3x - 4y - 2 = 0$, $4x - 3y + 4 = 0$.
14. $8x + 15y - 5 = 0$, $5x - 12y + 1 = 0$.
15. $24x - 7y + 1 = 0$, $3x + 4y - 5 = 0$.
16. $12x + 35y - 4 = 0$, $15y - 8x + 3 = 0$.
17. $x + y - 2 = 0$, $2x - 3 = 0$.
18. $2x + y + 3 = 0$, $y + 5 = 0$.

In Problems 19–24, find the distance between the given parallel lines.

19. $2x - 5y + 3 = 0$, $2x - 5y + 7 = 0$.
20. $x + 2y - 2 = 0$, $x + 2y + 5 = 0$.
21. $2x + y + 2 = 0$, $4x + 2y - 3 = 0$.
22. $4x - y + 2 = 0$, $12x - 3y + 1 = 0$.
23. $2x - y + 1 = 0$, $2x - y - 7 = 0$.
24. $3x + 2y = 0$, $6x + 4y - 5 = 0$.
25. Find the area of the triangle of Problem 11.
26. Find the area of the triangle of Problem 12.
27. The center of the circle inscribed in a triangle is the incenter of the triangle. The center of a circle which is tangent to one side and the extensions of the other two sides is an excenter of the triangle. Find the incenter and the three excenters of the triangle with vertices (3, 1), (5, 6), (−9/4, 31/10).

28. For what value(s) of m is the line $y = mx + 5$ at a distance 4 from the origin?
29. For what value(s) of m is the line $y = mx + 1$ at a distance 3 from (4, 1)?
30. For what value(s) of a is the line $(x/a) + (y/2) = 1$ at a distance 2 from the point (5, 4)?
31. For what value(s) of b is the line $(x/3) + (y/b) = 1$ at a distance 1 from the origin.
32. Prove that if $P(x_1, y_1)$ is a point not on the line $Ax + By + C = 0$ $(A \neq 0)$, then
    (a) A and $Ax_1 + By_1 + C$ agree in sign if P is to the right of the line;
    (b) A and $Ax_1 + By_1 + C$ have opposite signs if P is to the left of the line.
33. Prove that if $P(x_1, y_1)$ is a point not on the line $Ax + By + C = 0$ $(C \neq 0)$, then
    (a) C and $Ax_1 + By_1 + C$ agree in sign if P and the origin are on the same side of the line;
    (b) C and $Ax_1 + By_1 + C$ have opposite signs if P and the origin are on opposite sides of the line.
34. Find the center of the circle inscribed in the triangle with vertices $(a, 0)$, $(b, 0)$, $(0, c)$.
35. Find the points of tangency of the inscribed circle with the triangle of Problem 34.
36. Consider a line determined by a vertex of a triangle and the point of tangency of the inscribed circle with the opposite side. Prove that the three lines determined in this way are concurrent.
37. Suppose that α is the inclination of a line perpendicular (or normal) to the line l and p is the directed distance of l from the origin, p being positive if l is above the origin and

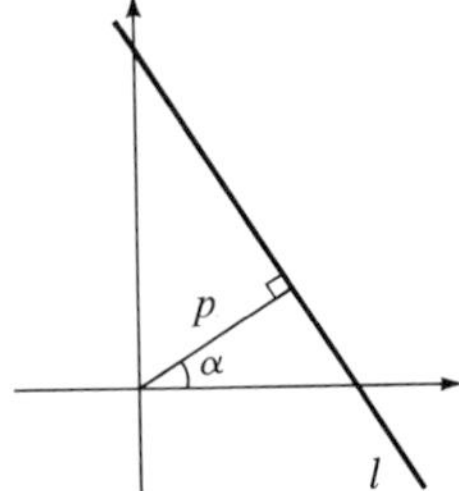

Figure 2.8

negative if l is below. Show that l can be put into the form

$$x \cos \alpha + y \sin \alpha - p = 0.$$

This is called the normal form of the line.

2.4

*Families of Lines**

The equation

$$y = 2x + b$$

is in the form $y = mx + b$, with $m = 2$, and thus it represents a line with slope 2 and y intercept b. But what is b? Clearly we could substitute many different values for b and get equations of many different lines. It is of interest then to consider the following

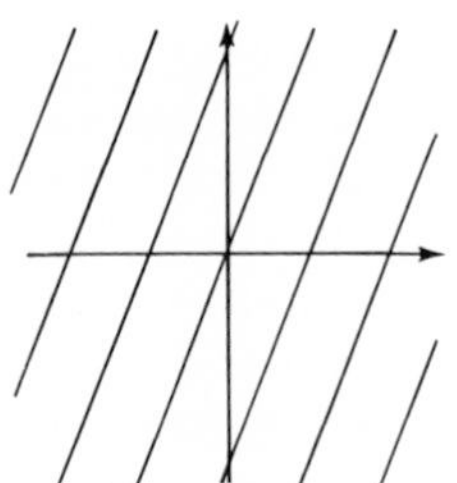

Figure 2.9

set, or family, of equations representing lines:

$$M = \{y = 2x + b \mid b \text{ real}\}.$$

M represents a set of parallel lines all having slope 2; in fact, it represents the set of *all* lines having slope 2 (see Figure 2.9). The b in $y = 2x + b$ is called a parameter. Since the equation has a single parameter, M is called a one-parameter family of lines. Let us consider a few more examples.

Example 1

$\{y - 2 = m(x - 1) \mid m \text{ real}\}$ represents a family of lines through the point (1, 2); however, it does not represent all such lines. The vertical line $x = 1$ (which has no slope) is not a member of this family. The set of *all* lines through the point (1, 2) is $\{y - 2 = m(x - 1) \mid m \text{ real}\} \cup \{x = 1\}$.

Example 2

$\left\{\frac{x}{2} + \frac{y}{b} = 1 \mid b \text{ real}, b \neq 0\right\}$ represents a family of lines, all having x intercept 2 and some y intercept. It represents all such lines. However, it does not represent all lines having x intercept 2, since the line $x = 2$ is not represented, nor does it represent all lines through (2, 0), since $x = 2$ and $y = 0$ are not included.

Example 3

$\{y = mx + b \mid m, b \text{ real}\}$ is a two-parameter family of lines representing all non-vertical lines.

Example 4

$\{x = k \mid k \text{ real}\}$ is the family of all vertical lines.

Example 5

$\{2x + 3y - 6 + k(4x - y + 2) = 0 \mid k \text{ real}\}$ represents a family of lines (no matter what value we choose for k, the resulting equation is linear) all containing the point of intersection of

$$2x + 3y - 6 = 0 \quad \text{and} \quad 4x - y + 2 = 0$$

(because any point satisfying $2x + 3y - 6 = 0$ and $4x - y + 2 = 0$ must satisfy

$$2x + 3y - 6 + k(4x - y + 2) = 0$$

no matter what value of k we choose). Again, it does not represent *all* such lines; the line $4x - y + 2 = 0$ is not a member of this family.

Example 6

$\{Ax + By + C = 0 \mid A, B, C \text{ real}\}$ is a three-parameter family representing all lines in the plane.

Let us now consider the use of families of lines. This concept is most useful in finding the equation of a line which cannot be represented in any of the standard forms that we have seen. Suppose we consider the following example.

Example 7

Find an equation(s) of a line(s) that contains the point (6, 0) and is a distance 5 from the point (1, 3).

$\{y = m(x - 6) \mid m \text{ real}\}$ represents a family of lines all containing the point (6, 0). Note that it does not represent all lines containing the point (6, 0); the only one not represented is the vertical line with equation $x = 6$. Thus, the family of all lines containing (6, 0) is (see Figure 2.10)

$$\{y = m(x - 6) \mid m \text{ real}\} \cup \{x = 6\}.$$

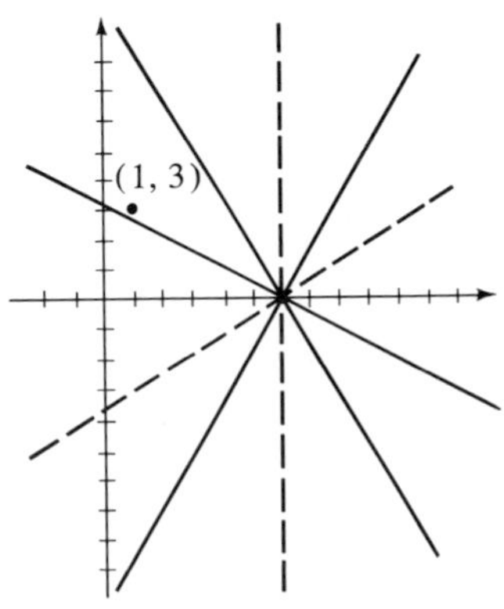

Figure 2.10

Now we must choose those members of the family that are at a distance 5 from (1, 3). We first consider those lines of the form $y = m(x - 6)$, which can be rewritten in the form

$$mx - y - 6m = 0.$$

The distance from this line to the point (1, 3) is

$$\frac{|m - 3 - 6m|}{\sqrt{m^2 + 1}} = 5.$$

Thus,

$$|-3 - 5m| = 5\sqrt{m^2 + 1},$$

$$9 + 30m + 25m^2 = 25m^2 + 25,$$

$$m = \frac{8}{15}.$$

Substituting this value back into the original equation, we get

$$y = \frac{8}{15}(x - 6),$$

$$8x - 15y - 48 = 0.$$

Now we must consider the line $x = 6$, which is a distance 5 from the point (1, 3). Thus, the two lines we want are

$$8x - 15y - 48 = 0 \quad \text{and} \quad x - 6 = 0.$$

Example 8

Find an equation(s) of the line(s) parallel to $3x - 5y + 2 = 0$ and containing the point (3, 8).

$\{3x - 5y = k \mid k \text{ real}\}$ is the family of all lines parallel to $3x - 5y + 2 = 0$ (including the given line). The member of the family which contains (3, 8) satisfies the condition

$$3 \cdot 3 - 5 \cdot 8 = k,$$
$$k = -31.$$

The equation desired is $3x - 5y + 31 = 0$. The above procedure is simple enough to carry out entirely in one's head, and a similar procedure can be used for perpendicular lines.

Example 9

Find an equation(s) of the line(s) perpendicular to $3x - 5y + 2 = 0$ and containing the point (3, 8).

$\{5x + 3y = k \mid k \text{ real}\}$ is the family of all lines perpendicular to $3x - 5y + 2 = 0$. The member that contains (3, 8) satisfies the conditions

$$5 \cdot 3 + 3 \cdot 8 = k,$$
$$k = 39.$$

The desired equation is $5x + 3y - 39 = 0$.

Problems

In Problems 1–14, describe the family of lines given. Indicate whether or not it contains *every* line of that description, and, if not, give all the lines with that description which are not included in the family.

1. $\{y - 4 = m(x + 1) \mid m \text{ real}\}$.
2. $\{y = mx - 5 \mid m \text{ real}\}$.
3. $\left\{\frac{x}{2} + \frac{y}{b} = 1 \mid b \text{ real}, b \neq 0\right\}$.
4. $\{x = ky \mid k \text{ real}\}$.
5. $\{Ax + By = 0 \mid A, B \text{ real}\}$.
6. $\{2x - 3y = k \mid k \text{ real}\}$.
7. $\left\{\frac{x}{a} + \frac{y}{b} = 1 \mid a, b, \text{ real}, a \neq 0, b \neq 0\right\}$.
8. $\{y = mx + b \mid m, b \text{ real}\}$.
9. $\{2x + 3y + 1 + k(4x + 2y - 5) = 0 \mid k \text{ real}\}$.
10. $\{x = k \mid k \text{ real}\}$.
11. $\left\{\frac{x}{a} + \frac{y}{2a} = 1 \mid a \text{ real}, a \neq 0\right\}$.
12. $\left\{\frac{x}{a} + \frac{y}{3 - a} = 1 \mid a \text{ real}, a \neq 0, a \neq 3\right\}$.
13. $\{y = mx + m \mid m \text{ real}\}$.
14. $\{y - a = m(x - a) \mid a, m \text{ real}\}$.

In Problems 15–24, give, in set notation, the family described.

15. All lines parallel to $3x - 5y - 7 = 0$.
16. All lines perpendicular to $3x - 5y - 7 = 0$.
17. All lines containing (2, 5).

18. All lines with x intercept twice the y intercept.
19. All lines containing the point of intersection of $3x - 5y + 1 = 0$ and $2x + 3y - 7 = 0$.
20. All horizontal lines.
21. All lines containing the origin.
22. All lines at a distance 3 from the origin.
23. All lines at a distance 5 from (6, 0).
24. All lines which form with the coordinate axes a triangle of area 4.

In Problems 25–28, find the lines satisfying the given condition that are (a) parallel and (b) perpendicular, respectively, to the given line.

25. Containing (5, 8); $3x - 5y + 1 = 0$.
26. Containing (3, 2); $2x + 3y - 7 = 0$.
27. y intercept 5; $4x + 2y - 5 = 0$.
28. x intercept 2; $3x + y + 2 = 0$.
29. Find an equation(s) of the line(s) with slope 5 at a distance 3 from the origin.
30. Find an equation(s) of the line(s) perpendicular to $3x - 4y + 1 = 0$ and at a distance 4 from (2, 3).
31. Find an equation(s) of the line(s) containing (5, 4) and at a distance 2 from (−1, −3).
32. Find an equation(s) of the line(s) containing (3, −1) and at a distance 4 from (−1, 3).
33. Find an equation(s) of the line(s) containing (7, 1) and at a distance 5 from (2, −5).
34. Find an equation(s) of the line(s) containing (−4, 3) and at a distance 5 from (−2, 2).
35. Find an equation(s) of the line(s) containing the point of intersection of $3x - y - 5 = 0$ and $2x + 2y - 3 = 0$ and having slope 2.
36. Find an equation(s) of the line(s) containing the point of intersection of $4x + 5y - 1 = 0$ and $3x - 2y + 1 = 0$ and the point (1, 1).
37. Find an equation(s) of the line(s) containing (4, −3) such that the sum of the intercepts is 5.
38. Find an equation(s) of the line(s) with slope 3 such that the sum of the intercepts is 12.
39. Find an equation(s) of the line(s) containing (2, 3) and forming with the coordinate axes a triangle of area 16.
40. Prove analytically that the bisector of an exterior angle determined by the two equal sides of an isosceles triangle is parallel to the third side.
41. An isosceles right triangle is circumscribed about the circle with center (2, 2) and radius 2. The coordinate axes are two of the sides. What is the third?
42. An isosceles right triangle is circumscribed about the circle with center (4, 2) and radius 2. The x axis is the hypotenuse. What are the other two sides?
43. An equilateral triangle is circumscribed about the circle with center (4, 2) and radius 2. The x axis is one side. What are the other two?

The Circle

3.1

The Standard Form for an Equation of a Circle

The standard form for an equation of a circle is a direct consequence of the definition and the length formula.

Definition

*A **circle** is the set of all points in a plane at a fixed positive distance (radius) from a fixed point (center).*

Theorem 3.1

A circle with center (h, k) and radius r has equation

$$(x-h)^2+(y-k)^2=r^2.$$

Proof

If (x, y) is any point on the circle, then the distance from the center (h, k) to (x, y) is r (see Figure 3.1):

$$r=\sqrt{(x-h)^2+(y-k)^2}.$$

Squaring, we have

$$(x-h)^2+(y-k)^2=r^2.$$

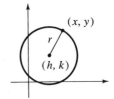

Since the steps above are reversible, we see that every point satisfying the equation of Theorem 3.1 is on the circle described.

Figure 3.1

Example 1

Give an equation for the circle with center $(3, -5)$ and radius 2.

From Theorem 3.1, an equation is

$$(x-3)^2 + [y-(-5)]^2 = 2^2,$$

or

$$(x-3)^2 + (y+5)^2 = 4.$$

Although the above form is a convenient one, in that it shows at a glance the center and radius of the circle, another form is usually used. It is called the general form and is comparable to the general form of a line. Before giving the generalized equation for this form, let us illustrate it with the result of Example 1. Squaring the two binomials and combining similar terms, we have

$$(x-3)^2 + (y+5)^2 = 4,$$
$$x^2 - 6x + 9 + y^2 + 10y + 25 = 4,$$
$$x^2 + y^2 - 6x + 10y + 30 = 0.$$

Normally an equation of a circle will be given in this form. Let us now repeat the above, starting with the standard form of Theorem 3.1.

$$(x-h)^2 + (y-k)^2 = r^2,$$
$$x^2 - 2hx + h^2 + y^2 - 2ky + k^2 = r^2,$$
$$x^2 + y^2 - 2hx - 2ky + (h^2 + k^2 - r^2) = 0,$$

which is in the form

$$x^2 + y^2 + D'x + E'y + F' = 0.$$

Upon multiplication by a nonzero constant, A, we have

$$Ax^2 + Ay^2 + Dx + Ey + F = 0 \quad (A \neq 0),$$

as the following theorem states.

Theorem 3.2

Every circle can be represented in the general form

$$Ax^2 + Ay^2 + Dx + Ey + F = 0 \quad (A \neq 0).$$

It is a simple matter to take an equation of a circle in the standard form and reduce it to the general form. We have already seen an example of this. However, it is somewhat more difficult to go from the general form to the standard form. The latter is accomplished by the process of "completing the square." To see how this is accomplished, suppose we consider the following:

$$(x+a)^2 = x^2 + 2ax + a^2.$$

The constant term a^2 and the coefficient of x have a definite relationship; namely, the constant term is the square of one-half the coefficient of x. Thus,

$$a^2 = \left[\frac{1}{2}(2a)\right]^2.$$

Note, however, that this relationship holds only when the coefficient of x^2 is 1.

This relationship suggests the following procedure. If the coefficients of x^2 and y^2 are not one, make them one by division. Group the x terms and the y terms on one side of the equation and take the constant to the other side. Then complete the square on both the x and the y terms. Remember that whatever is added to one side of an equation must be added to the other in order to maintain equality.

Example 2

Express $2x^2 + 2y^2 - 2x + 6y - 3 = 0$ in the standard form.

$$2x^2 + 2y^2 - 2x + 6y - 3 = 0,$$

$$x^2 + y^2 - x + 3y - \frac{3}{2} = 0,$$

$$(x^2 - x \quad\;) + (y^2 + 3y \quad\;) = \frac{3}{2},$$

$$\left(x^2 - x + \frac{1}{4}\right) + \left(y^2 + 3y + \frac{9}{4}\right) = \frac{3}{2} + \frac{1}{4} + \frac{9}{4},$$

$$\left(x - \frac{1}{2}\right)^2 + \left(y + \frac{3}{2}\right)^2 = 4.$$

Thus, the original equation represents a circle with center (1/2, −3/2) and radius 2.

The next two examples show that the converse of Theorem 3.2 is not true: that is, an equation of the form

$$Ax^2 + Ay^2 + Dx + Ey + F = 0$$

does not necessarily represent a circle.

Example 3

Express $x^2 + y^2 + 4x - 6y + 13 = 0$ in standard form.

$$x^2 + y^2 + 4x - 6y + 13 = 0,$$

$$(x^2 + 4x \quad\;) + (y^2 - 6y \quad\;) = -13,$$

$$(x^2 + 4x + 4) + (y^2 - 6y + 9) = -13 + 4 + 9,$$

$$(x + 2)^2 + (y - 3)^2 = 0.$$

Since neither of the two expressions on the left-hand side of the last equation can be negative, their sum can be zero only if both expressions are zero. This is possible only when $x = -2$ and $y = 3$. Thus, the point $(-2, 3)$ is the only point in the plane that satisfies the original equation.

Example 4

Express $x^2 + y^2 + 2x + 8y + 19 = 0$ in standard form.

$$
\begin{aligned}
x^2 + y^2 + 2x + 8y + 19 &= 0,\\
(x^2 + 2x \qquad) + (y^2 + 8y \qquad) &= -19,\\
(x^2 + 2x + 1) + (y^2 + 8y + 16) &= -19 + 1 + 16,\\
(x + 1)^2 + (y + 4)^2 &= -2.
\end{aligned}
$$

Again, since neither expression on the left-hand side of the last equation can be negative, their sum cannot possibly be negative. There is no point in the plane satisfying this equation. Its graph is the empty set.

Our results are stated in the next theorem.

Theorem 3.3

Every equation of the form

$$Ax^2 + Ay^2 + Dx + Ey + F = 0 \quad (A \neq 0)$$

represents either a circle, a point, or the empty set. (*The last two cases are called the degenerate cases of a circle.*)

Problems

In Problems 1–16, write an equation of the circle described in both the standard form and the general form. Sketch.

1. Center (1, 3); radius 5.
2. Center (0, 0); radius 1.
3. Center (5, −2); radius 2.
4. Center (0, 3); radius 1/2.
5. Center (1/2, −3/2); radius 2.
6. Center (−2/3, −1/2); radius 3/2.
7. Center (4, −2); (3, 3) on the circle.
8. Center (−1, 0); (4, −3) on the circle.
9. (2, −3) and (−2, 0) are the end points of a diameter.
10. (−3, 5) and (2, 4) are the end points of a diameter.
11. Radius 3; in the first quadrant and tangent to both axes.
12. Radius 5; in the fourth quadrant and tangent to both axes.
13. Radius 2; tangent to $x = 2$ and $y = -1$ and above and to the right of these lines.
14. Radius 3; tangent to $x = -3$ and $y = 4$ and below and to the left of these lines.
15. Tangent to both axes at (4, 0) and (0, −4).
16. Tangent to $x = -2$ and $y = 2$ at (−2, 0) and (−4, 2).

In Problems 17–28, express the equation in standard form. Sketch if the graph is nonempty.

17. $x^2 + y^2 - 2x - 4y + 1 = 0.$
18. $x^2 + y^2 + 4x - 6y - 3 = 0.$
19. $x^2 + y^2 + 6x - 16 = 0.$
20. $x^2 + y^2 - 10x + 4y + 29 = 0.$
21. $4x^2 + 4y^2 - 4x - 12y + 1 = 0.$
22. $9x^2 + 9y^2 - 12x - 24y - 13 = 0.$
23. $5x^2 + 5y^2 - 8x - 4y - 121 = 0.$
24. $9x^2 + 9y^2 - 18x - 12y - 23 = 0.$
25. $9x^2 + 9y^2 - 6x + 18y + 11 = 0.$
26. $36x^2 + 36y^2 - 36x + 24y - 23 = 0.$
27. $36x^2 + 36y^2 - 48x - 36y + 25 = 0.$
28. $8x^2 + 8y^2 + 24x - 4y + 19 = 0.$

29. Find the point(s) of intersection of

$$x^2 + y^2 - x - 3y - 6 = 0 \quad \text{and} \quad 4x - y - 9 = 0.$$

30. Find the point(s) of intersection of

$$x^2 + y^2 + 4x - 12y + 6 = 0 \quad \text{and} \quad 3x - 5y + 2 = 0.$$

31. Find the point(s) of intersection of

$$x^2 + y^2 + 5x + y - 26 = 0 \quad \text{and} \quad x^2 + y^2 + 2x - y - 15 = 0.$$

32. Find the point(s) of intersection of

$$x^2 + y^2 + x + 12y + 8 = 0 \quad \text{and} \quad 2x^2 + 2y^2 - 4x + 9y + 4 = 0.$$

33. What happens when we try to solve simultaneously

$$x^2 + y^2 - 2x + 4y + 1 = 0 \quad \text{and} \quad x - 2y + 2 = 0?$$

Interpret geometrically.

34. What happens when we try to solve simultaneously

$$x^2 + y^2 - 4x - 2y + 1 = 0 \quad \text{and} \quad x^2 + y^2 + 6x - 6y + 14 = 0?$$

Interpret geometrically.

35. Find the line through the points of intersection of

$$x^2 + y^2 - x + 3y - 10 = 0 \quad \text{and} \quad x^2 + y^2 - 2x + 2y - 11 = 0.$$

36. For what value(s) of k is the line $x + 2y + k = 0$ tangent to the circle

$$x^2 + y^2 - 2x + 4y + 1 = 0?$$

37. Prove analytically that if P_1 and P_2 are the ends of a diameter of a circle and Q is any point on the circle, then $\measuredangle P_1QP_2$ is a right angle.
38. A set of points in the plane has the property that every point in it is twice as far from (1, 1) as it is from (5, 3). What equation must be satisfied by every point (x, y) in the set?
39. Find the relation between A, D, E, and F of Theorem 3.2 in order that the equation represent (a) a circle, (b) a point, (c) the empty set. If the equation represents a circle, find h, k, and r in terms of A, D, E, and F.
40. In general, squaring both sides of an equation is not reversible (if $x = 2$, then $x^2 = 4$; but if $x^2 = 4$, then $x = \pm 2$). Yet, in the proof of Theorem 3.1, the argument was declared to be reversible even though both sides of an equation were squared. Why?

3.2

*Conditions to Determine a Circle**

We have seen two forms for equations of a circle: the standard form,

$$(x - h)^2 + (y - k)^2 = r^2,$$

with the three parameters h, k, and r, and the general form,

$$Ax^2 + Ay^2 + Dx + Ey + F = 0 \quad (A \neq 0),$$

with the parameters A, D, E, and F. However, since $A \neq 0$, we can divide through by A to obtain

$$x^2 + y^2 + D'x + E'y + F' = 0,$$

which, like the standard form, has only three parameters. Thus we need three equations in h, k, and r or in D', E', and F' in order to determine these parameters and give the equation desired. Since each condition on a circle determines one such equation, three conditions are required to determine a circle.

Example 1

Find an equation of the circle through points (1, 5), (−2, 3), and (2, −1).

The desired equation is

$$x^2 + y^2 + D'x + E'y + F' = 0$$

for suitable choices of D', E', and F'. Since the three given points are on the circle, they satisfy this equation. Thus

$$\begin{aligned} 1 + 25 + D' + 5E' + F' &= 0, \\ 4 + 9 - 2D' + 3E' + F' &= 0, \\ 4 + 1 + 2D' - E' + F' &= 0, \end{aligned}$$

or

$$\begin{aligned} D' + 5E' + F' &= -26, \\ -2D' + 3E' + F' &= -13, \\ 2D' - E' + F' &= -5. \end{aligned}$$

Solving simultaneously, we have $D' = -9/5$, $E' = -19/5$, and $F' = -26/5$. Thus the circle is

$$x^2 + y^2 - \frac{9}{5}x - \frac{19}{5}y - \frac{26}{5} = 0,$$

or

$$5x^2 + 5y^2 - 9x - 19y - 26 = 0.$$

Example 2

Find an equation(s) of the circle(s) of radius 4 with center on the line $4x + 3y + 7 = 0$ and tangent to $3x + 4y + 34 = 0$.

The three conditions lead to the following three relations involving h, k, and r (see Figure 3.2).

$$r = 4, \qquad (1)$$

$$4h + 3k + 7 = 0, \qquad (2)$$

$$\frac{|3h + 4k + 34|}{\sqrt{3^2 + 4^2}} = r. \qquad (3)$$

The first and third give

$$|3h + 4k + 34| = 20.$$

Solving the second for k, we have

$$k = -\frac{4h + 7}{3},$$

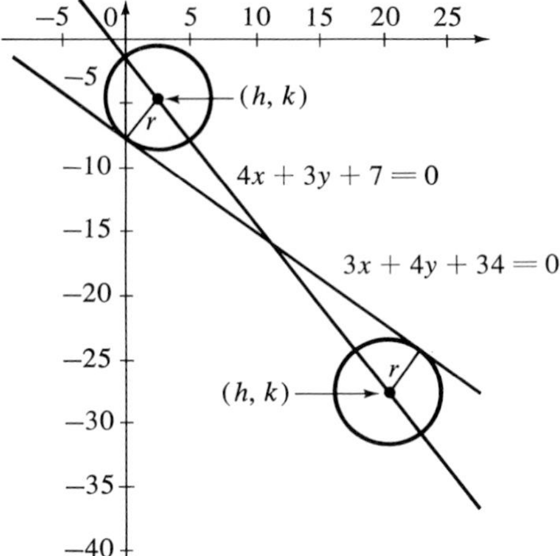

Figure 3.2

and substituting into $|3h + 4k + 34| = 20$, we have

$$|3h - \frac{16h + 28}{3} + 34| = 20,$$

$$|74 - 7h| = 60,$$

$$74 - 7h = \pm 60,$$

$$h = 2 \quad \text{or} \quad h = \frac{134}{7};$$

and $k = -5$ or $k = -195/7$, respectively. Thus the two solutions are

$$(x - 2)^2 + (y + 5)^2 = 16 \quad \text{and} \quad \left(x - \frac{134}{7}\right)^2 + \left(y + \frac{195}{7}\right)^2 = 16,$$

or

$$x^2 + y^2 - 4x + 10y + 13 = 0 \quad \text{and} \quad 49x^2 + 49y^2 - 1876x + 2730y + 55{,}197 = 0.$$

This problem can also be solved in the following way. Since the desired circle has radius 4 and is tangent to $3x + 4y + 34 = 0$, its center is on a line parallel to

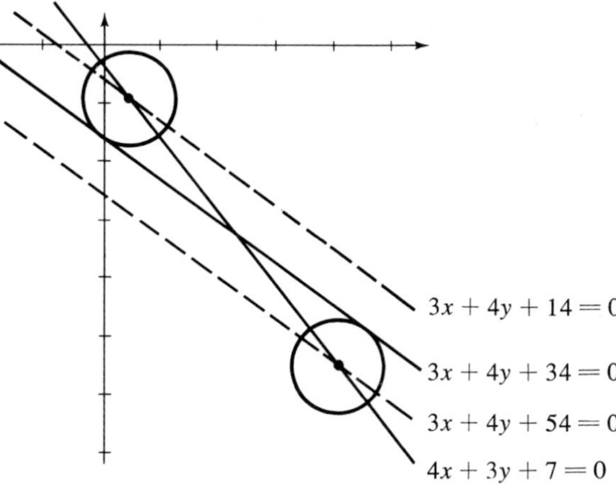

Figure 3.3

$3x + 4y + 34 = 0$ and at a distance 4 from it. There are two such lines (see Figure 3.3) given by

$$\frac{|3x + 4y + 34|}{5} = 4,$$

$$3x + 4y + 34 = \pm 20,$$

$$3x + 4y + 14 = 0 \quad \text{or} \quad 3x + 4y + 54 = 0.$$

Since the center is also on $4x + 3y + 7 = 0$, we can find its coordinates by solving this equation simultaneously with each of the two equations above. From

$$3x + 4y + 14 = 0 \quad \text{and} \quad 4x + 3y + 7 = 0,$$

we get center $(2, -5)$; from

$$3x + 4y + 54 = 0 \quad \text{and} \quad 4x + 3y + 7 = 0,$$

we get center $(134/7, -195/7)$. Using these centers with the given radius, 4, we have the desired circles.

Example 3

Find an equation(s) of the circle(s) tangent to both axes and containing the point $(-8, -1)$.

The three conditions give

$$h = -r, \tag{1}$$

$$k = -r, \tag{2}$$

$$(-8 - h)^2 + (-1 - k)^2 = r^2 \tag{3}$$

(see Figure 3.4). Substituting (1) and (2) into (3), we have

$$(-8 + r)^2 + (-1 + r)^2 = r^2,$$

$$r^2 - 18r + 65 = 0,$$

$$(r - 5)(r - 13) = 0,$$

$$r = 5 \quad \text{or} \quad r = 13.$$

Thus we have the circle with radius 5 and center $(-5, -5)$ with equation

$$(x + 5)^2 + (y + 5)^2 = 25,$$

or

$$x^2 + y^2 + 10x + 10y + 25 = 0;$$

or we have the circle with radius 13 and center $(-13, -13)$ with equation

$$(x + 13)^2 + (y + 13)^2 = 169$$

or

$$x^2 + y^2 + 26x + 26y + 169 = 0.$$

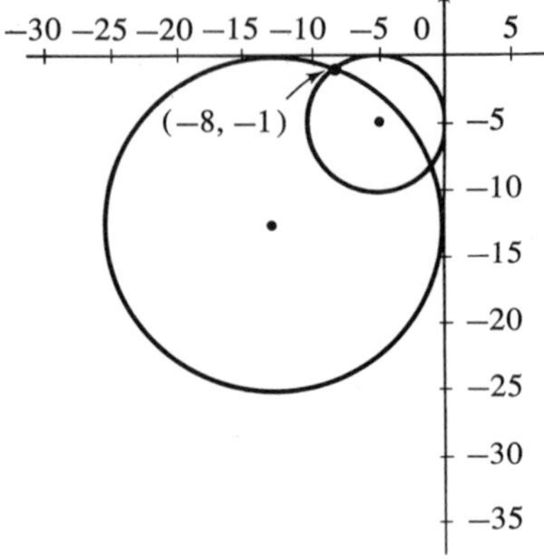

Figure 3.4

Example 4

Find an equation(s) of the circle(s) tangent to $3x - 4y - 4 = 0$ at $(0, -1)$ and containing the point $(-1, -8)$.

The center of the desired circle is on the line perpendicular to the tangent line at $(0, -1)$ (see Figure 3.5). An equation of this perpendicular is

$$4x + 3y = 4 \cdot 0 + 3(-1),$$

or

$$4x + 3y + 3 = 0.$$

Thus, for center (h, k), we have

$$4h + 3k + 3 = 0. \qquad (1)$$

The center is also on the perpendicular bisector of the line joining $(0, -1)$ and $(-1, -8)$ (see Figure 3.5). The slope of the line joining $(0, -1)$ and $(-1, -8)$ is

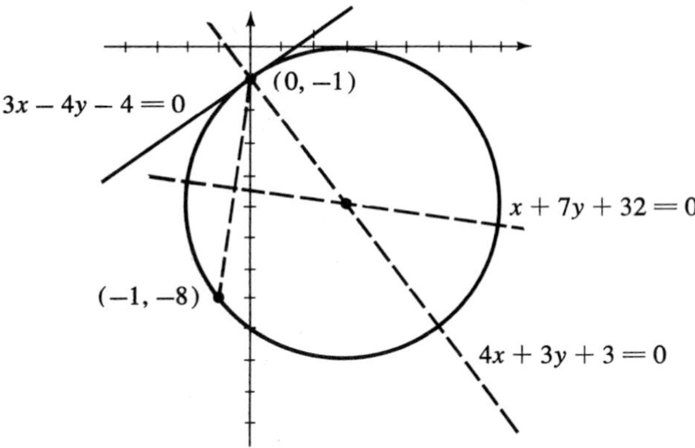

Figure 3.5

7; thus the slope of a perpendicular line is $-1/7$. The midpoint of the segment from $(0, -1)$ to $(-1, -8)$ is $(-1/2, -9/2)$. By the point-slope formula, the perpendicular bisector is

$$y + \frac{9}{2} = -\frac{1}{7}\left(x + \frac{1}{2}\right),$$

or

$$x + 7y + 32 = 0.$$

Thus,

$$h + 7k + 32 = 0. \qquad (2)$$

Solving (1) and (2) simultaneously, we have

$$h = 3 \quad \text{and} \quad k = -5.$$

Using this point with $(0, -1)$, we find the radius:

$$\begin{aligned} r &= \sqrt{(3-0)^2 + (-5+1)^2} \\ &= 5. \end{aligned}$$

Thus, the desired equation is

$$(x - 3)^2 + (y + 5)^2 = 25,$$

or

$$x^2 + y^2 - 6x + 10y + 9 = 0.$$

Problems

In Problems 1–23, find an equation(s) of the circle(s) described.

1. Through $(-1, 2)$, $(3, 4)$, and $(2, -1)$.
2. Through $(-2, -1)$, $(0, 3)$, and $(2, 0)$.
3. Circumscribed about the triangle with vertices $(2, 3)$, $(0, 5)$, and $(1, -1)$.
4. Circumscribed about the triangle with vertices $(1, 1)$, $(-2, 1)$, and $(1, 4)$.
5. Circumscribed about the triangle with sides $x - y = 0$, $x + 2y = 0$, and $4x + y = 35$.
6. Through $(2, 1)$, $(-4, 4)$, and $(6, -1)$. (*Watch out!*)
7. Tangent to the x axis; center on $2x + y - 1 = 0$; radius 5.
8. Tangent to $2x + 3y + 13 = 0$ and $2x - 3y - 1 = 0$; contains $(0, 4)$.
9. Tangent to $3x + 4y - 15 = 0$ at $(5, 0)$; contains $(-2, -1)$.
10. Tangent to $5x - 12y + 89 = 0$ at $(-1, 7)$; contains $(16, 0)$.
11. Tangent to $x + y = 0$ and $x - y - 6 = 0$; center on $3x - y + 3 = 0$.
12. Tangent to $x - 3y - 7 = 0$ and $3x + y - 21 = 0$; center on $x - 3y + 3 = 0$.
13. Tangent to $x - 3y = 0$ at $(0, 0)$; center on $2x + y + 1 = 0$.
14. Tangent to $x - y = 0$ at $(2, 2)$; center on $2x + 3y - 7 = 0$.
15. Contains $(-1, 4)$ and $(3, 2)$; center on $3x - y + 3 = 0$.
16. Contains $(5, 2)$ and $(-1, 6)$; center on $x = y$.
17. Tangent to $2x + 3y - 5 = 0$ at $(1, 1)$; tangent to $2x + 3y + 10 = 0$.
18. Tangent to $y = 0$ at $(4, 0)$; tangent to $3x - 4y - 17 = 0$.
19. Tangent to both axes; radius 3.
20. Tangent to $x = 0$; center on $x + y = 10$; contains $(2, 9)$.
21. Tangent to $3x - 4y + 3 = 0$ at $(-1, 0)$; radius 7.
22. Tangent to $x^2 + y^2 - 22x + 20y + 77 = 0$ at $(91/17, 10/17)$; containing $(0, 1)$.
23. Tangent to $x^2 + y^2 - 8x - 22y + 112 = 0$ and $3x + 4y + 19 = 0$; radius 5.
24. Show that if (x_1, y_1), (x_2, y_2), and (x_3, y_3) are three noncollinear points, then the circle containing these three points has equation
$$\begin{vmatrix} x^2 + y^2 & x & y & 1 \\ x_1^2 + y_1^2 & x_1 & y_1 & 1 \\ x_2^2 + y_2^2 & x_2 & y_2 & 1 \\ x_3^2 + y_3^2 & x_3 & y_3 & 1 \end{vmatrix} = 0.$$
25. Show that if (x_1, y_1), (x_2, y_2), and (x_3, y_3) are three collinear points, then the determinant of Problem 24 is linear.
26. Find an equation(s) of the line(s) tangent to $x^2 + y^2 + 4x - 10y + 4 = 0$ from the point $(3, 2)$.
27. Find an equation(s) of the line(s) tangent to $x^2 + y^2 - 8x + 2y - 152 = 0$ and having slope $1/3$.
28. If
$$A_1x^2 + A_1y^2 + D_1x + E_1y + F_1 = 0 \quad \text{and} \quad A_2x^2 + A_2y^2 + D_2x + E_2y + F_2 = 0$$
are equations of two intersecting circles, what is represented by
$$\{A_1x^2 + A_1y^2 + D_1x + E_1y + F_1 + k(A_2x^2 + A_2y^2 + D_2x + E_2y + F_2) = 0 \mid k \text{ real}\}?$$
Compare with Example 5, page 34.

The following problems are based upon the results of Problem 28.

29. Find an equation(s) of the circle(s) containing $(1, -4)$ and the points of intersection of

$$x^2 + y^2 + 2x - 4y + 1 = 0 \quad \text{and} \quad x^2 + y^2 + 4x + 6y - 3 = 0.$$

30. Find an equation(s) of the circle(s) containing $(2, 0)$ and the points of intersection of

$$x^2 + y^2 - 2x + 6y + 6 = 0 \quad \text{and} \quad x^2 + y^2 + 2x - 2y - 7 = 0.$$

31. Find an equation(s) of the circle(s) with center on $x + y - 2 = 0$ and containing the points of intersection of

$$x^2 + y^2 + 4x + 6y - 3 = 0 \quad \text{and} \quad x^2 + y^2 + 2x + 2y - 2 = 0.$$

32. Find an equation(s) of the line(s) containing the points of intersection of

$$x^2 + y^2 - 2x - 8y + 8 = 0 \quad \text{and} \quad x^2 + y^2 + 2x - 3 = 0.$$

33. Suppose you are asked to use the results of Problem 28 to find an equation(s) of the circle(s) containing $(3, 0)$ and the points of intersection of

$$x^2 + y^2 + 2x + 2y - 7 = 0 \quad \text{and} \quad x^2 + y^2 - 4x - 6y + 9 = 0.$$

What is the result? Does this represent all possible circles satisfying the given conditions? If not, why not? Sketch the given circles and the result.

34. Suppose you are asked to use the results of Problem 28 to find an equation(s) of the circle(s) containing $(-2, -1)$ and the points of intersection of

$$x^2 + y^2 + 4x - 8y + 16 = 0 \quad \text{and} \quad x^2 + y^2 - 4x - 2y + 1 = 0.$$

What is the result? Does this represent all possible circles satisfying the given conditions? If not, why not? Sketch the given circles and the result.

35. If there are two points P_1 and P_2 such that three different circles all contain P_1 and P_2, show that the centers of the circles are collinear.

Functions

Recall that the graph of an equation is the set of all points whose coordinates satisfy the equation and the points are represented by ordered pairs of real numbers. For example, the equation $y = x^2$ has the graph shown in Figure 4.1. Points on the graph are identified by their coordinates, which are ordered pairs of real numbers. If we bypass the graph of the equation, we see that the equation is represented by a set of ordered pairs of real numbers.

Finally, the example we have considered has a special property; for each value of x there is only one value of y. That is to say, we cannot find two ordered pairs in the set that have the same first numbers but different second ones. This does not exclude the possibility of having two ordered pairs with the same second numbers but different

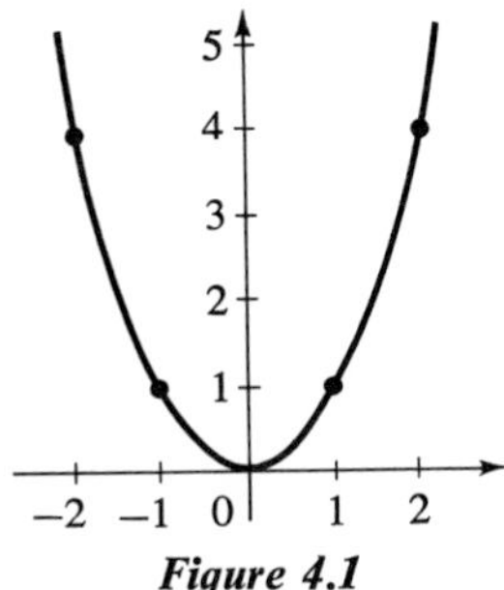

Figure 4.1

first ones. For example, we have the ordered pairs (2, 4) and (−2, 4) with the same second numbers; but we do not have another ordered pair with 2 as its first number.

A functional relationship between x and y values can still exist, even though we might not be able to express it in terms of a single equation (or any combination of equations). An example of this is the relationship between time and temperature at a given place. For any value of time (measured from a given starting time) there corresponds one and only one temperature. Although no equation is given to represent this relationship, there is no doubt that the relationship does exist. Thus the set of ordered pairs, rather than the equation, is the important concept in the idea of a function.

From the above discussion we now abstract a definition.

Definition

*A **function** f is a set of ordered pairs of objects such that no two ordered pairs of the set have the same first object but different second ones. The set of all first terms of the ordered pairs is the **domain** of f. The set of all second terms is the **range** of f.*

Note that a function is defined as a set of ordered pairs of "objects," rather than ordered pairs of real numbers. We do not wish to restrict the term "function" to refer only to a certain relationship between numbers. Although we shall be mainly interested in those functions that relate real numbers, we shall be dealing with others as well.

Example 1

The set of all ordered pairs (x, y) such that $y = x^2$ and x is a real number is a function. Its domain is $\{x \mid x \text{ real}\}$. Its range is $\{y \mid y \text{ real}, y \geq 0\}$.

Example 2

The set of all ordered pairs (x, y) such that $y = x^2$ and $x \geq 0$ is a function with domain $\{x \mid x \text{ real}, x \geq 0\}$ and range $\{y \mid y \text{ real}, y \geq 0\}$. Although the relationship between the first and second terms of the ordered pairs is the same as that of Example 1, this is a different function, since there are many ordered pairs of Example 1 that are not in this set—for example, $(-2, 4)$.

Example 3

Consider the correspondence between the circles in a plane and their areas. For each circle there is one and only one area. Thus the function involved is the set of all ordered pairs in which the first terms are circles in the given plane and each second term is the area of the circle given in the first term. The domain is the set of all circles in the given plane and the range is $\{y \mid y \text{ real}, y > 0\}$.

Example 4

The set of all ordered pairs whose first elements are themselves ordered pairs (x, y) of real numbers and whose second elements are $x + y$ represents a function. Its domain is $\{(x, y) \mid x, y \text{ real}\}$; its range is $\{z \mid z \text{ real}\}$.

In the examples above, the descriptions are rather cumbersome because we have no convenient notation for representing a function. In most of the cases we shall consider, the relationship between the first and second terms of the ordered pairs can be expressed in the form of an equation (or a combination of equations). For example, the equation $y = x^2$ expresses the relationship between the first and second terms of the ordered pairs given in Examples 1 and 2. If the ordered pair (x, y) is a member of some function named f, then y is called the value of the function at x, and is often represented by $f(x)$ (read "f of x"). Thus instead of $y = x^2$, we write $f(x) = x^2$. Knowing this relationship and the domain is enough to determine the function.

Thus the function of Example 1 is represented by

$$f\colon f(x) = x^2, \quad x \text{ real},$$

which is read "f is the function whose value at x is x^2 and whose domain is the set of all real numbers," or, more simply, "f of x is x^2, x real."

Similarly the function of Example 2 is represented by

$$f\colon f(x) = x^2, \quad x \text{ real}, x \geq 0.$$

Note that f is the function and $f(x)$ is the value of the function at x. Thus, a function is identified by its value at x and its domain. If we wish to talk about a function without specifying its value at x, we use the symbol f rather than $f(x)$.

Since we shall be dealing almost exclusively with real functions of real variables—that is, the range and domains of our functions are subsets of the set of real numbers—we shall omit the statement "x real." Therefore, when the domain is not stated, it is understood to be the set of all real numbers for which $f(x)$ is real. Thus,

$$f\colon f(x) = \frac{1}{x}$$

describes a function whose domain is the set of all real numbers except 0, and

$$f\colon f(x) = \sqrt{x}$$

describes a function whose domain is the set of all nonnegative real numbers.

The advantage of the notation $f(x) = x^2$ over $y = x^2$ can be seen in the following table.

$f(x) = x^2$	$y = x^2$
$f(1) = 1^2 = 1$	If $x = 1$, then $y = 1^2 = 1$.
$f(-1) = (-1)^2 = 1$	If $x = -1$, then $y = (-1)^2 = 1$.
$f(2) = 2^2 = 4$	If $x = 2$, then $y = 2^2 = 4$.
$f(2x + 3) = (2x + 3)^2$	If $x = 2x + 3$ (!), then $y = (2x + 3)^2$.

The notation $f(x) = x^2$ is more convenient in use. The last statement on the right really means "if the x in $y = x^2$ is replaced by $2x + 3$, then $y = (2x + 3)^2$." It is certainly simpler to say $f(2x + 3) = (2x + 3)^2$.

Example 5

Given $f\colon f(x) = x^2 + x + 1$, then

$$\begin{aligned}
f(0) &= 0^2 + 0 + 1 = 1,\\
f(1) &= 1^2 + 1 + 1 = 3,\\
f(-1) &= (-1)^2 + (-1) + 1 = 1,\\
f(z) &= z^2 + z + 1,\\
f(x + h) &= (x + h)^2 + (x + h) + 1,\\
\frac{f(x + h) - f(x)}{h} &= \frac{[(x + h)^2 + (x + h) + 1] - [x^2 + x + 1]}{h} = 2x + h + 1 \quad (h \neq 0).
\end{aligned}$$

Example 6

Given

$$f: f(x) = \begin{cases} 0 & \text{if } x \leq 0, \\ x & \text{if } x > 0, \end{cases}$$

then

$$f(0) = 0, \qquad f(1) = 1,$$
$$f(-1) = 0, \qquad f(3) = 3,$$
$$f(-10) = 0, \qquad f(.1) = .1;$$

$$f(1+h) = \begin{cases} 1+h & \text{if } h > -1, \\ 0 & \text{if } h \leq -1, \end{cases}$$

$$\frac{f(1+h) - f(1)}{h} = \begin{cases} \dfrac{(1+h)-1}{h} = 1 & \text{if } h > -1 \text{ and } h \neq 0, \\[2ex] \dfrac{0-1}{h} = -\dfrac{1}{h} & \text{if } h \leq -1. \end{cases}$$

Functions which are expressed in terms of more than one equation, like the one above, are called *compound functions.* This name does not describe an inherent property of the function; it is only a description of the representation. For example,

$$f: f(x) = |x| \quad \text{and} \quad f: f(x) = \begin{cases} x & \text{if } x \geq 0, \\ -x & \text{if } x < 0 \end{cases}$$

represent the same function, the first in simple form and the second in compound form.

Example 7

Given $f: f(x, y) = x^2 + y$, then

$$f(1, 2) = 1^2 + 2 = 3,$$
$$f(2, 1) = 2^2 + 1 = 5,$$
$$f(x+h, y) = (x+h)^2 + y,$$
$$f(x, y+h) = x^2 + y + h,$$
$$\frac{f(x+h, y) - f(x, y)}{h} = \frac{[(x+h)^2 + y] - [x^2 + y]}{h} = 2x + h \quad (h \neq 0),$$
$$\frac{f(x, y+h) - f(x, y)}{h} = \frac{(x^2 + y + h) - (x^2 + y)}{h} = 1 \quad (h \neq 0).$$

Functions of this type are called functions of two variables. The domain of this function is $\{(x, y) \mid x, y \text{ real}\}$ and the range is the set of all real numbers. Similarly, we may consider functions of three or more variables. An example of a function of three variables is

$$f(x, y, z) = x^2y + 2xz,$$

with domain $\{(x, y, z) \mid x, y, z \text{ real}\}$ and range the set of all real numbers.

Problems

In Problems 1–10, indicate whether or not the given equation determines y as a function of x.

1. $x + y = 1$.
2. $x^2 + y = 1$.
3. $x + y^2 = 1$.
4. $y = 2x - 5$.
5. $y = x^2$.
6. $x = y^2$.
7. $y = \sqrt{x}$.
8. $x^2 + y^2 = 1$.
9. $y = \pm\sqrt{x}$.
10. $x^2 + y^2 + 2x - 6y + 2 = 0$.

In Problems 11–34, indicate the domain and range of the given function.

11. $f: f(x) = x^2, \quad x \le 0$.
12. $f: f(x) = x^2, \quad x < 0$.
13. $f: f(x) = \dfrac{1}{x-1}$.
14. $f: f(x) = \dfrac{1}{x+1}$.
15. $f: f(x) = \dfrac{1}{x^2-1}$.
16. $f: f(x) = \dfrac{1}{x^2+x-6}$.
17. $f: f(x) = \sqrt{x-2}$.
18. $f: f(x) = \sqrt{x+3}$.
19. $f: f(x) = \sqrt{x^2 - x - 6}$.
20. $f: f(x) = \sqrt{6 + x - x^2}$.
21. $f: f(x) = x, \quad x = 1, 2, 3, \ldots.$
22. $f: f(x) = x^2, \quad x = 0, 1, 2, 3, \ldots.$
23. $f: f(x) = \dfrac{1}{x}, \quad x > 0$.
24. $f: f(x) = x + 1, \quad 1 \le x \le 2$.
25. $f: f(x) = \begin{cases} x & \text{if } x < 0, \\ 1 & \text{if } x \ge 0. \end{cases}$
26. $f: f(x) = \begin{cases} \dfrac{1}{x} & \text{if } x \ne 0. \\ 0 & \text{if } x = 0. \end{cases}$
27. $f: f(x) = \begin{cases} x & \text{if } x < 0, \\ 1 & \text{if } 0 < x \le 2, \\ x - 1 & \text{if } 2 < x. \end{cases}$
28. $f: f(x) = \begin{cases} x^2 & \text{if } x < 0, \\ 1 & \text{if } x = 0, \\ x & \text{if } 0 < x < 2. \end{cases}$
29. $f: f(x, y) = x^2 + y^2$.
30. $f: f(x, y) = xy$.
31. $f: f(x, y) = \sqrt{x^2 - y^2}$.
32. $f: f(x, y) = \sqrt{1 - (x^2 + y^2)}$.
33. $f: f(x, y, z) = x^2 + y^2 + z^2$.
34. $f: f(x, y, z) = \sqrt{1 - (x^2 + y^2 + z^2)}$.

In Problems 35–44, express the given function by giving the relation between x and $f(x)$ [or (x, y) and $f(x, y)$]. Give the domain.

35. $\{(x, f(x)) \mid f(x) = x^2, 0 \le x \le 1\}$.
36. $\{(x, f(x)) \mid f(x) = x + 1, x \ge 0\}$.
37. $\{(x, f(x)) \mid f(x) = x - 3, 0 < x \le 6\}$.
38. $\{(x, f(x)) \mid f(x) = 2x + 1, x \text{ real}\}$.
39. $\{(0, 0), (1, 1), (2, 2), (3, 3), (4, 4), (5, 5)\}$.
40. $\{(0, 0), (1, 1), (2, 4), (3, 9)\}$.
41. $\{(1, 2), (2, 4), (3, 6), \ldots, (n, 2n), \ldots\}$.
42. $\{(1, -1), (2, -2), (3, -3)\}$.
43. $\{(0, 0, 0), (0, 1, 1), (1, 0, 1), (0, 2, 2), (1, 1, 2), (2, 0, 2), (2, 1, 3), (1, 2, 3), (2, 2, 4)\}$.
44. $\{(0, 0, 0), (0, 1, 1), (1, 0, 1), (1, 1, 2), (2, 0, 4), (2, 1, 5), (2, 2, 8), (0, 2, 4), (1, 2, 5)\}$.
45. If $f: f(x) = 2x + 3$, find $f(0), f(1), f(5), f(-3)$.
46. If $f: f(x) = 4 - 3x$, find $f(-1), f(0), f(3), f(5)$.
47. If $f: f(x) = 1/x$, find $f(-1), f(0), f(2), f(x + 1)$.
48. If $f: f(x) = 1/(x - 1)$, find $f(-1), f(0), f(1), f(x + 1)$.
49. If $f: f(x) = \sqrt{x}$, find $f(0), f(4), f(x^2), f(x + h)$.
50. If $f: f(x) = \sqrt{x+1}$, find $f(0), f(3), f(x^2), f(x + h)$.
51. If $f: f(x) = x^2 + 1$, find $f(y), f(x + h), \dfrac{f(x+h) - f(x)}{h}$, where $h \ne 0$.

52. If $f: f(x) = \dfrac{x}{x+1}$, find $f(x+1), f(2+h), \dfrac{f(2+h)-f(2)}{h}$, where $h \neq 0$.

53. If $f: f(x) = \begin{cases} 0 & \text{if } x < 0, \\ x & \text{if } 0 \leq x \leq 1, \\ 1 & \text{if } 1 < x, \end{cases}$ find $f(-2), f(1/2), f(3)$.

54. If $f: f(x) = \begin{cases} x & \text{if } x \neq 0, \\ 1 & \text{if } x = 0, \end{cases}$ find $f(1), f(0), f(1+h), \dfrac{f(1+h)-f(1)}{h}$ $(h \neq 0)$.

55. If $f: f(x) = \begin{cases} \sin 1/x & \text{if } x \neq 0, \\ 0 & \text{if } x = 0, \end{cases}$ find $f(0), f(h)$ $(h \neq 0)$.

56. If $f: f(x) = \begin{cases} x \sin 1/x & \text{if } x \neq 0, \\ 0 & \text{if } x = 0, \end{cases}$ find $\dfrac{f(0+h)-f(0)}{h}$ $(h \neq 0)$.

57. If $f: f(x, y) = 1/(x^2 + y^2)$, find $f(0, 1), f(1, 0), f(1, 1), f(y, y), f(y, x)$.

58. If $f: f(x, y) = x^2 + xy$, find $f(0, 0), f(1, 1), f(x, x), f(y, x), f(x+h, y), f(x, y+h)$.

59. If $f: f(x, y) = x - y$, find

$$\frac{f(x+h, y) - f(x, y)}{h}, \qquad \frac{f(x, y+h) - f(x, y)}{h}.$$

60. If $f: f(x, y) = x^2 - y^2$, find

$$\frac{f(x+h, y) - f(x, y)}{h}, \qquad \frac{f(x, y+h) - f(x, y)}{h}.$$

The Derivative

5.1

The Slope of a Curve

Suppose we have the graph of $y = f(x)$ and we are presented with the problem of finding the slope of the curve at the point A (Figure 5.1). Before we ask, "What is the solution?" we might first ask, "What is the question?"

If our original curve had been a line, it would have been quite a simple problem. The slope of a line is simply the tangent of the inclination, or, if we had a pair of points on the line, we could find the slope by taking the difference between the y coordinates and dividing by the difference between the x coordinates taken in the same order. Since finding the slope of a line is so easy, we might try to relate the slope of a curve at a given point to the slope of some line. Let us consider Figure 5.2. Since the curve and the line have the same "direction" at the point A, they must have the same

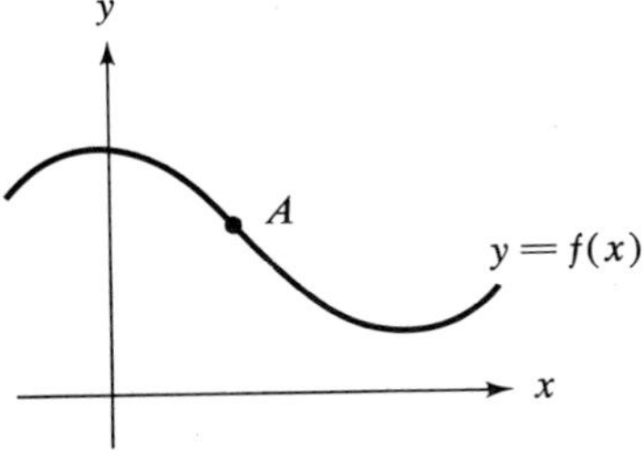

Figure 5.1

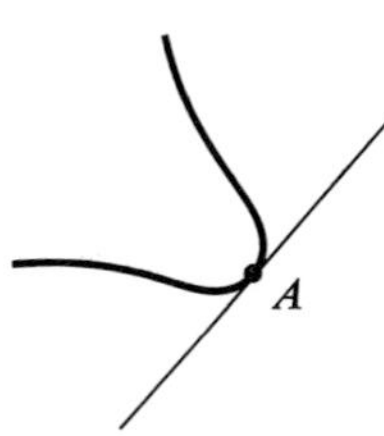

Figure 5.2

slope. What is the relationship between the curve and the line? It appears that the line is tangent to the curve at point A. With that, our problem of finding the slope of the curve at a given point reduces to one of finding the slope of the line tangent to the curve at the point.

But what is meant by the tangent to a curve at a given point? When we are dealing with circles, any line having exactly one point in common with the circle is defined as a tangent line, while any line having two points in common with it is called a secant line. But suppose we consider the two lines in Figure 5.3 and ask which of these is tangent to the curve at point A. If we use the same definition we used for a circle, we must conclude that m is tangent to the curve, while l is not. But this is exactly the reverse of what we intuitively think of as the tangent line. Perhaps we should cast off our intuitive idea and use this definition. However, it is not difficult to see that there are several lines that have only the point A in common with the curve of Figure 5.3. Thus it is easily seen that this definition of a tangent line—though quite suitable for circles—does not give us what we really want in the case of more general curves. What, then, do we mean by the tangent line to a curve at a given point? The fact that the line l intersects the curve at B as well as A seems, intuitively, to be rather unimportant when considering l as a tangent to the curve at A. Thus we seem to be interested only in the portion of the curve "near" A. Perhaps we can get the idea of a tangent line by considering secant lines joining A to the points of the curve "near" A. In Figure 5.4,

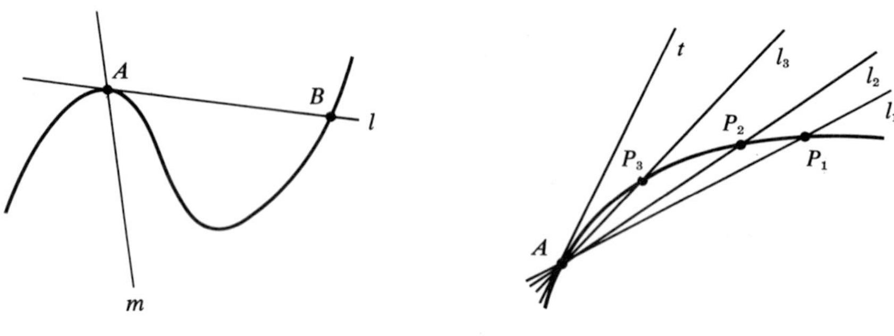

Figure 5.3

Figure 5.4

t is what we intuitively consider to be the tangent to the curve at A. Note that, when we take the points P_1, P_2, P_3 closer and closer to A, the secant lines joining A to P_1, P_2, P_3, are getting closer and closer to the line t. In fact, we can get as "close" as we please to the line t, provided we take a point P close enough to A. Thus we might define the tangent to a curve at a given point to be the limiting position of a secant line joining A to some point P of the curve, different from A, as P moves closer and closer to A. We might note that P can approach A from two sides. We are assuming that the secant line approaches the same limiting position as the point on the curve approaches A from either side (see Problem 25).

Now that we know what the question is, we have gone a long way toward finding an answer. If we want the slope of the curve at a given point, we are interested in the slope of the tangent line. If we want the tangent line, we must go through a limiting process with secant lines. Thus suppose we return to our original problem. Given the graph of $y = f(x)$ with the point A, suppose we identify the abscissa (x coordinate) of A by a (see Figure 5.5). The ordinate (y coordinate) of A is then $f(a)$. In order to get

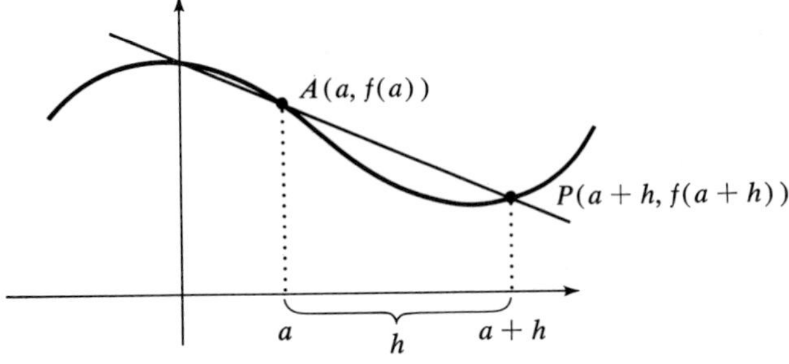

Figure 5.5

a secant line, we must select a point P of the curve different from A. Suppose we do it by choosing some number h and take P as the point of the curve with abscissa $a + h$. Note that while Figure 5.5 shows h to be positive, it need not be so—it may be negative; however, it may not be zero, since P is to be different from A. The slope of the line AP is easily found to be

$$m_{AP} = \frac{f(a+h) - f(a)}{(a+h) - a} = \frac{f(a+h) - f(a)}{h}.$$

If h is taken closer and closer to zero (but not equal to zero), AP then approaches the tangent to the curve at A. It would seem reasonable that if the line AP approaches the tangent line desired, then the slope of AP also approaches the slope of the tangent and thus the slope of the curve. Let us try the preceding approach with some specific examples.

Example 1

Find the slope of $f(x) = x^2$ at the point (1, 1).

Letting P be the point with abscissa $1 + h$, its ordinate, as indicated by the equation of the curve, is $(1 + h)^2$. Thus

$$m_{AP} = \frac{(1+h)^2 - 1}{h}.$$

Note that both the numerator and denominator of this fraction approach zero as h approaches zero. However, *the fact that both the numerator and denominator are approaching zero tells us nothing about what the fraction is approaching.* On simplifying the numerator, we have

$$m_{AP} = \frac{h^2 + 2h}{h}$$
$$= h + 2.$$

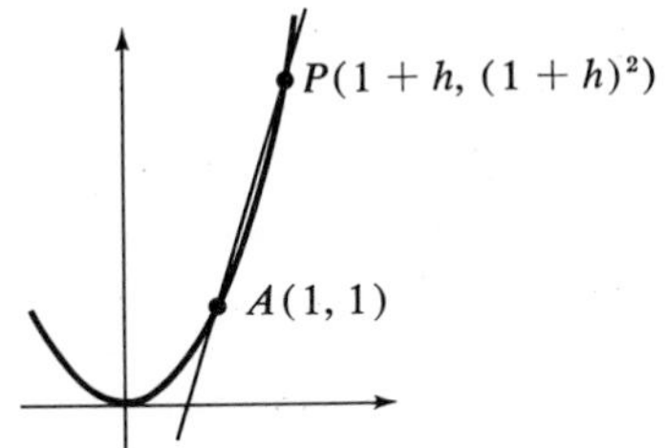

Figure 5.6

Note that the last two expressions are the same for all values of h except $h = 0$, but zero is the one value that h cannot have. Now as h approaches zero, m_{AP} approaches 2, which is the desired slope.

Example 2

Find the slope of $f(x) = x^2$ at the point (0, 0).

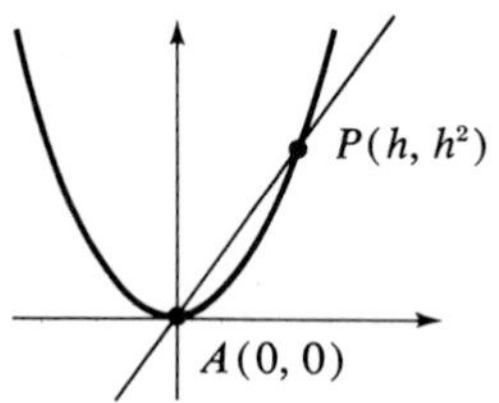

Figure 5.7

Before using the method given above, note that the x axis is what we intuitively think of as the tangent to $y = x^2$ at (0, 0), and it has slope 0. Thus, we know the answer before we start. This gives us a way of checking the validity of our new method—at least for this case. Letting $P = (h, h^2)$, we have

$$m_{AP} = \frac{h^2 - 0}{h} = h.$$

As h approaches zero, m_{AP} also approaches zero, which is the desired answer.

Problems

In Problems 1–12, find the slope of the curve at the point indicated.

1. $f(x) = x^2$ at $(-1, 1)$.
2. $f(x) = x^2$ at (2, 4).
3. $f(x) = x^3$ at (1, 1).
4. $f(x) = x^2 + x$ at (1, 2).
5. $f(x) = 3x^2 - 5x + 2$ at (2, 4).
6. $f(x) = (x + 2)(x - 1)$ at (2, 4).
7. $f(x) = (2x - 1)(x + 2)$ at $(0, -2)$.
8. $f(x) = (x^2 + 1)(x - 2)$ at (2, 0).
9. $f(x) = \dfrac{x + 1}{x - 1}$ at $(0, -1)$.
10. $f(x) = \dfrac{2x + 3}{x + 2}$ at (4, 11/6).
11. $f(x) = \sqrt{x}$ at (0, 0). What restrictions must be put on h here?
12. $f(x) = \sqrt{x}$ at (1, 1). What restrictions must be put on h here?

In Problems 13–18, find equations of the tangent and normal lines to the given curve at the point indicated. (The normal line is perpendicular to the tangent line at the point of contact.)

13. $f(x) = x^2$ at (2, 4).
14. $f(x) = x^2 + 1$ at (1, 2).
15. $f(x) = x^3 - x^2$ at (2, 4).
16. $f(x) = \dfrac{x}{x - 1}$ at (2, 2).
17. $f(x) = (x - 4)(2x + 1)$ at $(3, -7)$.
18. $f(x) = \sqrt{x}$ at (0, 0).
19. What is the slope of the curve $f(x) = |x|$ at $x = 1, 3, 8, -2, -5, -7, 0$? Sketch this curve.
20. At what point does $f(x) = 2x - x^2$ have slope 0?
21. At what point does $f(x) = x^2 - 4x$ have a horizontal tangent?
22. At what point does $f(x) = \sqrt{x}$ have no slope? (Do not confuse "no slope" with "slope 0.") Sketch the curve and the tangent line.
23. Use the method of this section to find the slope of $f(x) = 3x - 5$ at (2, 1). Repeat for the point $(0, -5)$. Repeat for the point with abscissa x. How does this compare with what you already know about the curve?
24. Find the slope of $f(x) = x^2$ at the point with abscissa x. What is the value of this slope when $x = 1$? When $x = 0$?
25. We noted above that P can approach A from two sides and that we were assuming the line AP to approach the same limiting position in either case. Give an example in which there are two different limiting positions, depending upon the side from which A is approached by P.

5.2

The Derivative of a Function

In the preceding section we found the slope of a curve by finding the slope of a secant line and using a certain limiting process. We saw that if the curve is represented by the function f and we are interested in the point with abscissa a, then

$$m_{AP} = \frac{f(a+h) - f(a)}{h}.$$

Note that if we are interested in the point with abscissa x, then

$$m_{AP} = \frac{f(x+h) - f(x)}{h}.$$

In particular, if $y = x^2$, then

$$\begin{aligned} m_{AP} &= \frac{(x+h)^2 - x^2}{h} \\ &= \frac{2hx + h^2}{h} \\ &= 2x + h. \end{aligned}$$

As h approaches 0, m_{AP} approaches $2x$. Thus the slope of $y = x^2$ at the point with abscissa x is $2x$. When $x = 1$, the slope is 2; when $x = 0$, the slope is 0. These are the results obtained in the preceding section by going through the entire process twice. Here we went through the process of finding the slope just once; but since we did it for a point with abscissa x, rather than for a particular point, we can assign particular values to x to find the slope at *any* point on the curve. Thus, by one simple process, we have found the slope of the given function at all of its points.

Suppose we formalize what has been done above. In dealing with a function f, we find a certain slope that is always in the form

$$\frac{f(x+h) - f(x)}{h}$$

and then note what number this approaches as h approaches 0. The number found in this way (if there is one) is called the limit of

$$\frac{f(x+h) - f(x)}{h}$$

as h approaches 0; it is written

$$\lim_{h \to 0} \frac{f(x+h) - f(x)}{h}.$$

Thus, finding the slope of the curve representing a function f is simply a matter of evaluating the above limit.

Now the slope of a curve is very important—much more so than might be apparent at first glance. In fact, it is important enough to give it the special name *derivative.*

Definition

The **derivative** *of a function f at x is*

$$f'(x) = \lim_{h \to 0} \frac{f(x+h) - f(x)}{h},$$

provided this limit exists.

To say that the function f is *differentiable* at x is to say that this limit exists. The process of finding the derivative is *differentiation.* A few words about the notation are in order here. If $y = f(x)$, then the derivative of y (or f) at x is represented by any one of the following notations:

$$y', \quad f'(x), \quad \frac{dy}{dx}, \quad \frac{d}{dx} f(x), \quad Dy, \quad \text{or} \quad Df(x).$$

These are all used interchangeably, and all mean exactly the same thing. It might be noted here that the notation dy/dx is particularly useful in certain cases. It is sometimes read "the derivative of y with respect to x." You might wonder about the point of the phrase "with respect to x." It is this: While in all our examples so far the y has been a function of x, it is also possible for it to be a function of something else. For instance, if $y = u^2$, where $u = x^2 + 1$, then y is a function of u, but at the same time it is, indirectly, a function of x; that is, $y = (x^2 + 1)^2$. Thus it is possible to take two derivatives of y, one with respect to x, which is dy/dx, and another with respect to u, which is dy/du. Whenever this ambiguity exists, we shall use the notation dy/dx, which is called the differential notation. However, resist the temptation to think of dy/dx as a quotient. While any number can be thought of as a quotient $(5 = 5/1)$, we have given no meanings to dy and dx individually (although we shall do so later, on page 131).

Note also that, although h appears in the definition of a derivative, it does not appear in the final value of it. Any symbol may be used in place of h. Thus we could just as well have defined the derivative as

$$\lim_{k \to 0} \frac{f(x+k) - f(x)}{k} \quad \text{or} \quad \lim_{z \to 0} \frac{f(x+z) - f(x)}{z}.$$

Many prefer to use Δx in place of h. This does not express a product but, rather, designates a difference between two values of x, which is what our h represents (see Figure 5.8). In the same way, the numerator $f(x+h) - f(x)$, which then becomes $f(x + \Delta x) - f(x)$, represents the difference between two values of y and is represented by Δy. Thus we would have

$$\lim_{\Delta x \to 0} \frac{f(x + \Delta x) - f(x)}{\Delta x} = \lim_{\Delta x \to 0} \frac{\Delta y}{\Delta x} = \frac{dy}{dx}.$$

When the differential notation for the derivative is used as it is above, the last equation presents the almost irresistible temptation to think of dy/dx as a fraction. Furthermore, it leads one to the *mistaken* notion that $\lim_{\Delta x \to 0} \Delta y = dy$ and $\lim_{\Delta x \to 0} \Delta x = dx$. The last two limits are both 0, and 0/0 is meaningless (remember, however, that the fact that both the numerator and denominator of a fraction approach 0, tells us nothing

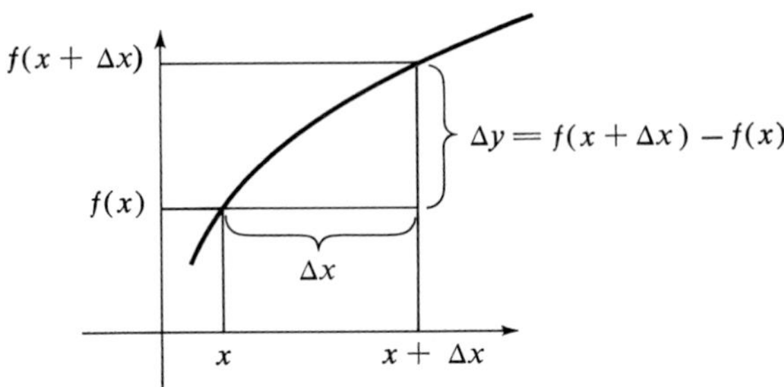

Figure 5.8

about what the fraction is approaching). We shall look at this notation again when we do give meanings to dy and dx; in the meantime, the "delta" notation will be avoided because of the temptations noted above.

Example 1

Differentiate $f(x) = x^2 - 2x$.

$$\begin{aligned} f'(x) &= \lim_{h \to 0} \frac{f(x+h) - f(x)}{h} \\ &= \lim_{h \to 0} \frac{[(x+h)^2 - 2(x+h)] - [x^2 - 2x]}{h} \\ &= \lim_{h \to 0} \frac{2hx + h^2 - 2h}{h} \\ &= \lim_{h \to 0} (2x + h - 2) \\ &= 2x - 2. \end{aligned}$$

Note that the derivative is the *limit* of $(f(x+h) - f(x))/h$; it is not merely $(f(x+h) - f(x))/h$. The "$\lim_{h \to 0}$" must be retained until the limit is actually taken at the last step. For instance,

$$f'(x) \neq 2x + h - 2;$$

rather,

$$f'(x) = \lim_{h \to 0} (2x + h - 2) = 2x - 2.$$

The "$\lim_{h \to 0}$" is dropped in the last expression, because the limit now has been taken and you no longer need a symbol which tells you to take the limit.

Example 2

Differentiate $f(x) = \dfrac{1}{x^2}$.

$$f'(x) = \lim_{h \to 0} \frac{f(x+h) - f(x)}{h}$$

$$= \lim_{h \to 0} \frac{\dfrac{1}{(x+h)^2} - \dfrac{1}{x^2}}{h}$$

$$= \lim_{h \to 0} \frac{x^2 - (x+h)^2}{hx^2(x+h)^2}$$

$$= \lim_{h \to 0} \frac{-2hx - h^2}{hx^2(x+h)^2}$$

$$= \lim_{h \to 0} \frac{-2x - h}{x^2(x+h)^2}$$

$$= -\frac{2x}{x^4} = -\frac{2}{x^3}.$$

Problems

In Problems 1–10, differentiate the given function.

1. $f(x) = 2x^2 - 4x + 1$.
2. $y = 3x^2 + x$.
3. $t = 4s^2 - s$.
4. $u = v^3 + 2v$.
5. $f(x) = \dfrac{1}{x+1}$.
6. $f(z) = \dfrac{z+4}{z-4}$.
7. $p = (q^2 + 1)(q^2 + 3)$.
8. $y = \sqrt{x}$.
9. $y = \sqrt[3]{x}$.
10. $f(s) = (s^2 + 1)^2$.

In Problems 11–16, find the derivative at the indicated points.

11. $f(x) = 4x^2 + x$ at $x = 1$.
12. $y = 5x^3 - 3x^2$ at $x = 2$; at $x = 1$.
13. $f(v) = \dfrac{v-4}{v+1}$ at $v = 0$; at $v = 2$.
14. $t = (s^2 + s)^2$ at $s = 1$; at $s = 3$.
15. $p = (q+1)^4$ at $q = 0$.
16. $y = \dfrac{x^2 + x + 1}{x+1}$ at $x = 1$.

In Problems 17–22, find the points at which the curve has horizontal tangents.

17. $f(x) = x^3$.
18. $y = x^3 - 6x$.
19. $y = x^2 - 2x - 1$.
20. $f(x) = x^3 + 3x$.
21. $f(x) = \dfrac{x^2 + 1}{x}$.
22. $y = x^2(x^2 - 4)$.
23. Find an equation of the line tangent to $f(x) = x^3$ at (1, 1).
24. Find an equation of the line tangent to $y = x^4$ at (1, 1).
25. Find an equation of the line tangent to $y = 4x^2 - x + 2$ at $(-1, 7)$.
26. Find an equation of the line tangent to $f(x) = x^3 - x^2 + x - 1$ at $(0, -1)$.
27. Find the points of $y = x^3$ at which the slope is 1.

28. Find the points of $y = x^3$ at which the slope is -1.
29. Find the angle of intersection of $y = x^2 - 1$ and $y = 4 - 4x^2$ measured from the first curve to the second at the point (1, 0).
30. Find the angle of intersection of $y = x^3$ and $y = 2 - x$ measured from the first curve to the second.
31. Find an equation(s) of the line(s) with slope 3 tangent to $y = 4x^2 - 5x + 1$.
32. Find an equation(s) of the line(s) with slope 1 tangent to $y = x^3 - 6x^2 + 10x - 10$.
33. Suppose the graph of a function is increasing as we go from left to right. What can be said about its derivative? What can be said about the derivative if the graph is decreasing?
34. Suppose the graph of a function is increasing (as we go from left to right) for all x up to $x = 1$ and is decreasing beyond $x = 1$. Assuming that the function is defined at $x = 1$, what does its graph look like there? What can be said about the derivative of the function at $x = 1$?

In Problems 35–38, use the interpretation of the derivative as the slope of the graph to sketch the function f' if the following are graphs of f.

35. 36. 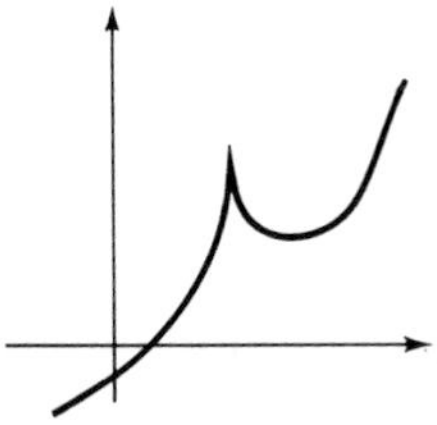 37. 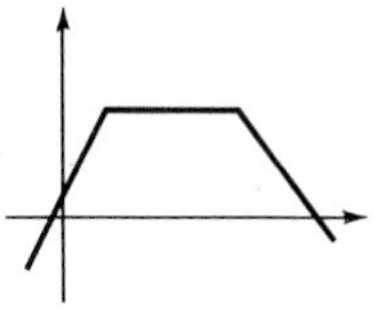 38.

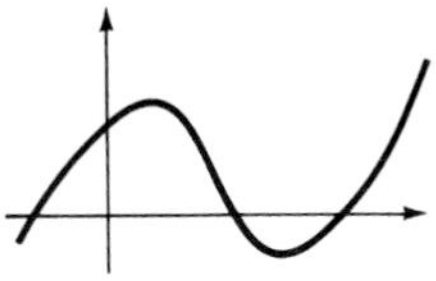

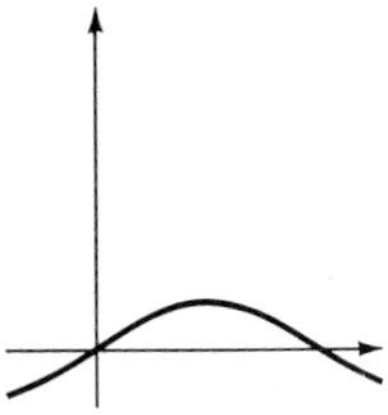

5.3

Derivative Formulas: Sum and Product Formulas

Although the derivative is a very important concept and one for which there are many applications, we have so far seen only the very simplest applications. Before looking at more important ones, it would be well for you to achieve a greater facility in finding derivatives of functions.

Until now we have relied on the definition to find derivatives of functions, and the process has been rather tedious even for the relatively simple functions with which we have been dealing. Imagine what a problem it would be to find the derivative of

$$y = \frac{x\sqrt{x+1}}{x^2 - 4} \quad \text{or} \quad y = \left(\frac{x^2+1}{x^2-1}\right)^{2/3}$$

by the definition! Obviously some easier method of taking derivatives is needed. We shall now begin to consider some short cuts.

Theorem 5.1

If f is a function such that $f(x) = c$, then $f'(x) = 0$. (In other words, the derivative of a constant is zero.)

Proof

$$\begin{aligned} f'(x) &= \lim_{h \to 0} \frac{f(x+h) - f(x)}{h} \\ &= \lim_{h \to 0} \frac{c - c}{h} \\ &= \lim_{h \to 0} 0 \\ &= 0. \end{aligned}$$

This result is quite obvious graphically. The graph of $f(x) = c$ is a horizontal line, which has slope 0 at every point.

Theorem 5.2

If f is a function such that $f(x) = x^n$, where n is a positive integer, then $f'(x) = nx^{n-1}$. (In other words, the derivative of x to a power is the exponent times x to the next lower power.)

Proof

$$\begin{aligned} f'(x) &= \lim_{h \to 0} \frac{f(x+h) - f(x)}{h} \\ &= \lim_{h \to 0} \frac{(x+h)^n - x^n}{h} \\ &= \lim_{h \to 0} \frac{x^n + nx^{n-1}h + [n(n-1)/2!]x^{n-2}h^2 + \cdots + h^n - x^n}{h} \\ &= \lim_{h \to 0} \left(nx^{n-1} + \frac{n(n-1)}{2!} x^{n-2}h + \cdots + h^{n-1} \right) \\ &= nx^{n-1}. \end{aligned}$$

With this formula we can see that if $y = x^2$, then $y' = 2x$, a fact we proved earlier with much more difficulty. Actually, this formula holds whether n is restricted to positive integers or not. We have already proved it for the case $n = 0$. If $y = x^0 = 1$, then $y' = 0 \cdot x^{0-1} = 0$. This same formula will be derived later with fewer restrictions on n.

Theorem 5.3

If u and v are differentiable at x and f is a function such that $f(x) = u(x) + v(x)$, then $f'(x) = u'(x) + v'(x)$. (That is to say, the derivative of a sum is the sum of the derivatives.)

Proof

$$\begin{aligned} f'(x) &= \lim_{h \to 0} \frac{f(x+h) - f(x)}{h} \\ &= \lim_{h \to 0} \frac{[u(x+h) + v(x+h)] - [u(x) + v(x)]}{h} \\ &= \lim_{h \to 0} \left(\frac{u(x+h) - u(x)}{h} + \frac{v(x+h) - v(x)}{h} \right) \\ &= u'(x) + v'(x). \end{aligned}$$

A similar result can be proved for the sum of three or more functions as well as for the difference of two functions (which may also be extended to more than two terms). Thus, if

$$f(x) = x^3 - x^2 + x - 3,$$

then

$$f'(x) = 3x^2 - 2x + 1.$$

Although it might be assumed that the same type of formula would work for products and quotients, it is easily seen that this is not the case; for if

$$u(x) = x,\ v(x) = x \quad \text{and} \quad f(x) = u(x) \cdot v(x) = x^2,$$

then

$$f'(x) = 2x \quad \text{but} \quad u'(x) \cdot v'(x) = 1 \cdot 1 = 1 \neq f'(x).$$

Thus the derivative of a product is *not* merely the product of the derivatives.

Theorem 5.4

(Product rule) If u and v are differentiable at x and f is a function such that

$$f(x) = u(x) \cdot v(x),$$

then

$$f'(x) = u(x) \cdot v'(x) + v(x) \cdot u'(x).$$

(The derivative of a product is the first factor times the derivative of the second plus the second factor times the derivative of the first.)

Proof

$$\begin{aligned} f'(x) &= \lim_{h\to 0} \frac{f(x+h) - f(x)}{h} \\ &= \lim_{h\to 0} \frac{u(x+h) \cdot v(x+h) - u(x) \cdot v(x)}{h} \\ &= \lim_{h\to 0} \frac{u(x+h) \cdot v(x+h) - u(x+h) \cdot v(x) + u(x+h) \cdot v(x) - u(x) \cdot v(x)}{h} \qquad \text{(See Note 1.)} \\ &= \lim_{h\to 0} \left[u(x+h) \frac{v(x+h) - v(x)}{h} + v(x) \frac{u(x+h) - u(x)}{h} \right] \\ &= u(x) \cdot v'(x) + v(x) \cdot u'(x). \qquad \text{(See Note 2.)} \end{aligned}$$

Note 1: All that was done here was to add and subtract $u(x + h) \cdot v(x)$ from the numerator. You might well ask, "How did you know to do that?" The answer "It works" is not very satisfactory. Let us look for a more reasonable answer. At the second step we had

$$\lim_{h\to 0} \frac{u(x+h) \cdot v(x+h) - u(x) \cdot v(x)}{h}.$$

In its place, we would like something that can be handled easily and looks almost like the expression we have. This expression would be much easier to handle if the $u(x)$ were, instead, $u(x+h)$—to match the $u(x+h)$ in the other term. That way the $u(x+h)$ could be factored out, and the limit of the expression which remains is a derivative.

Of course, if we want the new expression to be equal to the former one, we must compensate for it in some way. We do this by putting it in a second time, with the opposite sign. This same idea will be repeated several times later on. To summarize, when we do not have what we want, we simply put in what we do want and compensate for it to have equality.

Note 2: In taking the limit, we had $\lim_{h\to 0} u(x+h)$, which we assumed to be $u(x)$. As we shall see later, $\lim_{h\to 0} u(x+h)$ is not always $u(x)$. However, it is true for a certain class of functions which we might describe as "well behaved." Fortunately most of the functions that we shall be dealing with are "well behaved" and, until we take up this question in more detail, all of the functions we consider will satisfy the condition that $\lim_{h\to 0} u(x+h) = u(x)$.

Theorem 5.5

If u is differentiable at x and f is a function such that $f(x) = c \cdot u(x)$, then $f'(x) = c \cdot u'(x)$. (In other words, the derivative of a constant times a function of x is the constant times the derivative of the function.)

Proof

$$\begin{aligned} f'(x) &= c \cdot u'(x) + u(x) \cdot \frac{d}{dx} c, && \text{by Theorem 5.4,} \\ &= c \cdot u'(x) + u(x) \cdot 0, && \text{by Theorem 5.1,} \\ &= c \cdot u'(x). \end{aligned}$$

Example 1

Differentiate $y = 6x^3$.

$$y' = 6 \cdot 3x^2 = 18x^2.$$

Example 2

Differentiate $y = 4x^3 + 3x^2 - 2x + 2$.

$$\begin{aligned} y' &= 4 \cdot 3x^2 + 3 \cdot 2x - 2 \cdot 1 + 0 \\ &= 12x^2 + 6x - 2. \end{aligned}$$

With very little practice you should be able to omit the intermediate step and go directly to the final answer.

Example 3

Differentiate $y = (x^2 + x + 1)(x + 1)$.

There are two methods of differentiating. We can either differentiate by the product rule and simplify the result, or we can multiply first and differentiate the result. Both methods are given here.

$$\begin{aligned} y' &= (x^2 + x + 1)1 + (x + 1)(2x + 1) \\ &= x^2 + x + 1 + 2x^2 + 3x + 1 \\ &= 3x^2 + 4x + 2 \end{aligned}$$

or

$$\begin{aligned} y &= (x^2 + x + 1)(x + 1) \\ &= x^3 + 2x^2 + 2x + 1 \\ y' &= 3x^2 + 4x + 2. \end{aligned}$$

Problems

In Problems 1–12, differentiate the given function.

1. $y = 3x^2 + 5x - 2$.
2. $y = 4x^3 + 2x - 5$.
3. $y = x^5 + 5x^4$.
4. $y = x^4 + 1$.
5. $y = 7x^5 + 5x^3 + x - 3$.
6. $u = 5v^7 + 7v^5$.
7. $t = 4s^3 - 3s^2 - 12s$.
8. $y = (x^2 + 1)(x - 1)$.
9. $y = (x^2 + 2x - 1)(x^2 - 2x + 1)$.
10. $y = (x^4 + 1)(x^4 - 1)$.
11. $p = (q^3 + q)(q^2 + 1)$.
12. $y = x(x + 1)(x - 1)$.

In Problems 13–18, find the derivative at the indicated point.

13. $y = 3x^2 - 5x + 2$ at $(1, 0)$.
14. $y = 4x^3 - 4x$ at $(-1, 0)$.
15. $y = x^4 + 4x$ at $(2, 24)$.
16. $y = x^5 - 5x^3$ at $x = 5$.
17. $y = (x^4 + 1)(x^2 - 1)$ at $(1, 0)$.
18. $y = (2x^2 + 1)(x^3 - 1)$ at $x = -1$.
19. At what point(s) does the tangent to $y = x^2 + x$ have slope 1?
20. At what point(s) does the tangent to $y = (x^2 + 1)(2x - 1)$ have slope 2?
21. At what point(s) does $y = x^3 - 12x^2 + 45x - 55$ have a horizontal tangent?
22. At what point(s) does $y = x^4 - 2x^2$ have a horizontal tangent?
23. Find an equation of the line tangent to $y = x^3 + 2x + 1$ at the point $(1, 4)$.
24. Find an equation of the line tangent to $y = x^3$ at the point $(2, 8)$.
25. Prove that if $f(x) = u(x)v(x)w(x)$, then

$$f'(x) = u(x)v(x)w'(x) + u(x)v'(x)w(x) + u'(x)v(x)w(x).$$

If $f(x)$ is the product of four functions, what is $f'(x)$?

In Problems 26–29, use the results of Problem 25 to find the derivative.

26. $y = x(x - 2)(x + 1)$.
27. $y = (x + 1)(x + 2)(x + 3)$.
28. $y = (x^2 + 1)(x^2 + 2)(2x - 1)$.
29. $y = (x - 1)(x - 2)(x - 3)(x - 4)$.
30. Prove that if $f(x) = u(x) + v(x) + w(x)$, then $f'(x) = u'(x) + v'(x) + w'(x)$.
31. Prove that if $f(x) = u(x) - v(x)$, then $f'(x) = u'(x) - v'(x)$.
32. Prove Theorem 5.4 by adding and subtracting $u(x)v(x + h)$ instead of $u(x + h) \cdot v(x)$.
33. Give an example of a function $f(x)$ such that $\lim_{h\to 0} f(x + h) \neq f(x)$ for some value of x.
34. Prove that if $f(x) = u_1(x) + u_2(x) + u_3(x) + \cdots + u_n(x)$, where n is a positive integer, then

$$f'(x) = u_1'(x) + u_2'(x) + u_3'(x) + \cdots + u_n'(x).$$

5.4

Derivative Formulas: Quotient Rule and Chain Rule

Theorem 5.6

(Quotient rule) If u and v are differentiable at x, $v(x) \neq 0$, and f is a function such that $f(x) = u(x)/v(x)$, then

$$f'(x) = \frac{v(x) \cdot u'(x) - u(x) \cdot v'(x)}{v(x)^2}.$$

(The derivative of a quotient is the denominator times the derivative of the numerator minus the numerator times the derivative of the denominator, all divided by the denominator squared.)

Proof

$$f'(x) = \lim_{h \to 0} \frac{f(x+h) - f(x)}{h}$$

$$= \lim_{h \to 0} \frac{\dfrac{u(x+h)}{v(x+h)} - \dfrac{u(x)}{v(x)}}{h}$$

$$= \lim_{h \to 0} \frac{v(x) \cdot u(x+h) - v(x+h) \cdot u(x)}{v(x)v(x+h)h}$$

$$= \lim_{h \to 0} \frac{\dfrac{v(x) \cdot u(x+h) - v(x+h) \cdot u(x)}{h}}{v(x)v(x+h)}$$

$$= \lim_{h \to 0} \frac{\dfrac{v(x) \cdot u(x+h) - v(x) \cdot u(x) + v(x) \cdot u(x) - v(x+h)u(x)}{h}}{v(x)v(x+h)}$$

(See Note 1.)

$$= \lim_{h \to 0} \frac{v(x)\dfrac{u(x+h) - u(x)}{h} - u(x)\dfrac{v(x+h) - v(x)}{h}}{v(x)v(x+h)}$$

$$= \frac{v(x) \cdot u'(x) - u(x) \cdot v'(x)}{[v(x)]^2}.$$

(See Note 2.)

Note 1: (Note 1 of Theorem 5.4 also applies here.) We add and subtract $v(x) \cdot u(x)$. This particular expression is selected because we want a $v(x)$ to match the one in the first term so it can be factored out and a $u(x)$ so that

$$\frac{u(x-h) - u(x)}{h}$$

remains after the factoring.

Note 2: We also assume here that $\lim_{h \to 0} v(x+h) = v(x)$. Actually, this is true because of the hypothesis that v is differentiable at x.

Example 1

Differentiate $y = \dfrac{x+1}{x-2}$.

$$y' = \frac{(x-2)\cdot 1 - (x+1)\cdot 1}{(x-2)^2} = \frac{-3}{(x-2)^2}.$$

With Theorem 5.6, we can now extend Theorem 5.2.

Theorem 5.7

If f is a function such that $f(x) = x^n$, where n is an integer, then $f'(x) = nx^{n-1}$.

Proof

It has already been proved for the cases in which n is positive or zero. The only remaining case is that in which n is negative. In that case, there is a positive integer k such that $n = -k$. Thus,

$$f(x) = x^{-k} = 1/x^k.$$

By Theorems 5.6 and 5.2,

$$f'(x) = \frac{x^k \cdot 0 - 1 \cdot kx^{k-1}}{x^{2k}} = -kx^{-k-1} = nx^{n-1}.$$

Before considering other differentiation formulas, it is convenient to have another form for the derivative of a function—that is, a form different from the definition. To do so it is convenient to look back at the geometric motivation for the derivative. Compare (a) and (b) of Figure 5.9; basically, they represent the same thing, but they use different notation. Similarly, the slope of the line AP can be represented by

$$m_{AP} = \frac{f(x+h) - f(x)}{x+h-x} = \frac{f(x+h) - f(x)}{h}$$

or

$$m_{AP} = \frac{f(t) - f(x)}{t - x} = \frac{f(x) - f(t)}{x - t},$$

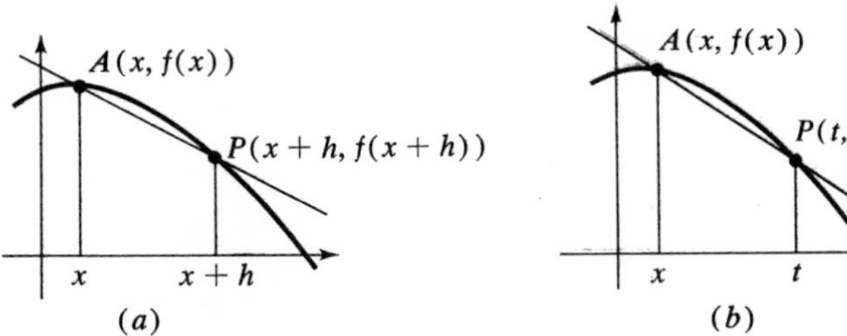

Figure 5.9

and as P approaches A, h approaches 0 and t approaches x. Thus, when we defined the derivative as

$$f'(x) = \lim_{h\to 0} \frac{f(x+h) - f(x)}{h},$$

we could just as easily have used

$$f'(x) = \lim_{t\to x} \frac{f(t) - f(x)}{t - x} = \lim_{t\to x} \frac{f(x) - f(t)}{x - t},$$

which is the statement of the next theorem.

Theorem 5.8

$$f'(x) = \lim_{t\to x} \frac{f(t) - f(x)}{t - x} = \lim_{t\to x} \frac{f(x) - f(t)}{x - t}.$$

This theorem can also be proved directly from the definition of derivative without recourse to the above geometric argument, by making the substitution $t = x + h$. For some purposes, this new form for the derivative is more convenient than the definition. Some authors use this as the definition and derive the other form from it.

Our next theorem uses the result of this one, but first let us take up a question touched upon earlier in connection with notation. Suppose y is a function of u while u is in turn a function of x, in which case y is a function of x as well as a function of u. Thus, if $y = f(u)$ and $u = g(x)$, then

$$y = f(g(x)) = F(x).$$

We may now consider two derivatives of y—the derivative of y with respect to u, which is dy/du, and the derivative of y with respect to x, which is dy/dx. Now when these derivatives are presented in the limit forms, how do we distinguish one from another? Basically it is done merely by noting that there are two different functions, $f(u)$ and $F(x)$. The important thing to note here is not the difference between u and x but the difference between the *functions* f and F. Thus

$$\frac{dy}{du} = \lim_{h\to 0} \frac{f(u+h) - f(u)}{h} = \lim_{t\to u} \frac{f(t) - f(u)}{t - u},$$

while

$$\frac{dy}{dx} = \lim_{h\to 0} \frac{F(x+h) - F(x)}{h} = \lim_{t\to x} \frac{F(t) - F(x)}{t - x}.$$

Since $u = g(x)$ and $F(x) = f(g(x))$, both can be written in other forms. Thus we get

$$\frac{dy}{du} = \lim_{t\to u} \frac{f(t) - f(u)}{t - u} = \lim_{g(s)\to g(x)} \frac{f(g(s)) - f(g(x))}{g(s) - g(x)},$$

simply by substituting $u = g(x)$ and $t = g(s)$. Note that the letters used here are immaterial; if t had not been used for something else, it might have been used instead of s, thus:

$$\frac{dy}{du} = \lim_{g(t)\to g(x)} \frac{f(g(t)) - f(g(x))}{g(t) - g(x)}.$$

Similarly,

$$\frac{dy}{dx} = \lim_{t\to x} \frac{F(t) - F(x)}{t - x} = \lim_{t\to x} \frac{f(g(t)) - f(g(x))}{t - x}.$$

Theorem 5.9

(Chain rule) If f and g are functions such that g is differentiable at x and f is differentiable at $u = g(x)$ and F is a function such that $F(x) = f(g(x))$, then

$$\frac{d}{dx} F(x) = \frac{d}{du} f(u) \cdot \frac{d}{dx} g(x).$$

A simpler, but less accurate statement of this theorem is: If $y = f(u)$ and $u = g(x)$, then

$$\frac{dy}{dx} = \frac{dy}{du} \cdot \frac{du}{dx}.$$

Note here that the differential notation is an aid to the memory. While you are reminded not to think of dy/du and du/dx as fractions, they seem to behave as if they were.

Proof

Since $y = f(u)$ and $u = g(x)$, $y = f(g(x)) = F(x)$.

$$\begin{aligned}\frac{dy}{dx} &= \lim_{t\to x} \frac{F(t) - F(x)}{t - x} \\ &= \lim_{t\to x} \frac{f(g(t)) - f(g(x))}{t - x}.\end{aligned}$$

Now let us stop and take stock. Given

$$\lim_{t\to x} \frac{f(g(t)) - f(g(x))}{t - x},$$

we prefer to have

$$\lim_{t\to x} \frac{g(t) - g(x)}{t - x}.$$

Normally we just put in the desired factor and compensate to give equality. This gives

$$\lim_{t\to x} \frac{f(g(t)) - f(g(x))}{g(t) - g(x)} \cdot \frac{g(t) - g(x)}{t - x}.$$

But this time we have a special problem—we have no assurance that $g(t) - g(x) \neq 0$. Let us split the argument into two cases.

Case I: $g(t) \neq g(x)$ for any t within a distance H of x. By choosing t close enough to x, we are assured that $g(t) - g(x) \neq 0$. Thus, for $|t - x|$ small enough,

$$\frac{dy}{dx} = \lim_{t \to x} \frac{f(g(t)) - f(g(x))}{g(t) - g(x)} \cdot \frac{g(t) - g(x)}{t - x}$$

$$= \frac{df(u)}{du} \cdot \frac{dg(x)}{dx} \qquad \text{(See Note.)}$$

$$= \frac{dy}{du} \cdot \frac{du}{dx}.$$

Case II: No matter how small H is, there is a number t within a distance H of x such that $g(t) = g(x)$. Note that this does not imply that $g(t) = g(x)$ for *all* t within a distance H of x; it does imply that $g(t) = g(x)$ for infinitely many values of t within a distance H of x. In any case

$$\lim_{t \to x} \frac{g(t) - g(x)}{t - x} = 0,$$

since we know that this limit (which is $g'(x)$) exists and

$$\frac{g(t) - g(x)}{t - x} = 0$$

for values of t arbitrarily close to x. Now let us consider

$$\lim_{t \to x} \frac{F(t) - F(x)}{t - x}.$$

First let M be the set of all numbers t of the domain of F such that t is within a distance H of x and $g(t) \neq g(x)$; let N be the set of all numbers t of the domain of F such that t is within a distance H of x and $g(t) = g(x)$. If M contains numbers arbitrarily close to x, then (by Case I)

$$\lim_{\substack{t \to x \\ t \text{ in } M}} \frac{F(t) - F(x)}{t - x} = \frac{dy}{du} \cdot \frac{du}{dx} = \frac{dy}{du} \cdot 0 = 0.$$

If M does not contain numbers arbitrarily close to x, we need not consider this limit. In addition,

$$\lim_{\substack{t \to x \\ t \text{ in } N}} \frac{F(t) - F(x)}{t - x} = \lim_{\substack{t \to x \\ t \text{ in } N}} \frac{f(g(t)) - f(g(x))}{t - x} = \lim_{\substack{t \to x \\ t \text{ in } N}} \frac{f(g(x)) - f(g(x))}{t - x}$$

$$= 0.$$

Thus the combination of these two limits gives

$$\frac{dy}{dx} = \lim_{t \to x} \frac{F(t) - F(x)}{t - x} = 0 = \frac{dy}{du} \cdot \frac{du}{dx}.$$

Note: While we had indicated that

$$\frac{dy}{du} = \lim_{g(t) \to g(x)} \frac{f(g(t)) - f(g(x))}{g(t) - g(x)},$$

the above limit is

$$\lim_{t \to x} \frac{f(g(t)) - f(g(x))}{g(t) - g(x)}.$$

We are assuming again that as t approaches x, $g(t)$ approaches $g(x)$. This is, in fact, the case because $g'(x)$ exists. Thus these two limits are equivalent.

The chain rule is very important and we shall use it to prove the next two theorems, as well as several others.

Theorem 5.10

If f is a function such that $f(x) = x^n$, where n is any rational number, then $y' = nx^{n-1}$.

Proof

First, $n = p/q$ where p and q are integers, and q is positive. Now we shall split the argument into two parts. We shall show first that $y' = nx^{n-1}$ if $n = 1/q$ (where q is a positive integer); then we shall use this together with the chain rule to prove the general case.

Suppose that $y = x^{1/q}$ where q is a positive integer. Then

$$y' = \lim_{t\to x} \frac{t^{1/q} - x^{1/q}}{t - x}.$$

Using the substitutions $z = x^{1/q}$ and $s = t^{1/q}$, we get

$$\begin{aligned}
y' &= \lim_{s^q\to z^q} \frac{s - z}{s^q - z^q} \\
&= \lim_{s\to z} \frac{s - z}{(s - z)(s^{q-1} + s^{q-2}z + s^{q-3}z^2 + \cdots + sz^{q-2} + z^{q-1})} \\
&= \lim_{s\to z} \frac{1}{(s^{q-1} + s^{q-2}z + s^{q-3}z^2 + \cdots + sz^{q-2} + z^{q-1})} \\
&= \frac{1}{qz^{q-1}} \\
&= \frac{1}{q}\, z^{1-q} \\
&= \frac{1}{q}\, (x^{1/q})^{1-q} \\
&= \frac{1}{q}\, x^{(1/q)-1}.
\end{aligned}$$

Thus, if $n = 1/q$ and $y = x^n$, then $y' = nx^{n-1}$.

Now suppose $y = x^{p/q}$ where p and q are integers and q is positive. Then $y = (x^{1/q})^p$. By substituting $u = x^{1/q}$ we have $y = u^p$.

$$\begin{aligned}
\frac{dy}{dx} &= \frac{dy}{du}\cdot\frac{du}{dx} \\
&= pu^{p-1}\cdot\frac{1}{q}\, x^{(1/q)-1} \\
&= \frac{p}{q}\, (x^{1/q})^{p-1} x^{(1/q)-1} \\
&= \frac{p}{q}\, x^{(p/q)-(1/q)} x^{(1/q)-1} \\
&= \frac{p}{q}\, x^{(p/q)-1}.
\end{aligned}$$

Thus, the formula which was first stated for positive integers in Theorem 5.2 was extended to all integers in Theorem 5.7 and now applies to all rational numbers. We shall not be in a position to prove it for all real numbers until Chapter 12 (see Theorem 12.6, page 271). Nevertheless, the extensions we have made allow us to find derivatives of a wide range of functions.

Example 2

Differentiate $y = \sqrt{x}$.

$$y = \sqrt{x} = x^{1/2},$$

$$y' = \frac{1}{2}x^{-1/2} = \frac{1}{2\sqrt{x}}.$$

Example 3

Differentiate $y = \dfrac{x+2}{\sqrt{x}}$.

There are several possible methods. Two are illustrated.

$$y = \frac{x+2}{x^{1/2}}, \qquad\qquad y = x^{1/2} + 2x^{-1/2},$$

$$y' = \frac{x^{1/2}\cdot 1 - (x+2)\dfrac{1}{2}x^{-1/2}}{x} \qquad\qquad y' = \frac{1}{2}x^{-1/2} - x^{-3/2}$$

$$= \frac{\sqrt{x} - \dfrac{x+2}{2\sqrt{x}}}{x} \qquad\qquad = \frac{1}{2x^{1/2}} - \frac{1}{x^{3/2}}$$

$$= \frac{2x - (x+2)}{2x^{3/2}} \qquad\qquad = \frac{x-2}{2x^{3/2}}.$$

$$= \frac{x-2}{2x^{3/2}}.$$

In this case we have avoided the relatively complicated quotient formula by carrying out the division and using negative exponents. While this method is not universally recommended, it sometimes simplifies a problem considerably.

Example 4

Differentiate $y = \dfrac{1}{x}$.

$$y' = \frac{x\cdot 0 - 1\cdot 1}{x^2} = \frac{-1}{x^2}.$$

However, by writing the original problem as $y = x^{-1}$, we get

$$y' = -x^{-2} = -\frac{1}{x^2}.$$

The use of negative exponents makes the problem simple enough to do in your head. This method cannot be used to advantage when the denominator is very complicated, and it is not always advisable when it is simple.

Problems

In Problems 1–22, differentiate.

1. $y = \dfrac{1}{x^2}$.

2. $y = \dfrac{1}{x^3}$.

3. $y = \dfrac{x^2+1}{x}$.

4. $y = \dfrac{x-1}{x^2}$.

5. $y = x^{2/3} - a^{2/3}$ (a is a constant).

6. $y = \dfrac{x}{x^2+1}$.

7. $y = \dfrac{x^2}{x-1}$.

8. $y = \dfrac{x^2-x}{x+1}$.

9. $s = t^{2/3} - t^{-1/3}$.

10. $s = \dfrac{3}{4}t^{4/3} + 3t^{1/3} + \dfrac{3}{2}t^{-2/3}$.

11. $u = \dfrac{v^2+2v+2}{v^2-2v-2}$.

12. $u = \dfrac{v^2+a^2}{v^2-a^2}$ (a is a constant).

13. $p = \dfrac{q^{2/3}+a^{2/3}}{q^{2/3}-a^{2/3}}$ (a is a constant).

14. $p = \dfrac{q^2-q^{1/3}}{q^{-2}-q^{-1/3}}$.

15. $y = \dfrac{(x^2-1)(2x+3)}{x}$.

16. $y = \dfrac{(2x-5)(3x+2)}{x+1}$.

17. $y = \dfrac{(x^2+x+1)(x-2)}{x^2+1}$.

18. $y = \dfrac{(x-1)(2x+1)}{(x+2)(3x-1)}$.

19. $s = \dfrac{(t^{1/3}-t)(t^{2/3}+t)}{t^2}$.

20. $u = \dfrac{(v^{1/2}-v^{-1/2})(v^2+1)}{v^{1/2}}$.

21. $y = \dfrac{\sqrt{x}+\sqrt[3]{x}}{\sqrt{x}-\sqrt[3]{x}}$.

22. $y = \dfrac{5\sqrt[5]{x}-3\sqrt[3]{x}}{5\sqrt[5]{x}+3\sqrt[3]{x}}$.

In Problems 23–28, find the derivative at the point indicated.

23. $y = x^{1/2} - x^{1/3}$ at $(1, 0)$.

24. $y = \dfrac{x+1}{x-2}$ at $(1, -2)$.

25. $y = \dfrac{x^2-3}{3x^2-1}$ at $x = 2$.

26. $y = \sqrt[3]{x} - 2$ at $(8, 0)$.

27. $y = \dfrac{x^3-1}{x^2+2}$ at $\left(-1, -\dfrac{2}{3}\right)$.

28. $y = \dfrac{\sqrt{x}+1}{\sqrt[3]{x}-1}$ at $x = 64$.

29. At what point(s) does the tangent to $y = 2x^3 - 3x^2 + 1$ have slope 12?
30. At what point(s) does the tangent to $y = 2x^3 - 3x^2 + 1$ have slope 0?
31. At what point(s) does $y = \dfrac{x^2}{x^2+1}$ have a horizontal tangent?
32. At what point(s) does $y = \sqrt[3]{x}$ have a vertical tangent?
33. Find an equation of the line tangent to $y = \sqrt{x}$ at the point $(4, 2)$.

34. Find an equation of the line tangent to $y = \dfrac{x+1}{x-1}$ at the point (2, 3).
35. Prove Theorem 5.6 by adding and subtracting $v(x+h) \cdot u(x+h)$ instead of $v(x) \cdot u(x)$.
36. Prove Theorem 5.2 by using Theorem 5.8 instead of the definition of derivative.

5.5

Derivative Formulas: Power Rule

We now extend Theorem 5.10 and, in proving the new theorem illustrate a second use of the chain rule. It will be used again to extend other theorems.

Theorem 5.11

(*Power rule*) *If u is a function that is differentiable at x and f is a function such that* $f(x) = [u(x)]^n$, *where n is a rational number, then*

$$f'(x) = n[u(x)]^{n-1} \cdot u'(x).$$

(*More simply, if* $y = u^n$, *then* $dy/dx = nu^{n-1} \cdot du/dx$.)

Proof

By the chain rule, we have

$$\frac{dy}{dx} = \frac{dy}{du} \cdot \frac{du}{dx}$$

$$= nu^{n-1} \cdot \frac{du}{dx}.$$

Example 1

Differentiate $y = (x^2+1)^2$.

$$y' = 2(x^2+1) \cdot 2x$$
$$= 4x(x^2+1).$$

Compare this with the power rule formula. The "u" here is x^2+1. Thus nu^{n-1} is $2(x^2+1)^1$, while $u' = 2x$. The derivative can be found here without using Theorem 5.11.

$$y = (x^2+1)^2 = x^4 + 2x^2 + 1,$$
$$y' = 4x^3 + 4x = 4x(x^2+1).$$

Example 2

Differentiate $y = (x^2 + 1)^{2/3}$.

$$y' = \frac{2}{3}(x^2 + 1)^{-1/3}2x$$

$$= \frac{4x}{3(x^2 + 1)^{1/3}}.$$

In this case, we cannot resort to the method of expansion by the binomial theorem—we must use Theorem 5.11. If you protest that the binomial theorem can be used even in this case, when the exponent is not a positive integer, a few things should be noted about that situation. First of all, the expansion cannot be given in finite terms—the result is an infinite series. This subject is better postponed until we are in a position to answer some of the questions that it brings up. What is an infinite series or infinite sum? Does the sum always exist? Does it ever exist? You might also look back to the place you first saw the binomial theorem for exponents other than positive integers. Very likely it appeared in an algebra book and was stated after the binomial theorem for positive integers; and while a proof was given for the binomial theorem for positive integers, none was given for the other cases. Even assuming that the expansion can be carried out, there is the problem of extending Theorem 5.3 to an infinite sum.

Of course, even if we determined that the expansion could be carried out and Theorem 5.3 could be extended to the infinite case, the question still arises, "Do we really want to do it this way when Theorem 5.11 gives us such a simple way of taking the derivative?" This question might arise in connection with the problem of finding the derivative of $y = (2x^3 - 5)^{12}$. While it is clear that this expression can be expanded and differentiated term by term, Theorem 5.11 offers a *far simpler* method of differentiation.

Example 3

Differentiate $y = \dfrac{(x + 1)^2}{(x - 2)^3}$.

By the quotient rule,

$$y' = \frac{(x - 2)^3 2(x + 1) - (x + 1)^2 3(x - 2)^2}{(x - 2)^6}$$

$$= \frac{(x + 1)(x - 2)^2[2(x - 2) - 3(x + 1)]}{(x - 2)^6}$$

$$= \frac{(x + 1)(-x - 7)}{(x - 2)^4}$$

$$= -\frac{(x + 1)(x + 7)}{(x - 2)^4}.$$

Example 4

Differentiate $y = \sqrt{\dfrac{2x-1}{2x+1}}$.

$$y = \left(\frac{2x-1}{2x+1}\right)^{1/2},$$

$$y' = \frac{1}{2}\left(\frac{2x-1}{2x+1}\right)^{-1/2} \frac{(2x+1)2-(2x-1)2}{(2x+1)^2}$$

$$= \frac{(2x+1)^{1/2}\cdot 4}{2(2x-1)^{1/2}(2x+1)^2}$$

$$= \frac{2}{(2x-1)^{1/2}(2x+1)^{3/2}}.$$

Problems

In Problems 1–22, differentiate.

1. $y = (x+1)^4$.
2. $y = (x^2+2)^3$.
3. $y = (4x+2)^5$.
4. $y = (3x-5)^4$.
5. $y = \sqrt{4x+2}$.
6. $y = \sqrt[3]{2x-5}$.
7. $p = (q^3-8)^{2/3}$.
8. $p = (8q-1)^{-1/3}$.
9. $y = \sqrt{\dfrac{x+1}{x-1}}$.
10. $y = \sqrt[3]{\dfrac{x^3+1}{x^3-1}}$.
11. $u = \dfrac{(v+1)^{2/3}}{(v-1)^{1/3}}$.
12. $u = \dfrac{v^2-v}{(v+1)^2}$.
13. $y = \left(\dfrac{2x-1}{2x+1}\right)^{2/3}$.
14. $y = (x^{2/3}-a^{2/3})^{1/3}$, a is a constant.
15. $y = x + \sqrt{x+1}$.
16. $y = x - \sqrt{x+1}$.
17. $y = (x^{-2}+x)^{-3}$.
18. $y = (x^{-2}+x^{-1})^{-2}$.
19. $y = \dfrac{x^{-2}+x^{-1}}{x^{-2}-x^{-1}}$.
20. $y = \sqrt{x+\sqrt{x+\sqrt{x}}}$.
21. $y = \dfrac{x\sqrt{x+1}}{x^2-4}$.
22. $y = \left(\dfrac{x^2+1}{x^2-1}\right)^{2/3}$.

In Problems 23–28, find the derivative at the point indicated.

23. $y = (x^2+1)^3$ at $x = 1$.
24. $y = (x^{1/3}-2)^3$ at $(8, 0)$.
25. $y = \dfrac{(x-1)^3}{(x+2)^2}$ at $(-1, -8)$.
26. $y = \dfrac{\sqrt{x+1}}{\sqrt[3]{3x-1}}$ at $x = 3$.
27. $y = (x^{-2}+x^{-1})^{-1}$ at $x = 1$.
28. $y = x - \sqrt{x^2+5}$ at $(2, -1)$.
29. For what value(s) of x does the tangent to $y = \dfrac{x+2}{x-3}$ have slope -5?
30. For what value(s) of x does the tangent to $y = (x-3)^3$ have slope 3?
31. For what value(s) of x does $y = (x-2)^2(x-3)^3$ have a horizontal tangent?
32. For what value(s) of x does $y = \dfrac{1}{(x-2)^2}$ have a vertical tangent?

33. Find an equation of the line tangent to $y = (x - 4)^2$ at the point (1, 9).
34. Find an equation of the line tangent to $y = (x - 1)^{2/3}$ at the point (1, 0).
35. Find the derivative of $y = \sqrt{x^2}$. What is the derivative for $x = 1, 3, 8, -2, -5, -7, 0$? Can you express y in a different form?
36. Repeat problem 35 for $y = \sqrt{(x - 1)^2}$.
37. Show that if $f(x) = (x - a)^n \cdot P(x)$, then $f'(x) = (x - a)^{n-1} \cdot Q(x)$. What does the graph of $f(x) = (x - 1)^2(x + 3)$ look like at $x = 1$?

5.6

Derivatives of Implicit Functions

Until now, all of the functions we have considered in this chapter have been stated explicitly in the form, $y = f(x)$. However, many functions are only implied by an equation. For example, the equation of a parabola $(x - 1)^2 = 4(y + 1)$ implies that y is some function of x, namely,

$$y = \frac{1}{4}(x - 1)^2 - 1,$$

although it is not explicitly stated. Unfortunately, the problem is not always so simple; even some relatively simple equations imply a combination of several functions, rather than a single function. For instance, the equation $x^2 + y^2 = 4$ implies that $y = \pm\sqrt{4 - x^2}$. It is easily seen that y is not a function of x, since some values of x determine two values of y. However, y can be represented as a combination of the two functions $\sqrt{4 - x^2}$ and $-\sqrt{4 - x^2}$, the first representing the top half of the original circle and the second representing the bottom half (see Figure 5.10). Thus an equation may imply that one of the variables can be represented as a function—or combination of functions—of the other. These are referred to as implicit functions.

Now suppose that we have a function (or combination of functions) defined implicitly by an equation and we wish to find the derivative of it. How do we proceed? One obvious method would be to determine the function or functions and proceed

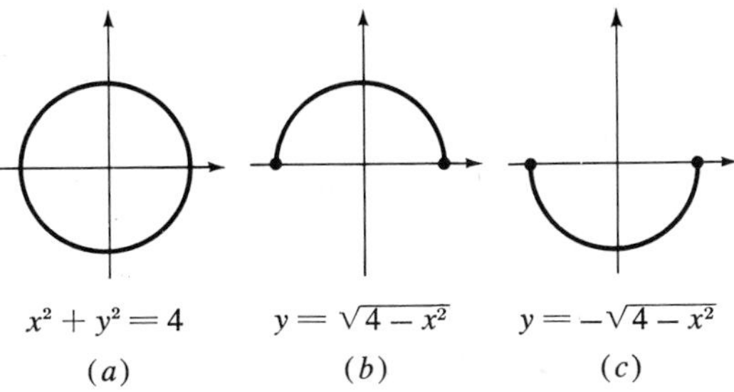

Figure 5.10

to find its derivative as in the past. For example, if we have $x^2 + y^2 = 4$, we find that

$$y = \sqrt{4 - x^2} \quad \text{or} \quad y = -\sqrt{4 - x^2}$$

and

$$y' = \frac{1}{2}(4 - x^2)^{-1/2}(-2x) \quad \text{or} \quad y' = -\frac{1}{2}(4 - x^2)^{-1/2}(-2x)$$

$$= \frac{-x}{\sqrt{4 - x^2}} \qquad\qquad = \frac{x}{\sqrt{4 - x^2}}.$$

Now if we want the derivative at a given point on the circle, we merely determine which of the two halves of the circle contains the point and use the derivative formula corresponding to that one. Thus, if we want the derivative at the point $(1, -\sqrt{3})$, we note that this point corresponds to

$$y = -\sqrt{4 - x^2} \quad \text{and} \quad y' = \frac{x}{\sqrt{4 - x^2}}$$

at $x = 1$, which gives $y' = 1/\sqrt{3}$.

This is all quite simple. But suppose we try to repeat this process with the equation $x^3 + 3x^2y + y^3 = 1$. We have considerably more trouble solving for y as a function of x. While we might be able to do so for this problem, we can easily imagine problems for which the solution is much more difficult or even impossible to find in the form we want. Nevertheless we feel that y can be represented as *some* function (or functions) of x. The fact that we cannot find it does not deny its existence. If we want the slope of the curve represented by some equation, must we give up if we cannot solve for y as a function of x, or is it still possible to find the slope without finding the function explicitly?

There is a way out. Since the general form is $F(x, y) = G(x, y)$, where y is some function of x, certainly the derivative of $F(x, y)$ with respect to x (remember that y is a function of x) equals the derivative of $G(x, y)$ with respect to x. Of course, since we have not solved for y as a function of x, we merely know that $y = f(x)$, but we do not know what $f(x)$ is. Thus, whenever we come to finding the derivative of y, we must simply leave it as dy/dx, or y'. Thus y' appears in the expression we get after taking derivatives of both $F(x, y)$ and $G(x, y)$ and sometimes we can solve for y' in terms of x and y.

Let us return to our equation for a circle,

$$x^2 + y^2 = 4.$$

Differentiating both sides (keep in mind that y is a function of x), we get

$$2x + 2yy' = 0, \quad \text{or} \quad y' = -\frac{x}{y}.$$

This process is called *implicit differentiation*. Now this result does not look at all like the result we had when solving for y and taking derivatives of the functions so obtained. Suppose we compare them.

$$\left.\begin{aligned} y' &= -\frac{x}{\sqrt{4-x^2}} \quad \text{when } y = \sqrt{4-x^2} \\ y' &= \frac{x}{\sqrt{4-x^2}} \quad \text{when } y = -\sqrt{4-x^2} \end{aligned}\right\} \text{from } x^2 + y^2 = 4$$

and

$$y' = -\frac{x}{y} \quad \text{when } x^2 + y^2 = 4.$$

The first thing to notice is that there are two forms for the derivative in the one case but only one in the other. Can the second result possibly be giving us as much as the first? Yes, because the second expression for the derivative has a "y" in it which is seen to be either $\sqrt{4-x^2}$ or $-\sqrt{4-x^2}$. When these are substituted for y, the second result looks like the first. Note that there is a certain advantage in using $y' = -x/y$, in that it gives us the derivatives of both functions at the same time. When we wanted the derivative at the point $(1, -\sqrt{3})$, we had to select the one of the two functions satisfied by the given point and substitute $x = 1$ into the derivative formula corresponding to that function. Now, since we have only one expression for the derivative and it has both x and y in it, we merely substitute $x = 1$ and $y = -\sqrt{3}$ into $y' = -x/y$ to get $y' = 1/\sqrt{3}$, the same result as before. Thus not only are we spared the chore of solving for y, but we have a simpler result to use.

Suppose we repeat this process for the more complicated equation

$$x^3 + 3x^2y + y^3 = 1;$$

$$3x^2 + 3(x^2y' + y \cdot 2x) + 3y^2y' = 0$$

$$x^2 + 2xy + (x^2 + y^2)y' = 0$$

$$y' = -\frac{x^2 + 2xy}{x^2 + y^2}.$$

As you can see, this is much simpler than first trying to solve for y and then differentiating.

Problems

In Problems 1–8, find dy/dx at the point indicated by (a) solving for y as a function(s) of x and finding the derivative of an explicit function and (b) using implicit differentiation.

1. $x^2 + 2y = 1$, $(1, 0)$.
2. $2x^2 + 3y - 5 = 0$, $(0, 5/3)$.
3. $y^2 = x$, $(4, 2)$.
4. $y^2 = 2x - 3$, $(2, -1)$.
5. $x^2 + y^2 + 2y = 0$, $(0, -2)$.
6. $4x^2 + 3xy - y^2 = 0$, $(3, -3)$.
7. $6x^2 - 5xy + y^2 + 2x - y = 0$, $(1, 4)$.
8. $x^3 + x^2y + y^2 - x = 0$, $(1, -1)$.

In Problems 9–26, find dy/dx.

9. $x^3 + y^3 = 5$.
10. $4x^2 - 5y^3 = 1$.
11. $x^{2/3} + y^{2/3} = 1$.
12. $\sqrt{x} + \sqrt{y} = 1$.
13. $x^{1/3} - y^{1/3} = 1$.
14. $x^{-1/3} + y^{-1/3} = 1$.

15. $xy = 4$.
16. $2x^2 - 2xy + y^2 = 1$.
17. $2xy - y^2 = 1$.
18. $(x + y)^2 = (x - y)^3$.
19. $(x + y)^2 = (x - y + 1)^2$.
20. $(x + y)^{2/3} = (x - y)^{2/3}$.
21. $x^3 + 3x^2y + y^3 = 8$.
22. $x^4 + 4x^2y^2 - y^4 = x + y$.
23. $(x^2 - y^2)^2 = x^2 + y^2$.
24. $\dfrac{x}{y} + \dfrac{y}{x} = x + y$.
25. $\dfrac{x + y}{x - y} = x^2 + y^2$.
26. $x + \sqrt{xy} - y = 4$.
27. At what point(s) does $x^2 + y^2 - 2x + 4y + 1 = 0$ have a horizontal tangent? A vertical tangent?
28. At what point(s) does $\sqrt{x} + \sqrt{y} = \sqrt{a}$ (a is a positive constant) have a horizontal tangent? A vertical tangent?
29. Find an equation of the line tangent to $x^2 + y^2 - 6x - 8y = 0$ at the point (6, 0).
30. Show that the line tangent to $y^2 = 4ax$ at the point (x_0, y_0) is $yy_0 = 2a(x + x_0)$.
31. Show that the line tangent to $x^2/a^2 + y^2/b^2 = 1$ at the point (x_0, y_0) is

$$\frac{xx_0}{a^2} + \frac{yy_0}{b^2} = 1.$$

32. Show that the tangent to $x^2/a^2 - y^2/b^2 = 1$ at the point (x_0, y_0) is

$$\frac{xx_0}{a^2} - \frac{yy_0}{b^2} = 1.$$

33. Find equations of the lines tangent to $x^2 + y^2 - 6x - 4y - 12 = 0$ and containing the point $(-4, 3)$.
34. Find equations of the lines tangent to $y^2 - 4x + 2y + 9 = 0$ and containing the origin.
35. If $4x^2 + 9y^2 + 36 = 0$, find dy/dx. What is the locus (graph) of the given equation? What conclusion can be drawn?
36. In Theorem 5.10, we extended the result of Theorem 5.2 to the case in which n is a rational number. To do this, we needed the chain rule. If $y = x^{p/q}$, where p and q are integers, then $y^q = x^p$. Use this fact to prove Theorem 5.10 without using the chain rule.
37. Find dy/dx at the points (2, 4), (2, 1), (3, 6), (3, 0), and (1, 2) of

$$2x^2 + xy - y^2 - 6x + 3y = 0.$$

Sketch the graph of the equation.

5.7

Multiple Derivatives

The derivative of a function is also a function. For example, if

$$f(x) = x^4,$$

then

$$f'(x) = 4x^3.$$

Since f' is itself a function, we can find its derivative (if it exists). The result, called the second derivative of f, is written f''. Thus, for the function above,

$$f''(x) = 12x^2.$$

We may continue indefinitely, taking the third, fourth, fifth, etc., derivatives, which are written f''', $f^{(4)}$, $f^{(5)}$, etc. Again, for the above function,

$$\begin{aligned} f'''(x) &= 24x, \\ f^{(4)}(x) &= 24, \\ f^{(5)}(x) &= 0, \\ f^{(6)}(x) &= 0, \end{aligned}$$

and so forth. The various notations used are as follows:

$$y', \quad y'', \quad y''', \quad y^{(4)}, \quad \text{etc.}$$

$$f'(x), \quad f''(x), \quad f'''(x), \quad f^{(4)}(x), \quad \text{etc.}$$

$$\frac{dy}{dx}, \quad \frac{d^2y}{dx^2}, \quad \frac{d^3y}{dx^3}, \quad \frac{d^4y}{dx^4}, \quad \text{etc.}$$

$$\frac{d}{dx}f(x), \quad \frac{d^2}{dx^2}f(x), \quad \frac{d^3}{dx^3}f(x), \quad \frac{d^4}{dx^4}f(x), \quad \text{etc.}$$

$$Dy, \quad D^2y, \quad D^3y, \quad D^4y, \quad \text{etc.}$$

$$Df(x), \quad D^2f(x), \quad D^3f(x), \quad D^4f(x), \quad \text{etc.}$$

Example 1

Find the first three derivatives of $y = x^2 + x^{1/2}$.

$$\begin{aligned} y' &= 2x + \frac{1}{2}x^{-1/2} = \frac{4x^{3/2}+1}{2\sqrt{x}}, \\ y'' &= 2 - \frac{1}{4}x^{-3/2} = \frac{8x^{3/2}-1}{4x^{3/2}}, \\ y''' &= \frac{3}{8}x^{-5/2} = \frac{3}{8x^{5/2}}. \end{aligned}$$

Example 2

Find d^2y/dx^2 for $x^2 + xy - y^2 = 2$.

$$2x + xy' + y - 2yy' = 0,$$

$$(2y - x)y' = 2x + y,$$

$$y' = \frac{2x+y}{2y-x};$$

$$y'' = \frac{(2y-x)(2+y') - (2x+y)(2y'-1)}{(2y-x)^2}$$

$$= \frac{(2y-x)\left(2+\dfrac{2x+y}{2y-x}\right) - (2x+y)\left(2\dfrac{2x+y}{2y-x}-1\right)}{(2y-x)^2}$$

$$= \frac{(2y-x)[2(2y-x)+(2x+y)] - (2x+y)[2(2x+y)-(2y-x)]}{(2y-x)^3}$$

$$= \frac{(2y-x)(5y)-(2x+y)(5x)}{(2y-x)^3}$$

$$= \frac{5(2y^2-2xy-2x^2)}{(2y-x)^3}$$

$$= \frac{-10(x^2+xy-y^2)}{(2y-x)^3}.$$

There still remain the questions of geometric interpretations and uses of the higher derivatives. Of course, the first derivative represents the slope of the original graph and the second derivative gives the slope of the graph of the first derivative, and so on, but there still remains the question of the relationship between the second derivative and the original function, which will be discussed in the next chapter.

Problems

In Problems 1–10, find the indicated derivative.

1. $f(x) = 3x^2 - 5x + 1$, $f''(x)$.
2. $g(x) = 4x^3 + 5x^2 + 2x - 3$, $g''(x)$.
3. $y = 7x^2 + 2x - 5$, y'''.
4. $p = 4q^3 - 2q + 1$, d^3p/dq^3.
5. $F(x) = x^{1/2} + x^{-1/2}$, $F''(x)$.
6. $f(x) = x^{3/2} - 3x^{1/2}$, $f''(x)$.
7. $f(v) = (v^2 + 1)^3$, $f'''(v)$.
8. $g(p) = \sqrt{p-1}$, $g'''(p)$.
9. $f(x) = \dfrac{1}{x^2-1}$, $f''(x)$.
10. $f(x) = \dfrac{x^2+1}{x^2-1}$, $f''(x)$.

In Problems 11–18, find the indicated derivative and express the result in terms of x and y.

11. $x^2 + y^2 = 16$, d^2y/dx^2.
12. $x^2 - y^2 = 4$, d^3y/dx^3.
13. $xy - y^2 = 5$, d^2y/dx^2.
14. $x^3 + y^3 = 3$, d^2y/dx^2.
15. $x^{2/3} + y^{2/3} = 1$, d^2y/dx^2.
16. $2x^2 - 2xy + y^2 = 1$, d^2y/dx^2.
17. $(x+y)^2 = xy + 1$, d^2y/dx^2.
18. $\sqrt{x} + \sqrt{y} = 1$, d^2y/dx^2.

In Problems 19–24, find $f(x)$, $f'(x)$, and $f''(x)$ for the indicated value of x.

19. $f(x) = 4x^2 - 2x + 1$, $x = 1$.
20. $f(x) = (2x-5)^4$, $x = 2$.
21. $f(x) = x^{1/3} + 1$, $x = 1$.
22. $f(x) = \dfrac{x+1}{x-1}$, $x = -1$.
23. $f(x) = \left(\dfrac{x+1}{x-1}\right)^2$, $x = 2$.
24. $f(x) = \sqrt{2x-3}$, $x = 2$.

In Problems 25–28, find dy/dx and d^2y/dx^2 at the indicated point.

25. $x^2 + y^2 = 25$, $(3, -4)$.
26. $2x^2 + xy - y^2 + 4 = 0$, $(1, 3)$.
27. $\sqrt{x} + \sqrt{y} = 1$, $(1/4, 1/4)$.
28. $(x + y)^2 = x - y$, $(3, -1)$.
29. Show that the second derivative of $f(x) = ax^2 + bx + c$ is $2a$.
30. Graph each of the following and compare the characteristics of the graphs with the corresponding second derivatives. What does this suggest about the second derivative?

    (a) $y = x^2$, (b) $y = x^2 - x$, (c) $y = 2x^2 + 1$,
    (d) $y = -x^2$, (e) $y = -x^2 - x$, (f) $y = -2x^2 + 1$.

In Problems 31–34, sketch the graphs of f' and f'' if the following are graphs of f.

31.

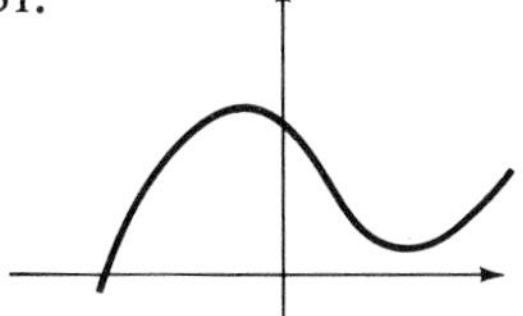

32.

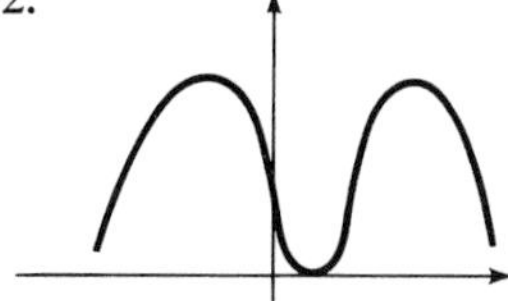

33.

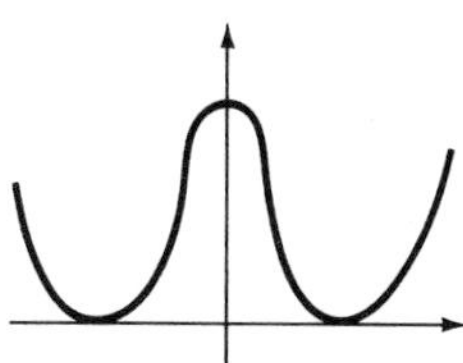

34.

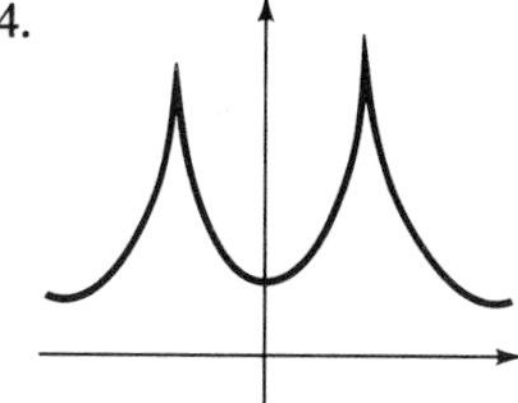

35. Show that if $f(x) = u(x) \cdot v(x)$, then

$$f''(x) = u(x) \cdot v''(x) + 2u'(x) \cdot v'(x) + u''(x) \cdot v(x)$$

and

$$f'''(x) = u(x) \cdot v'''(x) + 3u'(x) \cdot v''(x) + 3u''(x) \cdot v'(x) + u'''(x) \cdot v(x).$$

Compare with $(a + b)^2$ and $(a + b)^3$. Give an expression for $f^{(4)}(x)$.

5.8

Antiderivatives

We now consider the derivative problem in reverse—that is, given the derivative of a function, find the function. If $f'(x) = 2x$, we might be inclined to say that $f(x) = x^2$, because the derivative of x^2 is $2x$. But the derivative of $(x^2 + 1)$ is $2x$ and $d/dx(x^2 - 3) = 2x$: in fact, $d/dx(x^2 + C) = 2x$ no matter what number C represents. While it is certainly true that if $f(x) = x^2 + C$, then $f'(x) = 2x$, this fact does not necessarily imply that if $f'(x) = 2x$, then $f(x) = x^2 + C$ for some value of C. There still remains the possibility that there is some other expression not in the form $x^2 + C$ whose derivative is $2x$. This question is answered by the following theorem.

Theorem 5.12

If f and g are functions such that $f'(x) = g'(x)$ for all x, then $f(x) - g(x)$ is a constant.

The proof of this theorem (see Appendix B) requires the mean-value theorem, which we consider later (page 439). We shall assume it to be true at present. Once we have found one antiderivative, we know that any other differs from it by a constant. Thus, if $f'(x) = 2x$, then $f(x)$ must be in the form $x^2 + C$.

Let us see if we can get a general formula for finding antiderivatives. Suppose $f'(x) = x^n$; what is $f(x)$? First of all

$$\frac{d}{dx} x^{n+1} = (n+1)x^n \quad \text{and} \quad \frac{d}{dx} \frac{x^{n+1}}{(n+1)} = x^n.$$

Theorem 5.13

If $f'(x) = x^n$ $(n \neq -1)$, then

$$f(x) = \frac{x^{n+1}}{n+1} + C.$$

Example 1

If $f'(x) = \sqrt{x}$, find $f(x)$.

$$f'(x) = x^{1/2}.$$

$$f(x) = \frac{x^{(1/2)+1}}{(1/2)+1} + C = \frac{2x^{3/2}}{3} + C.$$

We can extend the use of this theorem by considering the results of Theorems 5.5 and 5.3. These theorems can be stated in antiderivative form in the following way.

Theorem 5.14

If $f'(x) = c \cdot u'(x)$ then

$$f(x) = c \cdot u(x) + C;$$

if $f'(x) = u'(x) + v'(x)$, then

$$f(x) = u(x) + v(x) + C.$$

Of course, the statement concerning the antiderivative of a sum holds for differences as well as for the sum of three or more terms.

Example 2

If $f'(x) = 3x$, find $f(x)$.

$$f(x) = 3 \cdot \frac{x^2}{2} + C = \frac{3x^2}{2} + C.$$

Example 3

If $f'(x) = 4x + 2$, find $f(x)$.

$$f(x) = 4 \cdot \frac{x^2}{2} + 2x + C = 2x^2 + 2x + C.$$

Example 4

If $f'(x) = \dfrac{x^4 - x^2 + 1}{x^2}$, find $f(x)$.

$$\begin{aligned} f'(x) &= \frac{x^4 - x^2 + 1}{x^2} \\ &= x^2 - 1 + x^{-2}; \\ f(x) &= \frac{x^3}{3} - x + \frac{x^{-1}}{-1} + C \\ &= \frac{x^3}{3} - x - \frac{1}{x} + C. \end{aligned}$$

A question that may have occurred to you is, "When we have an antiderivative involving two or more terms, why is there not a constant for each term?" The answer is that the constants we get for each term can all be combined into a single constant.

If we are given nothing but $f'(x)$, we cannot find the original function $f(x)$, because we cannot evaluate C; the best we can do is find a one-parameter family of functions all having the given derivative. But sometimes we are given additional information that allows us to choose the one member of the family we want.

Example 5

If $f'(x) = 6x^2 + 6x - 4$ and $f(1) = 3$, find $f(x)$.

$$\begin{aligned} f(x) &= 2x^3 + 3x^2 - 4x + C, \\ f(1) &= 2 \cdot 1^3 + 3 \cdot 1^2 - 4 \cdot 1 + C. \end{aligned}$$

Since $f(1) = 3$, we have

$$\begin{aligned} 3 &= 1 + C, \\ C &= 2. \end{aligned}$$

Thus

$$f(x) = 2x^3 + 3x^2 - 4x + 2.$$

Example 6

If $f''(x) = 32, f'(1) = 36$, and $f(1) = 16$, find $f(x)$.

$$\begin{aligned} f''(x) &= 32, \\ f'(x) &= 32x + C_1. \end{aligned}$$

Since $f'(1) = 36$, we have

$$\begin{aligned} 36 &= 32 + C_1, \\ C_1 &= 4, \\ f'(x) &= 32x + 4, \\ f(x) &= 16x^2 + 4x + C_2. \end{aligned}$$

Since $f(1) = 16$, we have

$$16 = 16 + 4 + C_2,$$
$$C_2 = -4.$$

Thus $f(x) = 16x^2 + 4x - 4$.

Example 7

If $f''(x) = 12$, $f(1) = 2$, and $f(2) = 15$, find $f(x)$.

$$f''(x) = 12,$$
$$f'(x) = 12x + C_1,$$
$$f(x) = 6x^2 + C_1x + C_2.$$

Using $f(1) = 2$ and $f(2) = 15$, we have

$$2 = 6 + C_1 + C_2, \qquad 15 = 24 + 2C_1 + C_2,$$
$$C_1 + C_2 = -4, \qquad 2C_1 + C_2 = -9,$$
$$C_1 = -5,$$
$$C_2 = 1.$$

Thus $f(x) = 6x^2 - 5x + 1$.

Problems

In Problems 1–30, find $f(x)$.

1. $f'(x) = 8x^3$.
2. $f'(x) = 3x^2$.
3. $f'(x) = x^{2/3}$.
4. $f'(x) = x^{4/3}$.
5. $f'(x) = \dfrac{1}{x^2}$.
6. $f'(x) = \dfrac{1}{\sqrt{x}}$.
7. $f'(x) = 12x^3 - 6x^2 + 3$.
8. $f'(x) = 48x^3 + 12x^2 - 4x$.
9. $f'(x) = \dfrac{x^2 - 1}{x^2}$.
10. $f'(x) = \dfrac{x^4 - x^2 + 1}{x^2}$.
11. $f'(x) = \dfrac{x^2 + x + 1}{\sqrt{x}}$.
12. $f'(x) = \dfrac{(x-1)^2}{x^{1/3}}$.
13. $f'(x) = (x-1)^2$.
14. $f'(x) = (x+1)(x-2)$.
15. $f'(x) = 4x^3$, $f(0) = 2$.
16. $f'(x) = x^{-1/2}$, $f(4) = 2$.
17. $f'(x) = x^{-1/3}$, $f(1) = 2$.
18. $f'(x) = x^{1/2} + x^{1/3}$, $f(1) = 1$.
19. $f'(x) = 6x^2 + 4x - 3$, $f(2) = 1$.
20. $f'(x) = 4x^3 - 6x^2 + 3$, $f(0) = 3$.
21. $f''(x) = 12$, $f'(1) = 3$, $f(1) = 4$.
22. $f''(x) = 4$, $f'(2) = 6$, $f(1) = 3$.
23. $f''(x) = -6$, $f(1) = 3$, $f(2) = 5$.
24. $f''(x) = 8$, $f(1) = -2$, $f(-1) = 2$.
25. $f''(x) = 6x + 2$, $f'(1) = 1$, $f(1) = 3$.
26. $f''(x) = 12x - 4$, $f(2) = 4$, $f(-1) = 3$.
27. $f''(x) = \sqrt{x}$, $f'(1) = 3$, $f(1) = 4$.
28. $f''(x) = x^{-5/3}$, $f(1) = 4$, $f(8) = 2$.
29. $f'''(x) = 6$, $f''(1) = 6$, $f'(1) = 4$, $f(1) = 0$.
30. $f'''(x) = -12$, $f(0) = 1$, $f(1) = 6$, $f(-1) = 4$.
31. Theorem 5.13 specifies that $n \neq -1$. If $f'(x) = 1/x$, we cannot find the antiderivative by Theorem 5.13. There is one, but it is not algebraic. Using the fact that $f'(x)$ is the slope of the graph and assuming that $f(1) = 0$, sketch the graph of f for $x > 0$.

Curve Sketching

6.1

Intercepts and Asymptotes

In the first chapter we sketched the graph of an equation by the tedious process of point-by-point plotting—a method that sometimes causes one to overlook some "interesting" portions of the graph or to sketch certain portions incorrectly. Suppose for example, you are asked to sketch the graph of

$$y = \frac{10x(x+8)}{(x+10)^2}.$$

The methods of Chapter 1 might lead you to the graph of Figure 6.1. A better sketch of the graph is given in Figure 6.2. While the earlier method produced correct results

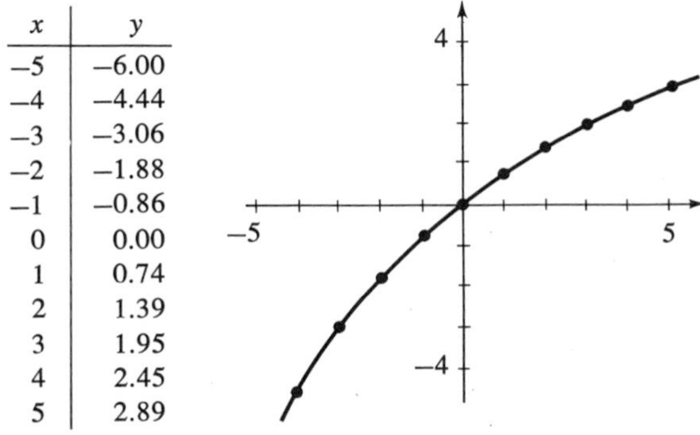

x	y
−5	−6.00
−4	−4.44
−3	−3.06
−2	−1.88
−1	−0.86
0	0.00
1	0.74
2	1.39
3	1.95
4	2.45
5	2.89

Figure 6.1

for the portion we were sketching, it provided no means for determining which portions of the curve are most "interesting."

Let us consider one more example. Suppose we want to graph

$$y = \frac{2x(2x-1)}{4x-1}.$$

The methods of Chapter 1 lead us to the set of points shown in Figure 6.3. Now, what does the graph look like? How would you join the points? Many would join them as indicated in (a) of Figure 6.4. The correct graph is shown in (b). These examples demonstrate the need for better methods of sketching curves. We begin by considering intercepts and asymptotes.

The intercepts of a curve are simply the points of the curve that lie on the coordinate axes; those on the x axis are the x intercepts, while those on the y axis are the y intercepts (the origin is both an x intercept and a y intercept). They are very simply determined by setting x and y equal to zero in turn and solving for y and x, respectively.

Example 1

Find the intercepts of $\frac{x^2}{4} + \frac{y^2}{9} = 1$.

When $y = 0$, $x^2 = 4$ and $x = \pm 2$. When $x = 0$, $y^2 = 9$ and $y = \pm 3$. Thus, the intercepts are $(2, 0)$, $(-2, 0)$, $(0, 3)$, and $(0, -3)$.

An equation frequently encountered is one of the type $y = P(x)$ or $y = P(x)/Q(x)$, where $P(x)$ and $Q(x)$ are polynomials having no common factor. If $P(x)$ can be factored in the form

$$P(x) = c(x - a_1)^{n_1}(x - a_2)^{n_2} \cdots (x - a_k)^{n_k},$$

where $c, a_1, \ldots, a_k$ are real numbers, then the x intercepts are $(a_1, 0)$, $(a_2, 0)$, ..., $(a_k, 0)$. The y intercept (there can only be one when the equation is in this form) is still found by setting x equal to zero.

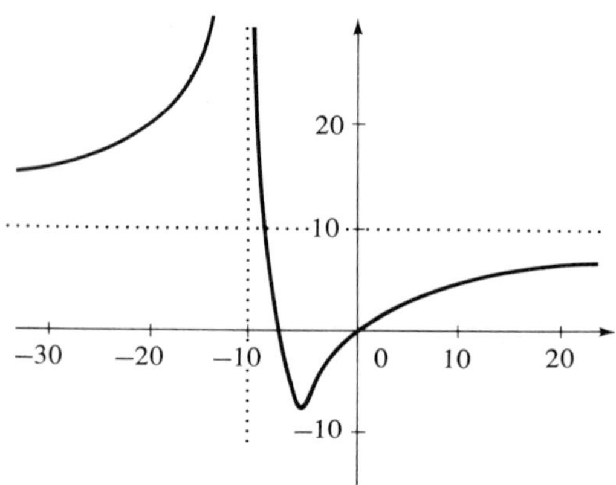

Figure 6.2

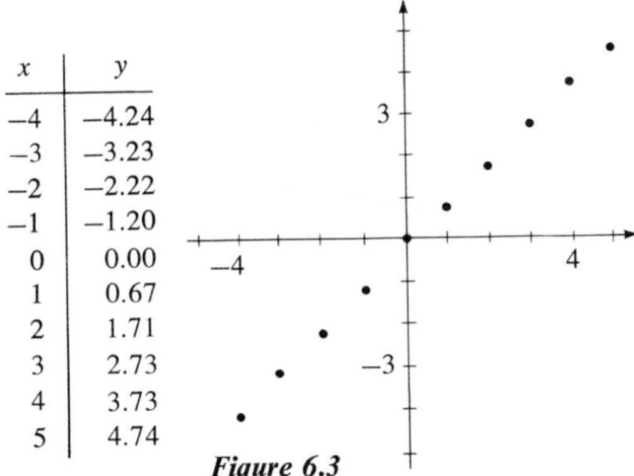

x	y
−4	−4.24
−3	−3.23
−2	−2.22
−1	−1.20
0	0.00
1	0.67
2	1.71
3	2.73
4	3.73
5	4.74

Figure 6.3

Example 2

Find the intercepts of $y = (x + 1)^2(x - 3)$.

The x intercepts can be taken from the two factors: $(-1, 0)$ from $(x + 1)^2$ and $(3, 0)$ from $(x - 3)$. When $x = 0$,

$$y = 1^2(-3) = -3.$$

Thus the y intercept is $(0, -3)$.

Example 3

Find the intercepts of

$$y = \frac{(x - 2)^2(x + 1)}{(x - 3)(x - 1)^2}.$$

From the factors $(x - 2)^2$ and $(x + 1)$, we get $(2, 0)$ and $(-1, 0)$. When $x = 0$, $y = -4/3$, and so the y intercept is $(0, -4/3)$. Note that the factors of the denominator have no part in determining the x intercepts.

Let us now turn to *asymptotes* (you are encouraged to study the spelling of that word). Rather than attempting a definition of an asymptote, which is rather difficult to define properly, let us consider some examples. In Figure 6.2, the lines $x = -10$

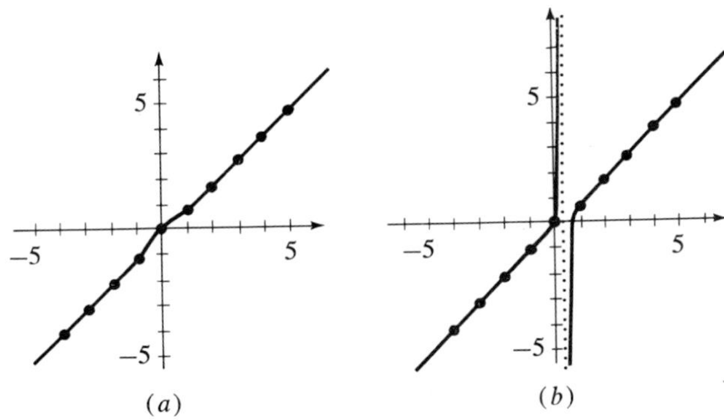

Figure 6.4

and $y = 10$ are asymptotes. We see that portions of the curve approach $x = -10$ and $y = 10$. This is the main feature to be considered in determining asymptotes. Note that the curve contains the point $(-25/3, 10)$ of the line $y = 10$. This does not prevent $y = 10$ from being an asymptote. A curve *can* have one or more (even infinitely many) points in common with its asymptote; however, a line is not an asymptote of itself, nor does $y = |x|$ have an asymptote. In Figure 6.4(b), the line $x = 1/4$ is an asymptote. Again we see that portions of the curve approach this line.

Although it is possible for any line to be an asymptote, we shall consider only horizontal and vertical asymptotes here (slant asymptotes are considered in Chapter 9). First we take up vertical asymptotes. In Figure 6.2 you can see that, as x approaches -10 from either side, y approaches no definite number but gets larger and larger. This is written

$$\lim_{x \to -10} y = +\infty.$$

As x approaches 1/4 from the right in Figure 6.4(b), y gets large and negative; and, as x approaches 1/4 from the left, y gets large and positive. These statements are symbolized as

$$\lim_{x \to 1/4^+} y = -\infty \quad \text{and} \quad \lim_{x \to 1/4^-} y = +\infty.$$

To find vertical asymptotes, we are not concerned with whether y gets large and positive or large and negative. We are interested only in determining values of x for which y gets large in absolute value. If the equation is in the form

$$y = \frac{P(x)}{Q(x)},$$

then, as x approaches a, y gets large in absolute value if $Q(x)$ approaches zero and $P(x)$ does not. Thus we need determine only the values of x which make $Q(x) = 0$ and $P(x) \neq 0$.

Example 4

Determine the vertical asymptotes of

$$y = \frac{(x+1)(x-3)}{(2x-1)(x+2)^2}.$$

The denominator is zero when either one of the two factors is zero.

$$2x - 1 = 0 \quad \text{gives} \quad x = 1/2.$$
$$x + 2 = 0 \quad \text{gives} \quad x = -2.$$

Since neither value of x gives zero for the numerator, $x = 1/2$ and $x = -2$ are the vertical asymptotes.

Let us now consider horizontal asymptotes. Of course, if the given equation is in the form

$$x = \frac{P(y)}{Q(y)},$$

or can easily be put into that form, we can simply use the methods given for vertical asymptotes. We merely reverse the role of the x and y here. Unfortunately, it is often difficult or impossible to solve for x as a function of y (consider the equation of Example 4), so another method must be found.

If $y = k$ is a horizontal asymptote for $y = f(x)$, then the distance between a point of the graph of $y = f(x)$ and the line $y = k$ must approach zero as x gets large in absolute value.

$$\lim_{x \to +\infty} [f(x) - k] = 0 \quad \text{or} \quad \lim_{x \to -\infty} [f(x) - k] = 0$$

giving

$$\lim_{x \to +\infty} f(x) = k \quad \text{or} \quad \lim_{x \to -\infty} f(x) = k.$$

Thus, we simply evaluate the limits; if one of them equals some number k, then $y = k$ is a horizontal asymptote.

Example 5

Determine the horizontal asymptote of

$$y = \frac{x^2 - 4}{x^2 + 3x}.$$

One of the limits we are interested in here is

$$\lim_{x \to +\infty} y = \lim_{x \to +\infty} \frac{x^2 - 4}{x^2 + 3x}.$$

As x gets large and positive, both the numerator and denominator are also getting large and positive. This fact alone tells us nothing about what the quotient is approaching (just as in the case in which both numerator and denominator approach zero). We must evaluate this limit by means of some trick. Suppose we alter the equation by dividing both numerator and denominator by x^2. Then

$$y = \frac{x^2 - 4}{x^2 + 3x} = \frac{1 - 4/x^2}{1 + 3/x}.$$

Now as x gets large,

$$\frac{4}{x^2} \to 0 \quad \text{and} \quad \frac{3}{x} \to 0.$$

Thus

$$\lim_{x \to +\infty} y = \lim_{x \to +\infty} \frac{1 - 4/x^2}{1 + 3/x} = 1,$$

and $y = 1$ is the horizontal asymptote. By the same argument,

$$\lim_{x \to -\infty} y = 1.$$

Thus the asymptote $y = 1$ is approached by the curve in both directions.

In evaluating this limit we first divided both numerator and denominator by the highest power of x (x^2 in this case) in the given expression. This trick often helps in evaluating limits of the forms

$$\lim_{x \to +\infty} f(x) \quad \text{and} \quad \lim_{x \to -\infty} f(x).$$

Example 6

Determine the horizontal asymptote of

$$y=\frac{(x+1)(x-3)}{(2x-1)(x+2)^2}.$$

If we multiplied out the numerator, the highest power of x would be x^2; in the denominator it would be x^3. Thus we shall divide the numerator and denominator by x^3 (do *not* divide the numerator by x^2 and the denominator by x^3; the result would *not* equal y).

$$y=\frac{(x+1)(x-3)}{(2x-1)(x+2)^2}=\frac{\left(\frac{x+1}{x}\right)\left(\frac{x-3}{x}\right)\left(\frac{1}{x}\right)}{\left(\frac{2x-1}{x}\right)\left(\frac{x+2}{x}\right)^2}=\frac{\left(1+\frac{1}{x}\right)\left(1-\frac{3}{x}\right)\left(\frac{1}{x}\right)}{\left(2-\frac{1}{x}\right)\left(1+\frac{2}{x}\right)^2}.$$

As x gets large, all of the expressions with x in the denominator approach zero and

$$\lim_{x\to+\infty} y=\lim_{x\to-\infty} y=\frac{(1+0)(1-0)(0)}{(2-0)(1+0)^2}=0.$$

Thus $y=0$ is the only horizontal asymptote.

Example 7

Find the horizontal asymptote of

$$y=\frac{x(x+1)(x-2)}{(x-4)(x+2)}.$$

The highest power of x in this expression is x^3. Dividing numerator and denominator by x^3, we have

$$y=\frac{x(x+1)(x-2)}{(x-4)(x+2)}=\frac{\left(\frac{x}{x}\right)\left(\frac{x+1}{x}\right)\left(\frac{x-2}{x}\right)}{\left(\frac{x-4}{x}\right)\left(\frac{x+2}{x}\right)\left(\frac{1}{x}\right)}=\frac{(1)\left(1+\frac{1}{x}\right)\left(1-\frac{2}{x}\right)}{\left(1-\frac{4}{x}\right)\left(1+\frac{2}{x}\right)\left(\frac{1}{x}\right)}.$$

As $x\to\pm\infty$, the numerator is approaching 1 and the denominator, 0. Thus the fraction becomes arbitrarily large as $x\to\pm\infty$, and so neither $\lim_{x\to+\infty} y$ nor $\lim_{x\to-\infty} y$ exists. There is no horizontal asymptote.

Problems

In Problems 1–16, find the intercepts.

1. $y=x^2+3x.$
2. $y=x^2-x-2.$
3. $y=(x+1)(x^2-1).$
4. $y=(2x-1)^2(3x+2)^3.$
5. $y=(4x+1)(x-2)(2x+3)^2.$
6. $y=(2x-1)^3(3x+2)^2(x-3).$
7. $y=(x-1)(x^2+1).$
8. $y=(2x+3)(x^2+x+1).$
9. $y=(3x-1)^2(x^2+2)^3(2x+1)^4.$
10. $y=(2x-5)(x^2-x+1)^3(x^2+2).$
11. $y=\frac{x}{x+1}.$
12. $y=\frac{(x+1)(x-2)}{(3x+1)^2}.$
13. $y=\frac{(x-3)^2}{2x+1}.$
14. $y=\frac{1}{3x+2}.$
15. $y=\frac{2}{x^2}.$
16. $y=\frac{(x+1)^2(x^2+1)}{x^2}.$

In Problems 17–34, find all horizontal and vertical asymptotes.

17. $y = (x+1)(x-2)$.

18. $y = (4x+3)(x-2)$.

19. $y = \dfrac{1}{x-1}$.

20. $y = \dfrac{4x-2}{x+1}$.

21. $y = \dfrac{x}{x+3}$.

22. $y = \dfrac{(x+1)^2}{2x(x-2)}$.

23. $y = \dfrac{2x(x-2)}{(x+1)^2}$.

24. $y = \dfrac{(x+1)(x-3)^2}{(x+2)^2}$.

25. $y = \dfrac{(2x-3)(x-2)}{(x+1)(x-3)^2}$.

26. $y = \dfrac{(4x-7)(x-1)^2}{(x+1)(x+2)(x+3)}$.

27. $y = \dfrac{(x+1)^2}{x^2+1}$.

28. $y = \dfrac{(2x+1)^2(x-2)^2}{x(4x-3)}$.

29. $y = \dfrac{(3x+2)^3(x-4)}{(2x+3)^2(x+1)^3}$.

30. $y = \dfrac{(2x+1)^2(x-3)^3}{x(2x-3)^2}$.

31. $y = x - \sqrt{x^2+1}$.
(*Hint*: Rationalize the numerator.)

32. $y = x + \sqrt{x^2+1}$.

33. $y = 2x - \sqrt{4x^2+3}$.

34. $y = 3x + \sqrt{9x^2-1}$.

35. If $y = \dfrac{a_n x^n + a_{n-1}x^{n-1} + \cdots + a_1 x + a_0}{b_m x^m + b_{m-1}x^{m-1} + \cdots + b_1 x + b_0}$, where $a_n \neq 0$ and $b_m \neq 0$, what can be said about horizontal asymptotes in case (a) $n < m$? (b) $n = m$? (c) $n > m$?

6.2

Symmetry, Sketching

Another characteristic that helps in sketching a curve is symmetry. There are two types: symmetry about a line and symmetry about a point. If a curve is symmetric about a line, then one-half of it is the mirror image of the other half, with the mirror as the line of symmetry. More precisely, for every point P of the curve, on one side of the line there is another point P' of the curve such that PP' is perpendicular to the line of symmetry and is bisected by it. An example of this type of symmetry occurs with the graph of $y = 1/x^2$, in which the y axis is the line of symmetry (see Figure 6.5).

A curve is symmetric about a point O if for every point $P \neq O$ of the curve, there corresponds a point P' such that PP' is bisected by the point O. The origin is the point of symmetry of the graph of $y = 1/x$ (see Figure 6.6).

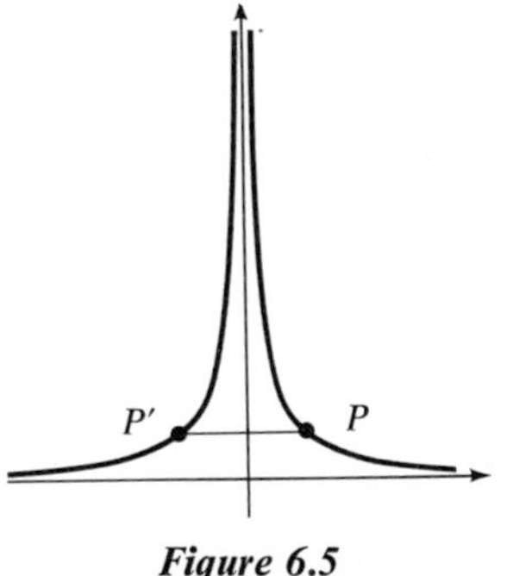

Figure 6.5

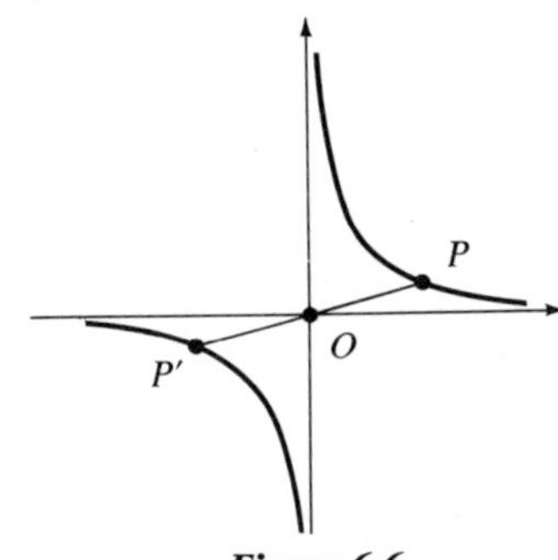

Figure 6.6

While there is no restriction on the lines or points that may be lines or points of symmetry, we shall consider here only symmetry about the axes and about the origin. We begin with symmetry about the y axis. If a curve is symmetric about the y axis, then, corresponding to every point $P(x, y)$ on the curve, there is a point $P'(-x, y)$ (see Figure 6.5) with the same y coordinate and an x coordinate that is the negative of the x coordinate of P. In this situation, we get the same value for y whether we substitute a positive number x into the equation or its negative, $-x$.

Theorem 6.1

If every x in an equation is replaced by $-x$ and the resulting equation is equivalent to the original (has the same graph), then its graph is symmetric about the y axis.

Example 1

We have already noted that $y = 1/x^2$ is symmetric about the y axis. We now test for symmetry. Replacing x by $-x$, we have

$$y = \frac{1}{(-x)^2}.$$

Since $(-x)^2 = x^2$, we see that the substitution has produced an equation equivalent to the original equation, proving symmetry about the y axis. A similar argument can be used to prove the next theorem.

Theorem 6.2

If every y in an equation is replaced by $-y$ and the resulting equation is equivalent to the original, then its graph is symmetric about the x axis.

If a curve is symmetric about the origin, then, for every point $P(x, y)$ on the curve, there is a point $P'(-x, -y)$ (see Figure 6.6). This is the statement of the next theorem.

Theorem 6.3

If every x in an equation is replaced by $-x$ and every y by $-y$ and the resulting equation is equivalent to the original, then its graph is symmetric about the origin.

Example 2

We test the theorem on $y = 1/x$, which we have already noted is symmetric about the origin. Replacing x by $-x$ and y by $-y$ gives

$$-y = \frac{1}{-x}.$$

This is equivalent to the original equation, since we get the original equation if we multiply both sides by -1.

Before using what we have observed about intercepts, asymptotes, and symmetry to sketch the curve, we shall look at one other characteristic that will help greatly in sketching curves represented by equations of the form

$$y = \frac{P(x)}{Q(x)}.$$

The factors of $P(x)$ determine the x intercepts, and the factors of $Q(x)$ determine the vertical asymptotes of the curve. It might be noted that these are the only two places at which y can change from positive to negative or from negative to positive. This is not to say that the value of y *must* change there—only that it cannot do so elsewhere. We can easily determine whether or not the change occurs at a given intercept or asymptote by considering the exponent on the factor that produces it.

Theorem 6.4

Given an equation of the form

$$y = \frac{P(x)}{Q(x)}$$

in reduced form, if $(x - a)^n$ *(where n is a positive integer) is a factor of either* $P(x)$ *or* $Q(x)$ *and if* $(x - a)^{n+1}$ *is a factor of neither, then*

(a) *the graph crosses the x axis at* $x = a$ *if and only if n is odd, and*
(b) *the graph stays on the same side of the x axis at* $x = a$ *if and only if n is even.*

The expression "the graph crosses the x axis" is not intended to mean that the graph has a point in common with the x axis. It means that the graph is above (or below) the x axis for $c < x < a$ and below (or above) for $a < x < d$ for some c and d.

Although the following discussion does not constitute a proof of this theorem, it serves to show why the theorem works. Let us consider the case in which $(x - a)^n$ is a factor of $P(x)$ (a similar argument can be used for the other case). Then

$$y = \frac{P(x)}{Q(x)} = \frac{R(x)}{Q(x)}(x - a)^n.$$

For all values of x at and "near" $x = a$, $R(x)/Q(x)$ is either positive throughout or negative throughout, not making any sign change. But

$$\begin{aligned} x - a < 0 &\quad \text{for} \quad x < a, \\ x - a = 0 &\quad \text{for} \quad x = a, \\ x - a > 0 &\quad \text{for} \quad x > a. \end{aligned}$$

In other words, $x - a$ changes sign at $x = a$. If n is odd, then $(x - a)^n$ also changes sign; thus y changes sign at $x = a$. If n is even, then $(x - a)^n$ is positive whether $x < a$ or $x > a$; that is, $(x - a)^n$ does not change sign and y does not change sign. Let us now use all of this information to sketch the graph of an equation.

Example 3

Sketch $y = (x - 3)(x + 1)^2$.

From the "numerator," we get x intercepts (3, 0) with an odd exponent and (−1, 0) with an even exponent. If $x = 0$, then $y = -3$, which gives (0, −3). Since the denominator is 1, there are no vertical asymptotes; and

$$\lim_{x \to +\infty} y = +\infty \quad \text{and} \quad \lim_{x \to -\infty} y = -\infty,$$

which means that there are no horizontal asymptotes. It is easy to see that no symmetry exists about either axis or the origin. Summing, up, we have:

Intercepts: (3, 0) odd, (−1, 0) even, (0, −3);
No asymptotes: $\lim_{x \to +\infty} y = +\infty, \quad \lim_{x \to -\infty} y = -\infty,$
No symmetry.

All of this is indicated in Figure 6.7. Let us sketch the graph, starting at the far left and working to the right (this choice is quite arbitrary; we might just as well go from right to left or start in the middle and work outward). We keep in mind that the curve must go through all intercepts and that y is a *function* of x; that is, it is single-valued. Since $\lim_{x \to -\infty} y = -\infty$, we start in the lower left-hand corner. Going to the right, we first reach the intercept (−1, 0). Since it is an even

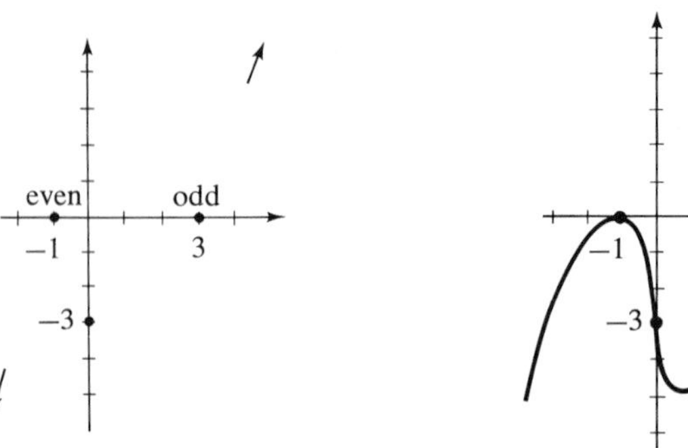

Figure 6.7 *Figure 6.8*

intercept, the graph merely touches the x axis but stays on the negative side. Next, the graph goes through (0, −3) and then turns back up in order to go through (3, 0). Since (3, 0) is an odd intercept, the graph crosses the x axis there and proceeds upward. The result is given in Figure 6.8.

Note that we put the lowest point of the "dip" at approximately $x = 1$. How did we know to put it there? We didn't. We made no attempt to locate it—we simply guessed. Without further work, the best we can say is that it is between $x = -1$ and $x = 3$. Furthermore, how do we know that the graph does not have some extra "turns" and "wiggles" and perhaps look like Figure 6.9? Again, we don't. As a general rule, unless there is some special reason to put in some extra "turn" or "wiggle," we shall leave it out. This rule will not necessarily give us the correct graph every time but there is no point in needlessly complicating the situation. These methods give only a general idea of the graph.

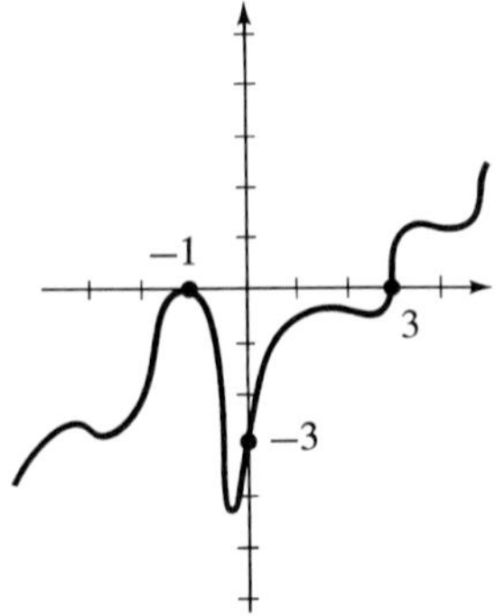

Figure 6.9

Note that, with the exception of the three intercepts, we have not plotted a single point! Yet we have some idea (within the restrictions noted above) of the main features of the curve. With a little practice, you should be able to sketch such curves quite quickly and thus achieve the principal aim here.

Example 4

Sketch

$$y = \frac{(2x-1)(x+2)^2}{(x+1)^2(x-3)}.$$

Intercepts:

$$(1/2, 0), \text{ odd}; \quad (-2, 0), \text{ even}; \quad (0, 4/3).$$

Asymptotes:
From the denominator:

$$x = -1, \text{ even}; \quad x = 3, \text{ odd},$$

$$\lim_{x \to \pm\infty} \frac{(2x-1)(x+2)^2}{(x+1)^2(x-3)} = \lim_{x \to \pm\infty} \frac{\left(\frac{2x-1}{x}\right)\left(\frac{x+2}{x}\right)^2}{\left(\frac{x+1}{x}\right)^2\left(\frac{x-3}{x}\right)} = \lim_{x \to \pm\infty} \frac{\left(2-\frac{1}{x}\right)\left(1+\frac{2}{x}\right)^2}{\left(1+\frac{1}{x}\right)^2\left(1-\frac{3}{x}\right)}$$

$$= \frac{2 \cdot 1}{1 \cdot 1} = 2.$$

Thus $y = 2$ is the horizontal asymptote.
No symmetry.

Again all of this information is summarized in Figure 6.10. If we begin sketching at one end or the other, we have the problem of not knowing whether the curve is approaching the asymptote from above or below. Similar problems exist at the vertical asymptotes and x intercepts. Suppose, then, we start at (0, 4/3). Going to the right, we first come to (1/2, 0). Since it is an odd intercept, the graph crosses the x axis there and then goes down to the vertical asymptote $x = 3$ (it cannot go up, since it

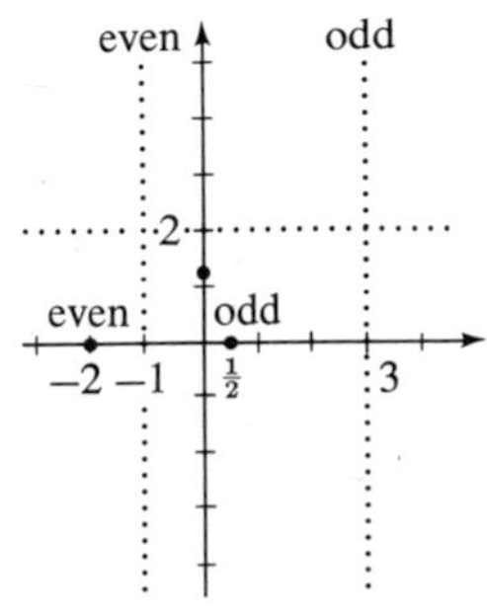

Figure 6.10

cannot cross the x axis anywhere between $x = 1/2$ and $x = 3$). Since this asymptote is also odd, the graph now jumps to the other side of the x axis. Finally it comes down to the horizontal asymptote $y = 2$.

Going back to $(0, 4/3)$ and proceeding to the left, we see that the graph must go up to the vertical asymptote $x = -1$ (remember there is nothing to prevent the graph from crossing a horizontal asymptote). Since $x = -1$ is an even asymptote, the curve stays above the x axis. It must then proceed down to the intercept $(-2, 0)$. This is also even, so the graph again remains above the x axis, finally going up to the horizontal asymptote. Thus, we have the graph indicated in Figure 6.11.

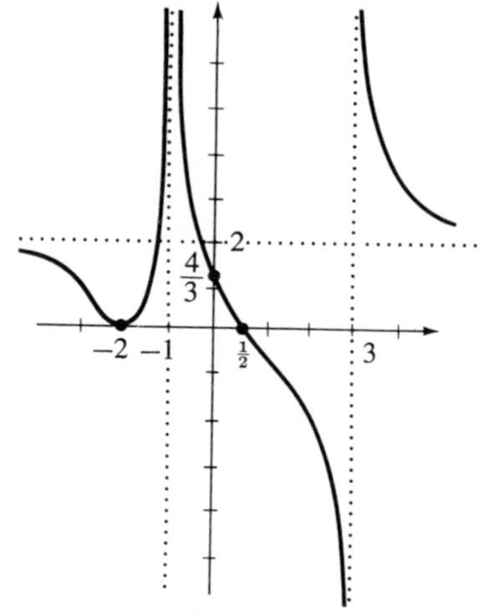

Figure 6.11

Problems

In Problems 1–10, check for symmetry about both axes and the origin.

1. $y = x^4 - x^2$.
2. $y = x^3 - x$.
3. $y = x^3 - x^2$.
4. $\dfrac{x^2}{4} + \dfrac{y^2}{9} = 1$.
5. $y^2 = \dfrac{x+1}{x}$.
6. $y^3 = \dfrac{x+1}{x}$.
7. $xy = 1$.
8. $x^2y^2 = 1$.
9. $y = \dfrac{x}{x^2+1}$.
10. $y = \dfrac{(x+1)(x-1)}{x^2}$.

In Problems 11–30, use the methods of this and the preceding section to sketch. Do not plot the graph point by point.

11. $y = (x+1)(x-3)$.
12. $y = (x+2)(x-1)^2$.
13. $y = x^2 - 5x - 6$.
14. $y = x^3 + x^2 - 2x$.
15. $y = x^4 - x^2$.
16. $y = x^3 - x$.
17. $y = \dfrac{x+1}{x}$.
18. $y = \dfrac{x-2}{x+2}$.
19. $y = \dfrac{(2x+1)(x-1)^2}{(x-2)(x+1)^2}$.
20. $y = \dfrac{x-3}{(x+1)(x-2)}$.
21. $y = \dfrac{(x+2)(x-4)}{x-1}$.
22. $y = \dfrac{x-1}{(x+2)(x-4)}$.
23. $y = \dfrac{(x+2)^2(x-4)}{(x-1)^2}$.
24. $y = \dfrac{x}{x^2+1}$.
25. $y = \dfrac{x^2+1}{x}$.
26. $xy = 2x + 1$.
27. $x^2y = 2x + 1$.
28. $x^2y - y = x^2$.
29. $x^2y - y = x^3$.
30. $x^2y - y = x$.
31. Show that if a graph has any two of the three types of symmetry—about the x axis, about the y axis, about the origin—then it must have the third.

32. Give an example of a curve with exactly two lines of symmetry.
33. Can a graph have two points of symmetry?
34. Give an example of a curve with infinitely many lines of symmetry.
35. Show that if two perpendicular lines are lines of symmetry of a given curve, then their point of intersection is a point of symmetry.

6.3

Radicals and the Domain of the Equation

Recall that two things can keep us from getting a value for y when we substitute a value of x into an equation: a zero in the denominator and an even root of a negative number. A zero in the denominator gives a vertical asymptote. Even roots of negative numbers simply cause gaps in the domain of the equation.

Example 1

$$\text{Sketch } y = \frac{2x}{\sqrt{x^2-4}} = \frac{2x}{\sqrt{(x+2)(x-2)}}.$$

Using the previous methods, we have:

Intercepts:

$$(0, 0) \text{ odd.}$$

Asymptotes:

$$x = 2, \quad x = -2.$$

The radical is equivalent to the one-half power, which is neither odd nor even. We have a special problem in finding the horizontal asymptotes. The highest power of x in the numerator is clearly x. The highest power in the denominator appears to be x^2. But it is under the radical; so the highest power is really $(x^2)^{1/2} = x$. Thus we shall want to divide the numerator and denominator by x. But we shall want to put the x under the radical in the denominator, which leads to further complications. The symbol $\sqrt{\ }$ means the *non-negative* square root. Thus $x = \sqrt{x^2}$ is true only when $x \geq 0$; when $x < 0$, $\sqrt{x^2} = -x$ (note that, since x itself is negative, $-x$ is positive), and we have two cases to consider:

$$\frac{2x}{\sqrt{x^2-4}} = \frac{\dfrac{2x}{x}}{\sqrt{\dfrac{x^2-4}{x^2}}} = \frac{2}{\sqrt{1-\dfrac{4}{x^2}}} \quad \text{when } x > 0,$$

$$\frac{2x}{\sqrt{x^2-4}} = \frac{\dfrac{2x}{-x}}{\sqrt{\dfrac{x^2-4}{x^2}}} = \frac{-2}{\sqrt{1-\dfrac{4}{x^2}}} \quad \text{when } x < 0.$$

Thus,

$$\lim_{x\to+\infty}\frac{2x}{\sqrt{x^2-4}}=\lim_{x\to+\infty}\frac{2}{\sqrt{1-\dfrac{4}{x^2}}}=2,$$

$$\lim_{x\to-\infty}\frac{2x}{\sqrt{x^2-4}}=\lim_{x\to-\infty}\frac{-2}{\sqrt{1-\dfrac{4}{x^2}}}=-2,$$

giving two horizontal asymptotes: $y=2$, which is approached on the right, and $y=-2$, which is approached on the left. Replacing x by $-x$ and y by $-y$ gives

$$-y=\frac{2(-x)}{\sqrt{(-x)^2-4}}=\frac{-2x}{\sqrt{x^2-4}},$$

which is equivalent to the original equation. Thus we have symmetry about the origin.

Finally, $\sqrt{x^2-4}$ represents a real number only when $x^2-4\geq 0$, which gives

$$x^2\geq 4 \quad \text{or} \quad \begin{cases} x\geq 2 \\ x\leq -2. \end{cases}$$

But y is real for one additional value of x, namely, $x=0$. If $x=0$, y equals zero divided by a complex number, which is still zero. Thus the domain is

$$\{x\mid x\geq 2 \text{ or } x\leq -2 \text{ or } x=0\}.$$

We see here that (0, 0) is an isolated point of the graph.

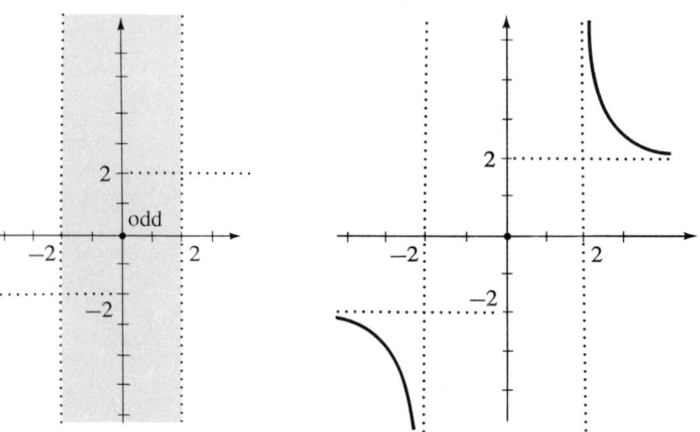

Figure 6.12 *Figure 6.13*

All of this information is represented graphically in Figure 6.12. We can now see that the fact that the intercept is odd is of no use, since it is an isolated point. Note one thing more: Since $\sqrt{x^2-4}$ is never negative, y is positive whenever x is positive and negative whenever x is negative. This additional information makes it easy for us to sketch the curve (see Figure 6.13).

Example 2

Sketch $y^2 = x^4 - x^2$.

To graph this equation, we use the following device: Since $y = \pm\sqrt{x^4 - x^2}$, we first graph $z = x^4 - x^2$ and then, from the values of z, get $y = \pm\sqrt{z}$. Graphing $z = x^4 - x^2 = x^2(x^2 - 1) = x^2(x+1)(x-1)$, we have

Intercepts:

(0, 0), even, (1, 0), odd, (−1, 0), odd.

No asymptotes.
Symmetry about the z axis (see Figure 6.14).

We see on the graph that, for each value of x, we have a value of $z = x^4 - x^2$. Now let us find the corresponding values for $y = \pm\sqrt{z}$. But first, we note the following points to keep in mind.

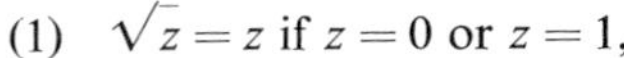

(1) $\sqrt{z} = z$ if $z = 0$ or $z = 1$,

(2) $\sqrt{z} > z$ if $0 < z < 1$,

(3) $\sqrt{z} < z$ if $z > 1$,

(4) $\sqrt{z}$ is not real if $z < 0$.

The final result is given by the solid graph of Figure 6.14. The origin is again an isolated point of this graph.

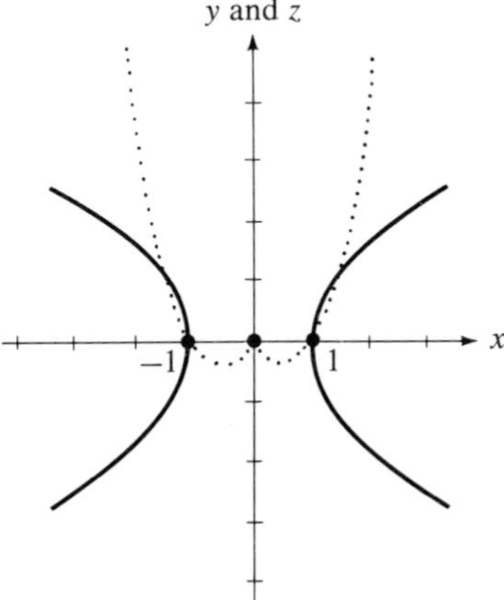

Figure 6.14

The same method could be used to sketch $y = \sqrt{x^4 - x^2}$. The only difference would be that we would have only the top half of the result in Figure 6.14. We might also have used this method in Example 1, starting with

$$y^2 = \frac{4x^2}{x^2 - 4}.$$

In that case, we would have to be careful which branch we chose; we would have to choose the top portion when x is positive and the bottom portion when x is negative.

One final point. Let us recall that when we had an equation of the form

$$y = \frac{P(x)}{Q(x)},$$

we noted that x intercepts come from factors in the numerator and vertical asymptotes from factors in the denominator, *provided there is no value of x for which both numerator and denominator are zero*. In the examples we have been considering, this is equivalent to the provision that there is no factor common to both numerator and denominator. What happens if there *are* common factors? The answer is simple. You simply cancel the common factors and sketch the resulting equation. But remember that if you cancel the factor $x - a$, the original equation is not defined at $x = a$ (it gives 0/0) and there is no point on the graph with x coordinate a.

Example 3

Sketch $y = \dfrac{x^2 - 1}{x - 1}$.

Since the numerator and denominator have the common factor $x - 1$, we cancel them to get

$$y = x + 1,$$

which gives a straight line. But recall that the original equation gives no value of y when $x = 1$. Thus the point $(1, 2)$ should be deleted from the graph, as in Figure 6.15.

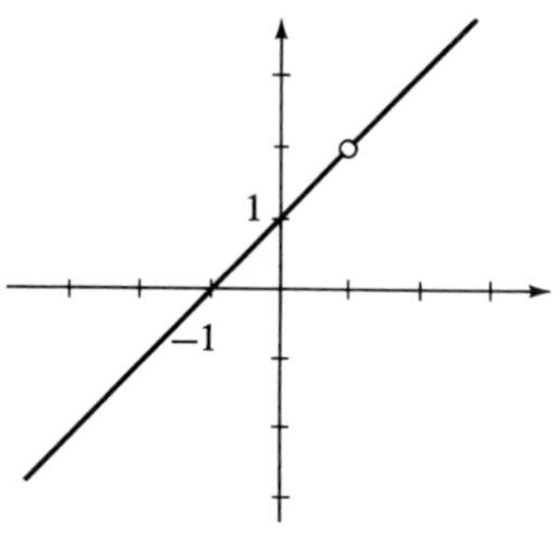

Figure 6.15

Problems

Sketch the graphs of the following equations.

1. $y = x\sqrt{x^2 - 1}$.
2. $y = \dfrac{x}{\sqrt{x - 1}}$.
3. $y = \dfrac{-x}{\sqrt{x^2 - 1}}$.
4. $y = \dfrac{x - 1}{\sqrt{x(x + 1)}}$.
5. $y = x + \sqrt{x^2 - 1}$.
6. $y = x - \sqrt{x^2 - 1}$.
7. $y^2 = \dfrac{x}{x + 1}$.
8. $y^2 = \dfrac{x^2}{(x + 1)(x - 2)}$.
9. $y^2 = \dfrac{2x}{(x - 1)^2}$.
10. $y^2 = \dfrac{(x - 1)^2}{x}$.
11. $y^2 = \dfrac{x(x + 1)}{(x - 2)^2}$.
12. $y^2 = \dfrac{x(x + 1)^2}{x - 2}$.
13. $y^2 = \dfrac{x(x - 1)}{(x + 1)^2}$.
14. $y^2 = \dfrac{x(1 - x)}{(x + 1)^2}$.
15. $y^2 = \dfrac{(x^2 - 1)^2}{x - 2}$.
16. $y^2 = (1 - x)(3 - x)^2$.
17. $y^2 = (x - 1)(x - 3)^2$.
18. $y^2 = -(x - 1)(x - 3)^2$.
19. $y = \dfrac{x^2 - 4}{x - 2}$.
20. $y = \dfrac{x^2 + x}{x}$.
21. $y = \dfrac{x^2 + x}{x^2}$.
22. $y = \dfrac{x^3 + x^2}{x}$.
23. $y = \dfrac{x(x + 1)^2}{(x - 1)(x + 1)^3}$.
24. $y = \dfrac{2x(x - 1)}{x(x + 1)}$.
25. $y = \dfrac{1 - (1 + h)^2}{h}$.
    (*Hint*: Simplify the numerator.)
26. $y = \dfrac{-1 - [(1 + h)^2 - 2(1 + h)]}{h}$.
27. $y = \dfrac{2 - \dfrac{2 + h}{1 + h}}{h}$.
28. $y = \dfrac{1 - \sqrt{1 + h}}{h}$.

6.4

Relative Maxima and Minima

Until now we have avoided using calculus in sketching the curves. We have also noted that our methods have left some things undetermined (see page 100). Whether or not we want to determine these things depends upon the use we plan for our sketch. Often we are not interested in locating highest or lowest points and we may not care how many "turns" or "wiggles" the graph has. But if we are interested in such things, we must use calculus to determine them.

First some new notation is needed.

Definition

*If a and b are real numbers, $a < b$, then the **open interval** (a, b) is the set $\{x \mid a < x < b\}$ and the **closed interval** $[a, b]$ is the set $\{x \mid a \le x \le b\}$. Similarly, $[a, b) = \{x \mid a \le x < b\}$ and $(a, b] = \{x \mid a < x \le b\}$; the latter two are **half-open intervals**.*

The notations for a point in the plane and for an open interval are the same, but it is easy to distinguish between them by context.

Definition

*The function f is **increasing** (or **decreasing**) on the interval (a, b) means that if $a < c < d < b$, then $f(c) < f(d)$ (or $f(c) > f(d)$). The function f is **nondecreasing** (or **nonincreasing**) on the interval (a, b) means that if $a < c < d < b$, then $f(c) \le f(d)$ (or $f(c) \ge f(d)$).*

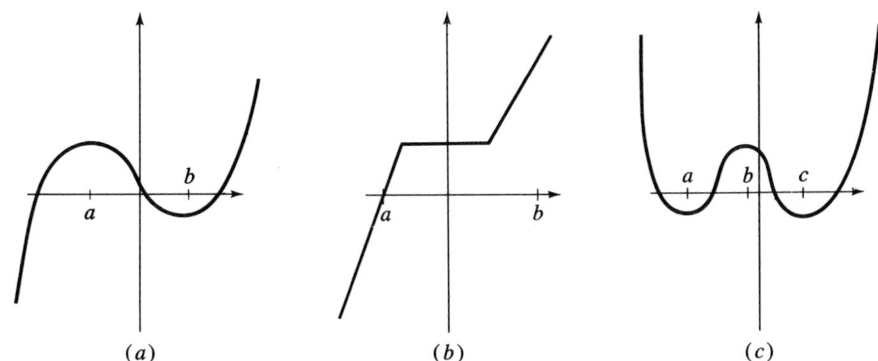

Figure 6.16

In (a) of Figure 6.16, the function is decreasing on the interval (a, b). In (b), it is nondecreasing on the interval (a, b). In (c), it is increasing on (a, b) and decreasing on (b, c). Now let us consider the relationship between increasing and decreasing functions and the derivative.

Theorem 6.5

If f is a function such that $f'(x) > 0$ for every x on (a, b), then f is increasing on (a, b); if $f'(x) < 0$ for every x on (a, b), then f is decreasing on (a, b).

We shall not attempt to prove this theorem. Intuitively, it is obvious; however, a proof (see Appendix B) requires the use of the mean-value theorem, which we shall consider later (page 439). It might be noted that the converse of this theorem is not true; that is, it does not follow that if f is increasing on (a, b), then $f'(x) > 0$ for every x on (a, b). Consider the function

$$f: f(x) = x^3.$$

It is increasing on the interval $(-1, 1)$ but $f'(0) = 0$. However, it is true that if f is increasing on (a, b), then for every x on (a, b), either $f'(x) \geq 0$ or $f'(x)$ does not exist.

Definition

*The point $A: (a, f(a))$ is a **relative maximum** (or **minimum**) of the graph of the function f means that there is an interval (b, c) containing a such that $f(a) \geq f(x)$ (or $f(a) \leq f(x)$) for any value of x in (b, c) which is in the domain of f.*

Definition

*The point $A: (a, f(a))$ is an **absolute maximum** (or **minimum**) of the graph of the function f means that $f(a) \geq f(x)$ (or $f(a) \leq f(x)$) for any value of x in the domain of f.*

Let us note, first of all, that we said *an* absolute maximum rather than *the* absolute maximum. There may be several "highest" points of the graph, all having the same y coordinate. Roughly speaking, an absolute maximum is a highest point of the graph (in the sense that there is none higher) while a relative maximum is at least as high as those points "near" it. Of course, an absolute maximum is also a relative maximum; in fact, if a graph has an absolute maximum, then it is the highest of the relative maxima. Note the qualifier, "if a graph has an absolute maximum." Do not just find a highest relative maximum and conclude that it is an absolute maximum—there may not be any absolute maximum (see (a) and (c) of Figure 6.16).

Now, let us suppose that the function f is defined on (b, c) and there is a number a in (b, c) such that $f'(x) > 0$ for x in (b, a) and $f'(x) < 0$ for x in (a, c). By Theorem 6.5, f is increasing on (b, a) and decreasing on (a, c); $(a, f(a))$ is a relative maximum. Since $f'(x)$ changes from positive to negative, either $f'(a) = 0$ or $f'(a)$ does not exist. A similar argument shows that, if $f'(x) < 0$ for x in (b, a) and $f'(x) > 0$ for x in (a, c), then $(a, f(a))$ is a relative minimum and either $f'(a) = 0$ or $f'(a)$ does not exist. Thus a first step in finding relative maxima and minima is to find those values of x that give either a zero derivative or no derivative.

Definition

*Those points of a graph at which the derivative is either zero or does not exist are called **critical points** and their x coordinates are **critical numbers** or **critical values**.*

A critical point is not necessarily a relative maximum or minimum—it may be neither. We can easily determine whether a given critical point is a relative maximum or minimum or neither by considering whether the graph is increasing or decreasing on each side of the point. The results are summarized below:

Type of Critical Point	Left of Point	Right of Point	Graphically
Relative maximum	Increasing	Decreasing	/ \
Relative minimum	Decreasing	Increasing	\ /
Neither	Increasing	Increasing	/ /
	Decreasing	Decreasing	\ \

Example 1

Find all relative maxima and minima of

$$y = x^3 - 3x^2 - 9x + 9.$$

$$\begin{aligned} y' &= 3x^2 - 6x - 9 \\ &= 3(x+1)(x-3). \end{aligned}$$

This gives critical values $x = -1$ and $x = 3$. Substituting back into the original equation to get the corresponding values of y, we have the points $(-1, 14)$ and $(3, -18)$.

Now we shall see where the graph is increasing and where it is decreasing in order to determine, in each case, whether the critical point is a relative maximum or minimum or neither. The only place that y' can change from positive to negative (or negative to positive) is at values of x that make $y' = 0$ or give no value for y' (compare this with a similar statement about y on page 99). Thus we need only determine the sign of y' to the left of -1, between -1 and 3, and to

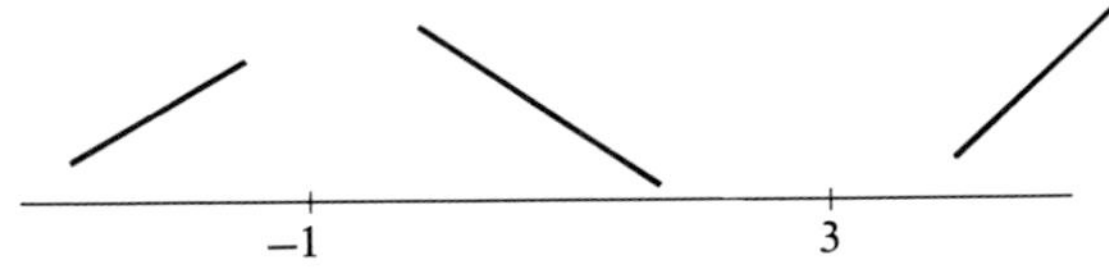

Figure 6.17

the right of 3 giving +, −, +, respectively. This is represented graphically in Figure 6.17, which shows that $(-1, 14)$ is a relative maximum and $(3, -18)$ is a relative minimum.

Example 2

Find all relative maximum and minima of $y = \dfrac{x^2+1}{x}$.

$$y' = \frac{x \cdot 2x - (x^2+1)}{x^2} = \frac{x^2-1}{x^2}.$$

The derivative is 0 when $x = \pm 1$ and there is no derivative when $x = 0$. These are *not* all critical values. A critical value is the x coordinate of a critical *point.*

When we put the values of x back into the original in order to find the y coordinates, we get $(-1, -2)$ and $(1, 2)$; but putting $x = 0$ into the original gives no value at all for y. Thus there is no value of y' at $x = 0$, because there is no value for y there, and $x = 0$ is a vertical asymptote.

Now in checking to see where the graph is increasing and where it is decreasing, we must take into consideration the fact that a change may occur at *any* value at which $y' = 0$ or y' does not exist. This includes the vertical asymptote $x = 0$. Thus we must check to the left of -1, between -1 and 0, between 0 and 1, and to the right of 1. The results are summarized graphically in Figure 6.18. Thus $(-1, -2)$ is a relative maximum and $(1, 2)$ is a relative minimum.

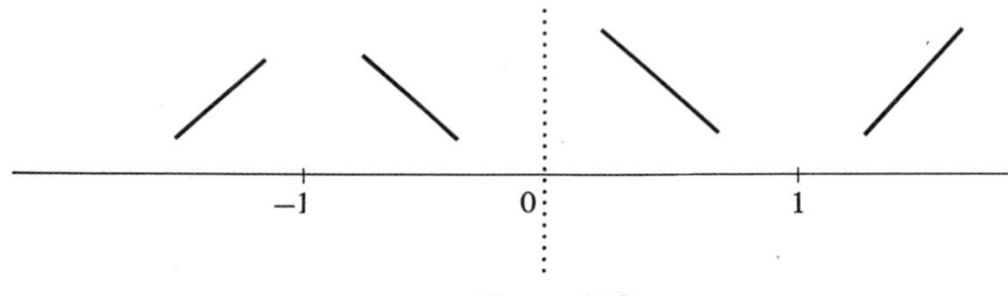

Figure 6.18

One thing about this result that may seem startling is that the lower of the two critical points is the relative maximum, while the higher one is the relative minimum. Thus the y coordinates give no hint as to which point is the relative maximum and which is the relative minimum! The graph of this equation is given in Figure 6.19. We shall say more about sketching the graph in the next section.

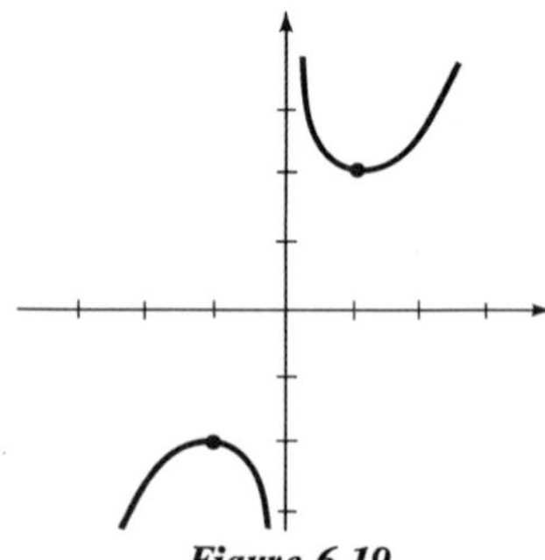

Figure 6.19

Example 3

Find all relative maxima and minima of $y = x^{2/3}$.

$$y' = \frac{2}{3}x^{-1/3} = \frac{2}{3x^{1/3}}.$$

We see that this derivative is never 0, but there is no derivative for $x = 0$. This time we see that it is a critical value, being the x coordinate of $(0, 0)$. Checking values of y' to the left and right of $x = 0$ gives us the result shown in Figure 6.20, so $(0, 0)$ is a relative minimum.

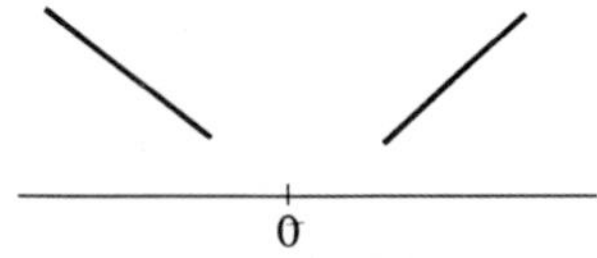

Figure 6.20

Example 4

Find all relative maxima and minima of $y = x^3$.

$$y' = 3x^2.$$

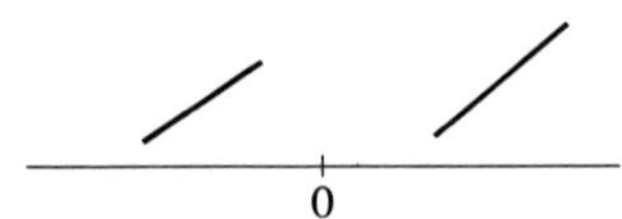

Figure 6.21

The only critical point is (0, 0). Checking the values of y' to the left and right of $x = 0$ gives the result that (0, 0) is neither a relative maximum nor minimum (see Figure 6.21). The graph $y = x^3$ is given in Figure 6.22. Note that, while (0, 0) is neither a relative maximum nor minimum, it does have a horizontal tangent at (0, 0).

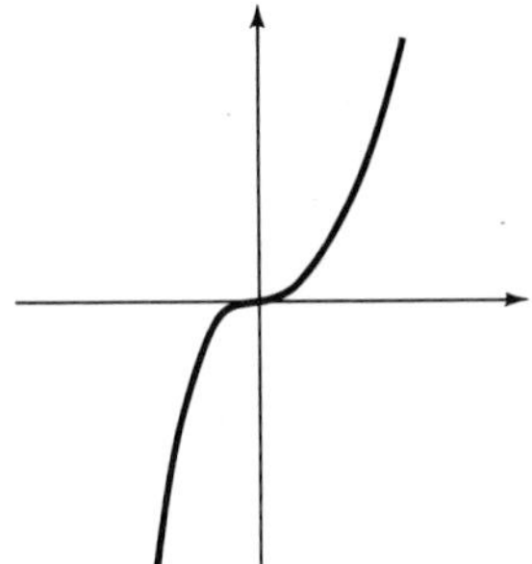

Figure 6.22

Problems

In Problems 1–34, find all relative maxima and minima.

1. $y = x^2 + 2x - 3.$
2. $y = 2x^2 + x - 5.$
3. $y = -x^2 + 6x + 2.$
4. $y = -3x^2 + 12x - 4.$
5. $y = x^3 - 3x^2 + 1.$
6. $y = x^3 + 3x^2 + 3x.$
7. $y = x^3 - 3x + 2.$
8. $y = 2x^3 + 9x^2 - 24x + 1.$
9. $y = 3x^4 + 4x^3.$
10. $y = x^4 - 2x^2 + 1.$
11. $y = -3x^4 + 8x^3 - 6x^2 + 16.$
12. $y = x^5 - 5x^4.$
13. $y = \dfrac{x}{x+1}.$
14. $y = \dfrac{x^2}{x^2+1}.$
15. $y = \dfrac{x^2+1}{x^2}.$
16. $y = \dfrac{x^2-1}{x^3}.$
17. $y = \dfrac{1}{x^2-1}.$
18. $y = \dfrac{x^2}{x^2-1}.$
19. $y = \dfrac{x^3}{(x-1)^2}.$
20. $y = \dfrac{x^3-1}{x^3+1}.$
21. $y = (x+1)^2(x-2).$
22. $y = x^4(x-1)^3.$
23. $y = (x-4)^4(x+2)^4.$
24. $y = x^3(x+2).$

25. $y = x^{1/3}$.

26. $y = x^{1/2}$.

27. $y = x^{2/3} + 1$.

28. $y = (x+1)^{2/3}$.

29. $y = (x-1)^{1/3}(x+2)^{2/3}$.

30. $y = \dfrac{(x-1)^{1/3}}{(x+2)^{2/3}}$.

31. $y = x^{2/3}(x-2)^{4/3}$.

32. $y = \dfrac{x^{2/3}}{(x-2)^{4/3}}$.

33. $y = x^{4/3} - x^{2/3}$.

34. $y = \dfrac{x^{4/3} - x^{2/3}}{x^{4/3} + x^{2/3}}$.

35. Show that if $(x-a)^b$, where $b > 0$ and $b \neq 1$, is a factor of $P(x)$ but not of $Q(x)$ in $f(x) = P(x)/Q(x)$, then $(a, 0)$ is a critical point.

36. Show that if $(x-a)^n$, where n is a positive even integer, is a factor of $P(x)$ but not of $Q(x)$ in $f(x) = P(x)/Q(x)$, then $(a, 0)$ is either a relative maximum or a relative minimum.

6.5

Second-Derivative Test and Points of Inflection

When we first introduced multiple derivatives, we did not attempt to give them a geometrical or physical interpretation. Let us do so now for the second derivative. Figure 6.23 gives three graphs; the top one gives y as a function of x, the middle one gives the derivative y' as a function of x, and the bottom one gives the second derivative, y'', as a function of x. How was the middle one derived from the top one? At the far left we see that y is increasing very rapidly; thus the corresponding value of y' is large and positive. As x increases, y is increasing more and more slowly until finally, at $x = a$, y stops increasing and the graph has a horizontal tangent; thus the corresponding values of y' become smaller and smaller and finally reach zero at $x = a$. As x goes from $x = a$ to $x = c$, the graph is decreasing, slowly at first, then faster and faster until it reaches $x = b$, at which time the rate of decrease begins slowing until it again reaches zero at $x = c$. The corresponding values of y', starting from zero at $x = a$, go negative, becoming numerically larger until, at $x = b$, y' attains the largest negative value. Then the value gets numerically smaller until it reaches zero at $x = c$. Beyond $x = c$, y increases faster and faster and y' gets larger and larger in the positive direction. The bottom graph is derived from the middle one in exactly the same way.

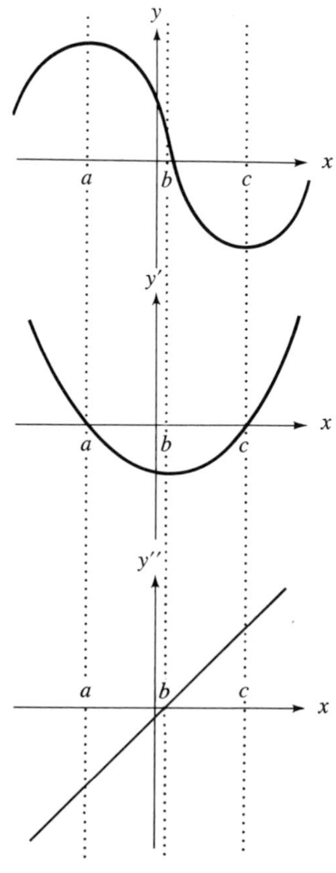

Figure 6.23

Now let us compare the second derivative with the original. We see that the second derivative is negative to the left of $x = b$, where the original is concave downward, and it is positive to the right of $x = b$, where the original is concave upward. At $x = b$, $y'' = 0$ and the original changes from concave downward to concave upward. All of this suggests the following theorem.

Theorem 6.6

If f is a function such that $f''(x)$ is positive (negative) for all x on (a, b), then the graph of f is concave upward (downward) on (a, b).

Of course the above discussion does not constitute a proof of this theorem and we shall not attempt one. A proof (see Appendix B) can be given using the mean-value theorem (see page 439). Again, as in Theorem 6.5, the converse is not true; the most that can be said is that if the graph is concave upward on (a, b), then $f''(x) \geq 0$ for all x on (a, b), at which $f''(x)$ exists. This gives us another method of testing a critical point to determine whether it is a relative maximum or minimum.

Theorem 6.7

If $A: (a, f(a))$ is a point of the graph of f such that $f'(a) = 0$ and $f''(a) < 0$, then A is a relative maximum; if $f'(a) = 0$ and $f''(a) > 0$, then A is a relative minimum.

Note that the only cases mentioned in the theorem are those in which the second derivative is either positive or negative. If the second derivative either is zero or does not exist, you are *not* justified in concluding that you have neither a relative maximum nor minimum—*you must resort to the first-derivative test* or some other analysis.

Example 1

Find all relative maxima and minima of $y = x^3 - 3x^2 - 9x + 9$.

$$y' = 3x^2 - 6x - 9 = 3(x + 1)(x - 3),$$
$$y'' = 6x - 6 = 6(x - 1).$$

From the first derivative we have critical values $x = -1$ and $x = 3$. From the second derivative we see that $f''(-1) = -12$ and $f''(3) = 12$. Thus $(-1, 14)$ is a relative maximum, and $(3, -18)$ is a relative minimum. This is the same result that we found in Example 1 of the previous section.

This second-derivative test is a nice, simple test when it works; unfortunately it does not work in every case. One case in which you can be sure that the second-derivative test will fail is for critical points at which the first derivative does not exist. If the first derivative does not exist for a given value of x, then the second derivative (which is the derivative of the first derivative) cannot possibly exist. Of course, there is no obligation to use this test even when it does work. If, after looking at the first derivative, you feel that you would rather do almost anything than take another derivative, then don't take another derivative—use the first-derivative test instead.

Another way in which the second derivative is useful is in locating those points at which the graph changes from concave upward to downward or vice versa.

Definition

If A: $(a, f(a))$ is a point of the graph of the function f such that there is an interval (b, a) and an interval (a, c) such that f is either concave upward in the first and concave downward in the second or vice versa, then A is a ***point of inflection.***

Points of inflection are determined in much the same way as critical points, by using the second derivative instead of the first. The second derivative changes from positive to negative or negative to positive at those points at which it is either zero or does not exist. Again, as with critical points, the points of the graph at which the second derivative is either zero or does not exist are only *possible* points of inflection. You must check to see whether or not the sign of the second derivative really does change by considering values to the left and right of the point in question.

Can one use the third derivative to make the check? Yes, you can, but it might be noted that the third-derivative test is not so valuable as it might seem at first glance. In most problems you will be interested in finding not only points of inflection, but also relative maxima and minima. Using the second-derivative test to determine relative maxima and minima, you would already be checking several values of the second derivative. Thus it sometimes happens that no further checking is needed when you consider points of inflection; when further checking is needed it is usually minimal.

If you do want to use the third-derivative test, it is much like the second-derivative test. If $f''(a) = 0$ and $f'''(a) \neq 0$, then $(a, f(a))$ is a point of inflection, with the graph changing from concave upward to downward if $f'''(a)$ is negative and from concave downward to upward if $f'''(a)$ is positive. If $f'''(a) = 0$, the test fails.

Example 2

Find all points of inflection and determine the concavity of the graph of $y = x^4 - 6x^2$.

$$y' = 4x^3 - 12x,$$
$$y'' = 12x^2 - 12 = 12(x - 1)(x + 1).$$

We see that $y'' = 0$ if $x = \pm 1$, and so we have two *possible* points of inflection, $(1, -5)$ and $(-1, -5)$.

To determine concavity we can use one of two methods. Checking the values of the second derivative to the left of -1, between -1 and 1, and to the right of 1 gives us Figure 6.24, which shows that the two points are really points of inflection, with the graph concave downward between them and concave upward elsewhere.

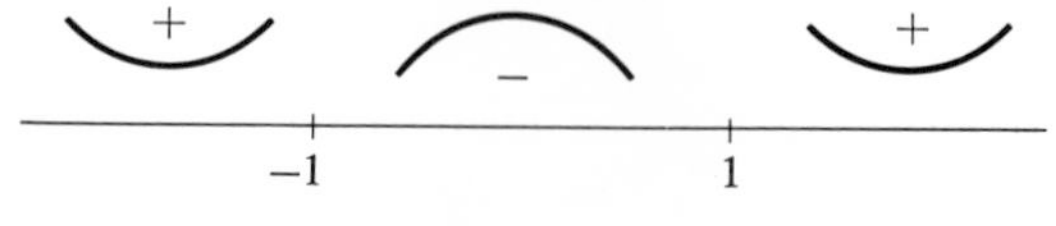

Figure 6.24

If we use the third-derivative test, we have $y''' = 24x$, which is clearly negative at $x = -1$ and positive at $x = 1$. Therefore, the graph changes from concave upward to downward at $x = -1$ and back to concave upward at $x = 1$.

Had we been asked to determine relative maxima and minima, there would be no point in using the third-derivative test. The critical values are $x = \pm\sqrt{3}$ and $x = 0$.

Using the second-derivative test to determine relative maxima and minima, you would check values of the second derivative to the left of -1 (at $-\sqrt{3}$), between -1 and 1 (at 0), and to the right of 1 (at $\sqrt{3}$). Thus no further checking would be needed when you consider points of inflection.

Problems

In Problems 1–12, use the second-derivative test where possible to determine relative maxima and minima.

1. $y = x^2 - x - 6.$
2. $y = x^2 + 4x - 2.$
3. $y = 2x^3 - x^2 - 4x + 2.$
4. $y = x^3 - 6x^2 + 9x + 1.$
5. $y = 3x^4 - 4x^3 - 12x^2 + 24.$
6. $y = 3x^4 - 8x^3 + 6x^2 + 1.$
7. $y = 4x^5 - 5x^4.$
8. $y = 4x^5 - x^4.$
9. $y = \dfrac{x^2}{x+1}.$
10. $y = \dfrac{x}{(x+1)^2}.$
11. $y = \dfrac{x^2+1}{x^2-1}.$
12. $y = \dfrac{x^3+1}{x^3-1}.$

In Problems 13–22, find all points of inflection and determine the concavity.

13. $y = x^2 - 2x - 1.$
14. $y = 1 - 4x - x^2.$
15. $y = x^3 - 3x^2 - 9x + 3.$
16. $y = x^3 + 2x^2 - 4x + 1.$
17. $y = x^4 - 6x^3.$
18. $y = x^4 + x^3 + 9x^2 - 9.$
19. $y = \dfrac{1}{x+1}.$
20. $y = \dfrac{x}{x+1}.$
21. $y = \dfrac{x}{x^2+1}$
22. $y = \dfrac{x}{x^2-1}.$

In Problems 23–32, find all relative maxima and minima and points of inflection.

23. $y = x^3 - 6x^2.$
24. $y = 4x^3 + 7x^2 - 10x + 1.$
25. $y = 4x^3 - 15x^2 - 18x + 10.$
26. $y = x^3 - 9x^2 + 15x - 5.$
27. $y = 2x^4 - x.$
28. $y = x^5 - 20x^2.$
29. $y = x^5 - 5x^4.$
30. $y = x^6 - 6x^5.$
31. $y = \dfrac{x^3}{x^2-1}.$
32. $y = \dfrac{x-1}{x^3}.$
33. Show that the graph of $y = (ax+b)/(cx+d)$ has no critical point and no point of inflection.

6.6

The Derivative as an Aid in Sketching Curves

With the ability to determine the relative maxima and minima and points of inflection of a given curve, you are in a much better position to sketch the curve.

Example 1

Sketch $y = (x - 3)(x + 1)^2$.

This is the same as Example 3 of Section 2, page 100. The information we found there is summed up graphically in Figure 6.7. Let us now determine maxima, minima, and points of inflection.

$$y' = (x + 1)(3x - 5), \qquad y'' = 2(3x - 1).$$

From these derivatives we have:

$(-1, 0)$ is a relative maximum,
$(5/3, -256/27)$ is a relative minimum,
$(1/3, -128/27)$ is a point of inflection.

We now see that the curve must look like Figure 6.25.

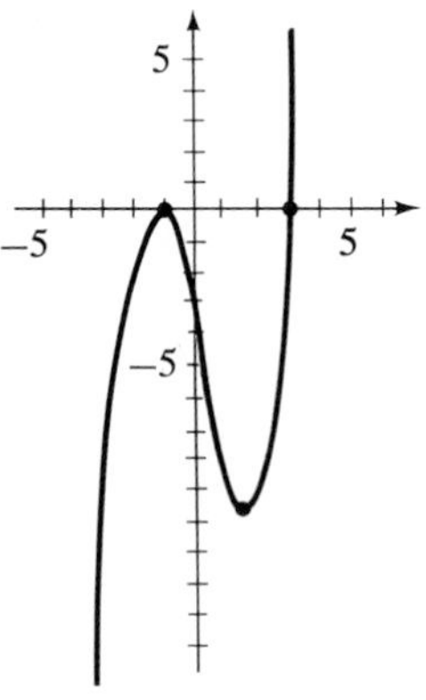

Figure 6.25

You might compare this with our best guess in Figure 6.8. You might also recall that we were not sure, when we first sketched the graph, that it did not look like Figure 6.9. We now know that it cannot have any more "turns," since we know that there cannot be any other relative maximum or minimum. Furthermore, there cannot even be a little "wiggle," since we found only one point of inflection. We now have a very accurate picture of the graph.

Example 2

Sketch $y = x^3 - 6x^2 + 9x + 1$.

Without calculus we know almost nothing about the graph. In order to find the x intercept(s), we would have to solve the equation $x^3 - 6x^2 + 9x + 1 = 0$! Since the left-hand side is not easily factorable, this seems to be too much work. Let's see if we can get along without it. The y intercept is $(0, 1)$. There are no asymptotes of any kind, but

$$\lim_{x \to +\infty} y = +\infty \quad \text{and} \quad \lim_{x \to -\infty} y = -\infty.$$

Taking derivatives we have

$$y' = 3x^2 - 12x + 9 = 3(x - 1)(x - 3),$$
$$y'' = 6x - 12 = 6(x - 2).$$

They give the following results:

$(1, 5)$ is a relative maximum,
$(3, 1)$ is a relative minimum,
$(2, 3)$ is a point of inflection.

The resulting graph is given in Figure 6.26.

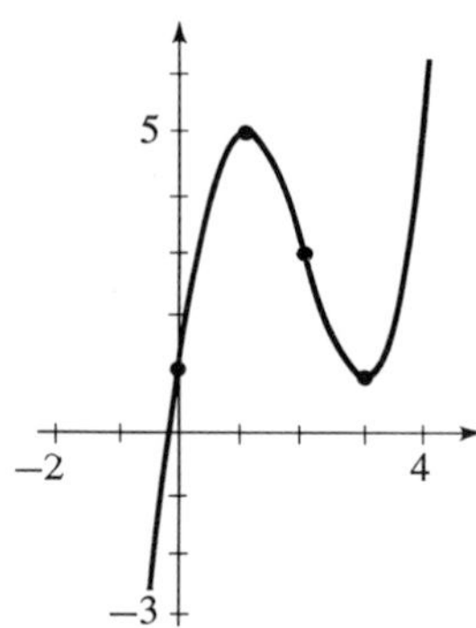

Figure 6.26

Example 3

Sketch $y = (x - 1)^{1/3}(x + 2)^{2/3}$.

The intercepts are $(1, 0)$ odd, $(-2, 0)$ even, and $(0, -\sqrt[3]{4})$. Even though the exponents are not integers, we may assign odd and even designations according to the numerator of the exponents. There are no asymptotes and no symmetry, but

$$\lim_{x \to +\infty} y = +\infty \quad \text{and} \quad \lim_{x \to -\infty} y = -\infty.$$

The first two derivatives,

$$y' = \frac{x}{(x-1)^{2/3}(x+2)^{1/3}}, \qquad y'' = \frac{-2}{(x-1)^{5/3}(x+2)^{4/3}},$$

give the following results:

$(0, -\sqrt[3]{4})$ is a relative minimum with horizontal tangent,

$(1, 0)$ is neither relative maximum nor minimum but has a vertical tangent,

$(-2, 0)$ is a relative maximum with a vertical tangent,

$(1, 0)$ is a point of inflection.

Note that, of the three critical values, $x = 0$, $x = 1$, and $x = -2$, only the first can be tested by the second derivative—there is no second derivative at $x = 1$ or $x = -2$.

The resulting graph is given in Figure 6.27.

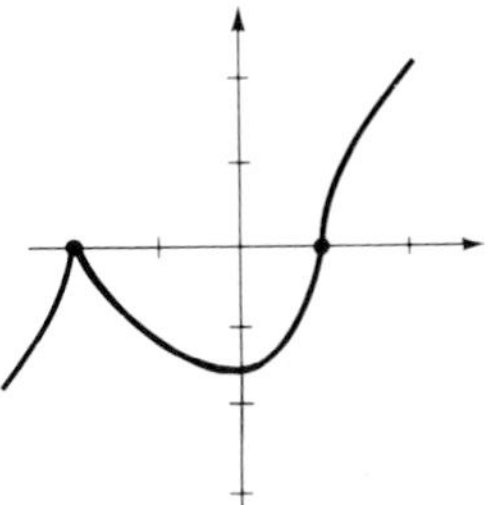

Figure 6.27

Note the basic difference between the critical point $(0, -\sqrt[3]{4})$ and the other two critical points, $(1, 0)$ and $(-2, 0)$. At $x = 0$, $y' = 0$; but at $x = 1$ and $x = -2$, y' does not exist. Thus when $y' = 0$, the tangent is horizontal; when y' does not exist (the denominator of the expression for y' is 0, but the numerator is not), the tangent is vertical. This is summed up graphically in Figure 6.28.

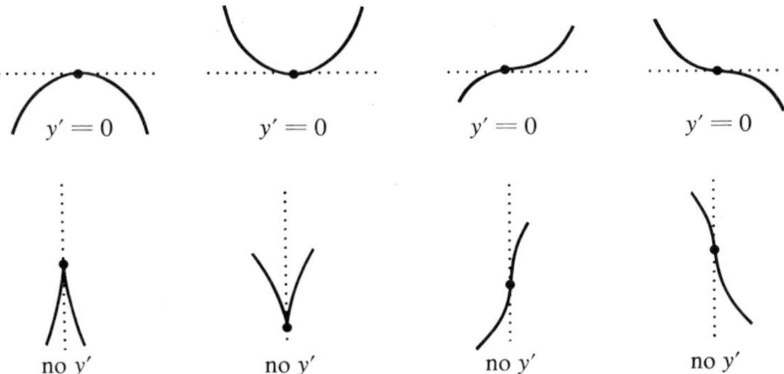

Figure 6.28

Example 4

Sketch $y^2 = \dfrac{27(x-1)^2}{x^3}$.

Suppose that we first sketch

$$z = \frac{27(x-1)^2}{x^3}.$$

We have intercept $(1, 0)$ even, vertical asymptote $x = 0$ odd, and horizontal asymptote $z = 0$ and no symmetry. The derivatives

$$z' = -\frac{27(x-1)(x-3)}{x^4} \quad \text{and} \quad z'' = \frac{54(x^2-6x+6)}{x^5}$$

give (for the graph of z)

$(1, 0)$ is a relative minimum,
$(3, 4)$ is a relative maximum,
$(3+\sqrt{3}, 3(3+\sqrt{3})/4)$ is a point of inflection,
$(3-\sqrt{3}, 3(3-\sqrt{3})/4)$ is a point of inflection.

In the resulting graph (Figure 6.29), z is represented by the dotted curve and y by the solid curve.

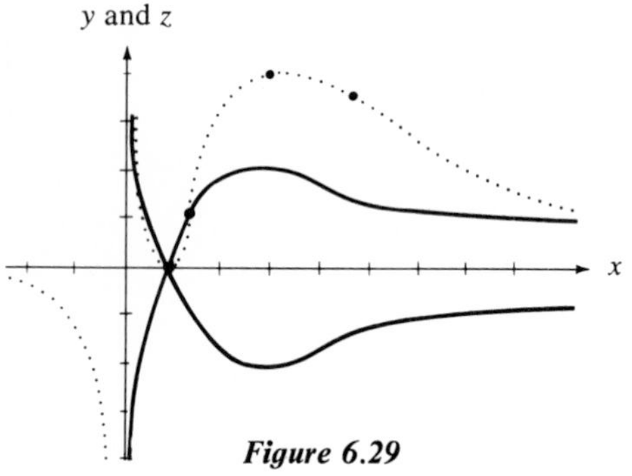

Figure 6.29

Problems

In Problems 1–16, find all relative maxima and minima and all points of inflection and sketch the curve.

1. $y = x^3 + 6x^2$.
2. $y = x^4 - 4x^3$.
3. $y = 2x^3 - x^2 - 4x + 2$.
4. $y = x^5 - 5x$.
5. $y = (x+1)^2(x-3)^3$.
6. $y = x^3(x-2)^4$.
7. $y = x(2x+1)(x-2)$.
8. $y = x^2(x^2-1)$.
9. $y = (x-1)^{1/3}(x+3)^{2/3}$.
10. $y = x^{2/3}(x-2)^{1/3}$.
11. $y = \sqrt{x}(x-1)$.
12. $y = x^{2/5}(x+1)^{3/5}$.
13. $y = \dfrac{x^2}{x+1}$.
14. $y = \dfrac{4(x+1)}{x^2}$.
15. $y = \dfrac{x^2+1}{x}$.
16. $y = \dfrac{1}{x^2-2x}$.

In Problems 17–24, find all relative maxima and minima and sketch the curve.

17. $y^2 = x^4 - 4x^3$.
18. $y^2 = -x^3 + 5x^2 - 7x + 35$.
19. $y^2 = 6x^2 - x^3$
20. $y^2 = (x-3)(x+3)^2$.
21. $y^2 = \dfrac{x-1}{x^3}$.
22. $y^2 = \dfrac{1}{x^2-1}$.
23. $y^2 = \dfrac{x}{(x-1)^3}$.
24. $y^2 = \dfrac{x^2(x-4)}{x-6}$.

Further Applications of the Derivative

7.1

Applications of Maxima and Minima

There are many practical applications of maxima and minima. The engineer wants to maximize the strength of structures, the businessman wants to minimize taxes, engineer and businessman alike want to maximize profit and minimize cost, and so on. Moreover, nature itself determines many maximum or minimum problems: light, when reaching an interface or a reflecting surface, takes a path that gives a minimum propagation time (see Problems 28 and 30); soap bubbles assume the shape with a minimum surface area. Thus the determination of maxima and minima can become a very practical problem. We, of course, are interested in an *absolute* maximum or minimum, not merely a relative maximum or minimum; however, finding the relative maxima or minima is a first step in determining the absolute maximum or minimum.

One must first determine an equation from the description of the situation and decide what is to be made a maximum or minimum and what is allowed to vary (there may be several quantities that vary). Then write an equation expressing the quantity that is to be a maximum or minimum in terms of *one* of the variables. Quite often it is relatively easy to get such an expression in terms of two variables. In such a case there will be some condition which gives a relationship between the two variables; thus, one variable can be expressed in terms of the other and substituted into the expression to be maximized or minimized. Once this has been done, merely proceed as in the previous chapter, remembering that you are looking for an absolute—not relative—maximum or minimum. This last condition is not so difficult a hurdle as it might seem. In many cases the physical situation will make it obvious whether or not there is a relative maximum or a relative minimum.

Example 1

A farmer wishes to fence a field bordering a straight stream with 1000 yards of fencing material. He will not fence the side bordering the stream. What is the area of the largest rectangular field he can fence?

Let us note, first of all, that the area is to be a maximum and the lengths of the sides, x and y (see Figure 7.1), are allowed to vary. It is a simple matter to express the area in terms of x and y:

$$A = xy.$$

Now we must eliminate either the x or y by finding a relationship between them.

Since he has 1000 yards of fencing material, we see that

$$2x + y = 1000, \quad \text{or} \quad y = 1000 - 2x.$$

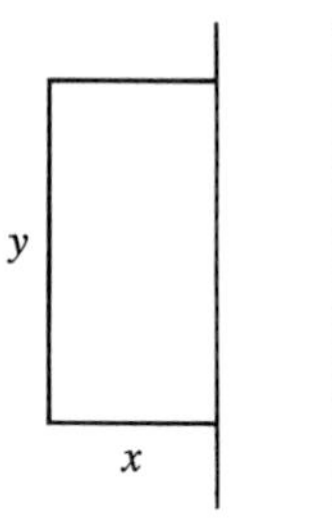

Figure 7.1

Thus,

$$A = x(1000 - 2x) = 1000x - 2x^2.$$

There are certain restrictions on x. Certainly $x > 0$ and $x < 500$ (if it were 500 or more, $y \leq 0$). Now we have the final relation we are looking for:

$$A = 1000x - 2x^2, \quad 0 < x < 500,$$
$$A' = 1000 - 4x = 0,$$
$$x = 250 \text{ yd},$$
$$A = 125{,}000 \text{ sq yd}.$$

The physical situation here makes it unnecessary to check to make sure that $x = 250$ gives the absolute maximum value for A. The area is nearly 0 when x is near the extreme values 0 and 500; it must reach a maximum value somewhere between these two extremes.

Example 2

Find the volume of the largest right circular cylinder that can be inscribed in a sphere of radius R.

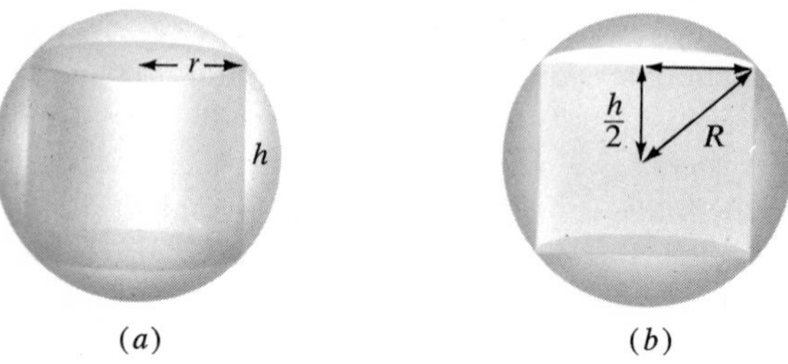

Figure 7.2

The volume of a cylinder (see Figure 7.2(a)) is $V = \pi r^2 h$. Let us consider a cross section through the center of the sphere. From the right triangle in Figure 7.2(b) we see that

$$R^2 = r^2 + \frac{h^2}{4}, \quad \text{or} \quad r^2 = R^2 - \frac{h^2}{4}.$$

Thus

$$V = \pi\left(R^2 - \frac{h^2}{4}\right)h$$

$$= \pi\left(R^2 h - \frac{h^3}{4}\right), \quad 0 < h < 2R,$$

$$V' = \pi\left(R^2 - \frac{3h^2}{4}\right) = 0,$$

$$h^2 = \frac{4R^2}{3},$$

$$h = \frac{2R}{\sqrt{3}},$$

$$V_{\max} = \frac{4\pi R^3}{3\sqrt{3}}.$$

Again, the physical situation tells us that we have the maximum, with no further checking.

Example 3

Find the area of the largest rectangle that can be inscribed in

$$\frac{x^2}{a^2} + \frac{y^2}{b^2} = 1.$$

The methods of the previous chapter show that the graph of the given equation is elliptical (see Figure 7.3). The inscribed rectangle must have all four corners on the ellipse, and thus its sides must be parallel to the axes. Suppose we label the corner in the first quadrant (x, y). Then

$$A = 4xy, \quad 0 < x < a, 0 < y < b.$$

Since (x, y) is on the ellipse, it satisfies the equation

$$\frac{x^2}{a^2} + \frac{y^2}{b^2} = 1,$$

and

$$y = \frac{b}{a}\sqrt{a^2 - x^2}.$$

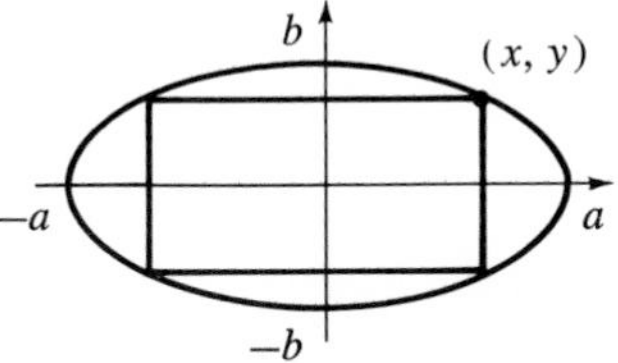

Figure 7.3

We are assuming here that a and b are positive, and we take only the positive square root, because y must be positive. Now

$$A = \frac{4b}{a} x\sqrt{a^2 - x^2}, \qquad 0 < x < a,$$

$$A' = \frac{4b}{a}\left(x \frac{-2x}{2\sqrt{a^2 - x^2}} + \sqrt{a^2 - x^2}\right) = \frac{4b}{a} \frac{a^2 - 2x^2}{\sqrt{a^2 - x^2}}.$$

$x = a/\sqrt{2}$ is the only critical point within the domain of our function. This must give the maximum desired, and

$$A = 2ab.$$

Example 4

Find the point of the curve $y = x^2$ that is closest to $(4, -1/2)$.

The distance between the point $(4, -1/2)$ and an arbitrary point (x, y) on the curve (see Figure 7.4) is given by

$$d = \sqrt{(x-4)^2 + (y+1/2)^2}.$$

Since (x, y) is on the curve, its coordinates satisfy the equation $y = x^2$; and

$$d = \sqrt{(x-4)^2 + (x^2+1/2)^2},$$

$$d' = \frac{2(x-4) + 2(x^2+1/2)2x}{2\sqrt{(x-4)^2 + (x^2+1/2)^2}}$$

$$= \frac{2x^3 + 2x - 4}{\sqrt{(x-4)^2 + (x^2+1/2)^2}}.$$

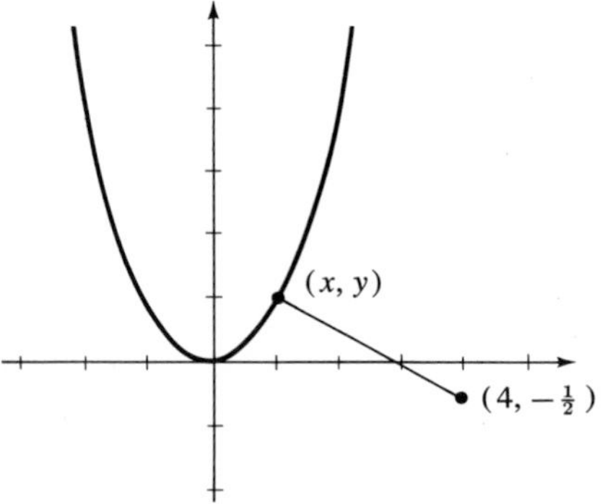

Figure 7.4

The only real value of x that makes the numerator zero is $x = 1$; the denominator cannot be zero (if it were, then $x - 4 = 0$ and $x^2 + 1/2 = y + 1/2 = 0$, which would give $(x, y) = (4, -1/2)$ and $(4, -1/2)$ is not a point of $y = x^2$). Thus, the point we are seeking is $(1, 1)$.

A trick that can used to some advantage here is to square d before taking the derivative.

$$D = d^2 = (x-4)^2 + (x^2+1/2)^2.$$

Since d is always positive, both d and D must have a maximum or minimum at the same value of x. The advantage is that the derivative of D is easier to find than the derivative of d.

$$D' = 2(x-4) + 2(x^2+1/2)2x$$
$$= 4x^3 + 4x - 8.$$

Not only is it easier to take the derivative, but the result is far simpler. This could also have been used in Example 3.

Problems

1. Find two numbers x and y whose sum is 48 and whose product is a maximum.
2. Find two numbers x and y whose sum is A such that the sum of their squares is a minimum.
3. A farmer wants to fence in 60,000 sq ft of land in a rectangular plot along a straight highway. The fence he plans to use along the highway costs \$1.00 per foot, while the fence for the other three sides costs \$.50 per foot. How much of each type of fence will he have to buy in order to keep expenses to a minimum? What is the minimum expense?
4. A farmer wants to fence in 60,000 sq ft of land in a rectangular plot and then divide it in half with a fence parallel to one pair of sides. What are the dimensions of the rectangular plot that will require the least amount of fence?

5. A farmer wants to fence in 180,000 sq ft of land in a rectangular plot and then divide it into three equal plots with a pair of fences both parallel to the same pair of sides (see (a) of Figure 7.5). What is the least amount of fence needed to accomplish this?

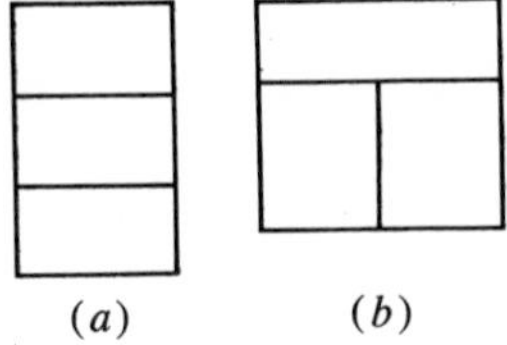

(*a*) (*b*)

Figure 7.5

6. The farmer in Problem 5 wonders if it would be cheaper to fence the same area (though not necessarily having the same dimensions) into three equal plots using the plan of Figure 7.5(b). Would this plan cost more than, less than, or the same amount as the earlier plan?
7. Suppose the farmer of Problem 5 wants to subdivide into four equal plots by either of the plans of Figure 7.6. Which plan (if either) is cheaper and what is the least amount of fence needed?

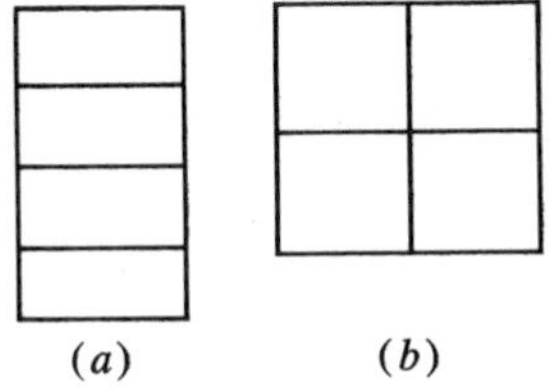

(*a*) (*b*)

Figure 7.6

8. Find the volume of the largest right circular cone which can be inscribed in a sphere of radius R.
9. Find the volume of the largest right circular cylinder which can be inscribed in a right circular cone of radius R and height H.
10. Find the volume of the smallest right circular cone which can be circumscribed about a sphere of radius R.
11. Find the dimensions of the right circular cylinder of greatest lateral surface that can be inscribed in a sphere of radius R.
12. A square piece of cardboard whose side is of length L has a square cutout at each corner. The sides are then turned up to form an open box. Find the side of the cut-out square that will produce a box of maximum volume.
13. A rectangular box, open at the top, with a square base, is to have a volume of 4000 cubic inches. What must be its dimensions if the box is to require the least possible material?
14. If the box of Problem 13 is to be closed at the top, what must be its dimensions?
15. A tin can is to be made with a capacity V. What dimensions for it will require the smallest amount of tin?
16. Find the dimensions of the rectangle of greatest area that can be inscribed in a circle of radius R.
17. Find the dimensions of the isosceles triangle of greatest area that can be inscribed in a circle of radius R.
18. Find the dimensions of the isosceles triangle of least area that can be circumscribed about a circle of radius R.
19. Find the dimensions of the trapezoid of greatest area inscribed in a circle of radius R and having one base a diameter of the circle.

20. Find the dimensions of the trapezoid of greatest area inscribed in $y = 16 - x^2$ and having its longer base on the x axis.
21. Find the dimensions of the rectangle of greatest area with its base on the x axis and its other two corners above the x axis and on $y = 16 - x^2$.
22. Find the point on $y^2 = 4x$ closest to $(3, 0)$.
23. Find the point in the first quadrant on $xy = 3$ closest to $(-8, 0)$.
24. A printed page has 1-in. margins at the top and bottom and 3/4-in. margins at the sides. If the area of the printed portion is to be 44 in.^{2}, what should the dimensions of the page be to use the least paper?
25. A Norman window consists of a rectangle surmounted by a semicircle. If the perimeter is to be P, what are the dimensions of the window admitting the most light?
26. The strength of a wooden beam of a given length is proportional to its width and the square of its height. Find the dimensions of the strongest beam that can be cut from a circular log of diameter 4 ft.
27. A ship is anchored 4 miles off a straight shore. Opposite a point 9 miles down the coast, another ship is anchored 8 miles from the shore. A boat from the first ship is to land a passenger on the shore and then proceed to the other ship to pick up another passenger before returning. At what point along the shore should the boat land the passenger in order to run the shortest course?
28. A ray of light from A is reflected to B in XY (see Figure 7.7). Find the value of x (in terms of a, b and c) such that the total time from A to B is a minimum. Show that, for this value of x, $\alpha = \beta$. Compare with Problem 27.
29. A man is in a boat 4 miles off a straight coast. He wants to reach a point 10 miles down the coast in the least possible time. If he can row 4 miles per hour and run 5 miles per hour, where should he land the boat?

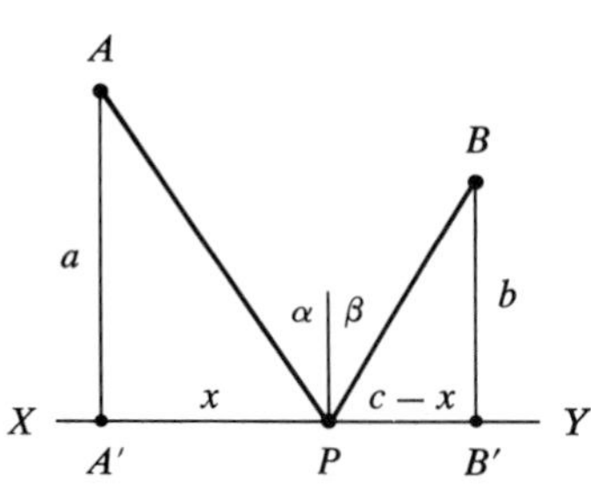

Figure 7.7

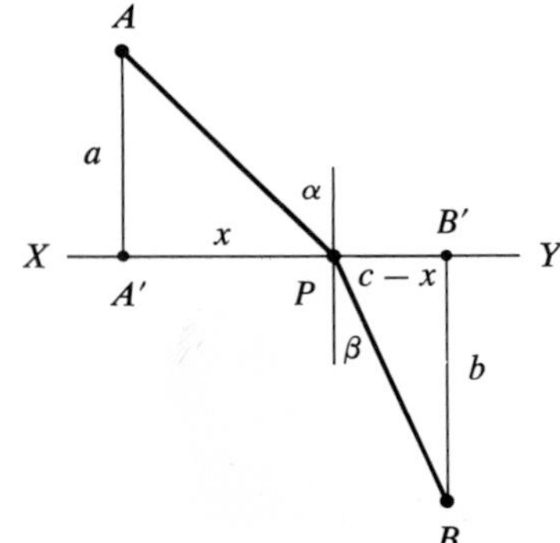

Figure 7.8

30. A ray of light is to move from A to B (see Figure 7.8) in the least possible time. Its velocity above XY is v_1; its velocity below XY is v_2. Show that

$$\frac{\sin \alpha}{\sin \beta} = \frac{v_1}{v_2}.$$

When v_1 is the velocity of light in a vacuum and v_2 is the velocity of light in some other medium, v_1/v_2 is called the index of refraction of the medium.

31. The current I in a voltaic cell is

$$I = \frac{E}{R + r},$$

where E is the electromotive force and R and r are the external and internal resistance, respectively. E and r are internal characteristics of the cell; they cannot be changed. The power developed is $P = RI^2$. Show that P is a maximum when $R = r$.

32. The efficiency of a screw is given by the formula

$$E = \frac{h(1 - h\mu)}{h + \mu},$$

where μ is the coefficient of friction and h is the tangent of the pitch angle of the screw. Find the value of h for which the efficiency is a maximum.

33. An impulse turbine consists of a high speed jet of water striking circularly mounted blades. The power P developed by such a turbine is directly proportional to the speed V of the jet, the speed U of the turbine and the speed of the jet relative to the turbine $V - U$. That is,

$$P = kVU(V - U).$$

For a given jet speed V, determine the turbine speed that will develop maximum power.

34. The cost of fuel used in propelling a ship varies as the cube of her speed, and is \$12.80 per hour when the speed is 8 miles per hour. The other expenses are \$50.00 per hour. Find the most economical speed and the minimum cost of a voyage of 1,000 miles.

35. Find the shortest distance from the point (x_1, y_1) to the line $Ax + By + C = 0$.

36. The lower corner of a page of width k is folded over so as just to reach the inner edge of the page (see Figure 7.9). Find the width x of the part folded over when the length of the crease y is a minimum.

37. In Problem 36, find the width of the part folded over when the area of the triangle folded over is a minimum.

38. The intensity of light at a distance d from a source of intensity I is kI/d^2. If two light sources have intensities I_1 and I_2 and are at a distance d from each other, find the point between them where the intensity is the least.

39. A steel pipe 25 feet long is carried down a narrow corridor 5.4 feet wide. At the end of the corridor is a right-angle turn into a wider hall. How wide must the hall be in order to get the pipe around the corner? (Assume that the pipe bends just enough so that you may neglect its width.)

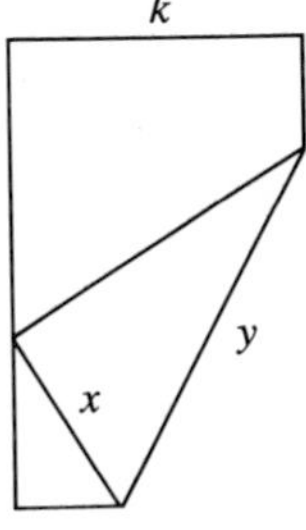

Figure 7.9

7.2

Position, Velocity, and Acceleration

Suppose we are to take a trip by car and keep a careful log of time t and distance s from the starting point. Suppose further that we represent all of this by means of a graph of position s (that is, distance from the starting point) as a function of time t (see Figure 7.10).

Now, if we want to determine our average speed during the trip, we simply divide the total distance, 80 miles, by the total driving time, two hours, to get 40 miles per hour. If we want the average speed during the first hour of the trip, we divide the distance covered in that hour, 35 miles, by the one hour, to get 35 miles per hour. For the average speed between $t = 1$ and $t = 3/2$, we have (letting $s = f(t)$)

$$\frac{f(3/2) - f(1)}{(3/2) - 1} = \frac{70 - 35}{1/2} = 70 \text{ miles per hour.}$$

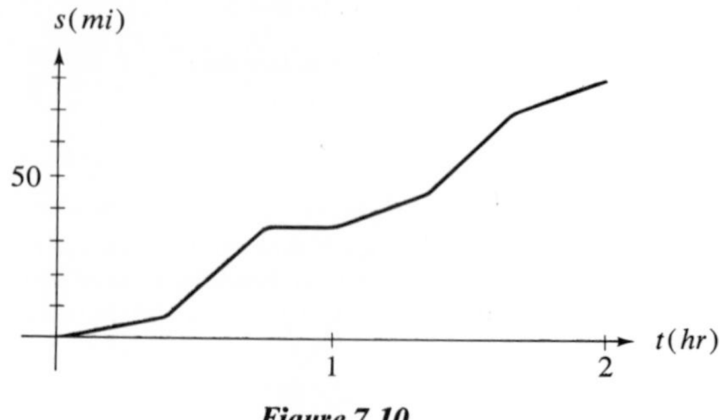

Figure 7.10

In fact, for the average speed between two times, t and $t + h$, we have

$$\frac{f(t+h) - f(t)}{(t+h) - t} = \frac{f(t+h) - f(t)}{h},$$

which represents the slope of the line joining the two points $(t, f(t))$ and $(t + h, f(t + h))$.

Of course, we cannot use this method to find the speed at any particular instant, since then the denominator would be zero. But the closer h gets to zero, the closer the average speed is to the instantaneous speed at t. Thus,

$$v = \lim_{h \to 0} \frac{f(t+h) - f(t)}{h} = \frac{ds}{dt};$$

the speed, which is the rate of change of position with respect to time, is the derivative of the position with respect to time. We are using the symbol v, which suggests velocity, for the speed. Actually, speed and velocity are not the same. Speed is a scalar, having magnitude only; while velocity is a vector, having both magnitude and direction (see pages 554–55). In this and the following section, we are concerned only with rectilinear, or straight-line, motion; therefore, speed and velocity are essentially the same and we shall use them interchangeably. When we get to Chapter 21, on vectors, we shall have to be a little more careful to distinguish between the scalar speed and the vector velocity.

The acceleration is defined to be the rate of change of velocity. Thus we have

$$s = f(t), \qquad v = \frac{ds}{dt}, \qquad a = \frac{dv}{dt} = \frac{d^2s}{dt^2}.$$

This allows us to proceed from position to velocity to acceleration by differentiation or from acceleration to velocity to position by antidifferentiation.

Example 1

An object has the equation of motion $s = t^3 - t$. Find the position, velocity, and acceleration at $t = 1$.

$$\begin{aligned} s &= t^3 - t, & \text{At } t = 1: \quad s &= 0, \\ v &= 3t^2 - 1, & v &= 2, \\ a &= 6t. & a &= 6. \end{aligned}$$

Example 2

An arrow is shot straight up into the air from ground level with an initial velocity of 128 ft/sec. How high will it go and when will it reach the ground?

We shall make two simplifying assumptions: first, we shall assume that the air resistance is negligible; second, we shall assume that the acceleration from gravity is constant at -32 ft/sec^2. Air does resist the motion of any object, and resistance increases with increased velocity. However, for the low velocities involved and the streamlined shape of an arrow, the resistance is slight. The acceleration caused by gravity is not a constant; it decreases in absolute value as the object moves farther away from the center of the earth. Again, for the small distance involved, the change in the acceleration is very slight. We might note that both of these assumptions would lead to very substantial errors if we were dealing with a missile traveling at high speeds to great heights. However, you will not be able to handle missile problems until you can solve the more difficult differential equations involved in them.

One more comment concerning a convention that we shall be using. It was noted that $a = -32$. The minus indicates that the acceleration is in the downward (or negative) direction. In falling-body problems, many authors use the convention that downward is the positive direction. It makes no difference which convention we use as long as we are consistent throughout a given problem. Throughout this section we shall continue to use the convention that downward is negative.

Now we have the differential equation (remember a is a derivative) $a = -32$ subject to the conditions that $v = 128$ and $s = 0$ when $t = 0$. Since $dv/dt = -32$, antidifferentiation gives

$$v = -32t + C_1.$$

Since $v = 128$ when $t = 0$, $C_1 = 128$. Then

$$v = -32t + 128, \qquad s = -16t^2 + 128t + C_2.$$

Since $s = 0$ when $t = 0$, $C_2 = 0$. Thus,

$$s = -16t^2 + 128t.$$

Since s is a maximum when $s' = v = 0$, the maximum height is reached when $t = 4$. At that time $s = 256$ ft. The arrow reaches the ground again when $s = 0$, which is when $t = 0$ or $t = 8$ sec. Of course, the second value of t is the one we want.

Problems

In Problems 1–10, find the position, velocity, and acceleration for the given value of t.

1. $s = t^2 + t - 1, \quad t = 4.$
2. $s = 3t^2 - 4t + 1, \quad t = 1.$
3. $s = 2t^3 - t^2 + 2, \quad t = 0.$
4. $s = t^3 - t^2 + t - 1, \quad t = 1.$
5. $s = t^4 - 1, \quad t = 2.$
6. $s = t^4 - t^2, \quad t = 2.$
7. $s = (t + 1)(t^2 + 1), \quad t = 2.$
8. $s = (t - 1)(t^2 - 1), \quad t = 1.$
9. $s = t^2(t + 1)^2, \quad t = 3.$
10. $s = \dfrac{1}{t^2 + 1}, \quad t = 0.$

In Problems 11–20, find the equation of motion, that is, find s as a function of t.

11. $a = -32$; $s = 0$ and $v = 64$ when $t = 0$.
12. $a = -32$; $s = 100$ and $v = -32$ when $t = 0$.

13. $a = 4t$; $s = 4$ and $v = 16$ when $t = 0$.
14. $a = 6t - 1$; $s = 9$ and $v = 48$ when $t = 0$.
15. $a = -32$; $s = 0$ when $t = 0$ and $s = 256$ when $t = 4$.
16. $a = -32$; $s = 0$ when $t = 0$ and again when $t = 16$.
17. $v = 4t + 1$; $s = 3$ when $t = 1$.
18. $v = 6t^2 - t$; $s = 4$ when $t = 2$.
19. $v = 12t^3 - 2t + 1$; $s = 6$ when $t = 0$.
20. $a = 20t^3 - 6t$; $s = 5$ and $v = 0$ when $t = 1$.
21. An arrow is shot straight up from ground level with velocity v_0. What is its velocity when it hits the ground? (*Moral*: Don't shoot arrows straight up.)
22. A ball is thrown upward from ground level with velocity v_0. What is its maximum height?
23. An object is thrown upward with initial velocity v_0 from an initial position s_0. Give its equation of motion.
24. A man is standing on top of a building 256 ft high. How long will it take a stone to hit the ground (a) if he simply drops it? (b) if he throws it downward with a velocity of 15 ft/sec? (c) if he throws it upward with a velocity of 15 ft/sec?
25. A ball is dropped from a height of 6 ft. One-fourth of its energy is absorbed when it hits the ground: that is, it bounces back up with a velocity that is three-fourths of its impact velocity. How high does it go after the first bounce? after the second bounce?
26. A car accelerates from 0 to 60 mph (88 ft/sec) in 30 seconds. Assuming the acceleration to be constant, what is that constant? Assuming that it is capable of continuing at the same acceleration for another 30 seconds, how fast will it be going then?
27. Suppose $a = kt$ in Problem 26. Find k. How fast will the car be going at the end of the first minute?

7.3

Related Rates

In many situations, two or more rates are related to each other in some way. For example, if a man is walking near a lamppost at night, the rate at which he is moving and the rate at which his shadow is moving are related.

In such problems, we must note all of the rates involved—both those given and those we want to find. For example, if they are dx/dt, dy/dt, and dz/dt, we must then find a relationship involving x, y, and z which is true at any time. Note that the x, y, and z are functions of time, since their values vary with time. Once we have this relationship in equation form, we simply need to take the derivatives of both sides of the equation with respect to time. After that, it is simply a matter of substitution of known quantities in order to determine an unknown one.

Example 1

A man six feet tall is walking away from a lamppost fifteen feet high at the rate of 6 ft/sec. At what rate is the end of his shadow moving away from the lamppost?

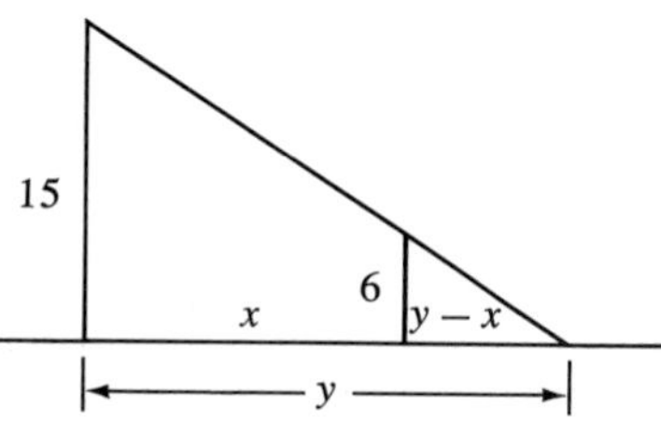

Figure 7.11

The two rates in which we are interested (see Figure 7.11) are

$$\frac{dx}{dt} = 6 \text{ ft/sec}, \qquad \frac{dy}{dt} \text{ (unknown)}.$$

By similar triangles,

$$\frac{y-x}{6} = \frac{y}{15}, \quad \text{or} \quad 3y = 5x.$$

Remembering that both x and y are functions of time, we take the derivative of both sides with respect to time:

$$3\frac{dy}{dt} = 5\frac{dx}{dt}.$$

Substituting $dx/dt = 6$ gives

$$\frac{dy}{dt} = 10 \text{ ft/sec}.$$

Example 2

The radius of a cylinder is decreasing at the rate of 4 ft/min, while the height is increasing at the rate of 2 ft/min. Find the rate of change of the volume when the radius is two feet and the height is six feet.

$$\frac{dr}{dt} = -4 \text{ ft/min}, \quad r = 2 \text{ ft},$$

$$\frac{dh}{dt} = 2 \text{ ft/min}, \quad h = 6 \text{ ft},$$

$$\frac{dV}{dt} \text{ (unknown)},$$

$$V = \pi r^2 h;$$

$$\begin{aligned}\frac{dV}{dt} &= \pi r^2 \frac{dh}{dt} + 2\pi r h \frac{dr}{dt} \\ &= \pi(2)^2(2) + 2\pi(2)(6)(-4) \\ &= -88\pi \text{ ft}^3\text{/min}.\end{aligned}$$

The minus here indicates that the volume is decreasing.

Example 3

Sand is being poured onto the top of a conical pile at the rate of 10 ft^3/min. The coefficient of friction of the sand is such that the height and the radius are always the same. At what rate is the height increasing when the pile is eight feet high?

$$\frac{dV}{dt} = 10 \text{ ft}^3/\text{min},$$

$$\frac{dh}{dt} \quad \text{(unknown)},$$

$$V = \frac{1}{3}\pi r^2 h = \frac{1}{3}\pi h^3 \quad (\text{since } r = h),$$

$$\frac{dV}{dt} = \pi h^2 \frac{dh}{dt},$$

$$10 = \pi(8)^2 \frac{dh}{dt},$$

$$\frac{dh}{dt} = \frac{10}{64\pi} \doteq 0.049 \text{ ft/min}.$$

(The symbol $\doteq$ indicates approximate equality.)

Problems

1. The three dimensions of a box are increasing at the rates of 5 in./min, 7 in./min, and 2 in./min. At what rate is the volume increasing at the moment when the box is a cube with edge 10 in? At what rate is the surface area increasing?
2. The base of a triangle is increasing at the rate of 4 in./min, while the altitude is decreasing at the same rate. At what rate is the area changing when (a) the base is 10 in. and the altitude 6 in.? (b) the base is 6 in. and the altitude 10 in.?
3. The side of an equilateral triangle is increasing at the rate of 2 in./min. At what rate is the area increasing when the side is 5 in.?
4. The area of an equilateral triangle is increasing at the rate of 4 in.^{2}/min. At what rate is the side increasing when the area is 10 in.^{2}?
5. The area of a circle is increasing at the rate of 4 in.^{2}/min. At what rate is the radius increasing when the area is 10 in.^{2}?
6. Helium is pumped into a spherical balloon at the rate of 4 ft^3/min. At what rate is the radius increasing (a) when the radius is 3 ft? (b) when the volume is 40 ft^3?
7. In Problem 6, find the rate at which the surface area is increasing (a) when the radius is 3 ft and (b) when the volume is 40 ft^3.
8. A man 6 ft tall is walking away from a lamppost 24 ft high at the rate of 4 ft/sec. At what rate is the end of his shadow moving away from the lamppost? At what rate is the end of his shadow moving away from him?
9. Ship A is steaming north at 10 miles per hour. Ship B, which is 5 miles west of ship A, is steaming east at 15 miles per hour. At what rate is the distance between them changing? At what rate will it be changing one hour from now?
10. If ship A in Problem 9 is steaming 30° west of north, at what rate is the distance between them changing? At what rate will it be changing one hour from now?
11. A gas has a volume of one liter at one atmosphere pressure. If the pressure is increasing at the rate of 0.1 atm/min, at what rate is the volume changing? Assume the gas to be ideal—that is, it satisfies the equation $pv = k$, where k is a constant.
12. If the gas of Problem 11 is not ideal, but satisfies the equation $pv = 22.41 + 0.01p$, at what rate is the volume changing?

13. A point is moving along the curve $y = x^2$ in such a way that its x coordinate is increasing at the rate of 2 units per minute. At what rate is y changing (a) when $x = 0$? (b) when $x = 1$? (c) when $x = 2$?
14. A point is moving along the curve $y = \sqrt{x}$ in such a way that its x coordinate is increasing at the rate of 3 units per minute. At what rate is y changing (a) when $x = 1$? (b) when $x = 4$?
15. A point is moving along the curve $y = \sqrt{x}$ in such a way that its y coordinate is increasing at the rate of 2 units per minute. At what rate is its x coordinate changing (a) when $x = 1$? (b) when $x = 4$?
16. A point is moving along the curve $y = \sqrt{x}$ in such a way that its x coordinate is increasing at the rate of 4 units per minute. At what rate is its slope changing (a) when $x = 1$? (b) when $x = 4$?
17. A tank has the shape of an inverted cone with height 10 ft and radius 4 ft. Water is being pumped into it at the rate of 5 ft^3/min. How fast is the depth of the water increasing when it is 5 ft deep?
18. A trough 12 ft long, 2 ft high, and 2 ft wide at the top has triangular ends. If water is put in at the rate of 1 ft^3/min, how fast is the depth increasing when it is 1.5 ft deep?
19. A trough has trapezoidal ends. It is 20 ft long, 2 ft high, 3 ft wide at the top, and 2 ft wide at the bottom. If water is being pumped in at the rate of 2 ft^3/min, how fast is the depth increasing when the water is 1 ft deep?

7.4

The Differential

We have seen that, given an equation of the form $y = f(x)$, y is a function of x. We have also seen functions of two or more variables. For instance, in $z = xy + y^2$, z is a function of x and y. In the equation $y = f(x)$, x is sometimes referred to as the independent variable and y as the dependent variable, because we may substitute values of x at random (as long as they are in the domain of the function) but the value we get for y is dependent upon the value we use for x. Similarly, x and y are the independent variables in the equation $z = xy + y^2$, while z is the dependent variable.

Let us now consider $y = f(x)$ and introduce a new independent variable, dx. It might be noted that dx is not a product—it is regarded as a single symbol. Corresponding to this is another new variable, dy, which is dependent upon both x and dx in the following way:

$$dy = f'(x)\, dx;$$

dy is called the *differential* of the function f. It is a function of two variables: x and dx. In our discussion of the derivative, dy/dx was not considered as a quotient, since we had not given meanings to dy and dx individually. Now that we have given meanings to dy and dx, we see that if $dx \neq 0$, then

$$\frac{dy}{dx} = f'(x).$$

A word of warning: One often finds differentials associated with such terms as "infinitesimals" or "infinitely small quantities." Moreover, these terms are often used synonymously. The idea of an "infinitely small quantity" is that it is smaller in absolute value than any positive number but is still not zero. Unfortunately for its proponents, there simply is no such thing—certainly no such real number! The absolute value of any number is either positive or zero. If the absolute value of an infinitely small quantity is less than any positive number, it cannot be positive itself; it must be zero—there is no other possibility. The word "infinitesimal" can be defined in a meaningful way—not as an "infinitely small quantity"; however, we shall not attempt to do so here.

The idea of an infinitely small quantity is a holdover from the dark ages of mathematics, when the idea of a limit was only dimly understood. We have already noted that when we take a derivative, we must evaluate

$$\lim_{h\to 0}\frac{f(x+h)-f(x)}{h}$$

or, in alternate notation (see page 62),

$$\lim_{\Delta x\to 0}\frac{\Delta y}{\Delta x}.$$

In the last limit, both the numerator and denominator approach zero. It was known by earlier mathematicians that 0/0 is not a number at all, but it was also known that the limit did exist in many cases; and that limit was called the derivative. To avoid situations like $0/0 = 5$, a bit of fiction was invented. It was maintained that Δy and Δx do not approach zero but, instead, approach the infinitely small quantities dy and dx, whose quotient is the derivative. Of course, all of this is nonsense; dy and dx are not infinitely small—the distance from here to the moon (expressed in millimeters) is a perfectly good value for a differential.

Figure 7.12 gives a geometric interpretation of differentials. We see that dx and dy are differences in x and y values, respectively, for a pair of points on the tangent line to the curve at $(x, f(x))$. Thus dy depends, not only on dx, but also on the tangent line, which is determined by x and the function.

Finding the differential of a given function is simply a matter of finding the derivative and multiplying by dx.

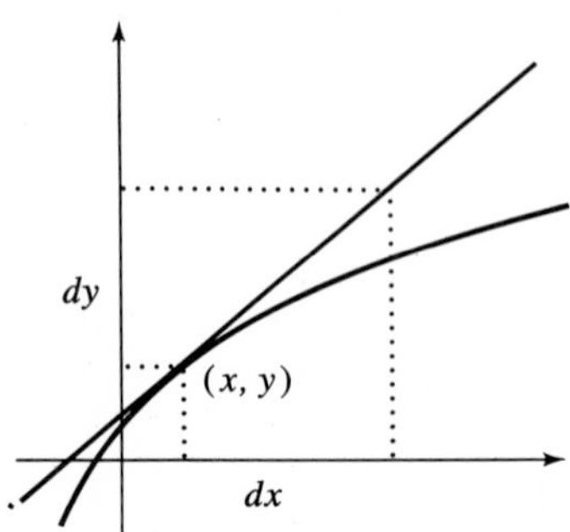

Figure 7.12

Example 1

Given $y = x^3 - 2x^2$, find dy.

Since $y' = 3x^2 - 4x$,

$$dy = (3x^2 - 4x)\,dx.$$

In the case of implicit functions, an alternate procedure may be followed.

Example 2

Given $y^2 - xy + 2x^2 = 5$, find dy.

$$2ydy - xdy - ydx + 4xdx = 0,$$

$$(2y - x)dy = (y - 4x)dx,$$

$$dy = \frac{y - 4x}{2y - x}\,dx.$$

Problems

In the following problems, find the differential dy.

1. $y = 3x - 5$.
2. $y = 4x - 2$.
3. $y = x^2 - 1$.
4. $y = 3x^2 - x$.
5. $y = x^3 - x^2$.
6. $y = x^4 + 1$.
7. $y = \dfrac{x + 1}{3x - 2}$.
8. $y = \dfrac{2x - 3}{x + 1}$.
9. $y = \dfrac{2x - 1}{x^2}$.
10. $y = \dfrac{x}{x^2 + 1}$.
11. $y = (x + 1)^2(3x - 2)^3$.
12. $y = x^3(3x - 4)^2$.
13. $y = \sqrt{x}\,(x - 4)$.
14. $y = \dfrac{\sqrt{x}}{x + 1}$.
15. $y = (x - 1)^{1/3}(x + 2)^{2/3}$.
16. $y = (3x + 1)^{1/3}(2x - 1)^{2/3}$.
17. $y = (x^2 + 1)^4$.
18. $y = (3x - 2)^5$.
19. $y = \left(\dfrac{x + 1}{x - 1}\right)^3$.
20. $y = \left(\dfrac{x^2}{x^2 + 1}\right)^{2/3}$.
21. $y = \dfrac{x^2(x - 1)}{(x + 2)^2}$.
22. $y = \dfrac{x(x + 1)}{(x - 1)(x + 3)}$.
23. $y = x + \sqrt{x^2 + 1}$.
24. $y = x - \sqrt{x^2 + 1}$.
25. $x^2 + y^2 = 4$.
26. $y^2 + xy = 3$.
27. $(x + y)^2 = x - y$.
28. $(x - y)^3 = (x + y)^2$.
29. $x + \sqrt{xy} - y = 4$.
30. $x^3 - 3x^2y + 3xy^2 = 5$.
31. $\left(\dfrac{x + y}{x - y}\right)^2 = xy$.
32. $\sqrt{x} + \sqrt{y} = 1$.

7.5

Approximations and Small Errors by the Differential

The number 10 is an approximation of π. This may come as a surprise to you. Perhaps you feel that 10 is not sufficiently close to π to qualify as an approximation. It certainly must be granted that it is not a very good approximation, but it is an approximation. Of course, there are many approximations of π that we might list: 35, 115, 4385, and so forth. That is to say, every number is an approximation of π; some numbers are better, some are worse.

Much the same situation arises in connection with "small" errors. Just how small is small. If we measure a certain length and make an error of two miles, is that a "small" error? Of course, it depends upon the length we are measuring. If we were trying to determine the circumference of the earth at the equator, we might concede that an error of two miles is small; if we were measuring the height of Mount Rainier, it is not likely that we would consider an error of two miles to be small. These are obvious cases. How do we decide in the "borderline" cases? For instance, suppose we are trying to measure the circumference of the earth at the equator. The actual value is approximately (!!?) 24,900 miles. Now where is the dividing line between a small error and one that is not small? We might arbitrarily set up the standard that an error in measuring x is small if it is 0.1% or less of the value of x. By that standard an error of 24.9 miles or less is "small"; anything larger is not. But a better approximation of the circumference of the earth is 24,902 miles. With this we see that an error of 24.902 now qualifies as "small," where it did not previously. The exact boundary line between a small error and one that is not small (big?) cannot be determined unless we have the exact value of x; and if we know that, it is highly unlikely that we will care to talk about errors at all. To complicate matters still more, it is obvious that no single standard (like 0.1%) is satisfactory in all cases. In some precision machining, we might insist that errors be less than 0.001% in order to qualify as "small."

With this we can see that "approximation" and "small" are certainly vague terms. Unfortunately, they are also commonly used terms, and we are forced to live with them whether we want to or not. Certainly we have some idea—however vague it might be—of what we mean by an approximation and by small errors. Very likely it was this idea that caused you to balk when 10 was given as an approximation of π. Thus we shall call upon this vague idea and use it as if we knew exactly what is meant by approximations and small errors.

Let us see how the differential can help us in computing small errors and making approximations. We have already seen that dx and dy are differences between pairs of values of x and of y, respectively, determined by the tangent line to $y = f(x)$. Similarly, Δx and Δy are differences between pairs of values of x and of y, respectively, determined by $y = f(x)$ at x. Now let us choose $dx = \Delta x$. The relationship between dy and Δy is given in Figure 7.13. Although dy and Δy are not necessarily the same, dy is a reasonable approximation of Δy provided $dx = \Delta x$ is "small" and $f(x)$ does not vary wildly for small values of x. Thus we can use differentials to compute dy as an approximation of Δy.

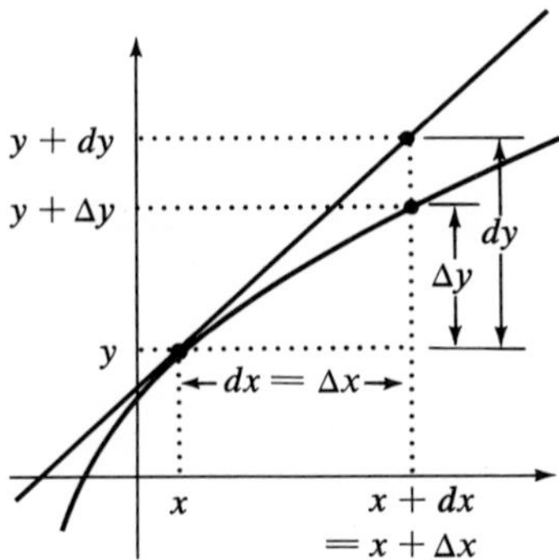

Figure 7.13

Example 1

The edge of a cube was measured and found to be ten inches. It is felt that this measurement is accurate to within 0.02 in. If the volume of the cube is computed using this measurement, what is the maximum error in the volume?

$$V = x^3.$$

We are given $x = 10.00$ with error $|\Delta x| \leq 0.02$. We want to find the maximum value of $|\Delta V|$ corresponding to Δx. Setting

$$|dx| = |\Delta x| \leq 0.02,$$

we compute dV.

$$\begin{aligned} |dV| &= |3x^2\, dx| \\ &\leq 3(10.00)^2(0.02) \\ &= 6. \end{aligned}$$

Thus $|\Delta V| \doteq |dV| \leq 6$ (we use the symbol $\doteq$ for approximate equality).

How good is our approximtaion? How does it compare with the actual value of $|\Delta V|$? We can easily compute $|\Delta V|$.

$$\begin{aligned} |\Delta V| &= |(x + \Delta x)^3 - x^3| \\ &\leq (10.02)^3 - (10.00)^3 \\ &= 6.012008. \end{aligned}$$

We see that $|dV| \leq 6$ is correct to two significant figures and it differs from $|\Delta V|$ by only 1 in the third figure. It might be noted here that, while we computed $|\Delta V|$ exactly, one would hardly be interested in more than the first two or three figures.

We see that, for the small value of Δx given, this method is quite accurate for estimating ΔV. This method becomes less accurate as Δx increases. For instance, suppose you use no measuring device to find x but simply estimate it to be ten inches with an error of at most one inch. The values of $|dV|$ and $|\Delta V|$ are:

$$|dV| \leq 300, \qquad |\Delta V| \leq 331.$$

We see that $|dV|$ is not nearly so good an estimate of $|\Delta V|$ in this case.

Example 2

Approximate $\sqrt{63}$ by differentials.

What we want here is a number y corresponding to $x = 63$ in the equation

$$y = \sqrt{x}.$$

If $x = 64$, then $y = 8$. Unfortunately, x is not 64; it is 63. We have the error $\Delta x = -1$, so that $x + \Delta x = 63$. Now we want to find $y + \Delta y$ corresponding to $x + \Delta x = 63$. Again let us take $dx = \Delta x = -1$ and compute $y + dy$, instead of $y + \Delta y$.

$$y = \sqrt{x} \qquad dy = \frac{dx}{2\sqrt{x}}$$

$$= \sqrt{64} \qquad = \frac{-1}{2\sqrt{64}}$$

$$= 8. \qquad = -0.0625.$$

$$y + dy = 7.938.$$

We have rounded off $y + dy$ to only three decimal places—remember this method gives only an approximation; do not try to push it too far. The actual value of $\sqrt{63}$ to three decimal places is 7.937.

An expression that is often more meaningful than the error is the relative error, or the percentage error.

$$\text{relative error in } x = \frac{\text{error in } x}{x}.$$

$$\text{percentage error in } x = \frac{\text{error in } x}{x} \cdot 100.$$

Example 3

If the percentage error in measuring the edge of a cube is 3%, what is the percentage error in finding its volume?

$$V = x^3,$$

$$dV = 3x^2\,dx,$$

$$\frac{dV}{V} = \frac{3x^2\,dx}{x^3} = 3 \cdot \frac{dx}{x},$$

$$\frac{dV}{V} \cdot 100 = 3 \cdot \frac{dx}{x} \cdot 100$$

$$= 3 \cdot 3\% = 9\%.$$

Problems

1. What is the error in determining the surface area in Example 1?
2. The radius of a circle was measured and found to be 5.35 ± 0.01 in. To what degree of accuracy can the circumference be found? the area?
3. The diameter of a circle was measured and found to be 7.38 ± 0.03. To what degree of accuracy can the circumference be found? the area?
4. The side of a square was measured and found to be $14.35 \pm .02$ in. What is the greatest error in computing the area? Approximate the error by differentials and find the exact value. Compare.
5. The relationship between centigrade and Fahrenheit temperatures is given by the formula

$$5F = 9C + 160.$$

   If a Fahrenheit thermometer can be read to the nearest 1°, to what degree of accuracy is the centigrade temperature known?
6. The radius of a sphere is measured and found to be 7.0 ± 0.1 cm. To what degree of accuracy can the volume be found? the surface area?
7. An unknown electrical resistance R is determined with a Wheatstone bridge by adjusting two things: a compensating resistance r read off a resistance box and the position x of a key along a slide wire of length l. R is then

$$R = r\frac{x}{l - x}.$$

   Suppose $r = 40$ ohms, $l = 100$ cm, and $x = 50 \pm 0.1$ cm. Find R and approximate its degree of accuracy.
8. Suppose the following figures are obtained from a Wheatstone bridge (see Problem 7): $r = 360$ ohms, $l = 100$ cm, and $x = 10 \pm 0.1$ cm. Find R and approximate its degree of accuracy. What do the results of this problem and Problem 7 suggest concerning the operation of a Wheatstone bridge for maximum accuracy?

In Problems 9–16, use differentials to approximate the numbers given.

9. $\sqrt{50}$.
10. $\sqrt{39}$.
11. $\sqrt[3]{25}$.
12. $\sqrt[3]{130}$.
13. $\sqrt[4]{80}$.
14. $\sqrt[5]{30}$.
15. $\dfrac{1}{\sqrt{27}}$.
16. $\dfrac{1}{\sqrt[3]{60}}$.
17. Show that if $y = mx$, the relative error in y is the same as the relative error in x.
18. Show that if $y = kx^n$, the relative error in y is n times the relative error in x.
19. If the volume of a cube is to be determined with a percentage error no greater than 3%, what is the greatest percentage error that can be tolerated in determining the edge?
20. If the volume of a sphere is to be determined with an error no greater than 3%, what is the greatest percentage error that can be tolerated in determining the radius?
21. The height and diameter of a right circular cone are known to be equal. If the volume is to be determined with an error no greater than 1%, what is the greatest percentage error that can be tolerated in determining the height?
22. If the lateral surface of the cone of Problem 21 is to be determined with an error no greater than 1%, what is the greatest percentage error that can be tolerated in determining the height?

The Integral

8.1

Sigma Notation

In the next few sections we shall consider sums with many terms—for instance,

$$1^2 + 3^2 + 5^2 + \cdots + 15^2$$

or

$$1 + 2 + 3 + \cdots + n.$$

In each case the dots are meant to indicate that the terms continue in the same form to the last term indicated. In the second example, the last term, of course, depends upon the value of n.

There are several disadvantages to the above notation. First of all, the form of the individual terms may not be clear from the first few terms. In addition, the second example looks a bit strange when n is one or two. Finally, this notation is rather long and tedious. For these reasons the sigma notation is often used. In this notation, the sum

$$1^2 + 3^2 + 5^2 + \cdots + 15^2$$

is represented by

$$\sum_{i=1}^{8} (2i - 1)^2.$$

The $\sum$ (uppercase sigma) is used to indicate that the given expression is a sum. The form of each term is $(2i-1)^2$, where the i represents an integer. The subscript ($i = 1$) and superscript (8) on $\sum$ indicate the values of i to be used for the first and last terms, respectively, of the sum. Thus the first term is

$$(2 \cdot 1 - 1)^2 = 1^2,$$

and the last term is

$$(2 \cdot 8 - 1)^2 = 15^2.$$

The intermediate terms are found by replacing i by consecutive integers between 1 and 8. The i in $(2i-1)^2$ is a "dummy variable"; that is, it does not appear in the expanded form. Any other symbol can be used in its place with the same result.

The second example above can be represented by

$$\sum_{i=1}^{n} i.$$

Example 1

Give the expanded form of

$$\sum_{i=1}^{10} \frac{1}{i(i+1)}.$$

$$\sum_{i=1}^{10} \frac{1}{i(i+1)} = \frac{1}{1(1+1)} + \frac{1}{2(2+1)} + \frac{1}{3(3+1)} + \cdots + \frac{1}{10(10+1)}$$

$$= \frac{1}{1 \cdot 2} + \frac{1}{2 \cdot 3} + \frac{1}{3 \cdot 4} + \cdots + \frac{1}{10 \cdot 11}.$$

Example 2

Give a sigma representation for $2 + 5 + 10 + \cdots + 122$.

We must find some expression $f(i)$ such that

$$f(1) = 2, \quad f(2) = 5, \quad \text{and} \quad f(3) = 10$$

(since we do not know the value of i corresponding to the last term, we cannot use it yet). Let us note that each term is one more than a perfect square: that is,

$$f(1) = 1 + 1 = 1^2 + 1,$$
$$f(2) = 4 + 1 = 2^2 + 1,$$
$$f(3) = 9 + 1 = 3^2 + 1.$$

Thus, all are in the form $i^2 + 1$. Furthermore, the last term is in the form $i^2 + 1$, with $i = 11$. Thus the above sum may be represented by

$$\sum_{i=1}^{11} (i^2 + 1).$$

The above representation is not the only one possible, as we can see by the following example.

Example 3

Show that

$$\sum_{i=1}^{12} (2i-1)^2 \quad \text{and} \quad \sum_{i=-1}^{10} (2i+3)^2$$

represent the same sum.

Let us write both in the expanded form:

$$\sum_{i=1}^{12} (2i-1)^2 = (2 \cdot 1 - 1)^2 + (2 \cdot 2 - 1)^2 + (2 \cdot 3 - 1)^2 + \cdots + (2 \cdot 12 - 1)^2$$
$$= 1^2 + 3^2 + 5^2 + \cdots + 23^2.$$

$$\sum_{i=-1}^{10} (2i+3)^2 = [2(-1) + 3]^2 + (2 \cdot 0 + 3)^2 + (2 \cdot 1 + 3)^2 + \cdots + (2 \cdot 10 + 3)^2$$
$$= 1^2 + 3^2 + 5^2 + \cdots + 23^2.$$

If all of the terms are known, it is a simple matter to find the sum. Thus,

$$\sum_{i=1}^{8} (2i-1)^2 = 1^2 + 3^2 + 5^2 + \cdots + 15^2 = 1184.$$

But what of the sum

$$\sum_{i=1}^{n} i = 1 + 2 + 3 + \cdots + n?$$

We cannot give the numerical value of this sum without knowing the value of n. But we can give a formula for the sum.

Theorem 8.1

If n is a positive integer, then

$$\sum_{i=1}^{n} i = \frac{n(n+1)}{2}.$$

Proof

Since we want to prove that the formula holds for any positive integer n, this theorem can be proved by mathematical induction. Let us recall that we must do two things. We must verify that the statement given by the formula is true when $n = 1$, and we must show that if it is true when $n = k$, then it is true when $n = k + 1$. If $n = 1$, then

$$\sum_{i=1}^{n} i = \sum_{i=1}^{1} i = 1$$

and

$$\frac{n(n+1)}{2} = \frac{1 \cdot 2}{2} = 1.$$

Suppose it is true when $n = k$, that is,

$$\sum_{i=1}^{k} i = \frac{k(k+1)}{2}.$$

Now

$$\sum_{i=1}^{k+1} i = \sum_{i=1}^{k} i + (k+1)$$

$$= \frac{k(k+1)}{2} + \frac{2(k+1)}{2}$$

$$= \frac{(k+1)(k+2)}{2}.$$

Thus it is true when $n = k + 1$. By mathematical induction, the formula holds for every positive integer n.

Theorem 8.2

If n is a positive integer, then

(a) $\sum_{i=1}^{n} 1 = n,$

(b) $\sum_{i=1}^{n} i = \frac{n(n+1)}{2},$

(c) $\sum_{i=1}^{n} i^2 = \frac{n(n+1)(2n+1)}{6},$

(d) $\sum_{i=1}^{n} i^3 = \frac{n^2(n+1)^2}{4},$

(e) $\sum_{i=1}^{n} i^4 = \frac{n(n+1)(6n^3 + 9n^2 + n - 1)}{30}.$

The formula of Theorem 8.1 is included in Theorem 8.2 for completeness. These formulas will be quite useful in the next section. All of them can be proved by mathematical induction as well as by other methods (see Problems 37–41).

Theorem 8.3

If f and g are functions, k is a number, and n is a positive integer, then

(a) $\sum_{i=1}^{n} kf(i) = k\sum_{i=1}^{n} f(i),$

(b) $\sum_{i=1}^{n} [f(i) + g(i)] = \sum_{i=1}^{n} f(i) + \sum_{i=1}^{n} g(i),$

(c) $\sum_{i=1}^{n} [f(i) - g(i)] = \sum_{i=1}^{n} f(i) - \sum_{i=1}^{n} g(i).$

Since these formulas are easily proved by writing them in the expanded form, the proof is left to the student.

Example 4

Simplify $\sum_{i=1}^{n}\left[\left(\frac{i}{n}\right)^2+\frac{i}{n}\right]\frac{1}{n}$.

$$\begin{aligned}\sum_{i=1}^{n}\left[\left(\frac{i}{n}\right)^2+\frac{i}{n}\right]\frac{1}{n} &= \sum_{i=1}^{n}\left(\frac{i^2}{n^3}+\frac{i}{n^2}\right)\\ &= \sum_{i=1}^{n}\frac{i^2}{n^3}+\sum_{i=1}^{n}\frac{i}{n^2}\\ &= \frac{1}{n^3}\sum_{i=1}^{n} i^2+\frac{1}{n^2}\sum_{i=1}^{n} i\\ &= \frac{1}{n^3}\cdot\frac{n(n+1)(2n+1)}{6}+\frac{1}{n^2}\cdot\frac{n(n+1)}{2}\\ &= \frac{(n+1)(2n+1)}{6n^2}+\frac{3n(n+1)}{6n^2}\\ &= \frac{(n+1)(5n+1)}{6n^2}\end{aligned}$$

Problems

In Problems 1–10, express the sum in the expanded form.

1. $\sum_{i=1}^{7} i^3$.
2. $\sum_{i=1}^{4} (i^2+2)$.
3. $\sum_{i=1}^{6} (2i-4)$.
4. $\sum_{i=-2}^{4} i^2$.
5. $\sum_{i=0}^{7} (2i+1)$.
6. $\sum_{i=1}^{n} i^4$.
7. $\sum_{i=1}^{n-1} i^3$.
8. $\sum_{i=1}^{n} (i^2-1)$.
9. $\sum_{i=1}^{n} (2i+1)$.
10. $\sum_{i=1}^{n-1} (i^2-i)$.

In Problems 11–20, express the sums in sigma notation.

11. $1+2+3+\cdots+10$.
12. $1+3+5+\cdots+21$.
13. $2+4+6+\cdots+22$.
14. $1+4+7+\cdots+31$.
15. $2+6+12+20+\cdots+72$.
16. $1^3+2^3+3^3+\cdots+(n-1)^3$.
17. $1+3+5+\cdots+(2n-1)$.
18. $\frac{1}{2}+\frac{2}{3}+\frac{3}{4}+\cdots+\frac{n}{n+1}$.
19. $10+17+26+\cdots+(n^2+1)$.
20. $\frac{2}{3}+\frac{3}{5}+\frac{4}{7}+\cdots+\frac{n}{2n-1}$.

In Problems 21–28, indicate whether or not the two given expressions are equal.

21. $\sum_{i=1}^{n} (2i-1)$, $\sum_{i=0}^{n-1} (2i+1)$.
22. $\sum_{i=1}^{n} (i+1)^3$, $\sum_{i=2}^{n+1} i^3$.
23. $\sum_{i=1}^{n} (2i+2)^2$, $\sum_{i=3}^{n+1} (2i-2)^2$.
24. $\sum_{i=0}^{n} (i^2+1)$, $\sum_{i=1}^{n+1} i^2$.
25. $\sum_{i=0}^{n} (i^2+1)$, $\sum_{i=1}^{n+1} [(i-1)^2+1]$.
26. $\sum_{i=1}^{n} i(i+1)$, $\sum_{k=2}^{n+1} k(k-1)$.
27. $\sum_{i=1}^{n-1} (i-2)$, $\sum_{i=2}^{n} (i-1)$.
28. $\sum_{i=1}^{n-1} (i^3-i^2)$, $\sum_{j=1}^{n} [(j-1)^3-(j-1)^2]$.

In Problems 29–36, simplify the given expression.

29. $\sum_{i=1}^{n} \left(\frac{i}{n}\right)^2 \frac{1}{n}$.

30. $\sum_{i=1}^{n} \left(\frac{i}{n}\right)^3 \frac{1}{n}$.

31. $\sum_{i=1}^{n} \left[\left(\frac{i}{n}\right)^2 - \frac{i}{n}\right] \frac{1}{n}$.

32. $\sum_{i=1}^{n} \left[\left(\frac{i}{n}\right)^3 + \frac{i}{n}\right] \frac{1}{n}$.

33. $\sum_{i=1}^{n} \left(\frac{i-1}{n}\right)^2 \frac{1}{n}$.

34. $\sum_{i=1}^{2n} \left(\frac{i}{n}\right)^2 \frac{1}{n}$.

35. $\sum_{i=1}^{n} \left(\frac{2i}{n}\right)^2 \frac{2}{n}$.

36. $\sum_{i=1}^{n} \left[3\left(\frac{i}{n}\right)^2 - \frac{i}{n}\right] \frac{1}{n}$.

37. Prove Theorem 8.2(a).

38. Prove Theorem 8.2(c).

39. Prove Theorem 8.2(d).

40. Prove Theorem 8.2(e).

41. Prove Theorem 8.2(b) (Theorem 8.1) by grouping the first and nth terms, the second and $(n-1)$-th terms, and so on.

42. Prove Theorem 8.3.

43. Find a formula for $\sum_{i=1}^{n} 2i$. Use your result and Theorem 8.2(b) to find a formula for

$$\sum_{i=1}^{n} (2i - 1).$$

8.2

The Area Under a Curve

Suppose we have the problem of determining the area "under the curve" $y = x^2$ from $x = 0$ to $x = 1$, that is, the area of the region bounded by $y = x^2$, the x axis, and the vertical lines $x = 0$ and $x = 1$ (see Figure 8.1). Before looking for an answer, we might ask what is meant by the area of a region. First of all, the area of a region is a nonnegative number. But this is not much help. The question still remains as to how a number is to be associated with a given region. Suppose we consider some simpler cases.

If the region in question is rectangular, the area is found quite simply; it is, by definition, the product of the length and width of the rectangle. Now we can find the

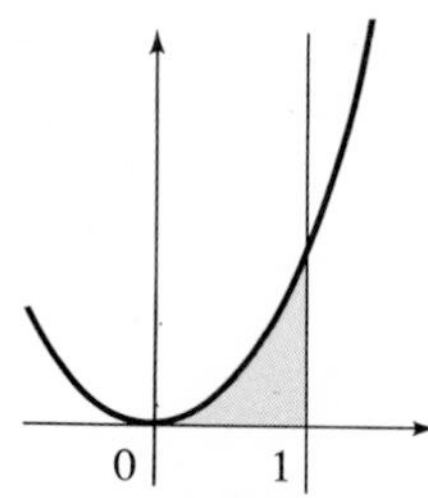

Figure 8.1

area of a right triangle, and that of any triangle, by using two very simple properties of area (in spite of the fact that we really do not know what area is, our intuitive idea of area demands that certain properties be satisfied). These are:

(1) If R_1 and R_2 are congruent regions, then their areas are equal.
(2) If $R = R_1 \cup R_2$, where R_1 and R_2 have only boundary points in common, then the area of R is the sum of the areas of R_1 and R_2.

Once we have the area of a triangle, we can find the area of any polygon by cutting it up into triangles.

But the region of Figure 8.1 has one curved side, while every area we have indicated as determinable has been an area of a region with straight sides. How can we make the transition? Suppose we take a lesson from our discussion of the slope of a graph. There we approximated the tangent line with a secant line and noted what happened to its slope as it moved closer and closer to the tangent line.

Let us try the same approach here. We shall subdivide the interval [0, 1] into n subintervals (see Figure 8.2) with the numbers

$$x_0 = 0, x_1, x_2, \ldots, x_{n-1}, x_n = 1.$$

Within each subinterval we select a number in any way we choose from the left- to the right-hand end point. Let us call these numbers

$$x_1^*, x_2^*, x_3^*, \ldots, x_n^*.$$

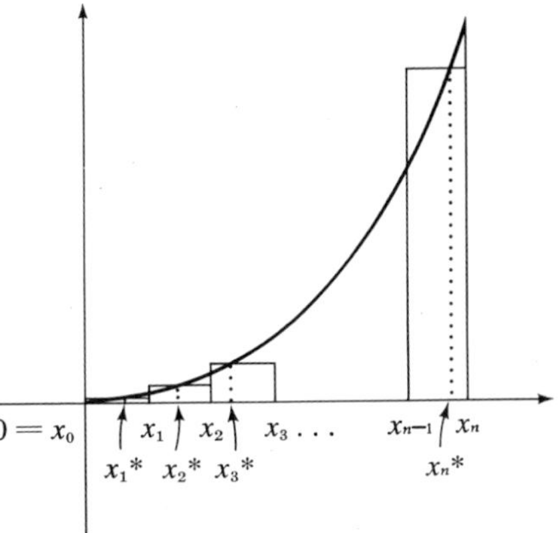

Figure 8.2

Now let us construct a rectangle for each subinterval, using the subinterval itself as the base and $f(x^*)$ as the altitude. Thus the sum of the areas of all of these rectangles gives an approximation (although perhaps a very poor one) of the area we seek. This sum is

$$f(x_1^*)(x_1 - x_0) + f(x_2^*)(x_2 - x_1) + f(x_3^*)(x_3 - x_2) + \cdots + f(x_n^*)(x_n - x_{n-1}) = \sum_{i=1}^{n} f(x_i^*)(x_i - x_{i-1}).$$

Finally we see that if we increase n in such a way that the lengths of all of the subintervals approach zero, the region formed by the rectangles is getting closer and closer to the region whose area we want; and the sum of the areas of the rectangles approaches the area we are seeking. Thus we shall *define* the area to be the limit (if it exists) of the above sum as the lengths of all the subintervals approach zero. Let us now apply this method to our original problem.

Example

Find the area under the curve $y = x^2$ from $x = 0$ to $x = 1$.

First of all, we must subdivide the interval [0, 1] and then choose the x^*'s. In order to simplify the algebra involved, let us subdivide the interval into n

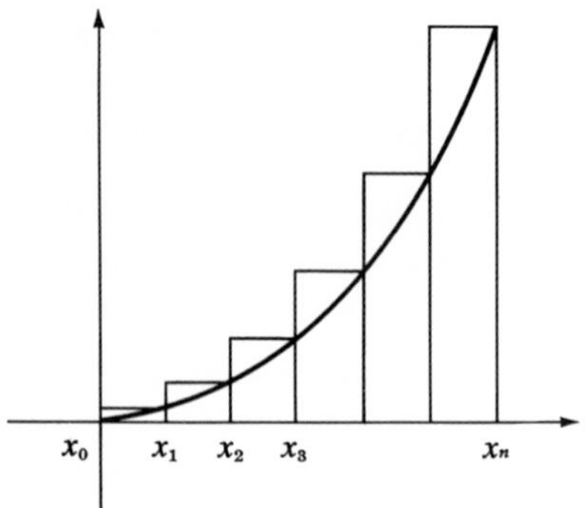

Figure 8.3

equal subintervals and choose the x^*'s to be the right-hand end points of the subintervals (see Figure 8.3). Thus

$$x_0 = \frac{0}{n} = 0, \quad x_1 = \frac{1}{n}, \quad x_2 = \frac{2}{n}, \quad \vdots \quad x_i = \frac{i}{n}, \quad \vdots \quad x_n = \frac{n}{n} = 1.$$

$$x_1^* = \frac{1}{n}, \quad x_2^* = \frac{2}{n}, \quad \vdots \quad x_i^* = \frac{i}{n}, \quad \vdots \quad x_n^* = \frac{n}{n} = 1,$$

We see that by choosing n equal subintervals, the length of each one of them is $1/n$ and the length of all of them is approaching zero as n gets large and positive. This last observation allows us to simplify our notation for the limit.

$$\begin{aligned}
A &= \lim_{n\to+\infty} \sum_{i=1}^{n} f(x_i^*)(x_i - x_{i-1}) \\
&= \lim_{n\to+\infty} \sum_{i=1}^{n} f\left(\frac{i}{n}\right)\left(\frac{i}{n} - \frac{i-1}{n}\right) \\
&= \lim_{n\to+\infty} \sum_{i=1}^{n} \frac{i^2}{n^2}\cdot\frac{1}{n} && \text{(See Note 1)} \\
&= \lim_{n\to+\infty} \frac{1}{n^3}\sum_{i=1}^{n} i^2 && \text{(By Theorem 8.3)} \\
&= \lim_{n\to+\infty} \frac{1}{n^3}\,\frac{n(n+1)(2n+1)}{6} && \text{(By Theorem 8.2(c))} \\
&= \lim_{n\to+\infty} \frac{\left(1+\frac{1}{n}\right)\left(2+\frac{1}{n}\right)}{6} && \text{(See Note 2)} \\
&= \frac{1}{3}.
\end{aligned}$$

Note 1: Since our original function is in the form $f(x) = x^2$, it follows that $f(i/n) = (i/n)^2 = i^2/n^2$.

Note 2: We have divided both numerator and denominator by n^3. In the numerator, each factor was divided by one of the n's.

Perhaps you feel that our answer in the example above is not correct, because we used the right-hand end points throughout, so that our approximating sums are *all* bigger than the area we want. If the answer is incorrect, it must be too large. Let us now use left-hand end points. Since the approximating sums are all smaller than the area we want (see Figure 8.4), we feel that the result will certainly not be greater than the area under the curve—either it will be the area we want, or it will be less than that area. In this case $x_i = i/n$ as before, but $x_i^* = (i - 1)/n$. Thus

$$
\begin{aligned}
A &= \lim_{n\to+\infty} \sum_{i=1}^{n} f(x_i^*)(x_i - x_{i-1}) \\
&= \lim_{n\to+\infty} \sum_{i=1}^{n} f\left(\frac{i-1}{n}\right)\left(\frac{i}{n} - \frac{i-1}{n}\right) \\
&= \lim_{n\to+\infty} \sum_{i=1}^{n} \frac{(i-1)^2}{n^2} \cdot \frac{1}{n} \\
&= \lim_{n\to+\infty} \frac{1}{n^3} \sum_{i=1}^{n} (i-1)^2 \\
&= \lim_{n\to+\infty} \frac{1}{n^3} \frac{(n-1)n(2n-1)}{6} \qquad \text{(See Note)} \\
&= \lim_{n\to+\infty} \frac{\left(1 - \frac{1}{n}\right)\left(2 - \frac{1}{n}\right)}{6} \\
&= \frac{1}{3}.
\end{aligned}
$$

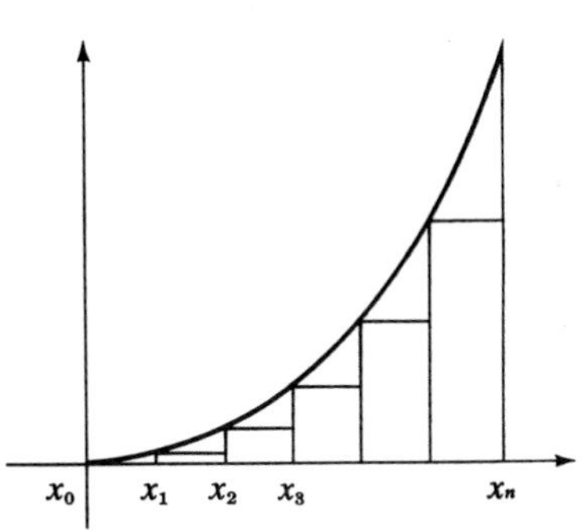

Figure 8.4

Note: Since

$$\sum_{i=1}^{n} i^2 = \frac{n(n+1)(2n+1)}{6},$$

it follows that

$$
\begin{aligned}
\sum_{i=1}^{n} (i-1)^2 &= 0^2 + 1^2 + 2^2 + \cdots + (n-1)^2 \\
&= \sum_{i=1}^{n-1} i^2 \\
&= \frac{[n-1][(n-1)+1][2(n-1)+1]}{6} \\
&= \frac{(n-1)n(2n-1)}{6}.
\end{aligned}
$$

We see that we have exactly the same result as in the previous case. It seems reasonable to expect that, if we get 1/3 in both of these extreme cases, we should get 1/3 in any case.

Problems

1. Use the area of a rectangle and the properties of area on page 145 to find the area of a triangle.
2. Use the area of a triangle and the properties of area on page 145 to find the area of a parallelogram.
3. Use the area of a triangle and the properties of area on page 145 to find the area of a trapezoid.
4. Find the area of the region bounded by $y = x^2$, the x axis, and $x = 1$, taking the x^*'s to be the midpoints of the subintervals. (See Problem 43 of the previous section.)
5. Find the area of the region bounded by $y = x$, the x axis, and $x = 1$. Since this region is triangular, it provides a method of checking the limit method against the method of Problem 1.
6. Find the area of the region bounded by $y = x^3$, the x axis, and $x = 1$, taking the x^*'s to be the right-hand end points of the subintervals.
7. Find the area of Problem 6, using the left-hand end points of the subintervals.

In Problems 8–18, find the area of the given region.

8. The region bounded by $y = x^4$, $y = 0$, and $x = 1$.
9. The region bounded by $y = x^2$ and $y = 0$ and between $x = 1$ and $x = 2$.
10. The region bounded by $y = x^2$, $y = 0$, and $x = 2$.
11. The region bounded by $y = x^3$ and $y = 0$ and between $x = 1$ and $x = 3$.
12. The region bounded by $y = x + x^2$ and $y = 0$ and between $x = 0$ and $x = 1$.
13. The region bounded by $y = 3x^2$, $y = 0$, and $x = 1$.
14. The region bounded by $y = 2x^2 + 3x$ and $y = 0$ and between $x = 0$ and $x = 1$.
15. The region bounded by $y = x^2 - x$ and $y = 0$ and between $x = 1$ and $x = 2$.
16. The region bounded $y = x^3 + 2x^2 + 3$ and $y = 0$ and between $x = 0$ and $x = 1$.
17. The region bounded by $y = x - x^2$ and $y = 0$.
18. The region bounded by $y = (x^2 - 1)^2$ and $y = 0$.

8.3

The Definite Integral

Let us now formalize the material of the preceding section as we did with the derivative. In each case we subdivided an interval $[a, b]$ into n subintervals with the numbers

$$x_0 = a, x_1, x_2, x_3, \ldots, x_n = b$$

(although we used *n equal* subintervals, this was just an algebraic convenience—we could have subdivided in any way). Then we selected a number x^* in each subinterval

$$x_{i-1} \leq x_i^* \leq x_i$$

and then found the sum

$$\sum_{i=1}^{n} f(x_i^*)(x_i - x_{i-1}).$$

Finally we took the limit of this sum as n increased indefinitely, in such a way that the lengths of all of the subintervals approached zero.

There is some notation to simplify the situation somewhat. The first is one we have considered before, namely, let

$$x_i - x_{i-1} = \Delta x_i.$$

Thus Δx_i is simply the length of the ith subinterval. With this, the approximating area is now

$$\sum_{i=1}^{n} f(x_i^*)\,\Delta x_i.$$

Finally, for a given subdivision $S = \{x_0 = a, x_1, x_2, \ldots, x_n = b\}$, we shall represent the length of a longest subinterval by $\|S\|$, called the norm of the subdivision. As $\|S\| \to 0$, the lengths of all of the subintervals must approach zero, and we can express the limit of the approximating sum as

$$\lim_{\|S\| \to 0} \sum_{i=1}^{n} f(x_i^*)\,\Delta x_i.$$

Just as the slope of a graph is far more important than it appeared to be at first glance, the above limit is also far more important than it appears to be. Although it was inspired by the problem of finding an area, we shall see that the same type of expression (with variations in f) can be used to find many things that have the properties of area given on page 145: volume, arc length, work, force, and many others. Because of its importance and wide application, we give it a special name and a special symbol that does not suggest area.

Definition

*If f is a bounded function defined on the interval $[a, b]$, if $S = \{x_0 = a, x_1, x_2, \ldots, x_n = b\}$ is a subdivision of $[a, b]$ with norm $\|S\|$ and if $x_{i-1} \le x_i^* \le x_i$, for $i = 1, 2, 3, \ldots, n$, and $\Delta x_i = x_i - x_{i-1}$, then the **definite integral** of f from a to b is*

$$\int_a^b f(x)\,dx = \lim_{\|S\| \to 0} \sum_{i=1}^{n} f(x_i^*)\,\Delta x_i,$$

provided this limit exists. If

$$\int_a^b f(x)\,dx$$

*exists, **f is integrable** on the interval $[a, b]$.*

This limit is actually much more complex than it appears to be. The approximating sum

$$\sum_{i=1}^{n} f(x_i^*)\,\Delta x_i$$

is dependent upon the function f, the limits a and b, the subdivision S of $[a, b]$, and the choice of the x^*'s. Furthermore, the condition that $\|S\| \to 0$ requires that the length of every subinterval approach zero. If this condition is to be met, the interval $[a, b]$ must be further subdivided repeatedly. Of course, there is no limit to the number of ways this can be done. Actually it can be proved (although we shall not attempt to do so) that, if f is integrable on $[a, b]$, then

$$\int_a^b f(x)\,dx$$

is independent of the subdivision S, the choice of the x^*'s, and the way in which $\|S\| \to 0$. Thus we shall continue to subdivide $[a, b]$ into equal subintervals.

Although we started out with a consideration of area, the definite integral is *not* defined in terms of area. We have not defined area except in certain restricted cases. Now that we have the integral, area can be defined in terms of it.

Definition

The ***area*** *of the region bounded by $y = f(x)$, the x axis, and the vertical lines $x = a$ and $x = b$ $(a < b)$ is*

$$A = \int_a^b |f(x)|\,dx.$$

If $f(x) \geq 0$, then $|f(x)| = f(x)$; but if $f(x) \leq 0$, then $|f(x)| = -f(x)$. You might note that in all of the problems of the previous section, $f(x) \geq 0$ for all x in $[a, b]$. If a portion of the graph is below the x axis, we must use $|f(x)| = -f(x)$ for that portion.

Example 1

Find the area of the region bounded by $y = x^2 - 1$, the x axis, and the vertical lines $x = 0$ and $x = 2$.

The region we want is indicated by the shaded portion of Figure 8.5. For $0 \leq x \leq 1$, $f(x) = y \leq 0$; for $1 \leq x \leq 2$, $f(x) = y \geq 0$. Thus,

$$\begin{aligned} A &= \int_0^2 |f(x)|\,dx \\ &= \int_0^1 -f(x)\,dx + \int_1^2 f(x)\,dx \\ &= \int_0^1 (1 - x^2)\,dx + \int_1^2 (x^2 - 1)\,dx. \end{aligned}$$

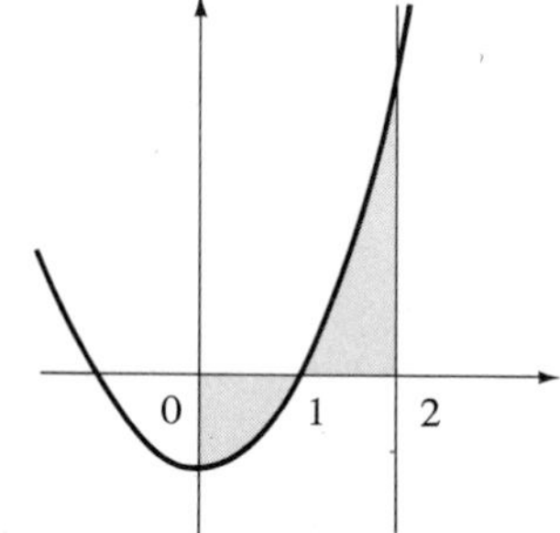

Figure 8.5

Each of these can be evaluated separately by the method of the preceding section, to get

$$A = \frac{2}{3} + \frac{4}{3} = 2.$$

We made use here of the following theorem.

Theorem 8.4

If $a < b < c$ and f is integrable on $[a, c]$, then

$$\int_a^c f(x)\,dx = \int_a^b f(x)\,dx + \int_b^c f(x)\,dx.$$

The theorem is intuitively obvious; we shall not prove it.

Example 2

Evaluate $\int_0^2 (x^2 - 1)\,dx$.

Subdividing [0, 2] and choosing x^*'s, we have (see Figure 8.6):

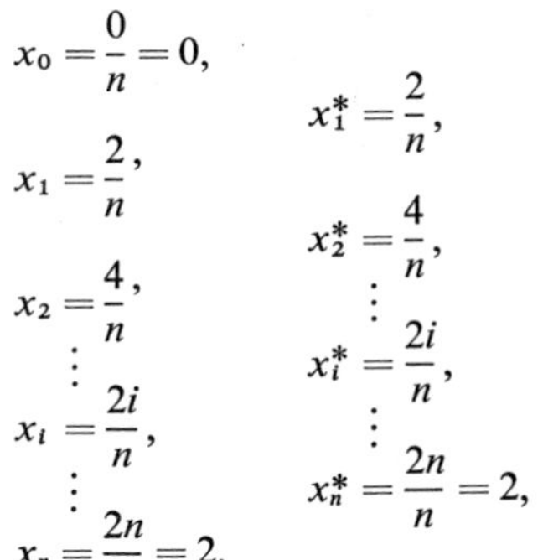

$$x_0 = \frac{0}{n} = 0,\quad x_1 = \frac{2}{n},\quad x_2 = \frac{4}{n},\quad \ldots,\quad x_i = \frac{2i}{n},\quad \ldots,\quad x_n = \frac{2n}{n} = 2.$$

$$x_1^* = \frac{2}{n},\quad x_2^* = \frac{4}{n},\quad \ldots,\quad x_i^* = \frac{2i}{n},\quad \ldots,\quad x_n^* = \frac{2n}{n} = 2,$$

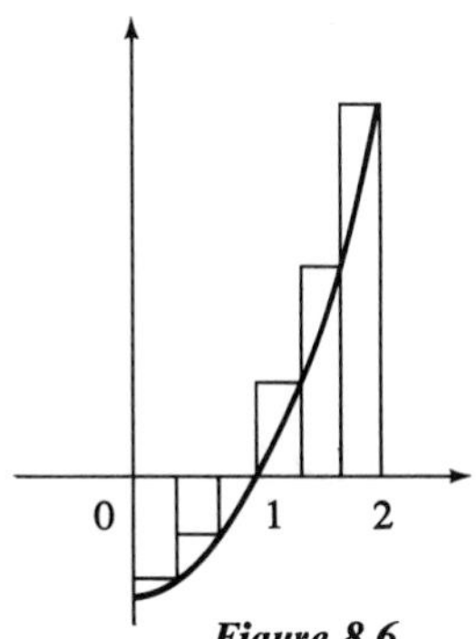

Figure 8.6

$$\begin{aligned}
\int_0^2 (x^2 - 1)\,dx &= \lim_{n\to+\infty} \sum_{i=1}^{n} f(x_i^*)\,\Delta x_i \\
&= \lim_{n\to+\infty} \sum_{i=1}^{n} f\left(\frac{2i}{n}\right)\frac{2}{n} \\
&= \lim_{n\to+\infty} \sum_{i=1}^{n} \frac{4i^2 - n^2}{n^2}\cdot\frac{2}{n} \\
&= \lim_{n\to+\infty} \frac{2}{n^3}\left[4\sum_{i=1}^{n} i^2 - n^2\sum_{i=1}^{n} 1\right] \\
&= \lim_{n\to+\infty} \frac{2}{n^3}\left[\frac{4n(n+1)(2n+1)}{6} - n^3\right] \\
&= \lim_{n\to+\infty} \left[\frac{4n(n+1)(2n+1)}{3n^3} - 2\right] \\
&= \lim_{n\to+\infty} \left[\frac{4\left(1+\frac{1}{n}\right)\left(2+\frac{1}{n}\right)}{3} - 2\right] \\
&= \frac{8}{3} - 2 = \frac{2}{3}.
\end{aligned}$$

Note that the result is not the area which we found in Example 1—it is really the area of the portion above the x axis minus the area of the portion below the x axis. This can easily be checked in Example 1, where these two areas were individually determined.

Problems

In Problems 1–10, evaluate the integrals.

1. $\int_0^3 (x^2 - 1)\,dx.$

2. $\int_{-1}^2 (x^2 - 1)\,dx.$

3. $\int_{-1}^{1} x^3\,dx.$

4. $\int_{-1}^{0} x^3\,dx.$

5. $\int_{0}^{1} x^3\,dx.$

6. $\int_{-1}^{1} x^2\,dx.$

7. $\int_{-1}^{0} x^2\,dx.$

8. $\int_{0}^{1} x^2\,dx.$

9. $\int_{0}^{1} (x^2 - x)\,dx.$

10. $\int_{3}^{4} (x^2 - 9)\,dx.$

In Problems 11–20, find the area of the given region.

11. The region bounded by $y = x^3$, $y = 0$, and $x = -1$.
12. The region bounded by $y = x^3$ and $y = 0$ and between $x = -1$ and $x = 1$.
13. The region bounded by $y = x^2 - x$ and $y = 0$ and between $x = 0$ and $x = 2$.
14. The region bounded by $y = x^2 - x$ and $y = 0$ and between $x = -1$ and $x = 0$.
15. The region bounded by $y = x^2 - 4x$ and $y = 0$.
16. The region bounded by $y = x^3 - x^2$ and $y = 0$ and between $x = 0$ and $x = 2$.
17. The region bounded by $y = x^3 - x^2$ and $y = 0$.
18. The region bounded by $y = x^3 - x$ and $y = 0$ and between $x = 0$ and $x = 2$.
19. The region bounded by $y = x^3 - x$ and $y = 0$.
20. The region bounded by $y = x^4 - 1$ and $y = 0$ and between $x = 0$ and $x = 2$.
21. A function f is odd if $f(-x) = -f(x)$; f is even if $f(-x) = f(x)$. What can be said about $\int_{-a}^{a} f(x)\,dx$ if f is odd? if f is even?
22. Show that the function f, where

$$f(x) = \begin{cases} 0 & \text{if } x \text{ is rational} \\ 1 & \text{if } x \text{ is irrational} \end{cases}$$

is not integrable on [0, 1]. *Hint:* Evaluate the approximating sum in two different ways. First use only rational values for all x^*'s; then use only irrational values.

8.4

The Fundamental Theorem of Integral Calculus

By this time you have probably had quite enough of the definition of the definite integral and are eager for a way to simplify the problem of integration. Fortunately, there is a simple relationship between the derivative and the integral which is given by the fundamental theorem of integral calculus. Perhaps you have heard that Newton and Leibniz invented calculus. Actually Archimedes, in the third century, B.C., used a method similar to the one of the preceding sections to find the areas of certain figures; and Fermat, in the seventeenth century, found tangents to algebraic curves. But, later in the seventeenth century, Newton and Leibniz, working independently, showed the relationship between the derivative and the integral and gave a systematic development of calculus. The relationship between the derivative and the integral is given in the fundamental theorem of integral calculus.

Theorem 8.5

(Fundamental theorem of integral calculus) If the function f is integrable on the interval $[a, b]$, then*

$$\int_a^b f(x)\,dx = F(b) - F(a),$$

where F is a function such that $F'(x) = f(x)$ for all x in $[a, b]$.

Proof

Let us make some simplifying assumptions about f (the theorem can be proved for the other cases as well, but the main ideas are to be found here). Let us assume that $f(x) \geq 0$ for all x, that $0 \leq a < b$, and that f is integrable on $[0, b]$. With

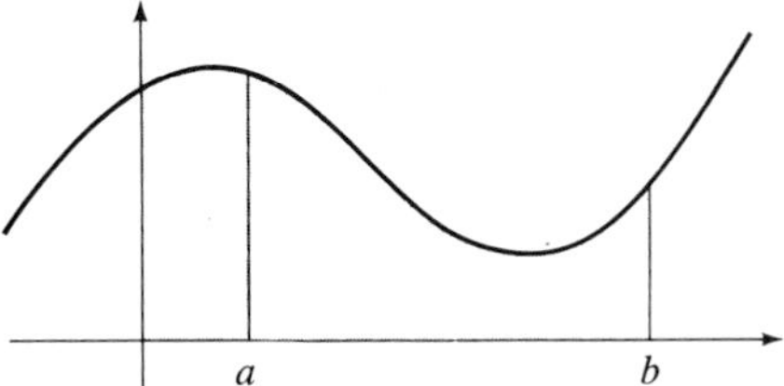

Figure 8.7

these assumptions, let $F(x)$ be the area "under the curve" from 0 to x. Since $F(b)$ is the area under the curve from 0 to b and $F(a)$ the area from 0 to a (see Figure 8.7), $F(b) - F(a)$ is the area from a to b, or

$$\int_a^b f(x)\,dx = F(b) - F(a).$$

We next show that F is an antiderivative of f. Let us consider one of the subdivisions of $[a, b]$: say $[x, x+h]$ (see Figure 8.8(a)). By the same argument used above, the area under the curve from x to $x+h$ is

$$F(x+h) - F(x).$$

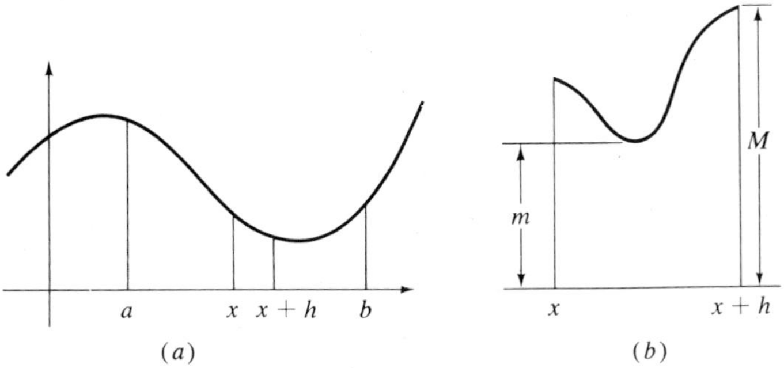

(a) (b)

Figure 8.8

Now let us compare this with the areas of rectangles that might be used in the definition of the definite integral. Let m and M be the minimum and maximum values, respectively, of $f(x)$ on $[x, x+h]$ (see Figure 8.8(b)). Since

*We again assume that f is "well-behaved." See Appendix B for a more precise statement and proof.

$m \le f(x^*) \le M$, mh and Mh represent the areas of the smallest and largest rectangles, respectively, with base $[x, x+h]$ and height $f(x^*)$, x^* in $[x, x+h]$. Thus

$$mh \le F(x+h) - F(x) \le Mh,$$

$$m \le \frac{F(x+h) - F(x)}{h} \le M.$$

Finally we want to take the limit as the widths of all subintervals approach zero or, in this case, as h approaches zero. Referring to Figure 8.8(b), we can see that m and M depend upon the value of h and that both approach $f(x)$ as h approaches zero.

$$\lim_{h\to 0} m = f(x),$$

$$\lim_{h\to 0} M = f(x),$$

$$\lim_{h\to 0} \frac{F(x+h) - F(x)}{h} = F'(x).$$

Thus

$$f(x) \le F'(x) \le f(x),$$

which requires that

$$F'(x) = f(x).$$

A complete proof of this theorem, using the mean-value theorem (see page 439), is given in Appendix B. This theorem now tells us that we can often avoid the complicated limit in the definition of an integral and just substitute into a function F whose derivative is f. Our problem is to find F. This is a problem we have already encountered in Chapter 5—the antiderivative.

Example 1

Evaluate $\int_0^1 x^2\,dx$.

$$F'(x) = x^2,$$

$$F(x) = \frac{x^3}{3} + C,$$

$$\int_0^1 x^2\,dx = F(1) - F(0)$$

$$= \left(\frac{1}{3} + C\right) - C$$

$$= \frac{1}{3}.$$

Note that the constant C cancels out in every case, since we are always taking the difference $F(b) - F(a)$. Since it always cancels out, we simply omit it. The notation is further shortened in the following way:

$$\int_0^1 x^2\,dx = \frac{x^3}{3}\Big|_0^1 = \frac{1}{3} - 0 = \frac{1}{3}.$$

Example 2

Evaluate $\int_1^2 x^3\,dx$.

$$\int_1^2 x^3\,dx = \frac{x^4}{4}\Big|_1^2 = 4 - \frac{1}{4} = \frac{15}{4}.$$

We see that we can now integrate much faster than before. Moreover, we can solve problems that we previously could not.

Example 3

Evaluate $\int_1^4 \sqrt{x}\,dx$.

$$\int_1^4 \sqrt{x}\,dx = \frac{2}{3}x^{3/2}\Big|_1^4 = \frac{16}{3} - \frac{2}{3} = \frac{14}{3}.$$

Problems

In Problems 1–20, evaluate the given integrals.

1. $\int_0^2 x^2\,dx.$
2. $\int_1^2 x^2\,dx.$
3. $\int_0^2 x^3\,dx.$
4. $\int_0^1 x^4\,dx.$
5. $\int_1^2 (3x^2 + 2x)\,dx.$
6. $\int_0^1 (x^3 - x)\,dx.$
7. $\int_0^1 x(x-1)^2\,dx.$
8. $\int_0^1 x(x^2-1)\,dx.$
9. $\int_1^2 x^2(x-1)\,dx.$
10. $\int_1^2 x(x-1)^2\,dx.$
11. $\int_1^4 (x + \sqrt{x})\,dx.$
12. $\int_0^4 (1 + \sqrt{x})^2\,dx.$

13. $\int_1^8 \sqrt[3]{x}\,dx.$

14. $\int_1^8 x^{2/3}\,dx.$

15. $\int_1^4 \frac{1}{\sqrt{x}}\,dx.$

16. $\int_4^9 (x^{1/2} + x^{-1/2})\,dx.$

17. $\int_1^2 \frac{1}{x^2}\,dx.$

18. $\int_1^2 \frac{2}{x^3}\,dx.$

19. $\int_1^4 \frac{x-1}{\sqrt{x}}\,dx.$

20. $\int_1^{64} (x^{1/2} + x^{1/3})\,dx.$

In Problems 21–30, find the area of the given region.

21. The region bounded by $y = x^2 + 1$, $y = 0$, $x = 0$, and $x = 1$.
22. The region bounded by $y = x^2 - 1$ and $y = 0$.
23. The region bounded by $y = x^4 - 1$ and $y = 0$.
24. The region bounded by $y = (x^2 - 1)^2$ and $y = 0$.
25. The region bounded by $y = (x - 1)^2$, $y = 0$, and $x = 0$.
26. The region bounded by $y = x(x - 1)^2$ and $y = 0$.
27. The region bounded by $y = 1/\sqrt{x}$ and $y = 0$ and between $x = 1$ and $x = 2$.
28. The region bounded by $y = 1/x^2$ and $y = 0$ and between $x = 1$ and $x = 2$.
29. The region bounded by $y = \sqrt{x}$, $y = 0$, and $x = 4$.
30. The region bounded by $y = x - \sqrt{x}$ and $y = 0$.
31. How would the proof of the fundamental theorem have to be altered if $a < 0$?
32. How would the proof of the fundamental theorem have to be altered if $f(x) < 0$ for some x?

8.5

Integration Formulas

We shall use the symbol $\int f(x)\,dx$ for the antiderivatives of $f(x)$. It is called the indefinite integral of $f(x)$. The results of Section 5.8 concerning the antiderivative can now be put into integral notation.

Theorem 8.6

If $u(x)$ and $v(x)$ are integrable, then

(a) $\int x^n\,dx = \frac{x^{n+1}}{n+1} + C \quad (n \neq -1),$

(b) $\int cv(x)\,dx = c\int v(x)\,dx,$

(c) $\int [u(x) + v(x)]\,dx = \int u(x)\,dx + \int v(x)\,dx.$

Example 1

Evaluate $\int (3x^2 - 4x)\,dx$.

$$\begin{aligned}\int (3x^2 - 4x)\,dx &= \int 3x^2\,dx - \int 4x\,dx \\ &= 3\int x^2\,dx - 4\int x\,dx \\ &= 3\cdot\frac{x^3}{3} - 4\cdot\frac{x^2}{2} + C \\ &= x^3 - 2x^2 + C.\end{aligned}$$

With very little practice, you should be able to write the answer directly without the intermediate steps. They have been put in here to show how Theorem 8.6 was used.

We might make one observation concerning the notation. It is possible to think of an expression like $\int x^2\,dx$ in two ways: one way is to think of $\int \cdots dx$ as one symbol indicating that whatever is inside is to be integrated with respect to x; the other way is to think of $\int$ as the symbol of integration, where $\int x^2\,dx$ means to integrate the differential $x^2\,dx$. Each point of view has its advantages as well as some disadvantages. We shall generally follow the former point of view.

One other useful formula follows from the power rule stated in Theorem 5.11.

Theorem 8.7

If n is a rational number different from -1, *then*

$$\int [u(x)]^n \cdot u'(x)\,dx = \frac{[u(x)]^{n+1}}{n+1} + C,$$

or, abbreviated,

$$\int u^n \cdot u'\,dx = \frac{u^{n+1}}{n+1} + C.$$

Since $du = u'\,dx$, this formula is often written

$$\int u^n\,du = \frac{u^{n+1}}{n+1} + C.$$

Example 2

Evaluate $\int (x^2 + 1)^3 \cdot 2x\,dx$.

This integral is in the form $\int u^3 \cdot u'\,dx$, with $u = x^2 + 1$. Thus

$$\int (x^2 + 1)^3 \cdot 2x\,dx = \frac{(x^2 + 1)^4}{4} + C.$$

A question many ask at this point is, Where did the $2x$ go? The only answer is a reminder that integration is the inverse of differentiation and that

$$\frac{d}{dx}\left[\frac{(x^2+1)^4}{4}+C\right]=(x^2+1)^3\cdot 2x.$$

Since $2x$ appears on differentiation, it must disappear on integration—wherever it comes from when we differentiate is where it must go when we integrate.

Example 3

Evaluate $\int (x^2-1)^4 \cdot x\,dx$.

If we let $u=x^2-1$, then $u'=2x$. Unfortunately we do not have $2x$; we have x. So, if we want something we do not have, we put it in and compensate with something else. Let us put in 2 and compensate with 1/2.

$$\begin{aligned}\int (x^2-1)^4\cdot x\,dx &= \int \frac{1}{2}(x^2-1)^4\cdot 2x\,dx\\ &= \frac{1}{2}\int (x^2-1)^4\cdot 2x\,dx \qquad \text{(By Theorem 8.6b)}\\ &= \frac{1}{2}\frac{(x^2-1)^5}{5}+C \qquad \text{(By Theorem 8.7)}\\ &= \frac{1}{10}(x^2-1)^5+C.\end{aligned}$$

This method works only when what we have and what we want differ by a *constant* factor, since Theorem 8.6(b) only allows us to take constants outside the integral sign.

Example 4

Evaluate $\int (x^2-1)^2\,dx$.

Letting $u=x^2-1$, we have $u'=2x$. Let us try the method of the preceding example and see why it fails here.

$$\begin{aligned}\int (x^2-1)^2\,dx &= \int \frac{1}{2x}(x^2-1)^2\cdot 2x\,dx\\ &\neq \frac{1}{2x}\int (x^2-1)^2\cdot 2x\,dx.\end{aligned}$$

Theorem 8.6(b) cannot be used here, because $1/(2x)$ is not a constant. The integration must be carried out as follows:

$$\begin{aligned}\int (x^2-1)^2\,dx &= \int (x^4-2x^2+1)\,dx\\ &= \frac{x^5}{5}-\frac{2x^3}{3}+x+C.\end{aligned}$$

Example 5

Evaluate $\int (3x - 2)^2\, dx$.

We can use the method of either Example 3 or Example 4. Let us try both methods.

$$\int (3x-2)^2\, dx \qquad\qquad \int (3x-2)^2\, dx$$

$$= \frac{1}{3}\int (3x-2)^2 \cdot 3\, dx \qquad = \int (9x^2 - 12x + 4)\, dx$$

$$= \frac{1}{9}(3x-2)^3 + C_1. \qquad = 3x^3 - 6x^2 + 4x + C_2.$$

The results we get by the two different methods look quite different. Are they equivalent? Let us see.

$$\frac{1}{9}(3x-2)^3 + C_1 = \frac{1}{9}(27x^3 - 54x^2 + 36x - 8) + C_1$$

$$= 3x^3 - 6x^2 + 4x - \frac{8}{9} + C_1$$

$$= 3x^3 - 6x^2 + 4x + C_2, \quad \text{where } C_2 = -\frac{8}{9} + C_1.$$

Although the two results look quite different, they are really equivalent with different constants of integration. Thus, two people could carry out an integration in two different ways, arrive at two different looking answers, and yet both be correct. One way to check is to differentiate the result. If differentiation gives the original expression, the integration is correct (assuming that the differentiation is correct).

Problems

Evaluate the following integrals.

1. $\int 2(2x-3)^2\, dx.$
2. $\int 2(2x-3)^{2/3}\, dx.$
3. $\int (x^2 - x)(2x-1)\, dx.$
4. $\int (x^2 - x)^2\, dx.$
5. $\int \sqrt{4x-3}\, dx.$
6. $\int \sqrt{2x+1}\, dx.$
7. $\int (x^2+4)^2 x\, dx.$
8. $\int (x^2+4)^2\, dx.$
9. $\int (x^2+4)^2 x^3\, dx.$
10. $\int (x^3+1)^2\, dx.$
11. $\int (x^3+1)^2 x^2\, dx.$
12. $\int \frac{(\sqrt{x}+1)^4}{\sqrt{x}}\, dx.$
13. $\int \frac{(x^{1/3}-1)^5}{x^{2/3}}\, dx.$
14. $\int (x^{-1}+1)^4 x^{-2}\, dx.$

15. $\int (x^{-2} + x)^5(1 - 2x^{-3})\, dx.$

16. $\int x\sqrt{3x^2 - 5}\, dx.$

17. $\int x\sqrt[3]{3x^2 - 5}\, dx.$

18. $\int (x^{-2} - 4)^{3/5}x^{-3}\, dx.$

19. $\int \frac{x^2 + 2x + 2}{(x+1)^2}\, dx.$

20. $\int \frac{(x^2 + 1)^2}{x^2}\, dx.$

21. $\int \frac{x^3 + 8x^2 + 20x + 20}{(x+2)^2}\, dx.$

22. $\int \frac{x^4 - 4x}{(x-1)^2}\, dx.$

23. $\int_0^2 (x^2 - 4)^2 x\, dx.$

24. $\int_0^1 (4x + 1)^2\, dx.$

25. $\int_1^2 (x^3 - x)^2(3x^2 - 1)\, dx.$

26. $\int_3^7 \sqrt{2x - 5}\, dx.$

27. $\int_1^{22} \sqrt{3x - 2}\, dx.$

28. $\int_0^1 (x^2 + 2)^2\, dx.$

29. $\int_1^2 (x^2 - 3)^3 x\, dx.$

30. $\int_0^1 4x\sqrt{x^2 + 1}\, dx.$

8.6

The Area between Two Curves

By altering the $f(x)$ in $\int_a^b f(x)\, dx$, we can extend considerably what we are able to do with the integral. Figure 8.9(a) shows a representative rectangle used to set up the

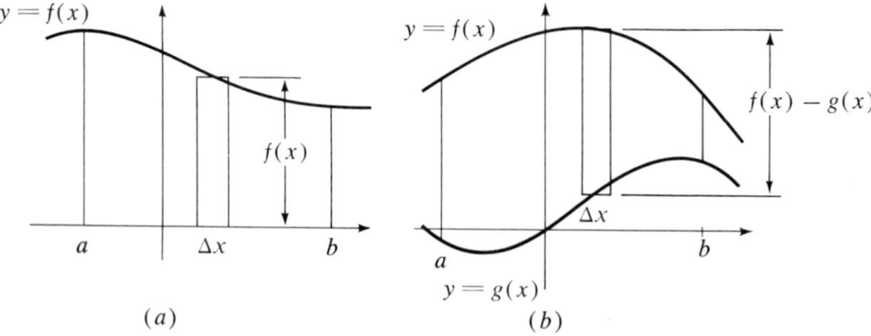

Figure 8.9

integral for the area. It is advisable to draw such rectangles in all cases, as an aid to setting up the integral—the integral $\int_a^b f(x)\, dx$ works only in the restricted case we have studied so far. Figure 8.9(b) shows a representative rectangle used to set up the integral for the area of the region bounded above by $y = f(x)$ and below by $y = g(x)$, and between the vertical lines $x = a$ and $x = b$. Basically, we have the same situation as before. The interval $[a, b]$ is subdivided and rectangles are formed. But this time, and this is the only difference, the top of the rectangle is on $y = f(x)$ and the bottom is on $y = g(x)$. Thus the height of the rectangle is the difference between the y coordinates: $f(x) - g(x)$. The relative position of the curves with respect to the x axis has no bearing on the situation (see page 3); the distance between two points on a vertical line is the larger y coordinate minus the smaller. Thus

$$A = \lim_{\|S\| \to 0} \sum_{i=1}^{n} [f(x_i^*) - g(x_i^*)]\, \Delta x_i$$
$$= \int_a^b [f(x) - g(x)]\, dx.$$

Example 1

Find the area of the region bounded by $y = 4 - 4x^2$ and $y = x^2 - 1$.

The graphs of the two curves are given in Figure 8.10. We see that the points of intersection are $(-1, 0)$ and $(1, 0)$, representing the left- and right-hand extremes, respectively, of the region under consideration. Since the height of the rectangle is $y_1 - y_2$ and the width is Δx, we have

$$A = \int_{-1}^{1} (y_1 - y_2)\, dx$$
$$= \int_{-1}^{1} (5 - 5x^2)\, dx$$
$$= 5x - \frac{5x^3}{3}\Big|_{-1}^{1}$$
$$= \left(5 - \frac{5}{3}\right) - \left(-5 + \frac{5}{3}\right) = \frac{20}{3}.$$

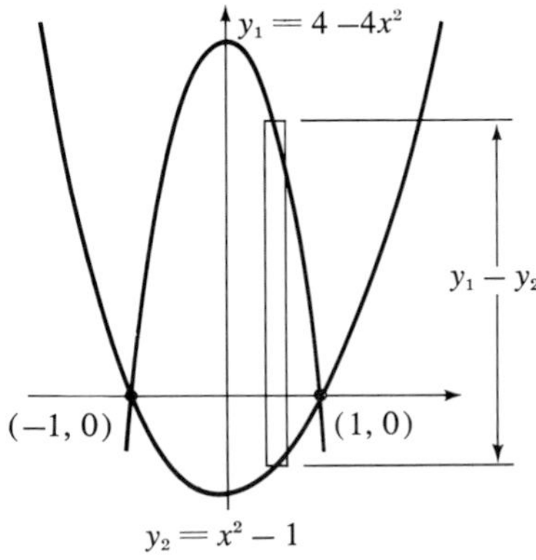

Figure 8.10

In this case you could have found the areas of the portion above the x axis and the portion below the x axis and added. This would have given

$$A = \int_{-1}^{1} y_1\, dx + \int_{-1}^{1} -y_2\, dx,$$

which is equivalent to

$$\int_{-1}^{1} (y_1 - y_2)\, dx.$$

Example 2

Find the area of the region bounded by $y^2 = x + 2$ and $y = x$.

The graphs are given in Figure 8.11. The points of intersection are found by solving the two equations simultaneously. In this case they do not represent the left- and right-hand extremes of the region. The extremes are $(-2, 0)$ and $(2, 2)$. Now we have a problem that we did not have in the previous example: both ends of the vertical strip are on the curve $y^2 = x + 2$ for $-2 \le x \le -1$, while the top end is on $y^2 = x + 2$ and the bottom on the line $y = x$

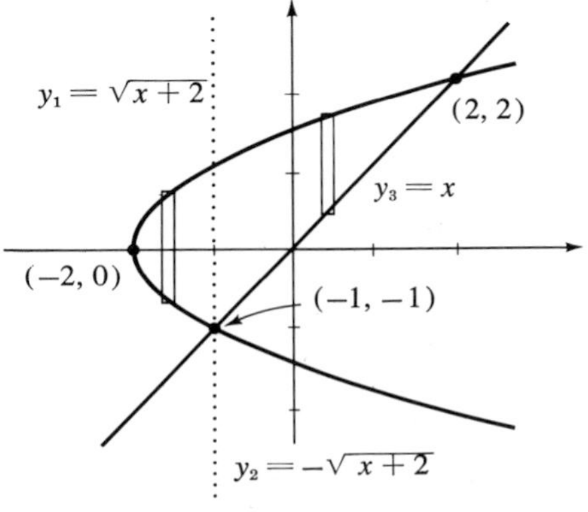

Figure 8.11

for $-1 \le x \le 2$. We shall find the areas of the two parts separately, noting that the top and bottom halves of $y^2 = x + 2$ are $y = \sqrt{x+2}$ and $y = -\sqrt{x+2}$, respectively. Now

$$A = \int_{-2}^{-1} (y_1 - y_2)\, dx + \int_{-1}^{2} (y_1 - y_3)\, dx$$

$$= \int_{-2}^{-1} (\sqrt{x+2} + \sqrt{x+2})\, dx + \int_{-1}^{2} (\sqrt{x+2} - x)\, dx$$

$$= \frac{4}{3}(x+2)^{3/2} \Big|_{-2}^{-1} + \left[\frac{2}{3}(x+2)^{3/2} - \frac{1}{2}x^2\right] \Big|_{-1}^{2}$$

$$= \frac{4}{3} + \frac{19}{6} = \frac{9}{2}.$$

The same result is found more simply by reversing the roles of x and y—that is, by using horizontal strips rather than vertical ones, noting that (2, 2) and (−1, −1) represent the top and bottom extremes of the region (see Figure 8.12). In this case, one end is always on $x = y^2 - 2$ and the other on $x = y$.

$$A = \int_{-1}^{2} (x_1 - x_2)\, dy$$

$$= \int_{-1}^{2} (y - y^2 + 2)\, dy$$

$$= \left(\frac{y^2}{2} - \frac{y^3}{3} + 2y\right) \Big|_{-1}^{2}$$

$$= \frac{9}{2}.$$

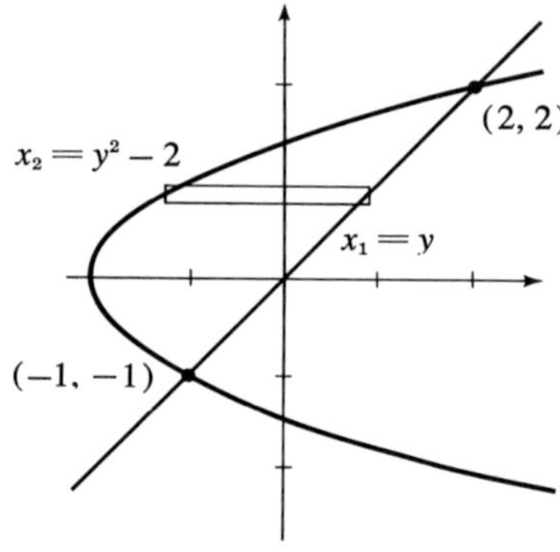

Figure 8.12

Problems

In Problems 1–20, find the area of the given region.

1. The region bounded by $y^2 - 2y + x = 0$ and $x = 0$.
2. The region bounded by $x = 2 + y - y^2$ and $x = 0$.
3. The region bounded by $x = y^2 - 5y + 4$ and $x = 0$.
4. The region in the second quadrant bounded by $x = y^2 - y - 6$, $x = 0$, and $y = 0$.
5. The region bounded by $x = y^2 - 4y$ and $x = 0$ and between $y = 2$ and $y = 5$.
6. The region bounded by $x = y^2 + 2y - 3$ and $x = 0$ and between $y = 0$ and $y = 2$.
7. The region bounded by $y = x^2$ and $x - y + 2 = 0$.
8. The region bounded by $y = x^2 - 1$ and $x - y + 1 = 0$.
9. The region bounded by $y = 2x - x^2$ and $x + y = 0$.
10. The region bounded by $y = 2 + x - x^2$ and $x + y + 1 = 0$.
11. The region bounded by $x = y^2$ and $x - y = 2$.
12. The region bounded by $x = y^2 - y - 2$ and $x - y = 6$.
13. The region bounded by $x^2y = 4$ and $3x + y = 7$.
14. The region bounded by $x - y = 0$, $x + 3y = 0$, and $3x + y = 8$.
15. The region bounded by $y = x(x-2)^2$ and $y = x$.

16. The region bounded by $x = y^3 - 3y^2$ and $x - y + 3 = 0$.
17. The region bounded by $y = x^2 + 2x$ and $y = 2 - x - x^2$.
18. The region bounded by $x = y^2 + 2y - 8$ and $x = 4 - y^2$.
19. The region bounded by $y = x^2 - 1$ and $y = x^3 - 1$.
20. The region bounded by $y = x^3 - x$ and $y = 3 - 3x^2$.
21. Find the area of the region bounded by $y = x^2$ and the line through (0, 0) and (2, 4).
22. Find the area of the region bounded by $y = x^2 - 2x$ and the line through (−1, 3) and (2, 0).
23. Find the area of the region bounded by $y = x^2 - x - 2$ and the line through (−2, 4) and (1, −2).
24. Find the area of the region bounded by $x = y^2 - 4$ and the line through (−3, 1) and (0, −2).
25. Find the area of the triangle with sides $x + 2y - 7 = 0$, $x - y - 4 = 0$, and $5x + y - 8 = 0$.
26. Find the area of the triangle with vertices (2, 3), (−1, 0), and (3, −2).

8.7

Work

We noted earlier that the integral is useful for much more than finding area. Let us now consider another application of the integral—that of determining the amount of work done. Work is defined as the product of the force exerted and the distance moved by the object on which the force is applied. For instance, if a five-pound weight is lifted ten feet, the work performed is the product, or 50 foot pounds.

Unfortunately, work problems are not all so simple. Consider the work done in stretching a spring. At first, relatively little force is needed to stretch it; but, as the spring is stretched more and more, it requires more and more force to continue stretching it. Since the force applied varies continuously as we stretch the spring, we cannot use any one number for the force. This is where the integral can help us.

Similarly, if water is pumped out of a tank over the top, it requires more work to pump out "the bottom layer" than the top, since it must be lifted farther. Many such instances of this type occur.

Example 1

A spring is stretched six inches by a force of 12 pounds. How much work is done in stretching the spring two feet?

First of all, let us assume that the spring obeys Hooke's law, which states that the force F required to stretch a spring a distance x is proportional to x. $F = kx$. Now k may be determined.

$$F = kx, \qquad 12 = k \cdot \frac{1}{2}, \qquad k = 24.$$

Thus, the force required to hold the spring stretched a distance x feet from the equilibrium position is

$$F = 24x \text{ lb.}$$

We can approximate the work done in the following way. Let us subdivide the interval [0, 2] into n subintervals (see Figure 8.13). Let Δx_i be the length of one such subinterval and let x_i^* be a number in that subinterval. For the ith subinterval, the force is approximately $24x_i^*$ and the distance is Δx_i. The work done throughout that subinterval is approximately

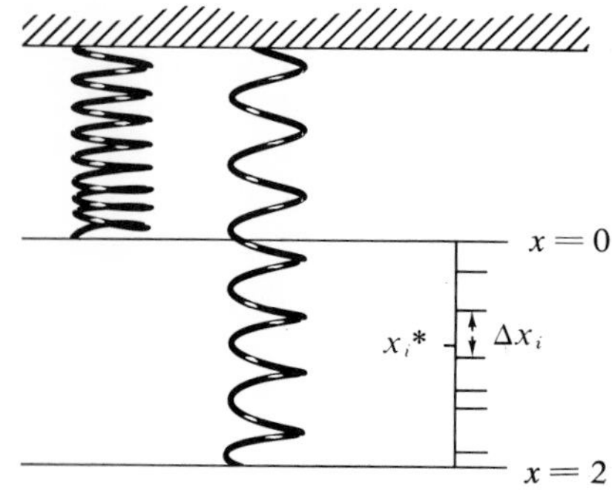

Figure 8.13

$$24x_i^* \, \Delta x_i,$$

and the total work from $x = 0$ to $x = 2$ is approximately

$$\sum_{i=1}^{n} 24x_i^* \, \Delta x_i.$$

But we do not want an approximation of the work done—we want the exact value. In order to find it, let us take the limit of our approximation as the lengths of the subintervals approach 0.

$$\begin{aligned} W &= \lim_{\|S\| \to 0} \sum_{i=1}^{n} 24x_i^* \, \Delta x_i \\ &= \int_0^2 24x \, dx \\ &= 12x^2 \Big|_0^2 \\ &= 48 \text{ ft lb.} \end{aligned}$$

We see here that defining an integral as a limit of a certain approximating sum is what allows us to extend its use from the computation of areas to other applications.

Example 2

A chain 50 feet long and weighing two pounds per foot is hanging from the top of a cliff. How much work is needed to pull 20 feet of it to the top?

The force needed to hold the chain is equal to the weight of the chain hanging down. Thus, if x feet of chain are hanging down,

$$F = 2x.$$

The work is then

$$\begin{aligned} W &= \int_{30}^{50} 2x \, dx \\ &= x^2 \Big|_{30}^{50} \\ &= 1600 \text{ ft lb.} \end{aligned}$$

Example 3

A cylindrical tank ten feet in diameter and ten feet high is full of water. How much work is required to pump the water out over the top?

We see (Figure 8.14) that different "layers" must be raised different distances to the top. If x represents the distance from the top of the tank, suppose we subdivide the interval [0, 10] into n subintervals. If Δx_i is the length of the ith subinterval and x_i^* is a number in that interval, then the weight of the ith layer is its volume times the density of water (62.4 lb/ft³).

$$F = (62.4)\pi \cdot 5^2 \cdot \Delta x_i$$
$$= 1560\pi \cdot \Delta x_i,$$

and the approximate work done in raising it to the top is

$$W = 1560\pi\ \Delta x_i \cdot x_i^*.$$

Taking the limit of the sum of all such layers gives

$$W = \int_0^{10} 1560\pi x\, dx$$
$$= 780\pi x^2 \Big|_0^{10}$$
$$= 78{,}000\pi \text{ ft lb}.$$

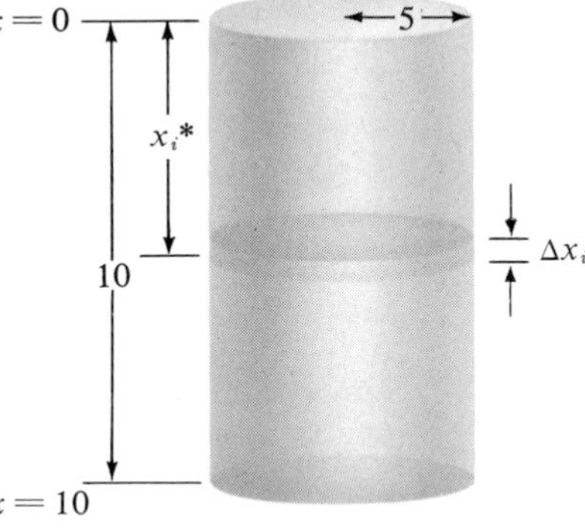

Figure 8.14

It might be noted that this same amount of work would be done *by* the water if it were allowed to run out the bottom of the tank.

Problems

1. A force of 3 lb stretches a spring 4 in. How much work is done in stretching the spring 1 ft?
2. How much work is done in stretching the spring of Problem 1 from 1 to 2 ft?
3. A force of 4 lb stretches a spring 1 ft. How much work is done in stretching the spring 6 in.?
4. A force of 2 lb stretches a spring 9 in. How much work is done in stretching the spring 2 ft?
5. A force of 5 lb stretches a spring 8 in. How much work is done in stretching the spring from 1 ft to 3 ft?
6. If the spring of Problem 5 is at the equilibrium position and 60 ft lb of work is expended in stretching it, how far is it stretched?
7. A cylindrical tank 8 ft in diameter across the top and 9 ft high is filled with water. How much work is done in pumping the water out over the top?
8. How much work is done in Problem 7 if only half of the water is pumped out?
9. If the tank of Problem 7 is emptied through a hole 6 ft from the bottom, what is the net amount of work done in emptying it? (Note that the water above the hole is doing work for us as it runs out the hole.) If the work done by the top 3 ft of water is lost, how much work must be done to empty the tank?
10. Suppose the tank of Problem 7 is elevated so that the bottom of the tank is 40 ft above the ground. How much work is done in filling the tank from a source of water at ground level if the water is pumped in over the top of the tank? What if it is pumped in through the bottom?

11. A conical tank (right circular cone) filled with water is 6 ft across the top and 5 ft high. How much work is done in pumping the water out over the top? How much work is done by the water if it runs out the bottom?
12. How much work is done in pumping the top 2.5 ft of water over the top of the tank of Problem 11? What portion of the entire volume of the tank does this represent?
13. A chain 50 ft long and weighing 1 lb/ft is hanging vertically. How much work is done in raising the chain to a horizontal position at the level of the top of the chain?
14. How much work is done on the chain of Problem 13 if only half is brought to the horizontal position and the other half left hanging?
15. Suppose the bottom of the chain of Problem 13 is raised to the level of the top so that the chain is doubled but still hanging vertically. How much work is expended in doing so?
16. A chain 10 ft long and weighing 0.5 lb/ft is lying on the floor. How much work is done if one end of the chain is taken and raised to a level of 15 ft?
17. A 100-lb weight is suspended from a 20-ft cable weighing 0.25 lb/ft. The weighted end is raised 15 ft, the other end remaining in its original position. How much work is done?
18. A bucket weighing 1 lb and holding 1 ft^3 of water is suspended by a rope weighing 0.1 lb/ft in a well 50 ft deep. How much work is necessary to bring the bucket of water to the top?
19. Suppose the water in the bucket of Problem 18 is leaking out at the rate of 0.01 ft^3/sec and the bucket is raised at the rate of 1 ft/sec. How much work is necessary to bring it to the top?
20. A ship has an anchor weighing 1000 lb out of water and 900 lb in the water. The anchor chain weighs 5 lb/ft out of water and 4.5 lb/ft in water. The deck of the ship is 10 ft above the water, and the ship is directly above the anchor with no slack in the anchor chain. If the water is 50 ft deep, how much work is done to weigh anchor?

8.8

Approximate Integration

Integration is generally a more difficult problem than differentiation. It is not unusual to encounter an integral that cannot be evaluated by antidifferentiation. In that case, we must resort to approximate integration. Among the many methods of approximate integration, two will be considered here. Both methods are based upon the interpretation of an integral as an area. We have already noted that we can determine areas by integrals. We now turn this idea around. Given an integral $\int_a^b f(x)\,dx$, which may come from a problem having nothing to do with area (for instance, a work problem), we can think of it as representing the "signed area" (with the portions below the x axis negative) under the curve $y = f(x)$ from $x = a$ to $x = b$. If we can approximate the area in some way, we shall have an approximation of the integral.

One way of approximating the area involves trapezoids (see Figure 8.15). The interval $[a, b]$ is subdivided into n equal subintervals, and the curve is approximated by straight-line segments forming n trapezoids. All have the common height

$$h = \frac{b-a}{n},$$

and the coordinates of the subdivisions are

$$\begin{aligned} x_0 &= a, \\ x_1 &= a + h, \\ x_2 &= a + 2h, \\ &\vdots \\ x_i &= a + ih, \\ &\vdots \\ x_n &= a + nh = b. \end{aligned}$$

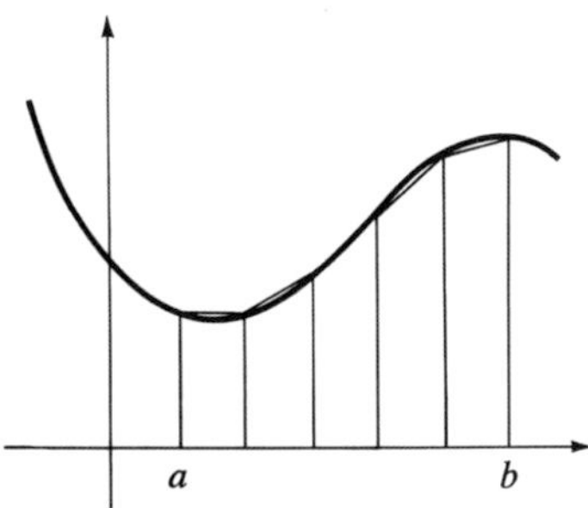

Figure 8.15

The area of the ith trapezoid is

$$A_i = \frac{h}{2}[f(x_{i-1}) + f(x_i)],$$

and the total area is

$$\begin{aligned} A &= \frac{h}{2}\{[f(x_0) + f(x_1)] + [f(x_1) + f(x_2)] + [f(x_2) + f(x_3)] + \cdots \\ &\quad + [f(x_{n-1}) + f(x_n)]\} \\ &= \frac{h}{2}[f(x_0) + 2f(x_1) + 2f(x_2) + \cdots + 2f(x_{n-1}) + f(x_n)] \\ &= \frac{h}{2}(y_0 + 2y_1 + 2y_2 + \cdots + 2y_{n-1} + y_n). \end{aligned}$$

This result is called the *trapezoidal rule.*

Example 1

Evaluate $\int_0^1 x^3\,dx$ by the trapezoidal rule, using $n = 4$.

$$h = \frac{1-0}{4} = 0.25;$$

$$\begin{aligned} x_0 &= 0, & y_0 &= 0, \\ x_1 &= 0.25, & y_1 &= 0.015625, \\ x_2 &= 0.5, & y_2 &= 0.125, \\ x_3 &= 0.75, & y_3 &= 0.421875, \\ x_4 &= 1. & y_4 &= 1. \end{aligned}$$

$$\begin{aligned} \int_0^1 x^3\,dx &\doteq \frac{h}{2}(y_0 + 2y_1 + 2y_2 + 2y_3 + y_4) \\ &= \frac{0.25}{2}(0 + 0.03125 + 0.25 + 0.84375 + 1) \\ &= 0.265625. \end{aligned}$$

In this case, integration in the usual way shows that the exact value is 1/4.

The other method of approximate integration uses what is called *Simpson's rule.* In this case, the interval $[a, b]$ is subdivided into n equal subintervals where *n is even.* Again,

$$h = \frac{b-a}{n} \quad \text{and} \quad x_i = a + ih.$$

This time the intervals are taken in pairs giving three points on the curve $y = f(x)$. For the first pair of intervals the points are (x_0, y_0), (x_1, y_1), and (x_2, y_2), where $y_i = f(x_i)$. A parabola (see Chapter 9) with axis parallel to the y axis may be passed through any three noncollinear points and the area under the parabola found (see Figure 8.16). Again, for the first pair of intervals, this area is

$$A = \frac{h}{3}(y_0 + 4y_1 + y_2)$$

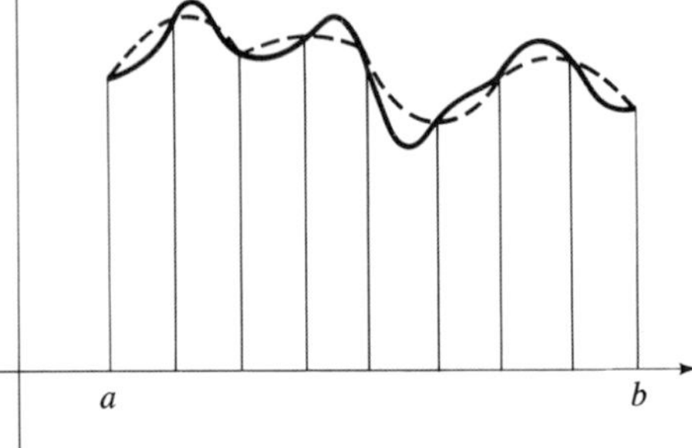

Figure 8.16

(see Problem 29, page 178 and Problem 29 of this section). Repeating this process for pairs of intervals from a to b and adding, we have

$$A = \frac{h}{3}[(y_0 + 4y_1 + y_2) + (y_2 + 4y_3 + y_4) + \cdots + (y_{n-2} + 4y_{n-1} + y_n)]$$

$$= \frac{h}{3}(y_0 + 4y_1 + 2y_2 + 4y_3 + 2y_4 + \cdots + 2y_{n-2} + 4y_{n-1} + y_n).$$

This is Simpson's rule. It generally gives a better approximation than the trapezoidal rule.

Example 2

Approximate $\int_0^1 x^3\,dx$ by Simpson's rule, using $n = 4$.

$$h = \frac{1-0}{4} = 0.25;$$

$$\begin{aligned} x_0 &= 0, & y_0 &= 0, \\ x_1 &= 0.25, & y_1 &= 0.015625, \\ x_2 &= 0.5, & y_2 &= 0.125, \\ x_3 &= 0.75 & y_3 &= 0.421875, \\ x_4 &= 1. & y_4 &= 1. \end{aligned}$$

$$\begin{aligned} \int_0^1 x^3\,dx &\doteq \frac{h}{3}(y_0 + 4y_1 + 2y_2 + 4y_3 + y_4) \\ &= \frac{0.25}{3}(0 + 0.0625 + 0.25 + 1.6875 + 1) \\ &= 0.25. \end{aligned}$$

In the above case, Simpson's rule gives the exact value of the integral. Of course this will not always occur (see Problem 30).

Problems

In Problems 1–10, evaluate the given integral by both the trapezoidal rule and Simpson's rule and compare with the exact value.

1. $\int_1^2 (x^2+1)\,dx, \quad n=4.$
2. $\int_1^2 (x^3-4)\,dx, \quad n=6.$
3. $\int_0^1 (x^2+1)^2\,dx, \quad n=4.$
4. $\int_0^1 x(x^2+1)^2\,dx, \quad n=4.$
5. $\int_0^1 \sqrt{x+1}\,dx, \quad n=4.$
6. $\int_0^1 \sqrt{x+1}\,dx, \quad n=8.$
7. $\int_0^1 2x\sqrt{x^2+1}\,dx, \quad n=4.$
8. $\int_0^1 2x(x^2+1)^{3/2}\,dx, \quad n=6.$
9. $\int_1^2 \frac{x^2+1}{x^2}\,dx, \quad n=4.$
10. $\int_0^1 \frac{2x\,dx}{\sqrt{x^2+1}}, \quad n=4.$

In Problems 11–16, evaluate the integral by the trapezoidal rule.

11. $\int_0^1 \sqrt{x^2+1}\,dx, \quad n=5.$
12. $\int_0^1 (x^2+1)^{3/2}\,dx, \quad n=10.$
13. $\int_1^3 \frac{x+1}{x}\,dx, \quad n=5.$
14. $\int_1^3 \frac{dx}{\sqrt{x^2+1}}, \quad n=4.$
15. $\int_0^4 \sqrt{16-x^2}\,dx, \quad n=4.$
16. $\int_0^7 \sqrt[3]{1+x}\,dx, \quad n=7.$

In Problems 17–22, evaluate the integral by Simpson's rule.

17. $\int_0^1 \sqrt{1-x^2}\,dx, \quad n=4.$
18. $\int_0^2 \sqrt{x^2+x}\,dx, \quad n=6.$
19. $\int_0^3 x\sqrt{1+x}\,dx, \quad n=6.$
20. $\int_0^3 \frac{x\,dx}{\sqrt{1+x}}, \quad n=6.$
21. $\int_0^1 \frac{x\,dx}{1+x}, \quad n=4.$
22. $\int_0^2 \sqrt[3]{1+x^2}\,dx, \quad n=4.$

In Problems 23–28, evaluate the integral by the trapezoidal rule and Simpson's rule.

23. $\int_2^4 x^2\sqrt{x^2-4}\,dx, \quad n=4.$
24. $\int_1^3 (9-x^2)^{2/3}\,dx, \quad n=4.$
25. $\int_1^3 \frac{x^2-1}{x}\,dx, \quad n=8.$
26. $\int_0^4 \frac{\sqrt{x}\,dx}{x+1}, \quad n=4.$
27. $\int_1^2 \sqrt{x^2-x}\,dx, \quad n=4.$
28. $\int_0^2 x\sqrt{4x+1}\,dx, \quad n=4.$
29. Suppose the coefficients a, b, and c of $f(x)=ax^2+bx+c$ are selected in such a way that the graph of $y=f(x)$ contains $(-h, y_0)$, $(0, y_1)$, and (h, y_2). Express a, b, and c in terms of h, y_0, y_1, and y_2. Show that
$$\int_{-h}^{h} f(x)\,dx = \frac{h}{3}(y_0+4y_1+y_2).$$
30. Evaluate
$$\int_{x_0}^{x_0+2h} x^3\,dx$$
and
$$\frac{h}{3}[x_0^3+4(x_0+h)^3+(x_0+2h)^3].$$
Compare. What does this imply about an approximation of $\int_a^b x^3\,dx$ by Simpson's rule?

Conic Sections

9.1

Conic Sections

Up to this point the only second-degree equations that we have considered systematically have been equations of circles. We shall see that equations of the second degree represent (with two trivial exceptions) conic sections—that is, curves formed by the intersection of a plane with a right circular cone. There are three general types of curves formed in this way, the parabola, the ellipse, and the hyperbola.

9.2

The Parabola

Definition

A ***parabola*** *is the set of all points in a plane equidistant from a fixed point (focus) and a fixed line (directrix) not containing the focus.*

Suppose we choose the focus to be the point $(c, 0)$ and the directrix to be $x = -c$, $c \neq 0$ (see Figure 9.1). Let us choose a point (x, y) on the parabola and see what condition must be satisfied by x and y. From the definition, we have

$$\overline{PF} = \overline{PD},$$

$$\sqrt{(x-c)^2 + y^2} = |x + c|, \qquad \text{(See Note 1)}$$

$$(x-c)^2 + y^2 = (x+c)^2, \qquad \text{(See Note 2)}$$

$$x^2 - 2cx + c^2 + y^2 = x^2 + 2cx + c^2,$$

$$y^2 = 4cx.$$

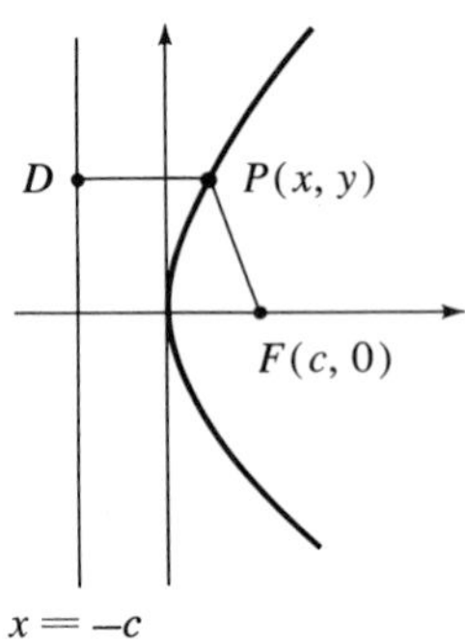

Figure 9.1

Note 1: Since $\overline{PD}$ is a horizontal distance,

$$\overline{PD} = |x - (-c)| = |x + c|.$$

You might feel that we should drop the absolute-value signs, since it is clear from Figure 9.1 that $x + c$ must be positive. However, we did not insist that c be positive (although Figure 9.1 is given for a positive value of c). If c is negative, x is also negative and $x + c$ is negative.

Note 2: When we square both sides of an equation, there is a possibility of introducing extraneous roots. For instance, (0, 1) is not a root of $x + y = x - y$, but it is a root of $(x + y)^2 = (x - y)^2$. The reason is that $x + y = 1$, while $x - y = -1$ for (0, 1), and $1^2 = (-1)^2 = 1$. In any case in which $(x + y)^2 = (x - y)^2$ and $x + y$ and $x - y$ are either both positive, both negative, or both zero, the above situation cannot occur. Since $\sqrt{(x-c)^2 + y^2}$ and $|x + c|$ must both be positive in any case, we have introduced no extraneous roots; that is, any point satisfying

$$(x-c)^2 + y^2 = (x+c)^2$$

must also satisfy

$$\sqrt{(x-c)^2 + y^2} = |x + c|.$$

We see then that if a point is on the parabola with focus $(c, 0)$ and directrix $x = -c$, it must satisfy the equation $y^2 = 4cx$. Furthermore, since Note 2 indicates that all steps in the above argument are reversible, any point satisfying the equation $y^2 = 4cx$ is on the given parabola.

Theorem 9.1

A point (x, y) is on the parabola with focus $(c, 0)$ and directrix $x = -c$ if and only if it satisfies the equation

$$y^2 = 4cx.$$

Let us observe some properties of this parabola before considering others. First of all, it has a line of symmetry—in this case the x axis. This line is called the *axis* of the parabola. It is perpendicular to the directrix and contains the focus (see Figure 9.2). The point of intersection of the axis and the parabola is the *vertex*. The vertex of the parabola $y^2 = 4cx$ is the origin. Finally, the line segment through the focus, perpendicular to the axis and having both ends on the parabola is the *latus rectum* (literally, straight side). Since the latus rectum of $y^2 = 4cx$ must be vertical and since

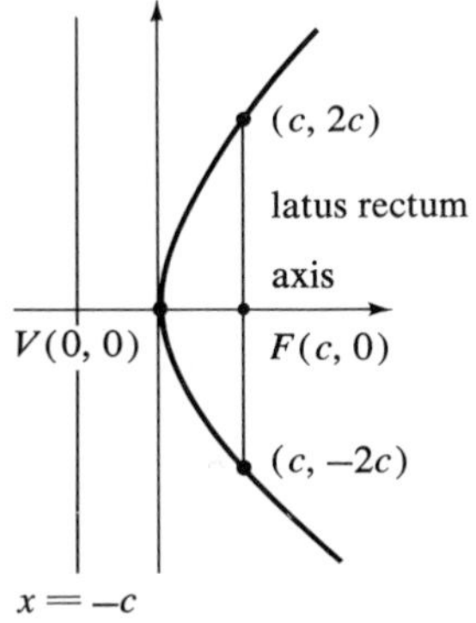

Figure 9.2

it contains $(c, 0)$, the x coordinate of both ends is c. Substituting $x = c$ into $y^2 = 4cx$, we have

$$y^2 = 4c^2,$$
$$y = \pm 2c.$$

Thus one end of the latus rectum is $(c, 2c)$ and the other $(c, -2c)$. Its length is $4|c|$.

Finally the role of the x and y may be reversed throughout, as the next theorem states.

Theorem 9.2

A point (x, y) *is on the parabola with focus* $(0, c)$ *and directrix* $y = -c$ *if and only if it satisfies the equation*

$$x^2 = 4cy.$$

Example 1

Sketch and discuss $y^2 = 8x$.

The equation is of the form

$$y^2 = 4cx,$$

with $c = 2$. Thus, it represents a parabola with vertex at the origin and axis on the x axis. The focus is at $(2, 0)$, and the directrix is $x = -2$. Finally, the length of the latus rectum is 8. This length may be used to determine the ends, $(2, \pm 4)$, of the latus rectum, which helps in sketching the curve (see Figure 9.3).

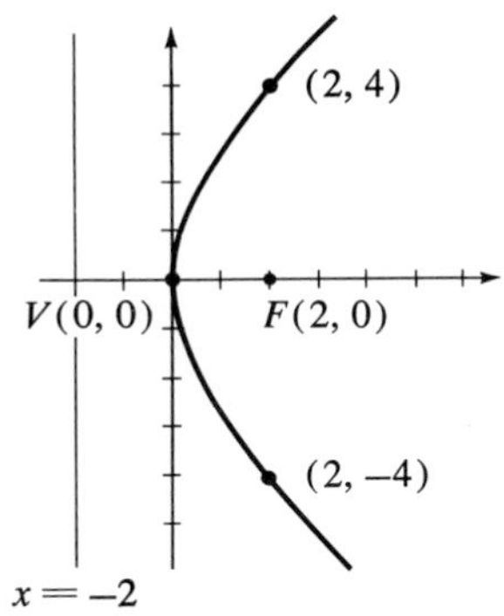

Figure 9.3

Example 2

Sketch and discuss $x^2 = -12y$.

This equation is in the form $x^2 = 4cy$, with $c = -3$. Thus, it is a parabola with vertex at the origin and axis on the y axis. The focus is $(0, -3)$, the length of the latus rectum is 12, and the equation of the directrix is $y = 3$ (see Figure 9.4).

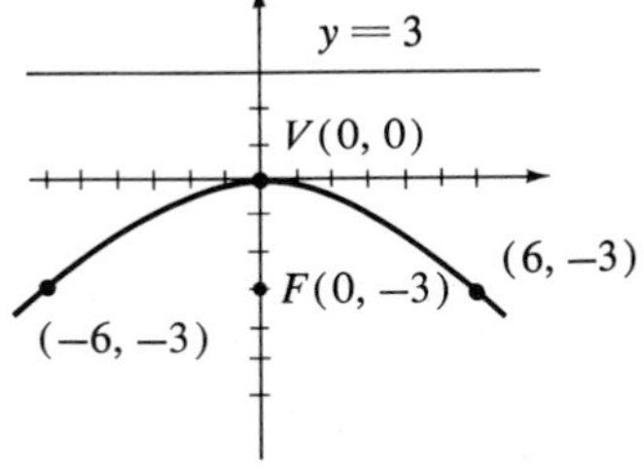

Figure 9.4

Example 3

Find an equation(s) of the parabola(s) with vertex at the origin and focus $(-4, 0)$.

Since the focus and vertex are on the x axis, the x axis is the axis of the parabola. Thus the equation is in the form $y^2 = 4cx$. Since the focus is $(-4, 0)$, $c = -4$ and the equation is $y^2 = -16x$.

Problems

In Problems 1–10, sketch and discuss the given parabola.

1. $y^2 = 16x$.
2. $y^2 = -12x$.
3. $x^2 = 4y$.
4. $x^2 = -8y$.
5. $y^2 = 10x$.
6. $x^2 = -7y$.
7. $x^2 = 5y$.
8. $y^2 = -9x$.
9. $x^2 = -2y$.
10. $y^2 = 3x$.

In Problems 11–18, find an equation(s) of the parabola(s) described.

11. Vertex: (0, 0); axis: x axis; contains (1, 5).
12. Vertex: (0, 0); axis: y axis; contains (1, 5).
13. Vertex: (0, 0); axis: x axis; length of latus rectum: 5.
14. Vertex: (0, 0); focus: (0, 5).
15. Focus: $(-3, 0)$; directrix: $x = 3$.
16. Focus: (0, 8); directrix: $y = -8$.
17. Vertex: (0, 0); contains (2, 3) and $(-2, 3)$.
18. Vertex: (0, 0); contains $(-3, -4)$ and $(-3, 4)$.
19. Prove Theorem 9.2.
20. Find an equation of the line tangent to $y^2 = 8x$ at (2, 4).
21. Find an equation of the line tangent to $x^2 = -5y$ at $(5, -5)$.
22. Find an equation of the line tangent to $y^2 = -16x$ and parallel to $x + y = 1$.
23. Find an equation of the line tangent to $x^2 = 6y$ and perpendicular to $x + 2y = 2$.
24. Find an equation(s) of the line(s) tangent to $y^2 = 4x$ and containing $(-2, 1)$.
25. Find an equation(s) of the line(s) tangent to $x^2 = -8y$ and containing (4, 0).
26. Show that the line tangent to $y^2 = 4cx$ at (x_0, y_0) is $yy_0 = 2c(x + x_0)$.
27. Prove that the ordinate of any point P of the parabola $y^2 = 4cx$ is the mean proportional between the length of the latus rectum and the abscissa of P.
28. If a ray of light strikes a curved reflecting surface at the point P, it is reflected as if it had struck a flat surface tangent to the curve at P. That is, the rays make equal angles with the tangent at P (see Figure 9.5). Suppose we have a parabolic mirror with a light source at the focus. Show that no matter what point P on the parabola is struck with a ray of light, the light is reflected in a line parallel to the axis.
29. Suppose V is the vertex of the parabola $y^2 = 4cx$, F is the focus, P is a point of the parabola different from V, T is the point of intersection of the tangent at P and the x axis, N is the point of intersection of the normal at P and the x axis, X is the foot of the perpendicular from P to the x axis, and Q is the point of intersection of the tangent and the y axis (see Figure 9.6). Show that
    (a) $TF = FP$,
    (b) $TV = VX$,
    (c) $XN = \frac{1}{2}$ (latus rectum),
    (d) $QF \perp TP$.

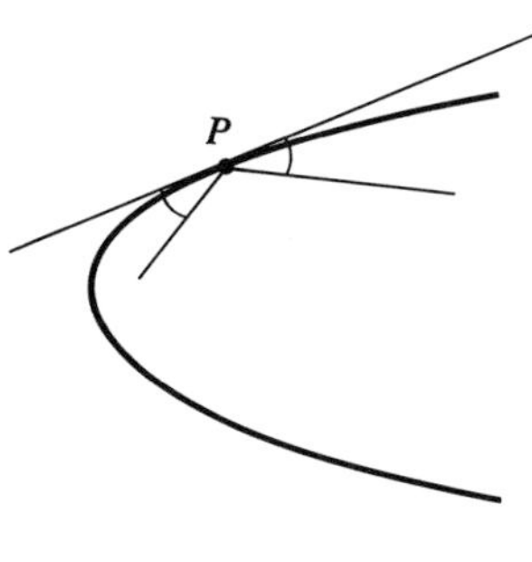

Figure 9.5

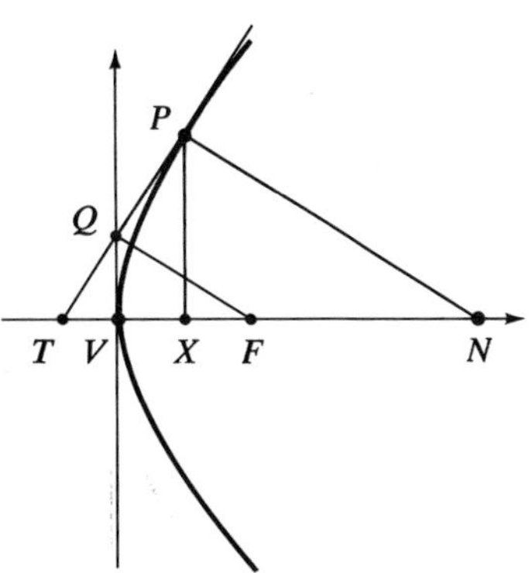

Figure 9.6

30. Suppose P_1 and P_2 are two points of a parabola, Q is the point of intersection of the tangents at P_1 and P_2, and F is the focus. Show that FQ bisects the angle P_1FP_2.
31. Suppose P_1 and P_2 are two points of a parabola and Q is the point of intersection of the tangents at P_1 and P_2. Show that the line through Q and parallel to the axis bisects P_1P_2.
32. Suppose P_1 and P_2 are two points of a parabola such that the line P_1P_2 contains the focus. Show that the point of intersection of the tangents at P_1 and P_2 is on the directrix.

9.3

Parabola with Vertex at (h, k)

Suppose we have a parabola with vertex at (h, k) and axis $y = k$ (see Figure 9.7). Let us put in a new pair of axes, the x' and y' axes, which are parallel to and in the same directions as the original axes and have their origin at the point (h, k) of the original system. Since the parabola's vertex is now at the origin of this coordinate system, its equation is

$$y'^2 = 4cx',$$

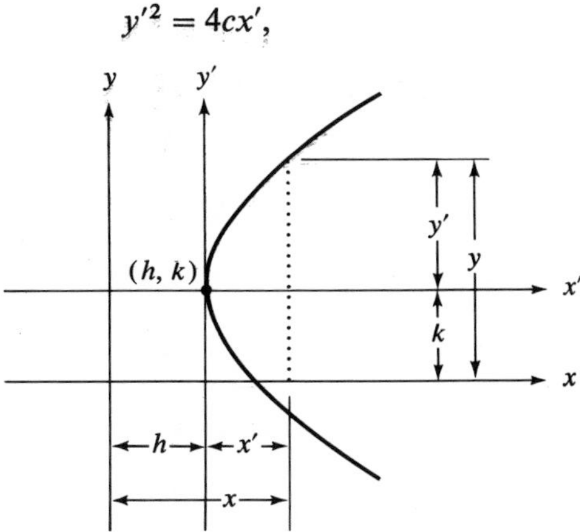

Figure 9.7

where $|c|$ is the distance from vertex to focus. Now the relationship between the old and new coordinates is (see Figure 9.7)

$$x = x' + h, \qquad y = y' + k$$

or

$$x' = x - h, \qquad y' = y - k.$$

Thus the equation of the parabola in the original coordinate system is

$$(y - k)^2 = 4c(x - h).$$

Theorem 9.3

A point (x, y) is on the parabola with focus $(h + c, k)$ and directrix $x = h - c$ if and only if it satisfies the equation

$$(y - k)^2 = 4c(x - h).$$

Theorem 9.4

A point (x, y) is on the parabola with focus $(h, k + c)$ and directrix $y = k - c$ if and only if it satisfies the equation

$$(x - h)^2 = 4c(y - k).$$

Theorem 9.4 can be proved by an argument similar to that for Theorem 9.3. Of course Theorems 9.1 and 9.2 are special cases of these two, with h and k both 0. The equation of Theorem 9.3 can be put into the form

$$y^2 - 4cx - 2ky + (k^2 + 4ch) = 0,$$

or

$$y^2 + D'x + E'y + F' = 0,$$

where $D' = -4c$, $E' = -2k$, and $F' = k^2 + 4ch$. Finally, if we multiply through by some number C, we have

$$Cy^2 + Dx + Ey + F = 0.$$

Similarly, the equation of Theorem 9.4 can be put into the form

$$Ax^2 + Dx + Ey + F = 0.$$

Theorem 9.5

A parabola with axis parallel to (or on) a coordinate axis can be represented by an equation in one of the two forms:

$$Ax^2 + Dx + Ey + F = 0, \quad A \neq 0,$$

$$Cy^2 + Dx + Ey + F = 0, \quad C \neq 0.$$

An equation of the form given in Theorem 9.5 is referred to as a *general form* for a parabola, while those of Theorems 9.3 and 9.4 are called *standard forms*. We have seen similar forms for equations of lines and circles.

Example 1

Sketch and discuss the parabola

$$(x-1)^2 = -8(y+2).$$

First of all, the vertex is $(1, -2)$. Since the square is on the x term, the axis is parallel to the y axis. Finally $c = -2$, giving focus $(1, -4)$ and directrix $y = 0$, and the length of the latus rectum is 8 (see Figure 9.8).

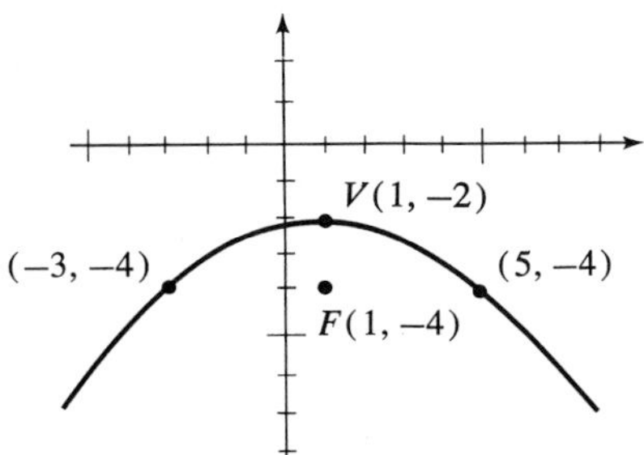

Figure 9.8

Example 2

Express $x^2 + 8x - 4y + 24 = 0$ in standard form.

We proceed in much the same way as we did with equations of circles—by completing the square.

$$\begin{aligned} x^2 + 8x - 4y + 24 &= 0, \\ x^2 + 8x &= 4y - 24, \\ x^2 + 8x + 16 &= 4y - 8, \\ (x+4)^2 &= 4(y-2). \end{aligned}$$

Once the equation is in standard form, we can determine vertex, focus, and so forth.

Example 3

Express $9y^2 + 36x - 6y + 25 = 0$ in standard form.

$$\begin{aligned} 9y^2 + 36x - 6y + 25 &= 0, \\ y^2 + 4x - \frac{2}{3}y + \frac{25}{9} &= 0, \\ y^2 - \frac{2}{3}y &= -4x - \frac{25}{9}, \\ y^2 - \frac{2}{3}y + \frac{1}{9} &= -4x - \frac{8}{3}, \\ \left(y - \frac{1}{3}\right)^2 &= -4\left(x + \frac{2}{3}\right). \end{aligned}$$

Unfortunately the converse of Theorem 9.5 is not true; that is, it is not true that every equation in one of the two forms

$$Ax^2 + Dx + Ey + F = 0, \quad A \neq 0,$$

or

$$Cy^2 + Dx + Ey + F = 0, \quad C \neq 0$$

represents a parabola. If $E = 0$ in the first form or $D = 0$ in the second, the resulting equation represents either a line (a pair of coincident lines), a pair of parallel lines or has no graph. These are sometimes referred to as degenerate cases of a parabola. We might note here that two of these cases—a pair of parallel lines and no graph—cannot be represented as the intersection of a plane and a cone.

Example 4

Sketch $y^2 + 2y - 3 = 0$.

We see that the equation cannot represent a parabola, since it does not involve both x and y. But, by factoring, we see that it represents a pair of parallel lines (see Figure 9.9).

$$y^2 + 2y - 3 = 0,$$

$$(y + 3)(y - 1) = 0;$$

$$y = -3, \qquad y = 1.$$

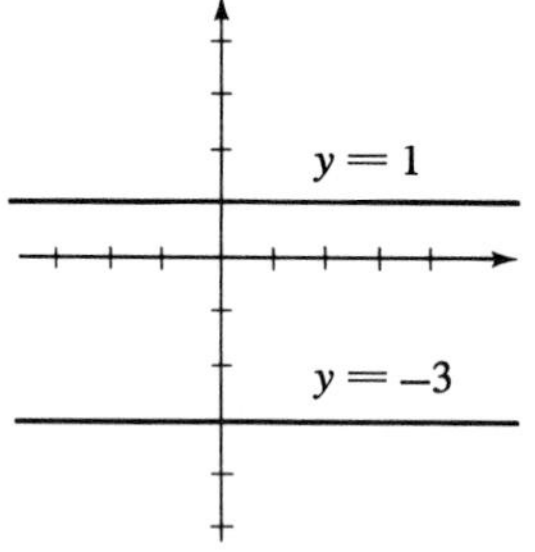

Figure 9.9

Problems

In Problems 1–16, sketch and discuss.

1. $(x - 3)^2 = 8(y - 2)$.
2. $(y + 1)^2 = -4(x - 1)$.
3. $(x + 5)^2 = 6(y + 2)$.
4. $(y - 4)^2 = 2x$.
5. $x^2 + 4x - 4y + 8 = 0$.
6. $x^2 + 6x - 4y - 3 = 0$.
7. $y^2 - x + 2y + 4 = 0$.
8. $y^2 - 5y + 6 = 0$.
9. $y^2 + 2x + 4 = 0$.
10. $4x^2 - 4x - 8y - 19 = 0$.
11. $2x^2 - 6x + 5 = 0$.
12. $16y^2 - 64x + 8y + 33 = 0$.
13. $25y^2 - 200x - 20y - 116 = 0$.
14. $4x^2 - 4x - 4y - 3 = 0$.
15. $12x^2 - 12x - 24y + 11 = 0$.
16. $9y^2 - 36x - 12y + 22 = 0$.

In Problems 17–24, find an equation(s) of the parabola(s) described.

17. Focus: (3, 5); directrix: $x = -1$.
18. Focus: (–2, 1); directrix: $y = 0$.
19. Vertex: (4, 1); focus: (4, 4).
20. Vertex: (3, 5); directrix: $x = 1$.
21. Vertex: (–2, 4); axis $y = 4$; length of latus rectum: 8.
22. Axis parallel to the x axis, contains (5, 3), (2, –3), and (10, 5).
23. Axis parallel to the y axis, contains (0, 6), (3, –6), and (8, 14).
24. Vertex: (1, –2); contains: (5, 2).
25. Find an equation of the line tangent to $y^2 + x + y - 1 = 0$ at (–1, 1).
26. Find an equation of the line tangent to $x^2 - 2x + 4y - 3 = 0$ at (1, 1).
27. Find an equation(s) of the line(s) tangent to $x^2 + 4x + y - 3 = 0$ and containing (1, 2).
28. Find an equation(s) of the line(s) tangent to $y^2 - x + 2y + 3 = 0$ and containing (2, –2).
29. Show that there is a parabola of the form $y = Ax^2 + Bx + C$ containing the points $(-h, y_0)$, $(0, y_1)$, and (h, y_2) and that

$$\int_{-h}^{h} y\,dx = \frac{h}{3}(y_0 + 4y_1 + y_2).$$

This is the basis of Simpson's rule (see page 168).

30. If a parabola with a vertical axis contains the points (x_0, y_0), (x_1, y_1), and (x_2, y_2), show that its equation can be put into the form

$$\begin{vmatrix} x^2 & x & y & 1 \\ x_0^2 & x_0 & y_0 & 1 \\ x_1^2 & x_1 & y_1 & 1 \\ x_2^2 & x_2 & y_2 & 1 \end{vmatrix} = 0.$$

31. What happens to the determinant of Problem 30 if the three given points are collinear? (*Hint*: See Problem 25, page 48.)

9.4

The Ellipse

Definition

An ***ellipse*** *is the set of all points (x, y) such that the sum of the distances from (x, y) to a pair of distinct fixed points (foci) is a fixed constant.*

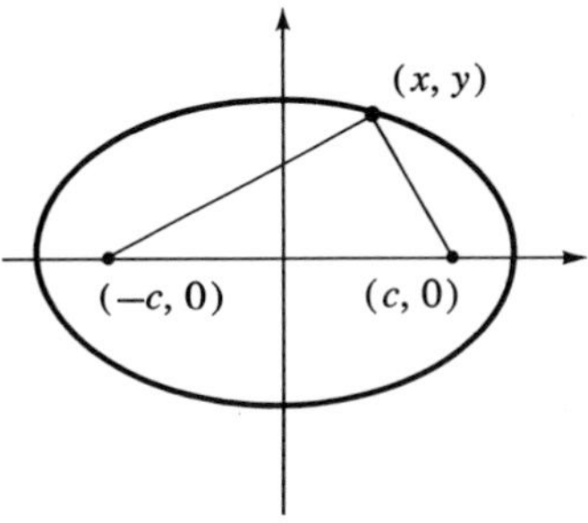

Figure 9.10

Let us choose the foci to be $(c, 0)$ and $(-c, 0)$ (see Figure 9.10) and let the fixed constant be $2a$. If (x, y) represents a point on the ellipse, we have

$$\sqrt{(x-c)^2+y^2}+\sqrt{(x+c)^2+y^2}=2a;$$

$$\sqrt{(x-c)^2+y^2}=2a-\sqrt{(x+c)^2+y^2},$$

$$x^2-2cx+c^2+y^2=4a^2-4a\sqrt{(x+c)^2+y^2}+x^2+2cx+c^2+y^2,$$

$$4a\sqrt{(x+c)^2+y^2}=4a^2+4cx,$$

$$\sqrt{(x+c)^2+y^2}=a+\frac{cx}{a},$$

$$x^2+2cx+c^2+y^2=a^2+2cx+\frac{c^2x^2}{a^2},$$

$$\frac{a^2-c^2}{a^2}x^2+y^2=a^2-c^2,$$

$$\frac{x^2}{a^2}+\frac{y^2}{a^2-c^2}=1.$$

The triangle of Figure 9.10, with vertices $(c, 0)$, $(-c, 0)$, and (x, y), has one side of length $2c$. The sum of the lengths of the other two sides is $2a$. Thus

$$2a > 2c,$$

$$a > c,$$

$$a^2 > c^2,$$

$$a^2 - c^2 > 0.$$

Since $a^2 - c^2$ is positive, we may replace it by another positive number, b^2. Thus

$$\frac{x^2}{a^2} + \frac{y^2}{b^2} = 1, \quad \text{where } b^2 = a^2 - c^2.$$

Note that we squared both sides of the equation at two of the steps. In both cases, both sides of the equation are nonnegative. Thus we have introduced no extraneous roots, and the steps may be reversed.

Note that there are two axes of symmetry: the x axis and the y axis. Furthermore $(\pm a, 0)$ are the x intercepts and $(0, \pm b)$ are the y intercepts where $a > b$ (since $b^2 = a^2 - c^2$). Thus the x axis is called the *major axis* and the y axis is the *minor axis*. The ends of the major axis, $(\pm a, 0)$, are called the *vertices*, the ends of the minor axis, $(0, \pm b)$, are the *covertices*, and the point of intersection, $(0, 0)$, is called the *center* (see Figure 9.11). The *foci* $(\pm c, 0)$ are on the major axis.

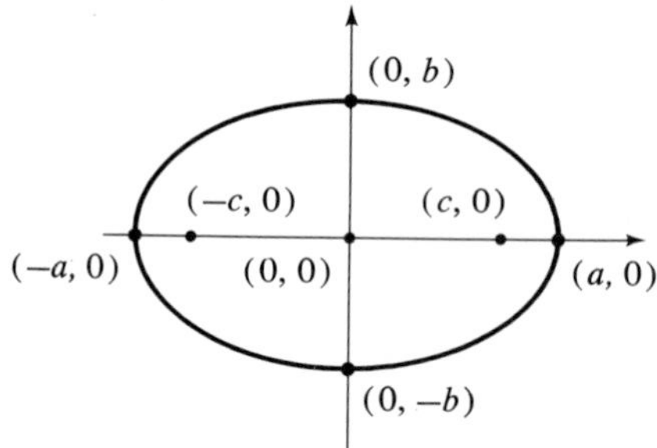

Figure 9.11

Theorem 9.6

A point (x, y) is on the ellipse with vertices $(\pm a, 0)$ and foci $(\pm c, 0)$ if and only if it satisfies the equation

$$\frac{x^2}{a^2} + \frac{y^2}{b^2} = 1,$$

where $b^2 = a^2 - c^2$.

An ellipse has two *latera recta* (plural of latus rectum), which are chords of the ellipse perpendicular to the major axis and containing the foci. If $x = \pm c$, then

$$\frac{c^2}{a^2} + \frac{y^2}{b^2} = 1,$$

$$\frac{y^2}{b^2} = \frac{a^2 - c^2}{a^2} = \frac{b^2}{a^2},$$

$$y^2 = \frac{b^4}{a^2},$$

$$y = \pm\frac{b^2}{a}.$$

Thus, one latus rectum has end points $(c, \pm b^2/a)$, while the other has end points $(-c, \pm b^2/a)$. In both cases the length is $2b^2/a$. This length may be used as an aid in sketching, as was done with the parabola; however, the vertices and covertices allow one to make a reasonable sketch.

Again, the role of the x and y may be reversed.

Theorem 9.7

A point (x, y) is on the ellipse with vertices $(0, \pm a)$ and foci $(0, \pm c)$ if and only if it satisfies the equation

$$\frac{y^2}{a^2} + \frac{x^2}{b^2} = 1,$$

where $b^2 = a^2 - c^2$.

One question that immediately arises is, How can we tell whether we have

$$\frac{x^2}{a^2} + \frac{y^2}{b^2} = 1 \quad \text{or} \quad \frac{y^2}{a^2} + \frac{x^2}{b^2} = 1?$$

The numbers in the denominator are not labeled a and b, so how do we know which is a and which is b? The answer is "size." In both cases $a > b$. Thus the larger denominator is a^2, and the smaller is b^2.

Example 1

Sketch and discuss $9x^2 + 25y^2 = 225$.

First, we put the equation into standard form by dividing through by 225:

$$\frac{x^2}{25} + \frac{y^2}{9} = 1.$$

Now

$$a^2 = 25, \quad b^2 = 9,$$

and

$$c^2 = a^2 - b^2 = 16.$$

This ellipse has center $(0, 0)$, vertices $(\pm 5, 0)$, covertices $(0, \pm 3)$, and foci $(\pm 4, 0)$. The latera recta have length $2b^2/a = 2 \cdot 9/5 = 3.6$ (see Figure 9.12).

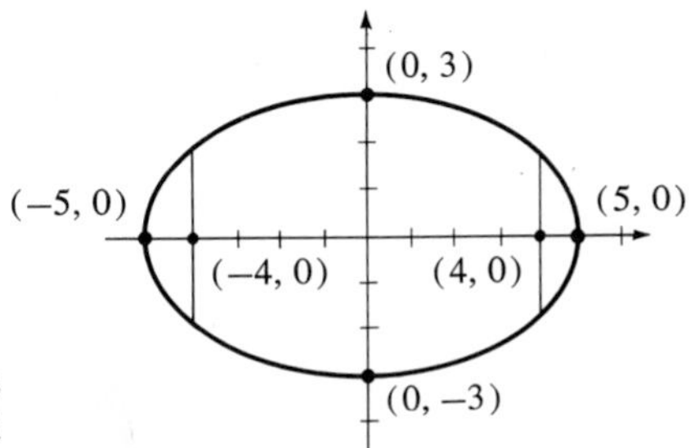

Figure 9.12

Example 2

Sketch and discuss $25x^2 + 16y^2 = 400$.

Putting the equation into standard form gives

$$\frac{x^2}{16} + \frac{y^2}{25} = 1.$$

Now

$$a^2 = 25, \quad b^2 = 16$$

and

$$c^2 = a^2 - b^2 = 9.$$

This ellipse has center (0, 0), vertices (0, ±5), covertices (±4, 0), and foci (0, ±3). The latera recta have length

$$2b^2/a = 2 \cdot 16/5 = 6.4$$

(see Figure 9.13).

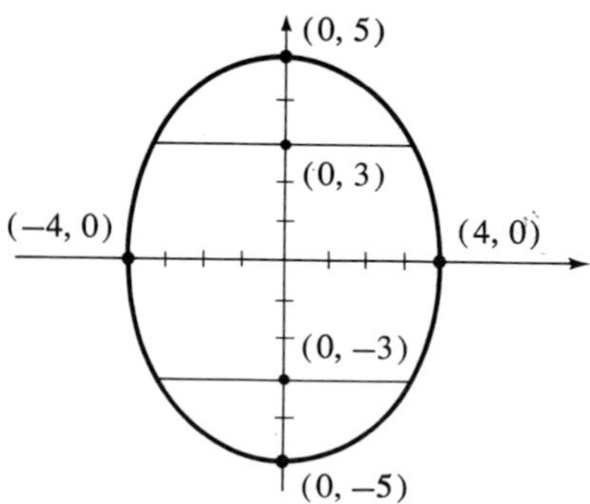

Figure 9.13

Example 3

Find an equation of the ellipse with vertices (0, ±8) and foci (0, ±5).

Since the vertices are on the y axis, we have the form

$$\frac{y^2}{a^2} + \frac{x^2}{b^2} = 1.$$

Furthermore, $a = 8$ and $c = 5$; thus $b^2 = a^2 - c^2 = 64 - 25 = 39$. The final result is

$$\frac{y^2}{64} + \frac{x^2}{39} = 1.$$

In addition to the quantities named, each ellipse is associated with a number, called the eccentricity. For any ellipse the *eccentricity* is

$$e = \frac{c}{a}.$$

The eccentricity of an ellipse satisfies the inequalities $0 < e < 1$. It gives a measure of the shape of the ellipse: the closer the eccentricity is to 0, the more nearly circular is the ellipse. For instance, in Example 1, $e = 4/5$, while in Example 2 $e = 3/5$. The ellipse of Example 2 is more nearly circular than the ellipse of Example 1, as can be easily seen by the sketches.

There is also a directrix associated with each focus of an ellipse. Associated with the focus $(c, 0)$ of the ellipse

$$\frac{x^2}{a^2} + \frac{y^2}{b^2} = 1$$

is the *directrix*

$$x = \frac{a}{e} = \frac{a^2}{c}.$$

If P is any point of the ellipse, the distance from P to the focus divided by the distance from P to the directrix is equal to the eccentricity. This is sometimes used as the definition of an ellipse.

Suppose we start with focus $(c, 0)$, directrix $x = a^2/c$, and eccentricity $e = c/a$. Now let us find the set of all points $P: (x, y)$ such that the distance from P to the focus divided by the distance from P to the directrix equals the eccentricity.

$$\frac{\sqrt{(x-c)^2 + y^2}}{\dfrac{a^2}{c} - x} = \frac{c}{a},$$

$$\sqrt{(x-c)^2 + y^2} = a - \frac{cx}{a},$$

$$x^2 - 2cx + c^2 + y^2 = a^2 - 2cx + \frac{c^2x^2}{a^2},$$

$$\frac{a^2 - c^2}{a^2}x^2 + y^2 = a^2 - c^2,$$

$$\frac{x^2}{a^2} + \frac{y^2}{a^2 - c^2} = 1.$$

With $b^2 = a^2 - c^2$, this becomes

$$\frac{x^2}{a^2} + \frac{y^2}{b^2} = 1.$$

The same result can be obtained using focus $(-c, 0)$, directrix $x = -a^2/c$, and eccentricity $e = c/a$.

For a parabola, the distance from a point on the parabola to the focus divided by the distance of the point from the directrix is always 1. Thus we define $e = 1$ for every parabola.

Problems

In Problems 1–10, sketch and discuss the given ellipse.

1. $\dfrac{x^2}{169} + \dfrac{y^2}{25} = 1.$
2. $\dfrac{x^2}{144} + \dfrac{y^2}{169} = 1.$
3. $\dfrac{x^2}{25} + \dfrac{y^2}{4} = 1.$
4. $\dfrac{x^2}{36} + \dfrac{y^2}{16} = 1.$
5. $\dfrac{x^2}{25} + \dfrac{y^2}{49} = 1.$
6. $x^2 + 4y^2 = 4.$
7. $9x^2 + 4y^2 = 36.$
8. $9x^2 + y^2 = 9.$
9. $16x^2 + 9y^2 = 144.$
10. $4x^2 + 25y^2 = 100.$

In Problems 11–18, find an equation(s) of the ellipse(s) described.

11. Center: (0, 0); vertex: (0, 13); focus: (0, −5).
12. Center: (0, 0); covertex: (0, 5); focus: (−12, 0).

13. Center: (0, 0); vertex: (5, 0); contains ($\sqrt{15}$, 2).
14. Center: (0, 0); axes on the coordinate axis; contains (2, 2) and (−4, 1).
15. Vertices: (±6, 0); length of latus rectum: 3.
16. Covertices: (±2, 0); length of latus rectum: 2.
17. Foci: (±6, 0); $e = 3/5$.
18. Foci: (±2, 0); directrices: $x = \pm 8$.
19. Prove Theorem 9.7.
20. Find an equation of the line tangent to $x^2 + 4y^2 = 20$ at (2, 2).
21. Find an equation of the line tangent to $2x^2 + 3y^2 = 11$ at (2, 1).
22. Find an equation of the line containing (3, −2) and tangent to $4x^2 + y^2 = 8$.
23. Find an equation of the line containing (2, 4) and tangent to $3x^2 + 8y^2 = 84$.
24. Show that the line tangent to

$$\frac{x^2}{a^2} + \frac{y^2}{b^2} = 1$$

at (x_0, y_0) is

$$\frac{xx_0}{a^2} + \frac{yy_0}{b^2} = 1.$$

25. Show that, given an elliptical mirror with a light source at one focus, no matter what point P on the ellipse is struck by a ray of light, the light is reflected to the other focus. (See Problem 28, page 174, for reflection by a curved surface.)
26. Find an expression for the length of a diameter (a chord through the center) of an ellipse. What is its maximum value? Its minimum value?
27. Suppose, in Figure 9.14, that A and B are fixed pins on the arm ABP and that AP and BP have lengths a and b, respectively. Show that if A is free to slide in channel XX' and B in channel YY', the point P traces an ellipse.

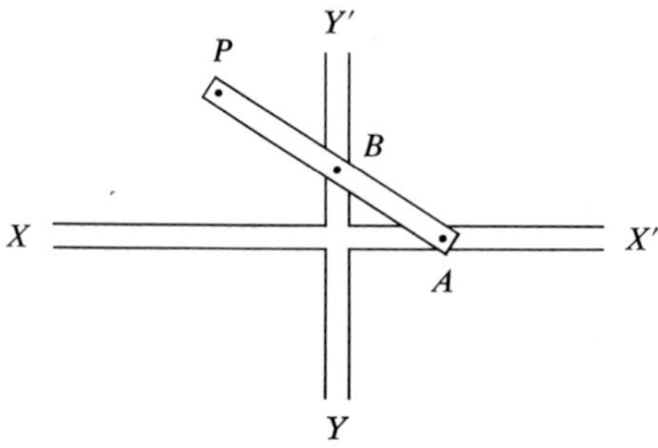

Figure 9.14

28. Given the focus $(-c, 0)$, directrix $x = -a^2/c$, and eccentricity $e = c/a$, show that these define the ellipse

$$\frac{x^2}{a^2} + \frac{y^2}{a^2 - c^2} = 1.$$

29. The earth moves in an elliptical orbit about the sun, with the sun at one focus. The least and greatest distances of the earth from the sun are 91,446,000 miles and 94,560,000 miles, respectively. What is the eccentricity of the ellipse?

9.5

Ellipse with Center (h, k)

Theorem 9.8

A point (x, y) is on the ellipse with center (h, k), vertices $(h \pm a, k)$, and covertices $(h, k \pm b)$ if and only if it satisfies the equation

$$\frac{(x-h)^2}{a^2} + \frac{(y-k)^2}{b^2} = 1.$$

The foci are $(h \pm c, k)$, where $c^2 = a^2 - b^2$.

Theorem 9.9

A point (x, y) is on the ellipse with center (h, k), vertices $(h, k \pm a)$, and covertices $(h \pm b, k)$ if and only if it satisfies the equation

$$\frac{(y-k)^2}{a^2} + \frac{(x-h)^2}{b^2} = 1.$$

The foci are $(h, k \pm c)$, where $c^2 = a^2 - b^2$.

These two theorems may be derived from Theorems 9.6 and 9.7, which are special cases of these, and they can be established by an argument similar to the one used for a point on the parabola with vertex (h, k).

Example 1

Sketch and discuss

$$\frac{(x-1)^2}{9} + \frac{(y+2)^2}{4} = 1.$$

The center of the ellipse is $(1, -2)$; the vertices are $(1 \pm 3, -2)$, and the covertices $(1, -2 \pm 2)$. Since $c^2 = a^2 - b^2 = 5$, the foci are $(1 \pm \sqrt{5}, -2)$. The length of the latera recta is

$$\frac{2b^2}{a} = 2 \cdot \frac{4}{3} = \frac{8}{3}$$

(see Figure 9.15).

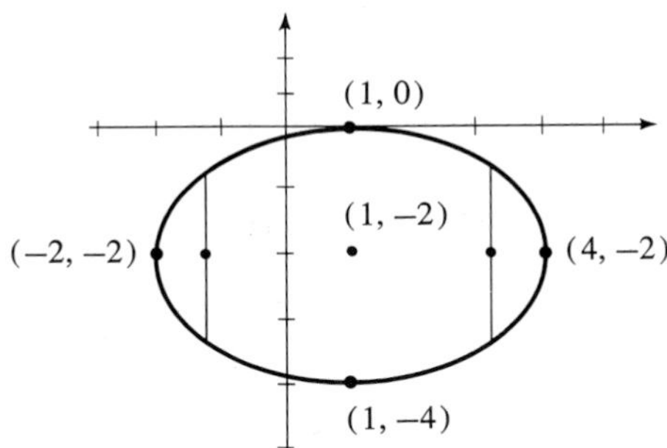

Figure 9.15

If the equations of Theorems 9.8 and 9.9 are cleared of fractions and multiplied out, we have

$$b^2x^2 + a^2y^2 - 2b^2hx - 2a^2ky + (b^2h^2 + a^2k^2 - a^2b^2) = 0$$

and

$$a^2x^2 + b^2y^2 - 2a^2hx - 2b^2ky + (a^2h^2 + b^2k^2 - a^2b^2) = 0.$$

Both of these are of the form

$$Ax^2 + Cy^2 + Dx + Ey + F = 0,$$

where A and C are both positive or both negative (if the equation were multiplied through by a negative number).

Theorem 9.10

An ellipse with axes parallel to (or on) the coordinate axes can be represented by an equation of the form:

$$Ax^2 + Cy^2 + Dx + Ey + F = 0,$$

where AC is positive.

Again, the form of the equation of Theorem 9.10 is called the *general form* of an ellipse, while those of Theorem 9.8 and 9.9 are called *standard forms.* It is a simple matter to change from a standard form to the general form, and the reverse is accomplished by completing squares.

Example 2

Express $25x^2 + 4y^2 + 50x - 24y - 39 = 0$ in standard form.

$$25(x^2 + 2x \qquad) + 4(y^2 - 6y \qquad) = 39$$

$$25(x^2 + 2x + 1) + 4(y^2 - 6y + 9) = 39 + 25 + 36,$$

$$25(x + 1)^2 + 4(y - 3)^2 = 100,$$

$$\frac{(x + 1)^2}{4} + \frac{(y - 3)^2}{25} = 1.$$

The converse of Theorem 9.10 is not true: that is, it is not true that every equation of the form

$$Ax^2 + Cy^2 + Dx + Ey + F = 0,$$

with AC positive, represents an ellipse. If $A = C$, the equation may represent a circle, a point, or no graph; if $A \neq C$, the equation may represent an ellipse, a point, or no graph. The circle, point, and no graph are called degenerate cases of an ellipse.

Example 3

Determine whether $9x^2 + 4y^2 + 36x + 8y + 40 = 0$ represents an ellipse or a degenerate form of an ellipse.

$$9(x^2 + 4x \quad\quad) + 4(y^2 + 2y \quad\quad) = -40,$$
$$9(x + 4x + 4) + 4(y^2 + 2y + 1) = -40 + 36 + 4,$$
$$9(x^2 + 2)^2 + 4(y + 1)^2 = 0.$$

We can now see that, since neither of the two expressions on the left can be negative, the sum is zero only if both terms are zero. Thus $(-2, -1)$ is the only point satisfying the equation.

If the constant 40 of this example is replaced by a larger number, then the right-hand side of the last equation is negative and there is no point in the plane satisfying the equation.

Problems

In Problems 1–14, sketch and discuss.

1. $x^2 + 4y^2 - 24y + 35 = 0.$
2. $x^2 + 4y^2 - 2x - 3 = 0.$
3. $9x^2 + 25y^2 + 72x - 50y - 56 = 0.$
4. $4x^2 + 9y^2 - 24x + 36y + 36 = 0.$
5. $4x^2 + y^2 + 8x + 10y + 13 = 0.$
6. $16x^2 + 25y^2 - 160x + 200y + 400 = 0.$
7. $8x^2 + 9y^2 + 64x - 54y + 209 = 0.$
8. $9x^2 + 4y^2 + 54x - 16y + 133 = 0.$
9. $4x^2 + 9y^2 + 8x - 36y + 4 = 0.$
10. $25x^2 + 16y^2 - 160y = 0.$
11. $25x^2 + 4y^2 - 150x + 40y + 350 = 0.$
12. $4x^2 + 4y^2 - 32x - 24y + 99 = 0.$
13. $4x^2 + 9y^2 + 48x - 144y + 684 = 0.$
14. $25x^2 + 4y^2 - 250x + 56y + 821 = 0.$

In Problems 15–26, find an equation(s) of the ellipse(s) described.

15. Vertices: $(1, 0)$ and $(1, -8)$; covertices: $(2, -4)$ and $(0, -4)$.
16. Vertices: $(3, 0)$ and $(3, 10)$; focus: $(3, 2)$.
17. Vertices: $(-1, 8)$ and $(-1, -2)$; contains $(1, 0)$.
18. Vertex: $(3, 5)$; covertex: $(1, 0)$.
19. Covertices: $(-5, 0)$ and $(1, 0)$; length of latera recta: $9/2$.
20. Foci: $(-1, 0)$ and $(-1, -6)$; length of latera recta: $32/5$.
21. Contains $(6, -1)$, $(-4, -5)$, $(6, -5)$, and $(-12, -3)$.
22. Contains $(1, 1)$, $(7, -3)$, $(-1, -1)$, and $(4, 5/2)$.
23. Vertex: $(8, -1)$; focus: $(6, -1)$; $e = 3/5$.
24. Focus: $(5, 2)$; corresponding directrix: $x = 11$; $e = 1/2$.
25. Center: $(-3, 1)$; focus: $(-3, 4)$; corresponding directrix: $y = 28$.
26. Focus: $(5, 2)$; vertex: $(7, 2)$; length of latera recta: $32/5$.
27. Find an equation of the line tangent to $x^2 + 4y^2 + 3x - 4y - 4 = 0$ at $(1, 1)$.
28. Find an equation of the line tangent to $2x^2 + 3y^2 - 4x + y - 4 = 0$ at $(2, 1)$.
29. Find an equation(s) of the line(s) tangent to $4x^2 + y^2 - 3x + 2y - 15 = 0$ and containing $(-32/3, -1)$.
30. Find an equation(s) of the line(s) tangent to $2x^2 + y^2 - 4x - 3y - 16 = 0$ and containing $(-7/2, 6)$.

9.6

The Hyperbola

Definition

*A **hyperbola** is the set of all points (x, y) in a plane such that the positive difference between the distances from (x, y) to a pair of distinct fixed points (foci) is a fixed constant.*

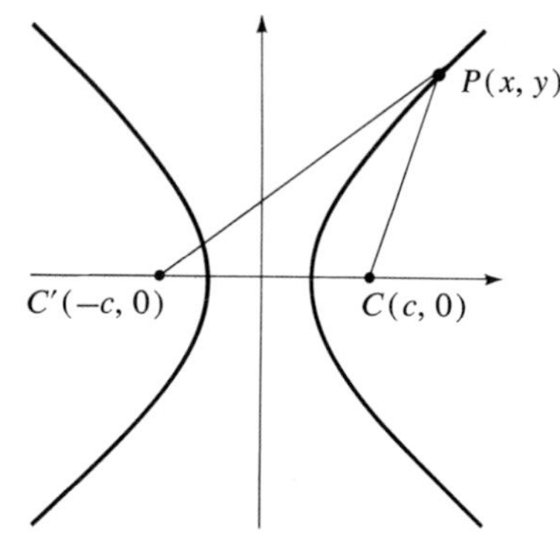

Figure 9.16

Again, let us choose the foci to be $(c, 0)$ and $(-c, 0)$ (see Figure 9.16) and choose the fixed constant to be $2a$. If (x, y) represents a point on the ellipse, we have

$$\sqrt{(x-c)^2+y^2}-\sqrt{(x+c)^2+y^2}=\pm 2a,$$

$$\sqrt{(x-c)^2+y^2}=\sqrt{(x+c)^2+y^2}\pm 2a,$$

$$x^2-2cx+c^2+y^2=x^2+2cx+c^2+y^2\pm 4a\sqrt{(x+c)^2+y^2}+4a^2,$$

$$\mp 4a\sqrt{(x+c)^2+y^2}=4a^2+4cx,$$

$$\mp\sqrt{(x+c)^2+y^2}=a+\frac{cx}{a},$$

$$x^2+2cx+c^2+y^2=a^2+2cx+\frac{c^2x^2}{a^2},$$

$$\frac{c^2-a^2}{a^2}x^2-y^2=c^2-a^2,$$

$$\frac{x^2}{a^2}-\frac{y^2}{c^2-a^2}=1.$$

In the triangle PCC' of Figure 9.16,

$$PC' < PC + CC'$$

$$PC' - PC < CC',$$

$$2a < 2c,$$

$$a < c,$$

$$c^2 - a^2 > 0.$$

Since $c^2 - a^2$ is positive, we may replace it by another positive number, b^2. Thus

$$\frac{x^2}{a^2}-\frac{y^2}{b^2}=1,$$

where $b^2 = c^2 - a^2$.

Again we squared both sides of the equation at two of the steps. The first time, both sides of the equation were positive; the second time, they were either both positive or both negative. Thus we have introduced no extraneous roots, and the steps may be reversed.

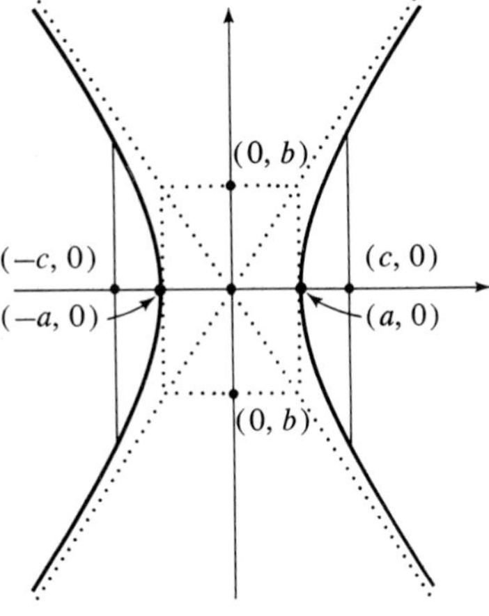

Figure 9.17

Again, both the x axis and the y axis are axes of symmetry and again $(\pm a, 0)$ are the x intercepts. However, there are no y intercepts; when $x = 0$, we have

$$-\frac{y^2}{b^2} = 1,$$

which is not satisfied by any real number y. The x axis (containing two points of the hyperbola) is called the *transverse axis*; the y axis is called the *conjugate axis*. The ends of the transverse axis, $(\pm a, 0)$, are called the *vertices*, and the point of intersection of the axes, (0, 0), is called the *center* (see Figure 9.17).

Theorem 9.11

A point (x, y) is on the hyperbola with vertices $(\pm a, 0)$ and foci $(\pm c, 0)$ if and only if it satisfies the equation

$$\frac{x^2}{a^2} - \frac{y^2}{b^2} = 1,$$

where $b^2 = c^2 - a^2$.

A hyperbola has a pair of asymptotes—something no other conic section has. Thus a hyperbola is not—as might appear from inaccurate diagrams—a pair of parabolas. The hyperbola

$$\frac{x^2}{a^2} - \frac{y^2}{b^2} = 1, \quad \text{or} \quad y = \pm\frac{b}{a}\sqrt{x^2 - a^2},$$

has asymptotes

$$y = \pm\frac{b}{a}x.$$

This can be proved by showing that

$$\lim_{x\to+\infty}\left[\left(\frac{b}{a}\sqrt{x^2 - a^2}\right) - \left(\frac{b}{a}x\right)\right] = 0,$$

$$\lim_{x\to+\infty}\left[\left(-\frac{b}{a}\sqrt{x^2 - a^2}\right) - \left(-\frac{b}{a}x\right)\right] = 0,$$

$$\lim_{x\to-\infty}\left[\left(\frac{b}{a}\sqrt{x^2 - a^2}\right) - \left(-\frac{b}{a}x\right)\right] = 0,$$

$$\lim_{x\to-\infty}\left[\left(-\frac{b}{a}\sqrt{x^2 - a^2}\right) - \left(\frac{b}{a}x\right)\right] = 0.$$

These are left to the student (see Problems 33 and 34). A convenient way of sketching the asymptotes is to plot both $(\pm a, 0)$ and $(0, \pm b)$ (even though the second pair of points is not on the hyperbola) and sketch the rectangle determined by them (see Figure 9.17). The diagonals of this rectangle are the asymptotes.

Again, two *latera recta* contain the foci and are perpendicular to the transverse axis. By using the same method as in the case of the parabola and ellipse, we can show their length to be

$$\frac{2b^2}{a}.$$

As with the parabola and the ellipse, the roles of x and y can be reversed.

Theorem 9.12

A point (x, y) is on the hyperbola with vertices $(0, \pm a)$ and foci $(0, \pm c)$ if and only if it satisfies the equation

$$\frac{y^2}{a^2} - \frac{x^2}{b^2} = 1,$$

where $b^2 = c^2 - a^2$.

It might be noted that a and b are determined by the sign of the term in which they appear; a^2 is always the denominator of the positive term and b^2 the denominator of the negative term. There is no requirement that a be greater than b, as there was for an ellipse.

The asymptotes of the hyperbola

$$\frac{y^2}{a^2} - \frac{x^2}{b^2} = 1$$

are

$$y = \pm \frac{a}{b} x.$$

Since the formulas for the asymptotes for the two cases are rather easy to confuse, a method that always works is to replace the 1 by 0 in the standard form and solve for y.

Example 1

Sketch and discuss.

$$\frac{x^2}{9} - \frac{y^2}{16} = 1.$$

We see that $a^2 = 9$, $b^2 = 16$, and $c^2 = a^2 + b^2 = 25$. This hyperbola has center $(0, 0)$, vertices $(\pm 3, 0)$, and foci $(\pm 5, 0)$. Its asymptotes are $y = \pm 4x/3$, and the length of the latera recta is $2b^2/a = 32/3$ (see Figure 9.18).

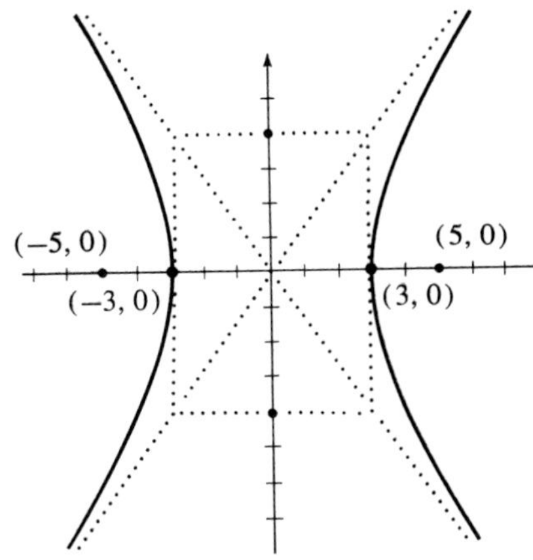

Figure 9.18

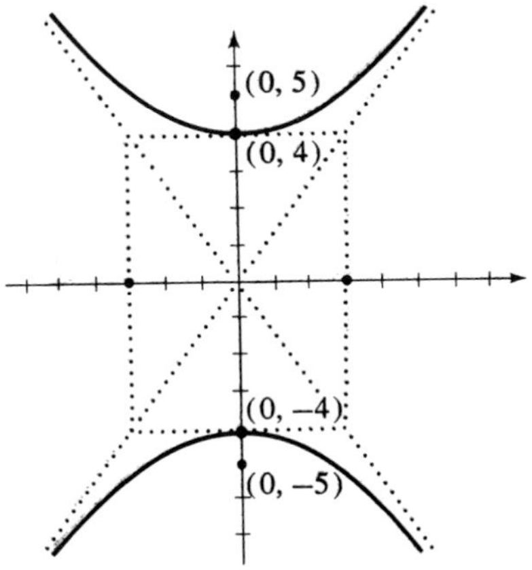

(0, 5)
(0, 4)
(0, −4)
(0, −5)

Figure 9.19

Example 2

Sketch and discuss $16x^2 - 9y^2 + 144 = 0$.

Putting this equation into standard form, we have

$$\frac{y^2}{16} - \frac{x^2}{9} = 1.$$

We see that $a^2 = 16$, $b^2 = 9$, and $c^2 = a^2 + b^2 = 25$. This hyperbola has center $(0, 0)$, vertices $(0, \pm 4)$ and foci $(0, \pm 5)$. Its asymptotes are $y = \pm 4x/3$ and the length of the latera recta is $2b^2/a = 9/2$ (see Figure 9.19).

Note the relationship between the equations of these two examples when in the standard forms; the left-hand sides are simply opposite in sign. Such hyperbolas are called *conjugate hyperbolas*.

Example 3

Find an equation of the hyperbola with foci $(\pm 4, 0)$ and vertex $(2, 0)$.

Since the foci are on the transverse axis and we are given that they are on the x axis, we must have the form

$$\frac{x^2}{a^2} - \frac{y^2}{b^2} = 1.$$

The foci tell us that $c = 4$, and the vertex gives $a = 2$; thus $b^2 = c^2 - a^2 = 12$. The resulting equation is

$$\frac{x^2}{4} - \frac{y^2}{12} = 1,$$

or

$$3x^2 - y^2 = 12.$$

Hyperbolas, as well as the other conic sections, can be determined by a single focus, a directrix, and an eccentricity. For the hyperbola

$$\frac{x^2}{a^2} - \frac{y^2}{b^2} = 1,$$

we have *eccentricity*

$$e = \frac{c}{a}$$

and *directrices*

$$x = \pm\frac{a}{e} = \pm\frac{a^2}{c},$$

where $x = a^2/c$ is used in conjunction with the focus $(c, 0)$ and $x = -a^2/c$ with the focus $(-c, 0)$. Since $c > a$, $e = c/a > 1$. Furthermore a single focus and directrix gives the entire hyperbola—not merely one branch. Either focus with its corresponding directrix generates a hyperbola.

Problems

In Problems 1–14, sketch and discuss.

1. $\frac{x^2}{16} - \frac{y^2}{9} = 1.$
2. $\frac{x^2}{4} - \frac{y^2}{1} = 1.$
3. $\frac{y^2}{9} - \frac{x^2}{4} = 1.$
4. $\frac{y^2}{1} - \frac{x^2}{9} = 1.$
5. $\frac{x^2}{144} - \frac{y^2}{25} = 1.$
6. $\frac{y^2}{25} - \frac{x^2}{144} = 1.$
7. $\frac{y^2}{25} - \frac{x^2}{9} = 1.$
8. $4x^2 - 9y^2 = 36.$
9. $4x^2 - y^2 = 4.$
10. $4x^2 - y^2 + 16 = 0.$
11. $x^2 - y^2 = 9.$
12. $16x^2 - 9y^2 = -36.$
13. $36y^2 - 100x^2 = 225.$
14. $9x^2 - 4y^2 - 9 = 0.$

In Problems 15–26, find an equation(s) of the hyperbola(s) described.

15. Vertices: $(\pm 2, 0)$; focus: $(-4, 0)$.
16. Foci: $(0, \pm 5)$; vertex: $(0, 2)$.
17. Asymptotes: $y = \pm 2x/3$; vertex: $(6, 0)$.
18. Asymptotes: $y = \pm 3x/4$; focus: $(0, -10)$.
19. Asymptotes: $y = \pm 4x/3$; contains $(3\sqrt{2}, 4)$.
20. Asymptotes: $y = \pm 3x/4$; length of latera recta: 9/2.
21. Vertices: $(\pm 5, 0)$; contains $(9/5, -4)$.
22. Foci: $(\pm 2\sqrt{61}, 0)$; contains $(65/6, 5)$.
23. Vertices: $(0, \pm 3)$; $e = 5/3$.
24. Foci: $(\pm 10, 0)$; $e = 5/2$.
25. Directices: $x = \pm 9/5$; $e = 5/3$.
26. Directrices: $y = \pm 25/13$; focus: $(0, -13)$.
27. Find an equation of the line tangent to $16x^2 - 9y^2 = 144$ at $(13/4, 5/3)$.
28. Find an equation of the line tangent to $x^2 - y^2 = 16$ at $(-5, 3)$.
29. Find an equation(s) of the line(s) tangent to $x^2 - y^2 = 9$ and containing $(9, 9)$.

30. Find an equation(s) of the line(s) tangent to $4x^2 - 9y^2 = 7$ and containing $(-7, 7)$.
31. Show that the line tangent to

$$\frac{x^2}{a^2} - \frac{y^2}{b^2} = 1$$

at the point (x_0, y_0) is

$$\frac{xx_0}{a^2} - \frac{yy_0}{b^2} = 1.$$

32. Show that there is a number k such that, if P is any point of a hyperbola, the product of the distances of P from the asymptotes of the hyperbola is k.
33. Show that $\lim_{x \to +\infty} \left[\left(\frac{b}{a}\sqrt{x^2 - a^2}\right) - \left(\frac{b}{a}x\right)\right] = 0$. (*Hint:* Rationalize the numerator.)
34. Show that $\lim_{x \to -\infty} \left[\left(\frac{b}{a}\sqrt{x^2 - a^2}\right) - \left(-\frac{b}{a}x\right)\right] = 0$.

9.7

Hyperbola with Center (h, k)

Theorem 9.13

A point (x, y) is on the hyperbola with center (h, k), vertices $(h \pm a, k)$, and foci $(h \pm c, k)$ if and only if it satisfies the equation

$$\frac{(x-h)^2}{a^2} - \frac{(y-k)^2}{b^2} = 1,$$

where $b^2 = c^2 - a^2$.

Theorem 9.14

A point (x, y) is on the hyperbola with center (h, k), vertices $(h, k \pm a)$, and foci $(h, k \pm c)$, if and only if it satisfies the equation

$$\frac{(y-k)^2}{a^2} - \frac{(x-h)^2}{b^2} = 1,$$

where $b^2 = c^2 - a^2$.

Example 1

Sketch and discuss

$$\frac{(x-1)^2}{4} - \frac{(y+3)^2}{9} = 1.$$

The center of the hyperbola is $(1, -3)$. $a^2 = 4$, $b^2 = 9$, and $c^2 = a^2 + b^2 = 13$. Thus the vertices are $(1 \pm 2, -3)$ and the foci are $(1 \pm \sqrt{13}, -3)$. The length of the latera recta is $2b^2/a = 2 \cdot 9/2 = 9$, and the equations of the asymptotes are

$$y + 3 = \pm \frac{3}{2}(x - 1),$$

or

$$3x - 2y - 9 = 0 \quad \text{and} \quad 3x + 2y + 3 = 0.$$

The method of replacing the 1 by 0 in the original equation is especially useful here (see Figure 9.20).

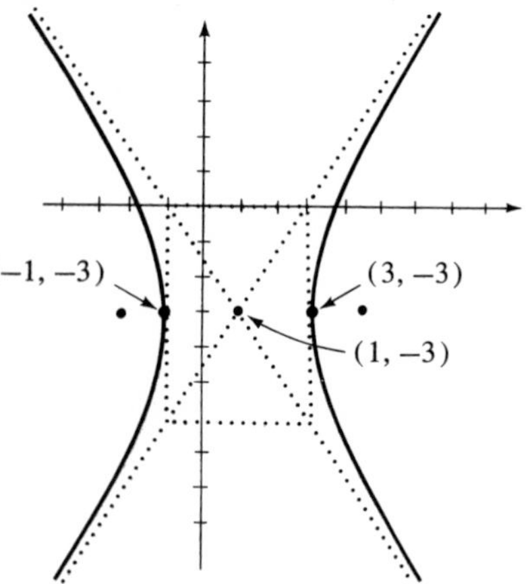

Figure 9.20

If we clear fractions and carry out the multiplication in the equations of Theorems 9.13 and 9.14, we have

$$b^2x^2 - a^2y^2 - 2b^2hx + 2a^2ky + (b^2h^2 - a^2k^2 - a^2b^2) = 0$$

and

$$-a^2x^2 + b^2y^2 + 2a^2hx - 2b^2ky + (-a^2h^2 + b^2k^2 - a^2b^2) = 0.$$

Both of these are in the form

$$Ax^2 + Cy^2 + Dx + Ey + F = 0$$

where A and C have opposite signs.

Theorem 9.15

A hyperbola with axes parallel to (or on) the coordinate axes can be represented by an equation of the form:

$$Ax^2 + Cy^2 + Dx + Ey + F = 0,$$

where AC is negative.

Again, the equations of Theorems 9.13 and 9.14 are called *standard forms* while that of equation 9.15 is called the *general form* of a hyperbola.

Example 2

Express $9x^2 - 4y^2 + 36x + 32y + 8 = 0$ in standard form,

$$9(x^2 + 4x \qquad) - 4(y^2 - 8y \qquad) = -8$$

$$9(x^2 + 4x + 4) - 4(y^2 - 8y + 16) = -8 + 36 - 64,$$

$$9(x + 2)^2 - 4(y - 4)^2 = -36,$$

$$\frac{(y - 4)^2}{9} - \frac{(x + 2)^2}{4} = 1.$$

Again, the converse of Theorem 9.15 is not true. Equations of the form

$$Ax^2 + Cy^2 + Dx + Ey + F = 0,$$

where AC is negative, may represent either a hyperbola or a pair of intersecting lines.

Example 3

Determine whether $25x^2 - 4y^2 - 150x - 16y + 209 = 0$ represents a hyperbola or a pair of intersecting lines.

$$25(x^2 - 6x \qquad) - 4(y^2 + 4y \qquad) = -209,$$

$$25(x^2 - 6x + 9) - 4(y^2 + 4y + 4) = -209 + 225 - 16,$$

$$25(x - 3)^2 - 4(y + 2)^2 = 0.$$

At this point we know that the equation represents a pair of intersecting lines. Continuing, we have

$$4(y + 2)^2 = 25(x - 3)^2,$$

$$2(y + 2) = \pm 5(x - 3),$$

$$5x - 2y - 19 = 0 \quad \text{and} \quad 5x + 2y - 11 = 0.$$

Problems

In Problems 1–12, sketch and discuss.

1. $16x^2 - 9y^2 + 54y - 225 = 0.$
2. $4x^2 - y^2 + 8x + 8 = 0.$
3. $x^2 - y^2 - 10x - 2y - 40 = 0.$
4. $4x^2 - 9y^2 - 4x + 36y - 71 = 0.$
5. $4x^2 - 16y^2 + 12x + 16y + 69 = 0.$
6. $16x^2 - y^2 - 16x + 6y - 1 = 0.$
7. $9x^2 - 4y^2 - 36x - 8y + 32 = 0.$
8. $9x^2 - 16y^2 + 18x - 16y - 139 = 0.$
9. $9x^2 - 9y^2 - 6x - 12y - 39 = 0.$
10. $25x^2 - 16y^2 + 200x + 160y = 0.$
11. $36x^2 - 36y^2 + 24x + 36y + 31 = 0.$
12. $4x^2 - y^2 - 2x - y - 16 = 0.$

In Problems 13–24, find an equation(s) of the hyperbola(s) described.

13. Vertices: (4, 1) and (0, 1); focus: (6, 1).
14. Foci: (−2, 5) and (−2, −3); vertex: (−2, 2).
15. Vertex: (6, −1); asymptotes: $3x - 2y - 6 = 0$ and $3x + 2y - 2 = 0$.
16. Asymptotes: $4x - 3y + 13 = 0$ and $4x + 3y - 5 = 0$; focus: (−1, −2).
17. Center: (2, 5); vertex: (2, 7); focus: (2, 0).
18. Asymptotes: $x - y - 7 = 0$ and $x + y - 3 = 0$; contains (0, 2).
19. Contains (2, −2), (−3, 8), (−1, −1), and (2, 8).
20. Contains (−1/4, 0), (9/4, 6), (0, 3), and (−1/4, 6).
21. Foci: (4, 0) and (−6, 0); $e = 5/2$.
22. Focus: (26/5, −2); directrix: $x = 2$; $e = 5/3$.
23. Vertices: (8, 1) and (2, 1); length of latera recta: 24.
24. Foci: (1, 14) and (1, −12); length of latera recta: 25/6.
25. Find an equation of the line tangent to $x^2 - 4y^2 + 2x + y = 0$ at (1, 1).
26. Find an equation(s) of the line tangent to $9x^2 - 4y^2 + x + 8y - 42 = 0$ at (2, 1).
27. Find an equation(s) of the line(s) tangent to $x^2 - 5y^2 + 2x + 10y - 24 = 0$ and containing the point (−1, −3).
28. Find an equation of the line(s) tangent to $x^2 - 5y^2 + x + 5 = 0$ and containing the point (−1/2, 19/20).

9.8

Translation

The *general second-degree equation* is

$$Ax^2 + Bxy + Cy^2 + Dx + Ey + F = 0.$$

We have seen that any conic section with axes parallel to the coordinate axes can be put into this form with $B = 0$ and A and C not both 0. Furthermore, any second-degree equation with $B = 0$ and A and C not both 0 is a conic section (or degenerate conic) with axes parallel to the coordinate axes. This is summarized in the following table.

Conic	AC	Degenerate cases
Parabola	0	One line (two coincident lines) Two parallel lines No graph
Ellipse	+	Circle Point No graph
Hyperbola	—	Two intersecting lines

The coordinate axes are something of an artificiality, which we introduced on the plane in order to represent points and curves algebraically. Since the axes are of this nature, their placement is quite arbitrary. Thus we might prefer to move them in order to simplify some equation. Any change in the position of the axes may be represented by a combination of a translation and a rotation. A translation of the axes gives a new set of axes parallel to the old ones (see Figure 9.21a), while in a rotation, the axes are rotated about the origin (see Figure 9.21b).

Let us consider translation first. If the axes are translated in such a way that the origin of the new coordinate system is the point (h, k) of the old system (see Figure 9.22), then every point has two representations: (x, y) in the old coordinate system,

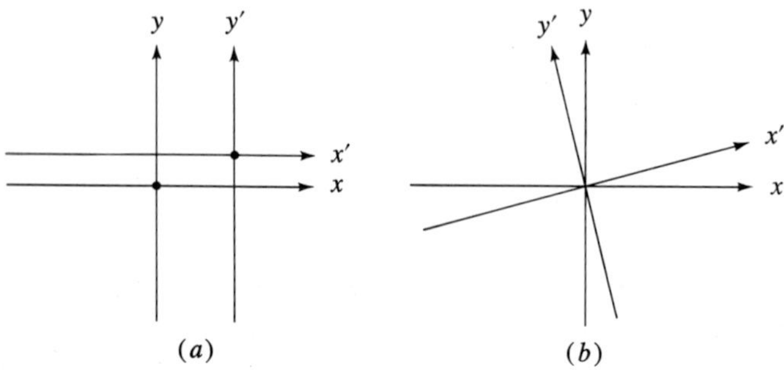

Figure 9.21

and (x', y') in the new. The relationship between the old and new coordinate system is easily seen from Figure 9.22 to be

$$x = x' + h \quad \text{or} \quad x' = x - h,$$
$$y = y' + k \quad \text{or} \quad y' = y - k.$$

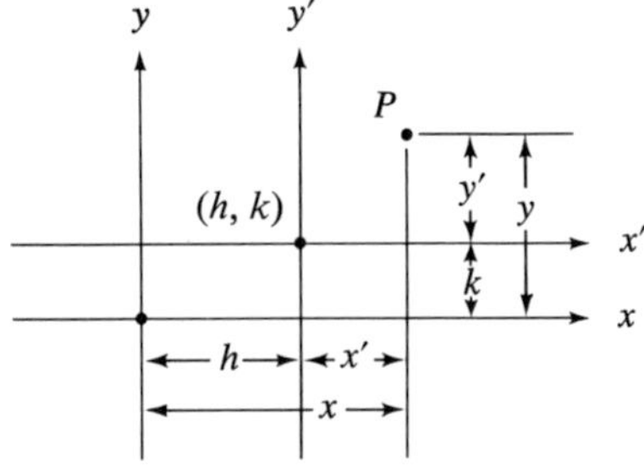

Figure 9.22

These equations (either set) are called equations of translation. This is exactly the situation we had in the discussion of parabolas in Section 9.3.

Thus, translation of the axes for a conic section consists of simply putting its equation into standard form and replacing $x - h$ by x' and $y - k$ by y'.

Example 1

Translate axes to eliminate the first-degree terms of $9x^2 + 4y^2 - 18x + 24y + 9 = 0$. Sketch, showing both the old and new coordinate systems.

Putting the equation into standard form, we have

$$\frac{(x-1)^2}{4} + \frac{(y+3)^2}{9} = 1.$$

The equations of translation,

$$x' = x - 1 \quad \text{and} \quad y' = y + 3,$$

transform this into the equation in the new coordinate system

$$\frac{x'^2}{4} + \frac{y'^2}{9} = 1.$$

The origin of the new coordinate system is the point $(1, -3)$ of the old system. Note that we have the same ellipse—it simply has a new representation in the new system (see Figure 9.23).

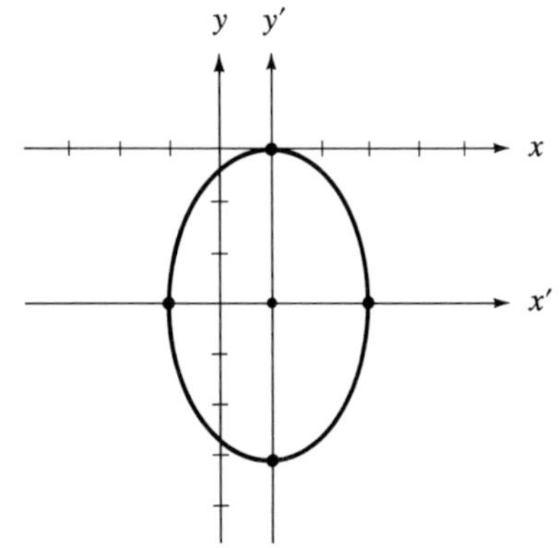

Figure 9.23

Note that any of the conic sections with axes parallel to the coordinate axes can be represented by a translation of the axes that puts the center or vertex at the origin. Thus we have the cases shown in the following table.

Conic	Before translation	After translation
Parabola	$Ax^2 + Dx + Ey + F = 0$ $Cy^2 + Dx + Ey + F = 0$	$Ax'^2 + Ey' = 0$ $Cy'^2 + Dx' = 0$
Ellipse Hyperbola	$Ax^2 + Cy^2 + Dx + Ey + F = 0$	$Ax'^2 + Cy'^2 + F' = 0$

The method of completing the square is simple to use, but it is rather limited in scope. It can be used only on second-degree equations with no xy term. If there is an xy term or if the equation is not of the second degree, another method, illustrated by the following example, can be used.

Example 2

Translate axes so that the constant and the x term of $y = x^3 - 5x^2 + 7x - 5$ are eliminated.

Since we do not know what values of h and k to choose, we simply use the equations of translation,

$$x = x' + h \quad \text{and} \quad y = y' + k,$$

and see what values of h and k are needed to eliminate the terms specified.

$$y' + k = (x' + h)^3 - 5(x' + h)^2 + 7(x' + h) - 5,$$

$$y' = x'^3 + (3h - 5)x'^2 + (3h^2 - 10h + 7)x' + (h^3 - 5h^2 + 7h - 5 - k).$$

Now we must choose h and k so that

$$3h^2 - 10h + 7 = 0,$$

$$h^3 - 5h^2 + 7h - 5 - k = 0.$$

The first of these two equations gives

$$h = 1 \quad \text{or} \quad h = 7/3.$$

Substituting these values into the second, we have

$$k = -2 \quad \text{or} \quad k = -86/27.$$

Using $h = 1$ and $k = -2$, we get

$$y' = x'^3 - 2x'^2.$$

Using $h = 7/3$ and $k = -86/27$, we get

$$y' = x'^3 + 2x'^2.$$

The graphs of both cases are given in Figure 9.24. While there are two different translations giving two different equations, both graphs are the same when referred to the original xy system. As an added bonus, this method has located the relative maximum, $(1, -2)$, and minimum, $(7/3, -86/27)$. This method can also be used on second-degree equations with no xy term, but completing the square is so much simpler that most would prefer to use it.

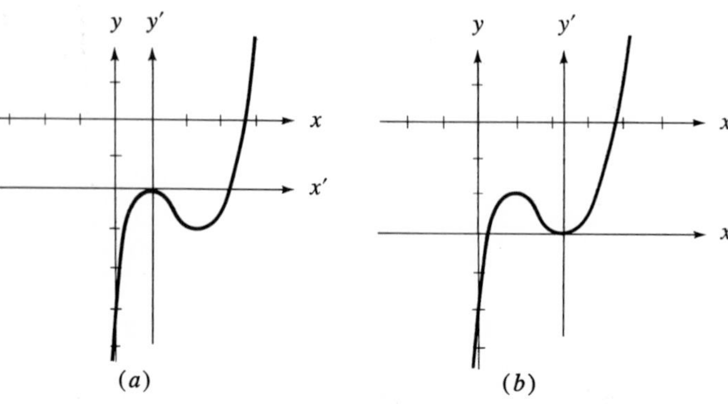

Figure 9.24

Problems

In Problems 1–10, translate so as to have the center or vertex of the conic section at the origin of the new coordinate system. Sketch the curve showing both the old and new axes.

1. $y^2 - 4x - 2y + 9 = 0$.
2. $x^2 - 8x - 8y + 8 = 0$.
3. $4x^2 + y^2 + 24x - 2y + 21 = 0$.
4. $x^2 + 9y^2 - 10x + 36y + 52 = 0$.
5. $9x^2 - 4y^2 + 90x + 32y + 125 = 0$.
6. $9x^2 - 16y^2 + 72x + 96y + 144 = 0$.
7. $9x^2 + 4y^2 - 72x + 16y + 160 = 0$.
8. $4x^2 - y^2 - 40x + 6y + 91 = 0$.
9. $4x^2 - 4x - 4y - 5 = 0$.
10. $16x^2 + 36y^2 + 48x - 180y + 257 = 0$.

In Problems 11–24, translate so as to eliminate the terms indicated.

11. $x^2 - 2xy + 4y^2 + 8x - 26y + 38 = 0$; first degree terms.
12. $2x^2 - xy - y^2 + 5x - 8y - 3 = 0$; first-degree terms.
13. $x^2 + 4xy - y^2 - 2x - 14y - 3 = 0$; first-degree terms.
14. $3x^2 + xy + y^2 - 16x - 10y + 30 = 0$; first-degree terms.
15. $xy - 5x + 4y - 4 = 0$; first-degree terms.
16. $x^2 + xy + 9x + 5y + 20 = 0$; first-degree terms.
17. $y = x^3 - 6x^2 + 11x - 8$; constant, x^2 term.
18. $y = x^3 - 3x + 6$; constant, x term.
19. $y = x^4 - 8x^3 + 24x^2 - 28x + 7$; constant, x term.
20. $y = x^4 - 10x^3 + 37x^2 - 120x + 138$; constant, x term.
21. $y = x^5 - 5x^4 + 8x^3 - 4x^2 + x - 3$; constant, x^2 term.
22. $y = x^5 + 7x^4 + 19x^3 + 25x^2 + 16x + 7$; constant, x term.
23. $x^2y - 2x^2 + 2xy + y - 4x - 6 = 0$; first-degree terms.
24. $x^2y + x^2 + 2xy + x + y - 1 = 0$; second-degree terms.
25. Suppose that a translation changes the equation
$$Ax^2 + Bxy + Cy^2 + Dx + Ey + F = 0$$
into
$$A'x'^2 + B'x'y' + C'y'^2 + D'x' + E'y' + F' = 0.$$
Show that $A' = A$, $B' = B$, and $C' = C$ for any translation. A, B, and C are said to be invariant under translation.

9.9

Rotation

The second transformation of the axes that we wish to consider is a rotation of the axes about the origin (see Figure 9.25). If the axes are rotated through an angle θ, then every point of the plane has two representations: (x, y) in the original coordinate system and (x', y') in the new coordinate system. The point P of Figure 9.25 has the representations

$$x = OQ, \qquad x' = OR,$$
$$y = PQ, \qquad y' = PR.$$

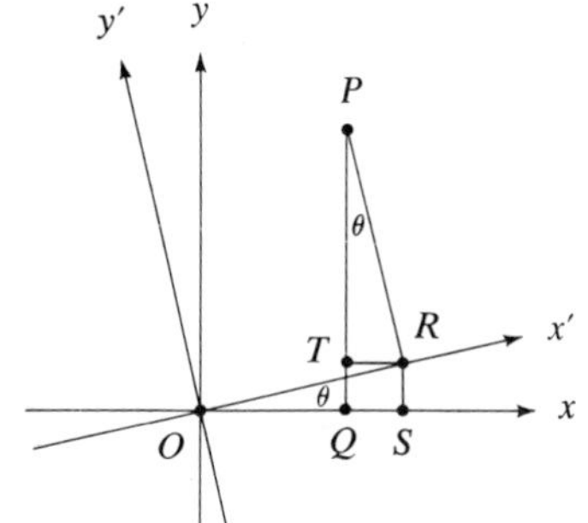

Figure 9.25

Let us now consider the relations between x and y, and x' and y'. Noting first of all that

$$\measuredangle ROQ = \measuredangle RPQ = \theta,$$

we find from triangle ORS

$$\sin\theta = \frac{RS}{OR}, \qquad \cos\theta = \frac{OS}{OR},$$

$$RS = OR\sin\theta \qquad OS = OR\cos\theta$$

$$= x'\sin\theta, \qquad = x'\cos\theta,$$

and from triangle PRT

$$\sin\theta = \frac{TR}{PR}, \qquad \cos\theta = \frac{PT}{PR},$$

$$TR = PR\sin\theta \qquad PT = PR\cos\theta$$

$$= y'\sin\theta, \qquad = y'\cos\theta.$$

Now

$$\begin{aligned} x &= OQ & y &= PQ \\ &= OS - QS & &= TQ + PT \\ &= OS - TR & &= RS + PT \\ &= x'\cos\theta - y'\sin\theta; & &= x'\sin\theta + y'\cos\theta. \end{aligned}$$

Thus we have the equations of rotation

$$x = x'\cos\theta - y'\sin\theta,$$
$$y = x'\sin\theta + y'\cos\theta.$$

Example 1

Find the new representation of

$$x^2 - xy + y^2 - 2 = 0$$

after rotating through an angle of 45°. Sketch the curve, showing both the old and new coordinate systems.

Since $\sin 45° = \cos 45° = 1/\sqrt{2}$, the equations of rotation are

$$x = \frac{x' - y'}{\sqrt{2}} \quad \text{and} \quad y = \frac{x' + y'}{\sqrt{2}}.$$

Substituting into the original equation, we have

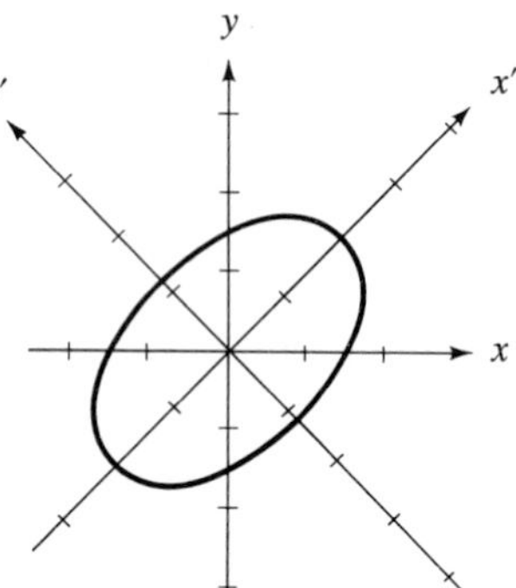

Figure 9.26

$$\frac{(x' - y')^2}{2} - \frac{x' - y'}{\sqrt{2}} \cdot \frac{x' + y'}{\sqrt{2}} + \frac{(x' + y')^2}{2} - 2 = 0,$$

$$\frac{x'^2 - 2x'y' + y'^2 - x'^2 + y'^2 + x'^2 + 2x'y' + y'^2}{2} = 2,$$

$$x'^2 + 3y'^2 = 4.$$

Figure 9.26 shows the final result.

Example 2

Find a new representation of $x^2 + 4xy - 2y^2 - 6 = 0$ after rotating through an angle $\theta = \text{Arctan } 1/2$. Sketch the curve, showing both the old and new coordinate systems.

Figure 9.27 shows that

$$\sin\theta = \frac{1}{\sqrt{5}} \quad \text{and} \quad \cos\theta = \frac{2}{\sqrt{5}},$$

giving equations of rotation

$$x = \frac{2x' - y'}{\sqrt{5}} \quad \text{and} \quad y = \frac{x' + 2y'}{\sqrt{5}}.$$

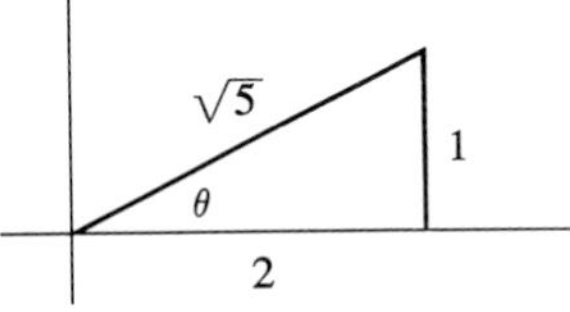

Figure 9.27

Substituting into the original equation, we have

$$\frac{(2x' - y')^2}{5} + 4\,\frac{2x' - y'}{\sqrt{5}} \cdot \frac{x' + 2y'}{\sqrt{5}} - 2\,\frac{(x' + 2y')^2}{5} - 6 = 0,$$

$$\frac{4x'^2 - 4x'y' + y'^2 + 8x'^2 + 12x'y' - 8y'^2 - 2x'^2 - 8x'y' - 8y'^2}{5} = 6,$$

$$2x'^2 - 3y'^2 = 6.$$

Figure 9.28 shows the final result. Note that Figure 9.27 can be used to determine the position of the new coordinate axes.

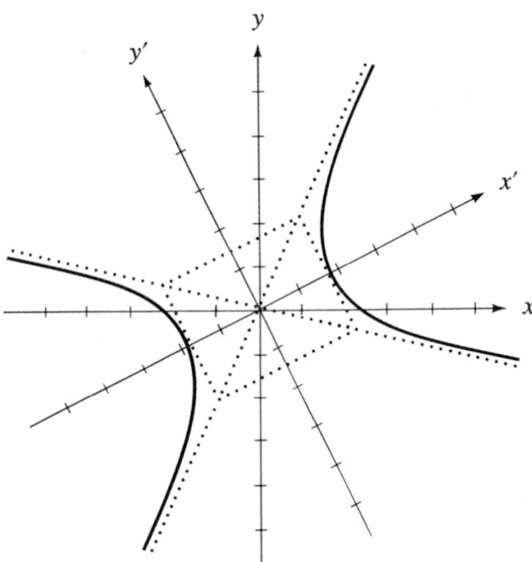

Figure 9.28

In both of these examples, we have seen that the given rotation has eliminated the xy term. Of course, not every rotation will do so—it must be specially chosen. We shall see in the next section how to choose θ to eliminate the xy term.

Problems

In Problems 1–10, find a new representation of the given equation after rotating through the given angle. Sketch the curve, showing both the old and new coordinate systems.

1. $2x + 3y = 6$; $\theta = \text{Arctan } 3/2$.
2. $3x - y = 5$; $\theta = \text{Arctan } 3$.

3. $xy = 4$; $\theta = 45°$.
4. $2x^2 - xy + 2y^2 - 15 = 0$; $\theta = 45°$.
5. $x^2 - 2xy + y^2 + x + y = 0$; $\theta = 45°$.
6. $31x^2 + 10\sqrt{3}xy + 21y^2 - 144 = 0$; $\theta = 30°$.
7. $x^2 + 2\sqrt{3}xy + 3y^2 + 8\sqrt{3}x - 8y = 0$; $\theta = 60°$.
8. $11x^2 - 50\sqrt{3}xy - 39y^2 + 576 = 0$; $\theta = 60°$.
9. $8x^2 + 5xy - 4y^2 - 4 = 0$; $\theta = \text{Arctan } 1/5$.
10. $6x^2 - 5xy - 6y^2 + 26 = 0$; $\theta = \text{Arctan } (-1/5)$.

In Problems 11–16, find a new representation of the given equation after rotating through the given angle.

11. $3x^2 - 3xy - y^2 + 4 = 0$; $\theta = \text{Arctan } (-1/2)$.
12. $4x^2 + 3xy - 5 = 0$; $\theta = \text{Arctan } 1/2$.
13. $4x^2 + 3xy - 5 = 0$; $\theta = 45°$.
14. $x^2 - 3xy + y^2 + 5 = 0$; $\theta = 30°$.
15. $3x^2 - 3xy - y^2 + 4 = 0$; $\theta = 60°$.
16. $x^2 - 5xy + 2 = 0$; $\theta = \text{Arctan } 1/5$.
17. Show that $x^2 + y^2 = 25$ is invariant under rotation through any angle.
18. Given the equation

$$Ax^2 + Bxy + Cy^2 + Dx + Ey + F = 0,$$

which yields

$$A'x'^2 + B'x'y' + C'y'^2 + D'x' + E'y' + F' = 0$$

after rotation through the angle θ, show that $A' + C' = A + C$ for any value of θ: that is, $A + C$ is invariant under rotation.
19. Show that, in the general equation of second degree, $B^2 - 4AC$ is invariant under rotation. (See Problem 18 for definition of invariant.)
20. Show that a second form for the equations of rotation is

$$x' = x \cos\theta + y \sin\theta,$$
$$y' = -x \sin\theta + y \cos\theta.$$

9.10

The General Equation of Second Degree

We have seen that any conic section with axes parallel to the coordinate axes can be represented by a second-degree equation with $B = 0$; furthermore, any second-degree equation with $B = 0$ represents a conic or degenerate conic with axes parallel to the coordinate axes. We now extend this concept to conic sections in any position. It is an easy matter to see that any conic can be represented by a second-degree equation, starting from our standard forms and translating and rotating.

Suppose, given a second-degree equation with $B \neq 0$, we rotate axes through an angle θ. If our assumption that this equation represents a conic or degenerate conic is correct, then a rotation of axes through some positive angle less than 90° should eliminate the xy term. Thus we shall assume throughout this discussion that $0° < \theta < 90°$ and

$$Ax^2 + Bxy + Cy^2 + Dx + Ey + F = 0.$$

Substituting the equations of rotation,

$$x = x' \cos\theta - y' \sin\theta,$$

$$y = x' \sin\theta + y' \cos\theta,$$

we have

$$\begin{aligned} A(x'\cos\theta - y'\sin\theta)^2 &+ B(x'\cos\theta - y'\sin\theta)(x'\sin\theta + y'\cos\theta) \\ &+ C(x'\sin\theta + y'\cos\theta)^2 + D(x'\cos\theta - y'\sin\theta) \\ &+ E(x'\sin\theta + y'\cos\theta) + F = 0. \end{aligned}$$

After carrying out the multiplication and combining similar terms, we find that the coefficient of $x'y'$ is

$$(C - A)2\sin\theta\cos\theta + B(\cos^2\theta - \sin^2\theta) = (C - A)\sin 2\theta + B\cos 2\theta.$$

We want this coefficient to be zero for the proper choice of θ. Let us set it equal to zero and see what θ should be.

$$(C - A)\sin 2\theta + B\cos 2\theta = 0,$$

$$(A - C)\sin 2\theta = B\cos 2\theta,$$

$$\frac{\sin 2\theta}{\cos 2\theta} = \frac{B}{A - C}, \quad A \neq C,$$

$$\tan 2\theta = \frac{B}{A - C}, \quad A \neq C.$$

We can easily solve this equation for θ, but it would involve us in inverse trigonometric functions—let us try to get around them. To do this we shall try to find expressions for $\sin\theta$ and $\cos\theta$ that we can use in the equations of rotation.

First, we note that if $A \neq C$, then $\tan 2\theta$ exists, $2\theta \neq 90°$, and $\theta \neq 45°$.

$$\sin^2 2\theta + \cos^2 2\theta = 1.$$

Dividing through by $\cos^2 2\theta$ (which is not zero since $\theta \neq 45°$), we get

$$\tan^2 2\theta + 1 = \frac{1}{\cos^2 2\theta}, \qquad \cos^2 2\theta = \frac{1}{1 + \tan^2 2\theta}, \qquad \cos 2\theta = \frac{\pm 1}{\sqrt{1 + \tan^2 2\theta}}.$$

The $\pm$ presents the question of which one to use. Since $0° < \theta < 90°$, $0° < 2\theta < 180°$. Both the tangent and cosine are positive for a first-quadrant angle and both are negative for a second-quadrant angle. Thus we choose the sign to agree with the sign of $\tan 2\theta$.

Now let us recall the half-angle identities

$$\sin\frac{A}{2} = \pm\sqrt{\frac{1 - \cos A}{2}} \quad \text{and} \quad \cos\frac{A}{2} = \pm\sqrt{\frac{1 + \cos A}{2}}.$$

Replacing A by 2θ and noting that both $\sin\theta$ and $\cos\theta$ must be positive since $0° < \theta < 90°$, we have

$$\sin\theta = \sqrt{\frac{1 - \cos 2\theta}{2}}, \qquad \cos\theta = \sqrt{\frac{1 + \cos 2\theta}{2}}.$$

Finally, if $A = C$, then

$$\begin{aligned} B\cos 2\theta &= 0, \\ \cos 2\theta &= 0, \\ 2\theta &= 90^\circ, \\ \theta &= 45^\circ. \end{aligned}$$

Thus, in either case, we are able to rotate axes to eliminate the xy term. The resulting equation must then represent a conic or degenerate conic.

Theorem 9.16

Any conic section can be represented by the second-degree equation

$$Ax^2 + Bxy + Cy^2 + Dx + Ey + F = 0$$

where A, B, and C are not all zero. Any second-degree equation represents either a conic or a degenerate conic.

If $B \neq 0$, then the axes may be rotated to eliminate the xy term in the following way:

$A = C$	$A \neq C$	
$\theta = 45^\circ$	$\tan 2\theta = \dfrac{B}{A - C}$	
	$\cos 2\theta = \dfrac{\pm 1}{\sqrt{1 + \tan^2 2\theta}}$	(sign agrees with the sign of $\tan 2\theta$)
	$\sin\theta = \sqrt{\dfrac{1 - \cos 2\theta}{2}}$	
	$\cos\theta = \sqrt{\dfrac{1 + \cos 2\theta}{2}}$	

Example 1

Rotate axes to eliminate the xy term of $x^2 + 4xy - 2y^2 - 6 = 0$. Sketch, showing both sets of axes.

$$\tan 2\theta = \frac{B}{A - C} = \frac{4}{1 - (-2)} = \frac{4}{3},$$

$$\cos 2\theta = \frac{1}{\sqrt{1 + \tan^2 2\theta}} \quad \text{(since } \tan 2\theta \text{ is positive, } \cos 2\theta \text{ is also positive)}$$

$$= \frac{1}{\sqrt{1 + \left(\frac{4}{3}\right)^2}} = \frac{3}{5},$$

$$\sin\theta = \sqrt{\frac{1-\cos 2\theta}{2}} = \sqrt{\frac{1-\frac{3}{5}}{2}} = \frac{1}{\sqrt{5}},$$

$$\cos\theta = \sqrt{\frac{1+\cos 2\theta}{2}} = \sqrt{\frac{1+\frac{3}{5}}{2}} = \frac{2}{\sqrt{5}},$$

$$\tan\theta = \frac{\sin\theta}{\cos\theta} = \frac{1}{2} \quad \text{(we shall use this for sketching);}$$

$$x = \frac{2x' - y'}{\sqrt{5}} \qquad y = \frac{x' + 2y'}{\sqrt{5}}.$$

Substituting these equations of rotation into the original equation (see Example 2 of the previous section), we have

$$2x'^2 - 3y'^2 = 6.$$

The sketch is given in Figure 9.28.

Example 2

Rotate axes to eliminate the xy term of

$$2x^2 - xy + 2y^2 - 2 = 0.$$

Sketch, showing both sets of axes.

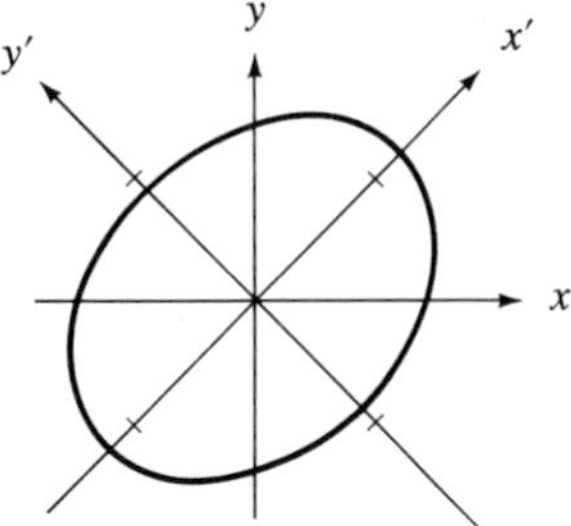

Figure 9.29

Since $A = C$, $\theta = 45°$ and the equations of rotation are

$$x = \frac{x' - y'}{\sqrt{2}}, \qquad y = \frac{x' + y'}{\sqrt{2}}.$$

Substituting these into the original equation, we have

$$2\frac{(x'-y')^2}{2} - \frac{x'-y'}{\sqrt{2}}\frac{x'+y'}{\sqrt{2}} + 2\frac{(x'+y')^2}{2} - 2 = 0,$$

$$\frac{2x'^2 - 4x'y' + 2y'^2 - \ x'^2 + y'^2 + 2x'^2 + 4x'y' + 2y'^2}{2} = 2,$$

$$3x'^2 + 5y'^2 = 4,$$

$$\frac{x'^2}{4/3} + \frac{y'^2}{4/5} = 1.$$

The sketch is given in Figure 9.29.

Problems

In Problems 1–14, rotate axes to eliminate the xy term. Sketch, showing both sets of axes.

1. $x^2 + xy + y^2 + 4\sqrt{2}x - 4\sqrt{2}y = 0.$
2. $5x^2 + 6xy + 5y^2 - 8 = 0.$
3. $7x^2 + 6xy - y^2 - 32 = 0.$
4. $4x^2 + 4xy + y^2 + 8\sqrt{5}x - 16\sqrt{5}y = 0.$
5. $241x^2 + 252xy + 136y^2 - 1300 = 0.$
6. $12x^2 + 10xy - 12y^2 + 13 = 0.$
7. $5x^2 - 4xy + 8y^2 - 36 = 0.$
8. $27x^2 - 78xy - 77y^2 + 360 = 0.$
9. $4x^2 + 12xy + 9y^2 + 8\sqrt{13}x + 12\sqrt{13}y - 65 = 0.$
10. $8x^2 - 12xy + 17y^2 + 20 = 0.$
11. $9x^2 - 6xy + y^2 - 12\sqrt{10}x - 36\sqrt{10}y = 0.$
12. $x^2 + 8xy + 7y^2 - 36 = 0.$
13. $8x^2 + 12xy - 8y^2 + 2\sqrt{10}x + 14\sqrt{10}y - 40 = 0.$
14. $5x^2 - 6xy + 5y^2 + 20\sqrt{2}x - 28\sqrt{2}y + 72 = 0.$
15. It can easily be seen graphically that two conic sections have at most four points in common. But

$$2x^2 + xy - y^2 + 3y - 2 = 0,$$
$$2x^2 + 3xy + y^2 - 6x - 5y + 4 = 0$$

have in common the five points $(1, 0)$, $(-2, 3)$, $(5, -4)$, $(-6, 7)$, and $(10, -9)$. Why?

9.11

Direct Sketching of Conics

By now you may feel you would rather do almost anything other than rotate axes. Let us see if we can determine some methods of sketching without going through the tedious process of rotating axes.

First of all, there is a method of determining which conic we have without rotating axes. It is based on the fact that certain expressions are invariant under rotation; that is, they have the same value before and after any rotation. Although there are several such expressions (see Problems 18 and 19 of Section 9.9), the one in which we are interested is $B^2 - 4AC$ for the equation

$$Ax^2 + Bxy + Cy^2 + Dx + Ey + F = 0.$$

Although a proof of the following theorem is not difficult, it is long and tedious and is omitted here.

Theorem 9.17

If the equation

$$Ax^2 + Bxy + Cy^2 + Dx + Ey + F = 0$$

is transformed into the equation

$$A'x'^2 + B'x'y' + C'y'^2 + D'x' + E'y' + F' = 0$$

by rotating the axes, then

$$B^2 - 4AC = B'^2 - 4A'C'.$$

If we choose the angle of rotation properly, $B' = 0$ and the type of conic can be determined by looking at A' and C' (see the table on page 196). Thus we have the following results.

Theorem 9.18

The equation

$$Ax^2 + Bxy + Cy^2 + Dx + Ey + F = 0$$

represents a hyperbola, ellipse, or parabola (or a degenerate case of one of these) according to whether $B^2 - 4AC$ is positive, negative, or zero, respectively.

This theorem gives us a general idea of the graph of an equation before we start. Remember that this test does not distinguish between the conics and their degenerate cases. Thus, for instance, if $B^2 - 4AC$ is positive, we may have either a hyperbola or two intersecting lines.

If we are dealing with a hyperbola, the greatest single aid in sketching the graph is determination of the asymptotes. If they are horizontal or vertical, the determination is relatively easy, so let us go to slant asymptotes. We shall consider two cases: the equation is linear in y ($C = 0$) and the equation is quadratic in y ($C \neq 0$). In either case, we first solve for y. Examples of each follow.

Example 1

Sketch $x^2 - xy - 3y - 1 = 0$ without rotating axes.

First of all, $B^2 - 4AC = (-1)^2 - 4(1)(0) = 1$, indicating that the conic is a hyperbola or a degenerate case of one. Solving for y, we have

$$y = \frac{x^2 - 1}{x + 3}.$$

The methods of Chapter 6 give intercepts $(\pm 1, 0)$, $(0, -1/3)$ and vertical asymptote $x = -3$. There is no horizontal asymptote, but we know that there must be a second asymptote. To find it, we carry out the division.

$$y = \frac{x^2 - 1}{x + 3} = x - 3 + \frac{8}{x + 3}.$$

We now see that, for numerically large values of x, $8/(x + 3)$ is almost zero and y is very near $x - 3$. Thus the slant asymptote is

$$y = x - 3.$$

With this we can easily sketch the hyperbola (see Figure 9.30).

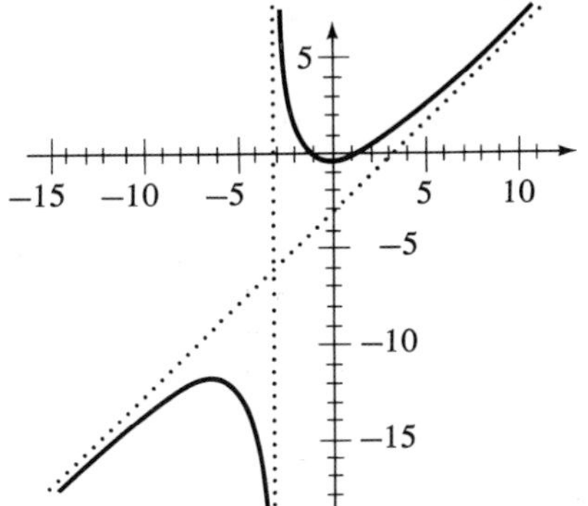

Figure 9.30

Example 2

Sketch $7x^2 + 6xy - y^2 - 32 = 0$ without rotating axes.

This equation is quadratic in y.

$$y^2 - 6xy + (32 - 7x^2) = 0.$$

Using the quadratic formula, we have

$$y = 3x \pm 4\sqrt{x^2 - 2}.$$

Again, for large values of x, $\sqrt{x^2 - 2}$ is almost $\sqrt{x^2}$, and y is very near $3x \pm 4x$. Thus, the slant asymptotes are

$$y = 7x \quad \text{and} \quad y = -x$$

(see Figure 9.31).
This and the intercepts give us a good idea of the curve.

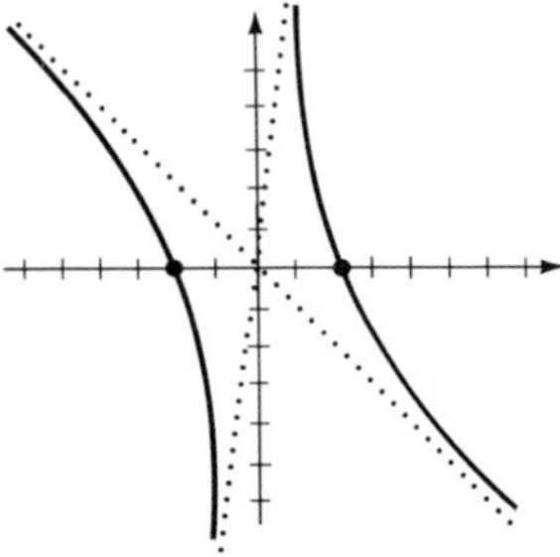

Figure 9.31

Another useful procedure in sketching conics (as well as other curves) is the method of addition of ordinates. Let us consider an example.

Example 3

Sketch $2x^2 - 2xy + y^2 - 9 = 0$ without rotating axes.

Since $B^2 - 4AC = -4$, the curve is an ellipse. Again, the equation is quadratic in y,

$$y^2 - 2xy + (2x^2 - 9) = 0.$$

By the quadratic formula, we have

$$y = x \pm \sqrt{9 - x^2}.$$

Instead of trying to sketch this curve directly let us sketch

$$y = x \quad \text{and} \quad y = \pm\sqrt{9 - x^2}.$$

By squaring both sides, we can put the second equation into the form

$$x^2 + y^2 = 9.$$

These two are easily sketched (see Figure 9.32). For each value of x in the interval $[-3, 3]$, there is an ordinate on the line and one (or two) on the circle. Adding them, we have the ellipse of Figure 9.32.

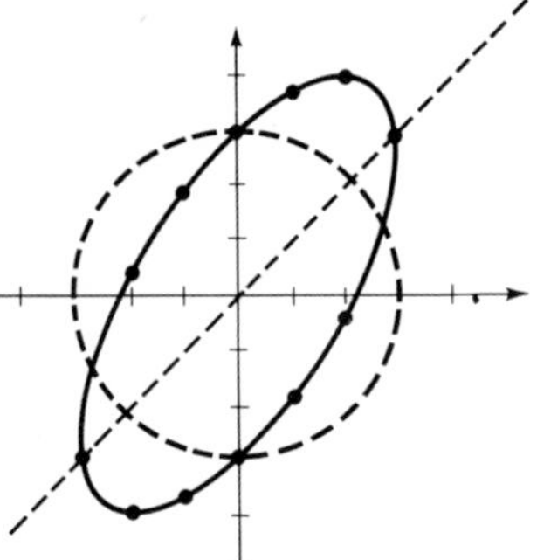

Figure 9.32

Since values of x outside the interval $[-3, 3]$ give complex values of y in the equation $y = x \pm \sqrt{9 - x^2}$, there is no graph to the right of $x = 3$ or to the left of $x = -3$.

Example 4

Sketch $4x^2 - 4xy + y^2 - 5x + 2y + 1 = 0$ without rotating axes.

Since $B^2 - 4AC = 0$, the curve is a parabola. Again solving for y, we have

$$y = 2x - 1 \pm \sqrt{x}.$$

This gives the two equations

$$y = 2x - 1 \quad \text{and} \quad y = \pm\sqrt{x},$$

where the latter can be written $y^2 = x$. Sketching these two and adding ordinates, we have the result given in Figure 9.33. The line $y = 2x - 1$ is *not* the axis of the parabola.

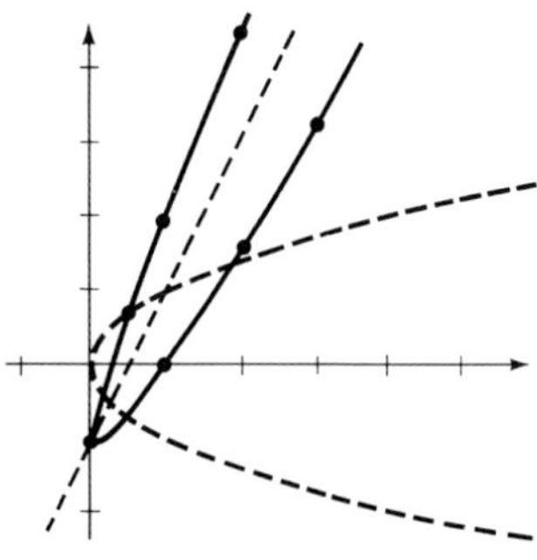

Figure 9.33

Addition of ordinates can be used for hyperbolas as well as for ellipses and parabolas. One disadvantage of this method is that the two curves must be graphed relatively accurately, or the final result is likely to be extremely inaccurate.

One final word; it is *not* maintained that the methods of this section will *always* provide the simplest method of sketching conics. They are alternate methods that are useful in many cases.

Problems

In Problems 1–20, sketch without rotating axes.

1. $xy - x + y + 3 = 0.$
2. $2xy - x - y - 2 = 0.$
3. $x^2 - xy - y - 4 = 0.$
4. $x^2 - xy + x + 2y = 0.$
5. $2x^2 - 2xy + y^2 - 1 = 0.$
6. $5x^2 - 4xy + y^2 - 4 = 0.$
7. $x^2 - 2xy + y^2 - x = 0.$
8. $x^2 - 2xy + y^2 + x - 2y + 2 = 0.$
9. $2xy - y^2 - 4 = 0.$
10. $2x^2 - 2xy + y^2 + 4x - 4y - 5 = 0.$
11. $2xy - y^2 + 6x - 6y - 18 = 0.$
12. $3x^2 - 4xy + y^2 - 4x + 2y + 5 = 0.$
13. $4x^2 + 4xy + y^2 - 3x + 2y + 1 = 0.$
14. $x^2 - 2xy + y^2 - 12x + 8y + 24 = 0.$
15. $3x^2 + 2xy - y^2 + 10x + 2y + 8 = 0.$
16. $x^2 - 2xy + y^2 - 2x + 2y - 3 = 0.$
17. $x^2 - xy - x - 2 = 0.$
18. $xy - y^2 - y + 2 = 0.$
19. $10x^2 - 6xy + y^2 + 12x - 4y + 4 = 0.$
20. $2xy + y^2 - 4 = 0.$
21. Show that $\sqrt{x} + \sqrt{y} = \sqrt{a}$ is a portion of a parabola.

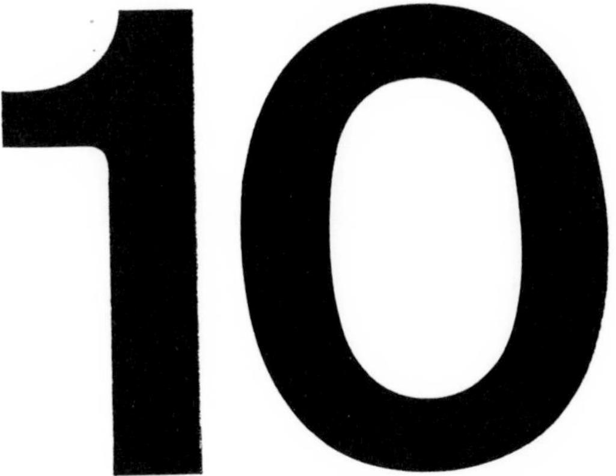

Limits and Continuity: A Geometric Approach

10.1

Limit Points of the Domain

In our previous work, which dealt with limits quite extensively, the derivative and the integral were defined in terms of certain limits (but not limits of the original function—more about this later), and the determination of asymptotes was seen as basically the evaluation of other limits (this time limits of the original function). Nevertheless, we have not considered a definition of a limit; we have only used an intuitive notion of its meaning.

Now we shall consider a definition of the expression

$$\lim_{x \to a} f(x) = b,$$

where a and b represent real numbers. In this chapter, we approach the definition from a purely geometric point of view. We assume throughout that the graph of $y = f(x)$ is well known. Later (in Chapter 17) we shall approach limits and continuity from an algebraic standpoint. Let us emphasize that *the definition given here and the one in Chapter 17 are equivalent*—they are merely in different dress.

First of all, some points must be identified. In the expression

$$\lim_{x \to a} f(x) = b,$$

the point (a, b), where a and b are identified by the above limit statement, is represented by P. Similarly, A represents the point $(a, f(a))$ if there is such a point. We might note the following facts about A and P:

(1) for a given function f and the given limit statement $\lim_{x\to a} f(x) = b$, the point P must necessarily exist but A may or may not exist;
(2) even in those cases in which A does exist, A and P are not necessarily the same point;
(3) A, when it exists, is a point of the graph of $y = f(x)$, while P may or may not be on the graph.

Suppose we consider a few examples:

Limit Statement	A	P
$\lim_{x\to a} f(x) = b$	$(a, f(a))$	(a, b)
$\lim_{x\to 0} x^2 = 0$	$(0, 0)$	$(0, 0)$
$\lim_{x\to 1} \frac{x^2 - 1}{x - 1} = 2$	does not exist	$(1, 2)$
$\lim_{x\to 2} (x^2 + 1) = 5$	$(2, 5)$	$(2, 5)$
$\lim_{x\to 2} (x^2 + 1) = 4$	$(2, 5)$	$(2, 4)$

You may object to the last limit statement, saying that $\lim_{x\to 2}(x^2 + 1)$ is not 4. You are quite right. Nevertheless, if we were asked to prove that the limit statement $\lim_{x\to 2}(x^2 + 1) = 4$ is not true, we would have to identify A and P in this case as well as for cases in which we want to show that a given limit statement is true.

One other convention is needed here. We shall use $\mathscr{G}$ to represent the graph of $y = f(x)$ and $\mathscr{G} - A$ to represent the set of all points of $\mathscr{G}$ except A. If A does not exist, $\mathscr{G} - A$ will be taken to mean $\mathscr{G}$. A thorough knowledge of the meanings of P, A, $\mathscr{G}$, and $\mathscr{G} - A$ are necessary for the definitions of this chapter.

Before considering a definition of a limit, we shall discuss a related term—a limit point of the domain of a function. We define it here only for a real-valued function of a single real variable.

Definition

*The number a is a **limit point** of the domain of the function f means that if h and k are two vertical lines with the line $x = a$ between them, then there is a point of $\mathscr{G} - A$ between them.*

Why do we refer to a *number* as a limit *point* of the domain? Why not a limit *number*? Remember that the class of functions with which we are dealing here is only one of many types of functions. In addition to functions of a single real number, there are functions of two or more real numbers, functions of one or more complex numbers, functions of vectors, and so forth. In order to have a single term for all types of functions, we use the term "limit *point.*" Thus, for our functions, a limit point is a real number. Other terms used in place of limit point are "point of accumulation" and "cluster point."

Now what does it mean? The number a is a limit point of the domain of f means, roughly speaking, that there are other numbers in the domain of f which are near a; in fact, there are other numbers in the domain "leading right up to" a. Let us consider some examples.

Example 1

Is the number 1 a limit point of the domain of $f(x) = x + 1$?

The graph $\mathscr{G}$ of $y = x + 1$ is given in Figure 10.1. The point A is $(1, f(1)) = (1, 2)$. If h and k are two vertical lines with $x = 1$ between them, then it is clear from Figure 10.1 that there is some point of $\mathscr{G} - A$ (that is, there is some point of the graph different from $(1, 2)$) that is also between h and k. Not only is this true for the lines h and k shown but it is also true for *any* pair of vertical lines with $x = 1$ between them. Thus the number 1 is a limit point of the domain of f.

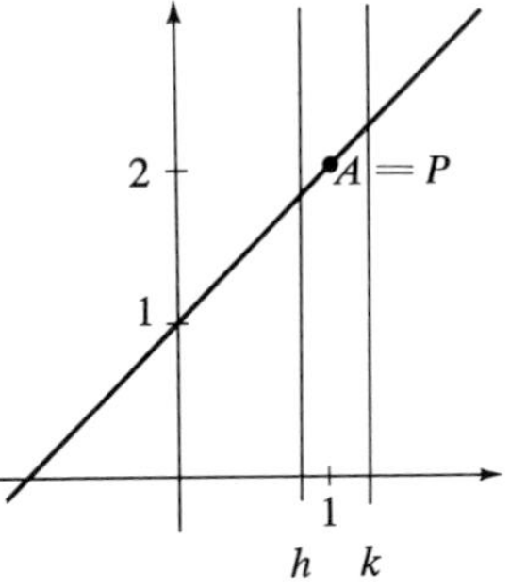

Figure 10.1

Perhaps you feel that it must be possible to find lines h and k close enough together so that A is the only point of $\mathscr{G}$ between them. If this were so, k would have to cross the x axis at the next point to the right of 1 and h would cross at the next point to the left of 1. But there is no "next point." If k crosses the x axis to the right of 1, then it has an equation of the form $x = c$, where $c > 1$. Now it is evident that there is a point on the x axis between 1 and c; one such point is the midpoint $(1 + c)/2$. Since the function $x + 1$ is defined for all x, there must be some point of $\mathscr{G}$ between A and k as well as a point of $\mathscr{G}$ between h and A.

Example 2

Is the number 0 a limit point of the domain of $f(x) = \sqrt{x^2(x^2 - 1)}$?

The graph $\mathscr{G}$ is given in Figure 10.2. The point A is $(0, f(0)) = (0, 0)$. We can see that A is an isolated point of $\mathscr{G}$. Let us choose h to be the line $x = -1/2$ and k to be the line $x = 1/2$ (see Figure 10.2). Now A is the only point of the graph between h and k; there is no point of $\mathscr{G} - A$ between h and k. Thus the number 0 is not a limit point of the domain.

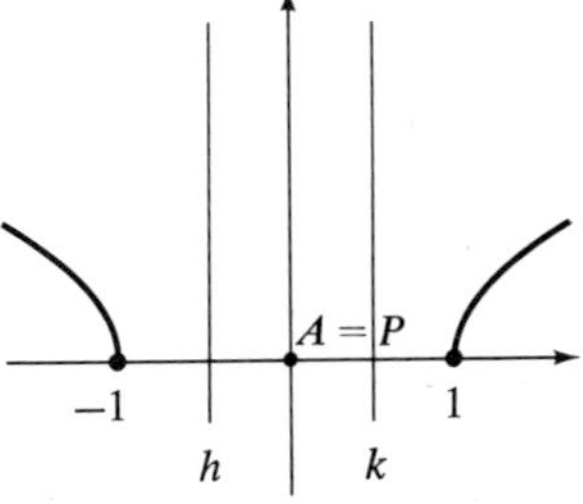

Figure 10.2

You may think that we are twisting things around to suit ourselves—that we could take h to be $x = -2$ and k to be $x = 2$ and thus find some point of $\mathscr{G} - A$ between h and k. Thus, you may be thinking, we can make zero a limit point of the domain or not as we choose. This is not really the case here. In order to show that zero is a limit point of the domain, we must show (as we did in Example 1) that, for *every* pair of vertical lines h and k with $x = 0$ between them, there is a point of $\mathcal{G} - A$ between them. To prove this statement false, we need exhibit only one pair of vertical lines with $x = 0$ between them but no point of $\mathcal{G} - A$ between them. This is what we did when we let h be $x = -1/2$ and k be $x = 1/2$. It is very much like the problem we have with the statement "Every person in this room is wearing a hat." In order to prove it false, we merely have to point out *one* person in this room who is not wearing a hat—it is not necessary to show that no one in the room is wearing a hat.

Example 3

Is the number 1 a limit point of the domain of

$$f(x) = \frac{x^2 - 1}{x - 1}?$$

The graph is given in Figure 10.3. Since this function is not defined for $x = 1$, there is no point A. Thus $\mathcal{G} - A$ is $\mathcal{G}$. The function is defined for all other values of x. Thus the $\mathcal{G} - A$ here is the same as the $\mathcal{G} - A$ of Example 1. By exactly the same argument we used there, the number 1 is a limit point of the domain of this function.

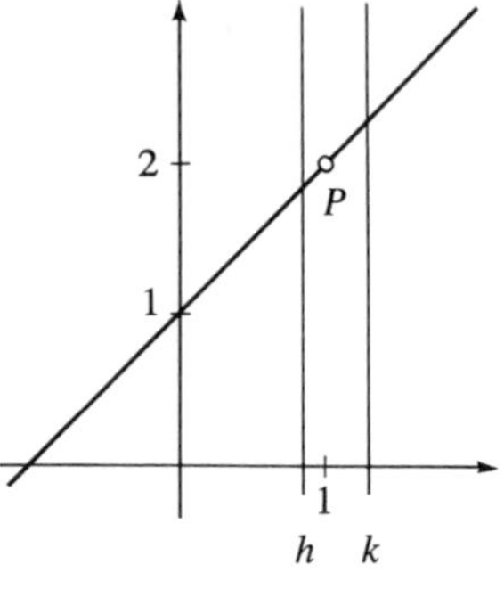

Figure 10.3

Note here that the existence or nonexistence of A has nothing to do with the number 1 being a limit point of the domain of f. Since we consider only $\mathcal{G} - A$, we are interested only in what happens near A, not at it.

Problems

In Problems 1–10, identify the points P and A for the given limit statement.

1. $\lim_{x \to 0} x^2 = 0.$
2. $\lim_{x \to 1} x^2 = 1.$
3. $\lim_{x \to 2} (x + 1) = 3.$
4. $\lim_{x \to 2} (x + 1) = 4.$
5. $\lim_{x \to 2} \frac{x^2 - 4}{x - 2} = 4.$
6. $\lim_{x \to 2} \frac{x^2 - 4}{x - 2} = 5.$
7. $\lim_{x \to 3} \frac{x^2 - 4}{x - 2} = 5.$
8. $\lim_{x \to 1} \sqrt{x} = 1.$
9. $\lim_{x \to 0} \sqrt{x} = 0.$
10. $\lim_{x \to -1} \sqrt{x} = 1.$

In Problems 11–25, indicate whether or not the given number is a limit point of the domain of the given function.

11. $0; f(x) = \sqrt{x}.$
12. $1; f(x) = \sqrt{x}.$
13. $-1; f(x) = \sqrt{x}.$
14. $0; f(x) = 1/x.$
15. $1; f(x) = 1/x.$
16. $0; f(x) = |x|.$
17. $0; f(x) = \begin{cases} 1 & \text{if } x > 0, \\ -1 & \text{if } x < 0. \end{cases}$
18. $1; f(x) = \begin{cases} 1 & \text{if } x = 1, \\ 2 & \text{if } x = 2, \\ 1 & \text{if } x = 3. \end{cases}$
19. $1; f(x) = \sqrt{x^2(x^2 - 1)}.$
20. $\frac{1}{2}; f(x) = \sqrt{x^2(x^2 - 1)}.$

21. $-1; f(x) = \sqrt{x^2(x+1)^2(x-1)}$.

22. $0; f(x) = \sqrt{x^2(x+1)^2(x-1)}$.

23. $1; f(x) = \sqrt{x^2(x+1)^2(x-1)}$.

24. $0; f(x) = \begin{cases} x-1 & \text{if } x \geq 1, \\ -x-1 & \text{if } x \leq -1. \end{cases}$

25. $1; f(x) = \begin{cases} x-1 & \text{if } x \geq 1, \\ -x-1 & \text{if } x \leq -1. \end{cases}$

10.2

The Limit

We are now ready to consider the definition of a limit.

Definition

$\lim_{x \to a} f(x) = b$ *(where a and b are real numbers) means:*

(a) *if h and k are two vertical lines with P between them, then there is a point of $\mathscr{G} - A$ between them, and*
(b) *if α and β are two horizontal lines with P between them, then there exists a pair of vertical lines l and m with P between them such that every point of $\mathscr{G} - A$ between l and m is also between α and β.*

The first part of this definition is easily seen to be a restatement of the condition that a is a limit point of the domain of f. Since P is (a, b), it is on the line $x = a$. Thus, two vertical lines with P between them also have the line $x = a$ between them. Recall that this assures us that there are points of the graph which are, roughly speaking, "close" to a in the x direction.

The second part of the definition says that no matter what pair of horizontal lines we are given with P between them, there is a pair of vertical lines, with P between them, close enough together so that every point of $\mathscr{G} - A$ which is between the vertical lines is also between the horizontal lines (see Figure 10.4). It does *not* say that there is one

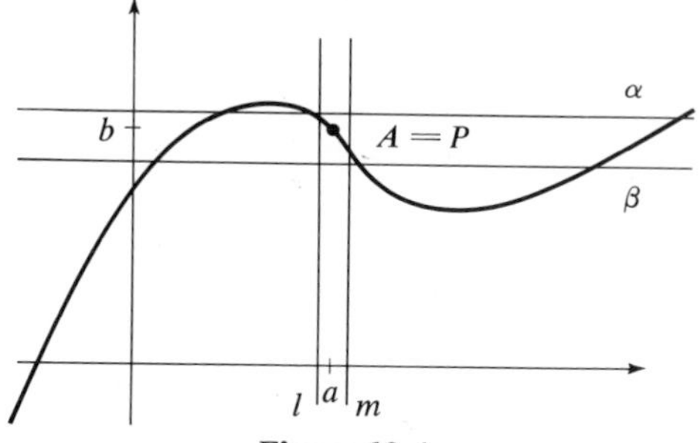

Figure 10.4

pair of vertical lines that works for every pair of horizontal lines; the choice of l and m depends, not only upon the function f and the number a, but also upon the horizontal lines α and β. In general, the closer together α and β are, the closer together l and m have to be.

Note that in both parts of the definition we are concerned with $\mathscr{G} - A$ rather than $\mathscr{G}$. We are not concerned with the graph at $x = a$ but only with that portion near $x = a$ (near because we consider only the portion between the vertical lines). Let us look at some specific examples.

Example 1

Show that

$$\lim_{x\to 0} \sqrt{x^2(x^2 - 1)}$$

does not exist.

We must show that, no matter what number b represents,

$$\lim_{x\to 0} \sqrt{x^2(x^2 - 1)} = b$$

is false. The first part of the definition (which has nothing to do with the number b) says that, for the limit statement to be true, zero must be a limit point of the domain of $f(x) = \sqrt{x^2(x^2 - 1)}$. We have already seen in Example 2 of the previous section that 0 is not a limit point of the domain of this function. Thus we need not consider the second part at all; the limit does not exist.

Example 2

Show that

$$\lim_{x\to 1} (x + 1) = 2.$$

We have already seen in Example 1 of the previous section that 1 is a limit point of the domain of $f(x) = x + 1$. Now let us consider the second part of the definition of a limit. First of all, $P = (1, 2)$ and $A = (1, f(1)) = (1, 2)$. If α and β are two horizontal lines with α above P and β below it, then each of these lines has exactly one point in common with the graph of $y = x + 1$. There is a point X to the right of P that is common to α and $\mathscr{G}$ and a point Y to the left of P that is common to β and $\mathscr{G}$ (see Figure 10.5). Letting l be the vertical line through Y and m the vertical line through X, we see that every piont of $\mathscr{G} - A$ between l and m is also between α and β. Thus the definition is satisfied and

$$\lim_{x\to 1} (x + 1) = 2.$$

While A itself is also between α and β, we are not interested in it—were it not between α and β, it would have no effect on the result (see Problem 7).

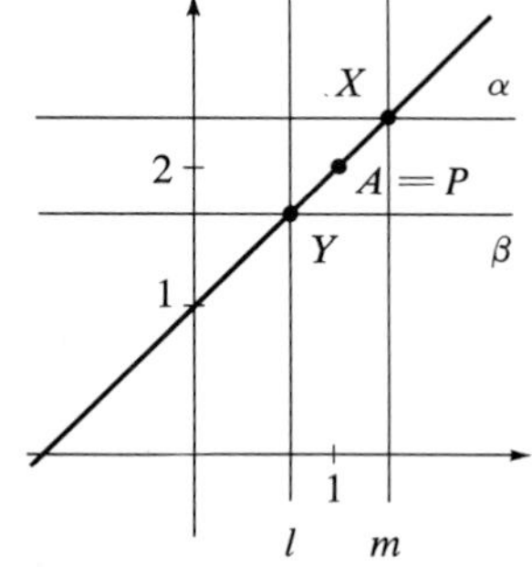

Figure 10.5

Example 3

Show that

$$\lim_{x\to 1} \frac{x^2-1}{x-1} = 2.$$

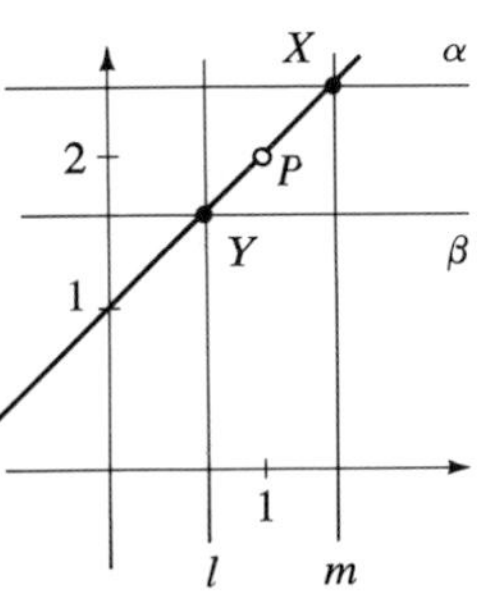

Figure 10.6

Note that $f(x)=(x^2-1)/(x-1)$ has the same graph as $f(x)=x+1$ except that it is not defined for $x=1$. Thus, while P is still the point (1, 2), there is no point A. The same arguments we used for both parts of the previous example can be used here—the absence of the point A has no effect on them whatsoever (see Figure 10.6). It must be remembered that $\mathscr{G}-A$ is the same as $\mathscr{G}$, since there is no A.

As this last example illustrates, the function f need not be defined at $x=a$ in order that $\lim_{x\to a} f(x)$ exist. On the other hand, the example using $\lim_{x\to 0}\sqrt{x^2(x^2-1)}$ illustrates that the mere existence of a functional value at $x=a$ is not enough to guarantee the existence of the limit.

Problems

In Problems 1–6, show whether or not part (a) of the definition of a limit is satisfied.

1. $\lim_{x\to 3} f(x)=1$, where $f(x)=\begin{cases}1 & \text{if } x=1,\\ 2 & \text{if } x=2,\\ 1 & \text{if } x=3.\end{cases}$

2. $\lim_{x\to 0}\sqrt{x}=0.$

3. $\lim_{x\to -4}\sqrt{x}=2.$

4. $\lim_{x\to 0}\frac{1}{x}=0.$

5. $\lim_{h\to 0}|h|=0.$

6. $\lim_{h\to 0} f(h)=0$, where $f(h)=\begin{cases}1 & \text{if } h>0,\\ -1 & \text{if } h<0.\end{cases}$

In Problems 7–20, show that the given limit statement is true.

7. $\lim_{x\to 1} f(x)=2$, where $f(x)=\begin{cases}x+1 & \text{if } x\neq 1,\\ 4 & \text{if } x=1.\end{cases}$

8. $\lim_{x\to 2}\frac{x^2-3x+2}{x-2}=1.$

9. $\lim_{x\to 0}\sqrt{x}=0.$

10. $\lim_{x\to 1}\frac{x-1}{\sqrt{x}-1}=2.$

11. $\lim_{x\to 1} f(x)=1$, where $f(x)=\begin{cases}2-x & \text{if } x<1,\\ x & \text{if } x\geq 1.\end{cases}$

12. $\lim_{x\to 1} f(x)=1$, where $f(x)=\begin{cases}2-x & \text{if } x<1,\\ x & \text{if } x>1.\end{cases}$

13. $\lim_{x\to 1} f(x)=1$, where $f(x)=\begin{cases}2-x & \text{if } x<1,\\ 2 & \text{if } x=1,\\ x & \text{if } x>1.\end{cases}$

14. $\lim_{x \to 0} |x| = 0.$

15. $\lim_{x \to 1} x^2 = 1.$

16. $\lim_{x \to 0} x^2 = 0.$

17. $\lim_{h \to 0} (3 + h) = 3.$

18. $\lim_{h \to 0} (2x + h + 1) = 2x + 1.$

19. $\lim_{u \to 2} (u^2 + 1) = 5.$

20. $\lim_{y \to -1} y^3 = -1.$

10.3

The Limit (Continued)

In considering the definition of a limit, we have only concerned ourselves with verifying that a given limit statement is true—except in those cases in which a is not a limit point of the domain of f. Now we shall consider the problem of showing that a limit statement is false. As we have already seen, one way to show that a limit statement is false is to show that it is not a limit point of the domain of f—that is, it fails to satisfy the first part of the definition. We should like to turn our attention now to the case in which the first part of the definition is satisfied but the second is not.

Now the second part of the definition states that for every pair of horizontal lines α and β with P between them, there exists a pair of vertical lines l and m with P between them satisfying the condition that every point of $\mathcal{G} - A$ between l and m is also between α and β. Suppose we take it in smaller pieces. According to the definition, for every pair of horizontal lines α and β with P between them, there exist two vertical lines l and m, with P between them, that satisfy certain conditions. In order for this to be false, it must be true that *there exists a pair of horizontal lines* α *and* β *with* P *between them, such that* no such pair of vertical lines l and m exists. Another way of saying that no such pair of vertical lines exists is to say that *for every pair of vertical lines* l *and* m *with* P *between them,* the condition is not satisfied. Now the condition we are considering here is that every point of $\mathcal{G} - A$ between l and m is also between α and β. In order that this condition not be satisfied, it must be that *there is some point of* $\mathcal{G} - A$ *between* l *and* m *which is not between* α *and* β. Now suppose we put all the pieces (the italicized portions above) together. If the second part of the definition is not true, then *there exists a pair of horizontal lines* α *and* β *with* P *between them such that, for every pair of vertical lines* l *and* m *with* P *between them, there is a point of* $\mathcal{G} - A$ *between* l *and* m *which is not between* α *and* β. Suppose we consider some specific examples.

Example 1

Show that, if

$$f(x) = \begin{cases} 0 & \text{if } x \le 0, \\ 1 & \text{if } x > 0, \end{cases}$$

then the limit statement

$$\lim_{x \to 0} f(x) = 0$$

is false.

First of all

$$A = P = (0, 0).$$

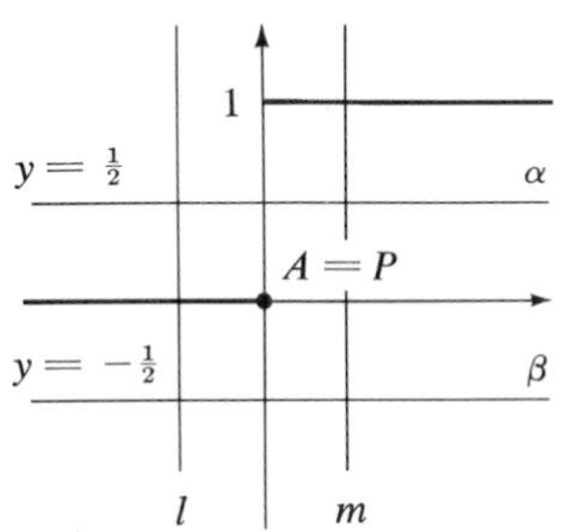

Figure 10.7

Since the function is defined for all x, the first part of the definition is easily seen to be satisfied. Thus if the limit is really not 0, it must be because the second part of the definition is not satisfied. To show this, we must simply exhibit a pair of horizontal lines α and β with P between them such that, no matter how the vertical lines l and m are chosen with P between them, there is some point of $\mathscr{G} - A$ between l and m which is not between α and β. The lines $y = 1/2$ and $y = -1/2$ constitute one such pair (see Figure 10.7). No matter how close to P we take m, there is some point between m and the y axis (and thus between l and m) having a y coordinate 1 which is above both $y = 1/2$ and $y = -1/2$. Thus, the second part of the definition is not satisfied, and

$$\lim_{x \to 0} f(x) \neq 0.$$

Example 2

Show that if f is the function of Example 1, then the limit statement

$$\lim_{x \to 0} f(x) = 1$$

is false.

Now

$$P = (0, 1) \quad \text{and} \quad A = (0, 0).$$

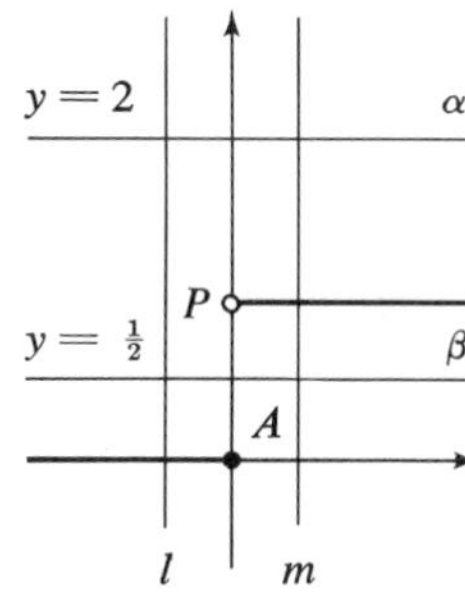

Figure 10.8

This time we choose α and β to be $y = 2$ and $y = 1/2$ (see Figure 10.8). Now no matter how close to P we take l, there is a point between l and the y axis (and thus between l and m) having a y coordinate 0, which is below both $y = 2$ and $y = 1/2$. Again, the second part of the definition is not satisfied and

$$\lim_{x \to 0} f(x) \neq 1.$$

We have seen that $\lim_{x \to 0} f(x)$ is neither zero nor one. This might lead you to suspect that this limit does not exist—that is, no matter what number we choose for b, the resulting limit statement is false. The problem of showing that this is the case seems to be quite formidable—after all, there are infinitely many choices for b, and we cannot repeat this argument infinitely many times! But there is a way of overcoming this difficulty, and that is by making one case handle infinitely many values of b.

Example 3

Show that, if f is the function of Example 1, then

$$\lim_{x \to 0} f(x)$$

does not exist; that is,

$$\lim_{x \to 0} f(x) = b$$

is false no matter what number b represents.

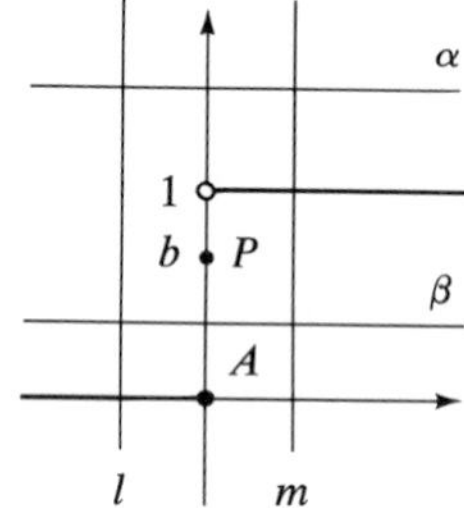

Figure 10.9

Let us consider two cases. First we assume that

$$\lim_{x \to 0} f(x) = b, \quad \text{where } b > 0.$$

Now $A = (0, 0)$, as always, and $P = (0, b)$. Let α be any horizontal line above P and β the line $y = b/2$ (see Figure 10.9). Note that $0 < b/2 < b$. No matter how we choose l and m, there is a point of $\mathcal{G} - A$ between them with negative abscissa and ordinate 0. This point, of course, is not between α and β.

$$\lim_{x \to 0} f(x) \neq b \quad \text{where } b > 0.$$

If this limit exists at all, it cannot be positive.

Now let us assume that

$$\lim_{x \to 0} f(x) = b \quad \text{where } b \leq 0,$$

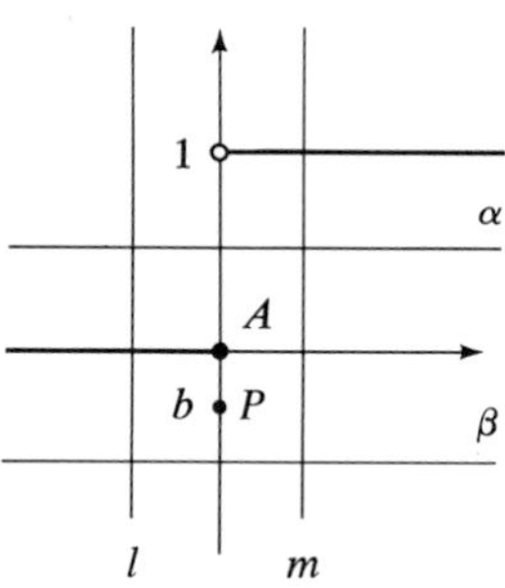

Figure 10.10

As in the previous case, $A = (0, 0)$ and $P = (0, b)$. Choose α to be the line $y = 1/2$ and β to be any horizontal line below P (see Figure 10.10). Again, no matter how we choose l and m, there is a point of $\mathcal{G} - A$ between them with positive abscissa and ordinate 1; and again this point is not between α and β. Thus, the limit cannot be zero, nor can it be negative either—the limit simply does not exist.

One final word. We seem to have been pulling α's and β's out of a hat—how do we know where to choose them? The following procedure is helpful. Let us ask whether or not it is always possible to choose an l and m satisfying the definition if we take the α and β closer and closer to P. If it is not always possible to find such vertical lines, it will be detected when α and β are "close" to P. Note that in the case we have been discussing, our arguments would not hold if α and β were very far apart—that is, if α were above $y = 1$ and β below $y = 0$. But remember, in order to prove the falsity of a limit statement, we need only produce one offending pair α and β.

Problems

In Problems 1–6, show that the given limit statement is false.

1. $\lim_{x \to 0} f(x) = 1 \quad \text{where} \quad f(x) = \begin{cases} 1 & \text{if } x \leq 0, \\ x & \text{if } x > 0. \end{cases}$
2. $\lim_{x \to 0} f(x) = 0 \quad \text{where} \quad f(x) = \begin{cases} 1 & \text{if } x \leq 0, \\ x & \text{if } x > 0. \end{cases}$
3. $\lim_{x \to 1} f(x) = 4 \quad \text{where} \quad f(x) = \begin{cases} x + 1 & \text{if } x \neq 1, \\ 4 & \text{if } x = 1. \end{cases}$
4. $\lim_{x \to 0} x^2 = 1.$
5. $\lim_{x \to 0} \frac{1}{x} = 0.$
6. $\lim_{x \to 1} \frac{1}{x - 1} = 1.$

In Problems 7–15, show whether the given limit statement is true or false

7. $\lim_{x\to 2} \dfrac{x^2 - x - 2}{x - 2} = 2.$ 8. $\lim_{x\to 2} \dfrac{x^2 - x - 2}{x - 2} = 3.$ 9. $\lim_{x\to 0} |x| = 0.$

10. $\lim_{x\to 0} f(x) = 0$ where $f(x) = \begin{cases} x & \text{if } x \geq 0, \\ -x & \text{if } x < 0. \end{cases}$

11. $\lim_{x\to 1} f(x) = 1$ where $f(x) = \begin{cases} 0 & \text{if } x \leq 0, \\ 1 & \text{if } x > 0. \end{cases}$

12. $\lim_{x\to 1} f(x) = 1$ where $f(x) = \begin{cases} x & \text{if } x \geq 1, \\ -x & \text{if } x < 1. \end{cases}$

13. $\lim_{x\to 0} \sin \dfrac{1}{x} = 0$ $\left(\textit{Hint:}\text{ Sketch } y = \sin \dfrac{1}{x} \text{ by plotting the points corresponding to } x = \dfrac{1}{\pi/2}, \dfrac{1}{\pi}, \dfrac{1}{3\pi/2}, \dfrac{1}{2\pi}, \dfrac{1}{5\pi/2}, \text{ etc.}\right).$

14. $\lim_{x\to 0} x \sin \dfrac{1}{x} = 0$ (See hint for Problem 13).

15. $\lim_{x\to 0} x^2 \sin \dfrac{1}{x} = 0$ (See hint for Problem 13).

In Problems 16–20, show that the given limit does not exist.

16. $\lim_{x\to 0} f(x)$ where $f(x) = \begin{cases} 1 & \text{if } x \leq 0, \\ x & \text{if } x > 0. \end{cases}$ 17. $\lim_{x\to 0} \dfrac{1}{x}.$

18. $\lim_{x\to 0} \dfrac{1}{x^2}.$ 19. $\lim_{x\to 1} f(x)$ where $f(x) = \begin{cases} 0 & \text{if } x < 1, \\ 1 & \text{if } x = 1, \\ x + 1 & \text{if } x > 1. \end{cases}$

20. $\lim_{x\to 0} \dfrac{1}{x} \sin \dfrac{1}{x}.$

10.4

One-Sided Limits

In the preceding section we considered in some detail the function

$$f(x) = \begin{cases} 0 & \text{if } x \leq 0, \\ 1 & \text{if } x > 0 \end{cases}$$

and the limit $\lim_{x\to 0} f(x)$, which we showed does not exist. However, it might be noted that if a point moves along the curve in such a way that its x coordinate approaches zero, the y coordinate approaches zero or one, depending upon whether the point approaches from the left or right. This leads directly to the definition of one-sided limits.

Definition

$\lim_{x\to a^+} f(x) = b$ *(this limit is called the right-hand limit of $f(x)$ as x approaches a or the limit of $f(x)$ as x approaches a from the right) means* $\lim_{x\to a} G(x) = b$, *where $G(x)$ is the function that coincides with $f(x)$ for all $x \geq a$ and is undefined for $x < a$.*

Definition

$\lim_{x\to a^-} f(x) = b$ means $\lim_{x\to a} g(x) = b$, where $g(x)$ is the function that coincides with $f(x)$ for all $x \le a$ and is undefined for $x > a$.

Example 1

Show that if

$$f(x) = \begin{cases} 0 & \text{if } x \le 0, \\ 1 & \text{if } x > 0, \end{cases}$$

then

$$\lim_{x\to 0+} f(x) = 1.$$

In order to show that $\lim_{x\to 0+} f(x) = 1$, we must show that $\lim_{x\to 0} G(x) = 1$, where

$$G(x) = \begin{cases} 0 & \text{if } x = 0, \\ 1 & \text{if } x > 0. \end{cases}$$

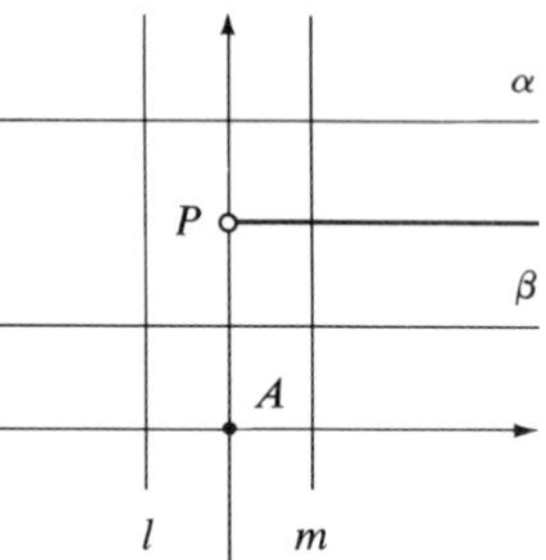

Figure 10.11

For this limit statement, $A = (0, 0)$ and $P = (0, 1)$. Since $G(x)$ is defined for $x \ge 0$, 0 is clearly a limit point of the domain of G. It is easily verified (see Figure 10.11), that if α and β are any pair of horizontal lines with P between them, then every point of $\mathscr{G} - A$ is between them no matter how l and m are selected.

Example 2

Show that if f is the function of Example 1, then

$$\lim_{x\to 0-} f(x) = 0.$$

Now $\lim_{x\to 0^-} f(x) = 0$ becomes $\lim_{x\to 0} g(x) = 0$, where

$$g(x) = 0 \quad \text{if } x \le 0.$$

For this limit statement, $A = P = (0, 0)$. Again, zero is clearly a limit point of the domain of $g(x)$. It is easy to verify (see Figure 10.12) that if α and β are any two horizontal lines with P between them, every point of $\mathscr{G} - A$ is between them no matter how l and m are selected.

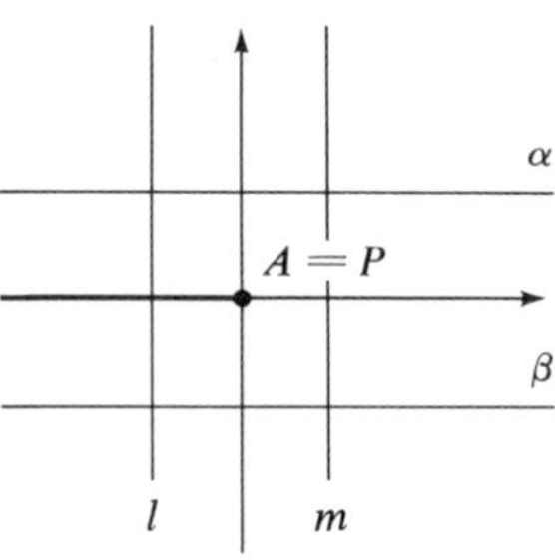

Figure 10.12

Since right- and left-hand limits are nothing more than ordinary limits of new functions, their existence or nonexistence is verified in exactly the same way that we have verified the existence or nonexistence of ordinary limits.

We might ask how the right- and left-hand limits of a given function are related to the limit of that function. We saw in the case of

$$f(x) = \begin{cases} 0 & \text{if } x \le 0, \\ 1 & \text{if } x > 0 \end{cases}$$

that $\lim_{x\to 0^-} f(x) = 0$ and $\lim_{x\to 0^+} f(x) = 1$, but $\lim_{x\to 0} f(x)$ does not exist. This is a special case of the following theorem.

Theorem 10.1

If $\lim_{x\to a^-} f(x) = b_1$ *and* $\lim_{x\to a^+} f(x) = b_2$, *where* $b_1 \neq b_2$, *then* $\lim_{x\to a} f(x)$ *does not exist.*

Proof

Let us suppose that $b_1 < b_2$. Since we want to prove that $\lim_{x\to a} f(x)$ does not exist, we must show that $\lim_{x\to a} f(x) = b$ is not true no matter what number we choose for b. To do this, we are going to consider two cases: $b > b_1$ and $b \leq b_1$. Before considering these cases, let us consider the points A and P for the three limits. Since all three are limits as x approaches a, $A = (a, f(a))$, for all three cases, provided $f(a)$ exists (if $f(a)$ does not exist, there is no point A in any of the three cases). Let $P_1 = (a, b_1)$, $P_2 = (a, b_2)$, and $P = (a, b)$; these are the P's for each of the three limit statements.

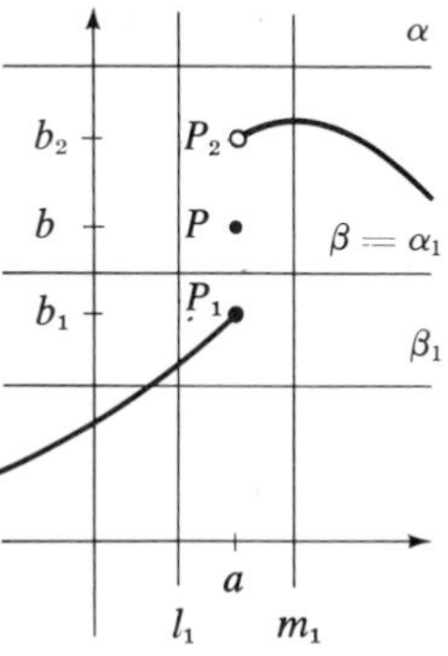

Figure 10.13

Assume that $\lim_{x\to a} f(x) = b$, where $b > b_1$. P and P_1 are on the same vertical line with P_1 below P (see Figure 10.13). Let α be any horizontal line above P, and let β be the line $y = (b + b_1)/2$ half-way between P and P_1. Now, since $\lim_{x\to a^-} f(x) = b_1$, it follows that no matter what pair of horizontal lines we choose with P_1 between them, there exists a pair of vertical lines l_1 and m_1 satisfying the conditions of the definition. Choose $\alpha_1 = \beta$ and let β_1 be any horizontal line below P_1. There is a pair of vertical lines l_1 and m_1 with P_1 between them such that every point of $\mathscr{G} - A$ between l_1 and m_1 and to the left of P_1 is between α_1 and β_1 (remember $\lim_{x\to a^-} f(x) = b_1$ is a left-hand limit). Now no matter how we choose l and m with P between them, some of these points are between them. But none of them is between α and β. Thus the assumption that $\lim_{x\to a} f(x) = b$, with $b > b_1$, is false.

The case in which $\lim_{x\to a} f(x) = b$ with $b \leq b_1$ is left to the student. This argument was made under the supposition that $b_1 < b_2$. A similar argument can be given for the case in which $b_1 > b_2$.

Theorem 10.2

If $\lim_{x\to a^+} f(x) = \lim_{x\to a^-} f(x) = b$, *then*

$$\lim_{x\to a} f(x) = b.$$

Proof

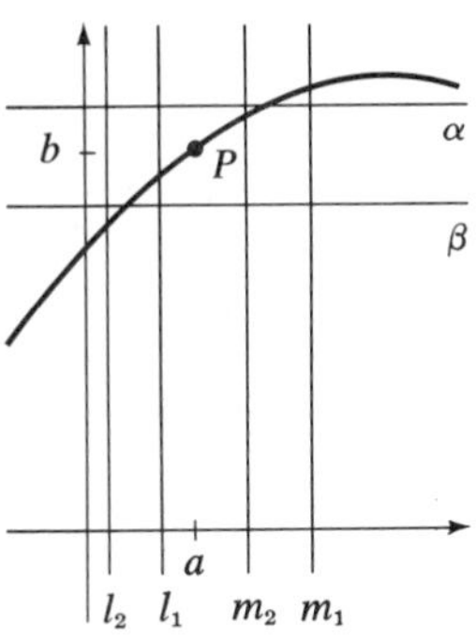

Figure 10.14

For all three limits, $A = (a, f(a))$ if it exists and $P = (a, b)$. The first part of the definition is easily seen to be satisfied, since it is satisfied for the points of $f(x)$ to the left (or right) of P. If α and β are two horizontal lines with P between them (see Figure 10.14), then since $\lim_{x\to a^-} f(x) = b$, there is a pair of vertical lines l_1 and m_1 such that every point of $\mathscr{G} - A$ between l_1 and m_1 and to the left of P is also between α and β. Similarly, since $\lim_{x\to a^+} f(x) = b$, there is a pair of vertical lines l_2 and m_2 such that every point of $\mathscr{G} - A$ between l_2 and m_2 and to the right of P is also between α and β. Now, let $l = l_1$ and $m = m_2$. Then every point of $\mathscr{G} - A$ between l and m is also between α and β. Thus $\lim_{x\to a} f(x) = b$.

The converses of the last two theorems are not true. This is obvious for Theorem 10.1. We have already seen many examples in which $\lim_{x\to a} f(x)$ did not exist, but neither right- nor left-hand limits existed either. It is not nearly so obvious that the converse of Theorem 10.2 is false; however, a consideration of the limits of Problem 15 shows that this is the case.

Problems

In Problems 1–4, show that the given limit statements are true.

1. $\lim_{x\to 0+} f(x) = 0$ where $f(x) = \begin{cases} 1 & \text{if } x \le 0, \\ x & \text{if } x > 0. \end{cases}$

2. $\lim_{x\to 0-} f(x) = 1$ where $f(x) = \begin{cases} 1 & \text{if } x \le 0, \\ x & \text{if } x > 0. \end{cases}$

3. $\lim_{x\to 1-} f(x) = 1$ where $f(x) = \begin{cases} x & \text{if } x \le 1, \\ 1 & \text{if } x > 1. \end{cases}$

4. $\lim_{x\to 1+} f(x) = 1$ where $f(x) = \begin{cases} x & \text{if } x \le 1, \\ 1 & \text{if } x > 1. \end{cases}$

In Problems 5–8, show that the given limit statements are false.

5. $\lim_{x\to 0+} f(x) = 0$ where $f(x) = \begin{cases} x & \text{if } x \le 0, \\ 1 & \text{if } x > 0. \end{cases}$

6. $\lim_{x\to 1+} f(x) = 2$ where $f(x) = \begin{cases} x-1 & \text{if } x \ne 1, \\ 2 & \text{if } x = 1. \end{cases}$

7. $\lim_{x\to 1-} f(x) = 2$ where $f(x) = \begin{cases} x-1 & \text{if } x \ne 1, \\ 2 & \text{if } x = 1. \end{cases}$

8. $\lim_{x\to 0+} \sin \dfrac{1}{x} = 0.$

In Problems 9–12, show that the given limits do not exist.

9. $\lim_{x\to 0+} \dfrac{1}{x}.$

10. $\lim_{x\to 0-} \sin \dfrac{1}{x}.$

11. $\lim_{x\to 0+} \log x.$

12. $\lim_{x\to 1-} f(x)$ where $f(x) = \begin{cases} \dfrac{1}{1-x} & \text{if } x < 1. \\ 1-x & \text{if } x > 1, \end{cases}$

In Problems 13–18, find $\lim_{x\to a^-} f(x)$, $\lim_{x\to a^+} f(x)$, and $\lim_{x\to a} f(x)$ for the given function and the given value of a.

13. $f(x) = \begin{cases} x+1 & \text{if } x < 1, \\ x-1 & \text{if } x > 1; \end{cases} \quad a = 1.$

14. $f(x) = \begin{cases} x & \text{if } x \ge 0, \\ -x & \text{if } x < 0; \end{cases} \quad a = 0.$

15. $f(x) = \sqrt{x}; a = 0.$

16. $f(x) = \dfrac{1}{x}; a = 0.$

17. $f(x) = \begin{cases} \dfrac{1}{x} & \text{if } x < 0, \\ 0 & \text{if } x \ge 0; \end{cases} \quad a = 0.$

18. $f(x) = \begin{cases} x+1 & \text{if } x < 1, \\ x-1 & \text{if } x > 1; \end{cases} \quad a = 0.$

19. Complete the proof of Theorem 10.1.

10.5

Infinite Limits

We have seen several ways in which a given limit might fail to exist. First of all, a may not be a limit point of the domain of the given function—that is, the first part of the definition might not be satisfied. In those cases in which a is a limit point of the domain, there are basically three different situations in which the limit might fail to exist.

The first type is the situation in which two different numbers are approached from the two different sides. We discussed this case in some detail in the preceding section dealing with right- and left-hand limits. A simple example (see Figure 10.10) of this type of nonexistence is

$$\left.\begin{array}{l}\lim\limits_{x\to 0^-} f(x) = 0 \\ \lim\limits_{x\to 0^+} f(x) = 1 \\ \lim\limits_{x\to 0} f(x) \text{ does not exist}\end{array}\right\} \text{where } f(x) = \begin{cases} 0 & \text{if } x \le 0, \\ 1 & \text{if } x > 0. \end{cases}$$

A second type of nonexistence occurs when no definite number is approached from either side but $f(x)$ gets large and positive as x approaches a (or $f(x)$ gets large and negative as x approaches a). This is exemplified (see Figure 10.15) by

$$\lim_{x\to 0} \frac{1}{x^2} \quad \text{does not exist.}$$

Figure 10.15

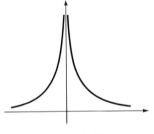

The third type may be illustrated (see Figure 10.16) by

$$\lim_{x\to 0} \sin\frac{1}{x} \quad \text{does not exist.}$$

In this case, no definite number is approached from either side, but the function does not get larger as x approaches zero.

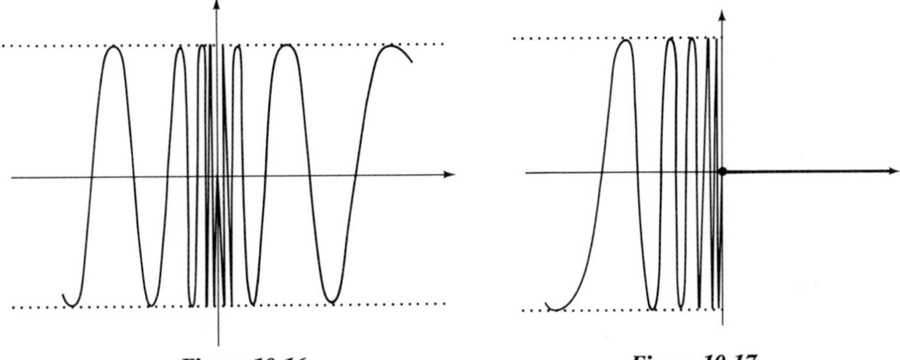

Figure 10.16 *Figure 10.17*

Of course there may be cases that combine two of these, such as (see Figure 10.17)

$$\lim_{x \to 0} f(x) \quad \text{where } f(x) = \begin{cases} \sin \dfrac{1}{x} & \text{if } x < 0, \\ 0 & \text{if } x \geq 0, \end{cases}$$

which combines the first and third types. Another is $\lim_{x\to 0} 1/x$ (see Figure 10.18), which combines the first two types; that is, $|f(x)|$ gets large as x approaches 0 from either side but $f(x)$ gets large and positive from one side and large and negative from the other.

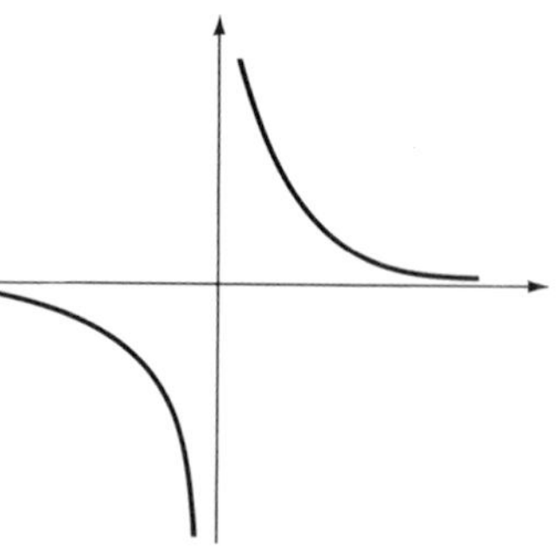

Figure 10.18

Since the second type of nonexistence occurs relatively frequently, special symbols are used to identify it. These symbols are $+\infty$ and $-\infty$. Thus $\lim_{x\to a} f(x) = +\infty$ means (roughly speaking) that $f(x)$ gets large and positive as x approaches a. Of course, this is unsatisfactory as a definition, because the meaning of the word "large" is quite vague. We shall use the following definition.

Definition

$\lim_{x\to a} f(x) = +\infty \ (-\infty)$ *means that*

(a) *if h and k are two vertical lines with $x = a$ between them, then there is a point of $\mathscr{G} - A$ between them, and*
(b) *if α is a horizontal line, then there exists a pair of vertical lines l and m with $x = a$ between them such that every point of $\mathscr{G} - A$ between l and m is above (below) α.*

Note here that A has the same meaning as before, but there is no point P. The first part of the definition is basically the same as the first part of the definition of $\lim_{x\to a} f(x) = b$; but the second part says that, no matter how high α may be, there is some point of $\mathscr{G} - A$ "close" to $x = a$ and higher than α.

Example 1

Show that

$$\lim_{x \to 0} \frac{1}{x^2} = +\infty.$$

The first part of the definition is easily seen to be satisfied, since $f(x) = 1/x^2$ has as its domain all real numbers different from zero. If α is a horizontal line above the x axis (see Figure 10.19), it intersects $\mathscr{G}$ at a pair of points X and Y. If l and m are vertical lines through X and Y, respectively, the second part of the definition is easily seen to be satisfied.

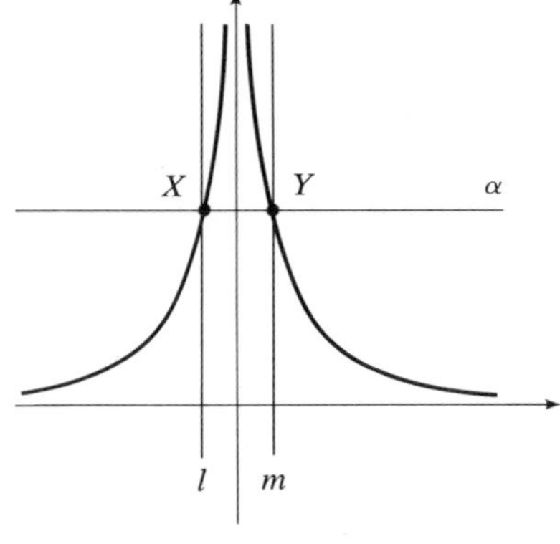

Figure 10.19

Remember here that the statement $\lim_{x\to a} f(x) = +\infty$ says that $\lim_{x\to a} f(x)$ does not exist (it is not equal to any number), but it is a certain special type of nonexistence.

$$\lim_{x\to a^+} f(x) = +\infty, \quad \lim_{x\to a^+} f(x) = -\infty, \quad \lim_{x\to a^-} f(x) = +\infty, \quad \text{and} \quad \lim_{x\to a^-} f(x) = -\infty$$

may be defined in a way that is self-evident. This is left to the student.

Now suppose we consider the limits

$$\lim_{x\to+\infty} f(x) \quad \text{and} \quad \lim_{x\to-\infty} f(x).$$

Since there is no numerical value for x to approach, there is neither an A nor a P.

Definition

$\lim_{x\to+\infty} f(x) = b$ means

(a) *if h is a vertical line, then there is a point of $\mathscr{G}$ to the right of h, and*
(b) *if α and β are two horizontal lines with $y = b$ between them, then there is a vertical line l such that every point of $\mathscr{G}$ to the right of l is between α and β.*

The definition of $\lim_{x\to-\infty} f(x) = b$ is the same except that "right" is replaced by "left."

The two parts of the definition correspond to the two parts of the definition of $\lim_{x\to a} f(x) = b$. The first part assures us that, no matter how far to the right we go, there is still some graph there. Thus $\lim_{x\to+\infty}\sqrt{-x}$ does not exist, because $\sqrt{-x}$ is not defined for any x to the right of $x = 0$.

Example 2

Show that

$$\lim_{x\to+\infty} \frac{x+1}{x} = 1.$$

Since $y = (x+1)/x$ is defined for all x except zero, the first part of the definition is easily seen to be satisfied. Suppose now that α and β are two horizontal lines with $y = 1$ between them (see Figure 10.20). If α is the higher one, α has a point X in common with the graph. Let l be the vertical line through X. Now every point of $\mathscr{G}$ to the right of l is below α and certainly above β. Thus the definition is seen to be satisfied.

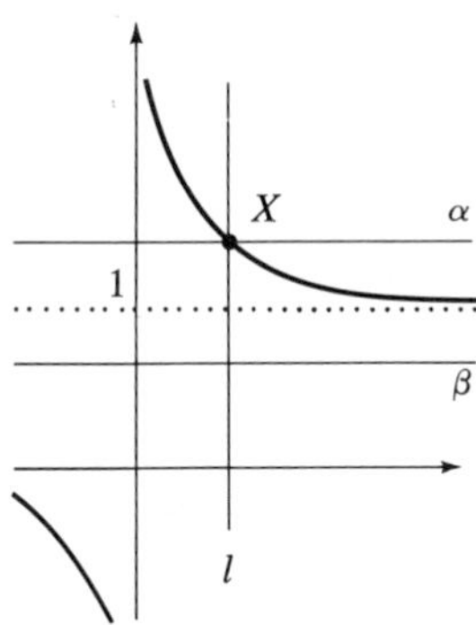

Figure 10.20

In what way, we might ask, might $\lim_{x\to+\infty} f(x)$ not exist? Of course, the first part of the definition might fail to be satisfied; we have already seen an example of this. However, instead of the basic three types of nonexistence we have seen for $\lim_{x\to a} f(x)$, there are only two. Obviously we cannot have the first type, in which two different numbers are approached from the two different sides, because you cannot approach $+\infty$ from both sides—you must approach it from the left. Thus the other two types of nonexistence are the only ones possible. They are illustrated by

$$\lim_{x\to+\infty} x^2 \quad \text{and} \quad \lim_{x\to+\infty} \sin x.$$

While neither limit exists, $\lim_{x \to +\infty} x^2$ is the special type of nonexistence given by $\lim_{x \to +\infty} x^2 = +\infty$ that we have seen before. The actual definitions of such expressions as

$$\lim_{x \to +\infty} f(x) = +\infty, \quad \lim_{x \to +\infty} f(x) = -\infty, \quad \lim_{x \to -\infty} f(x) = +\infty, \quad \text{and} \quad \lim_{x \to -\infty} f(x) = -\infty$$

are left to the student.

Problems

In Problems 1–8, verify that the given limit statements are true.

1. $\lim_{x \to 1} \frac{1}{(x-1)^2} = +\infty.$
2. $\lim_{x \to -1} \frac{1}{(x+1)^2} = +\infty.$
3. $\lim_{x \to 1} \frac{x-2}{(x-1)^2} = -\infty.$
4. $\lim_{x \to 2} \frac{x-2}{(x-1)^2} = 0.$
5. $\lim_{x \to +\infty} \frac{1}{x-1} = 0.$
6. $\lim_{x \to +\infty} \frac{x+1}{x-1} = 1.$
7. $\lim_{x \to -\infty} \frac{x+1}{x-1} = 1.$
8. $\lim_{x \to -\infty} \frac{2x^2+1}{x^2-1} = 2.$
9. Define $\lim_{x \to +\infty} f(x) = +\infty.$
10. Define $\lim_{x \to -\infty} f(x) = +\infty.$
11. Define $\lim_{x \to a+} f(x) = -\infty.$
12. Define $\lim_{x \to a-} f(x) = -\infty.$
13. Show that $\lim_{x \to 0-} \frac{1}{x} = -\infty$ and $\lim_{x \to 0+} \frac{1}{x} = +\infty$, but $\lim_{x \to 0} \frac{1}{x}$ is neither $+\infty$ nor $-\infty$.

In Problems 14–20, show whether the given limit statement is true or false.

14. $\lim_{x \to 0+} \frac{x+1}{x} = +\infty.$
15. $\lim_{x \to 0} \frac{x+1}{x} = +\infty.$
16. $\lim_{x \to +\infty} \frac{x+1}{x} = 1.$
17. $\lim_{x \to +\infty} x^2 = +\infty.$
18. $\lim_{x \to -\infty} x^2 = +\infty.$
19. $\lim_{x \to +\infty} (x - \sqrt{x^2+1}) = 0.$
20. $\lim_{x \to -\infty} (x - \sqrt{x^2+1}) = -\infty.$

10.6

Continuity

Although we have not mentioned it until now, another very important concept in calculus is that of continuity of a function. This concept is closely related to limits, as is apparent by the following definition.

Definition

The function f is **continuous at the point** *A of $\mathcal{G}$ means that if α and β are two horizontal lines with A between them, then there are two vertical lines l and m with A between them such that every point of $\mathcal{G}$ between l and m is also between α and β.*

This definition is very much like the definition of a limit. There are, however, two important differences. First, this is only a one-part definition; it contains nothing corresponding to the first part of the definition of a limit. The second difference seems to be quite minor but, in reality, is far more significant. It is the fact that, in considering the portion of the graph between the horizontal lines α and β and the vertical lines l and m, we are concerned with $\mathcal{G}$ rather than $\mathcal{G} - A$.

Suppose we consider the effect of these two differences. The first difference implies that $f(x) = \sqrt{x^2(x^2 - 1)}$ is continuous at the point (0, 0), which is an isolated point of its graph (see Figure 10.21). No matter what α and β are, l and m simply have to be taken close enough together so that the origin is the only point of $\mathcal{G}$ between l and m. Recall that $\lim_{x\to 0}\sqrt{x^2(x^2 - 1)}$ does not exist, because $x = 0$ is not a limit point of the domain.

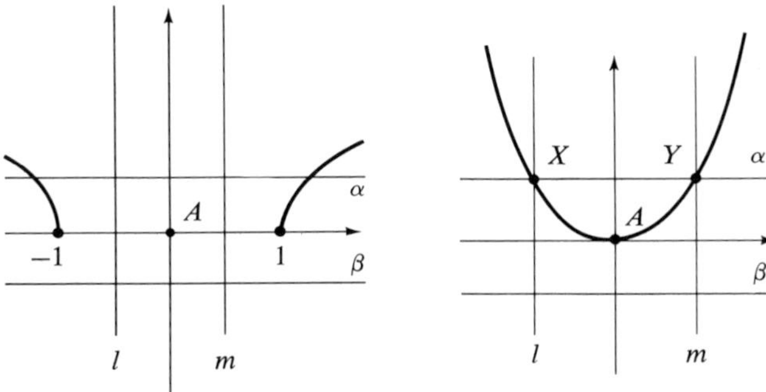

Figure 10.21 *Figure 10.22*

The effect of the second difference is that, roughly speaking, the point A is where you expect it to be. That is, $f(x) = x^2$ is continuous at (0, 0) (see Figure 10.22), while

$$f(x) = \begin{cases} x^2 & \text{if } x \neq 0, \\ 1 & \text{if } x = 0 \end{cases}$$

is not continuous at (0, 1); (0, 1) seems to be out of place (see Figure 10.23).

Example 1

Show that $f(x) = x^2$ is continuous at (0, 0).

The argument is basically the same as the one showing that $\lim_{x\to 0} x^2 = 0$ (see Figure 10.22). The horizontal line α has two points, X and Y, in common with $\mathcal{G}$. If l and m are vertical lines through X and Y, it is evident that every point (including the origin) of $\mathcal{G}$ between l and m is also between α and β.

Example 2

Show that

$$f(x) = \begin{cases} x^2 & \text{if } x \neq 0, \\ 1 & \text{if } x = 0 \end{cases}$$

is not continuous at (0, 1).

In order to show that this function is not continuous at $A = (0, 1)$ we must show that, for some pair of horizontal lines with A between them, no vertical lines can be found to satisfy the conditions of the definition (see Figure 10.23). Thus we select α to be any horizontal line above A and β to be the line $y = 1/2$. No matter how l and m are taken, there is some point of $\mathscr{G}$ between l and m but below both α and β. Thus this function is not continuous at A. Another way of saying this is to say that it is discontinuous at A.

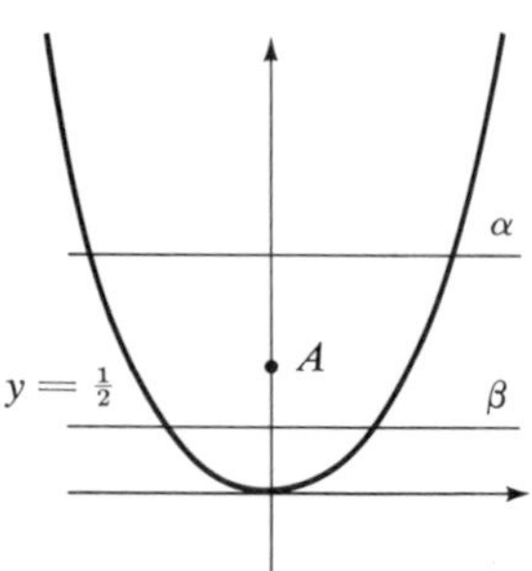

Figure 10. 23

Definition

The function f is ***discontinuous at the point*** *A of $\mathscr{G}$ means that it is not continuous at A.*

Note that we have defined a function to be continuous or discontinuous *at a point A of $\mathscr{G}$*. The function is neither continuous nor discontinuous at points not belonging to $\mathscr{G}$. Note also that we have defined continuity only at a point—not for the whole graph. However, we can easily extend our definitions to the following one.

Definition

A function is ***continuous*** *means that it is continuous at every one of its points. A function is* ***discontinuous*** *means that it is discontinuous at one or more of its points.*

Thus $f(x) = x^2$ and $f(x) = 1/x$ are continuous functions, since they are continuous at every one of their points. Some authors describe $f(x) = 1/x$ as a discontinuous function having a discontinuity at $x = 0$. Of course, there is no point of the graph with x coordinate 0; however, some authors define discontinuity, not only at points of the graph, but at values of x which are limit points of the domain (even when such points are not in the domain). Thus you need to remember this when reading other books or articles; some use the definition stated here, others use another—slightly different—definition. One must ascertain which definition an author is using before one can verify his statements concerning continuity.

Finally, how can we quickly observe discontinuities—that is, what does the curve look like at a discontinuity? Some take an opposite point of view and say that a continuous function is one that can be drawn without picking up the pencil. Actually, this is not quite true. While any function that can be drawn without picking up the pencil is continuous, there are other continuous functions that cannot. For example, $f(x) = 1/x$ is continuous at every one of its points; nevertheless, it cannot be drawn without picking up the pencil.

The following criterion is more reliable: A function is discontinuous if there is a vertical break in the graph that is not accompanied by a horizontal break. Thus, while there is a vertical break in the graph of $f(x) = 1/x$ at $x = 0$, there is also a horizontal break at $x = 0$. We grant that this horizontal break is only one point wide, but that is enough. If we were to plug up this hole with a point on the y axis, the resulting function would be discontinuous at that point, because then there would be a vertical break but no horizontal one. Similarly, the graph given in Figure 10.23 is discontinuous at $x = 0$ where there is a vertical break, but it is continuous everywhere else (there are no horizontal breaks in this curve, since it is defined for all real numbers x).

Problems

In Problems 1–18, indicate whether the given function is continuous, discontinuous, or neither at the point given and verify your result by means of the definition of continuity.

1. $y = x^2$; at (1, 1).
2. $y = x^3$; at (1, 1).
3. $y = \begin{cases} 0 & \text{if } x \le 0, \\ 1 & \text{if } x > 0; \end{cases}$ at (0, 0).
4. $y = \begin{cases} 0 & \text{if } x \le 0, \\ 1 & \text{if } x > 0; \end{cases}$ at (1, 1).
5. $y = \begin{cases} 0 & \text{if } x \le 0, \\ 1 & \text{if } x > 0; \end{cases}$ at (−1, 0).
6. $y = \dfrac{1}{x}$; at (1, 1).
7. $y = \dfrac{1}{x}$; at $\left(\dfrac{1}{100}, 100\right)$.
8. $y = \dfrac{x^2 - 1}{x - 1}$; at (1, 2).
9. $y = \begin{cases} x + 1 & \text{if } x \neq 1, \\ 2 & \text{if } x = 1; \end{cases}$ at (1, 2).
10. $y = \begin{cases} x + 1 & \text{if } x \neq 1, \\ 3 & \text{if } x = 1; \end{cases}$ at (1, 3).
11. $y = \begin{cases} \sin \dfrac{1}{x} & \text{if } x \neq 0, \\ 0 & \text{if } x = 0; \end{cases}$ at (0, 0).
12. $y = \begin{cases} x \sin \dfrac{1}{x} & \text{if } x \neq 0, \\ 0 & \text{if } x = 0; \end{cases}$ at (0, 0).
13. $y = \begin{cases} x^2 \sin \dfrac{1}{x} & \text{if } x \neq 0, \\ 0 & \text{if } x = 0; \end{cases}$ at (0, 0).
14. $y = \begin{cases} \dfrac{1}{x} \sin \dfrac{1}{x} & \text{if } x \neq 0, \\ 0 & \text{if } x = 0; \end{cases}$ at (0, 0).
15. $y = \begin{cases} \sin \dfrac{1}{x} & \text{if } x \neq 0, \\ 0 & \text{if } x = 0; \end{cases}$ at $\left(\dfrac{1}{2\pi}, 0\right)$.
16. $y = \begin{cases} x \sin \dfrac{1}{x} & \text{if } x \neq 0, \\ 0 & \text{if } x = 0; \end{cases}$ at $\left(\dfrac{1}{2\pi}, 0\right)$.
17. $y = \begin{cases} 1 & \text{if } x = 1, \\ 3 & \text{if } x = 2, \\ 7 & \text{if } x = 3; \end{cases}$ at (1, 1).
18. $y = x$ if $x = 0, 1, 2, \ldots$; at (1, 1).

In Problems 19–26, indicate whether the given function is continuous or discontinuous. If it is discontinuous, give all points of discontinuity.

19. $y = \dfrac{1}{x^2}$.
20. $y = \dfrac{x^2 - 1}{x - 1}$.
21. $y = \begin{cases} x + 1 & \text{if } x \neq 1, \\ 3 & \text{if } x = 1. \end{cases}$
22. $y = x$ if $x = 1, 2, 3, \ldots$.
23. $y = \begin{cases} 0 & \text{if } x \le 0; \\ x & \text{if } 0 < x < 1, \\ 0 & \text{if } 1 \le x. \end{cases}$
24. $y = \begin{cases} 1 & \text{if } x \le 0, \\ x & \text{if } 0 < x < 1, \\ 0 & \text{if } 1 \le x. \end{cases}$
25. $y = \begin{cases} 0 & \text{if } x \text{ is rational}, \\ 1 & \text{if } x \text{ is irrational}. \end{cases}$
26. $y = \begin{cases} 0 & \text{if } x \text{ is rational}, \\ x & \text{if } x \text{ is irrational}. \end{cases}$

10.7

Limits, Continuity, and Derivatives

In the last section we were concerned with the difference between limits and continuity. We shall now consider the similarities and their implications.

Perhaps you wonder, why all the fuss about limits? We've been taking limits for some time now, with no trouble. Why suddenly make it hard? Actually we have had no trouble with limits, because we have considered only the very simplest of limits for "well-behaved" functions. When the functions get more complicated and the limits more difficult, we would have considerable difficulty were we to rely on an intuitive idea of limits. You need a more exact idea of limits in order to evaluate the more difficult ones. Mathematics has a way of playing tricks on people who rely entirely on intuitive ideas and rules-of-thumb.

In past discussion, the determination of limits has seemed to be a matter of substitution. When will substitution give us the limit we want? The answer is found in the similarity of the definitions of limits and continuity.

Theorem 10.3

$\lim_{x\to a} f(x) = f(a)$ *if and only if f is continuous at $x = a$ and a is a limit point of the domain of f.*

Proof

Part I: Given that $\lim_{x\to a} f(x) = f(a)$, prove that $f(x)$ is continuous at $x = a$ and a is a limit point of the domain of f. Since $\lim_{x\to a} f(x) = f(a)$, it follows that a is a limit point of the domain of f (by the mere existence of the limit). It also follows that if α and β are two horizontal lines with P between them, then there exists a pair of vertical lines l and m with P between them such that every point of $\mathcal{G} - A$ between l and m is also between α and β. Since $A = P = (a, f(a))$, A is also between α and β. Thus, the earlier statement can be changed to read: If α and β are two horizontal lines with A between them, then there exists a pair of vertical lines l and m with A between them such that every point of $\mathcal{G}$ between l and m is also between α and β. But this *means* that f is continuous at $x = a$.

Part II: Given that f is continuous at $x = a$ and a is a limit point of the domain of f, prove that $\lim_{x\to a} f(x) = f(a)$. Since we are given that a is a limit point of the domain of f, the first part of the definition of the required limit statement is true. We merely have to verify that the second part is also true. Since f is given to be continuous at $x = a$, it must be defined at $x = a$ and $A = (a, f(a))$. By the definition of continuity, if α and β are two horizontal lines with A between them, then there exist two vertical lines l and m with A between them such that every point of $\mathcal{G}$ between l and m is also between α and β. Considering the limit statement that we want to prove, we have $P = A = (a, f(a))$. Since $P = A$, the above statement is true with A replaced by P. Furthermore, if every point of $\mathcal{G}$ between l and m is also between α and β, then every point of the smaller set $\mathcal{G} - P$ between l and m is also between α and β. Thus, the second part of the definition of limit is satisfied and $\lim_{x\to a} f(x) = f(a)$.

This theorem allows us to find limits like $\lim_{x\to 2} x^2 = 4$ by a simple substitution after noting that $f(x) = x^2$ is a continuous function and that $x = 2$ is a limit point of its domain. However, most of the limits with which we have dealt have been somewhat more complicated. Consider, for example,

$$\lim_{x\to 1} \frac{x^2 - 1}{x - 1}.$$

While $f(x) = (x^2 - 1)/(x - 1)$ is continuous at every one of its points, it simply is not defined at $x = 1$. Of course, if it is not defined at $x = 1$, it is not continuous there and we cannot use Theorem 10.3. We handle this by factoring the numerator and canceling factors to give

$$\lim_{x\to 1} \frac{x^2 - 1}{x - 1} = \lim_{x\to 1} (x + 1).$$

How do we justify this step? Let us note first that the functions $f(x) = (x^2 - 1)/(x - 1)$ and $g(x) = x + 1$ are not the same; however, they differ by only a single point. The point $(1, 2)$ is on the graph of g but not on the graph of f. This slight difference is not enough to give different limits, as the following theorem states.

Theorem 10.4

If the functions f and g are identical except for one point and $\lim_{x\to a} f(x)$ *exists, then* $\lim_{x\to a} g(x)$ exists and

$$\lim_{x\to a} f(x) = \lim_{x\to a} g(x).$$

Proof

Let $A_f = (a, f(a))$ and $A_g = (a, g(a))$, provided these points exist. Since $\lim_{x\to a} f(x)$ exists, it is equal to some number b and $P = (a, b)$. This point P is also used for the other limit, since we want to verify that $\lim_{x\to a} g(x) = b$. Now let us split the argument into two cases: that is, $A_f = A_g$ and $A_f \neq A_g$.

Case I: $A_f = A_g$. Since these points are identical, the graphs must differ at some other point. Now choose l and m close enough together so that the point of difference is not between them; thus, whatever we say about $\mathcal{G} - A_f$ between l and m can also be said about $\mathcal{G} - A_g$ between l and m. Since this is the portion of the graph we are concerned about in the definition of a limit, it follows that $\lim_{x\to a} f(x) = \lim_{x\to a} g(x)$.

Case II: $A_f \neq A_g$. Since these points are different, $\mathcal{G} - A_f = \mathcal{G} - A_g$. Again, this is the only portion of the graph we are concerned about in the definition of a limit. Thus $\lim_{x\to a} f(x) = \lim_{x\to a} g(x)$.

It might be noted that this theorem would still be true if f and g differed at any finite number of points. The proof is quite similar. Both of these theorems are used to evaluate

$$\lim_{x\to a} \frac{x^2 - a^2}{x - a}.$$

Theorem 10.4 is used to replace the function $(x^2 - a^2)/(x - a)$ by $x + a$, which is defined and continuous at $x = a$. Theorem 10.3 then allows us to evaluate the limit by a simple substitution. Thus, we see that these two theorems form the whole foundation for taking limits by the simple methods we have been using. It must be remembered, however, that in order for this to work the functions with which we are dealing must be continuous at $x = a$. Fortunately, *most* of the functions encountered in elementary calculus are continuous.

Theorem 10.5

A function f is continuous at $x = a$ and a is a limit point of the domain of f if and only if $\lim_{h \to 0} f(a + h) = f(a)$.

The proof of this follows quite directly from Theorem 10.3 by substituting $a + h$ for the x of that theorem. The details are left to the student.

We encountered $\lim_{h \to 0} f(x + h)$ in several of the proofs of theorems in Chapter 5 and assumed this limit to be $f(x)$. We noted there that this is not necessarily true for *all* functions, but that it is true for a certain class of functions that we called well-behaved. Theorem 10.5 now tells us that we may replace the vague term well-behaved by the defined term continuous. Thus, it might seem that Theorems 5.4 and 5.6 should specify that u (or v) be continuous. Actually, since we assume that $u'(x)$ exists, it is not necessary to say that u is continuous, since the derivative and continuity are related.

Let us turn our attention to the derivative. First of all, a derivative is a limit, but not every limit is a derivative. A derivative is a very special limit. If we are taking the derivative of the function f, we do not take the limit of f, but of the function

$$\frac{f(x + h) - f(x)}{h},$$

which is derived from f and which represents the slope of a certain line.

Let us consider the relationship between the derivative and continuity. First of all, the mere fact that a given function is continuous is not enough to guarantee the existence of a derivative. This is easily seen with the function defined by $y = |x|$. It is continuous at every one of its points, but it does not have a derivative at the origin (see Problem 12). But if a function has a derivative at a given point, it is necessarily continuous at that point.

Theorem 10.6

If f has a derivative at $x = a$, then it is continuous at $x = a$.

Proof

The proof is based upon two assumptions: The limit of a product is the product of the limits, and the limit of a difference is the difference of the limits, or

$$\lim_{x \to a} F(x) \cdot G(x) = \lim_{x \to a} F(x) \cdot \lim_{x \to a} G(x)$$

and

$$\lim_{x \to a} [F(x) - G(x)] = \lim_{x \to a} F(x) - \lim_{x \to a} G(x).$$

Similar statements can be made about the sum and quotient (provided the denominator is not 0) of two functions. Actually, these are properties of limits that we have been using for some time.

Let us use these assumptions to prove the theorem. Since

$$\begin{aligned}\lim_{h\to 0}[f(a+h)-f(a)] &= \lim_{h\to 0}\frac{f(a+h)-f(a)}{h}\cdot h\\ &= \lim_{h\to 0}\frac{f(a+h)-f(a)}{h}\cdot\lim_{h\to 0} h\\ &= f'(a)\cdot 0 = 0,\end{aligned}$$

it follows that

$$\begin{aligned}0 &= \lim_{h\to 0}[f(a+h)-f(a)] = \lim_{h\to 0} f(a+h) - \lim_{h\to 0} f(a)\\ &= \left[\lim_{h\to 0} f(a+h)\right] - f(a)\end{aligned}$$

and so

$$\lim_{h\to 0} f(a+h) = f(a).$$

By Theorem 10.5, f is continuous at $x = a$.

Problems

In Problems 1–10, evaluate the limits and indicate what theorem is used at each step.

1. $\lim_{x\to 0}\dfrac{x^2+x}{x^2-x}$.
2. $\lim_{x\to 2}\dfrac{x-2}{x^2-2x}$.
3. $\lim_{x\to 1}\dfrac{x^4-1}{x^2-1}$.
4. $\lim_{x\to 0}\dfrac{x^4-x^3-2x^2}{x^4+4x^3+3x^2}$.
5. $\lim_{h\to 0}\dfrac{(2+h)^2-4}{h}$.
6. $\lim_{h\to 0}\dfrac{(1+h)^3-1}{h}$.
7. $\lim_{h\to 0}\dfrac{\dfrac{1}{1+h}-1}{h}$.
8. $\lim_{h\to 0}\dfrac{\sqrt{1+h}-1}{h}$.
9. $\lim_{h\to 0}\dfrac{\dfrac{x+h}{x+h+1}-\dfrac{x}{x+1}}{h}$.
10. $\lim_{h\to 0}\dfrac{\sqrt{x+h}-\sqrt{x}}{h}$.
11. Supply the details for the proof of Theorem 10.5.
12. Show that $y = |x|$ is continuous at (0, 0) but has no derivative there.
13. Give an example of a function that is continuous everywhere but has no derivative at two of its points.
14. Give an example of a function that is continuous everywhere but has no derivative at infinitely many of its points.
15. Prove that Theorem 10.4 is still true if "one point" is replaced by "a finite number of points."

10.8

Derivatives of Compound Functions

In this chapter we have worked extensively with functions that are defined by more than one equation. We mentioned functions of this type in Chapter 4 (see page 54) and called them compound functions. Remember that the term compound does not describe an inherent property of the function but only a property of the way in which the function is represented. For example,

$$f(x) = \begin{cases} 0 & \text{if } x \leq 0, \\ 1 & \text{if } x > 0. \end{cases}$$

You may be very suspicious of functions of this type and regard them as somehow inferior to the simpler functions that can be defined by a single equation. Nevertheless, they are perfectly good functions and in no way inferior to the simpler ones. Among other places, compound functions are frequently encountered in probability theory.

Derivatives of compound functions can be considered in two parts—derivatives at "joints" and derivatives at all other points. The derivative of a compound function at points which are not "joints" is easily found. Suppose there is an open interval containing the number a such that the function f is defined by a single equation throughout that interval. By taking h small enough, we can determine $f(a + h)$ and $f(a)$ by the same equation. Since, in the derivative

$$f'(a) = \lim_{h \to 0} \frac{f(a + h) - f(a)}{h},$$

we are interested in the limit as h approaches zero, we need consider only small values of h. Thus the derivative at a is determined by a single equation, and it may be found by means of the derivative formulas.

The only problem we have in finding the derivative of a compound function is in connection with the derivative at the "joints." In that case we must use the definition of a derivative.

Example 1

Differentiate

$$f(x) = \begin{cases} 0 & \text{if } x \leq 0, \\ 1 & \text{if } x > 0. \end{cases}$$

The only "joint" is at $x = 0$. We can use differentiation formulas at all other values of x. Since $f(x) = 0$ if $x < 0$, $f'(x) = 0$ if $x < 0$. Since $f(x) = 1$ if $x > 0$, $f'(x) = 0$ if $x > 0$. Let us now consider the "joints." Here again we must start with the definition of a derivative. Suppose we consider the derivative of our given function at $x = 0$.

$$f'(0) = \lim_{h \to 0} \frac{f(0+h) - f(0)}{h}$$
$$= \lim_{h \to 0} \frac{f(h) - 0}{h}$$
$$= \lim_{h \to 0} \frac{f(h)}{h}.$$

Now we have something of a problem. What is $f(h)$? The answer to this question depends upon the value of h. If $h < 0$, $f(h) = 0$; if $h > 0$, $f(h) = 1$ (of course $h \neq 0$). Thus, we must consider two separate cases.

Case I $h < 0$:

$$\lim_{h \to 0-} \frac{f(h)}{h} = \lim_{h \to 0-} \frac{0}{h} = \lim_{h \to 0-} 0 = 0.$$

Case II $h > 0$:

$$\lim_{h \to 0+} \frac{f(h)}{h} = \lim_{h \to 0+} \frac{1}{h} = +\infty.$$

Since

$$\lim_{h \to 0-} \frac{f(h)}{h} \neq \lim_{h \to 0+} \frac{f(h)}{h},$$

$\lim_{h \to 0} f(h)/h$ does not exist. Thus there is no derivative at $x = 0$. This result also follows from Theorem 10.6. The derivative of the given function is

$$f'(x) = 0 \quad \text{if } x \neq 0.$$

Example 2

Differentiate

$$f(x) = \begin{cases} x + 1 & \text{if } x \neq 1, \\ 3 & \text{if } x = 1. \end{cases}$$

Of course $f'(x) = 1$ if $x \neq 1$. But

$$f'(1) = \lim_{h \to 0} \frac{f(1+h) - f(1)}{h}.$$

Since $1 + h \neq 1$,

$$f(1+h) = (1+h) + 1 = 2 + h;$$

and $f(1) = 3$. Thus,

$$f'(1) = \lim_{h \to 0} \frac{2 + h - 3}{h}$$
$$= \lim_{h \to 0} \frac{h - 1}{h}$$
$$= \lim_{h \to 0} \left(1 - \frac{1}{h}\right).$$

This limit does not exist, since $1 - 1/h$ gets large and negative as h approaches 0 from the right and large and positive as h approaches 0 from the left. Thus

$$f'(x) = 1 \quad \text{if } x \neq 1.$$

Problems

In Problems 1–10, find the derivative for all x.

1. $f(x) = \begin{cases} -x & \text{if } x \leq 0, \\ x^2 & \text{if } x > 0. \end{cases}$

2. $f(x) = \begin{cases} x^2 & \text{if } x \leq 0, \\ x^3 & \text{if } x > 0. \end{cases}$

3. $f(x) = \begin{cases} 0 & \text{if } x \leq 0, \\ x & \text{if } x > 0. \end{cases}$

4. $f(x) = \begin{cases} 1 & \text{if } x \leq 0, \\ x & \text{if } x > 0. \end{cases}$

5. $f(x) = \begin{cases} x & \text{if } x \neq 0, \\ 1 & \text{if } x = 0. \end{cases}$

6. $f(x) = \begin{cases} -x & \text{if } x \leq 0, \\ x & \text{if } x > 1. \end{cases}$

7. $f(x) = \begin{cases} -x & \text{if } x \leq 0, \\ 0 & \text{if } 0 < x < 1, \\ (x-1)^2 & \text{if } 1 \leq x. \end{cases}$

8. $f(x) = x \quad \text{if } 0 \leq x \leq 1.$

9. $f(x) = \begin{cases} 0 & \text{if } x < 0, \\ 3x^2 & \text{if } 0 \leq x \leq 1, \\ 0 & \text{if } 1 < x. \end{cases}$

10. $f(x) = \begin{cases} x & \text{if } x < 0, \\ 0 & \text{if } x \geq 0 \text{ and } x \neq 1, \\ 1 & \text{if } x = 1. \end{cases}$

In Problems 11–13, find the derivative at the point indicated.

11. $f(x) = \begin{cases} \sin \dfrac{1}{x} & \text{if } x \neq 0, \\ 0 & \text{if } x = 0; \end{cases}$ at (0, 0).

12. $f(x) = \begin{cases} x \sin \dfrac{1}{x} & \text{if } x \neq 0, \\ 0 & \text{if } x = 0; \end{cases}$ at (0, 0).

13. $f(x) = \begin{cases} x^2 \sin \dfrac{1}{x} & \text{if } x \neq 0, \\ 0 & \text{if } x = 0; \end{cases}$ at (0, 0).

14. Compare Problems 11–13 of this section with Problems 11–13 of Section 10.6, noting the relationship between the derivative and continuity.

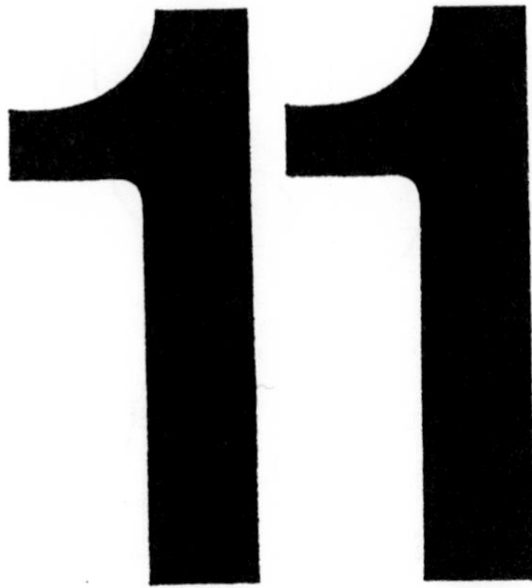

Trigonometric Functions

11.1

Graphs of Trigonometric and Inverse Trigonometric Functions

We now turn to some of the nonalgebraic (or transcendental) functions, beginning with the trigonometric functions and their inverses. Before considering the calculus of these functions, let us review some of their fundamental properties.

Although the measurement of angles in degrees is convenient for many purposes, you will find that, when we differentiate and integrate trigonometric functions, radian measure is the more natural way of measuring angles. We shall assume that all angles are measured in radians unless otherwise stated.

The graphs of the six common trigonometric functions are given in Figure 11.1. Note that all of them are periodic (repeating). The period of $y = \tan x$ and $y = \cot x$ is π; the other four functions have period 2π. Note also that four of them have vertical asymptotes, although there is no denominator to be zero. This is reasonable when we consider that all of them are defined as *ratios* of certain lengths. Let us see how these curves are altered by changing certain constants.

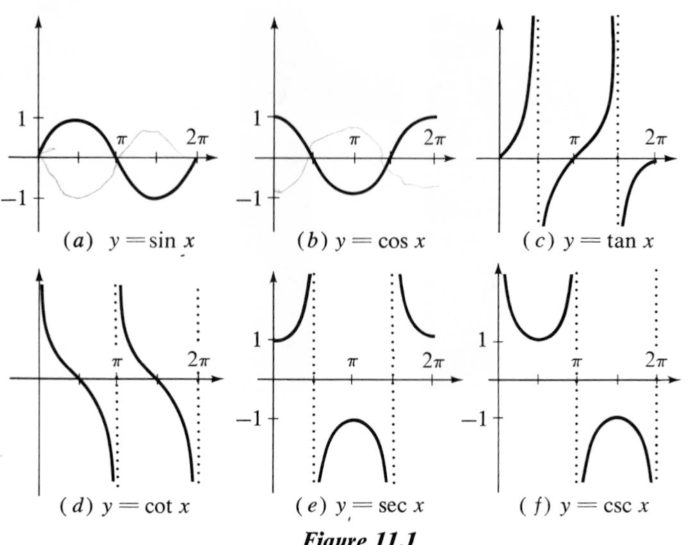

Figure 11.1

Example 1

Sketch $y = 3 \sin 2x$.

First of all, note that $-1 \leq \sin x \leq 1$. Thus the factor of 3 in $3 \sin 2x$ changes this range by a factor of 3. The fact that we have $\sin 2x$ instead of $\sin x$ does not alter the range. Now it takes one complete cycle for whatever we are taking the sine of to go from 0 to 2π; that is, we have one complete cycle for

$$0 \leq 2x \leq 2\pi \quad \text{or} \quad 0 \leq x \leq \pi.$$

Thus, the 3 in $3 \sin 2x$ triples the amplitude (or height) of the wave, while the 2 halves the period (or gives two complete cycles in the normal period of 2π). The result is shown in Figure 11.2.

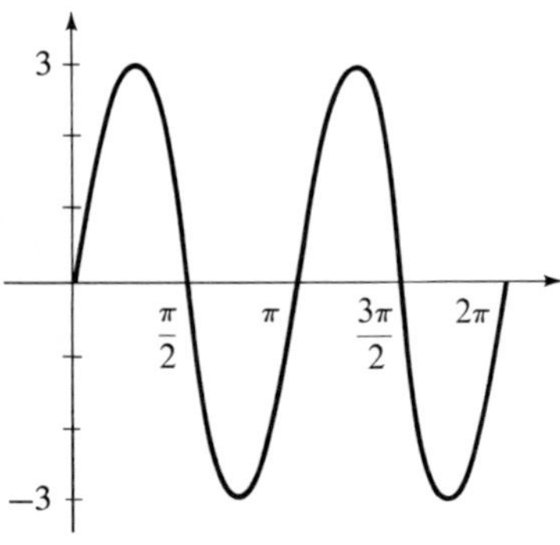

Figure 11.2

Example 2

Sketch $y = 4 \cos\left(2x + \dfrac{\pi}{2}\right)$.

First let us write the equation in the form

$$y = 4 \cos 2\left(x + \frac{\pi}{4}\right).$$

Now we see that the amplitude is 4 and the period is $2\pi/2 = \pi$. Now when $x = -\pi/4,\ \pi/4,\ 3\pi/4$, etc., $x + \pi/4 = 0,\ \pi/2,\ \pi$, etc. The $\pi/4$ has the effect of shifting the curve a distance $\pi/4$ to the left, as shown in Figure 11.3.

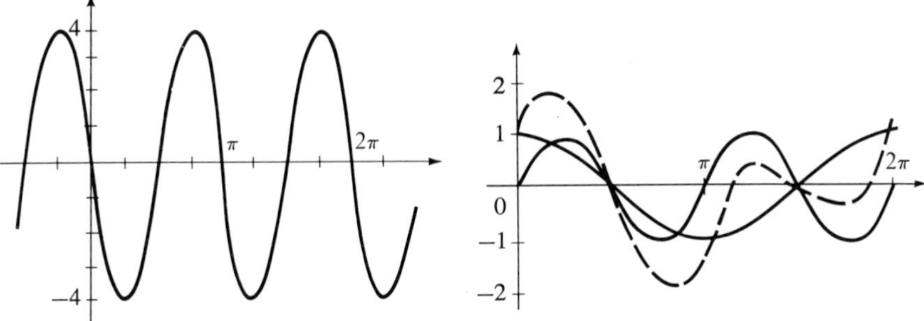

Figure 11.3

Figure 11.4

Example 3

Sketch $y = \cos x + \sin 2x$.

The method of addition of ordinates (see Section 9.11) is quite useful for equations of this type. Sketching $y = \cos x$ and $y = \sin 2x$ and adding the ordinates, we have the result given in Figure 11.4.

Example 4

Sketch $y = x + \sin x$.

Perhaps you wonder how we can add x and $\sin x$, if x is an angle and $\sin x$ is a number. Actually both x and $\sin x$ are numbers. We take trigonometric functions not of angles, but of numbers. The numbers are simply the *measures* of angles. It is quite possible to consider trigonometric functions of numbers quite independently of any angular interpretations; but if we do want to impose such an interpretation, the value of x is the measure of an angle in *radians*. Again, addition of ordinates works very well and Figure 11.5 is self-explanatory.

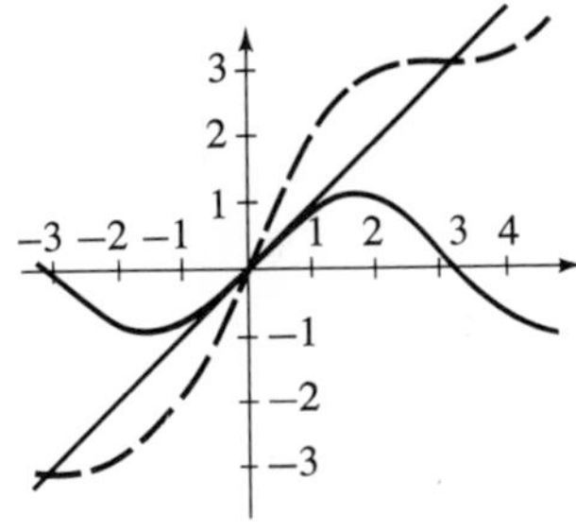

Figure 11.5

Suppose we have the equation $y = \sin x$ and want to express x in terms of y. To do so, we introduce a new notation for the solution,

$$x = \arcsin y \quad \text{or} \quad x = \sin^{-1} y.$$

This is read: x is an inverse sine of y. Thus $x = \arcsin y$ is equivalent to $y = \sin x$, or $y = \arcsin x$ is equivalent to $x = \sin y$. To graph $y = \arcsin x$, we merely graph $x = \sin y$ (see Figure 11.6). This looks exactly like the graph of $y = \sin x$ with the x and y reversed. Note that $\arcsin x$ is *not* a function, since one value of x gives many values of $\arcsin x$. (We shall restrict the values of $\arcsin x$ to give a function when we consider the derivatives.) The remaining five trigonometric functions have inverses that are defined analogously.

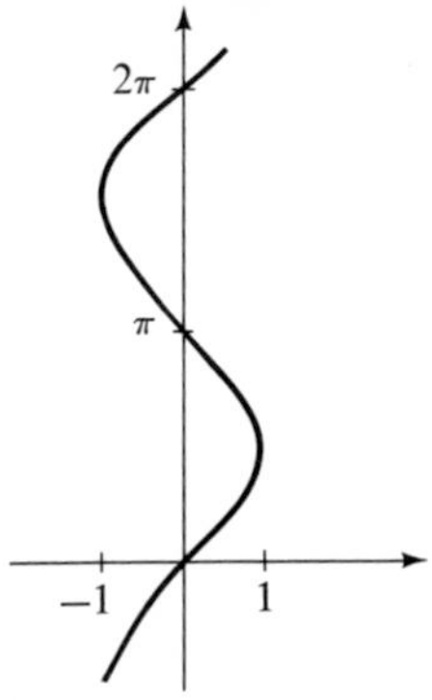

Figure 11.6

Example 5

Sketch $y = 2 \arcsin 3x$.

We first convert this to the equivalent equation involving the sine.

$$\frac{y}{2} = \arcsin 3x,$$

$$3x = \sin \frac{y}{2},$$

$$x = \frac{1}{3} \sin \frac{y}{2}.$$

Graphing this by the methods of Example 1, we have Figure 11.7.

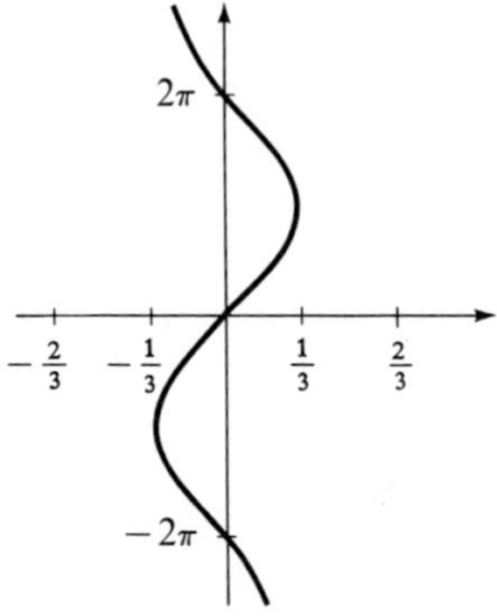

Figure 11.7

Problems

1. Express the following degree measures in radian measure: 45°, −210°, 270°, 30°, −180°, −60°, 135°, 150°.
2. Express the following radian measures in degree measure: $\pi/3$, π, $3\pi/4$, $-\pi/2$, $5\pi/6$, $-2\pi/3$, $3\pi/2$, $10\pi/6$.

In Problems 3–26, sketch one complete cycle.

3. $y = 3 \cos x$.
4. $y = 2 \sec x$.
5. $y = -2 \sin x$.
6. $y = 2 \tan 3x$.
7. $y = 4 \sin \pi x$.
8. $y = -2 \csc(\pi x/2)$.
9. $y = 3 \cos 4x$.
10. $y = 2 \sin(2x + \pi)$.
11. $y = 3 \cos(2\pi x + \pi/2)$.
12. $y = \tan(3x - \pi)$.
13. $y = 2 \sec(4x - 2\pi)$.
14. $y = -\cos(x - \pi/3)$.
15. $y = -2 \sin(\pi/4 - x)$.
16. $y = \sin x - \cos x$.
17. $y = 2 \sin x + \sin 2x$.
18. $y = \cos x - \sin 2x$.
19. $y = 3 \cos x + \sin x$.
20. $y = 4 \sin x + 2 \sin 2x - \sin 4x$.
21. $y = 2 \sin x - \sin 2x + \frac{2}{3} \sin 3x$.
22. $y = 1 - \cos x$.
23. $y = 4 \arcsin x$.
24. $y = 2 \arccos \frac{x}{3}$.
25. $y = \frac{1}{4} \operatorname{arcsec} \frac{x}{2}$.
26. $y = -\arcsin 2x$.

In Problems 27–30, sketch

27. $y = x - \sin x$.
28. $y = x^2 + \sin x$.
29. $y = x \sin x$.
30. $y = \frac{\sin x}{x}$.
31. Sketch

$$y = \frac{\pi}{2} + 2 \sin x, \qquad y = \frac{\pi}{2} + 2 \sin x + \frac{2}{3} \sin 3x,$$

and

$$y = \frac{\pi}{2} + 2 \sin x + \frac{2}{3} \sin 3x + \frac{2}{5} \sin 5x$$

on the same coordinates. What do you think the graph of

$$y=\frac{\pi}{2}+2\left(\sin x+\frac{1}{3}\sin 3x+\frac{1}{5}\sin 5x+\cdots\right)$$

looks like?

11.2

Derivatives of Trigonometric Functions

Before finding the derivatives of trigonometric functions, we shall first evaluate some difficult limits that will be useful later.

Theorem 11.1

$$\lim_{x\to 0}\frac{\sin x}{x}=1.$$

Proof

Note first that the previous methods we have used for evaluating limits cannot be used here. In the past, whenever both the numerator and denominator of a fraction approached zero, we (perhaps after some algebraic manipulation) canceled a factor to allow evaluation of the limit. This cannot be done here; we must try something entirely different.

Suppose we restrict the values of x to

$$0<x<\pi/2.$$

Now consider Figure 11.8, where the circle has radius one. Since $OA=OC=1$, we have

$$AB=OA\tan x=\tan x,$$
$$CD=OC\sin x=\sin x.$$

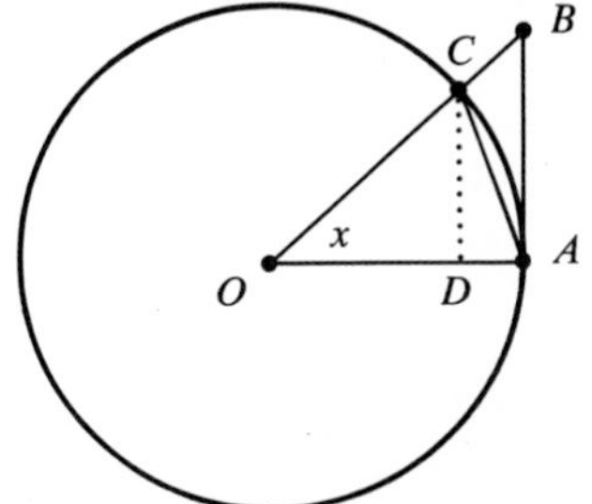

Figure 11.8

Comparing areas gives us

$$\triangle OAC<\text{sector } OAC<\triangle OAB,$$

$$\frac{1}{2}\cdot OA\cdot CD<\frac{1}{2}r^2x<\frac{1}{2}\cdot OA\cdot AB,$$

$$\frac{1}{2}\sin x<\frac{1}{2}x<\frac{1}{2}\tan x,$$

$$1<\frac{x}{\sin x}<\frac{1}{\cos x},$$

$$\cos x<\frac{\sin x}{x}<1. \qquad \text{(See Note 1)}$$

Taking limits, we have

$$\lim_{x\to 0+} 1 = 1 \quad \text{and} \quad \lim_{x\to 0+} \cos x = 1 \qquad \text{(See Note 2)}$$

and, for $0 < x < \pi/2$, $(\sin x)/x$ is between 1 and $\cos x$. Thus $(\sin x)/x$ must also approach 1, or

$$\lim_{x\to 0+} \frac{\sin x}{x} = 1.$$

Finally

$$\begin{aligned} \lim_{x\to 0-} \frac{\sin x}{x} &= \lim_{x\to 0+} \frac{\sin(-x)}{-x} \qquad \text{(See Note 3)} \\ &= \lim_{x\to 0+} \frac{-\sin x}{-x} \\ &= \lim_{x\to 0+} \frac{\sin x}{x} \\ &= 1. \end{aligned}$$

Since

$$\lim_{x\to 0+} \frac{\sin x}{x} = \lim_{x\to 0-} \frac{\sin x}{x} = 1,$$

it follows from Theorem 10.2 that

$$\lim_{x\to 0} \frac{\sin x}{x} = 1.$$

Note 1: If three positive numbers are replaced by their reciprocals, the inequalities are reversed. For example $2 < 3 < 4$, but $\frac{1}{2} > \frac{1}{3} > \frac{1}{4}$, or $\frac{1}{4} < \frac{1}{3} < \frac{1}{2}$ (see Problem 25, page 634).

Note 2: These must be right-hand limits, because of the restriction imposed on x, namely, $0 < x < \pi/2$.

Note 3: $\lim_{x\to 0^-} (\sin x)/x$ means the limit of $(\sin x)/x$ as x approaches zero, with x remaining negative throughout. The result is the same no matter what symbol is used in place of x. In particular, if x is replaced by $-x$, we have the limit of $\sin(-x)/-x$ as $-x$ approaches zero with $-x$ remaining negative throughout. But this means that x approaches zero with x remaining positive throughout, or

$$\lim_{x\to 0^+} \frac{\sin(-x)}{-x}.$$

Theorem 11.2

$$\lim_{x\to 0} \frac{\cos x - 1}{x} = 0.$$

Proof

Again, both the numerator and denominator are approaching zero. Let us use the result of Theorem 11.1 to evaluate this limit.

$$\begin{aligned}\lim_{x\to 0}\frac{\cos x-1}{x} &= \lim_{x\to 0}\frac{\cos^2 x-1}{x(\cos x+1)}\\ &= \lim_{x\to 0}\frac{-\sin^2 x}{x(\cos x+1)}\\ &= \lim_{x\to 0}\frac{\sin x}{x}\cdot\frac{-\sin x}{\cos x+1}\\ &= 1\cdot\frac{0}{2}\\ &= 0.\end{aligned}$$

Before using these two theorems, let us recall once more that they are true whether we use the symbol x or any other. In particular, if x is replaced by h, we have

$$\lim_{h\to 0}\frac{\sin h}{h}=1 \quad\text{and}\quad \lim_{h\to 0}\frac{\cos h-1}{h}=0.$$

Now let us make use of these limits.

Theorem 11.3

If $f(x)=\sin x$, *then* $f'(x)=\cos x$.

Proof

$$\begin{aligned}f'(x) &= \lim_{h\to 0}\frac{f(x+h)-f(x)}{h}\\ &= \lim_{h\to 0}\frac{\sin(x+h)-\sin x}{h}\\ &= \lim_{h\to 0}\frac{\sin x\cos h+\cos x\sin h-\sin x}{h}\\ &= \lim_{h\to 0}\left(\sin x\,\frac{\cos h-1}{h}+\cos x\,\frac{\sin h}{h}\right)\\ &= \sin x\cdot 0+\cos x\cdot 1\\ &= \cos x.\end{aligned}$$

Theorem 11.4

If $f(x)=\sin u(x)$, *then* $f'(x)=\cos u(x)\cdot u'(x)$.

Proof

This follows directly from Theorem 11.3 and the chain rule (Theorem 5.9). Letting $y=f(x)$ and abbreviating $u(x)$ to u, we get

$$\begin{aligned}\frac{dy}{dx} &= \frac{dy}{du}\cdot\frac{du}{dx}\\ &= \cos u\cdot\frac{du}{dx}.\end{aligned}$$

The last step uses Theorem 11.3 with the x replaced by u.

Theorem 11.5

If $f(x) = \cos u(x)$, *then* $f'(x) = -\sin u(x) \cdot u'(x)$.

Proof

Again abbreviating $u(x)$ to u, we have

$$\begin{aligned} f(x) &= \cos u = \sin(u + \pi/2), \\ f'(x) &= \cos(u + \pi/2) \cdot u' \\ &= -\sin u \cdot u'. \end{aligned}$$

Theorem 11.6

If $f(x) = \tan u(x)$, *then* $f'(x) = \sec^2 u(x) \cdot u'(x)$.

Proof

$f(x) = \tan u = \sin u/\cos u$. By the quotient rule,

$$\begin{aligned} f'(x) &= \frac{(\cos u)(\cos u \cdot u') - (\sin u)(-\sin u \cdot u')}{\cos^2 u} \\ &= \frac{(\sin^2 u + \cos^2 u)u'}{\cos^2 u} \\ &= \frac{1}{\cos^2 u} \cdot u' \\ &= \sec^2 u \cdot u'. \end{aligned}$$

Theorem 11.7

If $f(x) = \cot u(x)$, *then* $f'(x) = -\csc^2 u(x) \cdot u'(x)$.

Theorem 11.8

If $f(x) = \sec u(x)$, *then* $f'(x) = \sec u(x) \tan u(x) \cdot u'(x)$.

Theorem 11.9

If $f(x) = \csc u(x)$, *then* $f'(x) = -\csc u(x) \cot u(x) \cdot u'(x)$.

The proofs of these are similar to the proof of Theorem 11.6 and are left to the student. Summarizing the results of these theorems, we have:

$$\frac{d}{dx}\sin u = \cos u \cdot \frac{du}{dx}, \qquad \frac{d}{dx}\cos u = -\sin u \cdot \frac{du}{dx},$$

$$\frac{d}{dx}\tan u = \sec^2 u \cdot \frac{du}{dx}, \qquad \frac{d}{dx}\cot u = -\csc^2 u \cdot \frac{du}{dx},$$

$$\frac{d}{dx}\sec u = \sec u \tan u \cdot \frac{du}{dx}, \qquad \frac{d}{dx}\csc u = -\csc u \cot u \cdot \frac{du}{dx}.$$

You are urged to note certain similarities and differences that will make these formulas easier to remember.

Example 1

Differentiate $y = \sin x^2$.

$$y' = 2x \cos x^2.$$

Example 2

Differentiate $y = \sec (2x + 1)$.

$$y' = 2 \sec (2x + 1) \tan (2x + 1).$$

Example 3

Differentiate $y = \sin^2 x$.

First of all, let us compare this with Example 1 and note the difference. $\sin x^2$ indicates that we are to square x and take the sine of the result. $\sin^2 x$ indicates that we are to take the sine of x and square the result; it may also be written $(\sin x)^2$. In order to differentiate here, we must use the power rule.

$$\begin{aligned} y' &= 2 \sin x \cdot \frac{d}{dx} \sin x \\ &= 2 \sin x \cos x. \end{aligned}$$

Example 4

Differentiate $y = \dfrac{\sin x}{\cos x + 1}$.

$$\begin{aligned} y' &= \frac{(\cos x + 1)(\cos x) - (\sin x)(-\sin x)}{(\cos x + 1)^2} \\ &= \frac{\cos^2 x + \cos x + \sin^2 x}{(\cos x + 1)^2} \\ &= \frac{\cos x + 1}{(\cos x + 1)^2} \\ &= \frac{1}{\cos x + 1}. \end{aligned}$$

Example 5

Differentiate $y = \sqrt{\tan 2x}$.

$$\begin{aligned} y' &= \frac{1}{2} (\tan 2x)^{-1/2} \sec^2 2x \cdot 2 \\ &= \frac{\sec^2 2x}{\sqrt{\tan 2x}}. \end{aligned}$$

Problems

In Problems 1–22, differentiate and simplify.

1. $y = \sin 2x$.
2. $y = \cos x^2$.
3. $y = \tan 3x$.
4. $y = \csc (x^2 + 1)$.
5. $y = \sin^2 3x$.
6. $y = \cos^2 x^2$.
7. $y = (\cot 4x)^{3/2}$.
8. $y = \sec \sqrt{x}$.
9. $y = \sec x \tan x$.
10. $y = \sec^2 x + \tan^2 x$.
11. $y = (\sin x + \cos x)^2$.
12. $y = \dfrac{2 \sin x}{\sin 2x}$.
13. $y = \csc^2 x - \cot^2 x$.
14. $y = (\csc x - \cot x)^2$.
15. $y = \dfrac{\sin^2 x}{(1 - \cos x)^2}$.
16. $y = \dfrac{\sin x + \cos x}{\sin x - \cos x}$.
17. $y = \dfrac{\tan 2x}{2x}$.
18. $y = x \sin x$.
19. $y = x + \tan x$.
20. $y = \dfrac{\cot x}{1 + x^2}$.
21. $y = \sin \cos x$.
22. $y = \sec \tan x$.

In Problems 23–28, find the derivative for the given value of x.

23. $y = \sin x + \cos 2x, \quad x = \pi/4$.
24. $y = \sec^2 x + \tan^2 x, \quad x = \pi/6$.
25. $y = \sqrt{\sin 2x}, \quad x = \pi$.
26. $y = \dfrac{\sin x}{1 + \cos x}, \quad x = 5\pi/6$.
27. $y = \sin^2 x \tan^2 x, \quad x = 3\pi/4$.
28. $y = x \cos x, \quad x = \pi/4$.

In Problems 29–34, find dy/dx.

29. $\sin x = \cos y$.
30. $(\sin x + \sin y)^2 = 1$.
31. $\tan (x + y) = y$.
32. $\sec (x + y) = \tan (x - y)$.
33. $x + y = \cot (x - y)$.
34. $\sin (x + y) = (x - y)^2$.
35. Find an equation of the line tangent to $y = \sin x$ at $x = \pi/3$.
36. Find an equation of the line tangent to $y = \tan^2 x$ at $x = \pi/4$.
37. Show that $y = \sin 3x$ is a solution of $y'' + 9y = 0$. Show that $y = \cos 3x$ is also a solution.

11.3

Integrals Involving Trigonometric Functions

Since an indefinite integral is an antiderivative, we have an integral formula corresponding to every derivative formula. Corresponding to Theorems 11.4–11.9, we have the formulas of the following theorem.

Theorem 11.10

If u is a function of x, then

$$\int \sin u \cdot u'\,dx = -\cos u + C,$$

$$\int \cos u \cdot u'\,dx = \sin u + C,$$

$$\int \sec^2 u \cdot u'\,dx = \tan u + C,$$

$$\int \csc^2 u \cdot u'\,dx = -\cot u + C,$$

$$\int \sec u \tan u \cdot u'\,dx = \sec u + C,$$

$$\int \csc u \cot u \cdot u'\,dx = -\csc u + C.$$

Again, let us recall that $du = u'\,dx$. This substitution may be made on all of these formulas if desired.

Example 1

Evaluate $\int 2 \sin 2x\,dx$.

With $u = 2x$, $u' = 2$ and the integral is in the form $\int \sin u \cdot u'\,dx$. Thus

$$\int 2 \sin 2x\,dx = -\cos 2x + C.$$

Example 2

Evaluate $\int x \cos x^2\,dx$.

In this case $u = x^2$ and $u' = 2x$. Since we do not have the 2, we must adjust the constant in order to get it.

$$\int x \cos x^2\,dx = \frac{1}{2}\int 2x \cos x^2\,dx$$

$$= \frac{1}{2} \sin x^2 + C.$$

Example 3

Evaluate $\int \sec (2x - 1) \tan (2x - 1)\,dx$.

$$\int \sec (2x-1) \tan (2x-1)\,dx = \frac{1}{2}\int \sec (2x-1) \tan (2x-1) \cdot 2\,dx$$

$$= \frac{1}{2} \sec (2x-1) + C.$$

Example 4

Evaluate $\int \tan^2 x\, dx$.

None of our formulas allows us to evaluate this integral directly. However, we can put it into a form we can evaluate by using the identity $\tan^2 x = \sec^2 x - 1$.

$$\int \tan^2 x\, dx = \int (\sec^2 x - 1)\, dx = \tan x - x + C.$$

Example 5

Evaluate $\int \sin^2 x \cos x\, dx$.

Again, this does not fit any of the forms of Theorem 11.10. However, it is in the form $\int u^2 \cdot u'\, dx$, where $u = \sin x$. Thus,

$$\int \sin^2 x \cos x\, dx = \frac{\sin^3 x}{3} + C.$$

Example 6

Evaluate $\displaystyle\int \frac{\sin x}{\cos^2 x}\, dx$.

This integral may be evaluated either by the use of identities, as in Example 4, or by use of the power rule, as in Example 5. Let us use both methods.

$$\begin{aligned}\int \frac{\sin x}{\cos^2 x}\, dx &= \int \frac{1}{\cos x} \cdot \frac{\sin x}{\cos x}\, dx \\ &= \int \sec x \tan x\, dx \\ &= \sec x + C.\end{aligned}$$

$$\begin{aligned}\int \frac{\sin x}{\cos^2 x}\, dx &= -\int (\cos x)^{-2}(-\sin x)\, dx \\ &= -\frac{-1}{\cos x} + C \\ &= \sec x + C.\end{aligned}$$

Problems

Evaluate the integrals in Problems 1–26.

1. $\int \sin 2\theta\, d\theta$.
2. $\int \cos (2x - 1)\, dx$.
3. $\int \csc 3x \cot 3x\, dx$.
4. $\int \sec^2 4u\, du$.
5. $\int x^2 \sec x^3 \tan x^3\, dx$.
6. $\int x \sec^2 x^2\, dx$.

7. $\int (\sin x + \cos x)^2\, dx.$

8. $\int \tan^2 3x\, dx.$

9. $\int (\sin^2 x - \cos^2 x)\, dx.$

10. $\int \cot^2 4x\, dx.$

11. $\int \sin^3 2\theta \cos 2\theta\, d\theta.$

12. $\int \frac{\sec^2 x}{\tan^3 x}\, dx.$

13. $\int \frac{\tan x}{\sec^3 x}\, dx.$

14. $\int \csc^3 3x \cot 3x\, dx.$

15. $\int (\sec x + \tan x)^2\, dx.$

16. $\int (\csc x - \cot x)^2\, dx.$

17. $\int (1 - \csc x \cot x)^2\, dx.$

18. $\int (\sin x)^{2/3} \cos x\, dx.$

19. $\int \sqrt{\cot x}\, \csc^2 x\, dx.$

20. $\int \sec \theta (\sec \theta - \tan \theta)\, d\theta.$

21. $\int_0^{\pi/2} \sin 3x\, dx.$

22. $\int_0^{\pi/4} \sec x \tan x\, dx.$

23. $\int_{-\pi/4}^{\pi/4} \tan^2 x\, dx.$

24. $\int_{-\pi}^{\pi} \sin \theta \cos \theta\, d\theta.$

25. $\int_0^{2\pi} (1 - \sin x)\, dx.$

26. $\int_{\pi/4}^{\pi/2} \frac{dx}{\sin^2 x}.$

27. $\int \sec^2 x \tan x\, dx$ may be looked at from several different points of view. If we let $u = \tan x$, then $u' = \sec^2 x$ and we get

$$\frac{1}{2} \tan^2 x + C.$$

If we let $u = \sec x$, then $u' = \sec x \tan x$ and we get

$$\frac{1}{2} \sec^2 x + C.$$

Can both answers be correct? Explain.

11.4

Derivatives of Inverse Trigonometric Functions

As noted in Section 11.1, the trigonometric functions do not have single-valued inverses. Thus the inverses are not functions. In order to make them functions, we shall make them single-valued by restricting their ranges. Figure 11.9 gives the graphs of the principal inverse trigonometric functions together with their domains and ranges. The reason for restricting the ranges as we have will be apparent when we consider derivatives of these functions.

We shall use the following notation.

$$y = \arcsin x, \quad \text{or} \quad y = \sin^{-1} x$$

represents the inverse sine *relation* (not function) with domain $-1 \leq x \leq 1$ and unrestricted range.

$$y = \text{Arcsin } x, \quad \text{or} \quad y = \text{Sin}^{-1} x$$

represents the principal inverse sine *function* with domain $-1 \leq x \leq 1$ and range $-\pi/2 \leq y \leq \pi/2$. This same type of notation is used for the other five inverse trigonometric functions. Now that we are dealing with functions, we can proceed to find the derivatives.

Theorem 11.11

If $f(x) = \text{Arcsin } u(x)$, *then*

$$f'(x) = \frac{u'(x)}{\sqrt{1 - [u(x)]^2}}.$$

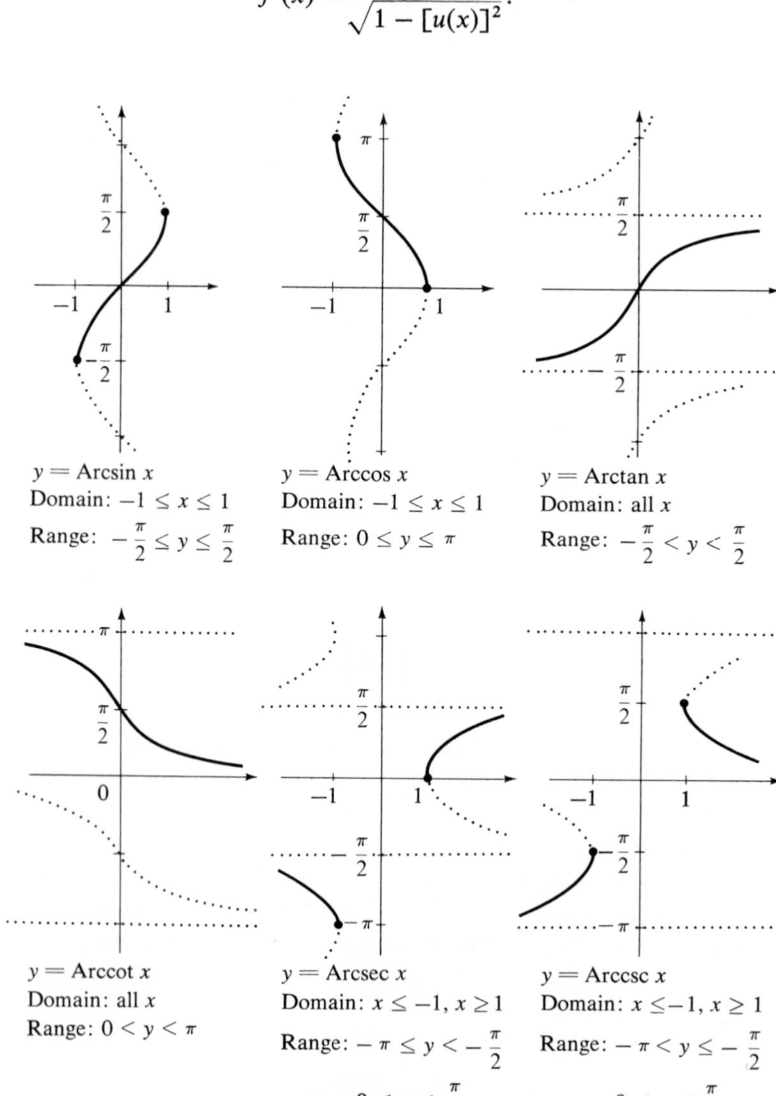

Figure 11.9

Proof

Let us abbreviate $u(x)$ to u and replace $f(x)$ by y, remembering that u and y are both functions of x. Now we have

$$y = \text{Arcsin } u$$

or

$$u = \sin y, \quad \text{where} \quad -\pi/2 \leq y \leq \pi/2.$$

Differentiating this implicit function, we have

$$u' = \cos y \cdot y',$$

$$y' = \frac{u'}{\cos y}.$$

Now since $\sin^2 y + \cos^2 y = 1$,

$$\cos y = \pm\sqrt{1 - \sin^2 y}$$

$$= \pm\sqrt{1 - u^2}.$$

Remembering that $-\pi/2 \leq y \leq \pi/2$, we see that $\cos y$ must be positive. Thus we may drop the $\pm$. Substituting this value of $\cos y$ back into the derivative, we have

$$y' = \frac{u'}{\sqrt{1 - u^2}}.$$

Theorem 11.12

If $f(x) = \text{Arccos } u(x)$, *then*

$$f'(x) = \frac{-u'(x)}{\sqrt{1 - [u(x)]^2}}.$$

The proof, which is similar to that of Theorem 11.11, is left to the student.

Theorem 11.13

If $f(x) = \text{Arctan } u(x)$, *then*

$$f'(x) = \frac{u'(x)}{1 + [u(x)]^2}$$

Proof

Again, using u and y for $u(x)$ and $f(x)$, respectively, we have

$$y = \text{Arctan } u,$$

$$u = \tan y, \text{ where } -\pi/2 < y < \pi/2,$$

$$u' = \sec^2 y \cdot y',$$

$$y' = \frac{u'}{\sec^2 y}$$

$$= \frac{u'}{1 + \tan^2 y}$$

$$= \frac{u'}{1 + u^2}.$$

Theorem 11.14

If $f(x) = \text{Arccot } u(x)$, *then*

$$f'(x) = \frac{-u'(x)}{1 + [u(x)]^2}$$

The proof is similar to that of Theorem 11.13.

Theorem 11.15

If $f(x) = \text{Arcsec } u(x)$, *then*

$$f'(x) = \frac{u'(x)}{u(x)\sqrt{[u(x)]^2 - 1}}.$$

Proof

Again, using u and y for $u(x)$ and $f(x)$, we have $y = \text{Arcsec } u$.

$$u = \sec y, \text{ where } -\pi \leq y < -\pi/2 \text{ or } 0 \leq y < \pi/2,$$

$$u' = \sec y \tan y \cdot y',$$

$$y' = \frac{u'}{\sec y \tan y}.$$

Now $\sec y = u$ and, from the identity $1 + \tan^2 y = \sec^2 y$, we get

$$\tan y = \pm\sqrt{\sec^2 y - 1}$$
$$= \pm\sqrt{u^2 - 1}.$$

Since y is either in the first or third quadrant, $\tan y$ is positive and we may again drop the $\pm$ giving

$$y' = \frac{u'}{u\sqrt{u^2 - 1}}.$$

Theorem 11.16

If $f(x) = \text{Arccsc } u(x)$, *then*

$$f'(x) = \frac{-u'(x)}{u(x)\sqrt{[u(x)]^2 - 1}}.$$

The proof, similar to the proof of Theorem 11.15, is left to the student. Summing up the results of Theorems 11.11–11.16, we have

$$\frac{d}{dx}\text{Arcsin } u = \frac{u'}{\sqrt{1 - u^2}}, \qquad \frac{d}{dx}\text{Arccos } u = \frac{-u'}{\sqrt{1 - u^2}},$$

$$\frac{d}{dx}\text{Arctan } u = \frac{u'}{1 + u^2}, \qquad \frac{d}{dx}\text{Arccot } u = \frac{-u'}{1 + u^2},$$

$$\frac{d}{dx}\text{Arcsec } u = \frac{u'}{u\sqrt{u^2 - 1}}, \qquad \frac{d}{dx}\text{Arccsc } u = \frac{-u'}{u\sqrt{u^2 - 1}}.$$

Example 1

Differentiate $y = \text{Arcsin } x^2$.

$$y' = \frac{2x}{\sqrt{1 - x^4}}.$$

Example 2

Differentiate $y = \text{Arctan } \dfrac{x}{a}$.

$$y' = \frac{\dfrac{1}{a}}{1 + \dfrac{x^2}{a^2}} = \frac{a}{a^2 + x^2}.$$

Example 3

Differentiate $y = x \text{ Arcsec } x$.

$$y' = x \frac{1}{x\sqrt{x^2 - 1}} + \text{Arcsec } x = \frac{1}{\sqrt{x^2 - 1}} + \text{Arcsec } x.$$

Example 4

Differentiate $y = \sin \text{Arccos } x$.

We can either simplify this expression and then take the derivative or take the derivative immediately. Differentiating the given expression, we have:

$$y' = \cos \text{Arccos } x \frac{-1}{\sqrt{1 - x^2}}$$

$$= x \frac{-1}{\sqrt{1 - x^2}}$$

$$= \frac{-x}{\sqrt{1 - x^2}}.$$

Simplifying first we have:

$$y = \sin \theta, \quad \text{where } \cos \theta = x \ (0 \leq \theta \leq \pi),$$

$$= \sqrt{1 - \cos^2 \theta} \ (\sin \theta \geq 0 \text{ for } 0 \leq \theta \leq \pi)$$

$$= \sqrt{1 - x^2}.$$

Differentiating this expression we get the same result as before.

Problems

In Problems 1–24, differentiate and simplify.

1. $y = \text{Arcsin } 2x$.
2. $y = \text{Arctan } x^2$.
3. $y = \text{Arccsc } 3x$.
4. $y = \text{Arccos } (2x - 1)$.

5. $y = \text{Arccot}(-2x)$.
6. $y = \text{Arcsec}\,\sqrt{x}$.
7. $y = \sqrt{1 - x^2} + \text{Arcsin}\, x$.
8. $y = \sqrt{1 - x^2} + \text{Arccos}\, x$.
9. $y = x - \text{Arctan}\, x$.
10. $y = \sqrt{x^2 - 1} + \text{Arccsc}\, x$.
11. $y = x\,\text{Arctan}\, x$.
12. $y = x^2\,\text{Arcsin}\, x$.
13. $y = \text{Arcsin}\,\sqrt{x}$.
14. $y = \text{Arccot}\,\sqrt{x}$.
15. $y = \dfrac{\text{Arcsin}\, x}{x}$.
16. $y = \dfrac{\text{Arcsin}\,\sqrt{x}}{\sqrt{x}}$.
17. $y = \text{Arcsin}\, x - x\sqrt{1 - x^2}$.
18. $y = -\dfrac{1}{8}\,[x\sqrt{1 - x^2}(2x^2 - 5) + 3\,\text{Arccos}\, x]$.
19. $y = \tan \text{Arcsin}\, x$.
20. $y = \sec \text{Arctan}\, x$.
21. $y = \text{Arcsin}\,\dfrac{1}{x}$.
22. $y = \text{Arctan}\,\dfrac{1}{x}$.
23. $y = \dfrac{x}{\sqrt{1 - x^2}} - \text{Arcsin}\, x$.
24. $y = x\,\text{Arcsin}\, x + \sqrt{1 - x^2}$.

In Problems 25–30, find the derivative at the given value of x.

25. $y = \text{Arcsin}\, x, \quad x = \dfrac{1}{2}$.
26. $y = \text{Arcsec}\, x, \quad x = 2$.
27. $y = x\,\text{Arccos}\, x, \quad x = -\dfrac{1}{2}$.
28. $y = x\,\text{Arctan}\, x, \quad x = 1$.
29. $y = \dfrac{\text{Arcsin}\, x}{x}, \quad x = \sqrt{3}/2$.
30. $y = \text{Arcsin}^2\, x, \quad x = 1/\sqrt{2}$.
31. Differentiate $y = \text{Arcsin}\, x - \text{Arcsec}\, x$. Watch out! (*Hint:* What is the domain of the function?)
32. Differentiate $y = \text{Arcsin}\, x + \text{Arccos}\, x$. Integrate the result.
33. Differentiate $y = \text{Arctan}\, x + \text{Arccot}\, x$. Integrate the result.

11.5

Integrals Involving Inverse Trigonometric Functions

Again the derivative formulas of Theorems 11.11–11.16 may be stated in integral form.

Theorem 11.17

If u is a function of x, then

$$\int \frac{u'\,dx}{\sqrt{1 - u^2}} = \text{Arcsin}\, u + C,$$

$$\int \frac{u'\,dx}{1+u^2} = \text{Arctan } u + C,$$

$$\int \frac{u'\,dx}{u\sqrt{u^2-1}} = \text{Arcsec } u + C.$$

Of course, this theorem gives the integral form of only three of the six derivative formulas. Since the derivatives of the other three principal inverse functions are simply the negatives of the three we have here and since constants can be adjusted, there is no need to consider the other three. For instance,

$$\int \frac{-u'\,dx}{\sqrt{1-u^2}} = \text{Arccos } u + C$$

or

$$\int \frac{-u'\,dx}{\sqrt{1-u^2}} = -\int \frac{u'\,dx}{\sqrt{1-u^2}} = -\text{Arcsin } u + C.$$

Example 1

Evaluate $\int \frac{dx}{\sqrt{1-x^2}}$.

This is in the form

$$\int \frac{u'\,dx}{\sqrt{1-u^2}},$$

with $u = x$. Thus

$$\int \frac{dx}{\sqrt{1-x^2}} = \text{Arcsin } x + C.$$

Example 2

Evaluate $\int \frac{x\,dx}{\sqrt{1-x^2}}$.

This is *not* in any of the forms given in Theorem 11.17. But, since the derivative of $1 - x^2$ is $-2x$, we can adjust the constant and use the power rule.

$$\begin{aligned}\int \frac{x\,dx}{\sqrt{1-x^2}} &= -\frac{1}{2}\int (1-x^2)^{-1/2}(-2x)\,dx \\ &= -\frac{1}{2}\frac{(1-x^2)^{1/2}}{1/2} + C \\ &= -\sqrt{1-x^2} + C.\end{aligned}$$

Example 3

Evaluate $\int \frac{dx}{4+x^2}$.

This again is not in any of the forms of Theorem 11.17, but this time it can be put into the form of one of them. The constant terms in all of the integrals of Theorem 11.17 are 1; thus, we need to get a 1 in place of the 4 we have. Let us divide both numerator and denominator by 4.

$$\int \frac{dx}{4+x^2} = \int \frac{\frac{1}{4}\,dx}{1+\frac{x^2}{4}}$$

$$= \frac{1}{2} \int \frac{\frac{1}{2}\,dx}{1+\left(\frac{x}{2}\right)^2}$$

$$= \frac{1}{2} \operatorname{Arctan} \frac{x}{2} + C.$$

Example 4

Evaluate $\int \frac{dx}{x\sqrt{x^2-9}}$.

$$\int \frac{dx}{x\sqrt{x^2-9}} = \frac{1}{3} \int \frac{\frac{1}{3}\,dx}{\frac{x}{3}\sqrt{\left(\frac{x}{3}\right)^2 - 1}}$$

$$= \frac{1}{3} \operatorname{Arcsec} \frac{x}{3} + C.$$

Example 5

Evaluate $\int \frac{dx}{\sqrt{2x-x^2}}$.

There are two ways of evaluating this integral. The first is by completing the square under the radical.

$$\sqrt{2x-x^2} = \sqrt{-(x^2-2x)}$$

$$= \sqrt{-(x^2-2x+1)+1}$$

$$= \sqrt{1-(x-1)^2};$$

$$\int \frac{dx}{\sqrt{2x-x^2}} = \int \frac{dx}{\sqrt{1-(x-1)^2}}$$

$$= \operatorname{Arcsin}(x-1) + C.$$

The other method is somewhat like that used in Example 3.

$$\int \frac{dx}{\sqrt{2x - x^2}} = \int \frac{\frac{1}{\sqrt{2x}}\,dx}{\sqrt{1 - \frac{x}{2}}}$$

$$= 2 \int \frac{\frac{1}{2\sqrt{2x}}\,dx}{\sqrt{1 - \left(\sqrt{\frac{x}{2}}\right)^2}}$$

$$= 2 \text{ Arcsin } \sqrt{\frac{x}{2}} + C_2 .$$

Although the two results look quite different, we can see by differentiating that both are correct.

Problems

In Problems 1–28, evaluate the integral.

1. $\int \frac{-x\,dx}{\sqrt{1 - x^2}}$.
2. $\int \frac{-x\,dx}{\sqrt{1 - x^4}}$.
3. $\int \frac{x\,dx}{1 + x^4}$.
4. $\int \frac{dx}{x\sqrt{4x^2 - 1}}$.
5. $\int \frac{dx}{\sqrt{1 - 9x^2}}$.
6. $\int \frac{x\,dx}{\sqrt{1 - 9x^2}}$.
7. $\int \frac{dx}{1 + 4x^2}$.
8. $\int \frac{dx}{1 + (x - 2)^2}$.
9. $\int \frac{dx}{\sqrt{1 - (2x + 1)^2}}$.
10. $\int \frac{dx}{(x + 2)\sqrt{(x + 2)^2 - 1}}$.
11. $\int \frac{dx}{x^2 - 2x + 2}$.
12. $\int \frac{dx}{\sqrt{-x^2 + 8x - 15}}$.
13. $\int \frac{dx}{(x - 2)\sqrt{x^2 - 4x + 3}}$.
14. $\int \frac{dx}{\sqrt{4x - 4x^2}}$.
15. $\int \frac{dx}{4x^2 + 12x + 10}$.
16. $\int \frac{dx}{\sqrt{-9x^2 + 12x - 3}}$.
17. $\int \frac{\cos x\,dx}{1 + \sin^2 x}$.
18. $\int \frac{\sec^2 x\,dx}{\sqrt{1 - \tan^2 x}}$.
19. $\int \frac{\sec^2 x \tan x\,dx}{\sqrt{1 - \tan^2 x}}$.
20. $\int \frac{\sec^2 x\,dx}{\tan x\sqrt{\tan^4 x - 1}}$
21. $\int \frac{\text{Arctan } x}{1 + x^2}\,dx$.
22. $\int \frac{\text{Arcsin } x}{\sqrt{1 - x^2}}\,dx$.
23. $\int_0^{1/2} \frac{dx}{\sqrt{1 - x^2}}$.
24. $\int_{-1/2}^{0} \frac{dx}{\sqrt{1 - x^2}}$.
25. $\int_0^1 \frac{dx}{1 + x^2}$.
26. $\int_0^{1/\sqrt{2}} \frac{x\,dx}{\sqrt{1 - x^4}}$.

27. $\displaystyle\int_{-2}^{-1} \frac{dx}{\sqrt{-x^2 - 2x}}$.

28. $\displaystyle\int_{0}^{\pi/4} \frac{\sin x\, dx}{1 + \cos^2 x}$.

29. Show that the two results of Example 5 are equivalent by showing that

$$\text{Arcsin}(x - 1) - 2\,\text{Arcsin}\sqrt{\frac{x}{2}}$$

is a constant. (*Hint:* Show that the sine of this expression is a constant.)

30. Evaluate $\displaystyle\int \frac{u'\,dx}{a^2 + u^2}$, where a is a constant and u is a function of x. Use the result to evaluate the integral of Example 3.

31. Evaluate $\displaystyle\int \frac{u'\,dx}{\sqrt{a^2 - u^2}}$, where a is a constant and u is a function of x.

32. Evaluate $\displaystyle\int \frac{u'\,dx}{u\sqrt{u^2 - a^2}}$, where a is a constant and u is a function of x.

Exponents, Logarithms, and Hyperbolic Functions

12.1

Exponential and Logarithmic Functions

Let us consider exponents and trace the development of a^n for various values of n. In your first encounter with exponents, you learned that, if n is a positive integer, then

$$a^n = a \cdot a \cdot a \cdots a \ (n \text{ factors}).$$

Later your knowledge of exponents was extended to include zero and negative integers:

$$a^0 = 1 \quad (a \neq 0),$$

$$a^{-n} = \frac{1}{a^n} \quad (a \neq 0, n \text{ a positive integer}),$$

Finally, this was extended to all rational numbers.

$$a^{p/q} = \sqrt[q]{a^p} = (\sqrt[q]{a})^p \quad (p, q \text{ integers}, q > 0, a \geq 0).$$

In the last extension negative values of the base a were ruled out, because they lead to problems like the following:

$$\sqrt{(-1)^2} = \sqrt{1} = 1, \qquad \sqrt{(-1)^3} = \sqrt{-1} = i,$$

$$(\sqrt{-1})^2 = i^2 = -1, \qquad (\sqrt{-1})^3 = i^3 = -i,$$

$$(-1)^{2/2} = ? \qquad (-1)^{3/2} = ?$$

We see that the order in which we carry out the operations makes a difference if the base is negative. To avoid this difficulty we restricted the base to positive numbers, for which the order of the operations is irrelevant.

All of the extensions from the original definition were made in such a way that the following properties of exponents, which were first derived for positive-integer exponents, remained true when exponents were extended to negative and, finally, to rational exponents.

I. $a^n \cdot a^m = a^{n+m}$.

II. $\dfrac{a^n}{a^m} = a^{n-m} \quad (a \neq 0)$.

III. $(a^n)^m = a^{nm}$.

IV. $(ab)^n = a^n b^n$.

Let us now make a final extension, to irrational exponents. In order to do so, let us consider the function

$$f(x) = a^x \quad (x \text{ rational}),$$

where a is any fixed positive constant.

Definition

$$a^n = \lim_{x \to n} f(x) \quad (n \textit{ real}).$$

Although we shall not attempt to do so here (proofs of the following statements can be found in Franklin*), the above limit can be shown to exist for all real values of n, and $\lim_{x \to n} f(x) = f(n)$ if n is rational. Furthermore properties I–IV are satisfied for real exponents, and the function

$$F(x) = a^x,$$

where a is a fixed positive constant, is continuous over the set of all real numbers.

The graph of $y = a^x$ for various values of a is given in Figure 12.1. The graph of $y = 1^x$ is the graph of $y = 1$, since $1^x = 1$ for all x. All of the others have the x axis as a horizontal asymptote. For $a > 1$, the graph rises steeply on the right and approaches the x axis on the left. The bigger the base, the more rapidly the graph increases on the right and the more rapidly it approaches zero on the left. For $a < 1$, the graph rises steeply on the left and approaches the x axis on the right. The smaller the base the more rapidly the graph increases on the left and the more rapidly it approaches zero on the right. All contain the point (0, 1).

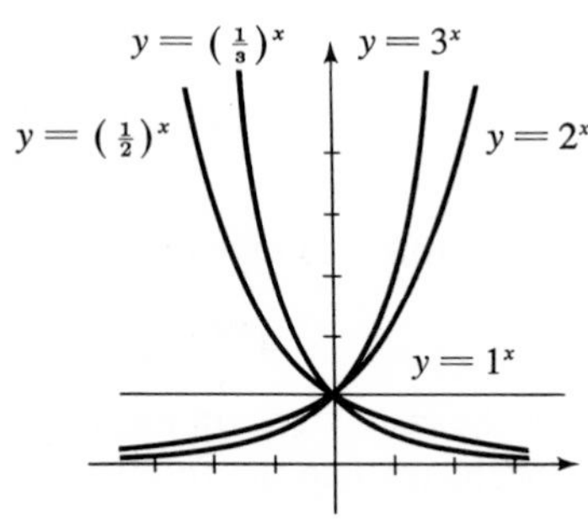

Figure 12.1

* Philip Franklin, *Treatise on Advanced Calculus* (New York, John Wiley, 1940), pp. 58–63.

Let us note at this time the distinction between $y = 2^x$ and $y = x^2$. The first, with a constant base and variable exponent, is an exponential function, which we are discussing here. The other, with a variable base and constant exponent, is a power function, which we have already discussed.

With this, we are in a position to define a logarithm in the customary way.

Definition

*The **logarithm**, base a $(a > 0,\ a \neq 1)$, of the number x $(x > 0)$ is the number y such that $a^y = x$. Thus,*

$$y = \log_a x \quad \textit{means} \quad x = a^y.$$

We see that the logarithm and exponential functions are inverses of each other; that is, $y = \log_a x$, which is equivalent to $x = a^y$, is simply the exponential function $y = a^x$ with the x and y reversed. Thus the fact that the range of all exponential functions with positive base other than one is the set of all positive numbers assures us that every positive number has a logarithm.

The graph of $y = \log_a x$ for various values of a is given in Figure 12.2. All have the set of positive numbers for their domain and the set of all numbers for their range. The y axis is a vertical asymptote and $y = \log_a x$ increases slowly for $a > 1$ and decreases slowly for $a < 1$. All contain the point (1, 0).

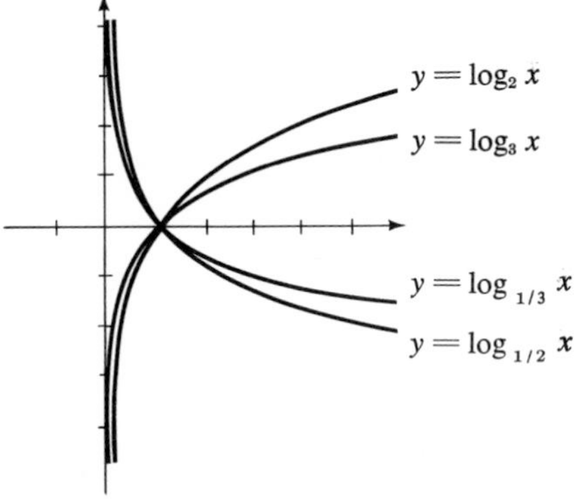

Figure 12.2

The laws of logarithms, which are easily derived from the laws of exponents are:

I. $\log_a mn = \log_a m + \log_a n$

II. $\log_a \dfrac{m}{n} = \log_a m - \log_a n.$

III. $\log_a n^m = m \log_a n.$

One other which we shall find useful is the equation for change of base.

IV. $\log_a n = \dfrac{\log_b n}{\log_b a}\cdot$

All of the laws of exponents and logarithms hold for any choice of the base a (provided $a > 0$ and $a \neq 1$). When working with logarithms in the past, you have probably worked almost exclusively with base 10. This is the most convenient base for computational work, since it coincides with the base of our system for representing numbers. But it is not very convenient in calculus. The most convenient base is the number e, which is defined as follows.

Definition

$$e = \lim_{x \to 0} (1 + x)^{1/x}.$$

This is a very difficult limit to evaluate. It appears at first glance that the limit must be 1, since the base approaches 1 and 1 to any power is still 1. Actually this is not the case. The graph of

$$y = (1 + x)^{1/x}$$

is given in Figure 12.3. It has domain $\{x \mid x > -1, x \neq 0\}$ and asymptotes $x = -1$ and $y = 1$. Although it is not defined at $x = 0$, the limit as x approaches zero exists and is a number between 2 and 3. This is the number we call e. The value of e to six significant figures is 2.71828.... Since the base 10 and the base e are used so frequently, logarithms with these bases are abbreviated. Throughout this book we shall use the conventions

$$\log_{10} x = \log x \quad \text{and} \quad \log_e x = \ln x.$$

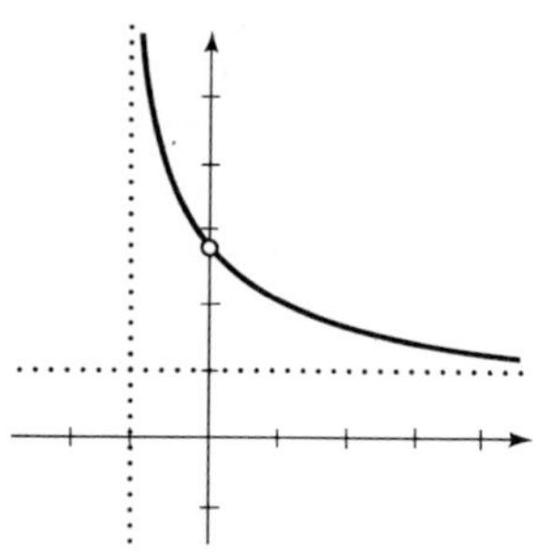

Figure 12.3

These are called the common logarithm and the natural logarithm, respectively. One word of warning: The abbreviations we are using are common in elementary mathematics texts as well as science and engineering texts; but most advanced mathematics books use $\log x$ to represent $\log_e x$. Thus, some confusion is inevitable, and you must check to see whether the base is 10 or e.

Problems

Sketch the graphs of the equations in Problems 1–16.

1. $y = 2^{x+1}$.
2. $y = 2^{x-1}$.
3. $y = 3^{-x}$.
4. $y = e^x$.
5. $y = 2^{|x|}$.
6. $y = 2^{x^2}$.
7. $y = 4^{2x}$.
8. $y = 3^{-2x}$.
9. $y = \log_2(x + 1)$.
10. $y = \log_2(x - 1)$.
11. $y = \log_3(-x)$.
12. $y = \ln x$.
13. $y = \log_2 |x|$.
14. $y = \log_2 x^2$.
15. $y = \log_4 2x$.
16. $y = \log_3(-2x)$.

In Problems 17–30, solve for x. Do not use tables.

17. $y = e^x$.
18. $y = \log_5 x$.
19. $y = \log_7(x - 1)$.
20. $y = 2^{\log_2 x}$.
21. $y = \log_3 3^x$.
22. $y = \ln x^2$.
23. $y = 4^{x+1}$.
24. $y = 3^{2x-5}$.
25. $\log x = 2 \log 3 - \log 4$.
26. $\log_2 x = \log_2 5 + \frac{1}{2} \log_2 4$.
27. $\log_3 x = \frac{1}{2} \log_3 5 + \log_3 4 - 2 \log_3 3$.
28. $\ln x = 4 \ln 2 - 2 \ln 3 - \ln 5$.
29. $\ln x^2 - \ln 2x = 4 \ln 3 - \ln 6$.
30. $\log x^2 = \frac{1}{2} \log 9 + 2 \log 4 - \log 5$.

In Problems 31–36, express the given logarithm in terms of simpler ones by the use of properties I–III of logarithms.

31. $\log x^2(x + 1)$.
32. $\log_3 \dfrac{x}{x - 2}$.
33. $\log_5 \dfrac{x^2(x + 3)}{x - 1}$.
34. $\log_2 \dfrac{\sqrt{x}(x - 4)}{(x + 1)^2}$.
35. $\ln \dfrac{(x + 1)^{3/2}(x - 2)^{1/2}}{(x + 3)^{1/3}}$.
36. $\log \sqrt{\dfrac{(x + 1)x}{(x - 2)}}$.

37. Prove laws I–III of logarithms.
38. Prove the change-of-base formula.
39. Use the definition of e to find a decimal approximation of e correct to two decimal places. *Hint:* Use the substitution $x = 1/n$ and expand the result by the binomial theorem (assuming n to be an integer).

12.2

Derivatives of Logarithmic Functions

Before finding derivatives of logarithmic functions, let us recall the definition of e.

$$e = \lim_{x \to 0} (1 + x)^{1/x}.$$

Although x appears in the limit expression, the number e has nothing to do with the choice of x. Any symbol may be used in place of x. In particular,

$$e = \lim_{h/x \to 0} \left(1 + \frac{h}{x}\right)^{x/h}.$$

Theorem 12.1

If $f(x) = \log_a x$, *then*

$$f'(x) = \frac{1}{x} \log_a e.$$

Proof

$$f'(x) = \lim_{h \to 0} \frac{f(x+h) - f(x)}{h}$$

$$= \lim_{h \to 0} \frac{\log_a(x+h) - \log_a x}{h}$$

$$= \lim_{h \to 0} \frac{\log_a \dfrac{x+h}{x}}{h} \qquad \text{(by law II)}$$

$$= \lim_{h \to 0} \frac{1}{h} \log_a\left(1 + \frac{h}{x}\right)$$

$$= \lim_{h \to 0} \frac{1}{x} \cdot \frac{x}{h} \log_a\left(1 + \frac{h}{x}\right)$$

$$= \lim_{h \to 0} \frac{1}{x} \log_a\left(1 + \frac{h}{x}\right)^{x/h} \qquad \text{(by law III)}$$

$$= \frac{1}{x} \log_a e. \qquad \text{(See Note)}$$

Note: We are assuming here that

$$\lim_{h\to 0} \frac{1}{x} \log_a\left(1+\frac{h}{x}\right)^{x/h} = \frac{1}{x} \log_a\left[\lim_{h\to 0}\left(1+\frac{h}{x}\right)^{x/h}\right].$$

Theorem 12.2

If $f(x) = \log_a u(x)$, *then*

$$f'(x) = \frac{u'(x)}{u(x)} \log_a e.$$

This follows directly from Theorem 12.1 and the chain rule. The factor $\log_a e$ is rather bothersome; but we can eliminate it by choosing $a = e$, since $\ln e = 1$.

Theorem 12.3

If $f(x) = \ln u(x)$, *then*

$$f'(x) = \frac{u'(x)}{u(x)}.$$

Example 1

Differentiate $y = \log_2(x^2 + 1)$.

$$y' = \frac{2x}{x^2+1} \log_2 e.$$

Example 2

Differentiate $y = \ln |x|$.

$$y = \ln |x| = \begin{cases} \ln x, & x > 0, \\ \ln(-x), & x < 0. \end{cases}$$

If $y = \ln x$, then $y' = 1/x$. If $y = \ln(-x)$, then $y' = (-1)/(-x) = 1/x$; thus $y' = 1/x$ in either case.

Example 3

Differentiate $y = \ln\sqrt{x}$.

Let us first differentiate this expression just as it stands:

$$y' = \frac{\dfrac{1}{2\sqrt{x}}}{\sqrt{x}} = \frac{1}{2x}.$$

We can get the same result more easily by simplifying the original expression:

$$y = \ln \sqrt{x} = \ln(x)^{1/2} = \frac{1}{2} \ln x.$$

Now the differentiation is simpler:

$$y' = \frac{1}{2} \cdot \frac{1}{x} = \frac{1}{2x}.$$

The second method was not much simpler than the first in this case, but let us consider another example.

Example 4

Differentiate $y = \ln \dfrac{x^2(x+1)}{(x-2)^3}$.

$$\begin{aligned} y &= \ln x^2 + \ln(x+1) - \ln(x-2)^3 \\ &= 2 \ln x + \ln(x+1) - 3 \ln(x-2). \\ y' &= \frac{2}{x} + \frac{1}{x+1} - \frac{3}{x-2} \\ &= -\frac{7x+4}{x(x+1)(x-2)}. \end{aligned}$$

Although there was some algebraic manipulation in simplifying the derivative, this method is still much simpler than differentiating the original expression. The use of logarithms can sometimes simplify complicated algebraic expressions.

Example 5

Differentiate $y = \dfrac{x^{2/3}(x-1)^{1/3}}{x+2}$.

Let us first take the natural logarithm of both sides of the equation.

$$\begin{aligned} \ln y &= \ln \frac{x^{2/3}(x-1)^{1/3}}{x+2} \\ &= \frac{2}{3} \ln |x| + \frac{1}{3} \ln(x-1) - \ln(x+2). \end{aligned}$$

Now we have an implicit function. Let us take the derivatives of both sides.

$$\frac{y'}{y} = \frac{2}{3x} + \frac{1}{3(x-1)} - \frac{1}{x+2},$$

$$y' = y\left(\frac{2}{3x} + \frac{1}{3(x-1)} - \frac{1}{x+2}\right).$$

If the result can be left in this form, we have saved a great deal of time. Unfortunately, the most useful form requires that we combine the three terms into a single one.

Example 6

Differentiate $y = x \ln x$.

$$\begin{aligned} y' &= x \cdot \frac{1}{x} + \ln x \cdot 1 \\ &= 1 + \ln x. \end{aligned}$$

Problems

In Problems 1–24, differentiate and simplify.

1. $y = \log 4x$.
2. $y = \log_3 x^2$.
3. $y = \ln(x^2 + 1)$.
4. $y = \ln \sqrt{x^2 + 1}$.
5. $y = \ln \dfrac{1}{x}$.
6. $y = \ln \dfrac{2x + 3}{3x + 2}$.
7. $y = \ln \sqrt{\dfrac{2x + 1}{2x - 1}}$.
8. $y = \ln \dfrac{x^2 - 1}{x^2 + 1}$.
9. $y = \log_5 \left(\dfrac{3x + 1}{3x - 1}\right)^{2/3}$.
10. $y = \log \dfrac{x(x - 1)}{x + 2}$.
11. $y = x^2 \ln x$.
12. $y = \sqrt{x} \ln \sqrt{x}$.
13. $y = \dfrac{\ln x}{x}$.
14. $y = \dfrac{\ln x}{x^2}$.
15. $y = \ln \sin x$.
16. $y = \ln \tan x$.
17. $y = \sin \ln x$.
18. $y = \ln (\sin^2 x + 1)$.
19. $y = \ln (x + \sqrt{x^2 - 1})$.
20. $y = \ln (x - \sqrt{x^2 - 1})$.
21. $y = \ln \ln x$.
22. $y = \ln \ln x^2$.
23. $y = \ln (x \ln x)$.
24. $y = \ln \ln \ln x$.

In Problems 25–30, find dy/dx.

25. $\ln y = \sin x$.
26. $\ln (x + y) = x - y$.
27. $\ln y = \sin (x + y)$.
28. $\ln \sqrt{xy} + \sqrt{xy} = 4$.
29. $x^2 + y^2 = \ln (x + y)$.
30. $xy = \ln \sin (x + y)$.

In Problems 31–34, use the method of Example 5 to differentiate.

31. $y = \sqrt{\dfrac{x(x - 1)}{x + 3}}$.
32. $y = \dfrac{x^2(x - 2)^5}{(x - 4)^3}$.
33. $y = \dfrac{x^{2/3}(x + 1)^{4/3}}{(x - 5)^{1/3}}$.
34. $y = \dfrac{(x - 2)^{3/2}(x + 1)^{1/2}}{x^{5/2}(x + 3)^{1/2}}$.

In Problems 35–40, find the derivative at the value of x indicated.

35. $y = \ln x, \quad x = 2$.
36. $y = \ln \sqrt{x}, \quad x = 4$.
37. $y = x \ln x, \quad x = 1$.
38. $y = \dfrac{\ln x}{x}, \quad x = 2$.
39. $y = \ln \cos x, \quad x = \dfrac{\pi}{4}$.
40. $y = \cos \ln x, \quad x = 1$.

12.3

Derivatives of Exponential Functions

Since logarithmic and exponential functions are inverses of each other, it is a simple matter to find the derivative of one if we know the derivative of the other.

Theorem 12.4

If $f(x) = a^{u(x)}$, *then* $f'(x) = a^{u(x)} \cdot u'(x) \cdot \ln a$.

Proof

Again let us abbreviate $u(x)$ to u and replace $f(x)$ by y.

$$y = a^u,$$

$$\log_a y = u,$$

$$\frac{y'}{y} \log_a e = u',$$

$$y' = \frac{y \cdot u'}{\log_a e}$$

$$= a^u \cdot u' \frac{1}{\log_a e}.$$

Using the formula for changing the base, we have

$$\log_a e = \frac{\ln e}{\ln a} = \frac{1}{\ln a}, \quad \text{or} \quad \frac{1}{\log_a e} = \ln a.$$

Thus

$$y' = a^u \cdot u' \ln a.$$

Of course, we could have left the derivative in the form

$$y' = a^u \cdot u' \frac{1}{\log_a e},$$

but $\log_a e$ will often have a form that makes division long and tedious. Replacing $1/\log_a e$ by $\ln a$ is usually simpler.

Theorem 12.5

If $f(x) = e^{u(x)}$, *then* $f'(x) = e^{u(x)} \cdot u'(x)$.

This follows directly from Theorem 12.4.

Example 1

Differentiate $y = 2^x$.

$$y' = 2^x \cdot 1 \cdot \ln 2 = 2^x \ln 2.$$

Example 2

Differentiate $y = e^x$.

$$y' = e^x \cdot 1 = e^x.$$

Perhaps you find this result a bit disappointing. All it means is that for any point on the graph of $y = e^x$, the y coordinate and the slope at that point are the same.

Example 3

Differentiate $y = e^{\sqrt{x}}$.

$$y' = e^{\sqrt{x}} \cdot \frac{1}{2\sqrt{x}} = \frac{e^{\sqrt{x}}}{2\sqrt{x}}.$$

Example 4

Differentiate $y = xe^x$.

Using the product rule, we have

$$y' = xe^x + e^x \cdot 1 = e^x(x + 1).$$

Example 5

Differentiate $y = x^2 \cdot 2^x$.

This illustrates the basic difference between a power function x^2, in which a variable base is raised to a constant power, and an exponential function, in which a constant base is raised to a variable power. Thus, the power rule is used on the first factor, while the derivative of an exponential function is used on the second. Of course, we must use the product rule, too.

$$\begin{aligned} y' &= x^2(2^x \cdot 1 \ln 2) + 2^x(2x) \\ &= x \cdot 2^x(x \ln 2 + 2). \end{aligned}$$

Let us note that there are four possible combinations of the base and exponent, two of which are illustrated in Example 5. They are:

$$\begin{aligned} &(\text{constant})^{(\text{constant})}, \\ &(\text{variable})^{(\text{constant})}, \\ &(\text{constant})^{(\text{variable})}, \\ &(\text{variable})^{(\text{variable})}. \end{aligned}$$

We can now differentiate three of these four forms. The first is quite trivial, since a constant base to a constant power is still a constant and its derivative is zero. The next two were illustrated in Example 5. Let us now consider the case in which both the base and the exponent are variable.

Example 6

Differentiate $y = x^x$.

We cannot differentiate by the power rule, since that requires a constant exponent. We cannot use the exponential formulas (Theorems 12.4 or 12.5), since they require a constant base. In the equation's present form, we cannot use any formula we have. Let us change its form by taking the logarithm of both sides.

$$\ln y = \ln x^x,$$
$$\ln y = x \ln x. \qquad \text{(by property III)}$$

Now we can take the derivative of this implicit function.

$$\frac{y'}{y} = x \cdot \frac{1}{x} + \ln x \cdot 1,$$
$$y' = y(1 + \ln x)$$
$$= x^x(1 + \ln x).$$

We may use any constant base we choose when taking the logarithm—we chose e because it is the simplest. This method of taking the logarithm of both sides can be used in any case involving exponents, but is unnecessary in those cases in which either the base or the exponent is constant, since we have formulas to handle these. Actually we have proved the power rule only for the case in which the exponent is rational (Theorem 5.10). We may use this method to extend that theorem to any n.

Theorem 12.6

If $f(x) = x^n$, where n is any real number, then $f'(x) = nx^{n-1}$.

The proof is left to the student.

Problems

In Problems 1–24, differentiate and simplify.

1. $y = 3^x$.
2. $y = e^{x^2}$.
3. $y = 2^{\sqrt{x}}$.
4. $y = 4^{x+1}$.
5. $y = e^{2x+2}$.
6. $y = e^{4x^2-1}$.
7. $y = 5^{2x^2+3}$.
8. $y = 2^{x^2+x}$.
9. $y = x + e^x$.
10. $y = \dfrac{e^x}{x}$.
11. $y = x^2 e^{x^2}$.
12. $y = \dfrac{1 - e^x}{x^2}$.
13. $y = 3^x(x^3 - 1)$.
14. $y = 2^e \cdot e^2$.
15. $y = e^x \cdot \ln x$.
16. $y = \ln (x + e^x)$.
17. $y = e^{x + \ln x}$.
18. $y = e^{\sin x}$.
19. $y = e^{\tan x}$.
20. $y = \sin e^x$.
21. $y = x^{x^2}$.
22. $y = x^{\sin x}$.
23. $y = (\sin x)^x$.
24. $y = x^{x^x}$.

In Problems 25–30, find dy/dx.

25. $\ln y = e^x$.
26. $e^{x+y} = \sin y$.
27. $e^{\sin (x+y)} = 1$.
28. $e^{x \ln y} = x^2 + y^2$.
29. $\ln \ln x = e^y$.
30. $\sin (x - y) = xe^x$.

In Problems 31–36, find the derivative at the value of x indicated.

31. $y = e^x, \quad x = 2$.
32. $y = xe^x, \quad x = 1$.
33. $y = e^{\sin x}, \quad x = \pi/2$.
34. $y = x^2 e^{x^2}, \quad x = 2$.
35. $y = 2^x, \quad x = 2$.
36. $y = e^{x^2+x}, \quad x = 1$.
37. Find a formula for the derivative of $y = u^v$, where u and v are functions of x.
38. Prove Theorem 12.6.
39. Show that $y = e^x$ is a solution of $y'' - 2y' + y = 0$. Show that $y = xe^x$ is also a solution.

12.4

Integrals Involving Logarithms and Exponentials

The theorems of the previous sections can be expressed in integral form. It would seem that the integral form of Theorem 12.3 is

$$\int \frac{u'}{u}\,dx = \ln u + C.$$

But this is unnecessarily restrictive; ln u exists only when $u > 0$. If $u < 0$,

$$\int \frac{u'}{u}\,dx = \int \frac{-u'}{-u}\,dx = \ln(-u) + C.$$

These two are combined in the next theorem.

Theorem 12.7

If u is a function of x, then

$$\int \frac{u'}{u}\,dx = \ln |u| + C.$$

It might be noted that this fills the gap left by the power rule. The power rule gives

$$\int u^n u'\,dx = \frac{u^{n+1}}{n+1} + C \quad (n \neq -1).$$

If $n = -1$, Theorem 12.7 is used. We do not give the integral form of Theorem 12.2, because none is needed.

$$\begin{aligned}\int \frac{u'}{u}\log_a e\,dx &= \log_a e \int \frac{u'}{u}\,dx \\ &= \log_a e \ln |u| + C \\ &= \log_a e \frac{\log_a |u|}{\log_a e} + C \\ &= \log_a |u| + C.\end{aligned}$$

The integral forms of Theorems 12.4 and 12.5 are given in Theorem 12.8, where we have changed the base of the logarithm in order to have the factor in the numerator.

Theorem 12.8

If u is a function of x, then

$$\int e^u \cdot u'\,dx = e^u + C,$$

$$\int a^u \cdot u'\,dx = \frac{a^u}{\ln a} + C = a^u \log_a e + C.$$

Example 1

Evaluate $\int \frac{x}{x^2+1}\,dx$.

If we take $u = x^2 + 1$, then $u' = 2x$. By adjusting the constant, we can put the integral into the form $\int \frac{u'}{u}\,dx$.

$$\int \frac{x}{x^2+1}\,dx = \frac{1}{2}\int \frac{2x}{x^2+1}\,dx$$

$$= \frac{1}{2}\ln|x^2+1| + C$$

$$= \frac{1}{2}\ln(x^2+1) + C.$$

The absolute value was dropped, because $x^2 + 1$ cannot be negative.

Example 2

Evaluate $\int \frac{x^3+3x^2-x+3}{x^2+1}\,dx$.

$$\int \frac{x^3+3x^2-x+3}{x^2+1}\,dx = \int \left(x+3-\frac{2x}{x^2+1}\right)dx$$

$$= \frac{x^2}{2} + 3x - \ln(x^2+1) + C.$$

Example 3

Evaluate $\int xe^{x^2}\,dx$.

$$\int xe^{x^2}\,dx = \frac{1}{2}\int 2xe^{x^2}\,dx$$

$$= \frac{1}{2}e^{x^2} + C.$$

Example 4

Evaluate $\int \frac{dx}{x\ln x}$.

If $u = \ln x$, then $u' = 1/x$. Thus

$$\int \frac{dx}{x\ln x} = \int \frac{\frac{1}{x}}{\ln x}\,dx$$

$$= \ln|\ln x| + C.$$

Problems

Evaluate the integrals in Problems 1–30.

1. $\int \frac{dx}{2x+1}$.
2. $\int \frac{dx}{3x-5}$.
3. $\int \frac{x^2+2x+2}{x-1}\, dx$.
4. $\int \frac{2x+1}{x^2+x-1}\, dx$.
5. $\int \frac{\sin x}{\cos x}\, dx$.
6. $\int \frac{\sec^2 x}{\tan x}\, dx$.
7. $\int \frac{e^x}{e^x+1}\, dx$.
8. $\int \frac{1}{e^x+1}\, dx$.
9. $\int \frac{2x+1}{\sqrt{x^2+x}}\, dx$.
10. $\int \frac{2x+1}{x^2+1}\, dx$.
11. $\int e^{-x}\, dx$.
12. $\int e^{4x}\, dx$.
13. $\int \sec^2 x\, e^{\tan x}\, dx$.
14. $\int (\sin x - \cos x) e^{\sin x + \cos x}\, dx$.
15. $\int \frac{e^{2x}+e^x+1}{e^x}\, dx$.
16. $\int \frac{dx}{x \ln \sqrt{x}}$.
17. $\int \frac{x^3+3x^2+5x+3}{(x+1)^2}\, dx$.
18. $\int \frac{dx}{(x^2+1)\text{Arctan}\, x}$.
19. $\int 10^x\, dx$.
20. $\int (e^x + e^{-x})\, dx$.
21. $\int (e^x - e^{-x})\, dx$.
22. $\int (e^x + e^{-x})^2\, dx$.
23. $\int \frac{3x^3-5x^2+x-4}{x}\, dx$.
24. $\int \frac{e^x+e^{-x}}{e^x-e^{-x}}\, dx$.
25. $\int_0^1 \frac{dx}{x+1}$.
26. $\int_0^1 \frac{dx}{e^x}$.
27. $\int_3^4 \frac{x^2-5}{x-2}\, dx$.
28. $\int_1^3 \frac{x\, dx}{x^2+4}$.
29. $\int_{\pi/6}^{\pi/2} \frac{\cos x}{\sin x}\, dx$.
30. $\int_0^1 x^2 e^{x^3}\, dx$.
31. It has been noted that $y' = y$ if $y = e^x$. In addition, $y' = y$ if $y = 0$. Is there any other function for which $y' = y$? If so, give one; if not, why not? (*Hint:* If $y' = y$, then $y'/y = 1$. Integrate both sides.)
32. For what function(s) (if any) does $y' = x$?

12.5

Hyperbolic Functions

The hyperbolic functions, which occur relatively frequently, are defined in terms of exponential functions, but they are like the trigonometric functions in many ways. They are called the hyperbolic sine, hyperbolic cosine, and so on, and are abbreviated sinh, cosh, and so forth, respectively.

Definition

(1) $\sinh x = \dfrac{e^x - e^{-x}}{2}$. (2) $\cosh x = \dfrac{e^x + e^{-x}}{2}$.

(3) $\tanh x = \dfrac{\sinh x}{\cosh x}$. (4) $\coth x = \dfrac{\cosh x}{\sinh x}$.

(5) $\operatorname{sech} x = \dfrac{1}{\cosh x}$. (6) $\operatorname{csch} x = \dfrac{1}{\sinh x}$.

The first two hyperbolic functions are easily graphed by addition of ordinates, and the remaining four by division of ordinates. For example, since

$$\sinh x = \frac{e^x}{2} - \frac{e^{-x}}{2},$$

we graph $y = e^x/2$ and $y = -e^{-x}/2$ and add the ordinates. This is given in (a) of Figure 12.4. The graph of $y = \tanh x$ is found by noting that

$$\tanh x = \frac{\sinh x}{\cosh x}.$$

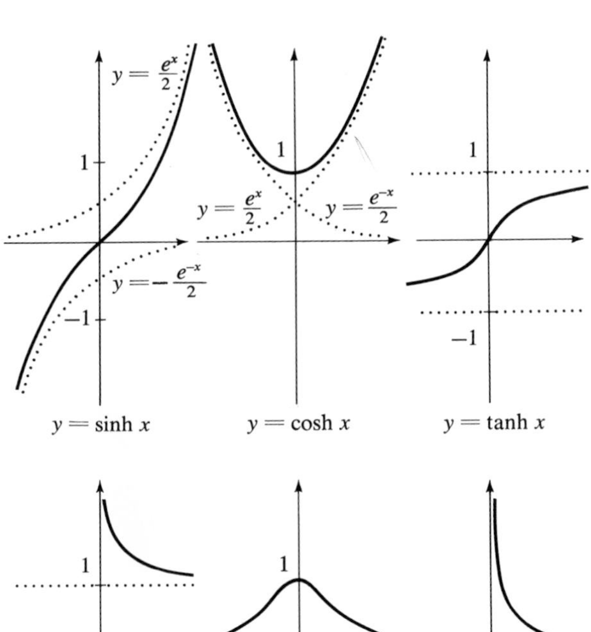

Figure 12.4

For each value of x, we divide $y_1 = \sinh x$ by $y_2 = \cosh x$ to find $\tanh x$. The result is given in Figure 12.4(c). The graphs of all six hyperbolic functions are given in the figure. They are not periodic functions as are the trigonometric functions; but there are many identities involving hyperbolic functions that are quite similar to those for the corresponding trigonometric functions. Some of the more important ones are given below.

$$\cosh^2 x - \sinh^2 x = 1.$$

$$1 - \tanh^2 x = \operatorname{sech}^2 x.$$

$$\coth^2 x - 1 = \operatorname{csch}^2 x.$$

$$\sinh (x \pm y) = \sinh x \cosh y \pm \cosh x \sinh y.$$

$$\cosh(x \pm y) = \cosh x \cosh y \pm \sinh x \sinh y.$$

$$\tanh (x \pm y) = \frac{\tanh x \pm \tanh y}{1 \pm \tanh x \tanh y}.$$

$$\sinh 2x = 2 \sinh x \cosh x.$$

$$\cosh 2x = \cosh^2 x + \sinh^2 x = 2 \cosh^2 x - 1 = 2 \sinh^2 x + 1.$$

$$\tanh 2x = \frac{2 \tanh x}{1 + \tanh^2 x}.$$

Example 1

Prove that $\cosh^2 x - \sinh^2 x = 1$.

$$\begin{aligned}\cosh^2 x - \sinh^2 x &= \left(\frac{e^x + e^{-x}}{2}\right)^2 - \left(\frac{e^x - e^{-x}}{2}\right)^2 \\ &= \frac{e^{2x} + 2 + e^{-2x}}{4} - \frac{e^{2x} - 2 + e^{-2x}}{4} \\ &= 1.\end{aligned}$$

Example 2

Prove that $\sinh (x + y) = \sinh x \cosh y + \cosh x \sinh y$.

$$\begin{aligned}\sinh x \cosh y + \cosh x \sinh y &= \frac{e^x - e^{-x}}{2} \cdot \frac{e^y + e^{-y}}{2} + \frac{e^x + e^{-x}}{2} \cdot \frac{e^y - e^{-y}}{2} \\ &= \frac{e^{x+y} + e^{x-y} - e^{-x+y} - e^{-x-y} + e^{x+y} - e^{x-y} + e^{-x+y} - e^{-x-y}}{4} \\ &= \frac{2e^{x+y} - 2e^{-x-y}}{4} \\ &= \frac{e^{x+y} - e^{-(x+y)}}{2} \\ &= \sinh (x+y).\end{aligned}$$

Example 3

Prove that $\sinh 2x = 2 \sinh x \cosh x$.

From Example 2,

$$\sinh(x+y) = \sinh x \cosh y + \cosh x \sinh y.$$

Replacing y by x, we have

$$\sinh 2x = 2 \sinh x \cosh x.$$

Example 4

If $\tanh x = 3/5$, find the values of the other five hyperbolic functions.

$$\coth x = \frac{1}{\tanh x} = 5/3.$$

$$\operatorname{sech}^2 x = 1 - \tanh^2 x = 1 - \left(\frac{3}{5}\right)^2 = \frac{16}{25}.$$

$$\operatorname{sech} x = \frac{4}{5} \quad \text{(it cannot be negative).}$$

$$\cosh x = \frac{1}{\operatorname{sech} x} = \frac{5}{4}.$$

$$\sinh^2 x = \cosh^2 x - 1 = \frac{25}{16} - 1 = \frac{9}{16}.$$

$$\sinh x = \frac{3}{4} \quad \text{(}\tanh x \text{ and } \sinh x \text{ agree in sign).}$$

$$\operatorname{csch} x = \frac{1}{\sinh x} = \frac{4}{3}.$$

Theorem 12.9

If u is a function of x, then

(1) $\dfrac{d}{dx} \sinh u = \cosh u \cdot u'$,

(2) $\dfrac{d}{dx} \cosh u = \sinh u \cdot u'$,

(3) $\dfrac{d}{dx} \tanh u = \operatorname{sech}^2 u \cdot u'$,

(4) $\dfrac{d}{dx} \coth u = -\operatorname{csch}^2 u \cdot u'$,

(5) $\dfrac{d}{dx} \operatorname{sech} u = -\operatorname{sech} u \tanh u \cdot u'$,

(6) $\dfrac{d}{dx} \operatorname{csch} u = -\operatorname{csch} u \coth u \cdot u'$.

Since the hyperbolic functions are defined in terms of exponential functions, it is a simple matter to prove the above theorem. The proof is left to the student.

Example 5

Differentiate $y = \cosh(3x + 1)$.

$$y' = 3 \sinh(3x + 1).$$

Example 6

Differentiate $y = x \sinh x$.

$$y' = x \cosh x + \sinh x.$$

Problems

In Problems 1–10, prove the identities.

1. $1 - \tanh^2 x = \operatorname{sech}^2 x$.
2. $\coth^2 x - 1 = \operatorname{csch}^2 x$.
3. $\cosh(x + y) = \cosh x \cosh y + \sinh x \sinh y$.
4. $\tanh(x + y) = \dfrac{\tanh x + \tanh y}{1 + \tanh x \tanh y}$.
5. $\sinh(x - y) = \sinh x \cosh y - \cosh x \sinh y$.
6. $\cosh 2x = \cosh^2 x + \sinh^2 x = 2 \sinh^2 x + 1 = 2 \cosh^2 x - 1$.
7. $\tanh 2x = \dfrac{2 \tanh x}{1 + \tanh^2 x}$.
8. $\sinh \dfrac{x}{2} = \pm \sqrt{\dfrac{\cosh x - 1}{2}}$.
9. $\cosh \dfrac{x}{2} = \sqrt{\dfrac{\cosh x + 1}{2}}$.
10. $\sinh 3x = 3 \sinh x + 4 \sinh^3 x$.

In Problems 11–16, find the values of the other hyperbolic functions.

11. $\sinh x = 4/3$.
12. $\cosh x = 5/4,\ x < 0$.
13. $\tanh x = -5/13$.
14. $\operatorname{sech} x = 15/17,\ x > 0$.
15. $\sinh x = -5/12$.
16. $\cosh x = 13/5,\ x > 0$.

In Problems 17–20, prove the given statement.

17. $\dfrac{d}{dx} \sinh u = \cosh u \cdot u'$.
18. $\dfrac{d}{dx} \cosh u = \sinh u \cdot u'$.
19. $\dfrac{d}{dx} \tanh u = \operatorname{sech}^2 u \cdot u'$.
20. $\dfrac{d}{dx} \operatorname{sech} u = -\operatorname{sech} u \tanh u \cdot u'$.

In Problems 21–34, differentiate and simplify.

21. $y = \sinh x^2$.
22. $y = x \cosh x$.
23. $y = \tanh(2x - 3)$.
24. $y = \sinh^2 2x$.
25. $y = \operatorname{sech} \sqrt{x}$.
26. $y = \operatorname{sech} x \tanh x$.
27. $y = \operatorname{csch}^2 x + \coth^2 x$.
28. $y = (9 \sinh x + \cosh x)^2$.
29. $y = \sinh^2 x + \cosh^2 x$.
30. $y = \ln \sinh x$.
31. $y = e^{\cosh x}$.
32. $y = \sin x \sinh x$.
33. $y = \cos \sinh x$.
34. $y = \sinh \cos x$.
35. Show that $y = \cosh 3x$ is a solution of $y'' - 9y = 0$. Show that $y = \sinh 3x$ is also a solution. Compare with Problem 37, page 248.

12.6

Inverse Hyperbolic Functions

We can consider the inverses of the hyperbolic functions just as we did those of the trigonometric functions. They are called the inverse hyperbolic sine, etc., and are represented by $\sinh^{-1}$, etc.

Definition

$y = \sinh^{-1} x$ means $x = \sinh y$. The other five inverse hyperbolic functions are defined similarly except for $\cosh^{-1} x$ and $\operatorname{sech}^{-1} x$, for which y must be non-negative.

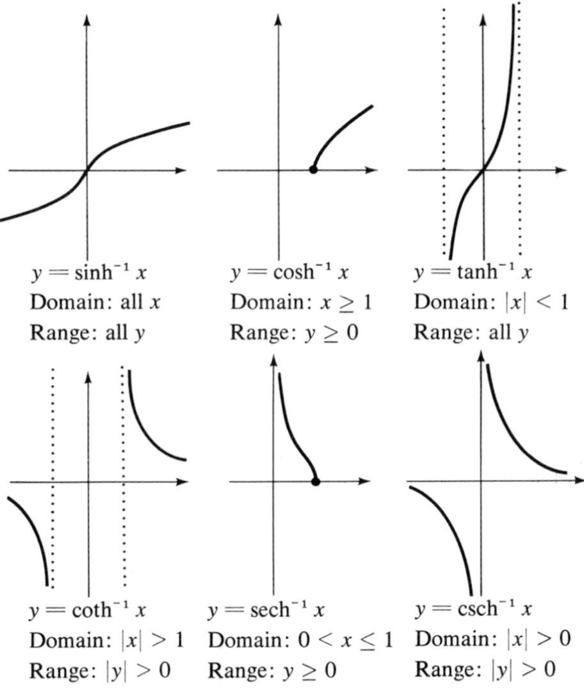

Figure 12.5

The graphs of these six functions, together with their domains and ranges, are given in Figure 12.5. Since the hyperbolic functions are defined in terms of exponential functions, it is reasonable to expect that the inverse hyperbolic functions can be expressed in terms of the inverse of the exponential functions—that is, in terms of the logarithmic functions. In fact, this is the case.

Theorem 12.10

(1) $\sinh^{-1} x = \ln(x + \sqrt{x^2 + 1})$;

(2) $\cosh^{-1} x = \ln(x + \sqrt{x^2 - 1}), \quad x \geq 1$;

(3) $\tanh^{-1} x = \dfrac{1}{2} \ln \dfrac{1+x}{1-x}, \quad |x| < 1;$

(4) $\coth^{-1} x = \dfrac{1}{2} \ln \dfrac{x+1}{x-1}, \quad |x| > 1;$

(5) $\operatorname{sech}^{-1} x = \ln \dfrac{1+\sqrt{1-x^2}}{x}, \quad 0 < x \le 1;$

(6) $\operatorname{csch}^{-1} x = \begin{cases} \ln \dfrac{1+\sqrt{1+x^2}}{x}, & x > 0, \\ -\ln \dfrac{1+\sqrt{1+x^2}}{-x}, & x < 0. \end{cases}$

Proof of (1)

$$y = \sinh^{-1} x,$$

$$x = \sinh y = \frac{e^y - e^{-y}}{2},$$

$$e^y - 2x - e^{-y} = 0,$$

$$e^{2y} - 2xe^y - 1 = 0.$$

This is now a quadratic equation in e^y. By the quadratic formula,

$$e^y = x \pm \sqrt{x^2+1}.$$

Since $\sqrt{x^2+1} > x$, $x - \sqrt{x^2+1} < 0$. But $e^y > 0$. Thus the only possibility is

$$e^y = x + \sqrt{x^2+1},$$

$$y = \ln (x + \sqrt{x^2+1}).$$

Proof of (4).

$$y = \coth^{-1} x,$$

$$x = \coth y = \frac{\cosh y}{\sinh y} = \frac{e^y + e^{-y}}{e^y - e^{-y}},$$

$$e^y(x-1) = e^{-y}(x+1),$$

$$e^{2y} = \frac{x+1}{x-1},$$

$$e^y = \sqrt{\frac{x+1}{x-1}},$$

$$y = \ln \sqrt{\frac{x+1}{x-1}} = \frac{1}{2} \ln \frac{x+1}{x-1}.$$

The proofs of the others, which are similar, are left to the student. These formulas give a convenient way of evaluating the inverse hyperbolic functions for particular values of x.

Example 1

Evaluate $\sinh^{-1} 2$.

$$\begin{aligned}\sinh^{-1} 2 &= \ln(2 + \sqrt{2^2 + 1})\\ &= \ln(2 + \sqrt{5}).\end{aligned}$$

This can now be approximated. We can either use a table of natural logarithms or change the base and use common logarithms, to get

$$\sinh^{-1} 2 \doteq 1.444.$$

We can find the derivatives of these functions by one of two methods: we may use the same method that was used to find the derivatives of the inverse trigonometric functions or we may use the results of Theorem 12.10.

Theorem 12.11

If u is a function of x, then

(1) $$\frac{d}{dx}\sinh^{-1} u = \frac{u'}{\sqrt{1+u^2}};$$

(2) $$\frac{d}{dx}\cosh^{-1} u = \frac{u'}{\sqrt{u^2-1}};$$

(3) $$\frac{d}{dx}\tanh^{-1} u = \frac{u'}{1-u^2};$$

(4) $$\frac{d}{dx}\coth^{-1} u = \frac{u'}{1-u^2};$$

(5) $$\frac{d}{dx}\operatorname{sech}^{-1} u = \frac{-u'}{u\sqrt{1-u^2}};$$

(6) $$\frac{d}{dx}\operatorname{csch}^{-1} u = \begin{cases}\dfrac{-u'}{u\sqrt{1+u^2}}, & u > 0,\\[2ex] \dfrac{u'}{u\sqrt{1+u^2}}, & u < 0.\end{cases}$$

Proof

We shall prove the first derivative formula by both methods.

By the first method:

$$\begin{aligned} y &= \sinh^{-1} u,\\ u &= \sinh y,\\ u' &= \cosh y \cdot y',\\ y' &= \frac{u'}{\cosh y}\\ &= \frac{u'}{\sqrt{1+\sinh^2 y}}\\ &= \frac{u'}{\sqrt{1+u^2}}.\end{aligned}$$

By Theorem 12.10,

$$y = \sinh^{-1} u = \ln(u + \sqrt{u^2 + 1})$$

$$y' = \frac{u' + \dfrac{uu'}{\sqrt{u^2+1}}}{u + \sqrt{u^2+1}} = \frac{u'(\sqrt{u^2+1} + u)}{(u + \sqrt{u^2+1})\sqrt{u^2+1}}$$

$$= \frac{u'}{\sqrt{u^2+1}}.$$

The other formulas can be proved similarly. Their proofs are left to the student.

Example 2

Differentiate $y = \sinh^{-1} x^2$.

$$y' = \frac{2x}{\sqrt{1+x^4}}.$$

Example 3

Differentiate $y = x \tanh^{-1} x$.

$$y' = x \frac{1}{1-x^2} + \tanh^{-1} x$$

$$= \frac{x}{1-x^2} + \tanh^{-1} x.$$

Problems

In Problems 1–6, give the value to three decimal places.

1. $\sinh^{-1} 3$.
2. $\tanh^{-1} 1/2$.
3. $\text{sech}^{-1} 1/\sqrt{2}$.
4. $\cosh^{-1} 2$.
5. $\coth^{-1} 3$.
6. $\text{csch}^{-1} 1$.

In Problems 7–20, differentiate and simplify.

7. $y = \cosh^{-1}(3x + 1)$.
8. $y = \tanh^{-1}(2x - 5)$.
9. $y = \sinh^{-1}\sqrt{x}$.
10. $y = x \sinh^{-1} x$.
11. $y = \dfrac{\coth^{-1} x}{x}$.
12. $y = \ln \cosh^{-1} x$.
13. $y = \tanh^{-1} e^x$.
14. $y = \text{sech}^{-1} \sin x$.
15. $y = \sqrt{1 + x^2} + \sinh^{-1} x$.
16. $y = \sqrt{1 + x} + \text{csch}^{-1}\sqrt{x}$.
17. $y = (\sinh^{-1} x)^2$.
18. $y = \sqrt{\cosh^{-1} x}$.
19. $y = (1 + \tanh^{-1} x)^2$.
20. $y = (\sinh^{-1} x + \sin^{-1} x)^2$.
21. Prove Theorem 12.10 (2).
22. Prove Theorem 12.10 (3).
23. Prove Theorem 12.10 (5).
24. Prove Theorem 12.10 (6).
25. Prove Theorem 12.11 (2).
26. Prove Theorem 12.11 (3).
27. Prove Theorem 12.11 (4).
28. Prove Theorem 12.11 (5).
29. Prove Theorem 12.11 (6).

12.7

Integrals Involving Hyperbolic and Inverse Hyperbolic Functions

---

The formulas for the derivatives of hyperbolic and inverse hyperbolic functions can be put into integral form.

Theorem 12.12

If u is a function of x, then

(1) $\int \sinh u \cdot u' \, dx = \cosh u + C,$

(2) $\int \cosh u \cdot u' \, dx = \sinh u + C,$

(3) $\int \operatorname{sech}^2 u \cdot u' \, dx = \tanh u + C,$

(4) $\int \operatorname{csch}^2 u \cdot u' \, dx = -\coth u + C,$

(5) $\int \operatorname{sech} u \tanh u \cdot u' \, dx = -\operatorname{sech} u + C,$

(6) $\int \operatorname{csch} u \coth u \cdot u' \, dx = -\operatorname{csch} u + C.$

Theorem 12.13

If u is a function of x, then

(1) $\int \frac{u' \, dx}{\sqrt{1 + u^2}} = \sinh^{-1} u + C,$

(2) $\int \frac{u' \, dx}{\sqrt{u^2 - 1}} = \cosh^{-1} u + C,$

(3) $\int \frac{u' \, dx}{1 - u^2} = \tanh^{-1} u + C, \quad |u| < 1,$

(4) $\int \frac{u' \, dx}{1 - u^2} = \coth^{-1} u + C, \quad |u| > 1,$

(5) $\int \frac{u' \, dx}{u\sqrt{1 - u^2}} = -\operatorname{sech}^{-1} |u| + C,$

(6) $\int \frac{u' \, dx}{u\sqrt{1 + u^2}} = \begin{cases} -\operatorname{csch}^{-1} u + C, & u > 0, \\ \operatorname{csch}^{-1} u + C, & u < 0. \end{cases}$

Compare these formulas with those of Theorem 11.17, pages 256–257. Theorem 12.14 combines Theorems 12.13 and 12.10.

Theorem 12.14

If u is a function of x, then

(1) $\displaystyle\int \frac{u'\,dx}{\sqrt{1+u^2}} = \ln(u+\sqrt{u^2+1}) + C,$

(2) $\displaystyle\int \frac{u'\,dx}{\sqrt{u^2-1}} = \ln(u+\sqrt{u^2-1}) + C,$

(3) $\displaystyle\int \frac{u'\,dx}{1-u^2} = \frac{1}{2}\ln\left|\frac{1+u}{1-u}\right| + C,$

(4) $\displaystyle\int \frac{u'\,dx}{u\sqrt{1-u^2}} = -\ln\frac{1+\sqrt{1-u^2}}{|u|} + C,$

(5) $\displaystyle\int \frac{u'\,dx}{u\sqrt{1+u^2}} = -\ln\frac{1+\sqrt{1+u^2}}{|u|} + C.$

Note that formulas (3) and (4) of Theorem 12.13 combine to give formula (3) here. Similarly, the two cases of formula (6) of Theorem 12.13 combine to give one result here.

Example 1

Evaluate $\int x \sinh x^2\,dx$.

$$\begin{aligned}\int x \sinh x^2\,dx &= \frac{1}{2}\int 2x\sinh x^2\,dx\\ &= \frac{1}{2}\cosh x^2 + C.\end{aligned}$$

Example 2

Evaluate $\displaystyle\int \frac{\operatorname{sech}\sqrt{x}\tanh\sqrt{x}}{\sqrt{x}}\,dx.$

$$\begin{aligned}\int \frac{\operatorname{sech}\sqrt{x}\tanh\sqrt{x}}{\sqrt{x}}\,dx &= 2\int \frac{\operatorname{sech}\sqrt{x}\tanh\sqrt{x}}{2\sqrt{x}}\,dx\\ &= -2\operatorname{sech}\sqrt{x} + C.\end{aligned}$$

Example 3

Evaluate $\int \tanh^2 x\,dx$.

We must first use an identity to put this into a form we can integrate.

$$\begin{aligned}\int \tanh^2 x\,dx &= \int (1-\operatorname{sech}^2 x)\,dx\\ &= x - \tanh x + C.\end{aligned}$$

Example 4

Evaluate $\int \frac{dx}{\sqrt{1+4x^2}}$.

$$\int \frac{dx}{\sqrt{1+4x^2}} = \frac{1}{2}\int \frac{2\,dx}{\sqrt{1+(2x)^2}}$$

$$= \frac{1}{2}\sinh^{-1} 2x + C \qquad \text{(by Theorem 12.13 (1))},$$

or

$$= \frac{1}{2}\ln(2x+\sqrt{1+4x^2}) + C \qquad \text{(by Theorem 12.14 (1))}.$$

Example 5

Evaluate $\int \frac{dx}{x^2+2x}$.

Let us begin by completing the square in the denominator.

$$\int \frac{dx}{x^2+2x} = \int \frac{dx}{(x^2+2x+1)-1}$$

$$= \int \frac{dx}{(x+1)^2-1}$$

$$= -\int \frac{dx}{1-(x+1)^2}$$

$$= \begin{cases} -\tanh^{-1}(x+1)+C & \text{if } |x+1|<1 \\ -\coth^{-1}(x+1)+C & \text{if } |x+1|>1 \end{cases} \qquad \text{(by Theorem 12.13 (3) and (4))},$$

or

$$= -\frac{1}{2}\ln\left|\frac{1+(x+1)}{1-(x+1)}\right| + C \qquad \text{(by Theorem 12.14 (3))}$$

$$= -\frac{1}{2}\ln\left|\frac{2+x}{x}\right| + C.$$

The advantage of Theorem 12.14 is clear here. But

$$\int_1^2 \frac{dx}{x^2+2x} = -\coth^{-1}(x+1)\Big|_1^2$$

$$= -\coth^{-1} 3 + \coth^{-1} 2$$

$$= \frac{1}{2}\ln 3 - \frac{1}{2}\ln 2$$

$$= \frac{1}{2}\ln\frac{3}{2},$$

or

$$\int_1^2 \frac{dx}{x^2+2x} = -\frac{1}{2}\ln\left|\frac{x+2}{x}\right|\Bigg|_1^2$$
$$= -\frac{1}{2}\ln 2 + \frac{1}{2}\ln 3$$
$$= \frac{1}{2}\ln\frac{3}{2}.$$

Problems

Evaluate the following integrals.

1. $\int \cosh(2x+1)\,dx.$
2. $\int \frac{\operatorname{sech}^2\sqrt{x}}{\sqrt{x}}\,dx.$
3. $\int \frac{\operatorname{sech}\frac{1}{x}\tanh\frac{1}{x}}{x^2}\,dx.$
4. $\int 2\tanh^2 2x\,dx.$
5. $\int \sinh^2 x\cosh x\,dx.$
6. $\int \frac{\operatorname{sech}^2 x}{\tanh x}\,dx.$
7. $\int \operatorname{csch}^4 x\coth x\,dx.$
8. $\int \frac{\sinh x}{\cosh x}\,dx.$
9. $\int \frac{dx}{x^2-1}.$
10. $\int \frac{dx}{\sqrt{9x^2-1}}.$
11. $\int \frac{dx}{\sqrt{4+x^2}}.$
12. $\int \frac{dx}{x\sqrt{1-4x^2}}.$
13. $\int \frac{dx}{x\sqrt{16+x^2}}.$
14. $\int \frac{dx}{\sqrt{x^2+4x+5}}.$
15. $\int \frac{dx}{\sqrt{x^2+2x}}.$
16. $\int \frac{dx}{(x-2)\sqrt{-x^2+4x-3}}.$
17. $\int \frac{dx}{\sqrt{4x^2+12x+10}}.$
18. $\int \frac{\cosh x\,dx}{1-\sinh^2 x}.$
19. $\int \frac{e^x\,dx}{\sqrt{1+e^{2x}}}.$
20. $\int \frac{dx}{x\sqrt{\ln^2 x-1}}.$
21. $\int_0^4 \sinh x\,dx.$
22. $\int_{-1/2}^1 \operatorname{sech}^2(2x+1)\,dx.$
23. $\int_0^1 \frac{x\,dx}{\sqrt{1+x^4}}.$
24. $\int_0^{1/2} \frac{dx}{1+x^2}.$
25. $\int_2^4 \frac{dx}{1-x^2}.$
26. $\int_1^2 \frac{dx}{x\sqrt{1+x^2}}.$
27. $\int_{-2}^{-1} \frac{dx}{x\sqrt{1+x^2}}.$
28. $\int_6^9 \frac{dx}{x^2-8x+15}.$
29. $\int_{\ln 2}^1 \frac{e^x\,dx}{\sqrt{e^{2x}-1}}.$

12.8

Applications

Of course, the applications of differentiation and integration apply to the functions of this and the preceding chapter just as they do to algebraic functions. Let us consider a few examples.

Example 1

Examine $y = xe^x$ for relative maxima and minima and points of inflection.

$$y' = xe^x + e^x \cdot 1 = (x+1)e^x,$$
$$y'' = (x+1)e^x + e^x \cdot 1 = (x+2)e^x.$$

There is a critical point at $(-1, -1/e)$ which is a relative minimum. There is a point of inflection at $(-2, -2/e^2)$.

Example 2

A lighthouse is two miles off a straight shore. Its light makes three revolutions per minute. How fast does the light beam move along a sea wall at a point two miles down the coast?

We can see from Figure 12.6 that

$$\tan \alpha = \frac{x}{2}.$$

We are given $x = 2$, which requires that $\alpha = \pi/4$. Furthermore $d\alpha/dt = 6\pi$ radians/min and we want to determine dx/dt.

$$x = 2 \tan \alpha,$$

$$\frac{dx}{dt} = 2 \sec^2 \alpha \cdot \frac{d\alpha}{dt},$$

$$= 2 \sec^2 \frac{\pi}{4} \cdot 6\pi,$$

$$= 24\pi \text{ mi/min}.$$

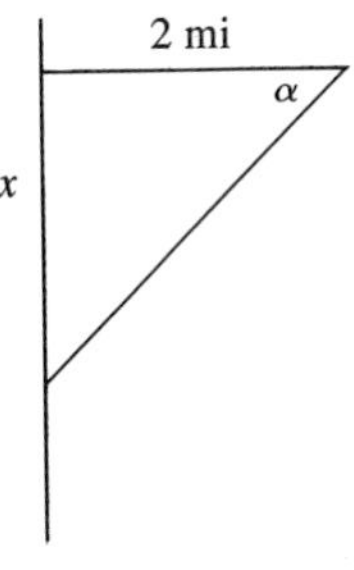

Figure 12.6

Example 3

Find the area under the first arch of the sine curve in Figure 12.7.

From the figure, we have

$$A = \int_0^\pi \sin x \, dx$$

$$= -\cos x \Big|_0^\pi$$

$$= 2.$$

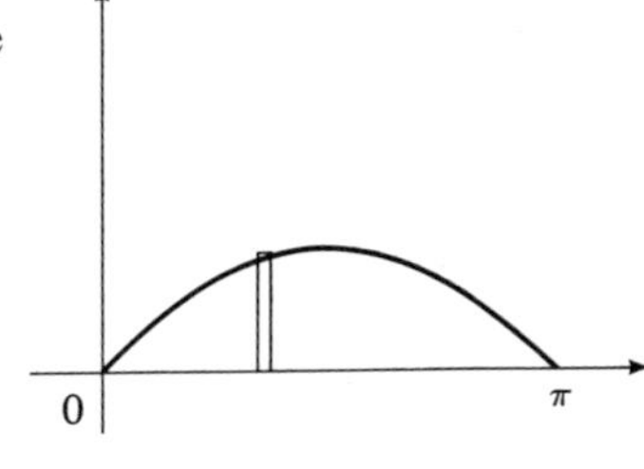

Figure 12.7

Example 4

Find the relative maxima and minima and sketch $y = e^{-x} \sin x$.

$$\begin{aligned} y' &= e^{-x} \cos x + \sin x(-e^{-x}) \\ &= e^{-x}(\cos x - \sin x). \end{aligned}$$

Since $e^{-x} \neq 0$ for any value of x, the maxima and minima occur when either

$$\cos x - \sin x = 0 \quad \text{or} \quad \cos x = \sin x.$$

Dividing both sides by $\cos x$, we have

$$\tan x = 1.$$

Thus the relative maxima and minima occur at

$$x = \frac{\pi}{4} + n\pi$$

for all integer values of n. Since

$$-1 \leq \sin x \leq 1,$$

it follows that

$$-e^{-x} \leq e^{-x} \sin x \leq e^{-x}.$$

Thus we have the graph shown in Figure 12.8. Note that, while $\sin x = \pm 1$ at $x = \pi/2 + n\pi$ and $e^{-x} \sin x = \pm e^{-x}$ at these values of x, these, nevertheless, are not the relative maxima and minima of $e^{-x} \sin x$.

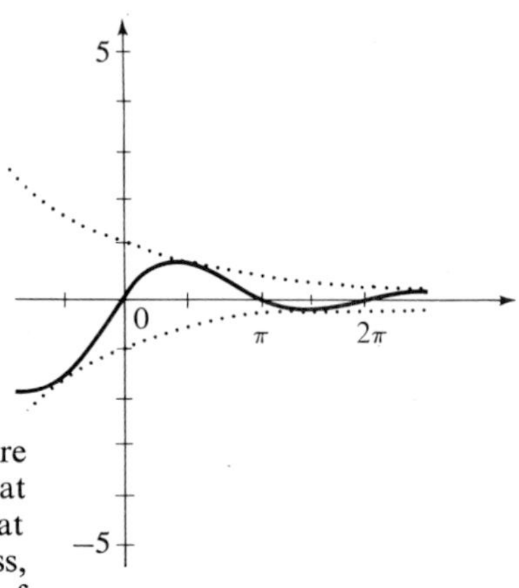

Figure 12.8

Problems

In Problems 1–10, find an equation of the tangent line to the curve at the indicated point.

1. $y = \sin x$, $(0, 0)$.
2. $y = \cos x$, $(\pi/3, 1/2)$.
3. $y = x + \sin x$, (π, π).
4. $y = \ln x$, $(1, 0)$.
5. $y = \ln x^2$, $(1, 0)$.
6. $y = e^x$, $(0, 1)$.
7. $y = \text{Arcsin } x$, $(-1/\sqrt{2}, -\pi/4)$.
8. $y = 1 + \cos^2 x$, $(\pi/4, 3/2)$.
9. $y = \sinh x$, $(0, 0)$.
10. $y = \cosh x$, $(0, 1)$.

In Problems 11–20, find all relative maxima and minima and sketch.

11. $y = x \ln x$.
12. $y = e^{-2x} \sin x$.
13. $y = e^{-x} \sin 2x$.
14. $y = e^{-x}$.
15. $y = \cos e^x$.
16. $y = 2x + \sin x$.
17. $y = a \sin x + b \cos x \quad (0 < b < a)$.
18. $y = \dfrac{\ln x}{x}$.
19. $y = x^2 e^x$.
20. $y = \cos \cos x$.

In Problems 21–26, find the area of the region bounded by the given curves.

21. $y = e^{-x}$, $y = 0$, $x = 0$, $x = 1$.
22. $y = e^{-2x}$, $y = 0$, $x = 0$, $x = 1$.
23. $y = \ln x$, $y = 0$, $x = 2$. (*Hint:* Use horizontal strips).
24. $y = \sin 2x$, $y = 0$, between $x = 0$ and $x = \pi/2$.

25. $y = \cosh x, y = 0, x = 0, x = 1.$

26. $y = \dfrac{e^x}{1 + e^x}, y = 0, x = 0, x = 1.$

27. Find the area of the region bounded by $y = e^{-x}$, both axes, and $x = k$, where $k > 0$. What is the limit of this area as k increases indefinitely? What does this limit represent?

28. The tractrix has equation $x = a \operatorname{sech}^{-1} y/a - \sqrt{a^2 - y^2}$. Find the distance from a point (x, y) on the tractrix and the x intercept of the line tangent to it at the point (x, y). Does this suggest a way of sketching the tractrix?

29. How fast does the light beam from the lighthouse of Example 2 move along a sea wall at a point 3.464 miles down the coast?

30. A submarine telegraph cable consists of a conducting circular core surrounded by a circular layer of insulation. If x is the ratio of the radius of the core to the thickness of the insulation, then the speed of the signal is proportional to $x^2 \ln 1/x$. For what value of x is the speed of the signal a maximum?

31. An object is thrown upward from ground level with a velocity of 100 ft/sec at an angle of 30° with the horizontal. What is the maximum height reached by the object? (*Hint:* The vertical component of the speed is 100 sin 30°. Disregard air resistance.)

32. A cannon fires a projectile with initial velocity V. What should be the angle of elevation α of the cannon for the projectile to go the farthest? (*Hint:* The vertical and horizontal components of the velocity are $V \sin \alpha$ and $V \cos \alpha$, respectively. Disregard air resistance.)

33. An advertising sign is to be made with letters three feet high. Most of the people who see it will be 100 feet from the wall on which it is to be placed. How high should the center of the letters be for them to appear the largest? (*Hint:* The letters appear largest when angle *TPB*, Figure 12.9, is a maximum.)

34. Show that an angle is a maximum when its tangent is a maximum.

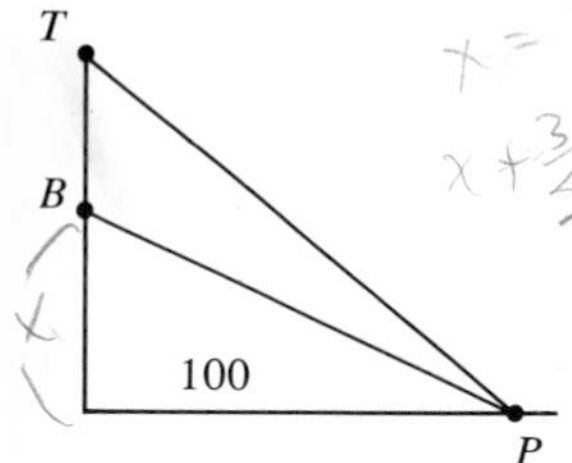

Figure 12.9

Parametric Equations

13.1

Parametric Equations

Up to now all of the equations we have dealt with have been in the form

$$y = f(x) \quad \text{or} \quad F(x, y) = 0.$$

In either case, a direct relationship between x and y is given. Another way of representing equations is to show x and y each as a function of a third variable or parameter; that is,

$$x = f(t), \qquad y = g(t).$$

Each value of the parameter t gives a value of x and a value of y.

For instance, in the parametric equations

$$x = \sin t, \qquad y = \cos t,$$

we see that, if $t = 0$, $x = 0$ and $y = 1$. Thus the point (0, 1) is a point of the graph. Note that we still have just the x and y axes; t does not appear on the graph. Let us continue with this process. The resulting graph is given in Figure 13.1. Of course, we could continue with values of t beyond 360°, but we would simply go over the same points again. Although the value of t need not appear anywhere on the graph, we have labeled several points with their corresponding values of t. Once the points are plotted, they are joined in the order of increasing (or decreasing) values of t.

The result seems to resemble a circle. How can we be *sure* it is a circle? If we had a single equation in x and y, we could easily see by the form of the equation whether

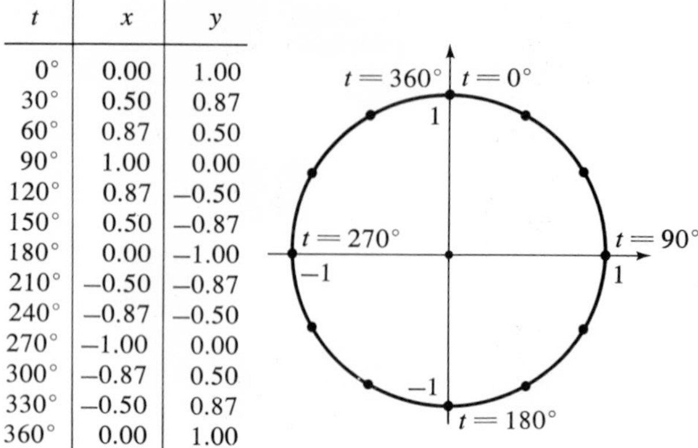

t	x	y
0°	0.00	1.00
30°	0.50	0.87
60°	0.87	0.50
90°	1.00	0.00
120°	0.87	−0.50
150°	0.50	−0.87
180°	0.00	−1.00
210°	−0.50	−0.87
240°	−0.87	−0.50
270°	−1.00	0.00
300°	−0.87	0.50
330°	−0.50	0.87
360°	0.00	1.00

Figure 13.1

or not we have a circle. Let us try to eliminate the parameter t between the equations $x = \sin t$ and $y = \cos t$:

$$\sin^2 t + \cos^2 t = 1,$$

$$x^2 + y^2 = 1.$$

We now see that we have a circle with center at the origin and radius 1.

Not only does elimination of the parameter assure us that this particular curve is a circle, it gives us a basis for sketching more rapidly that can be done by point-by-point plotting. However, we must be careful with the domain of the resulting equation. Let us illustrate this with some examples and see how the domain of $F(x, y) = 0$ plays an important role in sketching the graph.

Example 1

Graph the following two pairs of parameteric equations by eliminating the parameter.

$$x = t, \qquad x = t^2,$$

$$y = t; \qquad y = t^2.$$

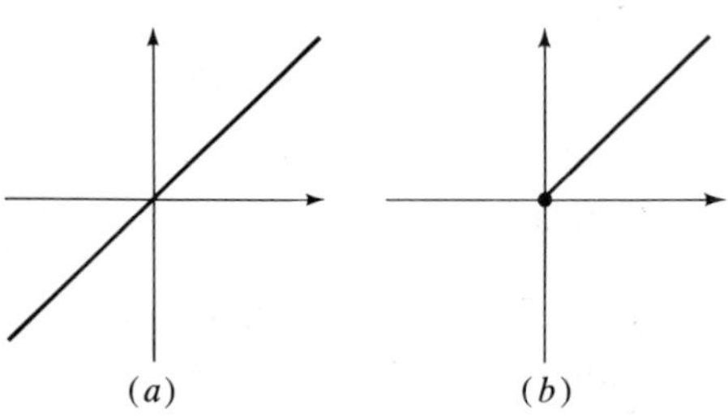

Figure 13.2

Elimination of the parameter gives $y = x$ in both cases. But the graphs are not the same, as the domains in the two cases will show. The domain can be determined from the first of the two parametric equations in each case. In the first case, $x = t$ and, since there is no restriction on t, there is none on x; the domain is the set of all real numbers. In the second case, $x = t^2$. The domain of $y = x$ is the range of $x = t^2$, which is $\{x \mid x \geq 0\}$. Thus we have a restricted domain here that we did not have in the first case. The graphs are given in Figure 13.2.

Example 2

Eliminate the parameter between $x = t + 1$ and $y = t^2 + 3t + 2$ and sketch.

Solving $x = t + 1$ for t, we have

$$t = x - 1.$$

If this is substituted into $y = t^2 + 3t + 2$, then

$$\begin{aligned} y &= (x-1)^2 + 3(x-1) + 2 \\ &= x^2 + x. \end{aligned}$$

Note that there is no restriction on x; the domain of $y = x^2 + x$ is the set of all real numbers. It is now a simple matter to sketch the curve; it is given in Figure 13.3.

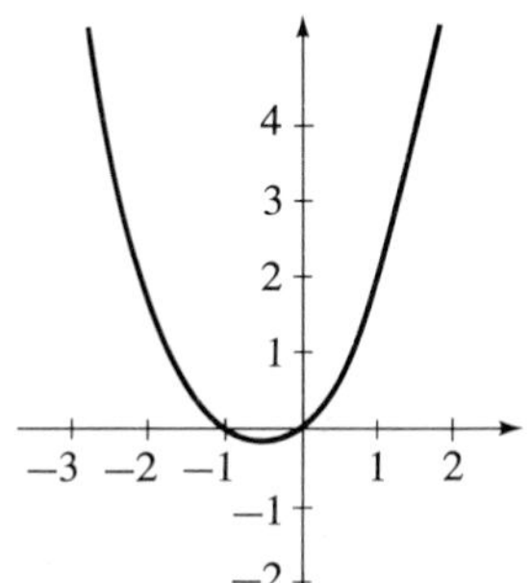

Figure 13.3

Occasionally it is difficult or impossible to eliminate the parameter. In such cases the curve must be plotted point by point. A question that must have occurred to you by this time is, "Why represent equations in parametric form?" The answer is that it is often simpler to deal with the x and y coordinates of a point separately, when trying to write a given equation, by relating each to a third variable. Let us consider an example.

Example 3

Suppose a gun is clamped into a horizontal position 10 feet from the ground and fired with an initial velocity of v_0 ft/sec. Neglecting air resistance, find parametric equations representing the path of the bullet.

This problem is quite simple if we handle the x and y coordinates separately. The velocity in the horizontal direction remains constant, since there is nothing to slow it down. Thus, if t is the number of seconds after firing,

$$x = v_0 t.$$

The vertical motion is governed by the laws of falling bodies. Thus

$$a = -32, \qquad v = -32t, \qquad y = -16t^2 + 10.$$

The path of the bullet, in parametric form, is

$$x = v_0 t \quad \text{and} \quad y = -16t^2 + 10.$$

Problems

In Problems 1–14, eliminate the parameter and sketch the curve.

1. $x = t^2 + 1, \quad y = t + 1.$
2. $x = t^2 + t - 2, \quad y = t + 2.$
3. $x = t - 1, \quad y = t^2 - 2t.$
4. $x = 2t^2 + t - 3, \quad y = t - 1.$
5. $x = t^2 + t, \quad y = t^2 - t.$
6. $x = t^2 + 1, \quad y = t^2 - 1.$
7. $x = t^3, \quad y = t^2.$
8. $x = e^t, \quad y = \sin t.$
9. $x = a \cos \theta, \quad y = b \sin \theta.$
10. $x = \theta - \sin \theta, \quad y = 1 - \cos \theta.$
11. $x = 2 + \cos \theta, \quad y = -1 + \sin \theta.$
12. $x = 3 - \cos \theta, \quad y = 2 + 4 \sin \theta.$
13. $x = 3 + \cosh \theta, \quad y = 2 + \sinh \theta.$
14. $x = 4 + 2 \cosh \theta, \quad y = 1 - 4 \sinh \theta.$

In Problems 15–18, sketch the curve.

15. $x = \cos \theta + \theta \sin \theta, \quad y = \sin \theta - \theta \cos \theta.$
16. $x = a \cos^3 \theta, \quad y = a \sin^3 \theta.$
17. $x = 2a \cos \theta - a \cos 2\theta, \quad y = 2a \sin \theta - a \sin 2\theta.$
18. $x = t - a \tanh \dfrac{t}{a}, \quad y = a \operatorname{sech} \dfrac{t}{a}.$
19. Sketch each of the following parametric equations and note the similarities and differences.
    (a) $x = t, \quad y = t;$
    (b) $x = t^2, \quad y = t^2;$
    (c) $x = |t|, \quad y = |t|;$
    (d) $x = \sin t, \quad y = \sin t;$
    (e) $x = \ln(-t), \quad y = \ln(-t);$
    (f) $x = \sqrt{(t-1)(t-2)}, \quad y = \sqrt{(t-1)(t-2)}.$

If, in Example 3, the gun is inclined at an angle θ, then the horizontal component of the velocity v_0 is $v_0 \cos \theta$, and the vertical component is $v_0 \sin \theta$. In Problems 20–22, find parametric equations representing the path of the bullet when the gun is at ground level and inclined at the angle indicated.

20. $\theta = 30°.$
21. $\theta = 45°.$
22. $\theta = 60°.$
23. At what angle should a gun be inclined to give a maximum range?

In Problems 24–27, represent the path described in parametric form.

24. A wheel of radius a is rolling along a flat plane. Find the path traced by a point on the circumference. Take the plane to be the x axis; the point starts at the origin.
25. Find the path traced by a point a distance b ($b < a$) from the center of the wheel in Problem 24. Again, take the plane to be the x axis and let the point be on the y axis.
26. Find the path traced by a point a distance b ($b > a$, as on a railroad wheel) from the center of the wheel in Problem 24. Again, take the plane to be the x axis and let the point be on the y axis.
27. Find the path traced by a point on the circumference of a circle of radius a which rolls inside a circle of radius $4a$. Take the center of the big circle to be the origin and the point on the little circle to be at $(4a, 0)$.

13.2

Derivatives of Parametric Equations

Suppose we are interested in finding the slope of a graph that is represented in parametric form. This means finding dy/dx. If we can eliminate the parameter to get an equation in x and y, we can use our previous methods to find the derivative.

Unfortunately, eliminating the parameter is sometimes difficult or impossible and, even if it can be done, the result may be extremely complicated. But we can find the derivative dy/dx nevertheless.

Theorem 13.1

If $x = f(t)$, $y = g(t)$, *and* $dx/dt \neq 0$, *then*

$$\frac{dy}{dx} = \frac{\dfrac{dy}{dt}}{\dfrac{dx}{dt}}.$$

Proof

Since our definition of dy/dx requires that y be a function of x and we cannot be sure that y is a function of x, we cannot use this definition directly. However, we can alter it to fit our purposes. The derivative was defined as a certain limit of the slope of a secant line. Keeping this in mind and considering Figure 13.4, we see that

$$\frac{dy}{dx} = \lim_{h \to 0} \frac{g(t+h) - g(t)}{f(t+h) - f(t)}.$$

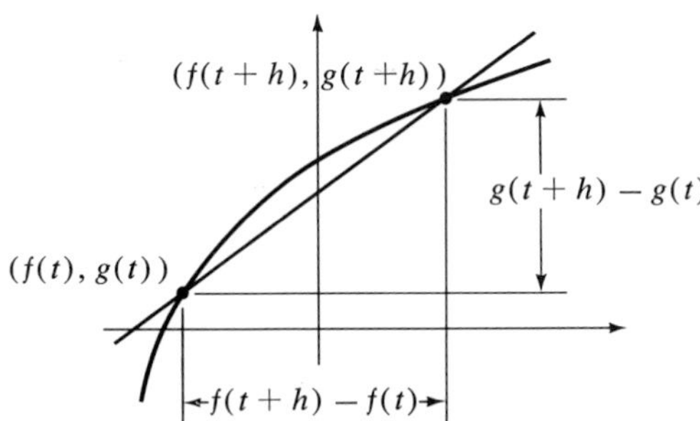

Figure 13.4

Dividing both numerator and denominator by h, we have

$$\frac{dy}{dx} = \lim_{h \to 0} \frac{\dfrac{g(t+h) - g(t)}{h}}{\dfrac{f(t+h) - f(t)}{h}} = \frac{\dfrac{dy}{dt}}{\dfrac{dx}{dt}}.$$

Example 1

Find dy/dx if $x = \sin t$, $y = \cos t$.

$$\frac{dy}{dx} = \frac{\dfrac{dy}{dt}}{\dfrac{dx}{dt}} = \frac{-\sin t}{\cos t} = -\tan t.$$

Suppose we want to take a second derivative, which is, of course, nothing more than the derivative of the first derivative. The first derivative is a function of the parameter t, while its derivative is taken with respect to x. By an argument similar to the one above, we have

$$\frac{d^2y}{dx^2} = \frac{\dfrac{d}{dt}\left(\dfrac{dy}{dx}\right)}{\dfrac{dx}{dt}}, \qquad \frac{d^3y}{dx^3} = \frac{\dfrac{d}{dt}\left(\dfrac{d^2y}{dx^2}\right)}{\dfrac{dx}{dt}}, \qquad \text{etc.}$$

Example 2

Find dy/dx and d^2y/dx^2 if $x = \sin t$, $y = 1 + \cos t$.

$$\frac{dy}{dx} = \frac{\dfrac{dy}{dt}}{\dfrac{dx}{dt}} = \frac{-\sin t}{\cos t} = -\tan t.$$

$$\frac{d^2y}{dx^2} = \frac{\dfrac{d}{dt}\left(\dfrac{dy}{dx}\right)}{\dfrac{dx}{dt}} = \frac{-\sec^2 t}{\cos t} = -\sec^3 t.$$

Example 3

Find dy/dx and d^2y/dx^2 at $t = 0$ if $x = e^t$, $y = e^{-t}$.

$$\frac{dy}{dx} = \frac{-e^{-t}}{e^t} = -e^{-2t}, \qquad \frac{d^2y}{dx^2} = \frac{2e^{-2t}}{e^t} = 2e^{-3t}.$$

At $t = 0$,

$$\frac{dy}{dx} = -1, \qquad \frac{d^2y}{dx^2} = 2.$$

Problems

In Problems 1–10, find dy/dx and d^2y/dx^2.

1. $x = t^2 + t, \quad y = t + 1.$
2. $x = t - 2, \quad y = t^2 - 2t.$
3. $x = t^2 + 7t + 10, \quad y = t + 3.$
4. $x = t^2 - 7t + 9, \quad y = t - 4.$
5. $x = t^2 + t, \quad y = t^2 - t.$
6. $x = 2t - 1, \quad y = 4t^2.$
7. $x = 1 + \cos t, \quad y = -2 + \sin t.$
8. $x = 3 + 2\cos t, \quad y = 1 - \sin t.$
9. $x = 2 + \cosh t, \quad y = -1 + \sinh t.$
10. $x = 3 + 2\cosh t, \quad y = -2 + 5\sinh t.$

In Problems 11–16, find dy/dx and d^2y/dx^2 at the given value of t.

11. $x = t - 3, \quad y = t^2 + 4t + 3; \quad t = 1.$
12. $x = t^3 - 3t^2 + 1, \quad y = t + 4; \quad t = 2.$
13. $x = t^3, \quad y = t^2; \quad t = -3.$
14. $x = 1 + \cos t, \quad y = 1 - \sin t; \quad t = \pi/2.$
15. $x = e^t + 1, \quad y = e^t + e^{-t}; \quad t = 0.$
16. $x = 1 + \cosh t, \quad y = 2 + \sinh t; \quad t = 0.$

In Problems 17–20, find an equation of the line tangent to the given curve at the given point.

17. $x = 2t - 1, \quad y = 4t^2 - 2t; \quad t = 1.$

18. $x = t + 1, \quad y = t^3 + 3t^2 + 4t + 2; \quad t = 0.$

19. $x = 3 \cos \theta, \quad y = 2 \sin \theta; \quad \theta = \pi/4.$

20. $x = 3 \cosh \theta, \quad y = 2 \sinh \theta; \quad \theta = 1.$

In Problems 21–29, find all points at which the curve has a horizontal or vertical tangent.

21. $x = t + 3, \quad y = t^3 - 3t^2.$

22. $x = t + 2, \quad y = (t^2 + 4t)^2.$

23. $x = 4 \cos \theta, \quad y = 2 \sin \theta.$

24. $x = 4 \cosh \theta, \quad y = 2 \sinh \theta.$

25. $x = \theta - \sin \theta, \quad y = 1 - \cos \theta.$

26. $x = \theta + \sin \theta, \quad y = 1 - \cos \theta.$

27. $x = \cos^3 \theta, \quad y = \sin^3 \theta.$

28. $x = \cos \theta + \theta \sin \theta, \quad y = \sin \theta - \theta \cos \theta.$

29. $x = t - \tanh t, \quad y = \operatorname{sech} t.$

Polar Coordinates

14.1

Polar Coordinates

Up to now, a point in the plane has been represented by a pair of numbers, (x, y), which represent (for perpendicular axes) the distances of the point from the y and x axes, respectively. Another way of representing points is by *polar coordinates*. In this case, we need only one axis (the *polar axis*) and a point on it (the *pole*). These correspond to the x axis and the origin of the rectangular coordinate system. Normally we shall include the y axis, even though it is not necessary to do so.

Before considering points in polar coordinates, let us recall that an angle in the standard position has its vertex at the origin (or pole) and its initial side on the positive end of the x axis (or polar axis). The terminal side is another ray (or half-line) with the origin as its end point. The ray with the same end point and on the same line as the terminal side is called the ray opposite the terminal side. For example, the terminal side of a 90° angle in standard position is the positive end of the y axis together with the origin; the ray opposite the terminal side is the negative end of the y axis together with the origin.

A point P is represented, in polar coordinates, by an ordered pair of numbers (r, θ). (See Figure 14.1.) It is determined in the following way: first find the terminal side of the angle θ in standard position; if $r \geq 0$, then P is on this terminal side and at a distance r from the pole; if $r < 0$, then P is on the ray opposite the terminal side

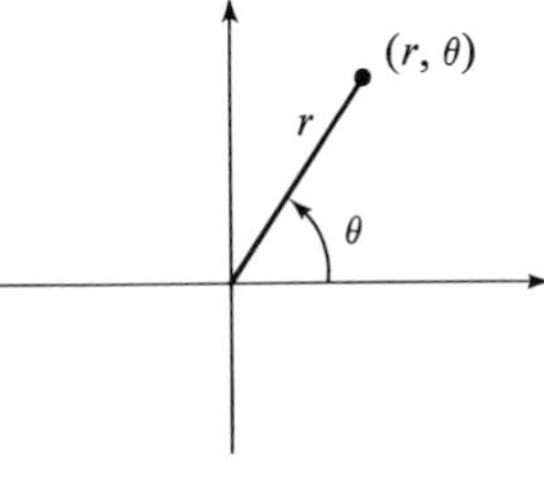

Figure 14.1

and at a distance $|r|$ from the pole. A few points are given with their polar coordinates in Figure 14.2.

It might be noted that while the terminal side of the angle $-\pi/3$ is in the fourth quadrant, $(-1, -\pi/3)$ is in the second quadrant. The quadrant that a point is in is *not* determined by the signs of the two polar coordinates, as it is with rectangular coordinates. It is determined by the size of θ and the sign of r. If r is positive, the point is in whatever quadrant θ is in; if r is negative, the point is in the opposite quadrant.

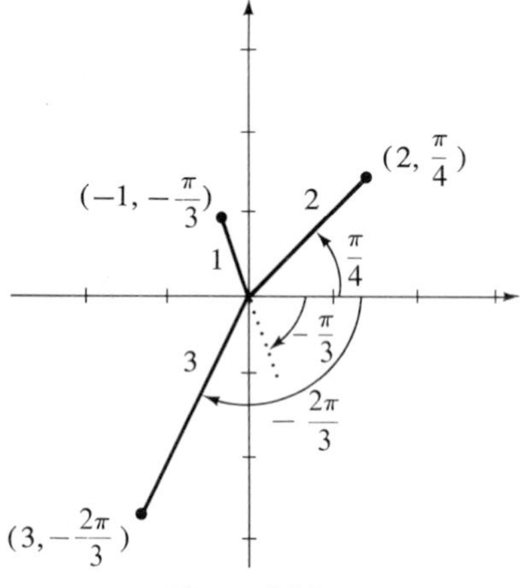

Figure 14.2

Polar coordinates present only one problem that we did not have with rectangular coordinates —a point has more than one representation in polar coordinates. For example: $(2, \pi/2)$ and $(-2, -\pi/2)$ represent the same point. In fact, if (r, θ) is one representation of a point, then $(r, \theta + \pi n)$, where n is an even integer, and $(-r, \theta + \pi n)$, where n is an odd integer, are representations of the same point. Furthermore, $(0, \theta)$ is the pole for any choice of θ.

14.2

Graphs in Polar Coordinates

Equations in polar coordinates can be graphed by point-by-point plotting, as we graphed rectangular coordinates.

Example 1

Graph $r = \sin \theta$.

Note in Figure 14.3 that we have the entire graph for $0° \leq \theta < 180°$. The remaining values of θ simply repeat the graph a second time, since $(0, 0°) = (0, 180°)$, $(.5, 30°) = (-.5, 210°)$, and so forth. Of course, values of θ outside the range $0° \leq \theta \leq 360°$ would give no new points.

This method of point-by-point plotting is quite cumbersome here, as it was in the case of rectangular coordinates. One way to simplify the proceedings is to represent the table of values of r and θ by means of a graph. This may sound as if we are going in circles—we can get the graph from a table of values of r and θ that is represented by a graph. Actually, this is not so bad as it sounds. We shall represent the table by a graph in *rectangular coordinates.*

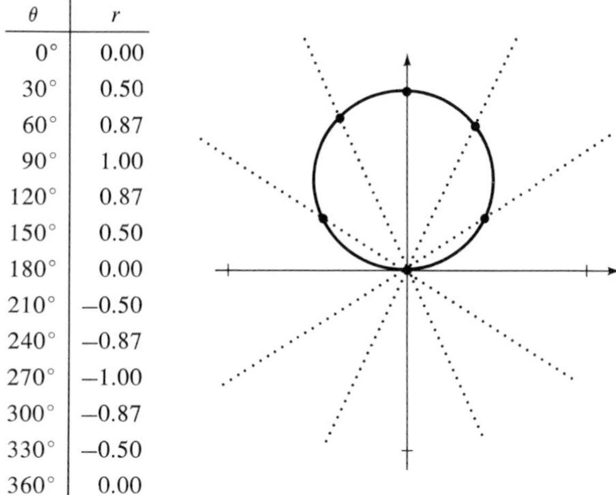

θ	r
0°	0.00
30°	0.50
60°	0.87
90°	1.00
120°	0.87
150°	0.50
180°	0.00
210°	–0.50
240°	–0.87
270°	–1.00
300°	–0.87
330°	–0.50
360°	0.00

Figure 14.3

Example 2

Graph $r = 1 + \cos\theta$.

We can easily graph this equation in rectangular coordinates by using addition of ordinates. The result is given in Figure 14.4. Now we can read off values of r and θ just as we would from a table. As θ increases from 0° to 90°, r goes from 2 to 1. This gives the portion of the curve shown in (a) of Figure 14.5. As θ goes from 90° to 180°, r goes from 1 down to 0 (shown in (b)). As θ goes from 180° to 270°, r goes from 0 back up to 1 (as in (c)); and finally, as θ goes from 270° to 360°,we see in (d) that θ goes from 1 to 2. The same path is traced for values of θ beyond 360° or less than 0°. Putting all of this together, we have the desired graph, shown in (e).

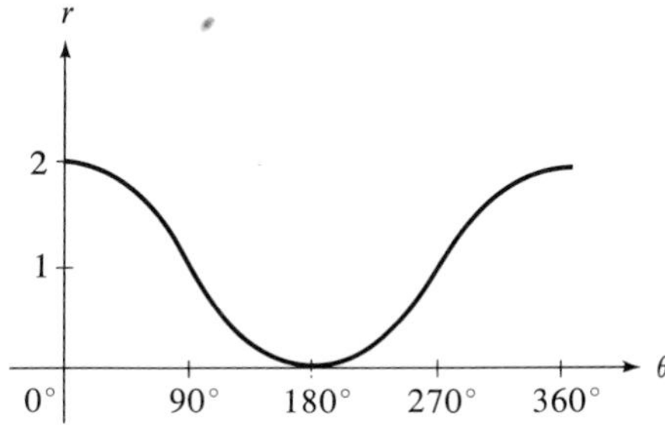

Figure 14.4

Example 3

Graph $r = \sin 2\theta$.

The graph is given in rectangular coordinates in (a) of Figure 14.6. This is then put on the polar graph shown in (b). Note that for θ in the range $90° < \theta < 180°$, r is negative. Thus instead of giving the loop in the second quadrant, it gives the one in the fourth quadrant. Similarly, r is negative for θ in the range $270° < \theta < 360°$. This gives the loop in the second quadrant.

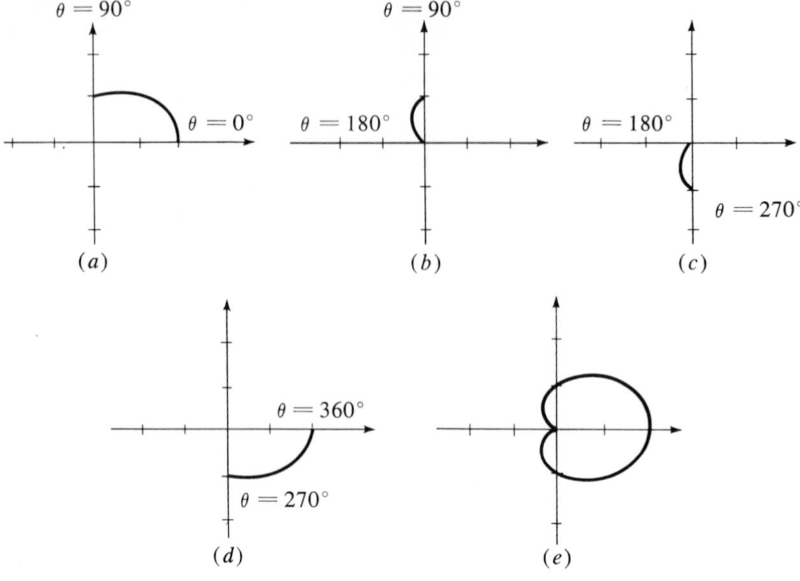

Figure 14.5

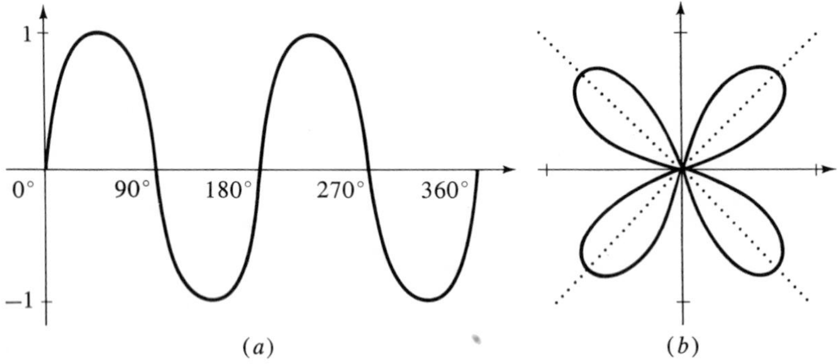

Figure 14.6

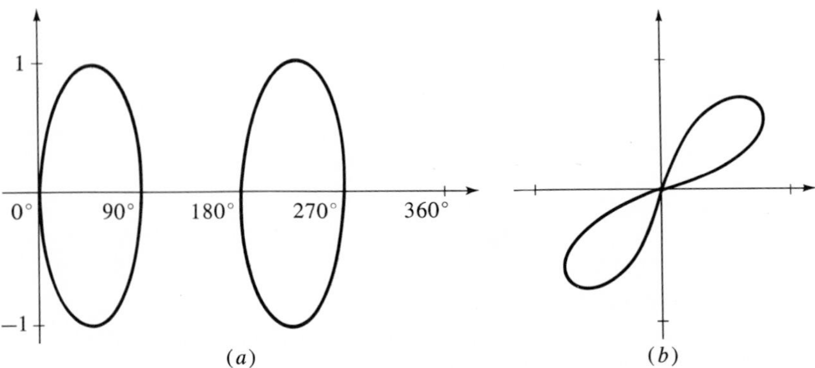

Figure 14.7

Example 4

Graph $r^2 = \sin 2\theta$.

Graphing in rectangular coordinates by the methods of Section 6.3, we have the result given in Figure 14.7(a). There are a couple of things of interest here. First of all, $r^2 = \sin 2\theta$ has two values of r for each θ in the ranges $0° < \theta < 90°$ and $180° < \theta < 270°$, while it has no value at all for $90° < \theta < 180°$ and $270° < \theta < 360°$. Since it has two values in the range $0° < \theta < 90°$, we get both loops for $0° \leq \theta \leq 90°$, shown in (b). Similarly we get both loops a second time for $180° \leq \theta \leq 270°$. Because there is no value of r for $90° < \theta < 180°$ and $270° < \theta < 360°$, there are no points of the graph in the second or fourth quadrants.

Problems

1. Plot the following points: $(1, \pi/3)$, $(2, 45°)$, $(0, 30°)$, $(-2, 90°)$, $(-1, 3\pi/4)$, $(2, 300°)$.
2. Give an alternate polar representation with $0° \leq \theta < 180°$: $(4, 330°)$, $(-2, 420°)$, $(1, 210°)$, $(0, 283°)$, $(-3, 270°)$, $(2, 240°)$.
3. Give an alternate polar representation with $r \geq 0$ and $0° \leq \theta < 360°$: $(-4, 120°)$, $(3, -60°)$, $(0, 530°)$, $(-1, 330°)$, $(-2, 390°)$, $(-2, 135°)$.
4. Give an alternate polar representation: $(1, 30°)$, $(-2, 180°)$, $(4, 210°)$, $(0, 60°)$, $(-1, 30°)$, $(2, 90°)$.

In Problems 5–34, sketch the graph of the given equation.

5. $r = \cos\theta$.
6. $r = 2\sin\theta$.
7. $r = 1 - \cos\theta$.
8. $r = 1 + \sin\theta$.
9. $r = 1 - \sin\theta$.
10. $r = \sin\theta - 1$.
11. $r = \cos 2\theta$.
12. $r = \sin 4\theta$.
13. $r = \sin 3\theta$.
14. $r = \cos 3\theta$.
15. $r = \cos 5\theta$.
16. $r = \sin 6\theta$.
17. $r = 1 + 2\sin\theta$.
18. $r = 1 - 2\cos\theta$.
19. $r = 2 + \cos\theta$.
20. $r = 2 + 3\sin\theta$.
21. $r = \tan\theta$.
22. $r = \sec\theta$.
23. $r^2 = \sin\theta$.
24. $r^2 = \cos 3\theta$.
25. $r^2 = \cos 4\theta$.
26. $r^2 = \sin^2\theta$.
27. $r^2 = 1 + \cos\theta$.
28. $r^2 = 1 - \sin\theta$.
29. $r = \theta$.
30. $r = |\theta|$.
31. $r^2 = \theta^2$.
32. $r = \dfrac{2}{1 - \cos\theta}$.
33. $r = \dfrac{2}{1 - 2\cos\theta}$.
34. $r = \dfrac{2}{2 - \cos\theta}$.
35. Show that if θ is replaced by $-\theta$ and the result is equivalent to the original equation, then the graph is symmetric about the x axis.
36. Show that if θ is replaced by $\pi - \theta$ and the result is equivalent to the original equation, then the graph is symmetric about the y axis.
37. Show that if r is replaced by $-r$ and the result is equivalent to the original equation, then the graph is symmetric about the pole.

14.3

Points of Intersection

Suppose we have a pair of equations in polar form that we solve simultaneously to obtain pairs of numbers satisfying both equations—that is, points of intersection of the two curves.

Example 1

Find the points of intersection of $r = 1$ and $r = 2 \sin \theta$.

Eliminating r from this pair of equations, we get

$$\sin \theta = \frac{1}{2}, \quad \text{or} \quad \theta = 30°, 150°,$$

giving the points (1, 30°) and (1, 150°). The graphs of these two curves, showing the two points of intersection are given in Figure 14.8.

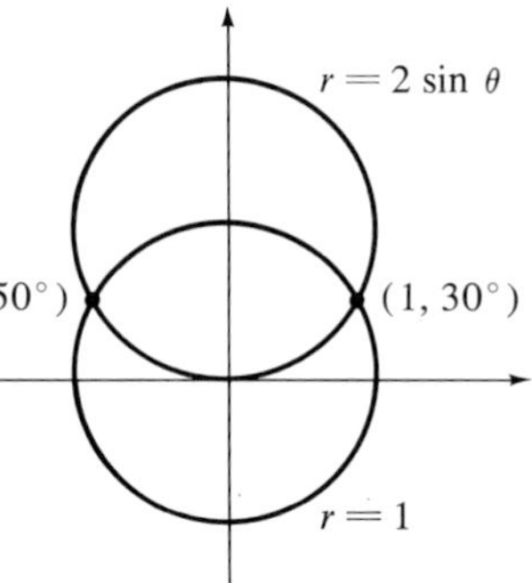

Figure 14.8

While the solutions of a pair of simultaneous equations must be points of intersection of the curves represented by the equations, some points of intersection cannot be found in this way. The reason is that they have different representations on the two curves. Thus *we must graph both curves* to be sure that we have found all points of intersection.

Example 2

Find the points of intersection of $r = \sin \theta$ and $r = \cos \theta$.

Eliminating r between the two equations, we have

$$\sin \theta = \cos \theta.$$

If we divide by $\cos \theta$, then

$$\tan \theta = 1 \quad \text{and} \quad \theta = 45° + 180° \cdot n.$$

In the range $0° \leq \theta < 360°$, we have $(1/\sqrt{2}, 45°)$ and $(-1/\sqrt{2}, 225°)$. But these are different representations for the same point. Thus we have found only one point of intersection. As we can see from Figure 14.9, there are really two points of intersection—the one we found and the pole.

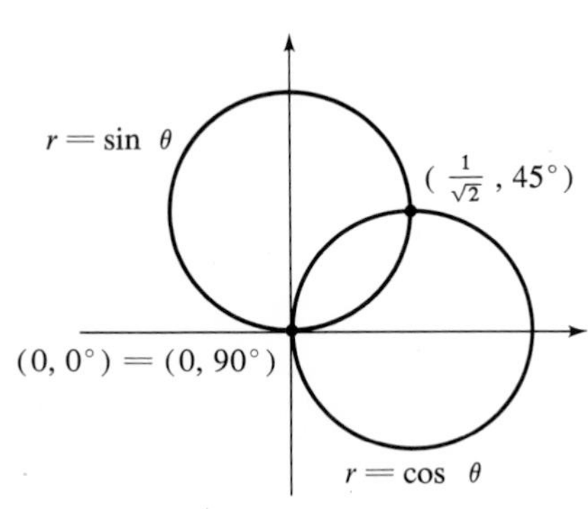

Figure 14.9

The pole has many different representations. On the curve $r = \sin\theta$ it is represented by $(0, 180° \cdot n)$; on $r = \cos\theta$ it is represented by $(0, 90° + 180° \cdot n)$. Thus, while the pole is common to both curves, it does not have a common representation that satisfies both equations. So we cannot find this point of intersection by finding simultaneous solutions of the two equations. We might represent this point by $(0, 0°) = (0, 90°)$.

Example 3

Find all points of intersection of $r = \cos 2\theta$ and $r = \sin\theta$.

$$\cos 2\theta = \sin\theta,$$
$$1 - 2\sin^2\theta = \sin\theta,$$
$$2\sin^2\theta + \sin\theta - 1 = 0,$$
$$(2\sin\theta - 1)(\sin\theta + 1) = 0;$$
$$\sin\theta = \frac{1}{2}, \quad \sin\theta = -1;$$
$$\theta = 30°, 150°, 270°.$$

Thus, we have the points $(1/2, 30°)$, $(1/2, 150°)$, and $(-1, 270°)$. In addition we can see from Figure 14.10 that the pole is a point of intersection; it may be represented by $(0, 45°) = (0, 0°)$. It might also be noted that the point $(-1, 270°)$ can also be written $(1, 90°)$, but this form satisfies only $r = \sin\theta$.

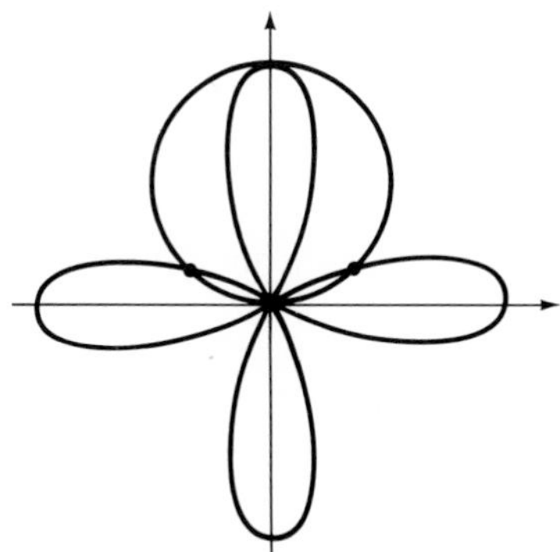

Figure 14.10

Problems

Find all points of intersection of the given curves.

1. $r = \sqrt{2}, r = 2\cos\theta.$
2. $r = \sqrt{3}, r = 2\sin\theta.$
3. $r = 2, r = \sin\theta + 2.$
4. $r = 1, r = 2\cos 2\theta.$
5. $r = \cos\theta, r = 1 - \cos\theta.$
6. $r = \cos\theta, r = 1 + \sin\theta.$
7. $r = \sin 2\theta, r = \sin\theta.$
8. $r = \sin 2\theta, r = \sqrt{2}\cos\theta.$
9. $r = \sec\theta, r = \csc\theta.$
10. $r = \sec\theta, r = \tan\theta.$
11. $r = 3\cos\theta + 4, r = 3.$
12. $r = \sin 2\theta, r = \cos 2\theta.$
13. $r = 2(1 + \cos\theta), r(1 - \cos\theta) = 1.$
14. $r = 1 - \sin\theta, r(1 - \sin\theta) = 1.$
15. $r = 1 - \sin\theta, r = 1 - \cos\theta.$
16. $r^2 = \sin\theta, r^2 = \cos\theta.$
17. $r^2 = \cos\theta, r^2 = \sec\theta.$
18. $r = 2\cos\theta + 1, r = 2\cos\theta - 1.$
19. $r^2 = \sin\theta, r = \sin\theta.$
20. $r^2 = \sin\theta, r = \cos\theta.$

14.4

Relationships between Rectangular and Polar Coordinates

There are some simple relationships between rectangular and polar coordinates. These can be found easily by a consideration of Figure 14.11.

$$x = r \cos \theta,$$

$$y = r \sin \theta,$$

$$r^2 = x^2 + y^2$$

$$\tan \theta = \frac{y}{x}.$$

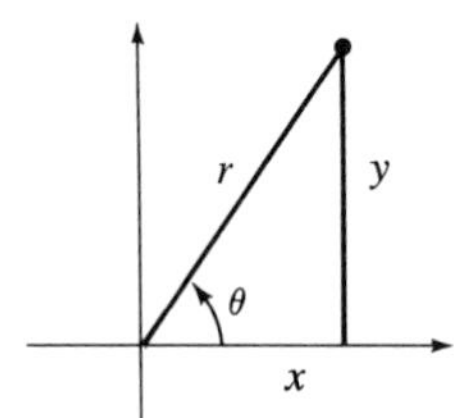

Figure 14.11

The last two, which may be solved for r and θ, would give us expressions involving $\pm$ and arctan. Thus, we prefer to leave them in their present form.

With these we can now change from one coordinate system to the other.

Example 1

Express (2, 30°) in rectangular coordinates.

$$\begin{aligned} x &= r \cos \theta & y &= r \sin \theta \\ &= 2 \cos 30^\circ & &= 2 \sin 30^\circ \\ &= 2 \cdot \frac{\sqrt{3}}{2} & &= 2 \cdot \frac{1}{2} \\ &= \sqrt{3}; & &= 1. \end{aligned}$$

Thus $(2, 30^\circ) = (\sqrt{3}, 1)$.

Example 2

Express (4, −4) in polar coordinates.

$$\begin{aligned} r^2 &= x^2 + y^2 & \tan \theta &= \frac{y}{x} \\ &= 16 + 16 & &= \frac{-4}{4} \\ &= 32 & &= -1 \\ r &= \pm 4\sqrt{2}; & \theta &= 135^\circ + 180^\circ \cdot n. \end{aligned}$$

We have a choice for both r and θ. The values of r and θ cannot be selected independently; the value we choose for one will limit the available choices for the other. In this case, the point (4, −4) is in the fourth quadrant. Thus, we may choose either a fourth-quadrant angle and a positive r or a second-quadrant angle and a negative r. Thus

$$(4, -4) = (4\sqrt{2}, 315^\circ) = (-4\sqrt{2}, 135^\circ) = (4\sqrt{2}, -45^\circ), \text{ etc.}$$

Of course we can use these equations to find a polar equation corresponding to one in rectangular coordinates, and vice versa.

Example 3

Express $y = x^2$ in polar coordinates.

$$\begin{aligned} y &= x^2, \\ r \sin \theta &= r^2 \cos^2 \theta, \\ \sin \theta &= r \cos^2 \theta \quad \text{or} \quad r = 0, \\ r &= \frac{\sin \theta}{\cos^2 \theta}, \\ r &= \sec \theta \tan \theta. \end{aligned}$$

Since $r = 0$ represents only the pole and it is included in $r = \sec \theta \tan \theta$, we may drop $r = 0$. The result is

$$r = \sec \theta \tan \theta.$$

Example 4

Express $r = 1 - \cos \theta$ in rectangular coordinates.

First, multiply through by r.

$$r^2 = r - r \cos \theta.$$

At this point we could make the substitutions $r^2 = x^2 + y^2$, $r \cos \theta = x$, and $r = \pm\sqrt{x^2 + y^2}$. The last is rather bothersome, since it involves a $\pm$. In order to avoid this, let us isolate r on one side of the equation and square.

$$\begin{aligned} r &= r^2 + r \cos \theta, \\ r^2 &= (r^2 + r \cos \theta)^2, \\ x^2 + y^2 &= (x^2 + y^2 + x)^2. \end{aligned}$$

We have done two things that might introduce extraneous roots: (1) Multiplying by r may introduce only a single point, the pole, to the graph. Since the pole is already a point of the graph of $r = 1 - \cos \theta$, no new point is introduced here. (2) Squaring may introduce several new points. The equation

$$r^2 = (r^2 + r \cos \theta)^2$$

is equivalent to

$$r = \pm(r^2 + r \cos \theta).$$

Now $r = r^2 + r \cos \theta$ is equivalent to our original equation, $r = 1 - \cos \theta$, while $r = -(r^2 + r \cos \theta)$ is equivalent to $r = -1 - \cos \theta$. Thus

$$x^2 + y^2 = (x^2 + y^2 + x)^2$$

is equivalent to $r = 1 - \cos \theta$ together with $r = -1 - \cos \theta$. But $r = 1 - \cos \theta$ and $r = -1 - \cos \theta$ have the same graph. Thus we have introduced no new points by squaring.

Problems

1. The following points are given in polar coordinates. Give the rectangular coordinate representation of each. $(1, \pi)$, $(\sqrt{3}, \pi/3)$, $(-1, 3\pi)$, $(\sqrt{2}, 3\pi/4)$, $(2\sqrt{3}, 5\pi/3)$, $(-3, 7\pi/6)$, $(0, 5\pi/4)$, $(4, 0)$, $(-2, 7\pi/4)$.

2. The following points are given in rectangular coordinates. Give a polar coordinate representation of each. $(\sqrt{2}, -\sqrt{2})$, $(-1, \sqrt{3})$, $(4, 0)$, $(-1, -1)$, $(0, -2)$, $(0, 0)$, $(-2\sqrt{3}, 2)$, $(-3, 1)$, $(4, 3)$, $(-2, 4)$.

In Problems 3–18, express the given equation in polar coordinates.

3. $x = 2$.
4. $y = 5$.
5. $x^2 + y^2 = 1$.
6. $x^2 - y^2 = 4$.
7. $y = x^2$.
8. $y = x^3$.
9. $(x + y)^2 = x - y$.
10. $x = y$.
11. $y = 3x$.
12. $y^2 = x^3$.
13. $x + 2y - 4 = 0$.
14. $x^2 + y^2 - 2x = 0$.
15. $x^2 + y^2 - 2x - 2y + 1 = 0$.
16. $x^2 + 9y^2 = 9$.
17. $xy = 1$.
18. $y = \dfrac{x}{x+1}$.

In Problems 19–34, express the given equation in rectangular coordinates.

19. $r = a$.
20. $\theta = \pi/4$.
21. $\theta = \pi/3$.
22. $r = 2 \sin \theta$.
23. $r = 4 \cos \theta$.
24. $r = \sin 2\theta$.
25. $r = \cos 2\theta$.
26. $r = 1 - \cos \theta$.
27. $r = 3 + 2 \sin \theta$.
28. $r^2 = \sin \theta$.
29. $r^2 = 1 + \sin \theta$.
30. $r^2 = \sin 2\theta$.
31. $r = \dfrac{1}{1 - \cos \theta}$.
32. $r = \dfrac{1}{1 + \sin \theta}$.
33. $r = 2 \sin \theta + 3 \cos \theta$.
34. $r = \sec \theta$.

14.5

Conics in Polar Coordinates

We found earlier that the equations of conic sections (in rectangular coordinates) have very simple forms if the center or vertex is at the origin and the axes are the coordinate axes. There are, however, three different forms corresponding to the three different types of conics. We find that conics can be easily represented in polar coordinates if a focus is at the origin and one axis is a coordinate axis. Furthermore, the same type of equation represents all three types of conics if we use the unifying concept of eccentricity.

Recall that any conic can be determined by a single focus, the corresponding directrix, and the eccentricity. If P is a point on the conic, then the distance from P to the focus divided by the distance from P to the directrix equals the eccentricity. The particular conic we get depends upon the eccentricity; the eccentricity is a positive number and

if $e < 1$, the conic is an ellipse,
if $e = 1$, the conic is a parabola,
if $e > 1$, the conic is a hyperbola.

If $P(r, \theta)$ is a point on a conic with focus 0, directrix $x = p$ (p positive), and eccentricity e, then

$$\frac{OP}{PD} = e, \quad \text{or} \quad \frac{|r|}{|p - r\cos\theta|} = e.$$

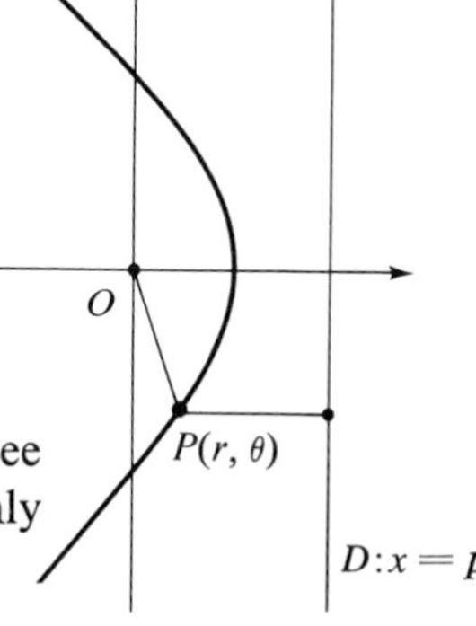

Figure 14.12

There are now two cases to consider:

$$\frac{r}{p - r\cos\theta} = e \quad \text{and} \quad \frac{r}{p - r\cos\theta} = -e.$$

Either of these yields an equation of the desired conic (see Problems 21 and 22); however, the first yields the commonly used form. Solving for r in this equation, we have

$$r = \frac{ep}{1 + e\cos\theta}.$$

If the directrix is $x = -p$ (p positive) then the equation is

$$r = \frac{ep}{1 - e\cos\theta}.$$

If the directrix is $y = \pm p$ (p positive), then the equation is

$$r = \frac{ep}{1 \pm e\sin\theta}.$$

Theorem 14.1

The conic section with focus at the origin, directrix $x = \pm p$ (p positive), and eccentricity e has polar equation

$$r = \frac{ep}{1 \pm e\cos\theta};$$

if the directrix is $y = \pm p$ (p positive), it has equation

$$r = \frac{ep}{1 \pm e\sin\theta}.$$

Example 1

Describe $r = \dfrac{6}{4 + 3\cos\theta}$.

Dividing numerator and denominator by 4, we have

$$r = \frac{\frac{3}{2}}{1 + \frac{3}{4}\cos\theta} = \frac{\frac{3}{4}\cdot 2}{1 + \frac{3}{4}\cos\theta}.$$

Thus the eccentricity is 3/4 and the directrix is $x = 2$. The conic is an ellipse with focus at the origin, directrix $x = 2$, and eccentricity 3/4.

Example 2

Sketch $r = \dfrac{15}{2 - 3\cos\theta}$.

Dividing by 2, we have

$$r = \frac{\frac{15}{2}}{1 - \frac{3}{2}\cos\theta} = \frac{\frac{3}{2}\cdot 5}{1 - \frac{3}{2}\cos\theta}.$$

Thus we have a hyperbola with focus at the origin, eccentricity 3/2, and directrix $x = -5$. The vertices are on the x axis, one between the focus and directrix and the other to the left of the directrix. When $\theta = 0°$, $r = -15$; when $\theta = 180°$, $r = 3$. Thus the vertices are $(-15, 0°)$ and $(3, 180°)$. When $\theta = 90°$ or $270°$, $r = 15/2$. Thus, the ends of one of the latera recta are $(15/2, 90°)$ and $(15/2, 270°)$. This information is enough to give a reasonably accurate picture of the hyperbola. If the asymptotes are desired, they can best be found by considering some of the above points in rectangular coordinates. Thus the vertices are $(-3, 0)$ and $(-15, 0)$, and the center is $(-9, 0)$, giving $a = 6$ and $c = 9$. We can now use the equation

$$b^2 = c^2 - a^2$$

to find $b^2 = 45$ or $b = 3\sqrt{5}$. Once we have this, the asymptotes are easily found (see Figure 14.13).

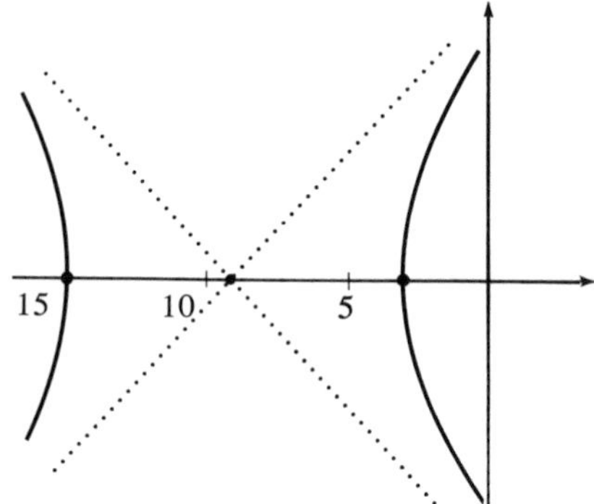

Figure 14.13

Example 3

Find a polar equation of the parabola with focus at the origin and directrix $y = -4$.

The equation is in the form

$$r = \frac{ep}{1 - e\sin\theta},$$

since the directrix is a horizontal line below the focus. Furthermore, $e = 1$, since the conic is a parabola, and directrix $y = -4$ gives $p = 4$. Thus the equation is

$$r = \frac{4}{1 - \sin\theta}.$$

Problems

In Problems 1–8, state the type of conic and give a focus and its corresponding directrix and the eccentricity.

1. $r = \dfrac{4}{1 + 2\cos\theta}$.

2. $r = \dfrac{12}{1 - 3\sin\theta}$.

3. $r = \dfrac{4}{3 + 2 \sin \theta}$.

4. $r = \dfrac{5}{4 - 4 \cos \theta}$.

5. $r = \dfrac{3}{1 + \sin \theta}$.

6. $r = \dfrac{10}{5 - 2 \cos \theta}$.

7. $r(3 + 2 \sin \theta) = 6$.

8. $r(2 - 4 \cos \theta) = 5$.

In Problems 9–14, sketch the given conic.

9. $r = \dfrac{2}{1 + \cos \theta}$.

10. $r = \dfrac{16}{5 - 3 \cos \theta}$.

11. $r = \dfrac{16}{4 - 5 \sin \theta}$.

12. $r(3 - 5 \cos \theta) = 9$.

13. $r(13 + 12 \sin \theta) = 25$.

14. $r(3 + 3 \sin \theta) = 4$.

In Problems 15–20, find a polar equation of the conic with focus at the origin and the given eccentricity and directrix.

15. Directrix: $x = 5$; $e = 2/3$.

16. Directrix: $y = -3$; $e = 2$.

17. Directrix: $y = 2$; $e = 1$.

18. Directrix: $x = -4$; $e = 1$.

19. Directrix: $x = 5$; $e = 5/4$.

20. Directrix: $y = 3$; $e = 3/4$.

21. Sketch $r = \dfrac{-2}{1 - \cos \theta}$. Compare with the conic of Problem 9 (see the following problem).

22. Show that the conic section with focus at the origin, directrix $x = p$ (p positive), and eccentricity e has polar equation

$$r = \frac{-ep}{1 - e \cos \theta}.$$

23. Suppose, in the equation $r = \dfrac{ep}{1 + e \cos \theta}$, $e \to 0$ and $p \to +\infty$ in such a way that ep remains constant. What happens to the shape of the conic? What happens to the equation of the conic?

24. Find a polar equation of a circle with center (k, α) and radius a by using the law of cosines (see Figure 14.14).

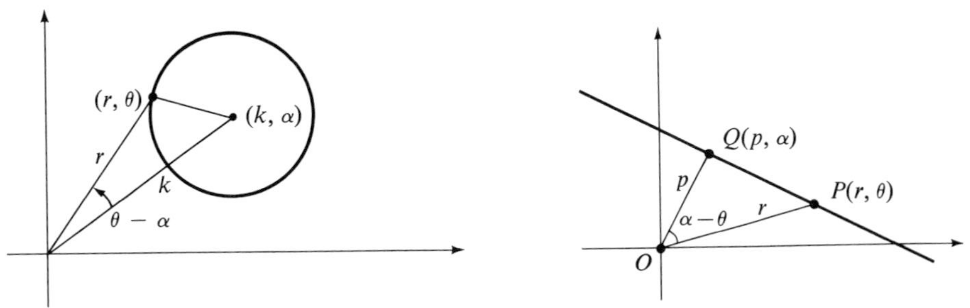

Figure 14.14

Figure 14.15

25. By using the trigonometry of right triangles, show that the line PQ (Figure 14.15) can be represented by the equation

$$x \cos \alpha + y \sin \alpha - p = 0.$$

This is called the *normal form* of the line, since it is expressed in terms of the polar coordinates of the point Q, which is the intersection of the original line and another perpendicular (or normal) to it and through the origin (see Problem 37, Section 2.3).

26. By using the identity

$$\sin^2 \alpha + \cos^2 \alpha = 1,$$

show that $Ax + By + C = 0$ can be put into the normal form by dividing through by $\pm\sqrt{A^2 + B^2}$ (see Problem 25 for the normal form).

27. Show that the distance from the point (x_1, y_1) to the line $Ax + By + C = 0$ is

$$d = \frac{|Ax_1 + By_1 + C|}{\sqrt{A^2 + B^2}}.$$

Hint: Put the original line and the one parallel to it and through (x_1, y_1) into the normal form (see Problems 25 and 26).

14.6

Derivatives in Polar Coordinates

If we are given the polar equation

$$r = f(\theta),$$

it is a simple matter to find the derivative $dr/d\theta$. The only trouble is that this does not represent the same thing as the derivative dy/dx, where $y = f(x)$. The latter represents the slope of the graph of $y = f(x)$. If we go back to the definition of the derivative, we see that

$$\frac{dr}{d\theta} = \lim_{h\to 0} \frac{f(\theta + h) - f(\theta)}{h}.$$

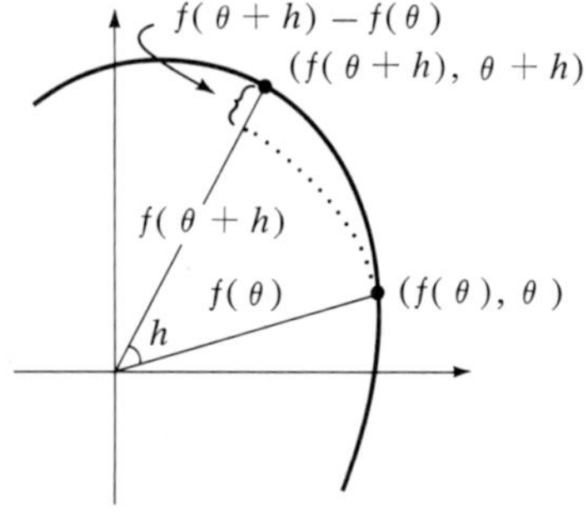

Figure 14.16

It is obvious from Figure 14.16 that this is not the slope.

Let us see if we can get the slope from some other expression. Since the slope of the graph is dy/dx, we are interested in expressing the equation

$$r = f(\theta)$$

in rectangular coordinates. Suppose we start with the relations

$$x = r \cos \theta \quad \text{and} \quad y = r \sin \theta.$$

By substituting $r = f(\theta)$, we get the desired equation in parametric form

$$x = f(\theta) \cos \theta \quad \text{and} \quad y = f(\theta) \sin \theta.$$

Now we are in a position to find the desired slope.

$$\frac{dy}{dx} = \frac{\dfrac{dy}{d\theta}}{\dfrac{dx}{d\theta}} = \frac{f'(\theta) \sin \theta + f(\theta) \cos \theta}{f'(\theta) \cos \theta - f(\theta) \sin \theta}$$

$$= \frac{r' \sin \theta + r \cos \theta}{r' \cos \theta - r \sin \theta}.$$

Example 1

Find the slope of the graph $r = 1 - \cos\theta$ at $\theta = \pi/2$.

$$\frac{dy}{dx} = \frac{r'\sin\theta + r\cos\theta}{r'\cos\theta - r\sin\theta} = \frac{\sin\theta\cdot\sin\theta + (1-\cos\theta)\cos\theta}{\sin\theta\cos\theta - (1-\cos\theta)\sin\theta}$$

$$= \frac{\sin^2\theta + \cos\theta - \cos^2\theta}{2\sin\theta\cos\theta - \sin\theta}.$$

At $\theta = \pi/2$,

$$\frac{dy}{dx} = \frac{1^2 + 0 - 0}{2\cdot 1\cdot 0 - 1} = -1.$$

Example 2

Find an equation (in rectangular coordinates) of the line tangent to $r = \sin 2\theta$ at $(1, \pi/4)$.

$$\frac{dy}{dx} = \frac{r'\sin\theta + r\cos\theta}{r'\cos\theta - r\sin\theta} = \frac{2\cos 2\theta\sin\theta + \sin 2\theta\cos\theta}{2\cos 2\theta\cos\theta - \sin 2\theta\sin\theta}.$$

At $\theta = \pi/4$,

$$\frac{dy}{dx} = \frac{2\cos\pi/2\sin\pi/4 + \sin\pi/2\cos\pi/4}{2\cos\pi/2\cos\pi/4 - \sin\pi/2\sin\pi/4}$$

$$= \frac{2\cdot 0\cdot 1/\sqrt{2} + 1\cdot 1/\sqrt{2}}{2\cdot 0\cdot 1/\sqrt{2} - 1\cdot 1/\sqrt{2}}$$

$$= -1.$$

Transforming the point $(1, \pi/4)$ into rectangular coordinates, we have

$$x = r\cos\theta = 1\cos\pi/4 = 1/\sqrt{2},$$
$$y = r\sin\theta = 1\sin\pi/4 = 1/\sqrt{2}.$$

Thus the desired equation is

$$y - 1/\sqrt{2} = -1\,(x - 1/\sqrt{2}) \quad\text{or}\quad x + y - \sqrt{2} = 0.$$

Example 3

Find the relative maxima and minima of $r = 1 + \sin\theta$.

$$\frac{dy}{dx} = \frac{r'\sin\theta + r\cos\theta}{r'\cos\theta - r\sin\theta} = \frac{\cos\theta\sin\theta + (1+\sin\theta)\cos\theta}{\cos^2\theta - (1+\sin\theta)\sin\theta}$$

$$= \frac{\cos\theta\,(2\sin\theta + 1)}{\cos^2\theta - \sin\theta - \sin^2\theta}.$$

The numerator is 0 if either

$$\cos\theta = 0 \quad\text{or}\quad \sin\theta = -\frac{1}{2}.$$

Thus

$$\theta = 90°, 270° \quad\text{and}\quad \theta = 210°, 330°$$

are critical values. Similarly the denominator is 0 if

$$\cos^2\theta - \sin\theta - \sin^2\theta = 0,$$
$$1 - \sin^2\theta - \sin\theta - \sin^2\theta = 0,$$
$$2\sin^2\theta + \sin\theta - 1 = 0,$$
$$(2\sin\theta - 1)(\sin\theta + 1) = 0;$$

$$\sin\theta = \frac{1}{2}, \qquad \sin\theta = -1;$$

$$\theta = 30°, 150°, 270°.$$

Since $\theta = 270°$ makes both numerator and denominator 0, one might expect both a horizontal and a vertical tangent. Actually there is a vertical tangent, as may be seen from Figure 14.17, although this cannot be determined from the derivative alone. We can also see from the figure that (3/2, 30°) and (3/2, 150°) are neither maxima nor minima. Thus, the relative maxima are (2, 90°) and (0, 270°), and the relative minima are (1/2, 210°) and (1/2, 330°).

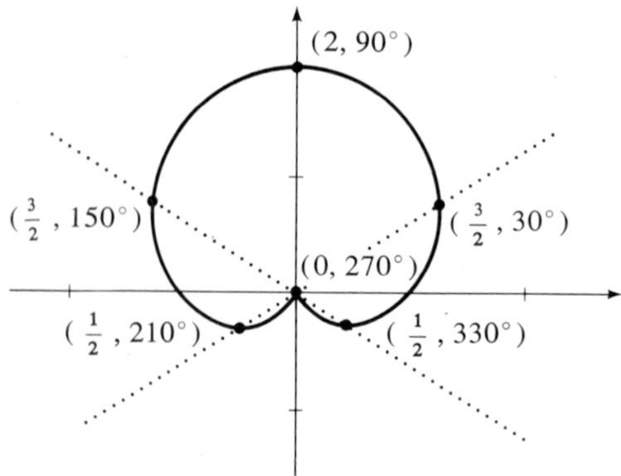

Figure 14.17

Problems

In Problems 1–10, find dy/dx.

1. $r = 1 + \cos\theta$.
2. $r = \dfrac{2 - \cos\theta}{2}$.
3. $r = 5\csc\theta$.
4. $r = \tan\theta$.
5. $r = \sin 3\theta$.
6. $r = \cos 2\theta$.
7. $r = \theta$.
8. $r = \sin\theta$.
9. $r = \dfrac{2}{1 - \sin\theta}$.
10. $r = \dfrac{\sin\theta}{1 + \cos\theta}$.

In Problems 11–16, find dy/dx for the given value of θ.

11. $r = 2\sin\theta,\ \theta = \pi/3$.
12. $r = 4\cos\theta,\ \theta = \pi/6$.
13. $r = 1 + \sin\theta,\ \theta = \pi/4$.
14. $r = 3 - 2\sin\theta,\ \theta = \pi$.
15. $r = \sin 3\theta,\ \theta = \pi/6$.
16. $r = \tan\theta,\ \theta = \pi/4$.

In Problems 17–22, find an equation (in rectangular coordinates) of the line tangent to the given curve at the given point.

17. $r = 1 + \cos\theta$ at $(1, \pi/2)$.
18. $r = 2\cos\theta$ at $(1, \pi/3)$.
19. $r = \cos 2\theta$ at $(-1, \pi/2)$.
20. $r = 4\sin\theta$ at $(2, \pi/6)$.
21. $r = 4\sin^2\theta$ at $(1, 5\pi/6)$.
22. $r = \tan\theta$ at $(1, \pi/4)$.

In Problems 23–28, find the relative maxima and minima.

23. $r = 1 - \cos\theta$.
24. $r = 1 - \sin\theta$.
25. $r = \sin 2\theta$.
26. $r = \cos^2\theta$.
27. $r = 1 + 2\cos\theta$.
28. $r = 2 - 3\sin\theta$.

29. The slope is not convenient for some purposes when dealing with polar coordinates. More convenient is $\tan\psi$ where ψ is the angle between the radius vector (joining the origin and the point P) and the tangent line (see Figure 14.18). Using the fact that

$$\psi = \varphi - \theta,$$

show that

$$\tan\psi = \frac{f(\theta)}{f'(\theta)}.$$

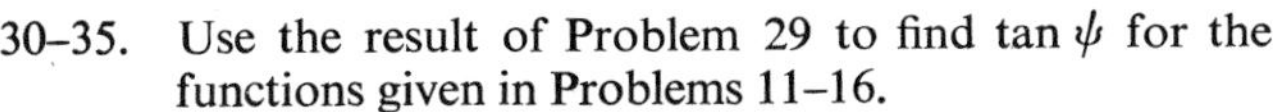

30–35. Use the result of Problem 29 to find $\tan\psi$ for the functions given in Problems 11–16.

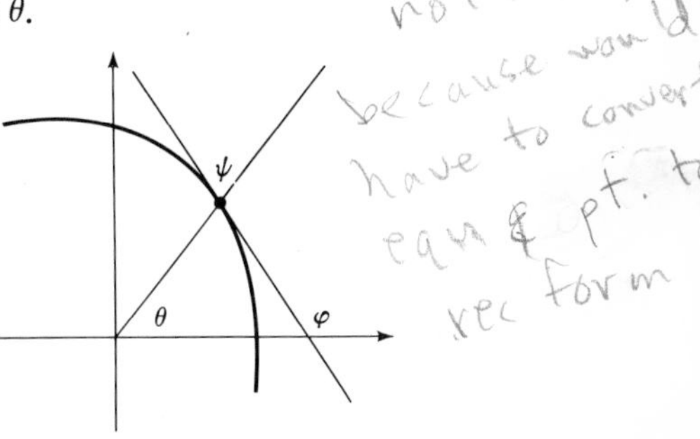

Figure 14.18

Methods of Integration

15.1

Fundamental Formulas

We had many integration formulas in Chapters 8, 9, and 12. Let us consider four more.

Theorem 15.1

$\int \tan u(x) \cdot u'(x)\, dx = -\ln |\cos u(x)| + C.$

Proof

Abbreviating $u(x)$ to u and $u'(x)$ to u', we have

$$\int \tan u \cdot u'\, dx = -\int \frac{-\sin u \cdot u'}{\cos u}\, dx.$$

The derivative of $\cos u$ is $-\sin u \cdot u'$. Our integral is in the form $\int \frac{v'}{v}\, dx$, where $v = \cos u$. Thus,

$$\int \tan u \cdot u'\, dx = -\ln |\cos u| + C.$$

Theorem 15.2

$\int \cot u(x) \cdot u'(x)\, dx = \ln |\sin u(x)| + C.$

The proof of this theorem is similar to that of Theorem 15.1. It is left to the student. Similar formulas can be derived for the hyperbolic functions.

Theorem 15.3

$$\int \sec u(x) \cdot u'(x)\, dx = \ln |\sec u(x) + \tan u(x)| + C.$$

Proof

Again, abbreviating $u(x)$ to u and $u'(x)$ to u', we have

$$\int \sec u \cdot u'\, dx = \int \frac{\sec^2 u + \sec u \tan u}{\sec u + \tan u}\, u'\, dx.$$

Again, this integral is in the form $\int \frac{v'}{v}\, dx$, where $v = \sec u + \tan u$. Thus

$$\int \sec u \cdot u'\, dx = \ln |\sec u + \tan u| + C.$$

Theorem 15.4

$$\int \csc u(x) \cdot u'(x)\, dx = \ln |\csc u - \cot u| + C.$$

The proof, similar to that of Theorem 15.3, is left to the student. We now have the following integration formulas.

1. $\int x^n\, dx = \frac{x^{n+1}}{n+1} + C \quad (n \neq -1).$

2. $\int u^n \cdot u'\, dx = \frac{u^{n+1}}{n+1} + C \quad (n \neq -1).$

3. $\int e^u \cdot u'\, dx = e^u + C.$

4. $\int a^u \cdot u'\, dx = a^u \cdot \log_a e + C.$

5. $\int \frac{u'}{u}\, dx = \ln |u| + C.$

6. $\int \sin u \cdot u'\, dx = -\cos u + C.$

7. $\int \cos u \cdot u'\, dx = \sin u + C.$

8. $\int \sec^2 u \cdot u'\, dx = \tan u + C.$

9. $\int \csc^2 u \cdot u'\, dx = -\cot u + C.$

10. $\int \sec u \tan u \cdot u'\, dx = \sec u + C.$

11. $\int \csc u \cot u \cdot u'\, dx = -\csc u + C.$

12. $\int \tan u \cdot u'\,dx = -\ln|\cos u| + C.$

13. $\int \cot u \cdot u'\,dx = \ln|\sin u| + C.$

14. $\int \sec u \cdot u'\,dx = \ln|\sec u + \tan u| + C.$

15. $\int \csc u \cdot u'\,dx = \ln|\csc u - \cot u| + C.$

16. $\int \sinh u \cdot u'\,dx = \cosh u + C.$

17. $\int \cosh u \cdot u'\,dx = \sinh u + C.$

18. $\int \operatorname{sech}^2 u \cdot u'\,dx = \tanh u + C.$

19. $\int \operatorname{csch}^2 u \cdot u'\,dx = -\coth u + C.$

20. $\int \operatorname{sech} u \tanh u \cdot u'\,dx = -\operatorname{sech} u + C.$

21. $\int \operatorname{csch} u \coth u \cdot u'\,dx = -\operatorname{csch} u + C.$

22. $\int \frac{u'}{1+u^2}\,dx = \operatorname{Arctan} u + C.$

23. $\int \frac{u'}{1-u^2}\,dx = \left.\begin{matrix} \tanh^{-1} u + C & (|u| < 1) \\ \coth^{-1} u + C & (|u| > 1) \end{matrix}\right\} = \frac{1}{2}\ln\left|\frac{1+u}{1-u}\right| + C.$

24. $\int \frac{u'}{\sqrt{1+u^2}}\,dx = \sinh^{-1} u + C = \ln(u + \sqrt{1+u^2}) + C.$

25. $\int \frac{u'}{\sqrt{1-u^2}}\,dx = \operatorname{Arcsin} u + C.$

26. $\int \frac{u'}{\sqrt{u^2-1}}\,dx = \cosh^{-1} u + C = \ln(u + \sqrt{u^2-1}) + C.$

27. $\int \frac{u'}{u\sqrt{1+u^2}}\,dx = \left\{\begin{matrix} -\operatorname{csch}^{-1} u + C & (u > 0) \\ \operatorname{csch}^{-1} u + C & (u < 0) \end{matrix}\right\} = -\ln\frac{1+\sqrt{1+u^2}}{|u|} + C.$

28. $\int \frac{u'}{u\sqrt{1-u^2}}\,dx = -\operatorname{sech}^{-1} u + C = -\ln\frac{1+\sqrt{1-u^2}}{|u|} + C.$

29. $\int \frac{u'}{u\sqrt{u^2-1}}\,dx = \operatorname{Arcsec} u + C.$

This is quite a long list of formulas to remember and it is a very unusual student who can remember them all for more than a week. However, things are not as bad as they seem. Only the first fifteen formulas are a must for you to memorize. The hyperbolic functions are defined in terms of exponentials. Thus if you forget an integral of a hyperbolic function, you can integrate by expressing it in terms of exponentials. Furthermore, hyperbolic functions are encountered rather infrequently. In addition, we shall consider methods of integration in this chapter that allow one to integrate any of the expressions of formulas 22–29. Thus, while you may find it convenient to memorize more than fifteen of the formulas, you will be relieved of the necessity of memorizing all of them.

In Formulas 23, 24, 26, 27, and 28 one has a choice of using either a hyperbolic form or a logarithmic form. The logarithmic form is used in both the examples and answers to problems in this chapter, because when several terms must be integrated, several logarithms can be combined to simplify the result (see Example 3, page 328).

Example 1

Evaluate $\int \frac{x^3 - 1}{x + 1}\, dx$.

Since the degree of the numerator is greater than that of the denominator, we shall divide until the remainder is of lower degree than that of the denominator.

$$\int \frac{x^3 - 1}{x + 1}\, dx = \int \left(x^2 - x + 1 - \frac{2}{x + 1}\right) dx.$$

Now we can integrate term by term.

$$\int \frac{x^3 - 1}{x + 1}\, dx = \frac{x^3}{3} - \frac{x^2}{2} + x - 2 \ln |x + 1| + C.$$

Example 2

Evaluate $\int e^x(e^x + 1)^2\, dx$.

This is in the form $\int u^2 \cdot u'\, dx$, where $u = e^x + 1$.

$$\int e^x(e^x + 1)^2\, dx = \frac{(e^x + 1)^3}{3} + C.$$

Example 3

Evaluate $\int \frac{\sin x}{1 + \cos x}\, dx$.

Since the derivative of the denominator is $-\sin x$, we adjust the constant factor and integrate.

$$\int \frac{\sin x}{1 + \cos x}\, dx = -\int \frac{-\sin x}{1 + \cos x}\, dx = -\ln (1 + \cos x) + C.$$

We dropped the absolute-value signs, since $1 + \cos x$ cannot be negative.

Example 4

Evaluate $\int \tan 3x\, dx$.

$$\int \tan 3x\, dx = \frac{1}{3} \int 3 \tan 3x\, dx = -\frac{1}{3} \ln |\cos 3x| + C.$$

Example 5

Evaluate $\int \frac{dx}{x^2+4}$.

This is almost in the form of Formula 22. The only difference is that we have a 4 where we want a 1. Let us get a 1 by dividing numerator and denominator by 4.

$$\int \frac{dx}{x^2+4} = \int \frac{\frac{1}{4}\,dx}{\frac{x^2}{4}+1} = \int \frac{\frac{1}{4}\,dx}{\left(\frac{x}{2}\right)^2+1}$$

$$= \frac{1}{2}\int \frac{\frac{1}{2}\,dx}{\left(\frac{x}{2}\right)^2+1} = \frac{1}{2}\operatorname{Arctan}\frac{x}{2} + C.$$

Example 6

Evaluate $\int \frac{dx}{x\sqrt{9-x^2}}$.

In order to get a 1 in place of the 9, divide numerator and denominator by $\sqrt{9}=3$.

$$\int \frac{dx}{x\sqrt{9-x^2}} = \int \frac{\frac{1}{3}\,dx}{x\sqrt{1-\frac{x^2}{9}}} = \int \frac{\frac{1}{3}\,dx}{x\sqrt{1-\left(\frac{x}{3}\right)^2}}.$$

This is almost in the form $\int \frac{u'}{u\sqrt{1-u^2}}\,dx$ with $u=\frac{x}{3}$. In order to get it into this form, let us divide numerator and denominator by another 3 and take part of the numerator outside the integral sign in order to keep 1/3, which is u'.

$$\int \frac{dx}{x\sqrt{9-x^2}} = \int \frac{\frac{1}{9}\,dx}{\frac{x}{3}\sqrt{1-\left(\frac{x}{3}\right)^2}} = \frac{1}{3}\int \frac{\frac{1}{3}\,dx}{\frac{x}{3}\sqrt{1-\left(\frac{x}{3}\right)^2}}$$

$$= \frac{1}{3}\ln \frac{1-\sqrt{1-\frac{x^2}{9}}}{\left|\frac{x}{3}\right|} + C$$

$$= \frac{1}{3}\ln \frac{3-\sqrt{9-x^2}}{|x|} + C.$$

Problems

Evaluate the following integrals.

1. $\int \frac{x^2+x-3}{x}\,dx.$

2. $\int \frac{x^2-5x+2}{x-1}\,dx.$

3. $\displaystyle\int \frac{4x^2 - x + 1}{2x + 1}\, dx.$

4. $\displaystyle\int \frac{y^3 + 1}{y - 1}\, dy.$

5. $\displaystyle\int \frac{u^3 + u}{u - 1}\, du.$

6. $\displaystyle\int \frac{4x^3 + 2x^2 - 6x + 1}{2x + 3}\, dx.$

7. $\displaystyle\int \sqrt{2x + 1}\, dx.$

8. $\displaystyle\int x(2x^2 - 3)^4\, dx.$

9. $\displaystyle\int (x + 1)(x^2 + 2x)^{2/3}\, dx.$

10. $\displaystyle\int (x^2 - 2)^3\, dx.$

11. $\displaystyle\int xe^{x^2}\, dx.$

12. $\displaystyle\int \sin x\, e^{\cos x}\, dx.$

13. $\displaystyle\int \frac{\ln x}{x}\, dx.$

14. $\displaystyle\int \frac{(3 - \ln x)}{x}\, dx.$

15. $\displaystyle\int \frac{1 - \cos x}{\sin x}\, dx.$

16. $\displaystyle\int \frac{\sin x}{1 - \cos x}\, dx.$

17. $\displaystyle\int \frac{du}{(1 - 2u)^4}.$

18. $\displaystyle\int \frac{e^x + 1}{e^x}\, dx.$

19. $\displaystyle\int \frac{e^x}{e^x + 1}\, dx.$

20. $\displaystyle\int \frac{e^x}{e^{2x} + 1}\, dx.$

21. $\displaystyle\int \frac{\sec^2 u}{1 + \tan u}\, du.$

22. $\displaystyle\int \sin x \cos x\, dx.$

23. $\displaystyle\int \sin 2x\, (\sin^2 x + 1)\, dx.$

24. $\displaystyle\int \sin 2\theta(\cos 2\theta + 1)\, d\theta.$

25. $\displaystyle\int \frac{\sinh x}{1 - \cosh x}\, dx.$

26. $\displaystyle\int \frac{\operatorname{csch}^2 x}{1 - \coth x}\, dx.$

27. $\displaystyle\int \frac{dx}{x^2 - 9}.$

28. $\displaystyle\int \frac{dx}{x\sqrt{x^2 - 9}}.$

29. $\displaystyle\int \frac{x\, dx}{x^4 + 1}.$

30. $\displaystyle\int \frac{dx}{\sqrt{x^2 + 2}}.$

31. $\displaystyle\int (\sec\theta + \tan\theta)^2\, d\theta.$

32. $\displaystyle\int (1 + \tan\theta)^2\, d\theta.$

33. $\displaystyle\int (1 + \sec\theta)^2\, d\theta.$

34. $\displaystyle\int \frac{\sin\theta \cos\theta\, d\theta}{\sin^2\theta + 1}.$

35. $\displaystyle\int \frac{\cos\theta\, d\theta}{\sin^2\theta + 1}.$

36. $\displaystyle\int \frac{e^{1/x}}{x^2}\, dx.$

37. $\displaystyle\int \left(\frac{\sec\theta}{1 - \tan\theta}\right)^2 d\theta.$

38. $\displaystyle\int \frac{(1 - \sqrt{x})^2}{\sqrt{x}}\, dx.$

39. $\displaystyle\int (1 - \sqrt{x})^2\, dx.$

40. $\displaystyle\int \frac{dx}{x\sqrt{x^4 - 1}}.$

41. $\displaystyle\int \frac{e^x - 1}{e^x + 1}\, dx.$

42. (a) Evaluate $\displaystyle\int \frac{dx}{e^x + 1}$ by dividing $1 + e^x$ into 1.
    (b) Evaluate by multiplying numerator and denominator by e^{-x}.
    (c) Show that the results above are equivalent.

43. Prove Theorem 15.2.

44. Prove Theorem 15.4.

45. Evaluate $\int \csc u \cdot u'\, dx$ by multiplying the numerator and denominator by $\csc u + \cot u$. Show that your result is equivalent to that given in Theorem 15.4.

46. Evaluate $\int \tanh u \cdot u'\, dx$.

47. Evaluate $\int \operatorname{sech} u \cdot u'\, dx$.

15.2

Integration by Substitution

In the method of integration by substitution, many different substitutions can be made, depending upon the particular expression we have to integrate. We shall consider only one type of substitution in this section—others will come later.

First, let us see what is involved. Given the integral $\int f(x)\,dx$ to evaluate, we want to find an $F(x)$ whose derivative with respect to x is $f(x)$:

$$\int f(x)\,dx = F(x).$$

Suppose u is a function of x, $u = g(x)$, such that $f(x)$ can be written in the form

$$\begin{aligned} f(x) &= h(g(x))g'(x) \\ &= h(u) \cdot u'. \end{aligned}$$

Then

$$\int f(x)\,dx = \int h(u) \cdot u'\,dx = H(u).$$

But $\int h(u) \cdot u'\,dx = H(u)$ means

$$\frac{d}{dx}H(u) = h(u) \cdot u'.$$

By the chain rule

$$\begin{aligned} \frac{d}{dx}H(u) &= \frac{d}{du}H(u) \cdot \frac{du}{dx} \\ &= \frac{d}{du}H(u) \cdot u'. \end{aligned}$$

Thus H is a function such that

$$\frac{d}{du}H(u) = h(u)$$

or, in integral form,

$$\int h(u)\,du = H(u).$$

Thus

$$F(x) = \int f(x)\,dx = \int h(u) \cdot u'\,dx = \int h(u)\,du = H(u) = H(g(x)).$$

The result is that *when making the substitution $u = g(x)$, we must substitute not only into the integrand $f(x)$ but also into the differential dx.*

Now let us consider a particular substitution. We have seen that we can easily integrate expressions of the form $(ax + b)^n$ for any value of n by using Formulas 2 or 5. When n is a positive integer, we can also expand $(ax + b)^n$ by the binomial theorem and integrate term by term. But when we have an expression of the form $x^m(ax + b)^n$, where $m \neq 0$, we cannot use Formulas 2 or 5. If n is a positive integer, we can still expand and integrate term by term, but we cannot integrate this expression for other values of n.

In particular, we cannot integrate expressions of the form $x^m\sqrt{ax + b}$. Because the radical prevents us from expanding, we would like to get rid of it. This is where a substitution is useful. If we make the substitution

$$u = \sqrt{ax + b},$$

we are rid of the radical. Solving for x, we have

$$x = \frac{u^2 - b}{a} \quad \text{and} \quad dx = \frac{2u\,du}{a},$$

Thus

$$\int x^m\sqrt{ax + b}\,dx = \int \left(\frac{u^2 - b}{a}\right)^m u \cdot \frac{2u}{a}\,du.$$

Now if m is a positive integer, we can expand and integrate term by term.

Let us consider some examples of this type of substitution.

Example 1

Evaluate $\int x\sqrt{x+1}\,dx$.

Since the derivative of $x+1$ (the expression under the radical) is 1 and we have a factor x, we cannot use the power rule. Because we have a radical, we cannot multiply it out. Our only alternative is to make a substitution. Let

$$u = \sqrt{x+1}.$$

Solving for x, we have

$$x = u^2 - 1 \quad \text{and} \quad dx = 2u\,du.$$

Thus

$$\begin{aligned}\int x\sqrt{x+1}\,dx &= \int (u^2 - 1)u \cdot 2u\,du \\ &= \int (2u^4 - 2u^2)\,du \\ &= \frac{2u^5}{5} - \frac{2u^3}{3} + C \\ &= \frac{2}{15}u^3(3u^2 - 5) + C.\end{aligned}$$

Finally, now that the original expression has been integrated, it must be put back in terms of x, since it was given in terms of x. Substituting

$$u = \sqrt{x+1},$$

we have

$$\int x\sqrt{x+1}\,dx = \frac{2}{15}(x+1)^{3/2}[3(x+1)-5]+C$$

$$= \frac{2}{15}(x+1)^{3/2}(3x-2)+C.$$

Example 2

Evaluate $\int x^2\sqrt{x-2}\,dx.$

Substituting

$$u = \sqrt{x-2}$$

and solving for x, we have

$$x = u^2 + 2 \quad \text{and} \quad dx = 2u\,du.$$

$$\int x^2\sqrt{x-2}\,dx = \int (u^2+2)^2 \cdot u \cdot 2u\,du$$

$$= \int (2u^6 + 8u^4 + 8u^2)\,du$$

$$= \frac{2u^7}{7} + \frac{8u^5}{5} + \frac{8u^3}{3} + C$$

$$= \frac{2u^3}{105}(15u^4 + 84u^2 + 140) + C.$$

Substituting $u = \sqrt{x-2}$, we have

$$\int x^2\sqrt{x-2}\,dx = \frac{2}{105}(x-2)^{3/2}[15(x-2)^2 + 84(x-2) + 140] + C$$

$$= \frac{2}{105}(x-2)^{3/2}(15x^2 + 24x + 32) + C.$$

Example 3

Evaluate $\int_0^5 x\sqrt{x+4}\,dx.$

First, note that the limits of integration are values of x, since we have an integral with respect to x. If we substitute to give an integral with respect to u, it is assumed then that the limits of integration are values of u unless something is said to the contrary.

There are two ways of handling the limits of integration when using a substitution. One way is to substitute, integrate, substitute back to get the result in terms of the original x, and then put in the limits of integration. The second method is to change the limits of integration to the corresponding values of u when the original substitution is made, thus eliminating the need to get the result back in terms of x. Both methods are illustrated here. In either case, we use the same substitution,

$$u = \sqrt{x+4}; \quad \text{when } x = 0,\ u = \sqrt{4} = 2,$$

$$x = u^2 - 4; \quad \text{when } x = 5,\ u = \sqrt{9} = 3,$$

$$dx = 2u\,du.$$

$$\begin{aligned}\int x\sqrt{x+4}\,dx &= \int (u^2-4)u\cdot 2u\,du\\ &= \int (2u^4-8u^2)\,du\\ &= \frac{2u^5}{5}-\frac{8u^3}{3}+C\\ &= \frac{2}{15}u^3(3u^2-20)+C\\ &= \frac{2}{15}(x+4)^{3/2}[3(x+4)-20]+C\\ &= \frac{2}{15}(x+4)^{3/2}(3x-8)+C;\end{aligned}$$

$$\begin{aligned}\int_0^5 x\sqrt{x+4}\,dx &= \frac{2}{15}(x+4)^{3/2}(3x-8)\Big|_0^5\\ &= \frac{2}{15}[9^{3/2}\cdot 7-4^{3/2}\cdot(-8)]\\ &= \frac{2}{15}\cdot 253\\ &= \frac{506}{15}.\end{aligned}$$

$$\begin{aligned}\int_0^5 x\sqrt{x+4}\,dx &= \int_2^3 (u^2-4)u\cdot 2u\,du\\ &= \int_2^3 (2u^4-8u^2)\,du\\ &= \frac{2u^5}{5}-\frac{8u^3}{3}\Big|_2^3\\ &= \frac{2}{15}u^3(3u^2-20)\Big|_2^3\\ &= \frac{2}{15}[3^3\cdot 7-2^3(-8)]\\ &= \frac{2}{15}\cdot 253\\ &= \frac{506}{15}.\end{aligned}$$

This method is not restricted to integrals of the form $\int x^m\sqrt{ax+b}\,dx$, as can be seen by the following example.

Example 4

Evaluate $\displaystyle\int \frac{x}{\sqrt{x+1}}\,dx.$

Let

$$u=\sqrt{x+1}, \qquad x=u^2-1, \qquad dx=2u\,du.$$

Then

$$\begin{aligned}\int \frac{x}{\sqrt{x+1}}\,dx &= \int \frac{u^2-1}{u}\,2u\,du\\ &= \int (2u^2-2)\,du\\ &= \frac{2u^3}{3}-2u+C\\ &= \frac{2}{3}u(u^2-3)+C\\ &= \frac{2}{3}\sqrt{x+1}\,(x-2)+C.\end{aligned}$$

Problems

Evaluate the following integrals.

1. $\int x\sqrt{x+2}\,dx.$
2. $\int x\sqrt{x-3}\,dx.$
3. $\int x^2\sqrt{x+2}\,dx.$
4. $\int x^2\sqrt{1-x}\,dx.$
5. $\int x\sqrt{2x+1}\,dx.$
6. $\int x\sqrt{2x-3}\,dx.$
7. $\int \frac{x}{\sqrt{x-2}}\,dx.$
8. $\int \frac{x}{\sqrt{x+3}}\,dx.$
9. $\int \frac{x^2}{\sqrt{x-1}}\,dx.$
10. $\int \frac{x^2}{\sqrt{2x-1}}\,dx.$
11. $\int \frac{x^3}{\sqrt{x-5}}\,dx.$
12. $\int \frac{x^3}{\sqrt{2x+3}}\,dx.$
13. $\int x\sqrt[3]{x+1}\,dx.$
14. $\int x\sqrt[3]{2x-1}\,dx.$
15. $\int x\sqrt[4]{x+1}\,dx.$
16. $\int x\sqrt[5]{x-2}\,dx.$
17. $\int (2x+3)\sqrt{2x+1}\,dx.$
18. $\int (x-4)\sqrt{x+1}\,dx.$
19. $\int \frac{2x+1}{\sqrt{x-3}}\,dx.$
20. $\int \frac{x^2+x}{\sqrt{x+1}}\,dx.$
21. $\int_3^4 x\sqrt{x-3}\,dx.$
22. $\int_0^4 x\sqrt{2x+1}\,dx.$
23. $\int_2^4 x^2\sqrt{2x-3}\,dx.$
24. $\int_5^7 \frac{x}{\sqrt{x-4}}\,dx.$
25. $\int_0^4 \frac{x^2}{\sqrt{2x+1}}\,dx.$
26. $\int_0^7 x\sqrt[3]{x+1}\,dx.$
27. $\int \sqrt{e^x+1}\,dx.$

15.3

Integrals Involving $ax^2 + b$

Integrals involving quadratic expressions in the denominator occur rather frequently. In this section we consider integrals involving $ax^2 + b$; in the next section we consider integrals involving the general quadratic expression $ax^2 + bx + c$.

When the numerator is a first-degree expression and the denominator is of the form $ax^2 + b$ or $\sqrt{ax^2 + b}$, the integral can be split into two simpler ones.

Example 1

Evaluate $\int \frac{2x+1}{x^2+1}\,dx.$

The derivative of the denominator is $2x$. Thus $2x/(x^2 + 1)$ can easily be integrated, and so can $1/(x^2+1)$. Thus we split the fraction into the sum of two fractions in the obvious way.

$$\int \frac{2x+1}{x^2+1}\,dx = \int \frac{2x}{x^2+1}\,dx + \int \frac{1}{x^2+1}\,dx$$

$$= \ln(x^2+1) + \text{Arctan}\, x + C.$$

Example 2

Evaluate $\int \frac{3x+1}{\sqrt{x^2+4}}\,dx$.

Again the derivative of x^2+4 is $2x$. Although we have $3x$ in the numerator, we can adjust the constant factor if we can get rid of the 1. Thus we split it into two fractions again.

$$\begin{aligned}
\int \frac{3x+1}{\sqrt{x^2+4}}\,dx &= \int \frac{3x}{\sqrt{x^2+4}}\,dx + \int \frac{1}{\sqrt{x^2+4}}\,dx \\
&= \frac{3}{2}\int \frac{2x}{\sqrt{x^2+4}}\,dx + \int \frac{1/2}{\sqrt{\dfrac{x^2}{4}+1}}\,dx \\
&= \frac{3}{2}\,\frac{\sqrt{x^2+4}}{\frac{1}{2}} + \ln\left(\frac{x}{2}+\sqrt{\frac{x^2}{4}+1}\right) + C \\
&= 3\sqrt{x^2+4} + \ln\frac{x+\sqrt{x^2+4}}{2} + C \\
&= 3\sqrt{x^2+4} + \ln\,(x+\sqrt{x^2+4}) - \ln 2 + C \\
&= 3\sqrt{x^2+4} + \ln\,(x+\sqrt{x^2+4}) + K.
\end{aligned}$$

Example 3

Evaluate $\int \frac{x-\sqrt{6}}{2x^2-3}\,dx$.

$$\begin{aligned}
\int \frac{x-\sqrt{6}}{2x^2-3}\,dx &= \int \frac{x}{2x^2-3}\,dx - \int \frac{\sqrt{6}}{2x^2-3}\,dx \\
&= \frac{1}{4}\int \frac{4x}{2x^2-3}\,dx - \int \frac{\dfrac{\sqrt{6}}{3}}{\dfrac{2x^2}{3}-1}\,dx \\
&= \frac{1}{4}\int \frac{4x}{2x^2-3}\,dx + \int \frac{\dfrac{\sqrt{2}}{\sqrt{3}}}{1-\left(\dfrac{\sqrt{2}\,x}{\sqrt{3}}\right)^2}\,dx \\
&= \frac{1}{4}\ln|2x^2-3| + \frac{1}{2}\ln\left|\frac{1+\dfrac{\sqrt{2}\,x}{\sqrt{3}}}{1-\dfrac{\sqrt{2}\,x}{\sqrt{3}}}\right| + C \\
&= \frac{1}{4}\ln|2x^2-3| + \frac{1}{2}\ln\left|\frac{\sqrt{3}+\sqrt{2}\,x}{\sqrt{3}-\sqrt{2}\,x}\right| + C
\end{aligned}$$

$$= \frac{1}{4} \ln |(\sqrt{2}x + \sqrt{3})(\sqrt{2}x - \sqrt{3})| + \frac{1}{4} \ln \left| \frac{(\sqrt{2}x + \sqrt{3})^2}{(\sqrt{2}x - \sqrt{3})^2} \right| + C$$

$$= \frac{1}{4} \ln \left| \frac{(\sqrt{2}x + \sqrt{3})^3}{\sqrt{2}x - \sqrt{3}} \right| + C.$$

If the denominator is of the form $ax^2 + b$ and the numerator is of the second degree or higher, divide first until the numerator is a first-degree expression or a constant.

Example 4

Evaluate $\int \frac{x^3 - 1}{x^2 + 4}\, dx$.

$$\int \frac{x^3 - 1}{x^2 + 4}\, dx = \int \left(x - \frac{4x + 1}{x^2 + 4} \right) dx$$

$$= \int x\, dx - \int \frac{4x}{x^2 + 4}\, dx - \int \frac{1}{x^2 + 4}\, dx$$

$$= \int x\, dx - 2 \int \frac{2x}{x^2 + 4}\, dx - \frac{1}{2} \int \frac{\frac{1}{2}}{\left(\frac{x}{2}\right)^2 + 1}\, dx$$

$$= \frac{x^2}{2} - 2 \ln (x^2 + 4) - \frac{1}{2} \operatorname{Arctan} \frac{x}{2} + C.$$

Problems

Evaluate the following integrals.

1. $\int \frac{2x + 1}{\sqrt{x^2 + 1}}\, dx.$
2. $\int \frac{x + 1}{1 - x^2}\, dx.$
3. $\int \frac{2x + 2}{x^2 - 2}\, dx.$
4. $\int \frac{3x - 1}{\sqrt{x^2 - 4}}\, dx.$
5. $\int \frac{4x + 1}{\sqrt{1 - x^2}}\, dx.$
6. $\int \frac{4x + 1}{2x^2 - 3}\, dx.$
7. $\int \frac{2x - 3}{3x^2 + 4}\, dx.$
8. $\int \frac{2x - 2}{\sqrt{4x^2 + 1}}\, dx.$
9. $\int \frac{x - 1}{\sqrt{3 - 2x^2}}\, dx.$
10. $\int \frac{2x - 1}{4 - 5x^2}\, dx.$
11. $\int \frac{(x + 1)^2}{x^2 + 1}\, dx.$
12. $\int \frac{(x + 1)^2}{x^2 - 1}\, dx.$
13. $\int \frac{x^2 + 2}{x^2 - 4}\, dx.$
14. $\int \frac{3x + 1}{\sqrt{2x^2 - 3}}\, dx.$
15. $\int_0^1 \frac{2x - 1}{x^2 + 1}\, dx.$
16. $\int_0^1 \frac{4x + 1}{\sqrt{1 - x^2}}\, dx.$
17. $\int_0^{\sqrt{2}} \frac{2x + 3}{\sqrt{x^2 + 2}}\, dx.$
18. $\int_0^1 \frac{x + 1}{2 - x^2}\, dx.$
19. $\int_2^{2\sqrt{2}} \frac{x + 1}{2 - x^2}\, dx.$
20. $\int_0^1 \frac{x^2 + 2x + 2}{x^2 - 2}\, dx.$
21. $\int_0^1 \frac{x + 1}{\sqrt{4 - 3x^2}}\, dx.$
22. $\int_0^{\sqrt{2}} \frac{4x - 1}{3x^2 + 2}\, dx.$

15.4

Integrals Involving $ax^2 + bx + c$

When the integral involves expressions of the form $ax^2 + bx + c$, it is necessary to complete the square in order to get the expression into the form $au^2 + d$. This is the same way we handled conics.

Example 1

Evaluate $\displaystyle\int \frac{dx}{x^2 + 2x + 10}$.

Let us complete the square on the first two terms of $x^2 + 2x + 10$.

$$\begin{aligned} x^2 + 2x + 10 &= x^2 + 2x + 1 - 1 + 10 \\ &= (x+1)^2 + 9; \end{aligned}$$

$$\begin{aligned} \int \frac{dx}{x^2 + 2x + 10} &= \int \frac{dx}{(x+1)^2 + 9} \\ &= \int \frac{\frac{1}{9}}{\frac{(x+1)^2}{9} + 1} dx \\ &= \frac{1}{3} \int \frac{\frac{1}{3}}{\left(\frac{x+1}{3}\right)^2 + 1} dx \\ &= \frac{1}{3} \operatorname{Arctan} \frac{x+1}{3} + C. \end{aligned}$$

Example 2

Evaluate $\displaystyle\int \frac{dx}{5 + 8x - 4x^2}$.

Again, we complete the square on the last two terms of the denominator.

$$\begin{aligned} 5 + 8x - 4x^2 &= 5 - 4(x^2 - 2x) \\ &= 5 + 4 - 4(x^2 - 2x + 1) \\ &= 9 - 4(x-1)^2; \end{aligned}$$

$$\begin{aligned} \int \frac{dx}{5 + 8x - 4x^2} &= \int \frac{dx}{9 - 4(x-1)^2} \\ &= \int \frac{\frac{1}{9}}{1 - \frac{4(x-1)^2}{9}} dx \end{aligned}$$

$$= \int \frac{\frac{1}{9}}{1 - \left[\frac{2(x-1)}{3}\right]^2}\, dx$$

$$= \frac{1}{6} \int \frac{\frac{2}{3}}{1 - \left[\frac{2(x-1)}{3}\right]^2}\, dx$$

$$= \frac{1}{12} \ln \left| \frac{1 + \frac{2(x-1)}{3}}{1 - \frac{2(x-1)}{3}} \right| + C$$

$$= \frac{1}{12} \ln \left| \frac{1+2x}{5-2x} \right| + C.$$

Example 3

Evaluate $\int \frac{dx}{\sqrt{4x^2 + 16x + 17}}$.

Completing the square under the radical, we have

$$\begin{aligned} 4x^2 + 16x + 17 &= 4(x^2 + 4x) + 17 \\ &= 4(x^2 + 4x + 4) - 16 + 17 \\ &= 4(x+2)^2 + 1; \end{aligned}$$

$$\begin{aligned} \int \frac{dx}{\sqrt{4x^2 + 16x + 17}} &= \int \frac{dx}{\sqrt{4(x+2)^2 + 1}} \\ &= \int \frac{dx}{\sqrt{(2x+4)^2 + 1}} \\ &= \frac{1}{2} \int \frac{2}{\sqrt{(2x+4)^2 + 1}}\, dx \\ &= \frac{1}{2} \ln (2x + 4 + \sqrt{4x^2 + 16x + 17}) + C. \end{aligned}$$

Problems

Evaluate the following integrals.

1. $\int \frac{dx}{x^2 + 2x + 2}$.
2. $\int \frac{dx}{x^2 + 4x + 8}$.
3. $\int \frac{dx}{\sqrt{x^2 - 4x + 3}}$.
4. $\int \frac{4\, dx}{\sqrt{-16x^2 - 32x - 15}}$.
5. $\int \frac{2\, dx}{4x^2 - 8x + 29}$.
6. $\int \frac{3\, dx}{2x^2 - 8x + 3}$.

7. $\int \frac{dx}{8x - 4x^2}$.

8. $\int \frac{dx}{9x^2 - 12x + 4}$.

9. $\int \frac{4\,dx}{\sqrt{x^2 - 2x + 5}}$.

10. $\int \frac{2\,dx}{\sqrt{3 + 2x - x^2}}$.

11. $\int \frac{-3\,dx}{\sqrt{4x^2 + 16x + 7}}$.

12. $\int \frac{3\,dx}{4x^2 + 12x}$.

13. $\int \frac{2\,dx}{9x^2 - 12x + 5}$.

14. $\int \frac{dx}{16x^2 - 8x + 17}$.

15. $\int \frac{dx}{4x^2 - 16x + 7}$.

16. $\int \frac{dx}{\sqrt{9x^2 + 30x + 25}}$.

17. $\int \frac{4\,dx}{\sqrt{9x^2 + 12x + 8}}$.

18. $\int \frac{dx}{4x^2 - 40x + 164}$.

19. $\int \frac{dx}{25x^2 - 40x + 16}$.

20. $\int \frac{dx}{\sqrt{-x^2 + 10x - 21}}$.

15.5

More Integrals Involving $ax^2 + bx + c$

Up to now the integrals we have seen with denominator of the form

$$ax^2 + bx + c \quad \text{or} \quad \sqrt{ax^2 + bx + c}$$

have all had constant numerators. We now consider the case in which the numerator is a first-degree expression. In this case the integral is split into two simpler integrals, as we did in Section 15.3; however, the way to make the split is not so obvious here as it was there. Let us consider an example.

Example 1

Evaluate $\int \frac{x - 5}{x^2 + 2x + 2}\,dx$.

First of all, note that the derivative of the denominator is $2x + 2$. Neither the $2x$ nor the 2 is in the numerator, where we want them. We can get the $2x$ in the numerator by multiplying the numerator by 2 (and compensating with a 1/2).

$$\int \frac{x - 5}{x^2 + 2x + 2}\,dx = \frac{1}{2}\int \frac{2x - 10}{x^2 + 2x + 2}\,dx.$$

Now we can get the 2 by simply adding it (and compensating with a -2).

$$\begin{aligned}\int \frac{x - 5}{x^2 + 2x + 2}\,dx &= \frac{1}{2}\int \frac{2x - 10}{x^2 + 2x + 2}\,dx \\ &= \frac{1}{2}\int \frac{(2x + 2) - 12}{x^2 + 2x + 2}\,dx.\end{aligned}$$

Now we split the integral into the sum of two others (remember the factor 1/2 goes with both of the new integrals).

$$\int \frac{x-5}{x^2+2x+2}\,dx = \frac{1}{2}\int \frac{2x+2}{x^2+2x+2}\,dx + \frac{1}{2}\int \frac{-12}{x^2+2x+2}\,dx$$

$$= \frac{1}{2}\int \frac{2x+2}{x^2+2x+2}\,dx - 6\int \frac{1}{x^2+2x+2}\,dx.$$

The first expression can easily be integrated to a logarithm, and the second can be handled by the method of the preceding section.

$$\int \frac{x-5}{x^2+2x+2}\,dx = \frac{1}{2}\int \frac{2x+2}{x^2+2x+2}\,dx - 6\int \frac{1}{(x+1)^2+1}\,dx$$

$$= \frac{1}{2}\ln(x^2+2x+2) - 6 \operatorname{Arctan}(x+1) + C.$$

Example 2

Evaluate $\int \frac{x+1}{\sqrt{x^2-4x}}\,dx$.

The derivative of the expression under the radical is $2x-4$. We adjust constants to get first the $2x$ and then the -4. Finally, we split the integral in two and integrate both terms.

$$\int \frac{x+1}{\sqrt{x^2-4x}}\,dx = \frac{1}{2}\int \frac{2x+2}{\sqrt{x^2-4x}}\,dx$$

$$= \frac{1}{2}\int \frac{(2x-4)+6}{\sqrt{x^2-4x}}\,dx$$

$$= \frac{1}{2}\int \frac{2x-4}{\sqrt{x^2-4x}}\,dx + \frac{1}{2}\int \frac{6}{\sqrt{x^2-4x}}\,dx$$

$$= \frac{1}{2}\int \frac{2x-4}{\sqrt{x^2-4x}}\,dx + 3\int \frac{1}{\sqrt{(x-2)^2-4}}\,dx$$

$$= \frac{1}{2}\int \frac{2x-4}{\sqrt{x^2-4x}}\,dx + 3\int \frac{\frac{1}{2}}{\sqrt{\left(\frac{x-2}{2}\right)^2-1}}\,dx$$

$$= \frac{1}{2}\,\frac{\sqrt{x^2-4x}}{\frac{1}{2}} + 3\ln\left(\frac{x-2}{2} + \sqrt{\left(\frac{x-2}{2}\right)^2-1}\right) + C$$

$$= \sqrt{x^2-4x} + 3\ln\frac{x-2+\sqrt{x^2-4x}}{2} + C$$

$$= \sqrt{x^2-4x} + 3\ln(x-2+\sqrt{x^2-4x}) + K.$$

Example 3

Evaluate $\int \frac{x-4}{\sqrt{-9x^2+36x-32}}\,dx.$

The derivative of the expression under the radical is $-18x+36$.

$$\int \frac{x-4}{\sqrt{-9x^2+36x-32}}\,dx$$

$$= -\frac{1}{18}\int \frac{-18x+72}{\sqrt{-9x^2+36x-32}}\,dx$$

$$= -\frac{1}{18}\int \frac{-18x+36}{\sqrt{-9x^2+36x-32}}\,dx - \frac{1}{18}\int \frac{36}{\sqrt{-9x^2+36x-32}}\,dx$$

$$= -\frac{1}{18}\int \frac{-18x+36}{\sqrt{-9x^2+36x-32}}\,dx - 2\int \frac{1}{\sqrt{4-9(x-2)^2}}\,dx$$

$$= -\frac{1}{18}\int \frac{-18x+36}{\sqrt{-9x^2+36-32}}\,dx - 2\int \frac{\frac{1}{2}}{\sqrt{1-\left[\frac{3(x-2)}{2}\right]^2}}\,dx$$

$$= -\frac{1}{18}\int \frac{-18x+36}{\sqrt{-9x^2+36x-32}}\,dx - \frac{2}{3}\int \frac{\frac{3}{2}}{\sqrt{1-\left(\frac{3x-6}{2}\right)^2}}\,dx$$

$$= -\frac{1}{18}\,\frac{\sqrt{-9x^2+36x-32}}{\frac{1}{2}} - \frac{2}{3}\,\mathrm{Arcsin}\,\frac{3x-6}{2} + C$$

$$= -\frac{1}{9}\sqrt{-9x^2+36x-32} - \frac{2}{3}\,\mathrm{Arcsin}\,\frac{3x-6}{2} + C.$$

Problems

Evaluate the following integrals.

1. $\int \frac{2x+1}{x^2+2x+2}\,dx.$
2. $\int \frac{2x+3}{x^2+4x+13}\,dx.$
3. $\int \frac{2x+1}{\sqrt{2x-x^2}}\,dx.$
4. $\int \frac{x-1}{\sqrt{x^2-4x+5}}\,dx.$
5. $\int \frac{5x+2}{4x^2-8x+13}\,dx.$
6. $\int \frac{3x-1}{\sqrt{4x^2-16x+41}}\,dx.$
7. $\int \frac{2-3x}{4x^2+24x+41}\,dx.$
8. $\int \frac{5x+1}{9x^2+36x+32}\,dx.$
9. $\int \frac{4x+1}{\sqrt{52+36x-9x^2}}\,dx.$
10. $\int \frac{3x+5}{\sqrt{-2x^2+20x-42}}\,dx.$
11. $\int \frac{x^2+4x+8}{x^2-4x+8}\,dx.$
12. $\int \frac{x^3+1}{x^2+2x}\,dx.$

13. $\int \frac{4x^4}{4x^2 - 8x + 13} dx.$

14. $\int \frac{81x^3}{9x^2 + 36x + 40} dx.$

15. $\int \frac{x - 2}{\sqrt{-5x^2 + 20x - 13}} dx.$

16. $\int \frac{x - 2}{6x^2 - 24x + 31} dx.$

15.6

Trigonometric Integrals

A very powerful method of integration is by trigonometric substitution. Before considering this method, let us first consider integration of trigonometric functions.

Case I: $\int \sin^m u \cos^n u \cdot u' \, dx$. We can use the identity

$$\sin^2 u + \cos^2 u = 1$$

to carry out the integration if either m or n is an odd positive integer. It is illustrated here for the case in which n is an odd positive integer.

$$\begin{aligned} \sin^m u \cos^n u &= \sin^m u \cos^{n-1} u \cos u \quad (n - 1 \text{ even}) \\ &= \sin^m u \, (\cos^2 u)^{(n-1)/2} \cos u \\ &= \sin^m u \, (1 - \sin^2 u)^{(n-1)/2} \cos u \\ &= f(\sin u) \cos u, \end{aligned}$$

where f is an ordinary polynomial. Thus,

$$\int \sin^m u \cos^n u \cdot u' \, dx = \int f(\sin u) \cos u \cdot u' \, dx.$$

Since $\cos u \cdot u'$ is the derivative of $\sin u$, this can easily be integrated term by term. A similar method can be used if m is an odd positive integer.

Example 1

Evaluate $\int \sin^2 x \cos^3 x \, dx$.

$$\begin{aligned} \int \sin^2 x \cos^3 x \, dx &= \int \sin^2 x \cos^2 x \cos x \, dx \\ &= \int \sin^2 x \, (1 - \sin^2 x) \cos x \, dx \\ &= \int (\sin^2 x - \sin^4 x) \cos x \, dx \\ &= \frac{\sin^3 x}{3} - \frac{\sin^5 x}{5} + C. \end{aligned}$$

Example 2

Evaluate $\int \sin^5 x \, dx$.

$$\begin{aligned}\int \sin^5 x \, dx &= \int \sin^4 x \sin x \, dx \\ &= \int (1 - \cos^2 x)^2 \sin x \, dx \\ &= -\int (1 - 2\cos^2 x + \cos^4 x)(-\sin x) \, dx \\ &= -\left(\cos x - \frac{2\cos^3 x}{3} + \frac{\cos^5 x}{5}\right) + C \\ &= -\cos x + \frac{2\cos^3 x}{3} - \frac{\cos^5 x}{5} + C.\end{aligned}$$

If m and n are both positive even integers, the above method does not work. (You are invited to try it and see why.) In this case we can use the identities

$$\cos 2x = 1 - 2\sin^2 x, \qquad \cos 2x = 2\cos^2 x - 1.$$

When these are solved for $\sin^2 x$ and $\cos^2 x$, respectively, we have

$$\sin^2 x = \frac{1 - \cos 2x}{2}, \qquad \cos^2 x = \frac{1 + \cos 2x}{2}.$$

In each case, we are replacing the second power of $\sin x$ or $\cos x$ by the first power of $\cos 2x$. Repeated applications of these identities will eventually lead to odd powers, which can be handled by the previous method.

Example 3

Evaluate $\int \sin^4 x \, dx$.

$$\begin{aligned}\int \sin^4 x \, dx &= \int (\sin^2 x)^2 \, dx \\ &= \int \left(\frac{1 - \cos 2x}{2}\right)^2 dx \\ &= \frac{1}{4}\int (1 - 2\cos 2x + \cos^2 2x) \, dx \\ &= \frac{1}{4}\int \left(1 - 2\cos 2x + \frac{1 + \cos 4x}{2}\right) dx \\ &= \frac{1}{8}\int (3 - 4\cos 2x + \cos 4x) \, dx \\ &= \frac{1}{8}\left(3x - 2\sin 2x + \frac{1}{4}\sin 4x\right) + C \\ &= \frac{3}{8}x - \frac{1}{4}\sin 2x + \frac{1}{32}\sin 4x + C.\end{aligned}$$

Example 4

Evaluate $\int \sin^2 2x \cos^2 2x \, dx$.

$$\begin{aligned}
\int \sin^2 2x \cos^2 2x \, dx &= \int \frac{1 - \cos 4x}{2} \frac{1 + \cos 4x}{2} \, dx \\
&= \frac{1}{4} \int (1 - \cos^2 4x) \, dx \\
&= \frac{1}{4} \int \left(1 - \frac{1 + \cos 8x}{2}\right) dx \\
&= \frac{1}{8} \int (1 - \cos 8x) \, dx \\
&= \frac{1}{8} \left(x - \frac{1}{8} \sin 8x\right) + C \\
&= \frac{1}{8} x - \frac{1}{64} \sin 8x + C.
\end{aligned}$$

Sometimes other trigonometric functions can be changed to sines and cosines and the above methods used.

Example 5

Evaluate $\int \sec^3 x \tan x \, dx$.

$$\begin{aligned}
\int \sec^3 x \tan x \, dx &= \int \frac{1}{\cos^3 x} \frac{\sin x}{\cos x} \, dx \\
&= -\int \frac{-\sin x}{\cos^4 x} \, dx \\
&= -\frac{(\cos x)^{-3}}{-3} + C \\
&= \frac{1}{3 \cos^3 x} + C \\
&= \frac{1}{3} \sec^3 x + C.
\end{aligned}$$

Problems

Evaluate the integrals in Problems 1–26.

1. $\int \sin^2 x \cos x \, dx$.
2. $\int \sin \theta \cos^2 \theta \, d\theta$.
3. $\int \sin \theta \cos^3 \theta \, d\theta$.
4. $\int \frac{\sin x}{\cos^3 x} \, dx$.
5. $\int \sin^3 x \cos^2 x \, dx$.
6. $\int \sin 4x \cos^4 4x \, dx$.

7. $\displaystyle\int \frac{\sin^3 2\theta}{\sqrt{\cos 2\theta}}\, d\theta.$

8. $\displaystyle\int \sin^2\theta \cos^5\theta\, d\theta.$

9. $\displaystyle\int \sin^2\theta \cos^4\theta\, d\theta.$

10. $\displaystyle\int \sin^2 2x \cos^2 2x\, dx.$

11. $\displaystyle\int \sin^4\theta \cos^2\theta\, d\theta.$

12. $\displaystyle\int \sin^6\theta\, d\theta.$

13. $\displaystyle\int \cos^4 2\theta\, d\theta.$

14. $\displaystyle\int \sin^5 2x \cos^2 2x\, dx.$

15. $\displaystyle\int \frac{\sin^3 x}{\cos^2 x}\, dx.$

16. $\displaystyle\int \frac{dx}{\cos^2 x}.$ easy

17. $\displaystyle\int \sin^{3/2} x \cos^3 x\, dx.$

18. $\displaystyle\int x \sin^2 x^2 \cos^2 x^2\, dx.$

19. $\displaystyle\int x \sin^3 x^2 \cos^2 x^2\, dx.$

20. $\displaystyle\int \tan^3\theta\, d\theta.$

21. $\displaystyle\int \sec^4\theta \tan\theta\, d\theta.$

22. $\displaystyle\int \csc\theta \cot^3\theta\, d\theta.$

23. $\displaystyle\int \sin^4\theta \cot^2\theta\, d\theta.$

24. $\displaystyle\int \sin^4\theta \cot^3\theta\, d\theta.$

25. $\displaystyle\int \sin^3 t \sqrt{\cos t}\, dt.$

26. $\displaystyle\int \sqrt{\sec x} \tan x\, dx.$

27. $\int \sin x \cos x\, dx$ can be evaluated by three different methods: by noting that $\cos x$ is the derivative of $\sin x$, by noting that $-\sin x$ is the derivative of $\cos x$, and by using the identity $\sin 2x = 2 \sin x \cos x$. Carry out the integration by all three methods and show that the three answers are equivalent.

28. Evaluate $\int \sin\theta \cos^3\theta\, d\theta$ by two different methods and show that the answers are equivalent.

29. Show why the use of the identity $\sin^2 u + \cos^2 u = 1$ does not allow us to evaluate $\int \sin^m u \cos^n u \cdot u'\, dx$ when both m and n are positive even integers.

15.7

Trigonometric Integrals (Continued)

Case II:

$$\int \sec^m u \tan^n u \cdot u'\, dx,$$

$$\int \csc^m u \cot^n u \cdot u'\, dx.$$

These integrals can be evaluated if either m is a positive even integer or n is a positive odd integer. Both depend upon the identities

$$\sec^2 u = 1 + \tan^2 u \quad \text{and} \quad \csc^2 u = 1 + \cot^2 u.$$

If m is a positive even integer, then

$$\begin{aligned}\int \sec^m u \tan^n u \cdot u'\,dx &= \int \sec^{m-2} u \tan^n u \sec^2 u \cdot u'\,dx \\ &= \int (\sec^2 u)^{(m-2)/2} \tan^n u \sec^2 u \cdot u'\,dx \\ &= \int (1 + \tan^2 u)^{(m-2)/2} \tan^n u \sec^2 u \cdot u'\,dx \\ &= \int f(\tan u)\sec^2 u \cdot u'\,dx.\end{aligned}$$

Since $\sec^2 u \cdot u'$ is the derivative of $\tan u$, the result is easily evaluated. A similar method can be used for $\int \csc^m u \cot^n u \cdot u'\,dx$.

Example 1

Evaluate $\int \sec^4 x\, tan^2\, x\,dx$.

$$\begin{aligned}\int \sec^4 x \tan^2 x\,dx &= \int \sec^2 x \tan^2 x \sec^2 x\,dx \\ &= \int (1 + \tan^2 x)\tan^2 x \sec^2 x\,dx \\ &= \int (\tan^2 x + \tan^4 x)\sec^2 x\,dx \\ &= \frac{\tan^3 x}{3} + \frac{\tan^5 x}{5} + C.\end{aligned}$$

Example 2

Evaluate $\int \sec^4 \theta\,d\theta$.

$$\begin{aligned}\int \sec^4 \theta\,d\theta &= \int \sec^2 \theta \sec^2 \theta\,d\theta \\ &= \int (1 + \tan^2 \theta)\sec^2 \theta\,d\theta \\ &= \tan \theta + \frac{\tan^3 \theta}{3} + C.\end{aligned}$$

If n is a positive odd integer, then

$$\begin{aligned}\int \sec^m u \tan^n u \cdot u'\,dx &= \int \sec^{m-1} u \tan^{n-1} u \sec u \tan u \cdot u'\,dx \\ &= \int \sec^{m-1} u(\tan^2 u)^{(n-1)/2} \sec u \tan u \cdot u'\,dx \\ &= \int \sec^{m-1} u(\sec^2 u - 1)^{(n-1)/2} \sec u \tan u \cdot u'\,dx \\ &= \int f(\sec u)\sec u \tan u \cdot u'\,dx.\end{aligned}$$

Since $\sec u \tan u \cdot u'$ is the derivative of $\sec u$, the result is easily evaluated. Again the same method can be used for $\int \csc^m u \cot^n u \cdot u'\,dx$.

Example 3

Evaluate $\int \sec^3 x \tan^3 x\, dx$.

$$\begin{aligned}\int \sec^3 x \tan^3 x\, dx &= \int \sec^2 x \tan^2 x \sec x \tan x\, dx\\ &= \int \sec^2 x\,(\sec^2 x - 1)\sec x \tan x\, dx\\ &= \int (\sec^4 x - \sec^2 x)\sec x \tan x\, dx\\ &= \frac{\sec^5 x}{5} - \frac{\sec^3 x}{3} + C.\end{aligned}$$

Example 4

Evaluate $\int \cot^3 x\, dx$.

$$\begin{aligned}\int \cot^3 x\, dx &= \int \frac{\cot^2 x}{\csc x} \csc x \cot x\, dx\\ &= \int \frac{\csc^2 x - 1}{\csc x} \csc x \cot x\, dx\\ &= \int \left(\frac{1}{\csc x} - \csc x\right)(-\csc x \cot x)\, dx\\ &= \ln|\csc x| - \frac{\csc^2 x}{2} + C.\end{aligned}$$

Case III: $\int \tan^n u \cdot u'\, dx$ and $\int \cot^n u \cdot u'\, dx$. The above method can be used here only if n is odd. The following method works for any positive integer n—odd or even. Of course, $\int \tan u \cdot u'\, dx$ and $\int \tan^2 u \cdot u'\, dx$ can be evaluated quite easily. If $n > 2$, then

$$\begin{aligned}\int \tan^n u \cdot u'\, dx &= \int \tan^{n-2} u \tan^2 u \cdot u'\, dx\\ &= \int \tan^{n-2} u\,(\sec^2 u - 1)u'\, dx\\ &= \int (\tan^{n-2} u \sec^2 u - \tan^{n-2} u)u'\, dx.\end{aligned}$$

The first term can easily be integrated, and the exponent on the second has been reduced by 2. If $n - 2 > 2$, this can be repeated until the exponent is down to 1 or 2.

Example 5

Evaluate $\int \tan^6 x\, dx$.

$$\begin{aligned}\int \tan^6 x\,dx &= \int \tan^4 x \tan^2 x\,dx \\ &= \int \tan^4 x\,(\sec^2 x - 1)\,dx \\ &= \int (\tan^4 x \sec^2 x - \tan^4 x)\,dx \\ &= \int (\tan^4 x \sec^2 x - \tan^2 x \tan^2 x)\,dx \\ &= \int [\tan^4 x \sec^2 x - \tan^2 x\,(\sec^2 x - 1)]\,dx \\ &= \int (\tan^4 x \sec^2 x - \tan^2 x \sec^2 x + \tan^2 x)\,dx \\ &= \int (\tan^4 x \sec^2 x - \tan^2 x \sec^2 x + \sec^2 x - 1)\,dx \\ &= \frac{\tan^5 x}{5} - \frac{\tan^3 x}{3} + \tan x - x + C.\end{aligned}$$

Example 6

Evaluate $\int \cot^3 x\,dx$.

This is the same problem as Example 4. Let us evaluate the integral by this new method.

$$\begin{aligned}\int \cot^3 x\,dx &= \int \cot x \cot^2 x\,dx \\ &= \int \cot x\,(\csc^2 x - 1)\,dx \\ &= \int (\cot x \csc^2 x - \cot x)\,dx \\ &= -\frac{\cot^2 x}{2} - \ln|\sin x| + C.\end{aligned}$$

Problems

Evaluate the integrals in Problems 1–30.

1. $\int \sec^2 x \tan^2 x\,dx$.
2. $\int \sec^4 \theta \tan^3 \theta\,d\theta$.
3. $\int \csc^4 x \cot^4 x\,dx$.
4. $\int \sec^6 2x \tan^2 2x\,dx$.
5. $\int \sec \theta \tan^3 \theta\,d\theta$.
6. $\int \csc \theta \cot^5 \theta\,d\theta$.
7. $\int \csc^3 x \cot x\,dx$.
8. $\int \sec^5 x \tan^3 x\,dx$.
9. $\int \sec^6 x\,dx$.
10. $\int \csc^4 2x\,dx$.
11. $\int \tan^3 \theta\,d\theta$.
12. $\int \cot^5 x\,dx$.

13. $\int \tan^5 2\theta \, d\theta.$

14. $\int \frac{\sin^2 \theta}{\cos^4 \theta} \, d\theta.$

15. $\int \frac{\sin^3 \theta}{\cos^4 \theta} \, d\theta.$

16. $\int \tan^2 x \, dx.$

17. $\int \cot^4 3x \, dx.$

18. $\int x \sec^4 x^2 \tan^2 x^2 \, dx.$

19. $\int \tan^4 (2x + 1) \, dx.$

20. $\int \csc^3 4x \cot^3 4x \, dx.$

21. $\int \frac{\tan \theta}{1 - \tan^2 \theta} \, d\theta.$

22. $\int (\cos^2 x - \sin^2 x) \, dx.$

23. $\int \frac{\sin^2 \theta}{1 - \cos \theta} \, d\theta.$

24. $\int \frac{1 - \cos \theta}{\sin^2 \theta} \, d\theta.$

25. $\int \frac{\sin \theta \cos \theta}{\sin^2 \theta - \cos^2 \theta} \, d\theta.$

26. $\int \frac{\tan \theta}{\sec^3 \theta} \, d\theta.$

27. $\int \frac{\csc^4 \theta}{\cot^2 \theta} \, d\theta.$

28. $\int \frac{\tan^3 \theta}{\sec^2 \theta} \, d\theta.$

29. $\int \frac{\tan^2 x}{\sec^3 x} \, dx.$

30. $\int \frac{\sec x + \tan x}{\sec^2 x} \, dx.$

31. $\int \sec^2 x \tan x \, dx$ can be integrated by three different methods—using the fact that the exponent on $\sec x$ is even, using the fact that the exponent on $\tan x$ is odd, and changing to $\sin x$ and $\cos x$. Carry out the integration by all three methods and show that the three results are equivalent.

32. Show that the results of Examples 4 and 6 are equivalent.

15.8

Trigonometric Substitutions

In the past two sections we have widened the range of trigonometric functions that we can integrate. But there are still many relatively simple trigonometric functions that we still cannot integrate. For example, $\int \sec^3 x \, dx$ cannot be integrated by any method we have had. We shall see more of this integral later in this section and in the next.

As we have noted, the attention we have given to trigonometric expressions is in preparation for integration by trigonometric substitutions. We have seen that integrals such as $\int x\sqrt{x + 1} \, dx$, in which the expression under the radical is linear, can be evaluated by means of the substitution $u = \sqrt{x + 1}$. Unfortunately, this type of substitution is usually of no avail if the expression under the radical is quadratic. When dealing with an integral involving the square root of a quadratic expression, we must resort to a trigonometric substitution.

Just as in the previous substitution, the trigonometric substitution is used to eliminate the radical. There are three substitutions to handle the three possible situations:

If the integral involves	use the substitution	and the identity
$\sqrt{a^2-u^2}$	$u=a\sin\theta$	$\cos^2\theta=1-\sin^2\theta$
$\sqrt{a^2+u^2}$,	$u=a\tan\theta$	$\sec^2\theta=1+\tan^2\theta$
$\sqrt{u^2-a^2}$,	$u=a\sec\theta$	$\tan^2\theta=\sec^2\theta-1$

Example 1

Evaluate $\int\frac{dx}{\sqrt{1-x^2}}$.

Although this integral can be evaluated by Formula 25 on page 319, it was promised there that you would have a method of integration that would relieve you of the necessity of memorizing Formulas 22–29. Trigonometric substitution is that method. Let us use the substitution

$$x=\sin\theta,$$

which gives

$$dx=\cos\theta\,d\theta;$$

then

$$\begin{aligned}\int\frac{dx}{\sqrt{1-x^2}}&=\int\frac{\cos\theta\,d\theta}{\sqrt{1-\sin^2\theta}}\\&=\int\frac{\cos\theta\,d\theta}{\sqrt{\cos^2\theta}}\\&=\int d\theta\\&=\theta+C.\end{aligned}$$

Having carried out the integration, we want to express the result in terms of x. The substitution $x=\sin\theta$ gives $\theta=\text{Arcsin}\,x$ and

$$\int\frac{dx}{\sqrt{1-x^2}}=\text{Arcsin}\,x+C.$$

Example 2

Evaluate $\int\frac{x^3}{\sqrt{x^2+4}}\,dx$.

Let us use the substitution

$$x=2\tan\theta,$$

which gives

$$dx=2\sec^2\theta\,d\theta;$$

then

$$\int \frac{x^3}{\sqrt{x^2+4}}\,dx = \int \frac{8\tan^3\theta \cdot 2\sec^2\theta}{\sqrt{4\tan^2\theta+4}}\,d\theta$$

$$= \int \frac{16\sec^2\theta\tan^3\theta}{\sqrt{4\sec^2\theta}}\,d\theta$$

$$= \int 8\sec\theta\tan^3\theta\,d\theta$$

$$= \int 8\tan^2\theta\sec\theta\tan\theta\,d\theta$$

$$= \int 8(\sec^2\theta - 1)\sec\theta\tan\theta\,d\theta$$

$$= 8\left(\frac{\sec^3\theta}{3} - \sec\theta\right) + C$$

$$= \frac{8}{3}\sec^3\theta - 8\sec\theta + C.$$

In order to express this result in terms of x, we see that the original substitution gives

$$\tan\theta = \frac{x}{2}.$$

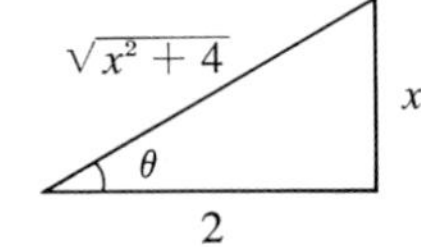

Figure 15.1

We can use either Figure 15.1 or the identity $\sec^2\theta = 1 + \tan^2\theta$ to get

$$\sec\theta = \frac{\sqrt{x^2+4}}{2}.$$

Thus

$$\int \frac{x^3}{\sqrt{x^2+4}}\,dx = \frac{8}{3}\frac{(x^2+4)^{3/2}}{8} - 8\frac{\sqrt{x^2+4}}{2} + C$$

$$= \frac{1}{3}\sqrt{x^2+4}\,[(x^2+4) - 12] + C$$

$$= \frac{1}{3}\sqrt{x^2+4}\,(x^2-8) + C.$$

Example 3

Evaluate $\displaystyle\int \frac{dx}{(4x^2-9)^{3/2}}$.

Since the 3/2 power gives a square root, this is handled in the same way as the other examples. Here we have $u^2 - a^2$, where $u = 2x$ and $a = 3$. Thus we want the substitution

$$2x = 3\sec\theta,$$

or

$$x = \frac{3}{2}\sec\theta,$$

$$dx = \frac{3}{2} \sec\theta \tan\theta \, d\theta;$$

$$\int \frac{dx}{(4x^2 - 9)^{3/2}} = \int \frac{\frac{3}{2} \sec\theta \tan\theta \, d\theta}{(9 \sec^2\theta - 9)^{3/2}}$$

$$= \int \frac{\frac{3}{2} \sec\theta \tan\theta \, d\theta}{(9 \tan^2\theta)^{3/2}}$$

$$= \int \frac{\frac{3}{2} \sec\theta \tan\theta \, d\theta}{3^3 \tan^3\theta}$$

$$= \frac{1}{18} \int \frac{\sec\theta}{\tan^2\theta} \, d\theta$$

$$= \frac{1}{18} \int \frac{\frac{1}{\cos\theta}}{\frac{\sin^2\theta}{\cos^2\theta}} \, d\theta$$

$$= \frac{1}{18} \int \frac{\cos\theta}{\sin^2\theta} \, d\theta$$

$$= \frac{1}{18} \cdot \frac{-1}{\sin\theta} + C$$

$$= -\frac{1}{18} \csc\theta + C.$$

Using our original substitution, we have $\sec\theta = 2x/3$. From Figure 15.2, we have

$$\csc\theta = \frac{2x}{\sqrt{4x^2 - 9}}.$$

Thus

$$\int \frac{dx}{(4x^2 - 9)^{3/2}} = -\frac{1}{18} \frac{2x}{\sqrt{4x^2 - 9}} + C$$

$$= \frac{-x}{9\sqrt{4x^2 - 9}} + C.$$

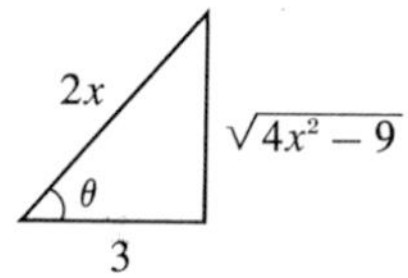

Figure 15.2

Example 4

Evaluate $\int \sqrt{x^2 + 2x + 2} \, dx$.

First of all let us complete the square on the first two terms under the radical. This gives

$$\int \sqrt{x^2 + 2x + 2} \, dx = \int \sqrt{(x + 1)^2 + 1} \, dx.$$

Now we are in a position to substitute.

$$x+1=\tan\theta$$
$$x=\tan\theta-1,$$
$$dx=\sec^2\theta\,d\theta.$$

$$\begin{aligned}\int\sqrt{x^2+2x+2}\,dx &= \int\sqrt{(x+1)^2+1}\,dx\\ &= \int\sqrt{\tan^2\theta+1}\,\sec^2\theta\,d\theta\\ &= \int\sec^3\theta\,d\theta.\end{aligned}$$

This is an integral which we cannot evaluate at this time. However, it is evaluated in the next section (see Example 9, page 353) and we shall use that result here:

$$\int\sqrt{x^2+2x+2}\,dx=\frac{1}{2}(\sec\theta\tan\theta+\ln|\sec\theta+\tan\theta|)+C.$$

Going back to our original substitution, we have

$$\tan\theta=x+1,$$

and, from Figure 15.3 or a trigonometric identity,

$$\sec\theta=\sqrt{x^2+2x+2}.$$

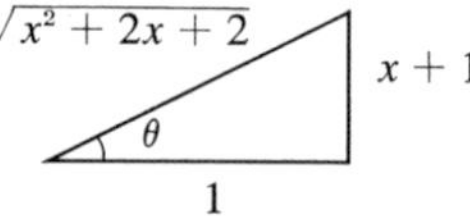

Figure 15.3

Thus

$$\int\sqrt{x^2+2x+2}\,dx=\frac{1}{2}\left[(x+1)\sqrt{x^2+2x+2}+\ln|\sqrt{x^2+2x+2}+x+1|\right]+C.$$

Example 5

Evaluate $\int_0^3\sqrt{9-x^2}\,dx$.

By making the substitution

$$x=3\sin\theta,$$

we get

$$dx=3\cos\theta\,d\theta.$$

Now when $x=0$, $\sin\theta=0$, and $\theta=0$; when $x=3$, $\sin\theta=1$, and $\theta=\pi/2$. Thus

$$\begin{aligned}\int_0^3\sqrt{9-x^2}\,dx &= \int_0^{\pi/2}\sqrt{9-9\sin^2\theta}\,3\cos\theta\,d\theta\\ &= \int_0^{\pi/2}9\cos^2\theta\,d\theta\\ &= \frac{9}{2}\int_0^{\pi/2}(1+\cos 2\theta)\,d\theta\\ &= \frac{9}{2}\left(\theta+\frac{1}{2}\sin 2\theta\right)\Big|_0^{\pi/2}\\ &= \frac{9}{2}\left[\left(\frac{\pi}{2}+\frac{1}{2}\sin\pi\right)-\left(0+\frac{1}{2}\sin 0\right)\right]\\ &= \frac{9\pi}{4}.\end{aligned}$$

If we had not changed the limits of integration we would have had to express

$$\frac{9}{2}\left(\theta + \frac{1}{2}\sin 2\theta\right)$$

in terms of x before putting in the limits of integration. In order to do so we would have had to use the identity $\sin 2\theta = 2 \sin\theta \cos\theta$.

$$\frac{9}{2}\left(\theta + \frac{1}{2}\sin 2\theta\right) = \frac{9}{2}(\theta + \sin\theta\cos\theta).$$

Now, since

$$\sin\theta = \frac{x}{3},$$

we have

$$\cos\theta = \frac{\sqrt{9 - x^2}}{3} \quad \text{and} \quad \theta = \operatorname{Arcsin}\frac{x}{3}.$$

$$\begin{aligned}\int_0^3 \sqrt{9 - x^2}\, dx &= \frac{9}{2}\left(\operatorname{Arcsin}\frac{x}{3} + \frac{x\sqrt{9 - x^2}}{9}\right)\Bigg|_0^3 \\ &= \frac{9}{2}[(\operatorname{Arcsin} 1 + 0) - (\operatorname{Arcsin} 0 + 0)] \\ &= \frac{9}{2}\frac{\pi}{2} \\ &= \frac{9\pi}{4}.\end{aligned}$$

It might be noted that the substitutions, as we have stated them, do not define θ as a function of x. The substitution $u = a\sin\theta$ is a more convenient way of saying $\theta = \operatorname{Arcsin}(u/a)$. It is this restriction on θ that allows us to say $\sqrt{\cos^2\theta} = \cos\theta$. The same holds for the other two substitutions. This is also why we were able to use the positive square roots in Figures 15.1–15.3.

Problems

Evaluate the integrals in Problems 1–22. If a substitution leads to $\int \sec^3\theta\, d\theta$, use the result of the next section,

$$\int \sec^3\theta\, d\theta = \frac{1}{2}(\sec\theta\tan\theta + \ln|\sec\theta + \tan\theta|) + C.$$

Do not use Formulas 22–29 on page 319.

1. $\displaystyle\int \frac{\sqrt{1 - x^2}}{x^2}\, dx.$

2. $\displaystyle\int \frac{x^2}{\sqrt{16 - x^2}}\, dx.$

3. $\displaystyle\int \frac{dx}{\sqrt{x^2 + 9}}.$

4. $\displaystyle\int \frac{dx}{(4 + x^2)^{3/2}}.$

5. $\displaystyle\int \frac{x^3\, dx}{\sqrt{4 - x^2}}.$

6. $\displaystyle\int \frac{x^2\, dx}{\sqrt{25 + x^2}}.$

7. $\int \frac{dx}{(x^2-5)^{3/2}}$.

8. $\int (4-x^2)^{3/2}\,dx$.

9. $\int \sqrt{9-4x^2}\,dx$.

10. $\int \sqrt{9x^2-1}\,dx$.

11. $\int \frac{\sqrt{4-3x^2}}{x^4}\,dx$.

12. $\int \frac{\sqrt{4x^2-25}}{x^3}\,dx$.

13. $\int \frac{x^3\,dx}{\sqrt{4x^2+9}}$.

14. $\int \frac{dx}{(5x^2+2)^{3/2}}$.

15. $\int \sqrt{x^2+4x+13}\,dx$.

16. $\int \frac{dx}{(x+3)\sqrt{x^2+6x+5}}$.

17. $\int \frac{dx}{(x^2+2x)^{3/2}}$.

18. $\int \sqrt{29+4x-x^2}\,dx$.

19. $\int_0^1 \frac{dx}{(x^2+1)^{3/2}}$.

20. $\int_0^{\sqrt{2}} \frac{x^3\,dx}{\sqrt{4-x^2}}$.

21. $\int_0^{3/2} x^2\sqrt{9-4x^2}\,dx$.

22. $\int_{\sqrt{3}}^{2} \frac{\sqrt{x^2-3}}{x}\,dx$.

23. Evaluate the integral of Problem 3 by using the substitution $x = 3\sinh t$. Compare with the answers obtained by the use of Formula 24 on page 319.

15.9

Integration by Parts

Perhaps the most powerful method of integration is integration by parts. It is based upon the formula for the derivative of a product,

$$\frac{d}{dx}(uv) = u\frac{dv}{dx} + v\frac{du}{dx},$$

where u and v are functions of x. In the integral form, it is written

$$uv = \int uv'\,dx + \int vu'\,dx$$

or

$$\int uv'\,dx = uv - \int vu'\,dx.$$

With this formula we are able to trade old integrals for new (and hopefully, simpler) ones.

Example 1

Evaluate $\int x \sin x\, dx$.

Suppose we let

$$u = x \quad \text{and} \quad v' = \sin x;$$

then

$$u' = 1 \quad \text{and} \quad v = -\cos x + C.$$

$$\begin{aligned}\int x \sin x\, dx &= x(-\cos x + C) - \int (-\cos x + C)\, dx \\ &= -x \cos x + Cx + \sin x - Cx + K \\ &= -x \cos x + \sin x + K.\end{aligned}$$

Note that the constant of integration, C, does not appear in the final answer above. This is not merely the case for this particular example—it always happens, because we always have

$$u \cdot C - \int u' \cdot C\, dx = u \cdot C - u \cdot C = 0.$$

Thus we may use any value of C we choose. Usually it is simplest to use $C = 0$, which we normally do, but occasionally it is more convenient to use some other value of C as in the following example from J. L. Borman.*

Example 2

Evaluate $\int x \operatorname{Arctan} x\, dx$.

Letting

$$u = \operatorname{Arctan} x, \qquad v' = x,$$

we have

$$u' = \frac{1}{1 + x^2}, \qquad v = \frac{x^2}{2} + C.$$

If we choose $C = 0$, then we have

$$\begin{aligned}\int x \operatorname{Arctan} x\, dx &= \frac{x^2}{2} \operatorname{Arctan} x - \int \frac{x^2}{2(1 + x^2)}\, dx \\ &= \frac{x^2}{2} \operatorname{Arctan} x - \frac{1}{2} \int \left(1 - \frac{1}{1 + x^2}\right) dx \\ &= \frac{x^2}{2} \operatorname{Arctan} x - \frac{1}{2} x + \frac{1}{2} \operatorname{Arctan} x + K \\ &= \frac{x^2 + 1}{2} \operatorname{Arctan} x - \frac{1}{2} x + K.\end{aligned}$$

* Borman, J. L., " A Remark on Integration by Parts " AMM. Vol. 51 (1944): pp. 32–33.

If we choose $C = 1/2$, then

$$\int x \text{ Arctan } x\, dx = \frac{x^2+1}{2} \text{ Arctan } x - \int \frac{x^2+1}{2(1+x^2)}\, dx$$

$$= \frac{x^2+1}{2} \text{ Arctan } x - \frac{1}{2} \int dx$$

$$= \frac{x^2+1}{2} \text{ Arctan } x - \frac{1}{2} x + K.$$

Perhaps you wonder how one knows which factor to call u and which v'. To a large extent, it is a matter of trial and error, but the following guide is helpful in many (but not all) cases: *Let v' be the most complicated part of the expression that can be easily integrated.* Suppose we try using this rule on other examples.

Example 3

Evaluate $\int x^3 e^{x^2}\, dx$.

Certainly e^{x^2} is a more "complicated" function than x^3, but we cannot integrate it. Let us then include a factor x, making it xe^{x^2}. This is even more complicated, and it can be integrated easily.

$$u = x^2, \qquad v' = xe^{x^2},$$

$$u' = 2x, \qquad v = \frac{1}{2} e^{x^2};$$

$$\int x^3 e^{x^2}\, dx = \frac{1}{2} x^2 e^{x^2} - \int xe^{x^2}\, dx$$

$$= \frac{1}{2} x^2 e^{x^2} - \frac{1}{2} e^{x^2} + C$$

$$= \frac{1}{2} e^{x^2}(x^2 - 1) + C.$$

Example 4

Evaluate $\int x \ln x\, dx$.

Again, $\ln x$ is the more complicated of the two factors, but it is not easily integrated. Thus x is the most complicated part that can still be integrated easily.

$$u = \ln x, \qquad v' = x,$$

$$u' = \frac{1}{x}, \qquad v = \frac{x^2}{2}.$$

$$\int x \ln x \, dx = \frac{x^2}{2} \ln x - \int \frac{x}{2} \, dx$$

$$= \frac{x^2}{2} \ln x - \frac{x^2}{4} + C$$

$$= \frac{x^2}{4} (2 \ln x - 1) + C.$$

Example 5

Evaluate $\int \ln x \, dx$.

We have only one factor, but we can easily have two, by using 1 as one of them. Since we cannot integrate $\ln x$ easily, we must choose

$$u = \ln x, \qquad v' = 1,$$

$$u' = \frac{1}{x}, \qquad v = x;$$

$$\int \ln x \, dx = x \ln x - \int dx$$

$$= x \ln x - x + C$$

$$= x (\ln x - 1) + C.$$

Sometimes more than one application of integration by parts is required, as the following example shows.

Example 6

Evaluate $\int x^2 \cos x \, dx$.

$$u = x^2, \qquad v' = \cos x,$$

$$u' = 2x, \qquad v = \sin x;$$

$$\int x^2 \cos x \, dx = x^2 \sin x - \int 2x \sin x \, dx.$$

Now the new integral, while it is better than the original, still cannot be evaluated by our integration formulas. Let us integrate by parts once more.

$$u = 2x, \qquad v' = \sin x,$$

$$u' = 2, \qquad v = -\cos x;$$

$$\int x^2 \cos x \, dx = x^2 \sin x - \left(-2x \cos x + \int 2 \cos x \, dx \right)$$

$$= x^2 \sin x + 2x \cos x - 2 \sin x + C.$$

When we can see from that start that more than one application of parts is needed, the process can be carried out more expeditiously by tabular integration. Let us note that the u and v' for the second application of parts corresponds to the u' and v from the first application. By telescoping the several applications of parts, we can make it into a table, as shown below. First we break up the integral into parts in the normal way. Then, instead of differentiating u only once, we repeat until we get 0. Similarly we integrate v' repeatedly. Finally, we take products diagonally, appending +, −, +, − as shown. The integral equals the sum of these products.

u	v'		
x^2	$\cos x$		
$2x$	$\sin x$	$(+)$	$\longrightarrow +x^2 \sin x$
2	$-\cos x$	$(-)$	$\longrightarrow -(-2x \cos x)$
0	$-\sin x$	$(+)$	$\longrightarrow +(-2 \sin x)$
		$(-)$	$\longrightarrow -0$

$$\int x^2 \cos x \, dx = x^2 \sin x + 2x \cos x - 2 \sin x + C.$$

Example 7

Evaluate $\int x^3 e^x \, dx$.

u	v'	
x^3	e^x	
$3x^2$	e^x	$(+)$
$6x$	e^x	$(-)$
6	e^x	$(+)$
0	e^x	$(-)$

$$\int x^3 e^x \, dx = x^3 e^x - 3x^2 e^x + 6x e^x - 6e^x + C.$$

Sometimes a repeated application of parts leads us back to our original integral. If so, it can be combined with the original integral, as the next example illustrates.

Example 8

Evaluate $\int e^x \sin x \, dx$.

$$u = e^x, \qquad v' = \sin x,$$
$$u' = e^x, \qquad v = -\cos x;$$

$$\int e^x \sin x \, dx = -e^x \cos x + \int e^x \cos x \, dx.$$

$$u = e^x, \qquad v' = \cos x,$$
$$u' = e^x, \qquad v = \sin x;$$

$$\int e^x \sin x \, dx = -e^x \cos x + e^x \sin x - \int e^x \sin x \, dx.$$

Now let us add $\int e^x \sin x\,dx$ to both sides.

$$2\int e^x \sin x\,dx = e^x(\sin x - \cos x),$$

$$\int e^x \sin x\,dx = \frac{1}{2}e^x(\sin x - \cos x) + C.$$

Example 9

Evaluate $\int \sec^3\theta\,d\theta$.

$$u = \sec\theta, \qquad v' = \sec^2\theta,$$
$$u' = \sec\theta\tan\theta, \qquad v = \tan\theta;$$

$$\begin{aligned}\int \sec^3\theta\,d\theta &= \sec\theta\tan\theta - \int \sec\theta\tan^2\theta\,d\theta \\ &= \sec\theta\tan\theta - \int \sec\theta(\sec^2\theta - 1)\,d\theta \\ &= \sec\theta\tan\theta + \int \sec\theta\,d\theta - \int \sec^3\theta\,d\theta,\end{aligned}$$

$$2\int \sec^3\theta\,d\theta = \sec\theta\tan\theta + \ln|\sec\theta + \tan\theta|,$$

$$\int \sec^3\theta\,d\theta = \frac{1}{2}(\sec\theta\tan\theta + \ln|\sec\theta + \tan\theta|) + C.$$

Problems

Evaluate the following integrals.

1. $\int x\cos x\,dx$.
2. $\int \theta\sin 2\theta\,d\theta$.
3. $\int xe^x\,dx$.
4. $\int 2xe^{-x}\,dx$.
5. $\int \ln x^2\,dx$.
6. $\int \ln 3x\,dx$.
7. $\int \frac{\ln x}{x^2}\,dx$.
8. $\int \frac{\ln(x-1)}{\sqrt{x-1}}\,dx$.
9. $\int \text{Arcsin}\,x\,dx$.
10. $\int \text{Arccos}\,2x\,dx$.
11. $\int \text{Arctan}\,x\,dx$.
12. $\int \text{Arccot}\sqrt{x}\,dx$.
13. $\int \sin\theta\ln\cos\theta\,d\theta$.
14. $\int \sinh^{-1}x\,dx$.
15. $\int \cosh^{-1}x\,dx$.
16. $\int x\,\text{Arcsin}\,x\,dx$.
17. $\int x^3\sqrt{4-x^2}\,dx$.
18. $\int \frac{x^3}{\sqrt{4-x^2}}\,dx$.
19. $\int x^5\sqrt{x^3+1}\,dx$.
20. $\int x^{2n-1}\sqrt{x^n+1}\,dx$.
21. $\int \sin\ln x\,dx$.
22. $\int x\sec^2 x\,dx$.

23. $\int \frac{\ln x \, dx}{(x-1)^2}$.

24. $\int x^2 \sin x \, dx$.

25. $\int x^4 \cos x \, dx$.

26. $\int x^3 \sin 2x \, dx$.

27. $\int x^3 e^x \, dx$.

28. $\int x^4 e^{-x} \, dx$.

29. $\int x^3 \ln^2 x \, dx$.

30. $\int x^n e^x \, dx$ (n a positive integer).

31. $\int e^x \cos x \, dx$.

32. $\int \csc^3 \theta \, d\theta$.

33. $\int \sec^5 \theta \, d\theta$.

34. $\int \sec^n \theta \, d\theta$.

35. $\int e^x \sin 2x \, dx$.

36. $\int \sin x \cos 3x \, dx$.

37. $\int \sin x \sin 3x \, dx$.

38. $\int \cos x \cos 5x \, dx$.

39. Evaluate $\int \sin^2 \theta \, d\theta$ by parts. Compare your answer with the one obtained using a double-angle formula and show that they are equivalent.

40. Evaluate $\int \cos^2 \theta \, d\theta$ by parts. Compare your answer with the one obtained using a double-angle formula and show that they are equivalent.

41. Evaluate the integral of Problem 37 by using the identity

$$\sin A \sin B = \frac{1}{2}[\cos(A-B) - \cos(A+B)].$$

15.10

Partial Fractions: Linear Factors

This section and the next are devoted to a method of integrating rational fractions. In the past we have seen many problems in which we were to add two or more fractions,

$$\frac{1}{x+1} + \frac{2}{x-2} - \frac{4}{x},$$

to give a single fraction

$$\frac{-x^2+4x+8}{x(x+1)(x-2)}.$$

What we would like to do here is to work this problem backward; that is, starting with

$$\frac{-x^2+4x+8}{x(x+1)(x-2)},$$

we would like to break it down into the sum of the partial fractions,

$$\frac{1}{x+1} + \frac{2}{x-2} - \frac{4}{x}.$$

Once this is done, we can easily integrate term by term. We shall not attempt to go into the theory of partial fractions—this is basically an algebraic problem.* We shall merely summarize the results.

First of all, the numerator must be of lower degree than the denominator. If this is not the case, we divide until the remainder term is in the proper form. Next, the denominator is factored so that every factor is either a linear or quadratic factor with real coefficients (this can always be done—but not always easily). Finally, this fraction can be broken down into partial fractions in a way that is dependent upon the factors of the denominator. There are four cases:

I. Nonrepeated linear factors,
II. Repeated linear factors,
III. Nonrepeated quadratic factors,
IV. Repeated quadratic factors.

We shall consider the first two cases in this section and the last two in the next section.

Case I Nonrepeated linear factors:

$$\frac{P(x)}{(a_1x+b_1)(a_2x+b_2)\cdots(a_nx+b_n)}=\frac{A_1}{a_1x+b_1}+\frac{A_2}{a_2x+b_2}+\cdots+\frac{A_n}{a_nx+b_n},$$

where $A_1, A_2, \ldots, A_n$ are constants.

Example 1

Evaluate $\displaystyle\int\frac{dx}{(x+1)(x-2)}$.

Let us break the fraction into partial fractions by the above rule.

$$\frac{1}{(x+1)(x-2)}=\frac{A}{x+1}+\frac{B}{x-2}.$$

Bear in mind that this equation (for the proper choices of A and B) is an identity; that is, it is true for all x for which both sides of the equation have meaning. This is an important consideration in determining A and B, which we shall now do. Multiplying both sides by $(x+1)(x-2)$, we have

$$\begin{aligned}1&=A(x-2)+B(x+1)\\&=(A+B)x+(-2A+B).\end{aligned}$$

Since this is also an identity, the coefficients must be the same on both sides of the equation: that is, the coefficient of x on the right, $A+B$, must equal the coefficient of x on the left, 0; and the constant term on the right, $-2A+B$, must equal the constant term on the left, 1.

$$A+B=0,$$

$$-2A+B=1.$$

Solving simultaneously, we have,

$$A=-\frac{1}{3}\quad\text{and}\quad B=\frac{1}{3}.$$

* Cf. M. Richardson, *College Algebra*, Alternate Edition, Prentice-Hall, 1958, pp. 427–435.

Thus,

$$\frac{1}{(x+1)(x-2)}=\frac{-\frac{1}{3}}{x+1}+\frac{\frac{1}{3}}{x-2}$$

and

$$\begin{aligned}\int\frac{dx}{(x+1)(x-2)}&=\int\left(-\frac{1}{3}\frac{1}{x+1}+\frac{1}{3}\frac{1}{x-2}\right)dx\\&=-\frac{1}{3}\ln|x+1|+\frac{1}{3}\ln|x-2|+C\\&=\frac{1}{3}\ln\left|\frac{x-2}{x+1}\right|+C.\end{aligned}$$

Example 2

Evaluate $\int\frac{x^3+1}{x^2-x}\,dx$.

Since the degree of the numerator is too high, we must divide before breaking it down into partial fractions.

$$\begin{aligned}\int\frac{x^3+1}{x^2-x}\,dx&=\int\left(x+1+\frac{x+1}{x^2-x}\right)dx\\&=\int\left(x+1+\frac{x+1}{x(x-1)}\right)dx.\end{aligned}$$

Using partial fractions, we have

$$\begin{aligned}\frac{x+1}{x(x-1)}&=\frac{A}{x}+\frac{B}{x-1},\\x+1&=A(x-1)+Bx\\&=(A+B)x-A.\end{aligned}$$

This gives

$$\begin{aligned}A+B&=1,\\-A&=1.\end{aligned}$$

Solving, we have

$$A=-1\quad\text{and}\quad B=2.$$

Thus

$$\begin{aligned}\int\frac{x^3+1}{x^2-x}\,dx&=\int\left(x+1-\frac{1}{x}+\frac{2}{x-1}\right)dx\\&=\frac{x^2}{2}+x-\ln|x|+2\ln|x-1|+C\\&=\frac{x^2}{2}+x+\ln\left|\frac{(x-1)^2}{x}\right|+C.\end{aligned}$$

Case II *Repeated linear factors:*

$$\frac{P(x)}{(ax+b)^n} = \frac{A_1}{ax+b} + \frac{A_2}{(ax+b)^2} + \cdots + \frac{A_n}{(ax+b)^n},$$

where $A_1, A_2, \ldots A_n$ are constants.

Example 3

Evaluate $\int \frac{x\,dx}{(x-2)^3}$.

$$\frac{x}{(x-2)^3} = \frac{A}{x-2} + \frac{B}{(x-2)^2} + \frac{C}{(x-2)^3}.$$

Multiplying by $(x-2)^3$, we have

$$\begin{aligned} x &= A(x-2)^2 + B(x-2) + C \\ &= Ax^2 + (-4A+B)x + (4A-2B+C). \end{aligned}$$

Equating coefficients, we have

$$\begin{aligned} A &= 0, \\ -4A + B &= 1, \\ 4A - 2B + C &= 0 \end{aligned}$$

or

$$A = 0, \qquad B = 1, \qquad C = 2.$$

Thus

$$\begin{aligned} \int \frac{x\,dx}{(x-2)^3} &= \int \left(\frac{1}{(x-2)^2} + \frac{2}{(x-2)^3}\right) dx \\ &= \frac{-1}{x-2} - \frac{1}{(x-2)^2} + C \\ &= \frac{1-x}{(x-2)^2} + C. \end{aligned}$$

Example 4

Evaluate $\int \frac{x-2}{x^2(x-1)^2}\,dx$.

$$\frac{x-2}{x^2(x-1)^2} = \frac{A}{x} + \frac{B}{x^2} + \frac{C}{x-1} + \frac{D}{(x-1)^2},$$

$$\begin{aligned} x - 2 &= Ax(x-1)^2 + B(x-1)^2 + Cx^2(x-1) + Dx^2 \\ &= (A+C)x^3 + (-2A+B-C+D)x^2 + (A-2B)x + B, \end{aligned}$$

$$\begin{aligned} A + C &= 0, \\ -2A + B - C + D &= 0, \\ A - 2B &= 1, \\ B &= -2. \end{aligned}$$

Solving simultaneously, we have

$$A = -3, \qquad B = -2, \qquad C = 3, \qquad D = -1.$$

Thus,

$$\int \frac{x-2}{x^2(x-1)^2}\,dx = \int \left(-\frac{3}{x} - \frac{2}{x^2} + \frac{3}{x-1} - \frac{1}{(x-1)^2}\right) dx$$

$$= -3\ln|x| + \frac{2}{x} + 3\ln|x-1| + \frac{1}{x-1} + C$$

$$= 3\ln\left|\frac{x-1}{x}\right| + \frac{3x-2}{x(x-1)} + C.$$

Problems

Evaluate the following integrals.

1. $\int \frac{dx}{x(x+1)}$.
2. $\int \frac{dx}{x(x-2)}$.
3. $\int \frac{x\,dx}{(x+1)(x+2)}$.
4. $\int \frac{dx}{x^2-4x-5}$.
5. $\int \frac{x^2+2}{x^2+2x}\,dx$.
6. $\int \frac{x^3-1}{x^2-3x}\,dx$.
7. $\int \frac{dx}{x^3-x}$.
8. $\int \frac{dx}{(x+1)(x+2)(x+3)}$.
9. $\int \frac{(x^3+2)\,dx}{x^3-3x^2+2x}$.
10. $\int \frac{x^3+4}{9x^3-4x}\,dx$.
11. $\int \frac{x\,dx}{(x-4)^2}$.
12. $\int \frac{x\,dx}{(x+1)^2}$.
13. $\int \frac{x^2\,dx}{(x+1)^2}$.
14. $\int \frac{x-2}{x(x-1)^2}\,dx$.
15. $\int \frac{dx}{x^3-x^2}$.
16. $\int \frac{dx}{x^2(x-3)^2}$.
17. $\int \frac{(x+2)\,dx}{x^4+2x^3-3x^2}$.
18. $\int \frac{dx}{(x-1)^2(x-2)^3}$.
19. $\int \frac{dx}{x(x-1)^2(x+1)^2}$.
20. $\int \frac{dx}{(2x+1)^2(x-2)^2}$.
21. $\int \frac{\cos x\,dx}{\sin^3 x + \sin^2 x}$. (*Hint*: let $u = \sin x$.)
22. $\int \frac{\cos x\,dx}{\sin^2 x - 2\sin x - 3}$.

15.11

Partial Fractions: Quadratic Factors

Case III Nonrepeated quadratic factors:

$$\frac{P(x)}{(a_1x^2+b_1x+c_1)\cdots(a_nx^2+b_nx+c_n)} = \frac{A_1x+B_1}{a_1x^2+b_1x+c_1} + \frac{A_2x+B_2}{a_2x^2+b_2x+c_2} + \dots + \frac{A_nx+B_n}{a_nx^2+b_nx+c_n}.$$

Example 1

Evaluate $\int \frac{dx}{x^3 + x}$.

The denominator can be factored to

$$x(x^2 + 1),$$

but the quadratic factor cannot be factored further without using complex coefficients. Thus,

$$\frac{1}{x(x^2 + 1)} = \frac{A}{x} + \frac{Bx + C}{x^2 + 1}.$$

The constants are now evaluated exactly as in the previous section.

$$\begin{aligned} 1 &= A(x^2 + 1) + (Bx + C)x \\ &= (A + B)x^2 + Cx + A, \end{aligned}$$

$$\begin{aligned} A + B &= 0, \\ C &= 0, \\ A &= 1. \end{aligned}$$

This gives

$$A = 1, \quad B = -1, \quad \text{and} \quad C = 0.$$

Thus

$$\begin{aligned} \int \frac{dx}{x^3 + x} &= \int \left(\frac{1}{x} - \frac{x}{x^2 + 1} \right) dx \\ &= \ln |x| - \frac{1}{2} \ln |x^2 + 1| + C \\ &= \ln \frac{|x|}{\sqrt{x^2 + 1}} + C. \end{aligned}$$

Example 2

Evaluate $\int \frac{dx}{x^4 + 5x^2 + 4}$.

Again the denominator can be factored to

$$(x^2 + 1)(x^2 + 4),$$

but neither factor can be factored further without using complex coefficients. Thus,

$$\frac{1}{(x^2 + 1)(x^2 + 4)} = \frac{Ax + B}{x^2 + 1} + \frac{Cx + D}{x^2 + 4},$$

$$\begin{aligned} 1 &= (Ax + B)(x^2 + 4) + (Cx + D)(x^2 + 1) \\ &= (A + C)x^3 + (B + D)x^2 + (4A + C)x + (4B + D); \end{aligned}$$

$$\begin{aligned} A + C &= 0, \\ B + D &= 0, \\ 4A + C &= 0, \\ 4B + D &= 1. \end{aligned}$$

Solving simultaneously, we have

$$A = 0, \quad B = 1/3, \quad C = 0, \quad \text{and} \quad D = -1/3.$$

Thus

$$\begin{aligned}\int \frac{dx}{x^4 + 5x^2 + 4} &= \int \left(\frac{\frac{1}{3}}{x^2 + 1} - \frac{\frac{1}{3}}{x^2 + 4} \right) dx \\ &= \int \left(\frac{1}{3}\frac{1}{x^2 + 1} - \frac{1}{6} \frac{\frac{1}{2}}{\left(\frac{x}{2}\right)^2 + 1} \right) dx \\ &= \frac{1}{3} \operatorname{Arctan} x - \frac{1}{6} \operatorname{Arctan} \frac{x}{2} + C.\end{aligned}$$

Case IV Repeated quadratic factors:

$$\frac{P(x)}{(ax^2 + bx + c)^n} = \frac{A_1 x + B_1}{ax^2 + bx + c} + \frac{A_2 x + B_2}{(ax^2 + bx + c)^2} + \cdots + \frac{A_n x + B_n}{(ax^2 + bx + c)^n}.$$

Example 3

Evaluate $\int \frac{(x-1)^2}{(x^2+1)^2} dx.$

$$\begin{aligned}\frac{(x-1)^2}{(x^2+1)^2} &= \frac{Ax + B}{x^2 + 1} + \frac{Cx + D}{(x^2 + 1)^2}, \\ x^2 - 2x + 1 &= Ax^3 + Bx^2 + Ax + B + Cx + D \\ &= Ax^3 + Bx^2 + (A + C)x + (B + D).\end{aligned}$$

Equating coefficients, we have

$$\begin{aligned}A &= 0, \\ B &= 1, \\ A + C &= -2, \\ B + D &= 1,\end{aligned}$$

or

$$A = 0, \quad B = 1, \quad C = -2, \quad \text{and} \quad D = 0.$$

Thus,

$$\begin{aligned}\int \frac{(x-1)^2}{(x^2+1)^2} dx &= \int \left(\frac{1}{x^2 + 1} - \frac{2x}{(x^2 + 1)^2} \right) dx \\ &= \operatorname{Arctan} x + \frac{1}{x^2 + 1} + C.\end{aligned}$$

Example 4

Evaluate $\int \frac{x^4 + x^3 + 8x^2 + 16}{x(x^2 + 4)^2} dx.$

$$\frac{x^4+x^3+8x^2+16}{x(x^2+4)^2} = \frac{A}{x} + \frac{Bx+C}{x^2+4} + \frac{Dx+E}{(x^2+4)^2},$$

$$\begin{aligned} x^4+x^3+8x^2+16 &= A(x^2+4)^2 + (Bx+C)x(x^2+4) + (Dx+E)x \\ &= (A+B)x^4 + Cx^3 + (8A+4B+D)x^2 + (4C+E)x + 16. \end{aligned}$$

Equating coefficients, we have

$$\begin{aligned} A+B &= 1, \\ C &= 1, \\ 8A+4B+D &= 8, \\ 4C+E &= 0, \\ 16A &= 16, \end{aligned}$$

or

$$A=1, \quad B=0, \quad C=1, \quad D=0, \quad \text{and} \quad E=-4.$$

Thus,

$$\int \frac{x^4+x^3+8x^2+16}{x(x^2+4)^2}\,dx = \int \left(\frac{1}{x} + \frac{1}{x^2+4} - \frac{4}{(x^2+4)^2}\right) dx.$$

Integrating term by term, we have

$$\int \frac{1}{x}\,dx = \ln|x| + C_1,$$

$$\int \frac{dx}{x^2+4} = \int \frac{\frac{1}{4}}{\frac{x^2}{4}+1}\,dx = \frac{1}{2}\int \frac{\frac{1}{2}}{\left(\frac{x}{2}\right)^2+1}\,dx = \frac{1}{2}\operatorname{Arctan}\frac{x}{2} + C_2.$$

The third term requires a substitution.

$$x = 2\tan\theta, \qquad dx = 2\sec^2\theta\,d\theta.$$

$$\begin{aligned} \int \frac{-4}{(x^2+4)^2}\,dx &= \int \frac{-4\cdot 2\sec^2\theta\,d\theta}{(4\tan^2\theta+4)^2} \\ &= \int \frac{-8\sec^2\theta\,d\theta}{16\sec^4\theta} \\ &= -\frac{1}{2}\int \frac{d\theta}{\sec^2\theta} \\ &= -\frac{1}{2}\int \cos^2\theta\,d\theta \\ &= -\frac{1}{4}\int (1+\cos 2\theta)\,d\theta \\ &= -\frac{1}{4}\left(\theta + \frac{1}{2}\sin 2\theta\right) + C_3 \\ &= -\frac{1}{4}(\theta + \sin\theta\cos\theta) + C_3 \\ &= -\frac{1}{4}\operatorname{Arctan}\frac{x}{2} - \frac{1}{4}\frac{x}{\sqrt{x^2+4}}\frac{2}{\sqrt{x^2+4}} + C_3 \\ &= -\frac{1}{4}\operatorname{Arctan}\frac{x}{2} - \frac{x}{2(x^2+4)} + C_3. \end{aligned}$$

Putting it all together, we have

$$\int \frac{x^4 + x^3 + 8x^2 + 16}{x(x^2+4)^2}\,dx = \ln|x| + \frac{1}{2}\operatorname{Arctan}\frac{x}{2} - \frac{1}{4}\operatorname{Arctan}\frac{x}{2} - \frac{x}{2(x^2+4)} + C$$

$$= \ln|x| + \frac{1}{4}\operatorname{Arctan}\frac{x}{2} - \frac{x}{2(x^2+4)} + C.$$

Problems

Evaluate the integrals.

1. $\displaystyle\int \frac{dx}{x(x^2+1)}.$
2. $\displaystyle\int \frac{dx}{(x+1)(x^2+4)}.$
3. $\displaystyle\int \frac{x\,dx}{x^3-1}.$
4. $\displaystyle\int \frac{x^2\,dx}{x^4-1}.$
5. $\displaystyle\int \frac{3\,dx}{x^3+x^2+x+1}.$
6. $\displaystyle\int \frac{(x-1)\,dx}{x^4+x^2}$
7. $\displaystyle\int \frac{dx}{(x^2+4)(x+2)^2}.$
8. $\displaystyle\int \frac{(x-1)\,dx}{x^3+x^2+x}.$
9. $\displaystyle\int \frac{x\,dx}{(x+1)(x^2+1)}.$
10. $\displaystyle\int \frac{x^3+8}{x(x^2+4)}\,dx.$
11. $\displaystyle\int \frac{x^2\,dx}{(x^2+1)^2}.$
12. $\displaystyle\int \frac{(x+1)^2\,dx}{(x^2+4)^3}.$
13. $\displaystyle\int \frac{dx}{x(x^2+4)^2}.$
14. $\displaystyle\int \frac{dx}{x^2(x^2+9)^2}.$
15. $\displaystyle\int \frac{x^4+4x^2+16}{(x^3-8)^2}\,dx.$
16. $\displaystyle\int \frac{dx}{(x^4-1)^2}.$
17. $\displaystyle\int \frac{x^2\,dx}{(x^2+1)(x^2+4)^2}.$
18. $\displaystyle\int \frac{x^2\,dx}{(x^2-1)(x^2+4)^2}.$
19. $\displaystyle\int \frac{dx}{x(x^2+2x+2)}.$
20. $\displaystyle\int \frac{x\,dx}{(x^2+2x+2)^2}.$

15.12

Miscellaneous Substitutions

If none of the previous methods works, there are still a few substitutions that may be tried. One of these is the rationalizing substitution. We have already seen this type of substitution, on simple problems, in Section 15.2. Let us consider some other examples of it.

Example 1

Evaluate $\int \frac{dx}{\sqrt{x} + \sqrt[3]{x}}$.

We can eliminate the square root by the substitution $u = \sqrt{x}$ or $x = u^2$, but then we still have the cube root to deal with. Similarly, we can eliminate the cube root by the substitution $u = \sqrt[3]{x}$ or $x = u^3$, but then we still have the square root to deal with. Instead of using the substitution $x = u^2$, so we can find its square root, or $x = u^3$, so we can find its cube root, we want a substitution that will allow us to find both the square root and the cube root without getting fractional exponents. Thus we want a substitution of the form $x = u^k$, where k is a multiple of both 2 and 3. Let us use the least common multiple, 6.

$$x = u^6, \qquad dx = 6u^5\, du.$$

$$\begin{aligned}
\int \frac{dx}{\sqrt{x} + \sqrt[3]{x}} &= \int \frac{6u^5\, du}{u^3 + u^2} \\
&= \int \frac{6u^3\, du}{u + 1} \\
&= \int \left(6u^2 - 6u + 6 - \frac{6}{u + 1}\right) du \\
&= 2u^3 - 3u^2 + 6u - 6 \ln |u + 1| + C \\
&= 2\sqrt{x} - 3\sqrt[3]{x} + 6\sqrt[6]{x} - 6 \ln |\sqrt[6]{x} + 1| + C.
\end{aligned}$$

Example 2

Evaluate $\int \frac{dx}{\sqrt{x - 1} + (x - 1)^{3/2}}$.

Let us use the substitution $u = \sqrt{x - 1}$ or $x = u^2 + 1$.

$$dx = 2u\, du.$$

Then

$$\begin{aligned}
\int \frac{dx}{\sqrt{x - 1} + (x - 1)^{3/2}} &= \int \frac{2u\, du}{u + u^3} \\
&= \int \frac{2\, du}{u^2 + 1} \\
&= 2 \text{ Arctan } u + C \\
&= 2 \text{ Arctan } \sqrt{x - 1} + C.
\end{aligned}$$

Another substitution helpful in evaluating trigonometric integrals is

$$u = \tan \frac{\theta}{2}.$$

This substitution allows us to evaluate certain difficult trigonometric integrals by rational fractions. By a trigonometric identity,

$$\tan^2 \frac{\theta}{2} = \frac{1 - \cos \theta}{1 + \cos \theta}.$$

Replacing $\tan \theta/2$ by u and solving for $\cos \theta$, we have

$$\cos \theta = \frac{1 - u^2}{1 + u^2}.$$

Using the identity

$$\tan \frac{\theta}{2} = \frac{\sin \theta}{1 + \cos \theta},$$

replacing $\tan \theta/2$ by u, and $\cos \theta$ by $(1 - u^2)/(1 + u^2)$ gives

$$\sin \theta = \left(1 + \frac{1 - u^2}{1 + u^2}\right)u, \quad \text{or} \quad \sin \theta = \frac{2u}{1 + u^2}.$$

Finally let us consider the relation between the differentials du and $d\theta$. From the original substitution, $u = \tan(\theta/2)$, we have

$$\theta = 2 \text{ Arctan } u.$$

Thus

$$d\theta = \frac{2\,du}{1 + u^2}.$$

Summing up, the substitution $u = \tan \theta/2$ gives

$$\sin \theta = \frac{2u}{1 + u^2}, \quad \cos \theta = \frac{1 - u^2}{1 + u^2}, \quad \text{and} \quad d\theta = \frac{2\,du}{1 + u^2}.$$

Now any trigonometric expression can be expressed in terms of u.

Example 3

Evaluate $\int \frac{d\theta}{3 - 5 \sin \theta}$.

Using the substitution $u = \tan(\theta/2)$, we have

$$\int \frac{d\theta}{3 - 5 \sin \theta} = \int \frac{\frac{2\,du}{1 + u^2}}{3 - 5\frac{2u}{1 + u^2}}$$

$$= \int \frac{2\,du}{3u^2 - 10u + 3}$$

$$= \int \frac{2\,du}{(3u - 1)(u - 3)}.$$

By use of partial fractions, we get

$$\int \frac{d\theta}{3 - 5\sin\theta} = \int \left(-\frac{3}{4}\frac{1}{3u-1} + \frac{1}{4}\frac{1}{u-3} \right) du$$

$$= -\frac{1}{4}\ln|3u - 1| + \frac{1}{4}\ln|u - 3| + C$$

$$= \frac{1}{4}\ln\left|\frac{u-3}{3u-1}\right| + C$$

$$= \frac{1}{4}\ln\left|\frac{\tan\frac{\theta}{2} - 3}{3\tan\frac{\theta}{2} - 1}\right| + C.$$

Example 4

Evaluate $\int \frac{d\theta}{1 + \sin\theta + \cos\theta}$.

Again using the substitution

$$u = \tan\frac{\theta}{2},$$

we have

$$\int \frac{d\theta}{1 + \sin\theta + \cos\theta} = \int \frac{\frac{2\,du}{1+u^2}}{1 + \frac{2u}{1+u^2} + \frac{1-u^2}{1+u^2}}$$

$$= \int \frac{2\,du}{2u + 2}$$

$$= \int \frac{du}{u + 1}$$

$$= \ln|u + 1| + C$$

$$= \ln\left|\tan\frac{\theta}{2} + 1\right| + C.$$

Problems

Evaluate the following integrals.

1. $\int \frac{x\,dx}{x + 1 + \sqrt{x+1}}$.
2. $\int \frac{dx}{x + 2\sqrt{x-2}}$.
3. $\int \frac{\sqrt{x}\,dx}{2x + \sqrt{x}}$.
4. $\int \frac{dx}{(x+1)^2 + \sqrt{x+1}}$.
5. $\int \frac{dx}{\sqrt{x} - \sqrt[3]{x}}$.
6. $\int \frac{dx}{\sqrt{x} + \sqrt[4]{x}}$.

7. $\int \frac{dx}{x^{1/2}+x^{2/3}}$.

8. $\int \frac{dx}{x^{2/3}-x^{3/4}}$.

9. $\int \frac{\sqrt{x}+1}{\sqrt{x}-1}\,dx$.

10. $\int \frac{\sqrt[3]{x}+1}{\sqrt[3]{x}-1}\,dx$.

11. $\int \frac{\sqrt{3x+1}}{x-2}\,dx$.

12. $\int \frac{\sqrt[3]{2x+1}}{x}\,dx$.

13. $\int \frac{d\theta}{\sin\theta-\cos\theta+2}$.

14. $\int \frac{d\theta}{3\cos\theta-2\sin\theta+1}$.

15. $\int \frac{dx}{\cos x-3\sin x-9}$.

16. $\int \frac{dx}{\sin x+\cos x+2}$.

17. $\int \frac{d\theta}{\sin\theta+\cos\theta}$.

18. $\int \frac{d\theta}{\sin\theta-\cos\theta+1}$.

19. $\int \frac{\sqrt{1-x^2}}{x}\,dx$.

20. $\int \frac{x^3}{\sqrt{x^2+1}}\,dx$.

21. $\int x^3\sqrt{x^2-4}\,dx$.

22. $\int \frac{\sqrt{x^2+2x+2}}{x+1}\,dx$.

15.13

Conclusion

It is certainly clear by this time that integration is considerably more difficult than differentiation. Moreover the methods of this chapter will not allow us to integrate all functions. In fact, there are some functions that cannot be integrated in finite terms; that is, there is no expression involving any finite combination of the algebraic or the transcendental functions we have considered that has one of these functions for derivative. For instance, none of the following can be integrated in finite terms:

$$\int \sin x^2\,dx, \qquad \int e^{-x^2}\,dx, \qquad \int \frac{dx}{\ln x},$$

$$\int x\tan x\,dx, \qquad \int \frac{\sin x}{x}\,dx, \qquad \int \frac{dx}{\sqrt{1+x^3}}.$$

We shall consider integrals of this type in Chapter 19, which deals with infinite series. Of course, when appropriate limits of integration are given, these integrals can be approximated as closely as we wish by, say, Simpson's rule or the trapezoidal rule.

Further Applications of the Integral

16.1

Improper Integrals

We saw in Chapter 8 that the integral can be used to determine the amount of work done in a physical problem as well as to find the area of a plane region. Before going on to further applications of the integral, let us extend the definition of the integral to include infinite limits and infinite integrands.

Suppose we consider the integral

$$\int_1^k \frac{dx}{x^2},$$

where $k > 1$. This integral can be evaluated to give

$$\int_1^k \frac{dx}{x^2} = -\frac{1}{x}\bigg|_1^k = 1 - \frac{1}{k}.$$

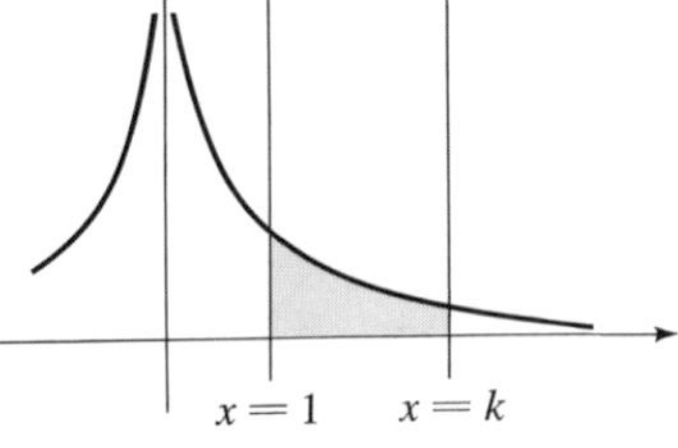

Figure 16.1

We now have the value of the integral for any value of $k\,(k > 1)$ we choose. Interpreting the integral geometrically, we see that it represents the area of the region bounded by $y = 1/x^2$, the x axis, and the vertical lines $x = 1$ and $x = k$ (see Figure 16.1). As k takes on larger and larger values, the area increases, getting closer and closer to the number 1; that is,

$$\lim_{k \to +\infty} \int_1^k \frac{dx}{x^2} = \lim_{k \to +\infty} \left(1 - \frac{1}{k}\right) = 1.$$

We shall represent the above limit by

$$\int_1^{+\infty} \frac{dx}{x^2}$$

and take it to be the area of the region between $y = 1/x^2$ and $y = 0$ and to the right of $x = 1$. More generally, we make the following definition.

Definition

$$\int_a^{+\infty} f(x)\,dx = \lim_{k \to +\infty} \int_a^k f(x)\,dx$$

and

$$\int_{-\infty}^{a} f(x)\,dx = \lim_{k \to -\infty} \int_k^a f(x)\,dx$$

whenever these limits exist.

Example 1

Evaluate $\int_{-\infty}^{0} e^x\,dx$.

$$\begin{aligned}\int_{-\infty}^{0} e^x\,dx &= \lim_{k \to -\infty} \int_k^0 e^x\,dx \\ &= \lim_{k \to -\infty} e^x \Big|_k^0 \\ &= \lim_{k \to -\infty} (1 - e^k) \\ &= 1.\end{aligned}$$

Example 2

Evaluate $\int_1^{+\infty} \frac{dx}{x}$.

$$\begin{aligned}\int_1^{+\infty} \frac{dx}{x} &= \lim_{k \to +\infty} \int_1^k \frac{dx}{x} \\ &= \lim_{k \to +\infty} \ln|x| \Big|_1^k \\ &= \lim_{k \to +\infty} \ln k \\ &= +\infty.\end{aligned}$$

Although the graphs of $y = 1/x$ and $y = 1/x^2$ are quite similar for x positive, we have seen that

$$\int_1^{+\infty} \frac{dx}{x^2} = 1, \quad \text{but} \quad \int_1^{+\infty} \frac{dx}{x} = +\infty.$$

Why should this be so when both have the x axis for a horizontal asymptote? We can see that the mere fact that $f(x)$ approaches 0 as x approaches $+\infty$ is not enough to guarantee the existence of $\int_a^{+\infty} f(x)\,dx$. The difference is that $1/x^2$ is approaching zero faster than $1/x$. In this case, the difference is enough to give a value of 1 for one of the integrals, while the other is infinite.

Let us now turn our attention to the integral

$$\int_\epsilon^1 \frac{dx}{\sqrt{x}}, \quad \text{where } 0 < \epsilon < 1.$$

Again, we can evaluate this integral for any allowable value of ϵ.

$$\int_\epsilon^1 \frac{dx}{\sqrt{x}} = 2\sqrt{x}\,\Big|_\epsilon^1$$
$$= 2 - 2\sqrt{\epsilon}.$$

Interpreted geometrically, the result represents the area of the region bounded by $y = 1/\sqrt{x}$, the x axis, and the vertical lines $x = \epsilon$ and $x = 1$ (see Figure 16.2). Again the area increases as ϵ approaches 0. In fact,

$$\lim_{\epsilon\to 0^+} \int_\epsilon^1 \frac{dx}{\sqrt{x}} = \lim_{\epsilon\to 0^+} (2 - 2\sqrt{\epsilon})$$
$$= 2.$$

This limit can be interpreted as the area of the region bounded by $y = 1/\sqrt{x}$, the x axis, and the vertical lines $x = 0$ and $x = 1$ or as

$$\int_0^1 \frac{dx}{\sqrt{x}}.$$

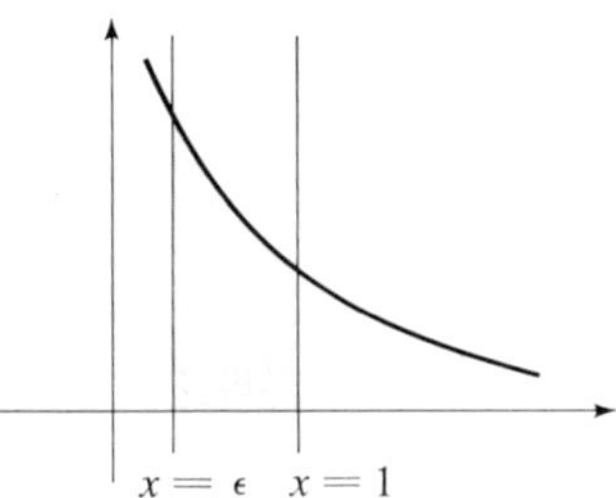

Figure 16.2

Definition

If f is continuous for $a < x \le b$ and if $x = a$ is a vertical asymptote, then

$$\int_a^b f(x)\,dx = \lim_{\epsilon\to 0^+} \int_{a+\epsilon}^b f(x)\,dx.$$

If f is continuous for $a \le x < b$ and $x = b$ is a vertical asymptote, then

$$\int_a^b f(x)\,dx = \lim_{\epsilon\to 0^+} \int_a^{b-\epsilon} f(x)\,dx.$$

If f is continuous for $a \le x < c$ and $c < x \le b$ and $x = c$ is a vertical asymptote, then

$$\int_a^b f(x)\,dx = \int_a^c f(x)\,dx + \int_c^b f(x)\,dx.$$

Similar definitions can be given when there are two or more (up to any finite number k) vertical asymptotes. Note that the definition of

$$\int_a^b f(x)\,dx$$

that was given in Chapter 8 (see page 149) considered bounded functions only.

Example 3

Evaluate $\int_0^1 \frac{dx}{x}$.

$$\begin{aligned}\int_0^1 \frac{dx}{x} &= \lim_{\epsilon\to 0+} \int_\epsilon^1 \frac{dx}{x}\\ &= \lim_{\epsilon\to 0+} \ln x\Big|_\epsilon^1\\ &= \lim_{\epsilon\to 0+} (-\ln \epsilon)\\ &= +\infty.\end{aligned}$$

Example 4

Evaluate $\int_0^1 \frac{dx}{(x-1)^{2/3}}$.

$$\begin{aligned}\int_0^1 \frac{dx}{(x-1)^{2/3}} &= \lim_{\epsilon\to 0+} \int_0^{1-\epsilon} \frac{dx}{(x-1)^{2/3}}\\ &= \lim_{\epsilon\to 0+} 3(x-1)^{1/3}\Big|_0^{1-\epsilon}\\ &= \lim_{\epsilon\to 0+} (3-3\epsilon^{1/3})\\ &= 3.\end{aligned}$$

Note that in the example above we used the definition of an improper integral to give

$$\int_0^1 \frac{dx}{(x-1)^{2/3}} = \lim_{\epsilon\to 0^+} \int_0^{1-\epsilon} \frac{dx}{(x-1)^{2/3}}.$$

We could just as well have used

$$\int_0^1 \frac{dx}{(x-1)^{2/3}} = \lim_{\epsilon\to 0^-} \int_0^{1+\epsilon} \frac{dx}{(x-1)^{2/3}}.$$

In the first case, we have $1-\epsilon < 1$, since $\epsilon > 0$; in the second, $1+\epsilon < 1$, since $\epsilon < 0$.

Example 5

Evaluate $\int_0^3 \frac{dx}{(x-1)^2}$.

In this case the vertical asymptote does not correspond to either end point of the interval of integration but rather to some value of x ($x = 1$) between 0 and 3. Thus

$$\begin{aligned}\int_0^3 \frac{dx}{(x-1)^2} &= \int_0^1 \frac{dx}{(x-1)^2} + \int_1^3 \frac{dx}{(x-1)^2}\\ &= \lim_{\epsilon\to 0+} \int_0^{1-\epsilon} \frac{dx}{(x-1)^2} + \lim_{\delta\to 0+} \int_{1+\delta}^3 \frac{dx}{(x-1)^2}\\ &= \lim_{\epsilon\to 0+} \frac{-1}{x-1}\Big|_0^{1-\epsilon} + \lim_{\delta\to 0+} \frac{-1}{x-1}\Big|_{1+\delta}^3\\ &= \lim_{\epsilon\to 0+} \left(\frac{1}{\epsilon} - 1\right) + \lim_{\delta\to 0+} \left(\frac{1}{\delta} - \frac{1}{2}\right).\end{aligned}$$

Neither limit exists (they are both $+\infty$); therefore

$$\int_0^3 \frac{dx}{(x-1)^2}$$

does not exist.

Some care must be taken to find this vertical asymptote and to take it into consideration when evaluating the integral. If it had not been considered here, we would have had the following *erroneous* result.

$$\int_0^3 \frac{dx}{(x-1)^2} = \left.\frac{-1}{x-1}\right|_0^3$$
$$= -\frac{3}{2}, \text{ which is false.}$$

Example 6

Evaluate $\displaystyle\int_{-1}^{1} \frac{dx}{x}$.

Again the vertical asymptote is at $x=0$, which is between -1 and 1. Thus,

$$\begin{aligned}\int_{-1}^{1} \frac{dx}{x} &= \int_{-1}^{0} \frac{dx}{x} + \int_{0}^{1} \frac{dx}{x} \\ &= \lim_{\epsilon\to 0+} \int_{-1}^{-\epsilon} \frac{dx}{x} + \lim_{\delta\to 0+} \int_{\delta}^{1} \frac{dx}{x} \\ &= \lim_{\epsilon\to 0+} \ln|x|\Big|_{-1}^{-\epsilon} + \lim_{\delta\to 0+} \ln|x|\Big|_{\delta}^{1} \\ &= \lim_{\epsilon\to 0+} \ln\epsilon + \lim_{\delta\to 0+} (-\ln\delta).\end{aligned}$$

Again, neither limit exists, since

$$\lim_{\epsilon\to 0+} \ln\epsilon = -\infty \quad \text{and} \quad \lim_{\delta\to 0+} (-\ln\delta) = +\infty.$$

Thus $\int_{-1}^{1} dx/x$ does not exist.

One might be tempted to consider this last case in a somewhat different light than the previous example. Since one of the two limits is $+\infty$ and the other is $-\infty$, there is the temptation to say that the given integral is zero. In fact, one might argue further that since

$$\lim_{\delta\to 0^+} \int_{\delta}^{1} \frac{dx}{x} = \lim_{\epsilon\to 0^+} \int_{\epsilon}^{1} \frac{dx}{x},$$

it then follows that

$$\begin{aligned}\int_{-1}^{1} \frac{dx}{x} &= \int_{-1}^{0} \frac{dx}{x} + \int_{0}^{1} \frac{dx}{x} \\ &= \lim_{\epsilon\to 0^+} \int_{-1}^{-\epsilon} \frac{dx}{x} + \lim_{\epsilon\to 0^+} \int_{\epsilon}^{1} \frac{dx}{x} \\ &= \lim_{\epsilon\to 0^+} \left(\int_{-1}^{-\epsilon} \frac{dx}{x} + \int_{\epsilon}^{1} \frac{dx}{x}\right) \\ &= \lim_{\epsilon\to 0^+} [\ln\epsilon + (-\ln\epsilon)] \\ &= \lim_{\epsilon\to 0^+} 0 \\ &= 0.\end{aligned}$$

This result is incorrect, because we are misapplying the statement

$$\lim_{x\to a} f(x) + \lim_{x\to a} g(x) = \lim_{x\to a} [f(x) + g(x)],$$

which is true, provided

$$\lim_{x\to a} f(x) \quad \text{and} \quad \lim_{x\to a} g(x)$$

both exist. In our case, neither

$$\lim_{\epsilon\to 0^+} \int_{-1}^{-\epsilon} \frac{dx}{x} \quad \text{nor} \quad \lim_{\epsilon\to 0^+} \int_{\epsilon}^{1} \frac{dx}{x}$$

exists; one is $+\infty$ and the other $-\infty$, both of which are special types of nonexistence.

Remember that if

$$\int_a^b f(x)\,dx = \int_a^c f(x)\,dx + \int_c^b f(x)\,dx,$$

then, in order to have $\int_a^b f(x)\,dx$ exist, *both integrals on the right must exist.* In this connection, it might also be noted that the results in Problem 21, page 152, hold if f is *continuous* on the interval $[-a, a]$; that is, $\int_{-a}^{a} f(x)\,dx = 0$ if f is odd and *continuous* on $[-a, a]$.

Problems

In Problems 1–20, evaluate the given integrals.

1. $\displaystyle\int_2^{+\infty} \frac{dx}{x^3}$.
2. $\displaystyle\int_{-\infty}^{-1} \frac{dx}{x}$.
3. $\displaystyle\int_1^{+\infty} \frac{dx}{(x+1)^2}$.
4. $\displaystyle\int_2^{+\infty} \frac{dx}{(x-1)^3}$.
5. $\displaystyle\int_1^{+\infty} \frac{dx}{2x+1}$.
6. $\displaystyle\int_{-\infty}^{0} \frac{dx}{(3x-1)^2}$.
7. $\displaystyle\int_1^{+\infty} \frac{dx}{\sqrt{2x-1}}$.
8. $\displaystyle\int_1^{+\infty} e^{-x}\,dx$.
9. $\displaystyle\int_1^{2} \frac{dx}{\sqrt{x-1}}$.
10. $\displaystyle\int_{-1}^{0} \frac{dx}{x}$.
11. $\displaystyle\int_{-1}^{0} \frac{dx}{(x+1)^3}$.
12. $\displaystyle\int_{-1}^{0} \frac{dx}{\sqrt[3]{2x+1}}$.
13. $\displaystyle\int_0^{2} \frac{dx}{(3x-1)^{2/3}}$.
14. $\displaystyle\int_0^{1} \frac{\ln x}{x}\,dx$.
15. $\displaystyle\int_0^{\pi/2} \tan x\,dx$.
16. $\displaystyle\int_{-1}^{0} \frac{dx}{\sqrt[3]{x}}$.
17. $\displaystyle\int_0^{+\infty} \frac{dx}{\sqrt{x}}$.
18. $\displaystyle\int_0^{+\infty} \frac{dx}{x^2}$.
19. $\displaystyle\int_{-\infty}^{+\infty} \frac{dx}{x^2+1}$.
20. $\displaystyle\int_{-1}^{1} \frac{dx}{x^2-1}$.

In Problems 21–26, find the area of the region bounded by the given curves.

21. $y = e^{-x}$, $y = 0$, right of $x = 0$.
22. $y = \dfrac{1}{\sqrt{x}}$, $y = 0$, between $x = 0$ and $x = 4$.
23. $y = \dfrac{1}{x^2}$, $y = 0$, right of $x = 2$.
24. $y = \dfrac{1}{x^2}$, $y = 0$, between $x = 0$ and $x = 2$.
25. $y = \dfrac{1}{(x-1)^{1/3}}$, $y = 0$, between $x = 0$ and $x = 2$.

26. $y = \dfrac{1}{\sqrt{x-1}}$, $y = 0$, right of $x = 5$.

27. Show that $\int_1^{+\infty} \dfrac{dx}{x^n}$ exists if and only if $n > 1$.

28. Show that $\int_0^1 \dfrac{dx}{x^n}$ exists if and only if $n < 1$.

16.2

Areas in Polar Coordinates

The problem of finding areas in polar coordinates is solved in basically the same way that it was in rectangular coordinates. Suppose we have a region bounded by $r = f(\theta)$ and the terminal sides of the angles α and β, where $\alpha < \beta$ (see Figure 16.3). Let us subdivide the (angular) interval $[\alpha, \beta]$ into n subintervals

$$\alpha = \theta_0, \theta_1, \theta_2, \ldots, \theta_n = \beta.$$

Now, for each value of i from 1 to n, let us choose θ_i^* such that

$$\theta_{i-1} \leq \theta_i^* \leq \theta_i.$$

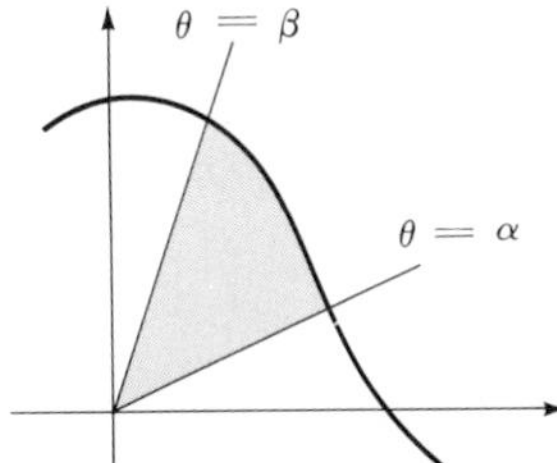

Figure 16.3

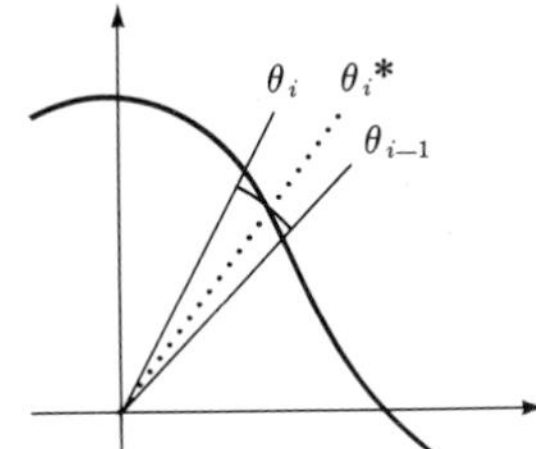

Figure 16.4

A typical such interval might look like the one in Figure 16.4. We can approximate the area within the ith subinterval by the area of a sector. Let us recall that the area of a sector of angle θ (in radians) and radius r is

$$\frac{1}{2}\theta r^2.$$

The angle of our sector is $\theta_i - \theta_{i-1}$, and we shall take the radius to be $f(\theta_i^*)$. Thus the area of the ith sector is

$$\frac{1}{2}(\theta_i - \theta_{i-1})[f(\theta_i^*)]^2,$$

and the sum of all of these areas is

$$\sum_{i=1}^{n} \frac{1}{2}(\theta_i - \theta_{i-1})[f(\theta_i^*)]^2, \quad \text{or} \quad \sum_{i=1}^{n} \frac{1}{2}[f(\theta_i^*)]^2 \, \Delta\theta_i,$$

where $\Delta\theta_i = \theta_i - \theta_{i-1}$. By taking the limit, we arrive at the desired area, which, by the definition of an integral is

$$A = \int_\alpha^\beta \frac{1}{2}[f(\theta)]^2 \, d\theta, \quad \text{or} \quad A = \int_\alpha^\beta \frac{1}{2} r^2 \, d\theta$$

(provided this integral exists). Of course it can be shown (although we shall not attempt to do so) that the area found in this way is the same as the area as defined in Chapter 8.

Example 1

Find the area in the first quadrant within $r = 1 - \cos\theta$.

The interval from $\theta = 0$ to $\theta = \pi/2$ is subdivided into intervals, and the area within each is approximated by the area of a sector (see Figure 16.5). The limit of the sum gives the integral

$$\begin{aligned}
\int_0^{\pi/2} \frac{1}{2} r^2 \, d\theta
&= \int_0^{\pi/2} \frac{1}{2}(1 - \cos\theta)^2 \, d\theta \\
&= \frac{1}{2}\int_0^{\pi/2} (1 - 2\cos\theta + \cos^2\theta) \, d\theta \\
&= \frac{1}{2}\int_0^{\pi/2} \left(1 - 2\cos\theta + \frac{1 + \cos 2\theta}{2}\right) d\theta \\
&= \frac{1}{2}\int_0^{\pi/2} \left(\frac{3}{2} - 2\cos\theta + \frac{1}{4}\cdot 2\cos 2\theta\right) d\theta \\
&= \frac{1}{2}\left(\frac{3}{2}\theta - 2\sin\theta + \frac{1}{4}\sin 2\theta\right)\Bigg|_0^{\pi/2} \\
&= \frac{3\pi - 8}{8}.
\end{aligned}$$

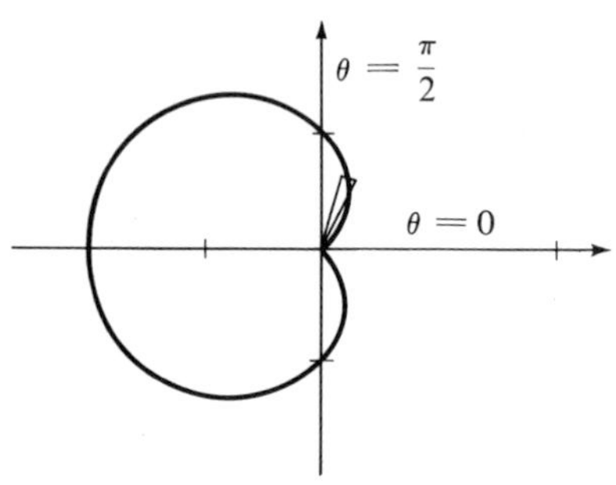

Figure 16.5

Example 2

Find the area within the inner loop of

$$r = 1 - 2\sin\theta.$$

The graph of $r = 1 - 2\sin\theta$ is given in Figure 16.6. The inner loop is determined by the interval $[\pi/6, 5\pi/6]$. The end points of this interval are found by noting that $r = 0$ at the ends of the loop. Thus

$$0 = 1 - 2\sin\theta,$$

$$\sin\theta = \frac{1}{2},$$

$$\theta = \pi/6, 5\pi/6.$$

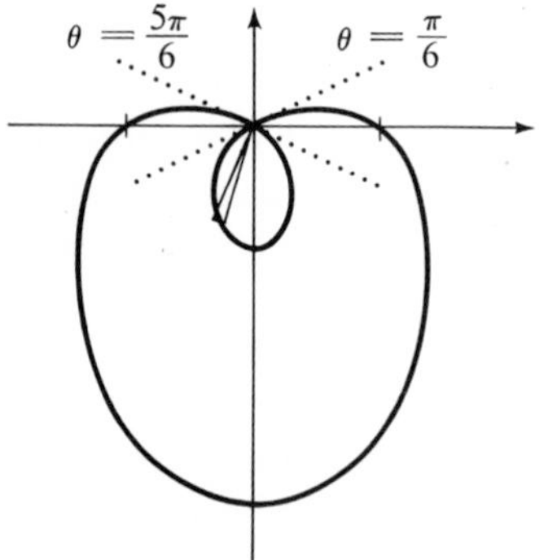

Figure 16.6

Although r is negative for all values of θ in $(\pi/6, 5\pi/6)$, we need not change the sign, since we use r^2 in the integral and r^2 is never negative. Thus

$$\begin{aligned}
A &= \int_{\pi/6}^{5\pi/6} \frac{1}{2} r^2 \, d\theta \\
&= \frac{1}{2} \int_{\pi/6}^{5\pi/6} (1 - 2 \sin \theta)^2 \, d\theta \\
&= \frac{1}{2} \int_{\pi/6}^{5\pi/6} (1 - 4 \sin \theta + 4 \sin^2 \theta) \, d\theta \\
&= \frac{1}{2} \int_{\pi/6}^{5\pi/6} \left(1 - 4 \sin \theta + 4 \cdot \frac{1 - \cos 2\theta}{2}\right) d\theta \\
&= \frac{1}{2} \int_{\pi/6}^{5\pi/6} (3 - 4 \sin \theta - 2 \cos 2\theta) \, d\theta \\
&= \frac{1}{2} (3\theta + 4 \cos \theta - \sin 2\theta) \Big|_{\pi/6}^{5\pi/6} \\
&= \frac{2\pi - 3\sqrt{3}}{2}.
\end{aligned}$$

Since the loop is symmetric about the y axis, we could have found the area of half of the loop (by integrating from $\theta = \pi/6$ to $\theta = \pi/2$) and then doubled the result.

Example 3

Find the area of the region inside both $r = \sin \theta$ and $r = 1 - \sin \theta$.

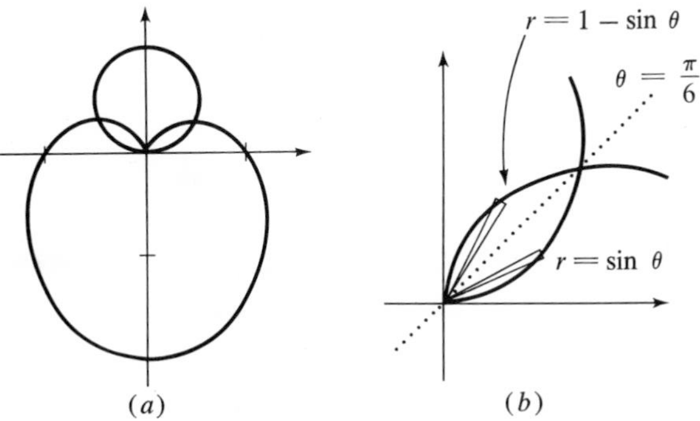

Figure 16.7

The graphs of these two equations are given in (a) of Figure 16.7. Since they are symmetric about the y axis, let us find the area in the first quadrant and double. We can see from (b) that the approximating sectors have their ends on either $r = \sin \theta$ or $r = 1 - \sin \theta$, depending upon the value of θ. For $0 \leq \theta \leq \pi/6$, the ends are on $r = \sin \theta$; for $\pi/6 \leq \theta \leq \pi/2$, the ends are on $r = 1 - \sin \theta$.

Thus the area is

$$A = 2\left[\int_0^{\pi/6} \frac{1}{2}\sin^2\theta\,d\theta + \int_{\pi/6}^{\pi/2} \frac{1}{2}(1-\sin\theta)^2\,d\theta\right]$$

$$= \int_0^{\pi/6} \frac{1-\cos 2\theta}{2}\,d\theta + \int_{\pi/6}^{\pi/2} (1 - 2\sin\theta + \sin^2\theta)\,d\theta$$

$$= \int_0^{\pi/6} \frac{1-\cos 2\theta}{2}\,d\theta + \int_{\pi/6}^{\pi/2} \left(1 - 2\sin\theta + \frac{1-\cos 2\theta}{2}\right)d\theta$$

$$= \int_0^{\pi/6} \left(\frac{1}{2} - \frac{1}{2}\cos 2\theta\right)d\theta + \int_{\pi/6}^{\pi/2} \left(\frac{3}{2} - 2\sin\theta - \frac{1}{2}\cos 2\theta\right)d\theta$$

$$= \left(\frac{1}{2}\theta - \frac{1}{4}\sin 2\theta\right)\Bigg|_0^{\pi/6} + \left(\frac{3}{2}\theta + 2\cos\theta - \frac{1}{4}\sin 2\theta\right)\Bigg|_{\pi/6}^{\pi/2}$$

$$= \frac{2\pi - 3\sqrt{3}}{24} + \frac{4\pi - 7\sqrt{3}}{8}$$

$$= \frac{7\pi}{12} - \sqrt{3}.$$

Problems

Find the area of the region described.

1. Inside $r = 2\sin\theta$.
2. Inside $r = \sin 2\theta$.
3. Inside $r = 1 + \cos\theta$.
4. Inside $r = 2 + \cos\theta$.
5. Inside $r = \sqrt{\sin\theta}$.
6. Inside $r^2 = \sin\theta$.
7. Inside $r = \sin\theta + \cos\theta$.
8. Inside $r = \sin\theta - \cos\theta$.
9. Inside $r = 3 - \sin\theta$.
10. Inside the inner loop of $r = 1 + 2\sin\theta$.
11. Inside $r^2 = 4\sin 2\theta$.
12. Inside $r^2 = 9\cos 3\theta$.
13. Inside $r = 1$ and $r = 1 + \cos\theta$.
14. Inside $r = 1$ and $r = 2\sin 2\theta$.
15. Inside $r = 1 + \cos\theta$ and $r = 1 + \sin\theta$.
16. Inside $r = 1 + \cos\theta$ and $r = 3\cos\theta$.
17. Inside $r = 1 + \sin\theta$ and outside $r = 1$.
18. Inside $r = 1 - \sin\theta$ and outside $r = 2\cos\theta$.
19. Inside $r = \sin\theta$ and $r = \sin 2\theta$.
20. Inside $r = 1$ and $r = 2\sin\theta$.

16.3

Volumes of Solids of Revolution: Disc Method

Suppose the region bounded by $y = f(x)$, the x axis, and the vertical lines $x = a$ and $x = b$ is rotated about the x axis (see Figure 16.8). What is the volume of the resulting solid? In order to answer this question, let us cut up the original plane region into vertical strips and rotate them along with the region. The result is a series of discs approximating the solid region.

Let us consider the ith disc. The original interval $[a, b]$ has been cut into subintervals by the subdivision

$$a = x_0, x_1, x_2, \ldots, x_n = b.$$

The ith subinterval is $[x_{i-1}, x_i]$, and a number x_i^* has been selected in this subinterval. Thus we have a rectangle of width $\Delta x_i = x_i - x_{i-1}$ and height $f(x_i^*)$. After rotation about the x axis, the rectangle sweeps out a cylinder with radius $f(x_i^*)$ and height Δx_i. Thus its volume is

$$\pi[f(x_i^*)]^2 \, \Delta x_i,$$

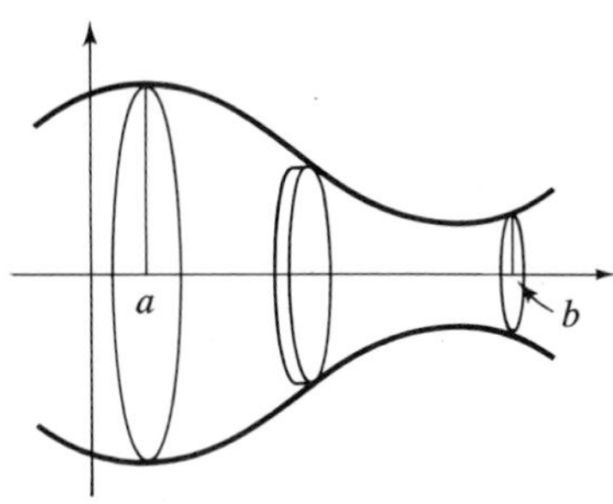

Figure 16.8

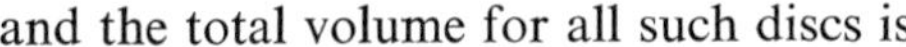

and the total volume for all such discs is

$$\sum_{i=1}^{n} \pi[f(x_i^*)]^2 \, \Delta x_i .$$

This is only an approximation of the original volume—the actual volume may be found by taking the limit of this expression as the norm of the subdivision, $\|S\|$, approaches zero. This limit is an integral.

$$\begin{aligned} V &= \lim_{\|S\| \to 0} \sum_{i=1}^{n} \pi[f(x_i^*)]^2 \, \Delta x_i \\ &= \int_a^b \pi[f(x)]^2 \, dx. \end{aligned}$$

The foregoing discussion does *not* constitute a proof that the formula gives the desired volume. In fact, we have not even *defined* "volume." If we were to try to do so, we should find ourselves in the same position as when we tried to define area—we have to define it in terms of an integral. We shall not attempt to give a formal definition here, but it is clear that we could do so (at least for solids of revolution).

What has been noted here holds throughout this chapter: namely, the discussions given are not intended as *proofs*—but simply to make the given applications of integration seem plausible.

Example 1

The region bounded by $y = x^2$, the x axis, and $x = 1$ is rotated about the x axis. Find the volume of the resulting solid.

A vertical strip in the original region would give the disc shown in Figure 16.9. Thus,

$$\begin{aligned} V &= \int_0^1 \pi y^2 \, dx \\ &= \pi \int_0^1 x^4 \, dx \\ &= \frac{\pi x^5}{5} \Big|_0^1 \\ &= \frac{\pi}{5}. \end{aligned}$$

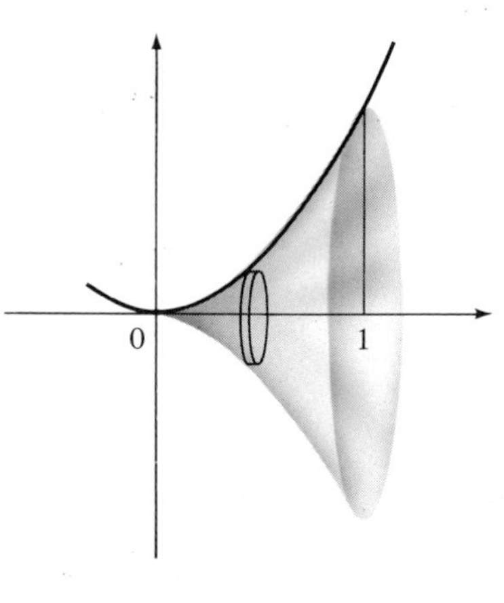

Figure 16.9

Although the above example fits the given integration formula perfectly, it is recommended that you do *not* memorize the formula. The only thing you need to memorize is the formula for the volume of a cylinder. Furthermore, it is best for you to draw a figure, including the disc, because the plane region can be rotated about *any* line—not merely about the x axis. It would be too difficult to try to catalog all possibilities and memorize a formula for each.

Example 2

The region bounded by $y = x^2$, the y axis, and $y = 1$ is rotated about the y axis. Find the volume of the resulting solid.

If the plane region is subdivided into horizontal strips and these are rotated about the y axis, we have discs with radius x and height Δy (see Figure 16.10). Thus,

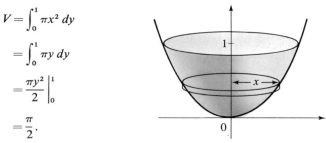

$$\begin{aligned} V &= \int_0^1 \pi x^2 \, dy \\ &= \int_0^1 \pi y \, dy \\ &= \frac{\pi y^2}{2}\bigg|_0^1 \\ &= \frac{\pi}{2}. \end{aligned}$$

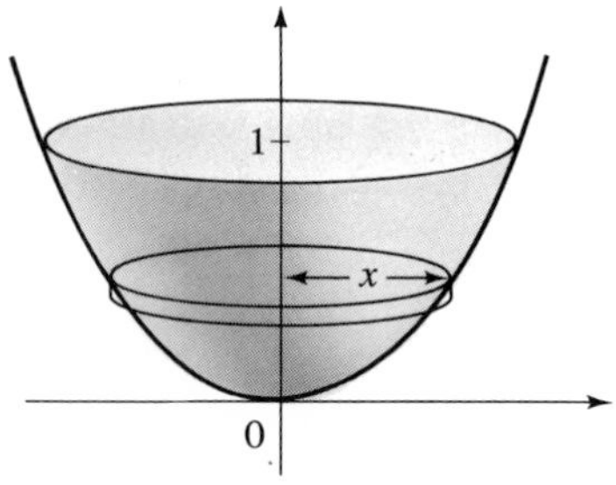

Figure 16.10

Example 3

Suppose the region of Example 1 is rotated about the line $x = 1$. Find the volume of the resulting solid.

A horizontal strip, when rotated (see Figure 16.11), gives a cylinder with radius $1 - x$ and height Δy. Thus

$$\begin{aligned} V &= \int_0^1 \pi(1 - x)^2 \, dy \\ &= \int_0^1 \pi(1 - \sqrt{y})^2 \, dy \\ &= \pi \int_0^1 (1 - 2\sqrt{y} + y) \, dy \\ &= \pi\left(y - \frac{4}{3} y^{3/2} + \frac{1}{2} y^2\right)\bigg|_0^1 \\ &= \frac{\pi}{6}. \end{aligned}$$

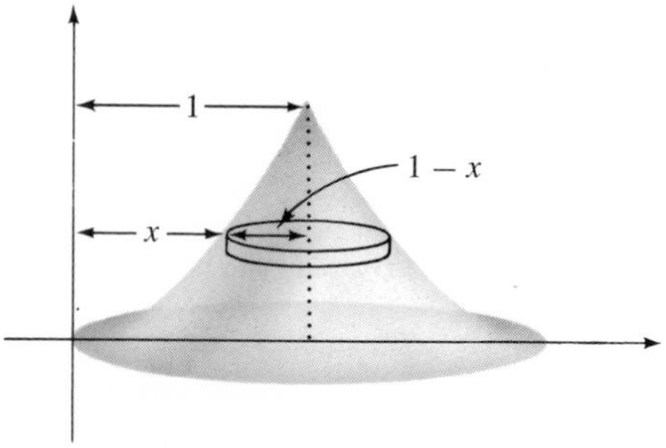

Figure 16.11

Example 4

Suppose the region of Example 1 is rotated about the y axis. Find the volume of the resulting solid.

If a horizontal strip is rotated about the y axis, the result is not a solid disc but a disc with a hole in it (see Figure 16.12). In order to find the volume of the disc with a hole in it, we simply find the volume of a solid disc and subtract the volume of the hole. If r and R are the smaller and larger radii, respectively, and h is the thickness of the disc, then

$$\begin{aligned} V &= \pi R^2 h - \pi r^2 h \\ &= \pi(R^2 - r^2)h. \end{aligned}$$

In our case the larger radius is 1, the smaller is x, and the thickness is Δy. Thus the volume of the disc is

$$v = \pi(1 - x^2)\,\Delta y,$$

and the volume of the solid is

$$\begin{aligned} V &= \int_0^1 \pi(1 - x^2)\,dy \\ &= \pi \int_0^1 (1 - y)\,dy \\ &= \pi\left(y - \frac{y^2}{2}\right)\Bigg|_0^1 \\ &= \frac{\pi}{2}. \end{aligned}$$

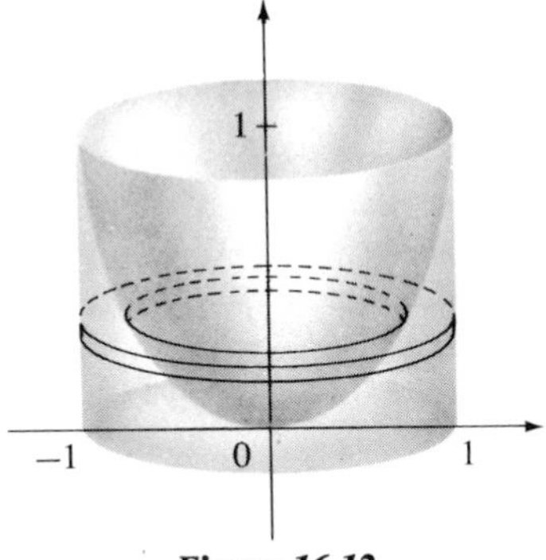

Figure 16.12

Problems

In Problems 1–10, the region bounded by the given curves is rotated about the x axis. Find the volume of the resulting solid.

1. $y = x^3$, x axis, $x = 1$.
2. $y = x^4$, x axis, $x = 1$.
3. $y = x^2 - x$, x axis.
4. $y = x^3 - x$, x axis, between $x = -1$ and $x = 1$.
5. $y = \sin x$, x axis, between $x = 0$ and $x = \pi$.
6. $y = e^x$, x axis, left of the y axis.
7. $y = \ln x$, x axis, between $x = 1$ and $x = e$.
8. $y = 1/x$, x axis, right of $x = 1$.
9. $y = x$, $y = x^2$.
10. $y = x$, $y = x^3$ (first quadrant).

In Problems 11–20, the region bounded by the given curves is rotated about the y axis. Find the volume of the resulting solid.

11. $y = x^3$, y axis, $y = 1$.
12. $y = x^4$, y axis, $y = 1$ (first quadrant).
13. $y = \cos x$, x axis, between $x = 0$ and $x = \pi/2$.
14. $y = \sin x$, x axis, between $x = 0$ and $x = \pi$.
15. $y = x^2 - x$, x axis.
16. $y = e^x$, x axis, left of the y axis. (Hint: $\lim_{\epsilon \to 0} \epsilon \ln \epsilon = 0$ and $\lim_{\epsilon \to 0} \epsilon \ln^2 \epsilon = 0$.)
17. $y = \ln x$, x axis, between $x = 0$ and $x = 1$.
18. $y = x^3$, x axis, $x = 1$.
19. $y = x$, $y = x^2$.
20. $y = x$, $y = x^3$ (first quadrant).

In Problems 21–30, the region bounded by the given curves is rotated about the line indicated. Find the volume of the resulting solid.

21. $y = x^3$, x axis, $x = 1$; about $x = 1$.
22. $y = x^3$, y axis, $y = 1$; about $y = 1$.
23. $y = x^3$, x axis, $x = 1$; about $y = 1$.
24. $y = \cos x$, x axis, between $x = 0$ and $x = \pi/2$; about $y = 1$.
25. $y = \cos x$, x axis, between $x = 0$ and $x = \pi/2$; about $x = \pi$.
26. $y = 1 - x$, both axes; about $x = 2$.
27. $x^2 + y^2 - 2x = 0$; about the y axis.
28. $x^2 + y^2 - 4x + 3 = 0$; about the y axis.
29. $y = x$, $y = x^2$; about $x = 1$.
30. $y = x$, $y = x^2$; about $y = x$.
31. Find the volume of a sphere of radius r.
32. Find the volume of a cone of radius r and height h.
33. Find the area of the region bounded by $y = 1/x$, $y = -1/x$ and to the right of $x = 1$. Find the volume of the solid generated by rotating this region about the x axis.

16.4

Volumes of Solids of Revolution: Shell Method

In Example 4 of the previous section we had the region bounded by $y = x^2$, the x axis, and $x = 1$ and rotated about the y axis. In that case we noted that a horizontal strip, when rotated about the y axis, generates a disc with a hole in it. Let us now consider what happens if a vertical strip is used. The result is a hollow shell (see Figure 16.13) much like a tin can with both ends removed. This shell is a cylinder with a cylindrical hole in it—its volume is easily found.

Let R_1 and R_2 be the radii of the inner and outer cylinders, respectively, and let h be the height. Then $R = (R_1 + R_2)/2$ is the average radius and $t = R_2 - R_1$ is the thickness of the shell. Thus, the volume is

$$\begin{aligned} V &= \pi R_2^2 h - \pi R_1^2 h \\ &= \pi h(R_2^2 - R_1^2) \\ &= \pi h(R_2 + R_1)(R_2 - R_1) \\ &= 2\pi h \frac{R_1 + R_2}{2}(R_2 - R_1) \\ &= 2\pi R h t. \end{aligned}$$

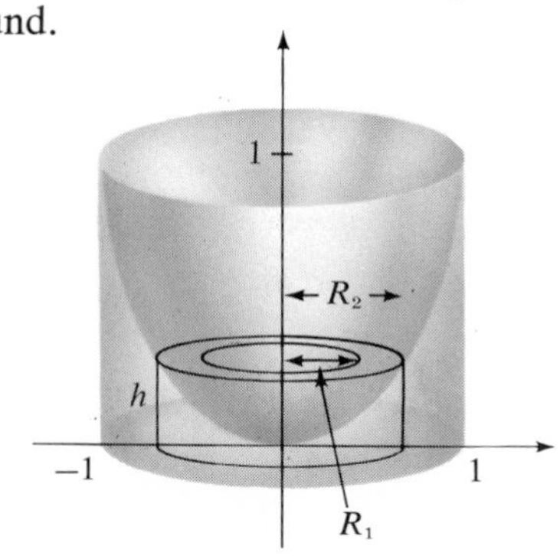

Figure 16.13

Another way of considering this volume is to imagine that the shell has been cut on one side from top to bottom and rolled flat. Then we have a flat plate with length h and width $2\pi R$ (the circumference of the cylinder) and thickness t. Its volume is

$$V = 2\pi R h t.$$

Example 1

Use the shell method to find the volume of the solid of Example 4 of the previous section.

From Figure 16.13 we have $R = x$, $h = y$, and $t = \Delta x$. Thus

$$\begin{aligned} V &= \int_0^1 2\pi xy \, dx \\ &= \int_0^1 2\pi x^3 \, dx \\ &= \frac{\pi x^4}{2} \bigg|_0^1 \\ &= \frac{\pi}{2}. \end{aligned}$$

One advantage this method has over the disc method is that the same formula may be used for the volume in any case—whether the original solid has a hole in it or not. We have seen a case in which the solid has a hole; let us consider the other case.

Example 2

Use the shell method to find the volume of the solid of Example 2 of the previous section.

From Figure 16.14 we see that a vertical strip, when rotated, gives a shell with radius x, height $1 - y$, and thickness Δx. Thus

$$\begin{aligned} V &= \int_0^1 2\pi x(1 - y) \, dx \\ &= 2\pi \int_0^1 x(1 - x^2) \, dx \\ &= 2\pi \int_0^1 (x - x^3) \, dx \\ &= 2\pi \left(\frac{x^2}{2} - \frac{x^4}{4} \right) \bigg|_0^1 \\ &= \frac{\pi}{2}. \end{aligned}$$

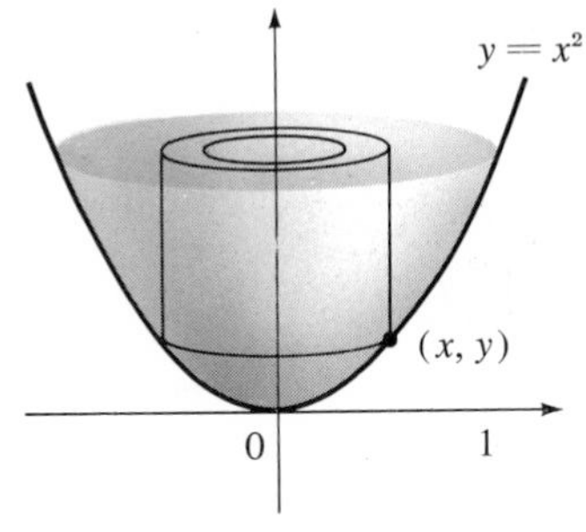

Figure 16.14

In many cases it is difficult, or impossible, to find a volume using the disc method, while the shell method works quite well.

Example 3

Find the volume of the solid generated by rotating about the y axis the region bounded by $y = x^2 - x^3$ and the x axis.

The graph of $y = x^2 - x^3$ is given in Figure 16.15(a). The relative maximum is at (2/3, 4/27) (the scale on the y axis is enlarged for convenience). Let us first

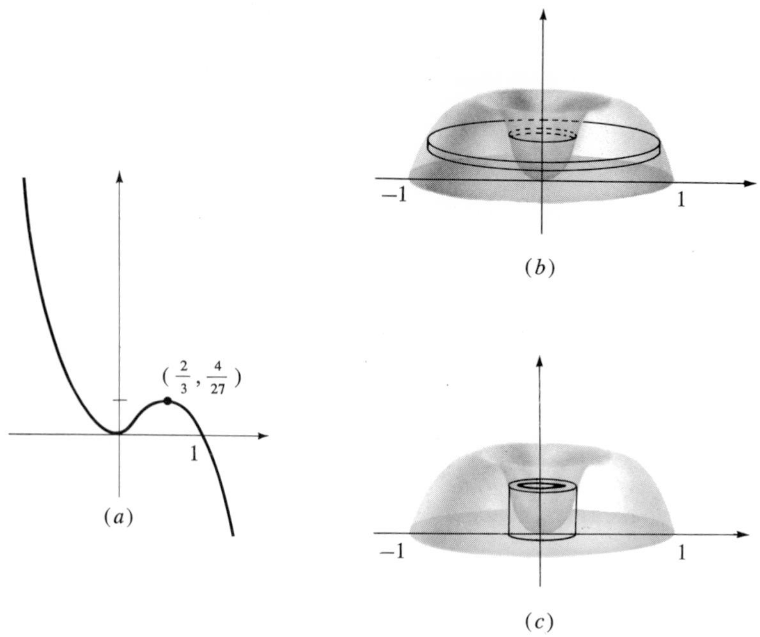

Figure 16.15

see what happens when we try to use the disc method. Figure 16.15(b) gives the solid and a representative disc. From this figure we get

$$V = \int_0^{4/27} \pi(x_2^2 - x_1^2)\,dy.$$

Now we are presented with the chore of solving $y = x^2 - x^3$ for x in terms of y. Not only that, but (since there are three values of x for a given value of y between 0 and 4/27) we must find the two positive values and assign x_2 as the larger and x_1 as the smaller. This is prohibitively difficult—we shall not attempt it.

Let us now consider the shell method. From Figure 16.15(c) we have

$$\begin{aligned} V &= \int_0^1 2\pi xy\,dx \\ &= 2\pi \int_0^1 x(x^2 - x^3)\,dx \\ &= 2\pi \int_0^1 (x^3 - x^4)\,dx \\ &= 2\pi\left(\frac{x^4}{4} - \frac{x^5}{5}\right)\Bigg|_0^1 \\ &= \frac{\pi}{10}. \end{aligned}$$

We see that this method gives the volume with very little work—not only do we not have to solve $y = x^2 - x^3$ for x, but we do not need to know the coordinates of the relative maximum. Of course it is not maintained that the shell method is always the easier of the two.

Example 4

Find the volume of the solid generated by rotating about the x axis the region bounded by $x = y^3 - y$ and the y axis, between $y = 0$ and $y = 1$.

The plane region is given in Figure 16.16(a). Notice that x is negative and y positive for the portion of the curve in which we are interested. Figure 16.16(b) gives the solid and a representative shell in it. From this figure we have

$$V = \int_0^1 2\pi y(-x)\,dy.$$

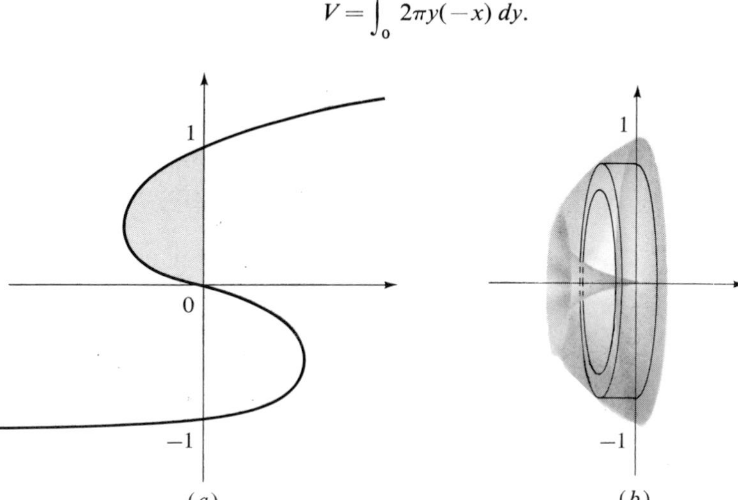

Figure 16.16

We have $-x$ rather than x, because x is negative and we want the corresponding positive number.

$$\begin{aligned} V &= 2\pi \int_0^1 y(y - y^3)\,dy \\ &= 2\pi \int_0^1 (y^2 - y^4)\,dy \\ &= 2\pi\left(\frac{y^3}{3} - \frac{y^5}{5}\right)\Big|_0^1 \\ &= \frac{4\pi}{15}. \end{aligned}$$

It might be noted again that this problem would be more difficult by the disc method.

Problems

In Problems 1–14, the region bounded by the given curves is rotated about the line indicated. Use the shell method to find the volume.

1. $y = x^2$, y axis, $y = 1$ (first quadrant); about x axis.
2. $y = x^2$, x axis, $x = 1$; about x axis.
3. $y = x^3$, x axis, $x = 1$; about y axis.

4. $y = x^3$, x axis, $x = 1$; about x axis.
5. $y = x^2$, x axis, $x = 1$; about $x = 1$.
6. $y = e^x$, x axis, between $x = 0$ and $x = 1$; about y axis.
7. $y = \ln x$, x axis, between $x = 1$ and $x = e$; about y axis.
8. $y = x^2 - x$, x axis; about y axis.
9. $y = x^2 - 4x + 3$, x axis; about y axis.
10. $x = y^2 - 4y$, y axis; about x axis.
11. $x = y^2 - 4y$, y axis; about y axis.
12. $y = 1/x$, x axis, right of $x = 1$; about x axis.
13. $y = 1/x$, x axis, right of $x = 1$; about y axis.
14. $y = 1/x$, x axis, right of $x = 1$; about $x = 1$.

In Problems 15–26, the region bounded by the given curves is rotated about the line indicated. Find the volume by any convenient method.

15. $y = x^2 - 2x - 3$, x axis; about x axis.
16. $y = x^2 - 6x + 8$, x axis; about y axis.
17. $y = x(x-2)^2$, x axis; about y axis.
18. $y = x(x-2)^2$, x axis; about x axis.
19. $y = x(x-2)^2$, x axis; about $x = 2$.
20. $y = x(x-2)^2$, x axis; about $y = 2$.
21. $y = \sin x$, x axis, between $x = 0$ and $x = \pi$; about y axis.
22. $y = e^x$, x axis, left of the y axis; about y axis.
23. $y = xe^x$, x axis, between $x = -2$ and $x = 0$; about x axis.
24. $y = xe^x$, x axis, between $x = -2$ and $x = 0$; about y axis.
25. $x = (y^2 - 1)^2$, y axis; about x axis.
26. $x = y^2(1 - y)$, y axis; about x axis.

16.5

Volumes of Other Solids

In many cases we are interested in the volumes of solids which are not solids of revolution. These can be found by using double or triple integrals (see Chapter 23). But certain special cases can be handled by the single integrals we have studied—in particular, whenever parallel cross sections all have the same simple shape (all squares, all triangles, and so on). It is based upon the volume of a disc (not necessarily circular) which is the product of the cross-sectional area and the thickness,

$$V = At.$$

Example 1

A solid has a circular base of radius 1. Parallel cross sections perpendicular to the base are squares. Find the volume of the solid.

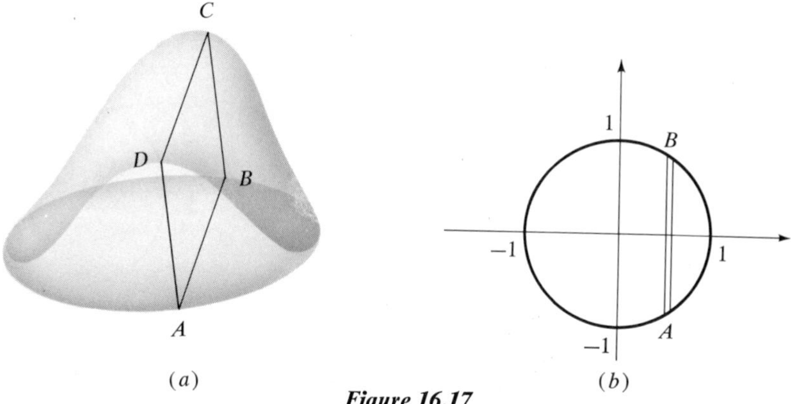

Figure 16.17

The solid is given in Figure 16.17(a) (although it is not necessary to know what the solid looks like in order to find the volume). One of the square cross-sections $ABCD$ is given. Suppose we represent the base (shown in (b)) by the equation

$$x^2 + y^2 = 1.$$

Then AB, the length of one side of the square cross section, is twice the y coordinate of B, or

$$2\sqrt{1 - x^2}.$$

Thus the cross-sectional area is

$$4(1 - x^2);$$

and, with thickness Δx, the volume of a cross-sectional square disc is

$$4(1 - x^2)\,\Delta x.$$

Thus,

$$\begin{aligned} V &= \int_{-1}^{1} 4(1 - x^2)\,dx \\ &= 4\left(x - \frac{x^3}{3}\right)\Big|_{-1}^{1} \\ &= \frac{16}{3}. \end{aligned}$$

Example 2

A solid has a circular base of radius 1. Parallel cross sections perpendicular to the base are equilateral triangles. Find the volume of the solid.

Figure 16.18(a) shows the resulting solid with the triangular cross section ABC. Again, if we represent the base by the equation

$$x^2 + y^2 = 1,$$

AB is of length

$$2\sqrt{1 - x^2},$$

and the altitude is $\sqrt{3}/2$ times the base, or

$$\sqrt{3}\sqrt{1 - x^2}.$$

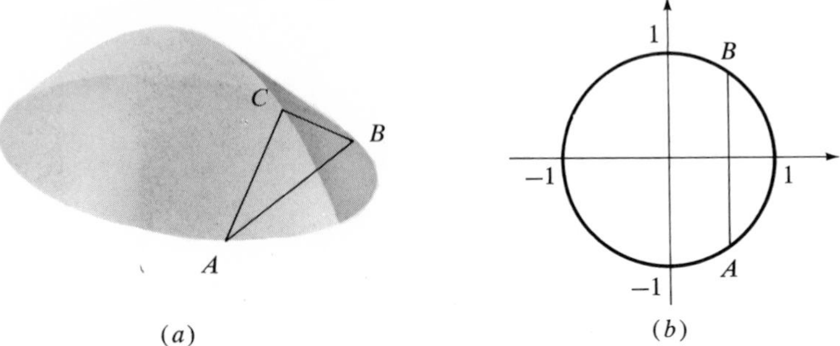

Figure 16.18

Thus,

$$
\begin{aligned}
V &= \int_{-1}^{1} \frac{1}{2} \cdot 2\sqrt{1-x^2}\,\sqrt{3}\,\sqrt{1-x^2}\,dx \\
&= \int_{-1}^{1} \sqrt{3}(1-x^2)\,dx \\
&= \sqrt{3}\left(x - \frac{x^3}{3}\right)\Big|_{-1}^{1} \\
&= \frac{4\sqrt{3}}{3}.
\end{aligned}
$$

Example 3

A circular cylinder of radius 1 is cut by two planes. One is perpendicular to the axis of the cylinder, and the other is inclined to the first at an angle of 45°, intersecting the first in a line that is a diameter of the cylinder. Find the volume of one of the wedges so formed.

There are two convenient ways of finding the volume. Both are illustrated here.

The wedge is illustrated in (a) of Figure 16.19. As can be seen there, cross sections perpendicular to the line of intersection of the two planes are right isosceles triangles. Let us again represent the base by the right half of the circle (shown in (b))

$$x^2 + y^2 = 1.$$

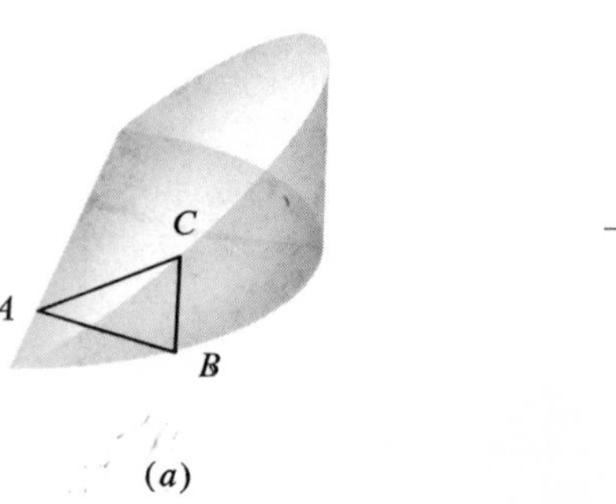

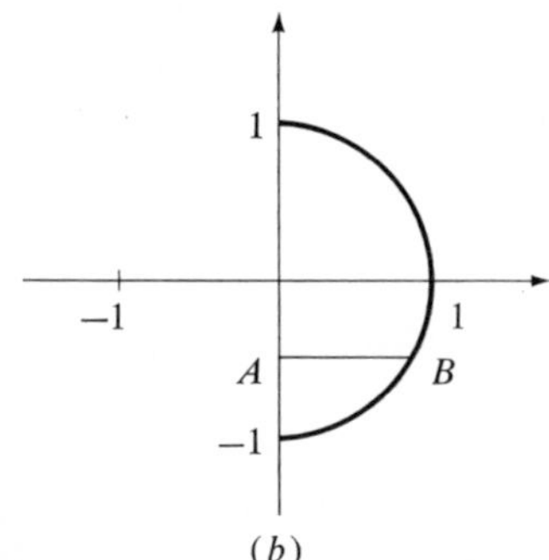

Figure 16.19

The length of AB is the x coordinate of B, or

$$\sqrt{1-y^2}.$$

Since $BC = AB$, the area of the triangular cross section is

$$\frac{1}{2}AB \cdot BC = \frac{1}{2}\sqrt{1-y^2}\sqrt{1-y^2} = \frac{1}{2}(1-y^2).$$

Thus

$$\begin{aligned} V &= \int_{-1}^{1} \frac{1}{2}(1-y^2)\,dy \\ &= \frac{1}{2}\left(y - \frac{y^3}{3}\right)\Big|_{-1}^{1} \\ &= \frac{2}{3}. \end{aligned}$$

If the cross sections are taken perpendicular to the base but parallel to the line of intersection of the two planes (see Figure 16.20(a)) then the cross section is a

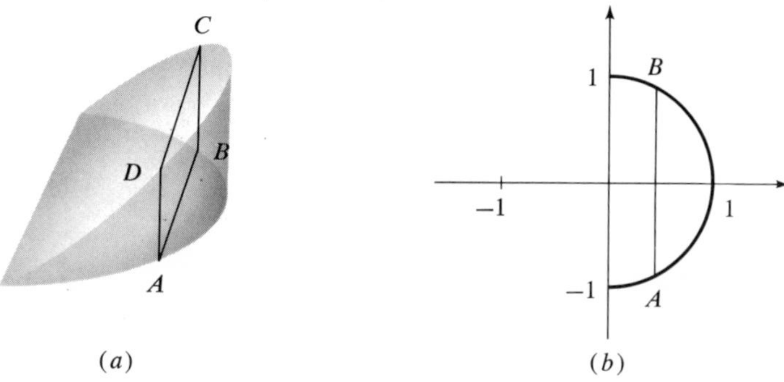

Figure 16.20

rectangle $ABCD$. Again representing the base as before, we see that the length of AB is twice the y coordinate of B, or

$$2\sqrt{1-x^2}.$$

Since the planes intersect at an angle of 45°, the length of AD is the same as the distance of AB from the y axis, or the x coordinate of B. Thus the area of $ABCD$ is

$$2x\sqrt{1-x^2},$$

and

$$\begin{aligned} V &= \int_{0}^{1} 2x\sqrt{1-x^2}\,dx \\ &= -\frac{2}{3}(1-x^2)^{3/2}\Big|_{0}^{1} \\ &= \frac{2}{3}. \end{aligned}$$

Problems

In Problems 1–6, we have a solid whose base is a circle of radius 1. The parallel cross sections taken perpendicular to the base are described. Find the volume.

1. Rectangles of height 1.
2. Isosceles triangles of height 1.
3. Isosceles right triangles with one leg as base.
4. Isosceles right triangles with the hypotenuse as base.
5. Semicircles.
6. Semi-ellipses of height 2.

Problems 7–14 involve a solid whose base is bounded by $y = 4 - x^2$ and the x axis. Cross sections perpendicular to the base and parallel to the x axis are described. Find the volume.

7. Squares.
8. Equilateral triangles.
9. Rectangles of height 2.
10. Isosceles triangles of height 1.
11. Isosceles right triangles with one leg as base.
12. Isosceles right triangles with the hypotenuse as base.
13. Semicircles.
14. Semi-ellipses of height 6.

Problems 15–22 concern a solid whose base is an ellipse with major axis 8 and minor axis 6. Cross sections perpendicular to the base and parallel to the minor axis are described. Find the volume.

15. Squares.
16. Equilateral triangles.
17. Rectangles of height 4.
18. Isosceles triangles of height 2.
19. Isosceles right triangles with one leg as base.
20. Isosceles right triangles with hypotenuse as base.
21. Semicircles.
22. Semi-ellipses of height 5.

In Problems 23–24, find the volume of the wedge described in Example 3, given that the second plane is inclined to the first at the given angle.

23. 30°.
24. 60°.
25. Two circular cylinders of radius 2 intersect each other in such a way that their axes intersect at right angles. Find the volume of the portion inside both cylinders.
26. Repeat Problem 25 with both cylinders of radius r.

16.6

Arc Length

Given a function f, suppose we want to find the length of the graph from $(a, f(a))$ to $(b, f(b))$. Since we can find straight-line distances very easily, let us again start by approximating the length by a series of straight-line distances (see Figure 16.21).

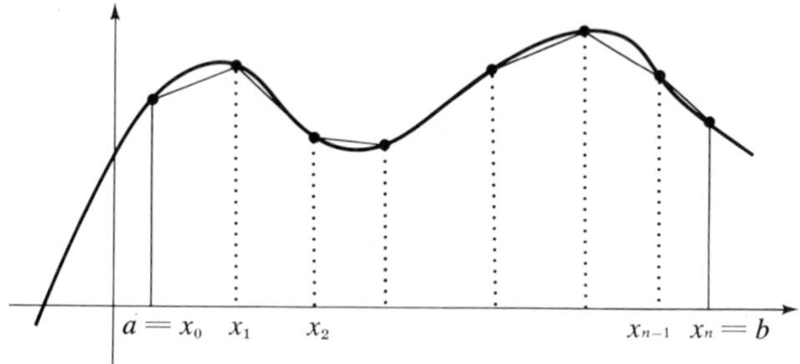

Figure 16.21

The length of the ith distance can be found by using the distance between two points. It is

$$l_i = \sqrt{(x_i - x_{i-1})^2 + [f(x_i) - f(x_{i-1})]^2}.$$

We now multiply and divide by $x_i - x_{i-1}$, noting that $x_i - x_{i-1} = \sqrt{(x_i - x_{i-1})^2}$, because $x_i - x_{i-1}$ is positive. Thus,

$$\begin{aligned} l_i &= \frac{\sqrt{(x_i - x_{i-1})^2 + [f(x_i) - f(x_{i-1})]^2}}{x_i - x_{i-1}}(x_i - x_{i-1}) \\ &= \sqrt{\frac{(x_i - x_{i-1})^2 + [f(x_i) - f(x_{i-1})]^2}{(x_i - x_{i-1})^2}}(x_i - x_{i-1}) \\ &= \sqrt{1 + \left(\frac{f(x_i) - f(x_{i-1})}{x_i - x_{i-1}}\right)^2}(x_i - x_{i-1}) \\ &= \sqrt{1 + \left(\frac{f(x_i) - f(x_{i-1})}{x_i - x_{i-1}}\right)^2}\Delta x_i, \end{aligned}$$

where $\Delta x_i = x_i - x_{i-1}$. The approximating sum is

$$\sum_{i=1}^{n} \sqrt{1 + \left(\frac{f(x_i) - f(x_{i-1})}{x_i - x_{i-1}}\right)^2}\Delta x_i.$$

Again we are interested in the exact value rather than an approximating sum; to get it, we take the limit of the approximating sum as the lengths of the subintervals approach zero.

$$L = \lim_{\|S\| \to 0} \sum_{i=1}^{n} \sqrt{1 + \left(\frac{f(x_i) - f(x_{i-1})}{x_i - x_{i-1}}\right)^2}\Delta x_i.$$

This limit is an integral. Note also that $x_i - x_{i-1}$ approaches 0 for all i, since $\|S\|$ approaches 0, and

$$\lim_{x_{i-1} \to x_i} \frac{f(x_i) - f(x_{i-1})}{x_i - x_{i-1}} = f'(x_i).$$

Thus

$$L = \int_a^b \sqrt{1 + [f'(x)]^2}\, dx.$$

Before using this formula, note that the preceding discussion is *not* a proof of the formula. We have not *defined* what is meant by the length of an arc. Our position is the same as when we first began to consider area; although we used our intuitive idea of area to determine what we meant by an integral, the actual definition of an integral was independent of area; in fact, area was defined in terms of the integral. Similarly we may now *define* arc length as

$$\int_a^b \sqrt{1+[f'(x)]^2}\,dx.$$

Example 1

Find the length of $y = x^{2/3}$ from (0, 0) to (8, 4).

$$y' = \frac{2}{3}x^{-1/3} = \frac{2}{3x^{1/3}},$$

$$\begin{aligned}
L &= \int_0^8 \sqrt{1+\left(\frac{2}{3x^{1/3}}\right)^2}\,dx \\
&= \int_0^8 \sqrt{1+\frac{4}{9x^{2/3}}}\,dx \\
&= \int_0^8 \sqrt{\frac{9x^{2/3}+4}{9x^{2/3}}}\,dx \\
&= \int_0^8 \frac{\sqrt{9x^{2/3}+4}}{3x^{1/3}}\,dx \\
&= \frac{1}{18}\int_0^8 6x^{-1/3}\sqrt{9x^{2/3}+4}\,dx \\
&= \lim_{\epsilon\to 0^+} \frac{1}{18}\int_\epsilon^8 6x^{-1/3}\sqrt{9x^{2/3}+4}\,dx \\
&= \lim_{\epsilon\to 0^+} \frac{1}{27}(9x^{2/3}+4)^{3/2}\Big|_\epsilon^8 \\
&= \lim_{\epsilon\to 0^+} \frac{1}{27}[80\sqrt{10} - (9\epsilon^{2/3}+4)^{3/2}] \\
&= \frac{8}{27}(10\sqrt{10}-1).
\end{aligned}$$

Example 2

Find the length of $y = \dfrac{x^2}{4} - \dfrac{\ln x}{2}$ from $x = 1$ to $x = 2$.

$$y' = \frac{x}{2} - \frac{1}{2x},$$

$$\begin{aligned}
L &= \int_1^2 \sqrt{1+\left(\frac{x}{2}-\frac{1}{2x}\right)^2}\,dx \\
&= \int_1^2 \sqrt{1+\frac{x^2}{4}-\frac{1}{2}+\frac{1}{4x^2}}\,dx \\
&= \int_1^2 \sqrt{\frac{x^2}{4}+\frac{1}{2}+\frac{1}{4x^2}}\,dx
\end{aligned}$$

$$= \int_1^2 \sqrt{\left(\frac{x}{2} + \frac{1}{2x}\right)^2}\, dx$$

$$= \int_1^2 \left(\frac{x}{2} + \frac{1}{2x}\right) dx$$

$$= \frac{x^2}{4} + \frac{\ln x}{2}\Big|_1^2$$

$$= \frac{3}{4} + \frac{1}{2}\ln 2.$$

If the original equation is not in the form $y = f(x)$, we must either put it into that form or find formulas to handle the form we have. In particular, if the equation is in the form $x = g(y)$, we have (by reversing the roles of the x and y above)

$$L = \int_c^d \sqrt{1 + [g'(y)]^2}\, dy.$$

Since the roles of the x and y have been reversed, it must be remembered that the derivative $g'(y)$ is a derivative with respect to y and the limits of integration are values of y.

Example 3

Find the length of $x = y^{3/2}$ from (0, 0) to (8, 4).

This is really the same problem as Example 1, the only difference being the form of the equation.

$$x' = \frac{3}{2} y^{1/2},$$

$$L = \int_0^4 \sqrt{1 + \frac{9}{4} y}\, dy$$

$$= \frac{4}{9} \int_0^4 \frac{9}{4} \sqrt{1 + \frac{9}{4} y}\, dy$$

$$= \frac{4}{9} \frac{\left(1 + \frac{9}{4} y\right)^{3/2}}{3/2}\Bigg|_0^4$$

$$= \frac{8}{27}\left(1 + \frac{9}{4} y\right)^{3/2}\Bigg|_0^4$$

$$= \frac{8}{27}(10\sqrt{10} - 1).$$

One other form for which we can derive a formula for arc length is the case in which the equation is given in the parametric form

$$x = f(t) \quad \text{and} \quad y = g(t).$$

Noting that

$$\frac{dy}{dx} = \frac{\dfrac{dy}{dt}}{\dfrac{dx}{dt}} \quad \text{and} \quad dx = \frac{dx}{dt} \cdot dt,$$

we can change our first arc-length formula to

$$L = \int_{t_1}^{t_2} \sqrt{\left(\frac{dx}{dt}\right)^2 + \left(\frac{dy}{dt}\right)^2}\, dt.$$

Example 4

Find the circumference of the circle $x = a \cos t$, $y = a \sin t$.

$$\frac{dx}{dt} = -a \sin t \quad \text{and} \quad \frac{dy}{dt} = a \cos t,$$

$$\begin{aligned} L &= \int_0^{2\pi} \sqrt{(-a \sin t)^2 + (a \cos t)^2}\, dt \\ &= \int_0^{2\pi} \sqrt{a^2 \sin^2 t + a^2 \cos^2 t}\, dt \\ &= \int_0^{2\pi} a\, dt \\ &= at \Big|_0^{2\pi} \\ &= 2\pi a. \end{aligned}$$

Of course there are other forms for the given equation. An important one is for implicit functions, which we shall consider in Chapter 22. Another case, which we defer to the problems (see Problem 25), is that in which the equation is given in polar coordinates. For the present, we shall content ourselves with the three forms

$$L = \int_{x_1}^{x_2} \sqrt{1 + (dy/dx)^2}\, dx \quad \text{if } y = f(x),$$

$$L = \int_{y_1}^{y_2} \sqrt{1 + (dx/dy)^2}\, dy \quad \text{if } x = g(y),$$

$$L = \int_{t_1}^{t_2} \sqrt{(dx/dt)^2 + (dy/dt)^2}\, dt \quad \text{if } x = f(t) \text{ and } y = g(t).$$

Problems

In Problems 1–22, find the length of the arc described.

1. $y = x^{3/2}$ from $x = 7/4$ to $x = 11/4$.
2. $y^3 = x^2$ from $x = 1$ to $x = 8$.
3. $y = x^2$ from $x = 0$ to $x = 2$.
4. $y = \ln x$ from $x = 1$ to $x = 2$.

5. $y = \ln \cos x$ from $x = 0$ to $x = \pi/4$.
6. $y = \ln \sin x$ from $x = \pi/6$ to $x = \pi/2$.
7. $y = \ln \csc x$ from $x = \pi/4$ to $x = 3\pi/4$.
8. $y = \ln (1 - x^2)$ from $x = 0$ to $x = 1/2$.
9. $y = \ln \dfrac{e^x + 1}{e^x - 1}$ from $x = 1$ to $x = 2$.
10. $y = \dfrac{x^3}{6} + \dfrac{1}{2x}$ from $x = 1$ to $x = 3$.
11. $x = \cosh y$ from $y = 0$ to $y = 1$.
12. $x = \dfrac{y^3}{3} + \dfrac{1}{4y}$ from $y = 1$ to $y = 3$.
13. $x = \text{Arcsin } e^y$ from $y = -1$ to $y = 0$.
14. $x = \dfrac{y^4}{4} + \dfrac{1}{8y^2}$ from $y = 1$ to $y = 2$.
15. $x = \text{Arccos}(1 - y) + \sqrt{2y - y^2}$ from $y = 0$ to $y = 1$.
16. $x = \text{sech}^{-1}\, y - \sqrt{1 - y^2}$ from $y = 1/2$ to $y = 1$.
17. $x = \cos^3 \theta,\ y = \sin^3 \theta$ from $\theta = 0$ to $\theta = \pi/2$.
18. $x = e^t \sin t,\ y = e^t \cos t$ from $t = 0$ to $t = \pi$.
19. $x = 8t^3,\ y = 4t^2$ from $t = 0$ to $t = 1$.
20. $x = 1 + t,\ y = t^2 + 2t + 1$ from $t = 0$ to $t = 1$.
21. $x = a(\theta - \sin \theta),\ y = a(1 - \cos \theta)$ from $\theta = 0$ to $\theta = \pi/2$.
22. $x = \cos \theta + \theta \sin \theta,\ y = \sin \theta - \theta \cos \theta$ from $\theta = 0$ to $\theta = \pi$.
23. Find the length of the loop of $9y^2 = x(x - 3)^2$.
24. Find the total length of $x^{2/3} + y^{2/3} = a^{2/3}$.
25. Show that if $r = f(\theta)$, then the length of the arc from $\theta = \theta_1$ to $\theta = \theta_2$ is

$$L = \int_{\theta_1}^{\theta_2} \sqrt{r^2 + \left(\frac{dr}{d\theta}\right)^2}\, d\theta.$$

In Problems 26–29, use the result of Problem 25 to find the length of the given arc.

26. $r = a\theta$ from $\theta = 0$ to $\theta = \pi$.
27. $r = e^\theta$ from $\theta = 0$ to $\theta = 2$.
28. $r = 1 + \cos \theta$ from $\theta = 0$ to $\theta = 2\pi$.
29. $r = 2 \sin^3 \dfrac{\theta}{3}$ from $\theta = 0$ to $\theta = \pi/2$.

16.7

Surfaces of Revolution

The area of a surface of revolution is based upon the area of the lateral surface of a frustum of a right circular cone. This area (see Figure 16.22) is

$$A = 2\pi \frac{r_1 + r_2}{2} s,$$

where $(r_1 + r_2)/2$ is the average radius and s is the slant height. This formula still holds if $r_1 = r_2$. In this case we have a cylinder for which the average radius is the radius of the cylinder and the slant height is the height of the cylinder.

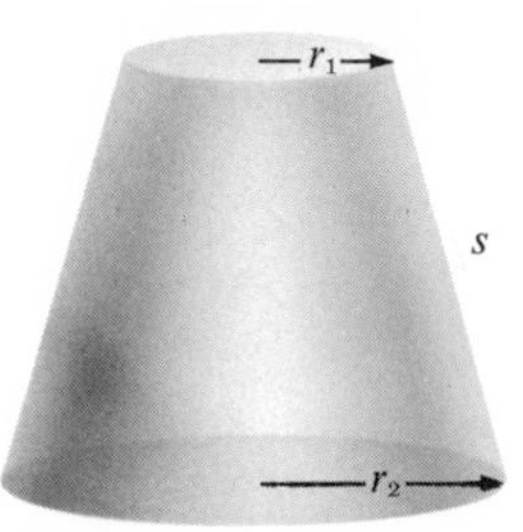

Figure 16.22

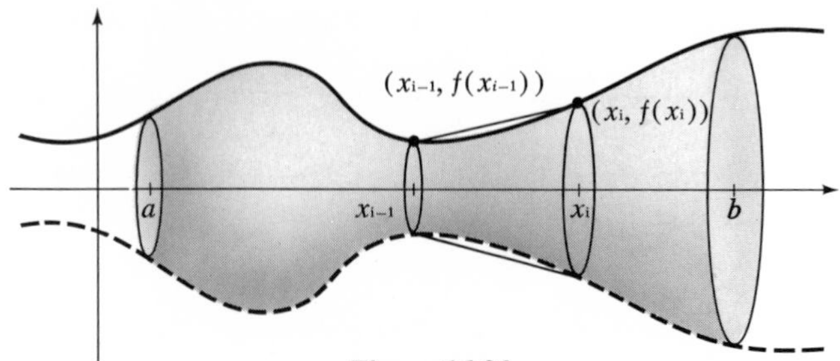

Figure 16.23

Now suppose we have a curve represented by the equation $y = f(x)$ and we rotate about the x axis the portion between $x = a$ and $x = b$ (see Figure 16.23). Suppose further that the straight-line segments used in the previous section to approximate the are length are rotated along with the curve. Each rotated segment gives a frustum of a cone (or a cylinder if it is parallel to the x axis). If the interval $[a, b]$ is subdivided to give

$$a = x_0, x_1, x_2, \ldots, x_n = b,$$

then the surface area for the ith interval is

$$2\pi\frac{f(x_{i-1}) + f(x_i)}{2}\sqrt{(x_i - x_{i-1})^2 + [f(x_i) - f(x_{i-1})]^2}.$$

Again multiplying and dividing by $x_i - x_{i-1}$, we have

$$2\pi\frac{f(x_{i-1}) + f(x_i)}{2}\sqrt{1 + \left(\frac{f(x_i) - f(x_{i-1})}{x_i - x_{i-1}}\right)^2}(x_i - x_{i-1})$$

$$= 2\pi\frac{f(x_{i-1}) + f(x_i)}{2}\sqrt{1 + \left(\frac{f(x_i) - f(x_{i-1})}{x_i - x_{i-1}}\right)^2}\,\Delta x_i.$$

Adding all of these and taking the limit as the lengths of all subintervals approach zero, we have

$$S_x = \lim_{\|s\| \to 0} \sum_{i=1}^{n} 2\pi\frac{f(x_{i-1}) + f(x_i)}{2}\sqrt{1 + \left(\frac{f(x_i) - f(x_{i-1})}{x_i - x_{i-1}}\right)^2}\,\Delta x_i$$

$$= \int_a^b 2\pi f(x)\sqrt{1 + (f'(x))^2}\,dx,$$

or

$$S_x = \int_a^b 2\pi y\sqrt{1 + \left(\frac{dy}{dx}\right)^2}\,dx.$$

In this discussion we have assumed that y is positive. If y is negative, we must use $|y|$, since it represents a radius, which is positive. Thus, we have

$$S_x = \int_a^b 2\pi|y|\sqrt{1 + \left(\frac{dy}{dx}\right)^2}\,dx.$$

As in the preceding section, if the given equation is in the form $x = g(y)$ or in parametric form, the resulting formulas are

$$S_x = \int_a^b 2\pi\, |y| \sqrt{1 + \left(\frac{dx}{dy}\right)^2}\, dy,$$

$$S_x = \int_a^b 2\pi\, |y| \sqrt{\left(\frac{dx}{dt}\right)^2 + \left(\frac{dy}{dt}\right)^2}\, dt.$$

This can be summarized by

$$S_x = \int_a^b 2\pi\, |y|\, ds,$$

where ds (sometimes called the differential of arc) is given by

$$ds = \sqrt{1 + \left(\frac{dy}{dx}\right)^2}\, dx \quad \text{if } y = f(x),$$

$$ds = \sqrt{1 + \left(\frac{dx}{dy}\right)^2}\, dy \quad \text{if } x = g(y),$$

$$ds = \sqrt{\left(\frac{dx}{dt}\right)^2 + \left(\frac{dy}{dt}\right)^2}\, dt \quad \text{if } x = f(t) \text{ and } y = g(t).$$

Of course the limits of integration are values of x, y, or t in the first, second, or third cases, respectively.

Example 1

Find the area of the surface formed by rotating about the x axis the arc $y = x^3/3$ from $x = 0$ to $x = 2$.

$y' = x^2$. Furthermore, $y \geq 0$ for all x in the interval [0, 2]. Thus $|y| = y$.

$$\begin{aligned} S_x &= \int_0^2 2\pi y \sqrt{1 + (y')^2}\, dx \\ &= \int_0^2 \frac{2\pi x^3}{3} \sqrt{1 + x^4}\, dx \\ &= \frac{\pi}{6} \int_0^2 4x^3 \sqrt{1 + x^4}\, dx \\ &= \frac{\pi}{6} \frac{(1 + x^4)^{3/2}}{3/2} \Big|_0^2 \\ &= \frac{\pi}{9} (1 + x^4)^{3/2} \Big|_0^2 \\ &= \frac{\pi}{9} (17^{3/2} - 1). \end{aligned}$$

Example 2

Find the area of the surface formed by rotating about the x axis the arc $x = 4 - t^2$, $y = t$ from $t = 0$ to $t = \sqrt{2}$.

$$\frac{dx}{dt} = -2t \quad \text{and} \quad \frac{dy}{dt} = 1.$$

Again $|y| = y$ for all values of t in $[0, \sqrt{2}]$.

$$S_x = \int_0^{\sqrt{2}} 2\pi y \sqrt{\left(\frac{dx}{dt}\right)^2 + \left(\frac{dy}{dt}\right)^2}\, dt$$

$$= \int_0^{\sqrt{2}} 2\pi t\sqrt{4t^2+1}\, dt$$

$$= \frac{\pi}{4}\int_0^{\sqrt{2}} 8t\sqrt{4t^2+1}\, dt$$

$$= \frac{\pi}{4}\,\frac{(4t^2+1)^{3/2}}{3/2}\bigg|_0^{\sqrt{2}}$$

$$= \frac{\pi}{6}\,(4t^2+1)^{3/2}\bigg|_0^{\sqrt{2}}$$

$$= \frac{\pi}{6}\,(27-1)$$

$$= \frac{13\pi}{3}.$$

By a similar process, it can be shown that if the region is rotated about the y axis, the surface area is

$$S_y = \int_a^b 2\pi\, |x|\, ds,$$

where the form of ds again depends upon the form of the equation.

Example 3

Find the area of the surface formed by rotating about the y axis the arc $x = y^3/6 + 1/(2y)$ from $(2/3, 1)$ to $(14/3, 3)$.

$$\frac{dx}{dy} = \frac{y^2}{2} - \frac{1}{2y^2}$$

Clearly, x is positive throughout the given interval. Thus $|x| = x$.

$$S_y = \int_1^3 2\pi x\sqrt{1+(x')^2}\, dy$$

$$= \int_1^3 2\pi\left(\frac{y^3}{6} + \frac{1}{2y}\right)\sqrt{1+\left(\frac{y^2}{2} - \frac{1}{2y^2}\right)^2}\, dy$$

$$= \int_1^3 2\pi\left(\frac{y^3}{6} + \frac{1}{2y}\right)\left(\frac{y^2}{2} + \frac{1}{2y^2}\right) dy$$

$$= 2\pi\int_1^3 \left(\frac{y^5}{12} + \frac{y}{3} + \frac{1}{4y^3}\right) dy$$

$$= 2\pi\left(\frac{y^6}{72} + \frac{y^2}{6} - \frac{1}{8y^2}\right)\bigg|_1^3$$

$$= \frac{208\pi}{9}.$$

Problems

1. Find the surface area of a sphere of radius R.
2. Find the lateral surface area of a cone of height h and radius r.
3. The ellipse $x^2/a^2 + y^2/b^2 = 1$ $(a > b)$ is rotated about the x axis. Find the area of the resulting surface.
4. The ellipse of Problem 3 is rotated about the y axis. Find the area of the resulting surface.
5. The portion of the circle $x^2 + y^2 = 4$ to the right of $x = 1$ is rotated about the x axis, forming a zone of the sphere. Find its surface area.
6. A zone of the sphere of Problem 5 is formed by rotating about the x axis the portion of the circle between $x = 0$ and $x = 1$. Find the surface area. Compare with the result of Problem 5.
7. A zone of the sphere of Problem 5 is formed by rotating about the x axis the portion of the circle between $x = -1/2$ and $x = 1/2$. Find the surface area. Compare with the results of Problems 5 and 6.
8. Find the surface area of a zone of height h of a sphere of radius r.

In Problems 9–22, the given arc is rotated about the x axis. Find the area of the resulting surface.

9. $y = \dfrac{x^3}{3} + \dfrac{1}{4x}$ from $x = 1$ to $x = 3$.
10. $y = \dfrac{x^2}{4} - \dfrac{\ln x}{2}$ from $x = 1$ to $x = 4$.
11. $y = \sin x$ from $x = 0$ to $x = \pi$.
12. $y = e^x$ left of $x = 0$.
13. $y = \cosh x$ from $x = -1$ to $x = 1$.
14. $y = a \cosh \dfrac{x}{a}$ from $x = -a$ to $x = a$.
15. $y^2 = 8x$ from (0, 0) to (2, 4).
16. $x^{2/3} + y^{2/3} = a^{2/3}$ from $(0, a)$ to $(a, 0)$.
17. $9y^2 = x(3 - x)^2$ from (0, 0) to (3, 0).
18. $8y^2 = x^2 - x^4$ from (0, 0) to (1, 0).
19. $x = a\theta - a \sin \theta$, $y = a - a \cos \theta$ from $\theta = 0$ to $\theta = \pi$.
20. $x = a \cos^3 \theta$, $y = a \sin^3 \theta$ from $\theta = 0$ to $\theta = \pi/2$.
21. $x = t^3$, $y = t^2$ from $t = 0$ to $t = 2$.
22. $x = t + 2$, $y = t^3$ from $t = 0$ to $t = 2$.

In Problems 23–30, the given arc is rotated about the y axis. Find the area of the resulting surface.

23. $y = \cosh x$ from $x = 0$ to $x = 1$.
24. $y = \dfrac{x^3}{3}$ from (0, 0) to (3, 9).
25. $y = \ln x$ from (1, 0) to $(e, 1)$.
26. $y = \dfrac{x^2}{4} - \dfrac{\ln x}{2}$ from $x = 1$ to $x = e$.
27. $x = y^{2/3}$ from $y = 0$ to $y = 1$.
28. $x = \sqrt{y}$ from $y = 0$ to $y = 4$.
29. $x = e^t \cos t$, $y = e^t \sin t$ from $t = 0$ to $t = \pi$.
30. $x = t + 1$, $y = t^2 - 1$ from $t = -1$ to $t = 1$.

16.8

Center of Gravity and Moments

The center of gravity of an object (or system of objects) is the point on which that object (or system) balances when at rest. For example, if weights are placed at the ends of a board, the point at which it balances is the center of gravity of the given system. If the object is not at rest, there may be inertial properties which partially or completely overcome the force of gravity. For example, a spinning gyroscope has different balancing properties than the same gyroscope at rest. The latter properties are all we are concerned with here.

In the previous sections we used integrals to determine areas, volumes, and so forth, because they are all additive; that is, the area of a large region can be found by cutting it up into smaller regions and adding all of their areas. The same is true for volume, arc length, and so forth. Unfortunately, we cannot do this with centers of gravity.

For example, suppose we have a barbell four feet long which we place on the x axis with one end at -2 and the other at 2. Suppose furthermore that we put a 100-pound weight at $x = -2$ and a ten-pound weight at $x = 2$. (When we say, "put a 100-pound weight at $x = -2$," we mean that the center of gravity—or balancing point—of the weight is at $x = -2$.) Since one center of gravity is at $x = -2$ and the other at $x = 2$, we find that the sum is $x = 0$, which is not the center of gravity of the barbell. Obviously the barbell would balance at a point nearer to the 100-pound weight than the 10-pound weight.

Since we cannot add centers of gravity, we must find something that is additive before we can even consider the use of the integral. Obviously, we need to consider not merely the location of the weights, but also their relative sizes. For this purpose, we consider the moment about a certain axis. The moment is the product of the weight and the distance from the axis.

The following problem illustrates the use of moments. We have a board lying on the x axis and balanced at the origin. A 100-pound weight is placed at $x = -2$. Where shall we put a 50-pound weight in order to have the board balance again? The moments should be the same on both sides. On the left, there is a weight of 100 pounds at a distance 2 from the origin; the moment is 200. On the right, there is a weight of 50 pounds at an unknown distance x from the origin; the moment is $50x$. Equating moments, we have

$$50x = 200, \quad \text{or} \quad x = 4.$$

Thus a 100-pound weight at $x = -2$ and a 50-pound weight at $x = 4$ balances at the origin; that is, its center of gravity is at the origin.

To use a more convenient method, we assign a $+$ or $-$ to the distance, depending upon the direction from the point of reference. Thus, if the point of reference is the origin, we can use the x coordinate of the point at which a weight is located, rather than the distance. In using this method in the last example, we should equate the sum of all moments to zero, rather than equating the moments on the two sides of the point of reference. Thus

$$\begin{aligned} -2 \cdot 100 + 50x &= 0, \\ x &= 4. \end{aligned}$$

This method also makes finding the center of gravity much simpler. In the last example we asked where to put a certain weight so that the center of gravity would be at the origin. If the center of gravity of the system is to be determined, the new method is easier.

Example 1

Find the center of gravity of a system consisting of a 100-pound weight at $x = -2$ and a 10-pound weight at $x = 2$.

Taking the origin as the point of reference, we have

$$\begin{aligned} M_0 &= 100(-2) + 10 \cdot 2 \\ &= -200 + 20 \\ &= -180. \end{aligned}$$

Since the sum of the moments of the individual weights equals the moment of the entire system, -180 is the moment about the origin of the entire system. If $\bar{x}$ is the coordinate of the center of gravity of the system, then

$$M_0 = 110\bar{x}.$$

Thus

$$110\bar{x} = -180,$$

$$\bar{x} = -\frac{18}{11}.$$

We see that the center of gravity can be determined by finding (a) the moment of the system about a given point and (b) the total weight. The center of gravity is then the moment divided by the weight. If the weights are distributed about a plane rather than along a line, we can find the center of gravity by dealing with the x and y coordinates separately. Thus we find the moments about the x and y axes and divide each by the total weight.

Example 2

Find the center of gravity of the system consisting of ten pounds at (1, 3), twenty pounds at (−2, 2), and four pounds at (−1, 8).

The moment about the x axis, M_x, is the product of the mass and the (directed) distance from the x axis, which is the *y coordinate*. Similarly M_y is the product of the mass and the distance from the y axis, which is the x coordinate. Thus

$$\begin{aligned} M_x &= 10 \cdot 3 + 20 \cdot 2 + 4 \cdot 8 \\ &= 102, \\ M_y &= 10 \cdot 1 + 20\,(-2) + 4\,(-1) \\ &= -34, \\ W &= 10 + 20 + 4 \\ &= 34, \\ \bar{x} &= \frac{M_y}{W} = \frac{-34}{34} = -1, \\ \bar{y} &= \frac{M_x}{W} = \frac{102}{34} = 3. \end{aligned}$$

Example 3

Find the center of gravity of the region shown in (a) of Figure 16.24. It is assumed to be of uniform density.

First of all let us choose a pair of coordinate axes. This choice is quite arbitrary—any convenient one will do. Let us put the axes in the position shown in (b) of the figure. Now the region can be subdivided into three rectangles. Because of their symmetry, the centers of gravity of the rectangles are at their

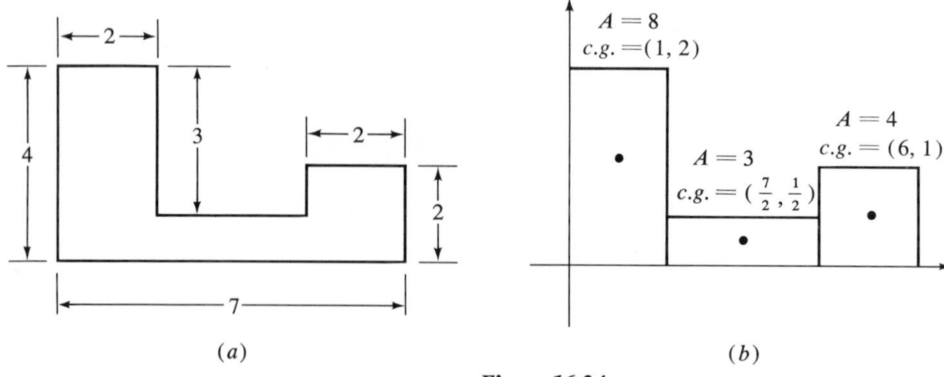

(*a*) (*b*)

Figure 16.24

geometric centers. Thus we have a rectangle of area 8 with center at (1, 2), another of area 3 with center at (7/2, 1/2), and a third of area 4 with center at (6, 1). Because the region is of uniform density, its weight is proportional to its area; thus the weight is the product of the area and the weight per unit area. Furthermore, the weight per unit area is a factor of both the total weight and any moment. Since the coordinates of the center of gravity are found by dividing the moments by the total weight, the weight per unit area cancels out—thus we shall neglect this factor. We now have

$$A = 8 + 3 + 4 = 15,$$

$$M_x = 8 \cdot 2 + 3 \cdot \frac{1}{2} + 4 \cdot 1 = \frac{43}{2},$$

$$M_y = 8 \cdot 1 + 3 \cdot \frac{7}{2} + 4 \cdot 6 = \frac{85}{2};$$

and

$$\bar{x} = \frac{M_y}{A} = \frac{85/2}{15} = \frac{17}{6},$$

$$\bar{y} = \frac{M_x}{A} = \frac{43/2}{15} = \frac{43}{30}.$$

Of course these are the coordinates of the center of gravity with respect to the chosen set of axes. If the axes had been in a different position, the result would give the same point but with a different representation.

Problems

In Problems 1–10, find the center of gravity of the system described.

1. 2 lb at (4, 0), 10 lb at (2, 0), 4 lb at (−6, 0).
2. 3 lb at (5, 0), 5 lb at (−4, 0).
3. 2 lb at (3, 0), 4 lb at (6, 0).
4. 4 lb at (1, 0), 2 lb at (4, 0), 1 lb at (−2, 0), 2 lb at (−3, 0).
5. 2 lb at (2, 4), 5 lb at (−1, 2), 3 lb at (4, −2).
6. 3 lb at (5, 5), 2 lb at (3, 4), 4 lb at (1, −1).
7. 5 lb at (1, 0), 3 lb at (3, 5), 2 lb at (−4, 1).
8. 4 lb at (0, 0), 5 lb at (2, 4), 2 lb at (−1, 2).

9. 10 lb at (2, 2), 3 lb at (5, −1), 7 lb at (0, −3).
10. 4 lb at (3, −1), 3 lb at (5, 4), 2 lb at (−2, 1), 1 lb at (0, −3).
11. There is a 5-lb weight at (5, 0) and a 3-lb weight at (−2, 0). Where should a 4-lb weight be placed in order to have the system balance at the origin?
12. There is a 3-lb weight at (1, 0), a 2-lb weight at (−3, 0), and a 2-lb weight at (4, 0). Where should a 2-lb weight be placed in order to have the system balance at the origin?
13. There is a 4-lb weight at (3, 0) and a 2-lb weight at (−1, 0). Where should a 3-lb weight be placed in order to have the system balance at (2, 0)?
14. There is a 10-lb weight at (3, 0), a 5-lb weight at (−5, 0), and a 20-lb weight at (5, 0). Where should a 10-lb weight be placed in order to have the system balance at (1, 0)?
15. There is a 2-lb weight at (5, 2) and a 4-lb weight at (−2, 4). Where should a 4-lb weight be placed in order to have the system balance at the origin?
16. There is a 3-lb weight at (4, −2), a 4-lb weight at (−1, −1), and a 2-lb weight at (−2, 4). Where should a 1-lb weight be placed in order to have the system balance at the origin?
17. There is a 4-lb weight at (2, 2) and a 2-lb weight at (−3, 4). Where should a 2-lb weight be placed in order to have the system balance at (−1, 1)?
18. There is a 5-lb weight at (−5, −1), a 10-lb weight at (4, 2), and a 15-lb weight at (5, 1). Where should a 20-lb weight be placed in order to have the system balance at (2, 2)?
19. The region of Figure 16.25(a) is of uniform density. Find its center of gravity.
20. The region of Figure 16.25(b) is of uniform density. Find its center of gravity.
21. The region of Figure 16.25(c) is of uniform density. Find its center of gravity.
22. The region of Figure 16.25(d) is of uniform density. Find its center of gravity.
23. The triangular portion of Figure 16.25(c) weighs twice as much per unit area as the square. Find the center of gravity of the entire region.
24. The square portion of Figure 16.25(c) weighs twice as much per unit area as the triangle. Find the center of gravity of the entire region.
25. The circular portion of Figure 16.25(d) weighs twice as much per unit area as the square. Find the center of gravity of the entire region.
26. The square portion of Figure 16.25(d) weighs three times as much per unit area as the circle. Find the center of gravity of the entire region.

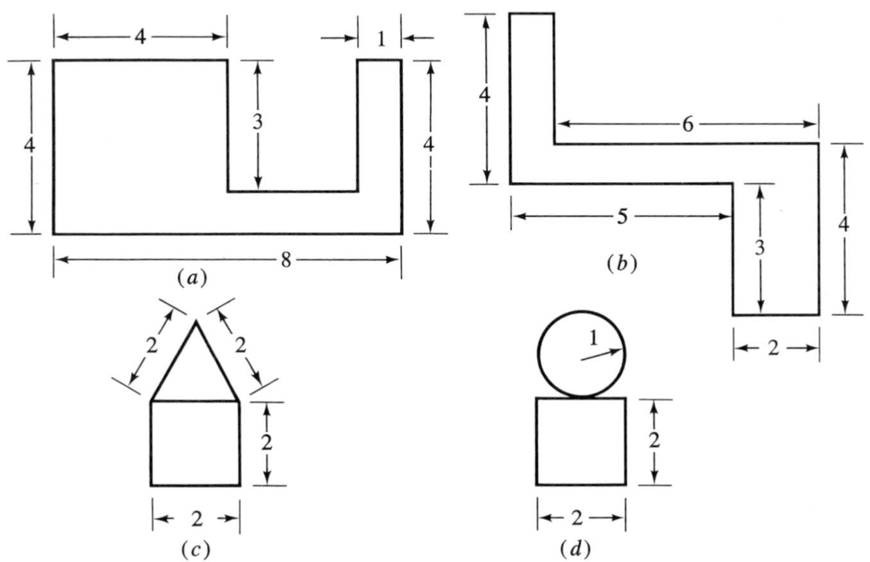

Figure 16.25

16.9

Centers of Gravity of Plane Regions

Suppose we have the problem of finding the center of gravity of a plane region of uniform density. Let us consider the case of a region bounded by $y = f(x)$ $(y \geq 0)$, the x axis, and the vertical lines $x = a$ and $x = b$ (see Figure 16.26). If we cut the

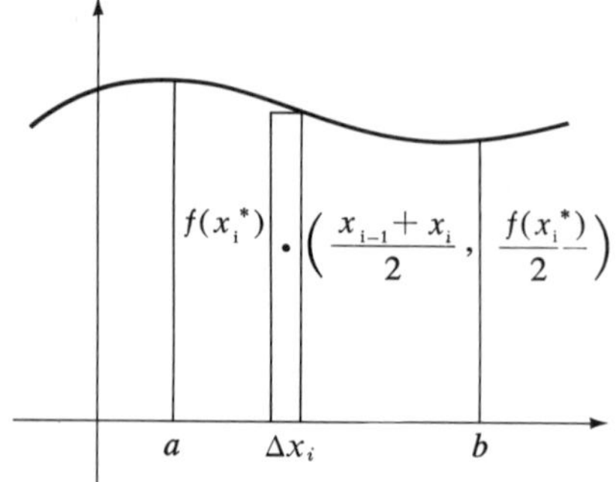

Figure 16.26

region into vertical strips, then the interval $[a, b]$ is subdivided and a number x_i^* $(i = 1, 2, 3, \ldots, n)$ is chosen in each subinterval. Then $f(x_i^*)$ is taken to be the height of the ith rectangle, and $\Delta x_i = x_i - x_{i-1}$ is the width. The center of gravity of each rectangle is at its geometric center, with coordinates

$$\left(\frac{x_{i-1} + x_i}{2}, \frac{f(x_i^*)}{2}\right)$$

(see Figure 16.26). Thus, the moments about the x and y axes for this strip are

$$m_x = \frac{f(x_i^*)}{2} \cdot f(x_i^*)\,\Delta x_i \quad \text{and} \quad m_y = \frac{x_{i-1} + x_i}{2} \cdot f(x_i^*)\,\Delta x_i.$$

Since moments can be added, we can approximate the moments for the desired region by adding the moments for all of the strips. Finally we get the exact values by taking the limit of this sum as the widths of all of them approach zero. Of course this gives integrals:

$$M_x = \int_a^b \frac{y^2}{2}\,dx, \qquad M_y = \int_a^b xy\,dx.$$

If these are compared with the integral for the area of this region,

$$A = \int_a^b y\,dx,$$

and if the center of gravity of the vertical strip is represented by $(x, y/2)$, we see that the moment about the x axis, M_x, is given by the integral for area with $y/2$ (the distance of the center of gravity of the strip from the x axis) as an additional factor. Similarly, the moment about the y axis is given by the integral for area, with x (the distance from the y axis) as an additional factor.

You are advised *not* to memorize these formulas. As in the case of area or volume, there are too many different possibilities to try to catalog all of them. *The important thing to remember is the method* leading to the above formulas rather than the formulas themselves.

Example 1

Find the center of gravity of the region bounded by $y = x^2$, $y = 0$, and $x = 1$.

We assume here that the region is of uniform density—we make this assumption throughout this section. The situation is illustrated graphically in Figure 16.27. This is exactly the same as the case illustrated previously. Thus,

$$A = \int_0^1 y\,dx = \int_0^1 x^2\,dx = \frac{x^3}{3}\bigg|_0^1 = \frac{1}{3},$$

$$M_x = \int_0^1 \frac{y^2}{2}\,dx = \int_0^1 \frac{x^4}{2}\,dx = \frac{x^5}{10}\bigg|_0^1 = \frac{1}{10},$$

$$M_y = \int_0^1 xy\,dx = \int_0^1 x^3\,dx = \frac{x^4}{4}\bigg|_0^1 = \frac{1}{4};$$

and

$$\bar{x} = \frac{M_y}{A} = \frac{1/4}{1/3} = \frac{3}{4},$$

$$\bar{y} = \frac{M_x}{A} = \frac{1/10}{1/3} = \frac{3}{10}.$$

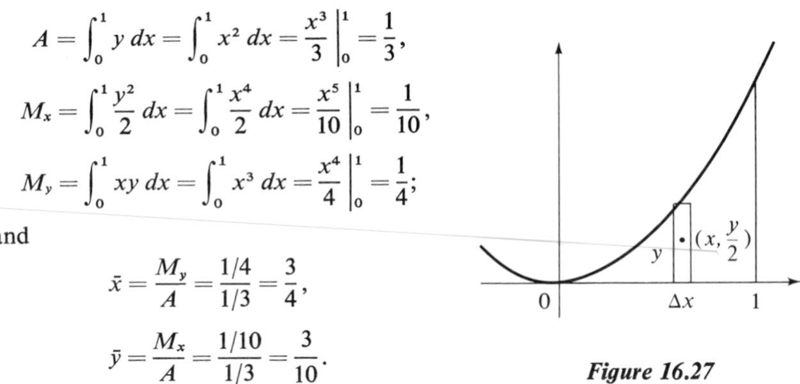

Figure 16.27

Example 2

Find the center of gravity of the region in the first quadrant bounded by $x = -y^2 + 2y + 3$.

The graph is given in Figure 16.28. In this case it is much easier to cut the region into horizontal strips than vertical ones. Thus

$$A = \int_0^3 x\,dy = \int_0^3 (-y^2 + 2y + 3)\,dy = -\frac{y^3}{3} + y^2 + 3y\bigg|_0^3 = 9,$$

$$M_x = \int_0^3 xy\,dy = \int_0^3 (-y^3 + 2y^2 + 3y)\,dy = -\frac{y^4}{4} + \frac{2y^3}{3} + \frac{3y^2}{2}\bigg|_0^3 = \frac{45}{4},$$

$$M_y = \int_0^3 \frac{x^2}{2}\,dy = \frac{1}{2}\int_0^3 (-y^2 + 2y + 3)^2\,dy$$

$$= \frac{1}{2}\int_0^3 (y^4 - 4y^3 - 2y^2 + 12y + 9)\,dy$$

$$= \frac{1}{2}\left(\frac{y^5}{5} - y^4 - \frac{2y^3}{3} + 6y^2 + 9y\right)\bigg|_0^3 = \frac{423}{10};$$

and

$$\bar{x} = \frac{M_y}{A} = \frac{423/10}{9} = \frac{47}{10},$$

$$\bar{y} = \frac{M_x}{A} = \frac{45/4}{9} = \frac{5}{4}.$$

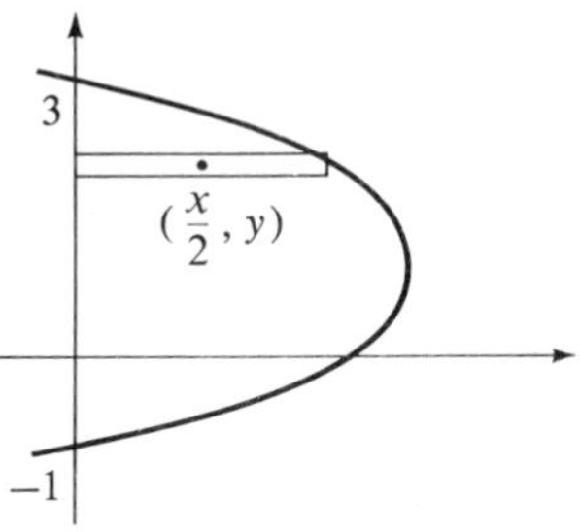

Figure 16.28

Example 3

Find the center of gravity of the region bounded by $y = x$ and $y = x^2$.

The graph is given in Figure 16.29. Let us note that the y coordinate of the center of gravity of the vertical strip is half-way between the top and bottom, which is the average of the y coordinates. Thus

$$A = \int_0^1 (y_1 - y_2)\,dx = \int_0^1 (x - x^2)\,dx$$

$$= \frac{x^2}{2} - \frac{x^3}{3}\Big|_0^1 = \frac{1}{6},$$

$$M_x = \int_0^1 (y_1 - y_2)\frac{y_1 + y_2}{2}\,dx$$

$$= \frac{1}{2}\int_0^1 (y_1^2 - y_2^2)\,dx = \frac{1}{2}\int_0^1 (x^2 - x^4)\,dx$$

$$= \frac{1}{2}\left(\frac{x^3}{3} - \frac{x^5}{5}\right)\Big|_0^1 = \frac{1}{15},$$

$$M_y = \int_0^1 (y_1 - y_2)x\,dx = \int_0^1 (x^2 - x^3)\,dx$$

$$= \frac{x^3}{3} - \frac{x^4}{4}\Big|_0^1 = \frac{1}{12};$$

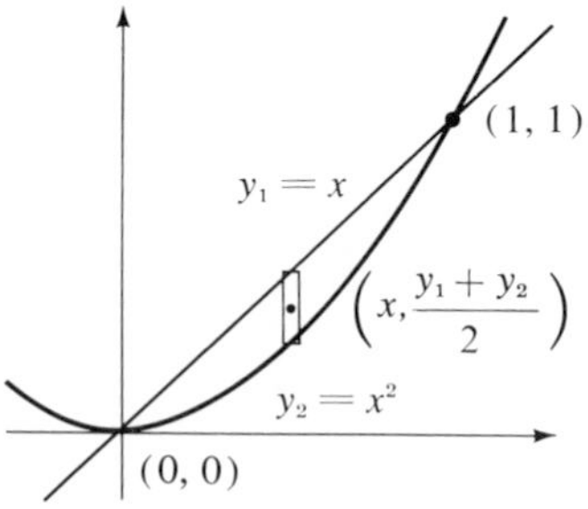

Figure 16.29

and

$$\bar{x} = \frac{M_y}{A} = \frac{1/12}{1/6} = \frac{1}{2},$$

$$\bar{y} = \frac{M_x}{A} = \frac{1/15}{1/6} = \frac{2}{5}.$$

Problems

In Problems 1–24, find the centers of gravity of the regions bounded by the given curves. They are of uniform density.

1. $y = x^2$, $y = 0$, $x = 2$.
2. $y = x^3$, $y = 0$, $x = 1$.
3. $y = x^4$, $y = 0$, $x = 1$.
4. $y = \sqrt{x}$, $y = 0$, $x = 1$.
5. $y = x^2$, $x = 0$, $y = 1$ (first quadrant).
6. $y = x^3$, $x = 0$, $y = 1$.
7. $y = x^3 - x^2$, $y = 0$.
8. $y = x(x - 1)^2$, $y = 0$.
9. $x = y^4 + 1$, $x = 0$, $y = 0$, $y = 1$.
10. $x = y^2 - 1$, $x = 0$.
11. $y = \sin x$, $y = 0$ between $x = 0$ and $x = \pi$.
12. $y = e^x$, $y = 0$, left of $x = 0$. (Hint: $\lim_{k \to -\infty} (k - 1)e^k = 0$.)
13. $y = \dfrac{1}{x^2 + 1}$, $y = 0$.
14. $y = 1/x^2$, $y = 0$, right of $x = 1$.
15. $y = x^3$, $y = x$ (first quadrant).
16. $y = x^4$, $y = x$.
17. $y = 4 - x^2$, $y = \dfrac{x^2}{4} - 1$.
18. $x^2/9 - y^2/16 = 1$, $x = 5$.
19. $x^2/a^2 + y^2/b^2 = 1$, $x = 0$, $y = 0$ (first quadrant).
20. $x^{2/3} + y^{2/3} = a^{2/3}$, $x = 0$, $y = 0$ (first quadrant).

21. $\sqrt{x}+\sqrt{y}=\sqrt{a}$, $x=0$, $y=0$.

22. $y=x^2$, $x-y+2=0$.

23. $x^2+y^2=4$, above $y=0$.

24. $x^2+y^2=4$, above $y=1$.

25. The First Theorem of Pappus states that if a region R is entirely on one side of a line, then the volume of the solid generated by rotating R about that line is the product of the area of R and the length of the path of the center of gravity of R. Verify this for the region bounded by $y=x^2$, the y axis, and $y=1$ rotated about the x axis.

26. Verify the First Theorem of Pappus (see Problem 25) for the region bounded by $y=x^2$, the x axis, and $x=1$ rotated about the x axis.

16.10

Centers of Gravity of Solids of Revolution

In considering the center of gravity of a solid, we need to find moments about planes, rather than axes. Just as we considered only moments about two axes in the plane, we shall consider only moments about two planes here. One of these contains the x axis and is perpendicular to the y axis; we call this the xz plane. The other contains the y axis and is perpendicular to the x axis; we call it the yz plane.

By an analysis similar to the one of the previous section, we can find moments for solids of revolution in much the same way that we did for plane regions: that is, the moment about the xz plane is given by the integral for volume with an additional factor, which is the distance (with appropriate sign) from the center of gravity of the disc or shell to the xz plane. Since the axis of revolution is also an axis of symmetry, the center of gravity is on it (we are considering only solids of uniform density). Thus, only one moment is needed.

Example 1

Find the center of gravity of the solid formed by rotating about the x axis the region bounded by $y=x^2$, $y=0$, and $x=1$.

The graph is given in Figure 16.30. Since the x axis is an axis of symmetry, the center of gravity is on it. All we need to find is its x coordinate. From Figure 16.30 we have

$$V=\int_0^1 \pi y^2\,dx=\pi\int_0^1 x^4\,dx$$

$$=\frac{\pi x^5}{5}\bigg|_0^1=\frac{\pi}{5},$$

$$M_{yz}=\int_0^1 \pi y^2 x\,dx=\pi\int_0^1 x^5\,dx$$

$$=\frac{\pi x^6}{6}\bigg|_0^1=\frac{\pi}{6},$$

and

$$\bar{x}=\frac{M_{yz}}{V}=\frac{\pi/6}{\pi/5}=\frac{5}{6}.$$

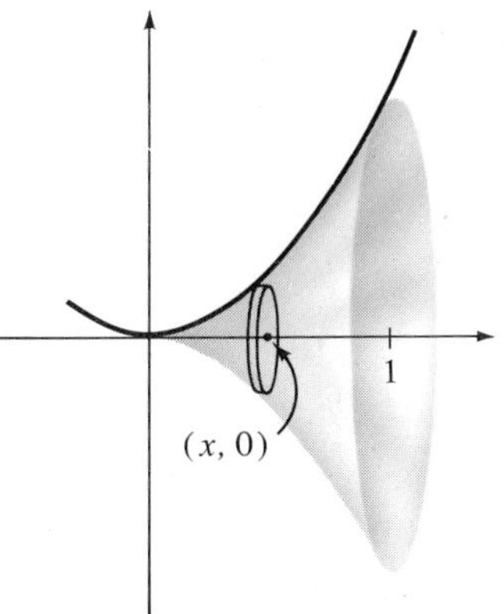

Figure 16.30

Example 2

The region of Example 1 is rotated about the y axis. Find its center of gravity.

By symmetry, the center of gravity is on the y axis—we need only find the y coordinate. Let us consider both the disc method and the shell method for finding the volume and moment. Figure 16.31 shows a representative disc. The center of gravity of the disc is in the center of the hole at $(0, y)$. From the figure, we have

$$V = \int_0^1 \pi(1 - x^2)\,dy = \pi \int_0^1 (1 - y)\,dy = \pi\left(y - \frac{y^2}{2}\right)\Bigg|_0^1 = \frac{\pi}{2},$$

$$M_{xz} = \int_0^1 \pi(1 - x^2)y\,dy = \pi \int_0^1 (y - y^2)\,dy = \pi\left(\frac{y^2}{2} - \frac{y^3}{3}\right)\Bigg|_0^1 = \frac{\pi}{6},$$

and

$$\bar{y} = \frac{M_{xz}}{V} = \frac{\pi/6}{\pi/2} = \frac{1}{3}.$$

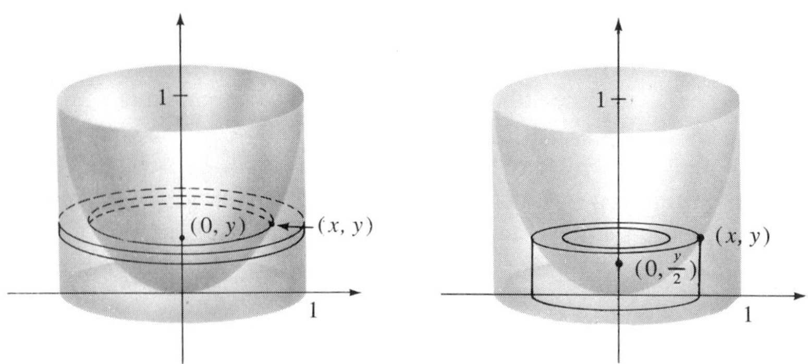

Figure 16.31 *Figure 16.32*

Figure 16.32 shows the same solid with a representative shell. Again, the center of gravity of the shell is in the center of the hole at $(0, y/2)$. Thus we have

$$V = \int_0^1 2\pi xy\,dx = 2\pi \int_0^1 x^3\,dx = \frac{\pi x^4}{2}\Bigg|_0^1 = \frac{\pi}{2},$$

$$M_{xz} = \int_0^1 2\pi xy \cdot \frac{y}{2}\,dx = \pi \int_0^1 x^5\,dx = \frac{\pi x^6}{6}\Bigg|_0^1 = \frac{\pi}{6},$$

and

$$\bar{y} = \frac{M_{xz}}{V} = \frac{\pi/6}{\pi/2} = \frac{1}{3}.$$

Although both the volume and moment were computed by both methods in the example above, there is no need to use the same method for both of them. If it is easier to find the volume by one method and the moment by the other, by all means do so.

Example 3

Find the center of gravity of the solid formed by rotating about the y axis the region bounded by $y = \cos x$ and $y = 0$, between $x = 0$ and $x = \pi/2$.

The solid is given in Figure 16.33 with a representative cylindrical shell (the use of circular discs is considerably more difficult). Thus we have

$$V = \int_0^{\pi/2} 2\pi xy\, dx$$

$$= 2\pi \int_0^{\pi/2} x \cos x\, dx \qquad \begin{cases} u = x, & v' = \cos x \\ u' = 1, & v = \sin x \end{cases}$$

$$= 2\pi(x \sin x + \cos x)\Big|_0^{\pi/2}$$

$$= \pi(\pi - 2)\,.$$

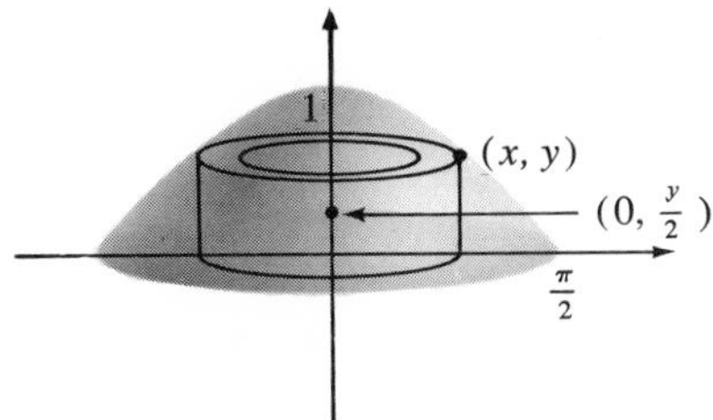

Figure 16.33

$$M_{xz} = \int_0^{\pi/2} \pi xy^2\, dx$$

$$= \pi \int_0^{\pi/2} x \cos^2 x\, dx \qquad \begin{cases} u = x, & v' = \cos^2 x = \dfrac{1 + \cos 2x}{2} \\ u' = 1, & v = \dfrac{x}{2} + \dfrac{1}{4} \sin 2x \end{cases}$$

$$= \pi\left(\frac{x^2}{4} + \frac{x}{4} \sin 2x + \frac{1}{8} \cos 2x\right)\Big|_0^{\pi/2}$$

$$= \frac{\pi(\pi^2 - 4)}{16};$$

and

$$\bar{y} = \frac{M_{xz}}{V} = \frac{\pi(\pi^2 - 4)/16}{\pi(\pi - 2)} = \frac{\pi + 2}{16}.$$

Of course, the center of gravity is on the y axis.

Problems

Find the center of gravity of the solid formed by rotating about the given axis the region bounded by the given curves. The solids are assumed to be of uniform density.

1. $y = x^3$, $y = 0$, $x = 1$; about the x axis.
2. $y = x^3$, $y = 0$, $x = 1$; about the y axis.
3. $y = (x - 1)^2$, $y = 0$, $x = 0$; about the y axis.

4. $y = 1 - x$, $x = 0$, $y = 0$; about the y axis.
5. $y = 2 - 2x$, $x = 0$, $y = 0$; about the y axis.
6. $y = 2x - x^2$, $x = 0$; about the y axis.
7. $x^2 + y^2 = 1$, right of $x = 0$; about the x axis.
8. $x^2 + y^2 = 4$, right of $x = 1$; about the x axis.
9. $x^2/a^2 + y^2/b^2 = 1$, right of $x = 0$; about the x axis.
10. $x^2/a^2 + y^2/b^2 = 1$, above $y = 0$; about the y axis.
11. $x^2 - y^2 = 1$, $x = 2$; about the x axis.
12. $x^2 - y^2 = 1$, $y = 0$, $y = 1$; about the y axis.
13. $y = 1/(x^2 + 1)$, $y = 0$, right of $x = 0$; about the y axis.
14. $y = \sin x$, $y = 0$, between $x = 0$ and $x = \pi/2$; about the x axis.
15. $y = \cos x^2$, $y = 0$, between $x = 0$ and $x = \sqrt{\pi/2}$; about the y axis.
16. $y = e^{-x}$, $y = 0$, right of $x = 0$; about the x axis. (Hint: $\lim_{k \to +\infty} (2k + 1)e^{-2k} = 0$.)
17. $y = \ln x$, $y = 0$, between $x = 1$ and $x = e$; about the y axis.
18. $y = x^2 - x$, x axis; about the y axis.
19. $x = y^2 - 4y$, y axis; about the x axis.
20. $y = 1/x^2$, $y = 0$, right of $x = 1$; about the x axis.

16.11

Centers of Gravity of Arcs and Surfaces

By an analysis similar to the one used for centers of gravity of plane regions in Section 16.9, we can find the center of gravity of an arc or a surface of revolution. For an arc we have

$$L = \int_a^b ds, \qquad M_x = \int_a^b y\, ds, \qquad M_y = \int_a^b x\, ds;$$

and

$$\bar{x} = \frac{M_y}{L}, \qquad \bar{y} = \frac{M_x}{L},$$

where ds is the differential of arc given in Section 16.7 (page 395).

If an arc is rotated about the x axis to give a surface of revolution, then

$$S_x = \int_a^b 2\pi\, |y|\, ds, \quad M_{yz} = \int_a^b 2\pi x\, |y|\, ds, \quad \text{and} \quad \bar{x} = \frac{M_{yz}}{S_x}.$$

Of course, the center of gravity is on the x axis by symmetry.

Similarly, if the arc is rotated about the y axis, then

$$S_y = \int_a^b 2\pi\, |x|\, ds, \quad M_{xz} = \int_a^b 2\pi\, |x|\, y\, ds, \quad \text{and} \quad \bar{y} = \frac{M_{xz}}{S_y}.$$

Example 1

Find the center of gravity of the arc $y=\sqrt{1-x^2}$.

The curve is a semicircle—its graph is given in Figure 16.34. We see by symmetry that $\bar{x}=0$; we need only find $\bar{y}$.

$$y'=\frac{-x}{\sqrt{1-x^2}},$$

$$\begin{aligned}L&=\int_{-1}^{1}\sqrt{1+(y')^2}\,dx\\&=2\int_0^1\sqrt{1+\frac{x^2}{1-x^2}}\,dx\\&=2\lim_{\epsilon\to 0^+}\int_0^{1-\epsilon}\frac{dx}{\sqrt{1-x^2}}\\&=2\lim_{\epsilon\to 0^+}\operatorname{Arcsin}x\Big|_0^{1-\epsilon}\\&=2\lim_{\epsilon\to 0^+}\operatorname{Arcsin}(1-\epsilon)=\pi;\end{aligned}$$

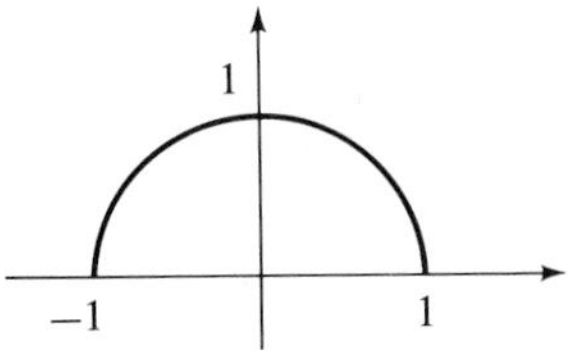

Figure 16.34

$$\begin{aligned}M_x&=\int_{-1}^{1}y\sqrt{1+(y')^2}\,dx\\&=\int_{-1}^{1}\sqrt{1-x^2}\,\frac{1}{\sqrt{1-x^2}}\,dx\\&=\int_{-1}^{1}dx\\&=x\Big|_{-1}^{1}\\&=2.\end{aligned}$$

Thus $\bar{y}=\dfrac{M_x}{L}=\dfrac{2}{\pi}$.

Example 2

Find the center of gravity of the arc of the circle $x=\cos\theta$, $y=\sin\theta$ in the first quadrant.

This is again a circle of radius one with center at the origin. The first quadrant corresponds to values of θ from $\theta=0$ to $\theta=\pi/2$.

$$\frac{dx}{d\theta}=-\sin\theta,\qquad \frac{dy}{d\theta}=\cos\theta;$$

$$\begin{aligned}L&=\int_0^{\pi/2}\sqrt{\left(\frac{dx}{d\theta}\right)^2+\left(\frac{dy}{d\theta}\right)^2}\,d\theta\\&=\int_0^{\pi/2}\sqrt{\sin^2\theta+\cos^2\theta}\,d\theta\\&=\int_0^{\pi/2}d\theta\\&=\theta\Big|_0^{\pi/2}\\&=\pi/2;\end{aligned}$$

$$M_x = \int_0^{\pi/2} y\sqrt{\left(\frac{dx}{d\theta}\right)^2 + \left(\frac{dy}{d\theta}\right)^2}\, d\theta$$

$$= \int_0^{\pi/2} \sin\theta\, d\theta$$

$$= -\cos\theta \Big|_0^{\pi/2}$$

$$= 1.$$

$$M_y = \int_0^{\pi/2} x\sqrt{\left(\frac{dx}{d\theta}\right)^2 + \left(\frac{dy}{d\theta}\right)^2}\, d\theta$$

$$= \int_0^{\pi/2} \cos\theta\, d\theta$$

$$= \sin\theta \Big|_0^{\pi/2}$$

$$= 1.$$

Thus

$$\bar{x} = \frac{M_y}{L} = \frac{1}{\pi/2} = \frac{2}{\pi},$$

$$\bar{y} = \frac{M_x}{L} = \frac{1}{\pi/2} = \frac{2}{\pi}.$$

Example 3

Find the center of gravity of the surface formed by rotating about the x axis the arc of Example 2.

$$S_x = \int_0^{\pi/2} 2\pi|y|\sqrt{\left(\frac{dx}{d\theta}\right)^2 + \left(\frac{dy}{d\theta}\right)^2}\, d\theta$$

$$= \int_0^{\pi/2} 2\pi \sin\theta\, d\theta$$

$$= -2\pi\cos\theta \Big|_0^{\pi/2}$$

$$= 2\pi;$$

$$M_{yz} = \int_0^{\pi/2} 2\pi x|y|\sqrt{\left(\frac{dx}{d\theta}\right)^2 + \left(\frac{dy}{d\theta}\right)^2}\, d\theta$$

$$= \int_0^{\pi/2} 2\pi \cos\theta \sin\theta\, d\theta$$

$$= \pi \sin^2\theta \Big|_0^{\pi/2}$$

$$= \pi.$$

Thus the center of gravity is on the x axis, with

$$\bar{x} = \frac{M_{yz}}{S_x} = \frac{\pi}{2\pi} = \frac{1}{2}.$$

Example 4

Find the center of gravity of the surface formed by rotating about the y axis the portion of $x^2 + y^2 = 1$ in the first quadrant.

This is basically the same problem as Example 3, except this time it is in rectangular coordinates and the arc is rotated about the y axis.

$$y = \sqrt{1 - x^2}, \qquad y' = \frac{-x}{\sqrt{1 - x^2}};$$

$$\begin{aligned}
S_y &= \int_0^1 2\pi |x| \sqrt{1 + (y')^2}\, dx \\
&= \lim_{\epsilon \to 0^+} \int_0^{1-\epsilon} 2\pi \frac{x}{\sqrt{1 - x^2}}\, dx \\
&= \lim_{\epsilon \to 0^+} -2\pi \sqrt{1 - x^2}\,\Big|_0^{1-\epsilon} \\
&= \lim_{\epsilon \to 0^+} [2\pi - 2\pi \sqrt{1 - (1 - \epsilon)^2}] = 2\pi; \\
M_{xz} &= \int_0^1 2\pi y |x| \sqrt{1 + (y')^2}\, dx \\
&= \int_0^1 2\pi x\, dx \\
&= \pi x^2 \Big|_0^1 \\
&= \pi.
\end{aligned}$$

Thus the center of gravity is on the y axis, with

$$\bar{y} = \frac{M_{xz}}{S_y} = \frac{\pi}{2\pi} = \frac{1}{2}.$$

Problems

In Problems 1–10 find the center of gravity of the given arc.

1. The portion of $x^{2/3} + y^{2/3} = a^{2/3}$ in the first quadrant.
2. $y^2 = 4x$ from $(1, -2)$ to $(1, 2)$.
3. $x^2 = 8y$ from $(-4, 2)$ to $(4, 2)$.
4. The portion of $x^2 + 4y = 4$ in the first quadrant.
5. $y = \cosh x$ from $x = -1$ to $x = 1$.
6. $x = \theta - \sin\theta$, $y = 1 - \cos\theta$ from $\theta = 0$ to $\theta = 2\pi$. (The curve is symmetric about $x = \pi$).
7. $x = a(\theta - \sin\theta)$, $y = a(1 - \cos\theta)$ from $\theta = 0$ to $\theta = \pi$.
8. $x = \cos^3\theta$, $y = \sin^3\theta$ from $\theta = 0$ to $\theta = \pi/2$.
9. $y = \dfrac{x^3}{6} + \dfrac{1}{2x}$ from $x = 1$ to $x = 3$.
10. $x = \dfrac{y^3}{3} + \dfrac{1}{4y}$ from $y = 1$ to $y = 3$.

In Problems 11–16, the given arc is rotated about the x axis. Find the center of gravity of the resulting surface.

11. All of $x = \sqrt{1 - y^2}$.
12. $x^2 + y^2 = 4$ from $(2, 0)$ to $(1, \sqrt{3})$ (first quadrant).
13. $y = \cosh x$ from $x = -1$ to $x = 1$.
14. $y = x$ from $(0, 0)$ to $(1, 1)$.

15. $y = \dfrac{x^3}{3} + \dfrac{1}{4x}$ from $x = 1$ to $x = 3$.

16. $x = \theta - \sin\theta$, $y = 1 - \cos\theta$ from $\theta = 0$ to $\theta = \pi/2$.

In Problems 17–20, the given arc is rotated about the y axis. Find the center of gravity of the resulting surface.

17. $x = \sqrt{y}$ from $y = 0$ to $y = 4$.

18. $y = hx/r$ from $(0, 0)$ to (r, h).

19. $y = \cosh x$ from $x = 0$ to $x = 1$.

20. Top half of $x^2 + y^2 - 2x = 0$.

21. The Second Theorem of Pappus states that if a plane arc lies entirely on one side of a line, then the area of the surface formed by rotating the arc about that line is the product of the length of the arc and the length of the path of the center of gravity of the arc. Verify this for the arc $y = \sqrt{1 - x^2}$ rotated about the x axis.

22. Verify the Second Theorem of Pappus (see Problem 21) for the arc $y = x^2$ from $(0, 0)$ to $(1, 1)$ rotated about the y axis.

16.12

Moments of Inertia

In previous sections we have dealt with moments in the determination of centers of gravity. In each case the moment was the product of the weight and a distance. This is called the first moment.

Let us consider another moment. If a weight w is concentrated at a distance x from a given line, then the moment of inertia of the weight about the line is defined to be

$$I = wx^2.$$

This is called the second moment. Inertia is the property of matter to resist motion when at rest and to resist a change in speed or direction when in motion. The moment of inertia is a measure of this tendency—the greater the moment of inertia, the greater the tendency to resist changes in motion.

Example 1

Find the moment of inertia about the y axis of a five-pound weight at $x = 3$.

$$\begin{aligned} I_y &= wx^2 \\ &= 5 \cdot 3^2 \\ &= 45. \end{aligned}$$

Example 2

Find the moment of inertia about the y axis of a system consisting of a five-pound weight at $x = 3$ and a five-pound weight at $x = -3$.

$$\begin{aligned} I_y &= w_1x_1^2 + w_2x_2^2 \\ &= 5 \cdot 3^2 + 5(-3)^2 \\ &= 90. \end{aligned}$$

We see by these examples that the symmetry of the system does not bring about a cancellation of the two moments as it did with first moments. Since the distance is squared, the individual moments are never negative; and, instead of canceling, the individual moments add up to give a bigger moment. Note also that here we are not using the moment to find something else as we did with first moments. Thus, the density will not cancel out as it did when finding centers of gravity. We must take density into consideration when finding a moment of inertia.

Example 3

Find the moment of inertia about the y axis of the region bounded by $y = x^2$, the x axis, and $x = 1$ where the region has a density of 2 g/cm². (The units for all of the equations are cm.)

$$I_y = \lim_{\|s\| \to 0} \sum_{i=1}^{n} x_i^2 w_i$$

$$= \lim_{\|s\| \to 0} \sum_{i=1}^{n} x_i^2 \cdot 2y_i \, \Delta x_i$$

$$= \int_0^1 x^2 \cdot 2y \, dx$$

$$= 2 \int_0^1 x^4 \, dx$$

$$= \frac{2x^5}{5} \Big|_0^1$$

$$= \frac{2}{5} \text{ gm cm}^2.$$

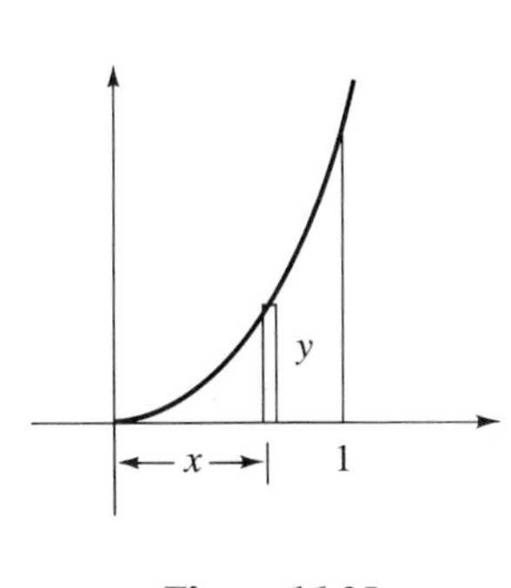

Figure 16.35

Example 4

Find the moment of inertia about the x axis of the region of Example 3.

We cannot use vertical strips as we did in Example 3, because the points on them are not all the same distance from the x axis (nor will they approach that in the limit). We must use horizontal strips (see Figure 16.36).

$$I_y = \int_0^1 y^2 \cdot 2(1 - x) \, dy$$

$$= 2 \int_0^1 y^2(1 - \sqrt{y}) \, dy$$

$$= 2 \int_0^1 (y^2 - y^{5/2}) \, dy$$

$$= 2\left(\frac{y^3}{3} - \frac{2}{7} y^{7/2}\right) \Big|_0^1$$

$$= \frac{2}{21} \text{ gm cm}^2.$$

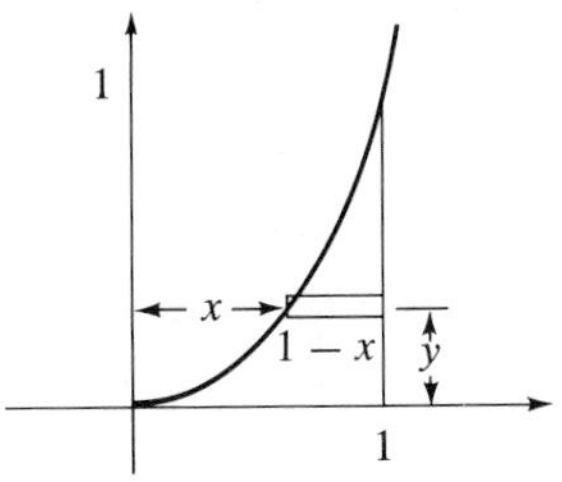

Figure 16.36

A quantity related to the moment of inertia is the radius of gyration. If the entire weight W of a region is located at a distance R from the axis of reference, then

$$I = WR^2, \quad \text{or} \quad R = \sqrt{1/W}.$$

Thus, for any region, the radius of gyration is given by $R = \sqrt{1/W}$.

Example 5

Find the radius of gyration about the y axis of the region of Example 3.

From Example 3, $I_y = 2/5$.

$$\begin{aligned} W &= \int_0^1 2y\,dx \\ &= 2\int_0^1 x^2\,dx \\ &= \frac{2x^3}{3}\bigg|_0^1 \\ &= \frac{2}{3}\text{ gm.} \end{aligned}$$

Thus

$$R = \sqrt{I/W} = \sqrt{\frac{2/5}{2/3}} = \sqrt{3/5}\,\text{cm.}$$

This indicates that, with respect to motion about the y axis, the region resists changes in motion as if all of the weight were concentrated $\sqrt{3/5}$ cm from the y axis. It might be noted that the density is not needed for finding the radius of gyration, since it must always cancel out.

Example 6

Find the radius of gyration about the x axis of the region of Example 4.

From Example 4, $I_x = 2/21$. From Example 5, $W = 2/3$, thus

$$R = \sqrt{I/W} = \sqrt{\frac{2/21}{2/3}} = \frac{1}{\sqrt{7}}\text{ cm.}$$

Problems

Find the moment of inertia and radius of gyration about the given axis.

1. 5-lb weight at $x = 2$, 2-lb weight at $x = -1$; about y axis.
2. 10-lb weight at $x = 1$, 10-lb weight at $x = 4$; about y axis.
3. 2-lb weight at $x = -2$, 4-lb weight at $x = -3$; about y axis.
4. 3-lb weight at $x = 5$, 2-lb weight at $x = -2$; about y axis.
5. The region bounded by $y = x^2$, the y axis, $y = 1$ (first quadrant); density 3 gm/cm²; about y axis.

6. The region of Problem 5; about x axis.
7. The region bounded by $y = x^3$, the x axis, $x = 1$; density 10 gm/cm²; about x axis.
8. The region of Problem 7; about y axis.
9. The region bounded by $y = x - x^2$ and the x axis; density 1 gm/cm²; about y axis.
10. The region of Problem 9; about x axis.
11. The region of Example 3; about $x = 1$.
12. The region of Example 3; about $y = 1$.
13. The region bounded by $y = \sin x$ and the x axis between $x = 0$ and $x = \pi$; density 1 gm/cm²; about y axis.
14. The region of Problem 13; about $x = \pi/2$.
15. The region bounded by $y = e^x$, the x axis and between $x = -1$ and $x = 0$; density 9 gm/cm²; about y axis.
16. The region of Problem 15; about $x = -1$.
17. The region bounded by $y = 1/x$, the x axis and between $x = 1$ and $x = 2$; density 8 gm/cm²; about y axis.
18. The region of Problem 17; about x axis.
19. Inside $x^2 + y^2 = 1$; density 1 gm/cm²; about y axis.
20. Inside $4x^2 + y^2 = 4$; density 1 gm/cm²; about y axis.
21. The region of Problem 20; about x axis.
22. The region bounded by $\sqrt{x} + \sqrt{y} = 1$ and both axes; density 3 gm/cm²; about x axis.

16.13

Fluid Force

Suppose a swimming pool is 15 feet wide and 30 feet long, has a horizontal bottom, and is 8 feet deep. Suppose further that we want to find the force of the water on the bottom of the pool. This is a relatively easy problem. The pressure (force per unit area) of the water on the bottom is the product of the depth and the density of water.

$$\begin{aligned} P &= 8(62.4) \\ &= 499.2 \text{ lb/ft}^2. \end{aligned}$$

The total force is then the product of the pressure and the area.

$$\begin{aligned} F &= P \cdot A \\ &= (499.2)(15.30) \\ &= 224{,}640 \text{ lb}. \end{aligned}$$

Now let us consider the problem of finding the force on one end of the pool. This problem is not so simple as the first. Since different parts of the wall are at different depths, the pressure is not a constant; it varies from 0 at the top to $8(62.4) = 499.2$ lb/ft² at the bottom. This continuous variation suggests the use of the integral. Let us introduce coordinate axes, as in Figure 16.37. Now we subdivide the interval [0, 8] on the y axis by

$$y_0 = 0, y_1, y_2, y_3, \ldots, y_{n-1}, \quad y_n = 8,$$

and select a number y^* in each subinterval such that

$$y_{i-1} \leq y_i^* \leq y_i.$$

Let us consider the force on a horizontal strip corresponding to the ith subinterval (see Figure 16.37). We can approximate the depth below the surface by $8 - y_i^*$.

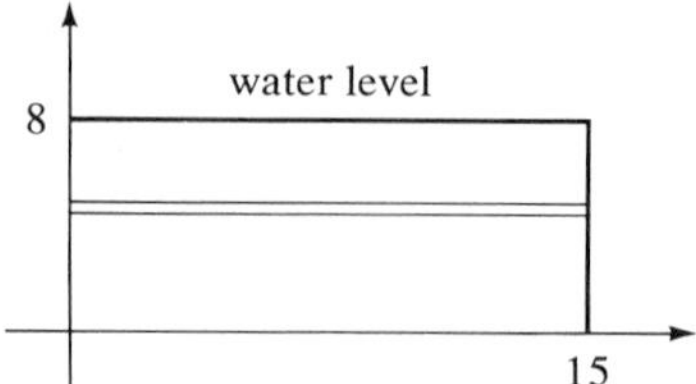

Figure 16.37

Although the points of the strip are not all at this depth, none differs by more than the width of the interval $y_i - y_{i-1}$. Thus the pressure is $62.4(8 - y_i^*)$, and the force on the horizontal strip is the product of this pressure and the area of the strip,

$$62.4(8 - y_i^*)15(y_i - y_{i-1}) = 936(8 - y_i^*)\,\Delta y_i,$$

where $\Delta y_i = y_i - y_{i-1}$. We can approximate the total force on the wall by adding together the forces for all of the horizontal strips. The exact value is found by taking the limit of this approximating sum as the lengths of all the subintervals approach 0.

$$\begin{aligned} F &= \lim_{\|s\| \to 0} \sum_{i=1}^{n} 936(8 - y_i^*)\,\Delta y_i \\ &= \int_0^8 936(8 - y)\,dy \\ &= 936\left(8y - \frac{y^2}{2}\right)\Bigg|_0^8 \\ &= 29{,}952 \text{ lb.} \end{aligned}$$

While this is a simple case, it illustrates how the integral may be used to determine fluid forces.

Example 1

A swimming pool is ten feet wide and twenty feet long. The bottom is flat (but not horizontal) and the sides are vertical. The water is three feet deep at one end and ten feet deep at the other. Find the force of the water on one twenty-foot side.

Coordinate axes are put in the position shown in Figure 16.38. Notice that the downward direction is taken to be positive so that we can deal with positive numbers throughout. The equation of the line through (20, 3) and (0, 10) is $7x + 20y = 200$. We see from Figure 16.38 that, while the horizontal strips always have their left ends on the y axis, the right ends are sometimes on

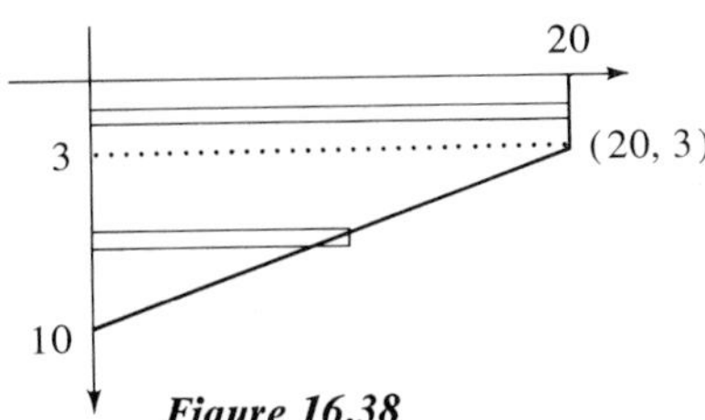

Figure 16.38

the vertical line $x = 20$ and sometimes on $7x + 20y = 200$. Thus we need two integrals.

$$F = \int_0^3 (62.4)y(20)\,dy + \int_3^{10} (62.4)y\left(\frac{200 - 20y}{7}\right) dy$$

$$= 1248 \int_0^3 y\,dy + \frac{1248}{7} \int_3^{10} (10y - y^2)\,dy$$

$$= 624y^2 \Big|_0^3 + \frac{1248}{7}\left(5y^2 - \frac{y^3}{3}\right)\Big|_3^{10}$$

$$= 28{,}960 \text{ lbs.}$$

Of course, the placement of the axes has no effect on the final result. You are encouraged to see this for yourself by repeating this problem with the axes in another position.

Example 2

Find the force on a circular gate of diameter four feet in a vertical dam where the center of the gate is twenty feet below the surface of the water.

First let us put the coordinate axes in the position indicated in Figure 16.39. The circular gate is then represented by the equation $x^2 + y^2 = 4$. Thus we have

$$F = \int_{-2}^{2} 62.4(20 - y)2x\,dy$$

$$= 124.8 \int_{-2}^{2} (20 - y)\sqrt{4 - y^2}\,dy.$$

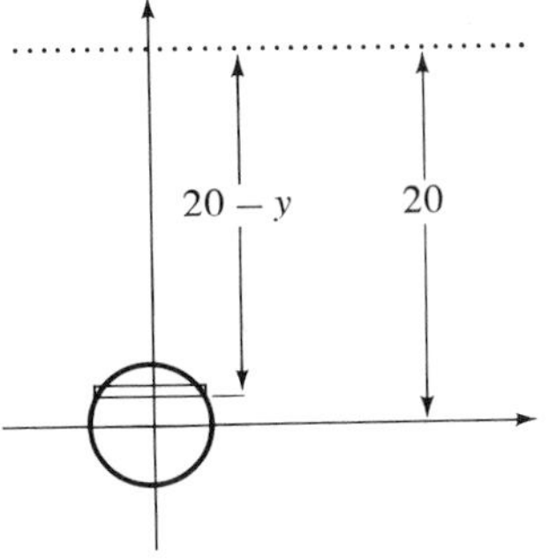

Figure 16.39

Using the substitution $y = 2 \sin \theta$, we have

$$F = 124.8 \int_{-\pi/2}^{\pi/2} (20 - 2 \sin \theta)\sqrt{4 - 4 \sin^2 \theta}\; 2 \cos \theta\, d\theta$$

$$= 124.8 \int_{-\pi/2}^{\pi/2} 8(10 - \sin \theta)\cos^2 \theta\, d\theta$$

$$= 998.4 \int_{-\pi/2}^{\pi/2} [5(1 + \cos 2\theta) - \sin \theta \cos^2 \theta]\, d\theta$$

$$= 998.4\left[5\theta + \frac{5}{2} \sin 2\theta + \frac{1}{3} \cos^3 \theta\right]\Big|_{-\pi/2}^{\pi/2}$$

$$= 4992\,\pi \text{ lbs.}$$

Problems

1. A dam contains a vertical rectangular gate 10 ft wide and 4 ft high. The top of the gate is horizontal and 10 ft below the surface of the water. Find the force on the gate.
2. A vertical wall of a swimming pool is 10 ft wide and 8 ft high. Find the force of water on the wall if the pool is half full.
3. A hollow metal cube has a 1-ft edge. It is suspended under water with the top face horizontal and 10 ft below the surface. Find the total force on all six faces.
4. A dam has a square gate with side 2-ft long and one diagonal vertical. The highest point of the gate is 10 ft below the water surface. Find the force on the gate.
5. An irrigation ditch has a vertical head gate that is a circle of diameter 1 ft. Find the force on the head gate if the water is level with the top of the gate.
6. Find the force on the head gate of Problem 5 if the level of the water is half-way up from the bottom.
7. Find the force on the head gate of Problem 5 if the level of the water is h ft $(0 \leq h \leq 1)$ from the bottom.
8. Find the force on the head gate of Problem 5 if the level of the water is h ft $(h \geq 0)$ above the top of the gate.
9. A trough is 10 ft long and 1 ft high. Vertical cross sections are equilateral triangles with the top side horizontal. Find the force on one end if the trough is filled with water.
10. A trough is 10 ft long and 1 ft high. Vertical cross sections are isosceles right triangles with the hypotenuse horizontal. Find the force on one end if the trough is filled with water.
11. Find the force on one side of the trough of Problem 9.
12. Find the force on one side of the trough of Problem 10.
13. Find the force on the bottom half of a vertical ellipse with major axis 10 and minor axis 6 if the major axis is on the surface of the water.
14. Find the force on the bottom half of the ellipse of Problem 13 if the minor axis is on the surface of the water.
15. A dam has a vertical gate that is an isosceles trapezoid with upper base 6 ft, lower base 8 ft, and height 3 ft. Find the force on the gate if the upper base is 10 ft below the surface.
16. Suppose the gate of Problem 15 were inverted. Find the force on it.
17. A dam is in the shape of a parabola 10 ft high and 8 ft across the top. Find the force on it when filled to the top.
18. Find the force on the dam of Problem 17 when filled half-way to the top.
19. A dam has a vertical gate which is 10 ft wide and 4 ft high. Its top is horizontal and it can withstand a force of 35,000 lb. What is the highest level to which the dam can be filled?
20. A dam has a vertical, circular gate of radius 2 ft. It can withstand a force of 16,000 lb. What is the highest level to which the dam can be filled?
21. A swimming pool is in the form of a circular cylinder of radius 10 ft. What is the force on the wall of the pool if it is filled to a level of 4 ft?
22. Suppose that the gate of Problem 1 is inclined at an angle of 60° with the horizontal. What is the force on it?
23. Suppose that the gate of Problem 1 is inclined at an angle of 45° with the horizontal. What is the force on it?
24. Suppose that the gate of Example 2 is inclined at an angle of 60° with the horizontal. What is the force on it?
25. Show that the force on the vertical face of a dam is the product of the density of the water, the area of the face, and the depth of the center of gravity of the face.

Limits and Continuity: The Epsilon-Delta Approach

17.1

The Limit

Since absolute values and inequalities are used quite extensively throughout this chapter, a review of these topics is given in Appendix A for those who need it. In Chapter 10 we considered limits and continuity by means of a geometric definition. The main disadvantage of that definition is that it depends upon knowledge of an accurate graph of the function in question. Furthermore, you are not likely to encounter that definition for limit in other books. We now consider a more standard definition of limit.

Definition

$\text{Lim}_{x \to a} f(x) = b$ *means*

(a) *if δ is a positive number, then there is a number x in the domain of f such that*

$$0 < |x - a| < \delta, \text{ and}$$

(b) *if ϵ is a positive number, then there is a positive number δ such that*

$$|f(x) - b| < \epsilon$$

for every number x in the domain of f for which

$$0 < |x - a| < \delta.$$

The two parts of this definition correspond exactly to the two parts of the definition in Chapter 10. In order to see the similarity, note first that $|x - a|$ can be interpreted as the horizontal distance between points with x coordinates x and a; similarly, $|f(x) - b|$ can be interpreted as the vertical distance between points with y coordinates $f(x)$ and b. The first part of this definition states that no matter how small a number δ we choose, there is some number x in the domain of f such that $x \neq a$ (since $0 < |x - a|$), and the distance between x and a is less than δ. In other words, there are numbers in the domain of f as close as we please to the number a. This is exactly what was stated by the first part of the definition in Chapter 10. Let us recall that the number a is a limit point of the domain of f if it satisfies the first part of the definition.

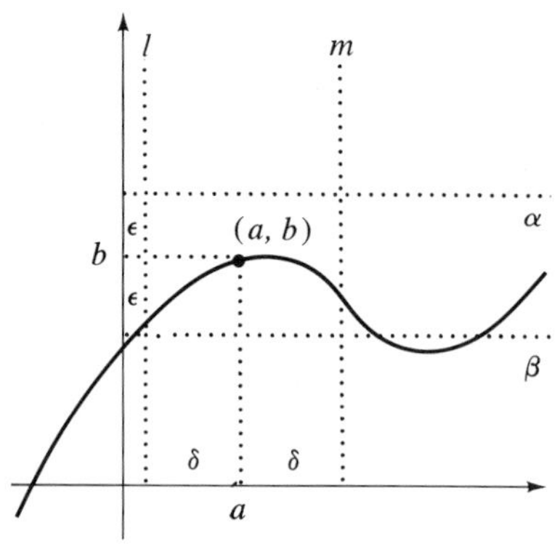

Figure 17.1

Given a positive number ϵ, we see that it determines a pair of horizontal lines α and β (see Figure 17.1), which are a distance ϵ above and below (a, b). Thus, having a positive number ϵ is equivalent to having a pair of horizontal lines α and β with (a, b) between them. Similarly, the positive number δ determines a pair of vertical lines l and m, which are a distance δ to the right and left of the point (a, b). Now the set of all numbers x belonging to the domain of f and satisfying

$$0 < |x - a| < \delta$$

corresponds to the set of all points of the graph between l and m except the one with x coordinate a. Similarly the set of all numbers $f(x)$ in the range of f and satisfying

$$|f(x) - b| < \epsilon$$

corresponds to the set of all points of the graph between α and β. This explanation shows that the new definition is equivalent to the one given in Chapter 10. Let us now see how we can work with this definition.

Example 1

Show, by means of the definition, that $\lim_{x \to 1}(x + 1) = 2$.

Since the function $f(x) = x + 1$ is defined for all x, the first part of the definition is satisfied. Suppose we are given a positive number ϵ. We must now find a positive number δ, such that $|f(x) - 2| < \epsilon$ whenever $0 < |x - 1| < \delta$. Let us suppose that $0 < |x - 1| < \delta$ for some choice of δ. Then

$$\begin{aligned} |f(x) - 2| &= |(x + 1) - 2| \\ &= |x - 1| < \delta. \end{aligned}$$

We want $|f(x) - 2|$ to be less than ϵ. We get it if we choose $\delta = \epsilon$. Since we are able to find a δ in terms of the given ϵ, we see that, for any value of ϵ, there is a value of δ satisfying the condition that $|f(x) - 2| < \epsilon$ for any x in the domain such that $0 < |x - 1| < \delta$. Thus the given limit statement is true.

Example 2

Show that $\lim_{x\to 1} x^2 = 1$.

Again $f(x) = x^2$ is defined for all x, and the first part of the definition holds. Given a positive number ϵ, we now want to find a positive number δ such that

$$|x^2 - 1| < \epsilon$$

whenever

$$0 < |x - 1| < \delta.$$

Again, suppose that $0 < |x - 1| < \delta$ for some choice of δ. The situation is not so simple here as it was in the previous example. But we do know this much: no matter what value of δ we choose, $|x^2 - 1|$ can be broken down into two factors, $|x + 1|$ and $|x - 1|$, one of which is always less than δ. All we need to do is limit the size of the other factor. We can do that by restricting the size of δ. Let us arbitrarily choose $\delta \leq 1$; that is, we shall never choose a value of δ greater than one, although we may choose a smaller value. Now

$$\begin{aligned} |x - 1| &< \delta \leq 1, \\ |x - 1| &< 1, \\ -1 < x - &1 < 1, \\ 1 < x + &1 < 3, \\ |x + 1| &< 3. \end{aligned}$$

Thus, if $|x - 1| < \delta$ and $\delta \leq 1$, then

$$|x^2 - 1| = |x + 1| \cdot |x - 1| < 3\delta.$$

Now if we let $3\delta = \epsilon$ or $\delta = \epsilon/3$, then $|x^2 - 1| < \epsilon$. But this is also based on the assumption that $\delta \leq 1$. If $\epsilon > 3$, then $\epsilon/3 \not\leq 1$. Thus we must choose δ to be the smaller of the two numbers $\epsilon/3$ and 1, and we write it

$$\delta = \min\{\epsilon/3, 1\}.$$

In this last example, how did we know to choose $\delta \leq 1$? Why not $\delta \leq 3$ or $\delta \leq 1/2$? Actually we could have started with any of these restrictions. The choice of $\delta \leq 1$ was quite arbitrary; any other choice would work as well. This is not always the case, as the next example shows.

Example 3

Show that $\lim_{x\to 1}(1/x) = 1$.

Again, the first part of the definition is obviously satisfied. Now we must show that if ϵ is a positive number, then there is a positive number δ such that

$$\left|\frac{1}{x} - 1\right| < \epsilon$$

whenever $x \neq 0$ and $|x - 1| < \delta$. Suppose $0 < |x - 1| < \delta$. Then

$$\begin{aligned} \left|\frac{1}{x} - 1\right| &= \left|\frac{1 - x}{x}\right| \\ &= \frac{|1 - x|}{|x|} \\ &= \frac{1}{|x|}\,|x - 1|. \end{aligned}$$

Again one of the two factors is less than δ, but the value of the other must be restricted. The only way we can do this is to restrict the value of δ. Let us try $\delta \leq 1$. Then

$$|x-1| < \delta \leq 1,$$
$$|x-1| < 1,$$
$$-1 < x-1 < 1,$$
$$0 < x < 2,$$
$$\frac{1}{x} > \frac{1}{2},$$
$$\frac{1}{|x|} > \frac{1}{2}.$$

Unfortunately this does not get us anywhere. We want to be able to say that $1/|x|$ is less than something. But because $0 < x < 1$, there is no limit on how big $1/x$ can be. Our problem is that, by choosing $\delta \leq 1$, we did not restrict x enough. This restriction merely requires that $|x-1| < 1$. Figure 17.2 shows the points satisfying this inequality. The points of the graph that satisfy this inequality have y coordinates $(=1/x)$ without an upper limit. We can see from this figure that if the width of the band were narrowed, there would be an upper limit to $1/x$. With this in mind, let us choose $\delta \leq 1/2$. Now

$$|x-1| < \delta \leq \frac{1}{2},$$
$$|x-1| < \frac{1}{2},$$
$$-\frac{1}{2} < x-1 < \frac{1}{2},$$
$$\frac{1}{2} < x < \frac{3}{2},$$
$$\frac{2}{3} < \frac{1}{x} < 2,$$
$$\frac{2}{3} < \frac{1}{|x|} < 2.$$

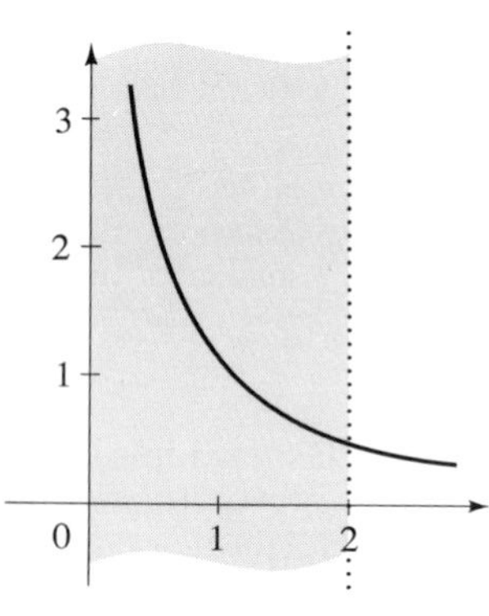

Figure 17.2

Actually the only inequality we want is $1/|x| < 2$. Now we have

$$\left|\frac{1}{x} - 1\right| = \frac{1}{|x|}\,|x-1| < 2\delta.$$

Thus we choose $2\delta = \epsilon$ or $\delta = \epsilon/2$, provided $\epsilon/2 \leq 1/2$, or

$$\delta = \min\{\epsilon/2,\ 1/2\}.$$

Problems

In Problems 1–10, determine whether or not a is a limit point of the domain of the given function.

1. $f(x) = x + 1$, $a = 1$.

2. $f(x) = \dfrac{x^2-1}{x-1}$, $a = 1$.

3. $f(x) = \dfrac{x^2 - 1}{x - 1}$, $a = 0$.

4. $f(x) = \sqrt{x}$, $a = 0$.

5. $f(x) = \sqrt{x}$, $a = -1$.

6. $f(x) = \sqrt{x^4 - 4x^2}$, $a = 0$.

7. $f(x) = \sqrt{x^4 - 4x^2}$, $a = 2$.

8. $f(x) = \sqrt{x^4 - 4x^2}$, $a = 1$.

9. $f(x) = \dfrac{1}{x}$, $a = 0$.

10. $f(x) = \operatorname{Arcsin} x$, $a = 2$.

11. Show that $\lim_{x \to 1} x^2 = 1$ by using $\delta \leq 3$.
12. Show that $\lim_{x \to 1} x^2 = 1$ by using $\delta \leq 1/2$.

In Problems 13–32, use the definition of a limit given in this section to show that the given limit statements are true.

13. $\lim_{x \to 1} (x - 4) = -3$.

14. $\lim_{x \to 1} (2x + 1) = 3$.

15. $\lim_{x \to 2} \dfrac{x^2 - 4}{x - 2} = 4$.

16. $\lim_{x \to 1} \dfrac{x^2 - 4}{x - 2} = 3$.

17. $\lim_{x \to 0} x^2 = 0$.

18. $\lim_{x \to 2} x^2 = 4$.

19. $\lim_{x \to -1} x^2 = 1$.

20. $\lim_{x \to 1} (x^2 + x) = 2$.

21. $\lim_{x \to 1} (x^2 - x) = 0$.

22. $\lim_{x \to 1} (x^2 + 2x) = 3$.

23. $\lim_{x \to 1} x^3 = 1$.

24. $\lim_{x \to 2} x^3 = 8$.

25. $\lim_{x \to 0} x^3 = 0$.

26. $\lim_{x \to 1} x^4 = 1$.

27. $\lim_{x \to 2} \dfrac{1}{x} = \dfrac{1}{2}$.

28. $\lim_{x \to 0} \dfrac{1}{x + 1} = 1$.

29. $\lim_{x \to 0} \dfrac{1}{x - 1} = -1$.

30. $\lim_{x \to 1} \dfrac{1}{x^2} = 1$.

31. $\lim_{x \to 1} \sqrt{x} = 1$.

32. $\lim_{x \to 0} \sqrt{x} = 0$.

33. Give an ϵ-δ definition of $\lim_{x \to a^+} f(x) = b$. Can you give a definition which does not use a new function with restricted domain?
34. Repeat Problem 33 for $\lim_{x \to a^-} f(x) = b$.

17.2

The Limit (Continued)

The examples of the previous section only required us to verify that a given limit statement is true. We now consider the problem of showing that a given limit statement is false. Again there are *two* ways for a given limit statement to be false: it can fail to satisfy the first part of the definition *or* it can fail to satisfy the second part. It is easy to show whether or not the first part of the definition is satisfied; the second part is more difficult.

When considering the geometric definition of limit, we noted that if the second condition fails to hold, it fails for horizontal lines that are "close" together. Since these are related to the ϵ of our new definition, we see that if the second condition of this definition fails to hold, it fails for "small" values of ϵ. A more precise way of saying this is that if the second part of the definition fails for one value of ϵ, it fails for any smaller value. Again, in order to show that the second part of the definition fails, we must find *one* value of ϵ for which there is *no* δ satisfying the given conditions. Let us consider some examples.

Example 1

Show that $\lim_{x \to 0} f(x) \neq 1$ if

$$f(x) = \begin{cases} 0, & x \leq 0, \\ 1, & x > 0. \end{cases}$$

Since $f(x)$ is defined for all real numbers, the first part of the definition is clearly satisfied—zero is a limit point of the domain of f. The graph of this function is given in Figure 17.3. If we were working with horizontal and vertical lines, we would choose β high enough so that the portion of the graph on the x axis is not between α and β. Thus no matter how we choose l and m, there is some point of the graph between l and m that is not between α and β. This corresponds to a choice of ϵ less than or equal to 1. Let us choose $\epsilon = 1/2$. We now want to show that we cannot find a value of δ that satisfies the definition. Let us assume that there is a value of δ satisfying the definition. Then if x satisfies the inequality

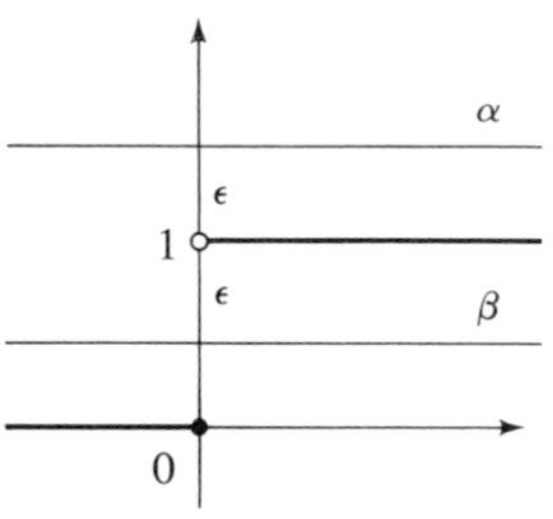

Figure 17.3

$$0 < |x - 0| < \delta,$$

we have $0 < |x| < \delta$, or

$$-\delta < x < \delta \quad \text{and} \quad x \neq 0.$$

For those values of x for which $-\delta < x < 0$, we see that $f(x) = 0$ and

$$|f(x) - 1| = |0 - 1| = 1 > \epsilon.$$

This contradicts the definition of limit. Thus, for $\epsilon = 1/2$, there is no value of δ that satisfies the definition of a limit,

$$\lim_{x \to 0} f(x) \neq 1.$$

Of course there are some values of x satisfying $0 < |x - 0| < \delta$ which also satisfy $|f(x) - 1| < 1/2$. We are not interested in them. We have shown that it is not true that *every* x satisfying $0 < |x - 0| < \delta$, also satisfies $|f(x) - 1| < 1/2$.

What happens here if we try to proceed as we did in the previous section? Suppose $0 < |x - 0| < \delta$. Then

$$|f(x) - 1| = \begin{cases} |0 - 1| = 1 & \text{if } x \leq 0, \\ |1 - 1| = 0 & \text{if } x > 0. \end{cases}$$

Now, can we choose δ in such a way that $|f(x) - 1| < \epsilon$, no matter what positive number ϵ represents? If $\epsilon \leq 1$, we cannot. No matter what δ we choose, there is a number x such that $-\delta < x < 0$ and $|f(x) - 1| = 1 \not< \epsilon$.

Example 2

Show that $\lim_{x \to 0} 1/x \neq 1$.

Again 0 is a limit point of the domain of f. The graph of f (see Figure 17.4) makes it obvious that any choice of ϵ will give us a contradiction. Let us arbitrarily choose $\epsilon = 1$. Now suppose that δ represents some positive number. We want to show now that, no matter what positive number δ might be, there is a value of x satisfying

$$0 < |x - 0| < \delta$$

but not

$$|f(x) - 1| < 1.$$

The last condition is equivalent to

$$\left|\frac{1}{x} - 1\right| < 1,$$

$$-1 < \frac{1}{x} - 1 < 1,$$

$$0 < \frac{1}{x} < 2,$$

$$x > \frac{1}{2}.$$

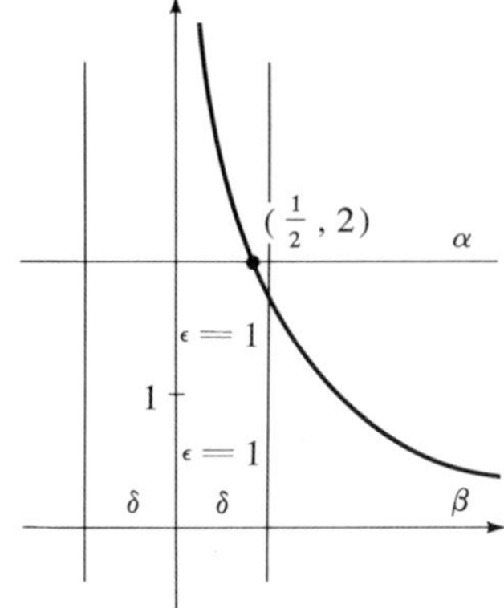

Figure 17.4

We want to find a value of x for which this is not true; that is, we want $x \leq 1/2$. Let us choose $0 < x < 1/2$. Then $|f(x) - 1| \nless 1$. The only question that remains is, "Does x satisfy the inequality $0 < |x - 0| < \delta$?" Of course, the answer depends upon the value of δ. Let us choose

$$0 < x < \min\{1/2, \delta\}.$$

If $d \leq 1/2$, then $0 < x < \delta \leq 1/2$. Thus $x < 1/2$ or $|f(x) - 1| \nless 1$, and $|x| < \delta$. If $\delta > 1/2$, then $0 < x < 1/2 < \delta$. Again, $x < 1/2$ or $|f(x) - 1| \nless 1$; and, since $0 < x < \delta$, $|x| < \delta$. Thus, no matter how we choose δ, there is some x satisfying $0 < |x - 0| < \delta$ but not $|f(x) - 1) < \epsilon$. Thus

$$\lim_{x \to 0} \frac{1}{x} \neq 1.$$

As we saw in Chapter 10, the above limit does not exist; that is, it does not equal any number. Let us show that here.

Example 3

Show that $\lim_{x \to 0} 1/x$ does not exist.

In order to show that $\lim_{x \to 0} 1/x$ does not exist we must show that, no matter what number we choose for b, $\lim_{x \to 0} 1/x = b$ is not true. Again 0 is a limit point of the domain of the given function. Thus the first part of the definition is satisfied no matter what number b represents. Let us now arbitrarily choose $\epsilon = 1$. We must now show that, for this choice of ϵ and for any choice of b, we cannot find a positive number δ satisfying the conditions of the definition. In order to simplify the problem, let us break it down into two cases depending on the value of b.

Case I $b \geq 0$: Now we want to find a value of x satisfying $0 < |x - 0| < \delta$ but not satisfying $|f(x) - b| < 1$. If

$$|f(x) - b| < 1,$$

then

$$\left|\frac{1}{x} - b\right| < 1,$$

$$-1 < \frac{1}{x} - b < 1,$$

$$b - 1 < \frac{1}{x} < b + 1.$$

Since $b \geq 0$, $b + 1$ is positive; if x is also positive, then

$$x > \frac{1}{b+1} > 0.$$

Let us choose

$$0 < x < \min\left\{\delta, \frac{1}{b+1}\right\}.$$

Clearly $0 < |x| < \delta$. Since $0 < x < 1/(b+1)$,

$$\frac{1}{x} \geq b + 1.$$

Thus $|f(x) - b| \not< 1$.

Case II $b < 0$: Again we want to find a value of x satisfying $0 < |x - 0| < \delta$ but not $|f(x) - b| < 1$. Again,

$$|f(x) - b| < 1$$

leads to

$$b - 1 < \frac{1}{x} < b + 1.$$

Since $b < 0$, $b - 1$ is negative; if x is also negative, then

$$x < \frac{1}{b-1} < 0.$$

Let us choose

$$\max\left\{-\delta, \frac{1}{b-1}\right\} < x < 0.$$

Since $-\delta < x < 0$, $0 < |x| = -x < \delta$. Since $1/(b-1) < x < 0$,

$$\frac{1}{x} < b - 1.$$

Thus $|f(x) - 1| \not< 1$. The definition of limit fails to hold for any choice of b and $\lim_{x \to 0} 1/x$ does not exist.

As we have seen before, this is a special type of nonexistence. We shall consider it in more detail in the next section.

Problems

In Problems 1–12, show, by means of the definition of limit, that the given limit statement is false.

1. $\lim_{x\to 1}(x+1)=3.$
2. $\lim_{x\to 1}(2x+1)=2.$
3. $\lim_{x\to 1} f(x)=3$, where $f(x)=\begin{cases} x+1 & \text{if } x\neq 1, \\ 3 & \text{if } x=1. \end{cases}$
4. $\lim_{x\to 2} f(x)=1$, where $f(x)=\begin{cases} x-2 & \text{if } x\neq 2, \\ 1 & \text{if } x=2. \end{cases}$
5. $\lim_{x\to 0} f(x)=0$, where $f(x)=\begin{cases} 0 & \text{if } x\leq 0, \\ 1 & \text{if } x>0. \end{cases}$
6. $\lim_{x\to 0} f(x)=1$, where $f(x)=\begin{cases} 0 & \text{if } x\leq 0, \\ 1 & \text{if } x>0. \end{cases}$
7. $\lim_{x\to 0} f(x)=0$, where $f(x)=\begin{cases} 1 & \text{if } x<0, \\ x & \text{if } x>0. \end{cases}$
8. $\lim_{x\to 0} f(x)=1$, where $f(x)=\begin{cases} 1 & \text{if } x<0, \\ x & \text{if } x>0. \end{cases}$
9. $\lim_{x\to 0}\frac{1}{x^2}=0.$
10. $\lim_{x\to 0}\frac{1}{x^2}=1.$
11. $\lim_{x\to 1}\frac{1}{x-1}=0.$
12. $\lim_{x\to 2} f(x)=1$, where $f(x)=\begin{cases} 1 & \text{if } x \text{ is rational}, \\ -1 & \text{if } x \text{ is irrational}. \end{cases}$

In Problems 13–18, indicate whether the given limit statement is true or false and show, by means of the definition of limit, that your answer is correct.

13. $\lim_{x\to 1}\frac{x^2-1}{x-1}=2.$
14. $\lim_{x\to 1} f(x)=2$, where $f(x)=\begin{cases} x+1 & \text{if } x\neq 1, \\ 3 & \text{if } x=1. \end{cases}$
15. $\lim_{x\to 1} f(x)=3$, where $f(x)=\begin{cases} x+1 & \text{if } x\neq 1, \\ 3 & \text{if } x=1. \end{cases}$
16. $\lim_{x\to 1}\frac{1}{x}=1.$
17. $\lim_{x\to 0}\frac{1}{x}=0.$
18. $\lim_{x\to 0} f(x)=0$, where $f(x)=\begin{cases} \frac{1}{x} & \text{if } x\neq 0, \\ 0 & \text{if } x=0. \end{cases}$

In Problems 19–24, show that the given limit does not exist.

19. $\lim_{x\to 0} f(x)$, where $f(x)=\begin{cases} 0 & \text{if } x\leq 0, \\ 1 & \text{if } x>0. \end{cases}$
20. $\lim_{x\to 0} f(x)$, where $f(x)=\begin{cases} 1 & \text{if } x\leq 0, \\ x & \text{if } x>0. \end{cases}$

21. $\lim_{x \to 0} f(x)$, where $f(x) = \begin{cases} x^2 & \text{if } x < 0, \\ x + 1 & \text{if } x \geq 0. \end{cases}$

22. $\lim_{x \to 0} f(x)$, where $f(x) = \begin{cases} 0 & \text{if } x \leq 0, \\ \dfrac{1}{x} & \text{if } x > 0. \end{cases}$

23. $\lim_{x \to 1} \dfrac{1}{x - 1}$.

24. $\lim_{x \to 0} \dfrac{1}{x^2}$.

17.3

Infinite Limits

As we have already noted, $\lim_{x \to 0} 1/x^2$ does not exist. But this is an example of a special type of nonexistence which we want to distinguish from other types. We had a geometric definition of $\lim_{x \to a} f(x) = +\infty$ in Chapter 10; we now consider an algebraic definition.

Definition

$\text{Lim}_{x \to a} f(x) = +\infty$ *means*

(a) *if δ is a positive number, then there is a number x in the domain of f such that $0 < |x - a| < \delta$, and*

(b) *if N is a number, then there is a positive number δ such that*

$$f(x) > N$$

for every number x in the domain of f for which $0 < |x - a| < \delta$.

The first part of the definition is exactly the same as the first part of the definition of $\lim_{x \to a} f(x) = b$. In the second part, ϵ has been replaced by N, which may be thought of as a large number. Then, roughly speaking, the second part of the definition says that no matter how big N is, all values of x sufficiently near a have their functional values even bigger.

Example 1

Show that $\lim_{x \to 0} \dfrac{1}{x^2} = +\infty$.

Since the given function is defined for all x except 0, the first part of the definition is satisfied. If $N \leq 0$, the entire graph is above $y = N$ (see Figure 17.5).

Thus, for any choice of δ, $f(x) > N$ for every number in the domain for which $0 < |x - 0| < \delta$. If N is positive, then $y = N$ has two points in common with the graph, namely, $(\pm 1/\sqrt{N}, N)$. Now if $|x| < 1/\sqrt{N}$, then

$$f(x) = \frac{1}{x^2} = \frac{1}{|x|^2} > (\sqrt{N})^2 = N.$$

Let us choose $\delta = 1/\sqrt{N}$. It now follows that, if N is any number, there is a positive number δ such that $f(x) > N$ for every number x in the domain of f for which $0 < |x - 0| < \delta$. Thus

$$\lim_{x \to 0} \frac{1}{x^2} = +\infty.$$

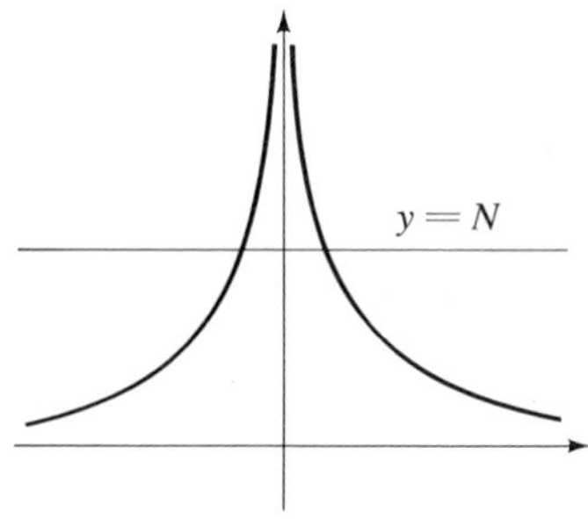

Figure 17.5

We can define $\lim_{x \to a} f(x) = -\infty$ similarly.

Definition

$\text{Lim}_{x \to a} f(x) = -\infty$ *means*

(a) *if δ is a positive number, then there is a number x in the domain of f such that* $0 < |x - a| < \delta$, *and*

(b) *if N is a number, then there is a positive number δ such that*

$$f(x) < N$$

for every number x in the domain of f for which $0 < |x - a| < \delta$.

Example 2

Show that $\lim_{x \to 0} \frac{1}{x}$ is neither $+\infty$ nor $-\infty$ but $\lim_{x \to 0^-} \frac{1}{x} = -\infty$.

Let us first show that $\lim_{x \to 0} 1/x$ is neither $+\infty$ nor $-\infty$. In each of the two cases, we must find a particular value of N for which there is no value of δ satisfying the given conditions. Let us choose $N = 0$. There is a value of x $(x = -\delta/2)$ in the domain of f satisfying $0 < |x - 0| < \delta$ but not $f(x) > 0$. Similarly there is a value of x $(x = \delta/2)$ in the domain of f satisfying $0 < |x - 0| < \delta$ but not $f(x) < 0$. Thus, $\lim_{x \to 0} 1/x$ is neither $+\infty$ nor $-\infty$.

In order to show that $\lim_{x \to 0^-} 1/x = -\infty$, we want to consider only the portion of the graph to the left of $x = 0$. Alternatively, we may consider the whole graph but, instead of considering values of x satisfying

$$0 < |x| < \delta,$$

which is equivalent to

$$-\delta < x < 0 \quad \text{or} \quad 0 < x < \delta,$$

we shall consider only those x satisfying

$$-\delta < x < 0.$$

Now if $N \geq 0$, then, no matter what positive number δ represents, $f(x) < N$ if $-\delta < x < 0$. Suppose $N < 0$. If $f(x) = 1/x$ is to be less than N, then we must choose x such that

$$x > \frac{1}{N}.$$

Thus if $N < 0$, choose $\delta = -1/N$. Now if

$$-\delta < x < 0,$$

then

$$\frac{1}{N} < x < 0$$

and $f(x) = 1/x < N$. Thus $\lim_{x \to 0^-} 1/x = -\infty$.

Let us now consider limits in which $x \to +\infty$ or $x \to -\infty$.

Definition

$\text{Lim}_{x \to +\infty} f(x) = b$ *means*

(a) *if M is a number, then there is a number x in the domain of f such that $x > M$, and*

(b) *if ϵ is a positive number, then there is a number N such that*

$$|f(x) - b| < \epsilon$$

for every number in the domain of f for which $x > N$.

Again, the two parts of this definition correspond exactly to the two parts of the definition given in Chapter 10. The first part says that, no matter how big M is, there is a number x in the domain that is still bigger. This is equivalent to saying that, no matter what vertical line we choose, there is some point of the graph to the right of it. The second part says that, for large enough values of x, $f(x)$ is near (within a distance ϵ of) b. Of course, the same type of definition is used if $x \to -\infty$.

Definition

$\text{Lim}_{x \to +\infty} f(x) = b$ *means*

(a) *if M is a number, then there is a number x in the domain of f such that $x < M$, and*

(b) *if ϵ is a positive number, then there is a number N such that*

$$|f(x) - b| < \epsilon$$

for every number in the domain of f for which $x < N$.

Example 3

Show that $\lim_{x \to +\infty} \frac{1}{x} = 0.$

The first part of the definition is easily seen to be satisfied, since the domain of the function is the set of all real numbers different from 0. Suppose ϵ is a positive number. We want to show that there is a number N big enough so that, if $x > N$, then

$$|f(x) - 0| < \epsilon.$$

Let us find those values of x for which the last inequality is true.

$$\left|\frac{1}{x} - 0\right| < \epsilon,$$

$$-\epsilon < \frac{1}{x} < \epsilon,$$

$$x < -\frac{1}{\epsilon} \quad \text{or} \quad x > \frac{1}{\epsilon}.$$

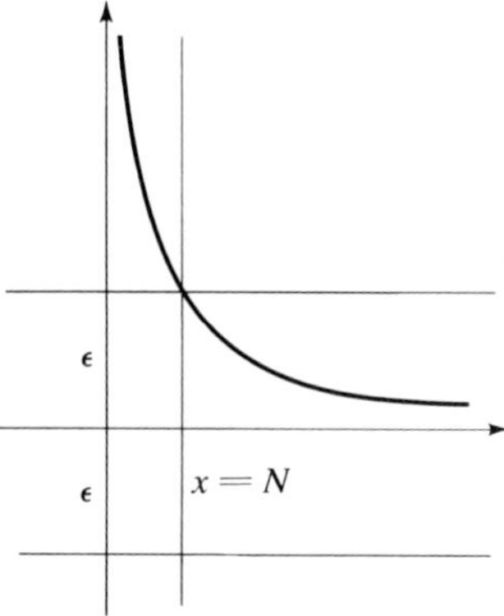

Figure 17.6

We are concerned with a limit as $x \to +\infty$; thus we are only interested in "large" values of x (those bigger than some number N). So we are interested in the second of the last two inequalities ($x > 1/\epsilon$). Let us then choose $N = 1/\epsilon$. Thus if

$$x > N = \frac{1}{\epsilon},$$

then

$$f(x) = \frac{1}{x} < \epsilon \quad \text{and} \quad |f(x) - 0| < \epsilon.$$

The given limit statement is therefore true.

Problems

In Problems 1–12, show that the given limit statement is true.

1. $\lim\limits_{x\to 0} \dfrac{1}{x^4} = +\infty.$
2. $\lim\limits_{x\to 1} \dfrac{1}{(x-1)^2} = +\infty.$
3. $\lim\limits_{x\to 0} \dfrac{-1}{x^2} = -\infty.$
4. $\lim\limits_{x\to -1} \dfrac{-1}{(x+1)^2} = -\infty.$
5. $\lim\limits_{x\to -1+} \dfrac{1}{x+1} = +\infty.$
6. $\lim\limits_{x\to -1-} \dfrac{1}{x+1} = -\infty.$
7. $\lim\limits_{x\to +\infty} \dfrac{1}{x^2} = 0.$
8. $\lim\limits_{x\to -\infty} \dfrac{1}{x^2} = 0.$
9. $\lim\limits_{x\to -\infty} \dfrac{x}{x+1} = 1.$
10. $\lim\limits_{x\to +\infty} \dfrac{x+1}{x} = 1.$
11. $\lim\limits_{x\to -\infty} e^x = 0.$
12. $\lim\limits_{x\to 0} \ln x = -\infty.$

In Problems 13–20, show that the given limit statement is false.

13. $\lim\limits_{x\to 0} \dfrac{1}{x^3} = +\infty.$
14. $\lim\limits_{x\to 0} \dfrac{1}{x^3} = -\infty.$

15. $\lim_{x\to 0} f(x) = +\infty$, where $f(x) = \begin{cases} 0 & \text{if } x < 0, \\ \dfrac{1}{x} & \text{if } x > 0. \end{cases}$

16. $\lim_{x\to 0} f(x) = +\infty$, where $f(x) = \begin{cases} 0 & \text{if } x < 0, \\ 1 & \text{if } x > 0. \end{cases}$

17. $\lim_{x\to +\infty} (x-1) = 1.$

18. $\lim_{x\to -\infty} (2x+1) = 3.$

19. $\lim_{x\to +\infty} \dfrac{x^2-1}{x-1} = 1.$

20. $\lim_{x\to +\infty} \sqrt{\dfrac{1-x^2}{1+x^2}} = 1.$

21. Define $\lim_{x\to +\infty} f(x) = +\infty$.

22. Define $\lim_{x\to -\infty} f(x) = +\infty$.

23. Show that $\lim_{x\to +\infty} x^2 = +\infty$ (see Problem 21).

24. Show that $\lim_{x\to -\infty} x^2 = +\infty$ (see Problem 22).

17.4

Continuity

Let us now consider an ϵ-δ definition of continuity.

Definition

The function f is **continuous** *at the point* $(a, f(a))$ *means that, if* ϵ *is a positive number, then there is a positive number* δ *such that*

$$|f(x) - f(a)| < \epsilon$$

for all x in the domain of f for which

$$|x - a| < \delta.$$

This concept of continuity at a point can be extended to continuity of the whole function and to discontinuity at a point in exactly the same way as was done in Chapter 10. We include those definitions here.

Definition

The function f is **discontinuous** *at the point* $(a, f(a))$ *means that it is not continuous at* $(a, f(a))$.

Definition

A function is **continuous** *means that it is continuous at every one of its points. A function is* **discontinuous** *means that it is discontinuous at one or more of its points.*

Example 1

Show that $f(x) = x^2$ is continuous at (1, 1).

The method of showing continuity here is similar to that of showing that $\lim_{x\to 1} x^2 = 1$, which was done in Example 2 of Section 17.1. You are invited to compare them. We need to show that if ϵ is a positive number, then there is a positive number δ such that

$$|x^2 - 1| < \epsilon$$

whenever

$$|x - 1| < \delta.$$

Again, note that

$$|x^2 - 1| = |x + 1|\,|x - 1|,$$

and we are restricting $|x - 1|$ to values less than δ. In order to restrict the value of $|x + 1|$, let us choose δ so that

$$\delta \leq 1.$$

Then

$$\begin{aligned} |x - 1| &< \delta \leq 1, \\ |x - 1| &< 1, \\ -1 < x - 1 &< 1, \\ 1 < x + 1 &< 3, \\ |x + 1| &< 3. \end{aligned}$$

Thus

$$|x^2 - 1| = |x + 1|\,|x - 1| < 3\delta.$$

Now let us choose $\delta = \epsilon/3$ but subject to the condition that $\delta \leq 1$. Thus, if we choose

$$\delta = \min\left\{1, \frac{\epsilon}{3}\right\},$$

it follows that if

$$|x - 1| < \delta,$$

then

$$|x^2 - 1| < \epsilon.$$

Example 2

Show that

$$f(x) = \begin{cases} 0, & x \leq 0, \\ 1, & x > 1 \end{cases}$$

is discontinuous at (0, 0).

We need to exhibit an ϵ for which no δ can be found that satisfies the conditions for continuity. Since the graph jumps from 0 to 1 at $x = 0$, let us choose $\epsilon = 1/2$ (any number ≤ 1 will do). Now we want to show that, for this choice of ϵ, there is no number δ such that

$$|f(x) - 0| < \epsilon$$

whenever

$$|x - 0| < \delta.$$

Assume there is such a number δ. Then let x be a number such that

$$0 < x < \delta.$$

For this choice of x,

$$|x - 0| < \delta,$$

but

$$|f(x) - 0| = |1 - 0| \not< \epsilon.$$

Thus, no such δ can be found, and the given function is discontinuous at (0, 0).

Of course, the relationship between limits and continuity that we considered in Chapter 10 is still valid for our new definitions of these terms. Recall that we assumed the following theorem.

Theorem 17.1

If $\lim_{x\to a} f(x) = L$ *and* $\lim_{x\to a} g(x) = M$, *where* L *and* M *are real numbers (not* $\pm\infty$), then

$$\lim_{x\to a} [f(x) + g(x)] = L + M,$$

$$\lim_{x\to a} [f(x) - g(x)] = L - M,$$

$$\lim_{x\to a} f(x)g(x) = L \cdot M, \quad \textit{and}$$

$$\lim_{x\to a} \frac{f(x)}{g(x)} = \frac{L}{M}, \quad \textit{provided } M \neq 0.$$

We omit the proof of this theorem*. A direct result of this and the connection between limits and continuity is stated next.

Theorem 17.2

If f and g are continuous at $x = a$, then $f + g$, $f - g$, and fg are continuous at $x = a$, and f/g is continuous at $x = a$, provided $g(a) \neq 0$.

We shall use this result in a later section.

Problems

In Problems 1–14, show, by means of the definition of continuity, that the following functions are continuous at the given point.

1. $f(x) = x$, at (0, 0).
2. $f(x) = x$, at (1, 1).
3. $f(x) = 2x + 1$, at (1, 3).
4. $f(x) = x - 4$, at (1, −3).
5. $f(x) = \dfrac{x^2 - 1}{x - 1}$, at (0, 1).
6. $f(x) = x^2$, at (0, 0).

* For a proof of this theorem see Walter Rudin, Principles of Mathematical Analysis (2nd ed.) (New York, McGraw-Hill, 1964), pp. 73–74.

7. $f(x) = x^2$, at (2, 4).

8. $f(x) = x^3$, at (0, 0).

9. $f(x) = x^3$, at (1, 1).

10. $f(x) = \dfrac{1}{x}$, at (1, 1).

11. $f(x) = \dfrac{1}{x}$, at (2, 1/2).

12. $f(x) = \dfrac{1}{x^2}$, at (1, 1).

13. $f(x) = \begin{cases} 0 & \text{if } x \leq 0, \\ 1 & \text{if } x > 0; \text{ at } (1, 1). \end{cases}$

14. $f(x) = \begin{cases} 0 & \text{if } x \leq 0, \\ x & \text{if } x > 0; \text{ at } (1, 1). \end{cases}$

In Problems 15–21, show, by means of the definition of continuity, that the following functions are discontinuous at the given point.

15. $f(x) = \begin{cases} x+1 & \text{if } x \neq 1, \\ 3 & \text{if } x = 1; \text{ at } (1, 3). \end{cases}$

16. $f(x) = \begin{cases} 1 & \text{if } x \leq 0, \\ x & \text{if } x > 0; \text{ at } (0, 1). \end{cases}$

17. $f(x) = \begin{cases} x^2 & \text{if } x \leq 0, \\ x+1 & \text{if } x > 0; \text{ at } (0, 0). \end{cases}$

18. $f(x) = \begin{cases} x-2 & \text{if } x \neq 2, \\ 1 & \text{if } x = 2; \text{ at } (2, 1). \end{cases}$

19. $f(x) = \begin{cases} x^2 & \text{if } x \neq 0, \\ 1 & \text{if } x = 0; \text{ at } (0, 1). \end{cases}$

20. $f(x) = \begin{cases} x+4 & \text{if } x < 1, \\ x & \text{if } x \geq 1; \text{ at } (1, 1). \end{cases}$

21. $f(x) = \begin{cases} \sin \dfrac{1}{x} & \text{if } x \neq 0, \\ 0 & \text{if } x = 0; \text{ at } (0, 0). \end{cases}$

17.5

Rolle's Theorem

You will recall our mentioning earlier that several of the theorems that were stated but not proved might be proved by using the mean-value theorem. It should be clear by now that the mean-value theorem is a very important and powerful theorem. In this section we consider Rolle's theorem, which is a special case of the mean-value theorem as well as an aid in proving it. The mean-value theorem itself is stated in the next section. The following theorem will provide a basis for proving Rolle's theorem.

Theorem 17.3

If a function f is continuous on an interval $[a, b]$, *then there is a number* x_0 *in* $[a, b]$ *such that* $f(x_0) \geq f(x)$ *for all x in* $[a, b]$; *similarly, there is a number* x_1 *in* $[a, b]$ *such that* $f(x_1) \leq f(x)$ *for all x in* $[a, b]$.

First of all, note that f is defined on $[a, b]$ because it is given that f is continuous on $[a, b]$; if f is continuous at x, it is also defined at x.

Instead of proving this theorem,* let us simply show that all of the conditions are necessary. We can see by Figure 17.7(a) that if f is not continuous, because it is not

* For a proof of this theorem, see Walter Rudin, Principles of Mathematical Analysis (2nd ed.) (New York, McGraw-Hill, 1964), p. 77.

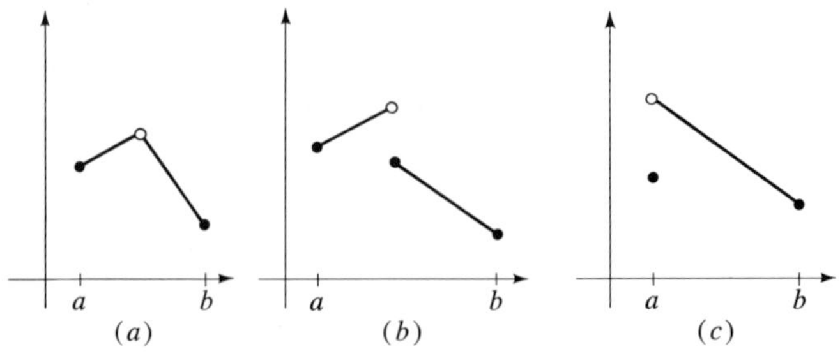

Figure 17.7

defined at some number between a and b, then the number x_0 does not necessarily exist. Figure 17.7(b) shows that if f is discontinuous for some number between a and b, then x_0 need not exist. Finally, (c) shows that the interval must be closed, since there is no number x_0 of (a, b) satisfying the conditions of the theorem. We are now ready to consider Rolle's theorem.

Theorem 17.4

(*Rolle's theorem*) *If a and b are numbers* $(a < b)$ *and f is a function such that*

(a) *f is continuous on* $[a, b]$,
(b) *$f'(x)$ exists for all x in* (a, b), *and*
(c) $f(a) = f(b) = 0$,

then there is a number x_0 between a and b such that $f'(x_0) = 0$.

The theorem says, roughly speaking, that if the graph of f has no horizontal or vertical jumps and no sharp points and if the ends are on the x axis, then there is at least one point between a and b at which the graph has a horizontal tangent. All three of the conditions are needed, although the third condition can be weakened somewhat (see Problem 22). Figure 17.8 shows that there need not be such a number x_0 if (a) f is not continuous on $[a, b]$, (b) $f'(x)$ does not exist for some x in (a, b), and (c) $f(a)$ and $f(b)$ are not both 0. Note that if one or more of the conditions of Rolle's theorem is not satisfied, this does *not* mean that no such number x_0 exists. The theorem merely states what follows if the three conditions *are* satisfied; if they are not all satisfied, the theorem says absolutely nothing concerning the existence of the number x_0.

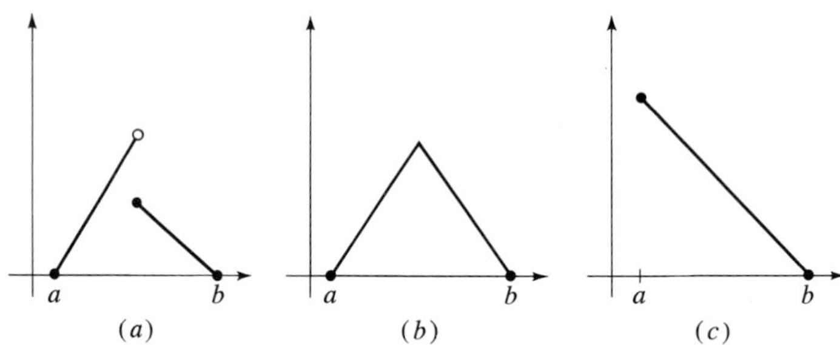

Figure 17.8

Proof

The proof of Rolle's theorem consists of three separate cases, which cover all possible functions f: Case I, $f(x) > 0$ for some x between a and b; Case II, $f(x) < 0$ for some x between a and b; Case III, $f(x) = 0$ for all x between a and b.

Case I $f(x) > 0$ for some x between a and b: By Theorem 17.3, there is a number x_0 in $[a, b]$ such that $f(x_0) \geq f(x)$ for every x in $[a, b]$. Since $f(x) > 0$ for some x between a and b and $f(x_0) \geq f(x)$, it follows that $f(x_0) > 0$. Thus, x_0 is neither a nor b, since $f(a) = f(b) = 0$, and x_0 is between a and b. Now define a function F by

$$F(x) = \frac{f(x_0) - f(x)}{x_0 - x}$$

for all x except x_0 in $[a, b]$. Since $f(x_0) \geq f(x)$ for all x in $[a, b]$,

$$f(x_0) - f(x) \geq 0$$

for all such values of x. If $x < x_0$, then $x_0 - x > 0$ and $F(x) \geq 0$. If $x > x_0$, then $x_0 - x < 0$ and $F(x) \leq 0$. By definition,

$$\lim_{x \to x_0} F(x) = \lim_{x \to x_0} \frac{f(x_0) - f(x)}{x_0 - x} = f'(x_0).$$

Since we are given that $f'(x)$ exists for all x in (a, b), we know that $\lim_{x \to x_0} F(x)$ is some number L. Let us assume L to be positive. If $\epsilon = L/2$, then, by the definition of limit, there is a positive number δ such that

$$|F(x) - L| < \frac{L}{2}$$

whenever

$$0 < |x - x_0| < \delta.$$

Suppose $x < b$ and $x_0 < x < x_0 + \delta$. For this choice of x, $|x - x_0| < \delta$. But, since $x > x_0$, $F(x) \leq 0$ and

$$F(x) - L \leq -L.$$

Thus

$$|F(x) - L| \geq L > \frac{L}{2},$$

which is a contradiction. Thus, the assumption that L is positive is wrong.

Assume now that L is negative. If $\epsilon = -L/2$, then, by the definition of limit, there is a positive number δ such that

$$|F(x) - L| < -\frac{L}{2}$$

whenever

$$0 < |x - x_0| < \delta.$$

Suppose $x > a$ and $x_0 - \delta < x < x_0$. For this choice of x, $|x - x_0| < \delta$. But, since $x < x_0$, $F(x) \geq 0$ and

$$F(x) - L \geq -L > 0.$$

Thus

$$|F(x) - L| \geq -L > -\frac{L}{2},$$

which is a contradiction. The assumption that L is negative is also wrong. Since L is neither positive nor negative, L must be 0, which means $f'(x_0) = 0$.

Case II $f(x) < 0$ for some x between a and b: Again by Theorem 17.3, there is a number x_0 in $[a, b]$ such that $f(x_0) \leq f(x)$ for every x in $[a, b]$. We can, by an argument similar to that used for Case I, show that x_0 is between a and b and $f'(x_0) = 0$.

Case III $f(x) = 0$ for all x between a and b: In this case, $f'(x) = 0$ for all x between a and b and, in particular, for some x_0 between a and b.

Thus, in any case, there is a number x_0 between a and b such that $f'(x_0) = 0$.

Example 1

Verify Rolle's theorem for the function $f(x) = x^2 - x$.

First of all $f(x) = 0$ if $x = 0$ or $x = 1$. These must be the values of a and b. This function is continuous for all x—certainly for all x in $[0, 1]$. $f'(x) = 2x - 1$ exists for all x and thus for all x in $(0, 1)$. Thus the three conditions of Rolle's theorem are satisfied; the theorem tells us that there must be a number x_0 between 0 and 1 such that $f'(x_0) = 0$. Let us verify that this is the case. $f'(x) = 0$ if $2x - 1 = 0$, or $x = 1/2$. Thus the number x_0 is $1/2$, which is between 0 and 1. Rolle's theorem is verified for this function.

Example 2

Does Rolle's theorem tell us anything about the function $f(x) = x^{2/3} - 1$? If so, what? If not, why not?

Again $f(x) = 0$ if $x = \pm 1$. Thus $a = -1$ and $b = 1$. This function is continuous for all x and thus for all x in $[-1, 1]$. But

$$f'(x) = \frac{2}{3} x^{-1/3} = \frac{2}{3x^{1/3}}.$$

There is no derivative when $x = 0$. We *cannot* say that $f'(x)$ exists for all x in $(-1, 1)$—the conditions of Rolle's theorem are not satisfied. Thus, Rolle's theorem tells us nothing about this function.

Note that Rolle's theorem does *not* say that there is no number between -1 and 1 for which the derivative is 0. It is possible to find functions for which the conditions of Rolle's theorem are not satisfied but for which there does exist a number x_0 between a and b for which $f'(x_0) = 0$. If the three conditions of Rolle's theorem are not satisfied, the theorem tells us absolutely nothing about the function.

Problems

In Problems 1–10, verify Rolle's theorem for the given function.

1. $f(x) = x^2 - 4x$.
2. $f(x) = x^2 + 2x$.
3. $f(x) = x^2 - x - 2$.
4. $f(x) = x^2 - x - 6$.
5. $f(x) = x^3 - x^2$.
6. $f(x) = x(x + 2)^2$.
7. $f(x) = x^3 - x$; $a = -1$, $b = 0$.
8. $f(x) = x^3 - x$; $a = 0$, $b = 1$.
9. $f(x) = \sin x$; $a = 0$, $b = \pi$.
10. $f(x) = \sin x$; $a = \pi$, $b = 4\pi$.

In Problems 11–20, does Rolle's theorem tell us anything about the given function? If so, what? If not, why not?

11. $f(x) = x - x^{1/3}$; $a = 0$, $b = 1$.
12. $f(x) = x - x^{1/3}$; $a = -1$, $b = 1$.
13. $f(x) = x^{4/5} - 1$.
14. $f(x) = x^{1/3} - 1$.
15. $f(x) = \begin{cases} x & \text{if } x \leq 1, \\ 2 - x & \text{if } x > 1. \end{cases}$
16. $f(x) = \begin{cases} x & \text{if } x < 1, \\ 1 & \text{if } 1 \leq x \leq 2, \\ 3 - x & \text{if } x > 2. \end{cases}$
17. $f(x) = \begin{cases} x^2 - 1 & \text{if } x \leq 0, \\ x^3 - 1 & \text{if } x > 0. \end{cases}$
18. $f(x) = \tan x$; $a = 0$, $b = \pi$.
19. $f(x) = \ln |x|$.
20. $f(x) = x \ln x$.
21. Complete the proof of Rolle's theorem.
22. Prove that if the third condition of Rolle's theorem were changed to $f(a) = f(b)$, the resulting statement would be true.

17.6

The Mean-Value Theorem

Now that we have proved Rolle's theorem let us consider the mean-value theorem, to which we have been leading.

Theorem 17.5

(*Mean-value theorem*) *If a and b are numbers ($a < b$) and f is a function such that*

(a) *f is continuous on $[a, b]$, and*
(b) *$f'(x)$ exists for all x in (a, b),*

then there is a number x_0 between a and b such that

$$f'(x_0) = \frac{f(b) - f(a)}{b - a}.$$

Note that the conditions on f stated here are two of the three conditions of Rolle's theorem. Also note that

$$\frac{f(b) - f(a)}{b - a}$$

is the slope of the line joining $(a, f(a))$ and $(b, f(b))$ (see Figure 17.9). Thus, roughly speaking, the mean-value theorem says that if the graph of f has no horizontal or vertical jumps and no sharp points, then there is at least one point between a and b at which the tangent to the graph is parallel to the line joining the ends.

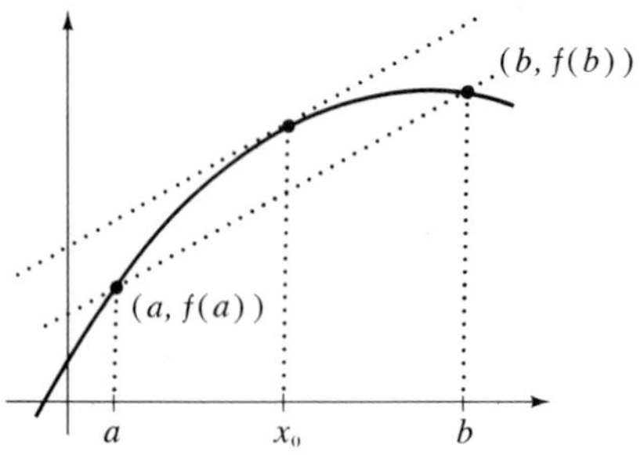

Figure 17.9

Proof

In order to prove the mean-value theorem, we would like to find a new function F in terms of f such that F still satisfies the two conditions of continuity and differentiability as well as the third condition of Rolle's theorem. Thus, we shall take the new function F to be the difference between the y coordinates of the given function and the line joining the end points. First, let us find an equation for that line. The slope of the line is

$$\frac{f(b)-f(a)}{b-a},$$

and it contains the point $(a, f(a))$. Using the point-slope formula, we have

$$y-f(a)=\frac{f(b)-f(a)}{b-a}(x-a),$$

or

$$y=f(a)+\frac{f(b)-f(a)}{b-a}(x-a).$$

Thus the new function F is defined by

$$F(x)=f(x)-f(a)-\frac{f(b)-f(a)}{b-a}(x-a).$$

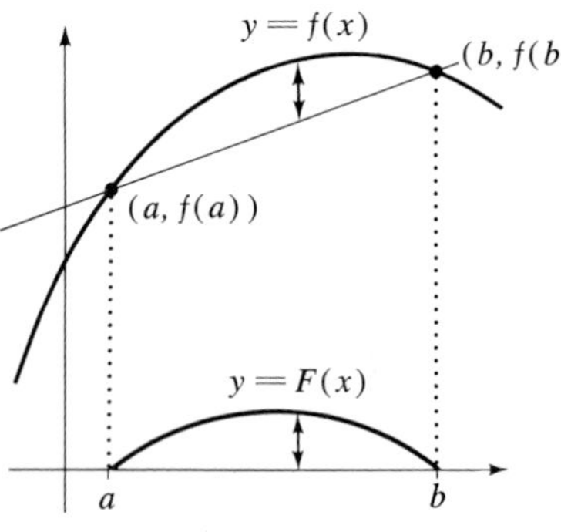

Figure 17.10

We now check that F satisfies the three hypotheses of Rolle's theorem. First of all, F is the difference of two functions—one is f and the other represents a line. Since these two are both continuous, F is continuous by Theorem 17.2. Finding the derivative, we have

$$F'(x)=f'(x)-\frac{f(b)-f(a)}{b-a}. \tag{1}$$

Since $f'(x)$ exists for every x in (a, b), $F'(x)$ exists for every x in (a, b). Finally

$$F(a)=f(a)-f(a)-\frac{f(b)-f(a)}{b-a}(a-a)=0-0=0,$$

$$F(b)=f(b)-f(a)-\frac{f(b)-f(a)}{b-a}(b-a)=[f(b)-f(a)]-[f(b)-f(a)]=0.$$

Thus, all the conditions of Rolle's theorem are satisfied. Then, by Rolle's theorem, there is a number x_0 between a and b such that

$$F'(x_0)=0. \tag{2}$$

But now (1) and (2) imply

$$f'(x_0) - \frac{f(b)-f(a)}{b-a} = 0,$$

$$f'(x_0) = \frac{f(b)-f(a)}{b-a}.$$

Example 1

Verify the mean-value theorem for $f(x) = x^2$, where $a = 0$ and $b = 1$.

Clearly f is continuous and differentiable everywhere; so f satisfies the conditions of the mean-value theorem. Thus the mean-value theorem asserts that there is a number x_0 between 0 and 1 such that

$$f'(x_0) = \frac{f(1)-f(0)}{1-0}.$$

Let us now verify that there is such a number.

$$\frac{f(1)-f(0)}{1-0} = \frac{1^2-0^2}{1-0} = 1,$$

$$f'(x) = 2x.$$

We now see that if $x_0 = 1/2$, then

$$f'(x_0) = \frac{f(1)-f(0)}{1-0}.$$

Thus the theorem is verified.

The following useful theorem is related to the mean-value theorem.

Theorem 17.6

(*Extended mean-value theorem*) *If a and b are numbers $(a < b)$ and f and g are functions such that*

(a) *f and g are continuous on $[a, b]$,*
(b) *$f'(x)$ and $g'(x)$ exist for x all in (a, b), and*
(c) *$g'(x) \neq 0$ for each x in (a, b),*

then there is a number x_0 between a and b such that

$$\frac{f'(x_0)}{g'(x_0)} = \frac{f(b)-f(a)}{g(b)-g(a)}.$$

The choice $g(x) = x$ reduces the extended mean-value theorem to the mean-value theorem. This gives us a hint as to how the generalized version might be proved. In proving the mean-value theorem, we used the function

$$F(x) = f(x) - f(a) - \frac{f(b)-f(a)}{b-a}(x-a).$$

If $g(x) = x$, then $g(a) = a$ and $g(b) = b$, so it might be reasonable to replace x, a, and b by $g(x)$, $g(a)$, and $g(b)$, respectively. Thus, in order to prove the extended mean-value theorem, we shall consider the new function

$$F(x) = f(x) - f(a) - \frac{f(b) - f(a)}{g(b) - g(a)} [g(x) - g(a)].$$

By use of this new function, the theorem can be proved in exactly the same way as the mean-value theorem. The details of the proof are left to the student (see Problem 22). Actually, there is one additional problem here that was not encountered in the proof of the mean-value theorem. We cannot be sure that the expression for $F(x)$ is meaningful unless we can be sure that $g(b) - g(a) \neq 0$, for this expression appears as a denominator in $F(x)$. This can be shown by use of Rolle's theorem (see Problem 21).

Example 2

Verify the extended mean-value theorem for $f(x) = x^2 - 1$, $g(x) = x - 1$, $a = 0$, and $b = 1$.

Clearly, both functions are defined and continuous, as well as differentiable, everywhere. Furthermore, $g'(x) = 1$ for all x and so it is not 0 for any x. Thus the extended mean-value theorem asserts the existence of a number x_0 between 0 and 1 such that

$$\frac{f'(x_0)}{g'(x_0)} = \frac{f(1) - f(0)}{g(1) - g(0)}.$$

Let us verify that this is the case. If there is such a number x_0, then

$$\frac{2x_0}{1} = \frac{0-(-1)}{0-(-1)} \quad \text{or} \quad x_0 = \frac{1}{2}.$$

Since $0 < 1/2 < 1$, the theorem is verified for this case.

In earlier chapters several proofs of theorems were omitted because they required the use of the mean-value theorem. The omitted proofs are given in Appendix B. A review of these theorems and their proofs will demonstrate the importance of the mean-value theorem in theoretical work. The extended mean-value theorem also has important applications, one of which is considered in the next chapter.

Problems

In Problems 1–10, verify the mean-value theorem for the given function and the given values of a and b.

1. $f(x) = x^2$; $a = -1$, $b = 2$.
2. $f(x) = x^2 + 1$; $a = -2$, $b = 3$.
3. $f(x) = x^3$; $a = 0$, $b = 2$.
4. $f(x) = x^3$; $a = -1$, $b = 1$.
5. $f(x) = \dfrac{1}{x}$; $a = 1$, $b = 2$.
6. $f(x) = \dfrac{1}{x^2}$; $a = 1$, $b = 3$.
7. $f(x) = \dfrac{1}{x+1}$; $a = 0$, $b = 1$.
8. $f(x) = \dfrac{x}{x+1}$; $a = 0$, $b = 4$.
9. $f(x) = e^x$; $a = 0$, $b = 1$.
10. $f(x) = \tan x$; $a = 0$, $b = \pi/4$.

In Problems 11–16, does the mean-value theorem tell you anything about the given function? If so what? If not, why not?

11. $f(x) = \dfrac{1}{x}$; $a = -1$, $b = 1$.

12. $f(x) = |x|$; $a = 0$, $b = 1$.

13. $f(x) = |x|$; $a = -1$, $b = 2$.

14. $f(x) = \begin{cases} x & \text{if } x \leq 0, \\ 0 & \text{if } x > 0; \end{cases}$ $a = -1$, $b = 1$.

15. $f(x) = \ln |x|$; $a = -1$, $b = 1$.

16. $f(x) = |\ln x|$; $a = 1/2$, $b = 2$.

In Problems 17–20, verify the extended mean-value theorem for the given functions.

17. $f(x) = 2x + 1$, $g(x) = x^2$; $a = 0$, $b = 1$.
18. $f(x) = x^2 + 1$, $g(x) = \dfrac{1}{x}$; $a = 1$, $b = 2$.
19. $f(x) = x^3$, $g(x) = \dfrac{1}{x+1}$; $a = 0$, $b = 1$.
20. $f(x) = (x + 1)^2$, $g(x) = 2x - 1$; $a = 1$, $b = 3$.
21. Show that if g is continuous on $[a, b]$ and if $g'(x) \neq 0$ for all x in (a, b), then $g(a) \neq g(b)$ (see Problem 22 of the previous section).
22. Complete the proof of the extended mean-value theorem.

Indeterminate Forms

18.1

The Forms 0/0 *and* ∞/∞

Some of the very simple limits we have dealt with—such as

$$\lim_{x\to 1}\frac{x}{x+1}=\frac{1}{2},$$

can be evaluated simply by substitution. On the other hand, there have been limits such as

$$\lim_{x\to 1}\frac{x^2-1}{x-1}$$

that cannot be evaluated by substitution, because both the numerator and denominator approach 0 as x approaches 1. When we first encountered limits of this type, we observed that the mere fact that both numerator and denominator approach 0 tells us nothing about the limit of the quotient. This particular form of limit is called an indeterminate form. The two types we have encountered most frequently in the past have been the forms 0/0 and ∞/∞, by which is meant both the numerator and denominator approach 0 or else the numerator approaches $+\infty$ or $-\infty$ and the denominator approaches $+\infty$ or $-\infty$ (numerator and denominator not necessarily agreeing in sign).

Of course, we had little trouble evaluating limits like

$$\lim_{x\to 1}\frac{x^2-1}{x-1}.$$

We simply factored the numerator and canceled the factors $x - 1$. Unfortunately we could not evaluate

$$\lim_{x \to 0} \frac{\sin x}{x}$$

so simply. In that case we went through a rather elaborate geometric argument in order to find the limit. Because the method of canceling factors has only a very limited application, we should like to find a more general method of handling indeterminate forms. A method which works for a very wide range of functions is called L'Hôpital's (pronounced low′-pee-tahl) rule.

In order to simplify the statements of L'Hôpital's rule, let us introduce the concept of a deleted neighborhood. If a is a real number, then a deleted neighborhood of a is the set of all numbers except a in an open interval (b, c) which contains a. For example: a deleted neighborhood of 3 is

$$\{x \mid x \text{ is in } (0, 4) \text{ and } x \neq 3\} = \{x \mid 0 < x < 3 \text{ or } 3 < x < 4\}.$$

Of course, there are many other deleted neighborhoods of 3. A deleted neighborhood of $+\infty$ is the set of all numbers greater than some real number N. Likewise, a deleted neighborhood of $-\infty$ is the set of all numbers less than some real number N.

Now let us consider L'Hôpital's rule. It is stated here as two separate theorems.

Theorem 18.1

(L'Hôpital's rule—0/0) If a is a real number, $+\infty$, or $-\infty$ and f and g are functions such that

(a) *$f'(x)$ and $g'(x)$ exist for all x in some deleted neighborhood of a and $g'(x) \neq 0$ for all x in that neighborhood,*
(b) *$\lim_{x \to a} f(x) = \lim_{x \to a} g(x) = 0$, and*
(c) *$\lim_{x \to a} f'(x)/g'(x) = L$, where L is a real number, $+\infty$, or $-\infty$, then*

$$\lim_{x \to a} \frac{f(x)}{g(x)} = L.$$

Proof

Let us consider the case in which a is a real number and the deleted neighborhood is $\{x \mid b < x < a \text{ or } a < x < c\}$. Let us further restrict ourselves to the right-hand limit.

The statement of the theorem gives no assurance that either $f(a)$ or $g(a)$ exists. Thus, let us consider two new functions F and G such that

$$F(x) = \begin{cases} f(x) & x \neq a, \\ 0 & x = a, \end{cases} \qquad G(x) = \begin{cases} g(x) & x \neq a. \\ 0 & x = a. \end{cases}$$

Then F and G are continuous at $x = a$. If $a < x < c$, then F and G are defined and continuous on $[a, x]$. (We have already noted that they are continuous at $x = a$; since they are differentiable, they are continuous at every other number in $[a, x]$.) Also, $F' = f'$ and $G' = g'$ exist at every number in (a, x) and $G' \neq 0$ everywhere in (a, x). By the extended mean-value theorem, there is a number y between a and x such that

$$\frac{F(x) - F(a)}{G(x) - G(a)} = \frac{F'(y)}{G'(y)}.$$

But $F(a) = G(a) = 0$. Thus,

$$\frac{F(x)}{G(x)} = \frac{F'(y)}{G'(y)}.$$

As $x \to a^+$, we also have $y \to a^+$, because $a < y < x$. Therefore,

$$\lim_{x\to a+} \frac{f(x)}{g(x)} = \lim_{x\to a+} \frac{F(x)}{G(x)} = \lim_{y\to a+} \frac{F'(y)}{G'(y)} = \lim_{y\to a+} \frac{f'(y)}{g'(y)} = L.$$

A similar argument shows that

$$\lim_{x\to a-} \frac{f(x)}{g(x)} = L,$$

which gives

$$\lim_{x\to a} \frac{f(x)}{g(x)} = L$$

for the case in which a is a real number.

Suppose $a = +\infty$. Let us introduce a new variable t such that

$$x = \frac{1}{t}.$$

Then

$$\lim_{x\to+\infty} \frac{f(x)}{g(x)} = \lim_{t\to 0+} \frac{f\left(\frac{1}{t}\right)}{g\left(\frac{1}{t}\right)}$$

$$= \lim_{t\to 0+} \frac{\frac{d}{dt} f\left(\frac{1}{t}\right)}{\frac{d}{dt} g\left(\frac{1}{t}\right)}$$

$$= \lim_{t\to 0+} \frac{-t^2 \frac{d}{dt} f\left(\frac{1}{t}\right)}{-t^2 \frac{d}{dt} g\left(\frac{1}{t}\right)}$$

$$= \lim_{x\to+\infty} \frac{\frac{d}{dx} f(x)}{\frac{d}{dx} g(x)} \qquad \text{(See Note)}$$

$$= \lim_{x\to+\infty} \frac{f'(x)}{g'(x)} = L.$$

A similar argument handles the case in which $a = -\infty$.

Note: Since $x = 1/t$, $f(x) = f(1/t)$. By the chain rule,

$$\frac{d}{dt} f\left(\frac{1}{t}\right) = \frac{d}{dx} f(x) \cdot \frac{d}{dt}\left(\frac{1}{t}\right)$$

$$= \frac{d}{dx} f(x)\left(-\frac{1}{t^2}\right),$$

$$-t^2 \frac{d}{dt} f\left(\frac{1}{t}\right) = \frac{d}{dx} f(x).$$

Theorem 18.2

(*L'Hôpital's rule*—∞/∞) *If a is a real number*, $+\infty$, *or* $-\infty$ *and f and g are functions such that*

(a) $f'(x)$ *and* $g'(x)$ *exist for all x in some deleted neighborhood of a and* $g'(x) \neq 0$ *for each x in that neighborhood*,
(b) $\lim_{x\to a} |f(x)| = \lim_{x\to a} |g(x)| = +\infty$, *and*
(c) $\lim_{x\to a} f'(x)/g'(x) = L$, *where L is a real number*, $+\infty$, *or* $-\infty$, *then*

$$\lim_{x\to a} \frac{f(x)}{g(x)} = L.$$

The proof for this case is more difficult. We omit it.*

It might appear at first glance that the conditions on the use of L'Hôpital's rule are quite stringent and that only a few functions satisfy all of them. Actually, quite the opposite is true. Differentiability is a condition that almost all of the functions we have encountered satisfy at all but a finite number of points. Furthermore, by taking the interval small enough, we can assure ourselves that the derivative of the denominator is not 0 for all values of x "near" $x = a$. The only thing we need to do for our simple functions (and it must always be done) is make sure we have one of the indeterminate forms 0/0 or ∞/∞.

Example 1

Evaluate $\lim_{x\to 0} \dfrac{\sin x}{x}$.

$$\lim_{x\to 0} \frac{\sin x}{x} \begin{matrix}\to 0\\ \to 0\end{matrix} = \lim_{x\to 0} \frac{\cos x}{1} = \frac{1}{1} = 1.$$

This, of course, agrees with the result we obtained in Chapter 11 (see pages 243–244). That is not to say that we could have used L'Hôpital's rule at that time. In order to use it, we need to know the derivative of sin x. We did not know it then; in fact, we used the value of this limit to find the derivative of sin x.

It might be noted that we did *not* take the derivative of (sin x)/x; we took the derivatives of the numerator and denominator individually.

Example 2

Evaluate $\lim_{x\to +\infty} \dfrac{e^x}{x}$.

$$\lim_{x\to +\infty} \frac{e^x}{x} \begin{matrix}\to +\infty\\ \to +\infty\end{matrix} = \lim_{x\to +\infty} \frac{e^x}{1} = +\infty.$$

* For a proof of this theorem see Walter Rudin, *Principles of Mathematical Analysis* (2nd ed.) (New York, McGraw-Hill, 1964), pp. 94–95.

Example 3

Evaluate $\lim_{x\to 0} \dfrac{1-\cos x}{x^2}$.

$$\lim_{x\to 0} \frac{1-\cos x}{x^2} \quad \begin{matrix}\to 0\\ \to 0\end{matrix} \quad = \lim_{x\to 0} \frac{\sin x}{2x} \quad \begin{matrix}\to 0\\ \to 0.\end{matrix}$$

At this point you might feel that L'Hôpital's rule has failed us, since we are still left with the indeterminate form 0/0. But there is nothing to prevent us from using L'Hôpital's rule a second time. The result is

$$\lim_{x\to 0} \frac{1-\cos x}{x^2} = \lim_{x\to 0} \frac{\cos x}{2} = \frac{1}{2}.$$

Example 4

Evaluate $\lim_{x\to 0} \dfrac{x-\sin x}{2+2x+x^2-2e^x}$.

$$\begin{aligned}\lim_{x\to 0} \frac{x-\sin x}{2+2x+x^2-2e^x} \quad \begin{matrix}\to 0\\ \to 0\end{matrix} \quad &= \lim_{x\to 0} \frac{1-\cos x}{2+2x-2e^x} \quad \begin{matrix}\to 0\\ \to 0\end{matrix}\\ &= \lim_{x\to 0} \frac{\sin x}{2-2e^x} \quad \begin{matrix}\to 0\\ \to 0\end{matrix}\\ &= \lim_{x\to 0} \frac{\cos x}{-2e^x} = -\frac{1}{2}.\end{aligned}$$

Example 5

Evaluate $\lim_{x\to 0+} \dfrac{\cot x}{\cot 2x}$.

$$\begin{aligned}\lim_{x\to 0+} \frac{\cot x}{\cot 2x} \quad \begin{matrix}\to +\infty\\ \to +\infty\end{matrix} \quad &= \lim_{x\to 0+} \frac{-\csc^2 x}{-2\csc^2 2x} \quad \begin{matrix}\to -\infty\\ \to -\infty\end{matrix}\\ &= \lim_{x\to 0+} \frac{2\csc^2 x \cot x}{4\csc^2 2x \cot 2x} \quad \begin{matrix}\to +\infty\\ \to +\infty.\end{matrix}\end{aligned}$$

At this point let us stop and take stock. The derivative of $\cot x$ is $-\csc^2 x$; the derivative of $\csc x$ is $-\csc x \cot x$. Furthermore,

$$\lim_{x\to 0+} \cot x = +\infty \quad \text{and} \quad \lim_{x\to 0+} \csc x = +\infty.$$

Thus, by taking derivatives of $\cot x$ and $\csc x$, we can only get a new expression involving $\cot x$ and $\csc x$, and the limit in either case is $+\infty$. Thus, continued application of L'Hôpital's rule will get us nowhere. Let us return to the beginning and try something different.

$$\begin{aligned}\lim_{x\to 0+} \frac{\cot}{\cot 2x} = \lim_{x\to 0+} \frac{\tan 2x}{\tan x} \quad \begin{matrix}\to 0\\ \to 0\end{matrix}\\ = \lim_{x\to 0+} \frac{2\sec^2 2x}{\sec^2 x} = 2.\end{aligned}$$

Example 6

Evaluate $\lim_{x\to 0+} \frac{e^x}{x}$.

$$\lim_{x\to 0+} \frac{e^x}{x} \begin{matrix}\to 1 \\ \to 0^+\end{matrix} = +\infty.$$

We see that L'Hôpital's rule is not necessary here; in fact, it cannot be used, since we do not have one of the indeterminate forms. A blind application of the rule gives

$$\lim_{x\to 0+} \frac{e^x}{x} = \lim_{x\to 0+} \frac{e^x}{1} = 1,$$

which is incorrect. Before using L'Hôpital's rule *you must make sure you have one of the indeterminate forms* 0/0 or ∞/∞.

Problems

In Problems 1–28, evaluate the given limit.

1. $\lim_{x\to 1} \frac{x^2-1}{x-1}$.
2. $\lim_{x\to 2} \frac{x^2-x-2}{x-2}$.
3. $\lim_{x\to a} \frac{\sqrt{x}-\sqrt{a}}{x-a}$.
4. $\lim_{x\to a} \frac{\sqrt[3]{x}-\sqrt[3]{a}}{x-a}$.
5. $\lim_{x\to +\infty} \frac{x^2+x}{x^2-1}$.
6. $\lim_{x\to -\infty} \frac{x-4}{x^2+2}$.
7. $\lim_{x\to 0} \frac{e^x-1}{\sin x}$.
8. $\lim_{x\to 0} \frac{\tan x}{x}$.
9. $\lim_{x\to 1} \frac{\ln x}{\sqrt{1-x}}$.
10. $\lim_{x\to 0} \frac{\sin x}{e^x}$.
11. $\lim_{x\to 0} \frac{\tan x - \sin x}{x^3}$.
12. $\lim_{x\to \pi/2} \frac{\sec x}{\sec 2x}$.
13. $\lim_{x\to +\infty} \frac{\ln x}{x}$.
14. $\lim_{x\to 0} \frac{\ln x}{x}$.
15. $\lim_{x\to +\infty} \frac{\ln x}{x^n}$ (n a positive integer).
16. $\lim_{x\to 0} \frac{\ln x}{1/x}$.
17. $\lim_{x\to 0} \frac{a^x-b^x}{x}$.
18. $\lim_{x\to \pi/2} \frac{\cos x - \sin x + 1}{\cos x + \sin x - 1}$.
19. $\lim_{x\to 0} \frac{e^x-e^{-x}-2x}{x-\sin x}$.
20. $\lim_{x\to 0} \frac{\sin x}{e^x-e^{-x}}$.
21. $\lim_{x\to 0} \frac{\ln \tan x}{\ln \tan 2x}$.
22. $\lim_{x\to 0} \frac{1-\ln x}{e^{1/x}}$.
23. $\lim_{x\to 0} \frac{x - \text{Arcsin}\, x}{\sin^3 x}$.
24. $\lim_{x\to \pi/2} \frac{\ln (x-\pi/2)}{\tan x}$.
25. $\lim_{x\to 1} \frac{x^x - x}{1-x+\ln x}$.
26. $\lim_{x\to 0} \frac{\text{Arcsin}\,(1-x)}{\sqrt{2x-x^2}}$.
27. $\lim_{x\to 0} \frac{\sin x - x\cos x}{x-\sin x}$.
28. $\lim_{x\to \pi/4} \frac{\sec^2 x - 2\tan x}{1+\cos 4x}$.

29. Prove that $\lim_{x \to a^-} \dfrac{f(x)}{g(x)} = L$ under the conditions of Theorem 18.1.

30. Prove that $\lim_{x \to -\infty} \dfrac{f(x)}{g(x)} = L$ under the conditions of Theorem 18.1.

18.2

The Forms $0 \cdot \infty$ *and* $\infty - \infty$

Let us emphasize that L'Hôpital's rule handles only the two indeterminate forms 0/0 and ∞/∞. However, some other indeterminate forms can be put into one of these two forms. We consider two of them here. The first is the form $0 \cdot \infty$: that is,

$$\lim_{x \to a} f(x) \cdot g(x),$$

where

$$\lim_{x \to a} f(x) = 0 \quad \text{and} \quad \lim_{x \to a} |g(x)| = +\infty.$$

One factor tends to make the product large in absolute value, while the other tend. to make it small. Thus, the outcome is in doubt, and $0 \cdot \infty$ is an indeterminate forms It can be put into the form 0/0 or ∞/∞ by one of the following methods.

$$\lim_{x \to a} f(x) \cdot g(x) = \lim_{x \to a} \frac{f(x)}{1/g(x)} \quad \begin{matrix} \to 0 \\ \to 0. \end{matrix}$$

$$\lim_{x \to a} f(x) \cdot g(x) = \lim_{x \to a} \frac{g(x)}{1/f(x)} \quad \begin{matrix} \to \pm\infty \\ \to \pm\infty. \end{matrix}$$

Either way gives a form that L'Hôpital's rule can handle; the choice depends upon which of the two is easier.

Example 1

Evaluate $\lim_{x \to 0} x \ln x$.

$$\lim_{x \to 0} x \ln x \quad \to 0(-\infty) \quad = \lim_{x \to 0} \frac{\ln x}{\frac{1}{x}} \quad \begin{matrix} \to -\infty \\ \to +\infty \end{matrix}$$

(Since $\ln x$ is defined only for positive values of x, $x \to 0^+$)

$$= \lim_{x \to 0} \frac{\frac{1}{x}}{\frac{-1}{x^2}} \quad \begin{matrix} \to +\infty \\ \to -\infty \end{matrix}$$

$$= \lim_{x \to 0} (-x) = 0.$$

In this example we had a choice of changing $x \ln x$ to

$$\frac{\ln x}{\frac{1}{x}} \quad \text{or} \quad \frac{x}{\frac{1}{\ln x}}.$$

Since the derivative of $1/\ln x$ is relatively complicated, we chose the other, simpler form. After using L'Hôpital's rule once, we were still left with the indeterminate form ∞/∞. Continued use of L'Hôpital's rule would have gotten us nowhere; but simplifying the expression algebraically led to an answer directly. Remember that L'Hôpital's rule is not a cure for all ills; sometimes another method works where it fails.

Example 2

Evaluate $\lim\limits_{x \to \pi/2-} \sec 3x \cos 5x$.

$$\lim_{x \to \pi/2-} \sec 3x \cos 5x \quad \to (-\infty)0 \quad = \lim_{x \to \pi/-2} \frac{\cos 5x}{\cos 3x} \quad \begin{matrix} \to 0 \\ \to 0 \end{matrix}$$

$$= \lim_{x \to \pi/-2} \frac{-5 \sin 5x}{-3 \sin 3x} = \frac{-5}{3}.$$

Another form that will lead to either $0/0$ or ∞/∞ is generally referred to as "$\infty - \infty$." In the past we have used ∞ without a $+$ or $-$ (as in ∞/∞ or $0 \cdot \infty$), when it made no difference if we had the $+$ or the $-$. It does make a difference in this case; in fact, *the signs must be watched carefully*. The form $\infty - \infty$ is a convenient notation for all of the following: $(+\infty)-(+\infty)$, $(-\infty)-(-\infty)$ and $(+\infty)+(-\infty)$. Again, one term tends to make the expression large while the other tends to make it small, giving an indeterminate form.

Unfortunately there is no generally applicable, simple procedure for converting to one of the forms $0/0$ or ∞/∞. All that can be said is: combine the two terms into a single fraction and try to get one of the previous forms from that.

Example 3

Evaluate $\lim\limits_{x \to \pi/2-} (\sec x - \tan x)$.

$$\lim_{x \to \pi/2-} (\sec x - \tan x) \quad \to (+\infty) - (+\infty) \quad = \lim_{x \to \pi/2-} \left(\frac{1}{\cos x} - \frac{\sin x}{\cos x} \right)$$

$$= \lim_{x \to \pi/2-} \frac{1 - \sin x}{\cos x} \quad \begin{matrix} \to 0 \\ \to 0 \end{matrix}$$

$$= \lim_{x \to \pi/2-} \frac{-\cos x}{-\sin x} = \frac{0}{-1} = 0.$$

Example 4

Evaluate $\lim\limits_{x \to 1+} \left(\dfrac{1}{x-1} - \dfrac{2}{x^2-1} \right)$.

$$\lim_{x\to 1+}\left(\frac{1}{x-1}-\frac{2}{x^2-1}\right) \to (+\infty)-(+\infty) \quad = \lim_{x\to 1+}\left(\frac{x+1}{x^2-1}-\frac{2}{x^2-1}\right)$$

$$= \lim_{x\to 1+}\frac{x-1}{x^2-1} \quad \begin{matrix}\to 0\\ \to 0\end{matrix}$$

$$= \lim_{x\to 1+}\frac{1}{2x}=\frac{1}{2}.$$

While we used L'Hôpital's rule here, we had a choice of that or canceling factors.

Example 5

Evaluate $\lim_{x\to 0+}\left(\frac{1}{x}-\ln x\right)$.

$$\lim_{x\to 0+}\frac{1}{x}=+\infty, \qquad \lim_{x\to 0+}\ln x=-\infty.$$

Since the second term is subtracted from the first, the two terms are pulling in the same direction. This is *not* an indeterminate form and L'Hôpital's rule is not needed.

$$\lim_{x\to 0+}\left(\frac{1}{x}-\ln x\right)=+\infty.$$

Problems

Evaluate the following limits.

1. $\lim_{x\to 0}x^2\ln x$.
2. $\lim_{x\to 0}x^n\ln x$ (n a positive integer).
3. $\lim_{x\to 0}\sin x\ln x$.
4. $\lim_{x\to 0}\tan x\ln x$.
5. $\lim_{x\to \pi/4-}(1-\tan x)\sec 2x$.
6. $\lim_{x\to \pi/2-}\sec x\cos 5x$.
7. $\lim_{x\to \pi/2-}\sec 3x\cos 7x$.
8. $\lim_{x\to 1-}(1-x)\tan\frac{\pi x}{2}$.
9. $\lim_{x\to +\infty}e^{-x}\ln x$.
10. $\lim_{x\to 0+}e^{-x}\ln x$.
11. $\lim_{x\to \pi/2-}\sec x\left(x\sin x-\frac{\pi}{2}\right)$.
12. $\lim_{x\to a+}\ln(x-a)\tan(x-a)$.
13. $\lim_{x\to +\infty}x\ln\left(1+\frac{a}{x}\right)$ $(a>0)$.
14. $\lim_{x\to 0+}\ln x\ln(1+x)$.
15. $\lim_{x\to 1+}\left(\frac{1}{\ln x}-\frac{1}{x-1}\right)$.
16. $\lim_{x\to 1}\left(\frac{1}{\ln x}-\frac{x}{\ln x}\right)$.
17. $\lim_{x\to \pi/2-}(2x\tan x-\pi\sec x)$.
18. $\lim_{x\to 0}\left(\frac{2}{\sin^2 x}-\frac{1}{1-\cos x}\right)$.
19. $\lim_{x\to 1}\left(\frac{x}{x-1}-\frac{1}{\ln x}\right)$.
20. $\lim_{x\to 0}\left(\frac{1}{2x}-\frac{1}{x(e^x+1)}\right)$.
21. $\lim_{x\to 0}\left(\frac{1}{x^2}-\frac{1}{x\tan x}\right)$.
22. $\lim_{x\to 0}\left(\frac{1}{x(1+x)}-\frac{\ln(1+x)}{x^2}\right)$.
23. $\lim_{x\to +\infty}\left[x-x^2\ln\left(1+\frac{1}{x}\right)\right]$.
24. $\lim_{x\to 0}\left(\frac{x}{\sin^3 x}-\cot^2 x\right)$.

18.3

The Forms 0^0, ∞^0, *and* 1^∞

Let us now consider the limit

$$\lim_{x\to a}[f(x)]^{g(x)},$$

where

(a) $\lim_{x\to a} f(x) = 0$ and $\lim_{x\to a} g(x) = 0 \quad (0^0)$,

(b) $\lim_{x\to a} |f(x)| = +\infty$ and $\lim_{x\to a} g(x) = 0 \quad (\infty^0)$,

(c) $\lim_{x\to a} f(x) = 1$ and $\lim_{x\to a} |g(x)| = +\infty \quad (1^\infty)$.

All three of these cases are handled in the same way. This method depends upon the equality

$$\ln \lim_{x\to a} F(x) = \lim_{x\to a} \ln F(x).$$

Although we shall not prove either this special case or the more general one, the equality is true, not only for the logarithm, but for any continuous function G. Thus we need evaluate, not the limit of the original function, but the limit of the logarithm, which can be reduced to a product. Let us consider some examples.

Example 1

Evaluate $\lim_{x\to 0+} x^x$.

We see that this is the indeterminate form 0^0. Thus

$$\begin{aligned}
\ln \lim_{x\to 0+} x^x &= \lim_{x\to 0+} \ln x^x \\
&= \lim_{x\to 0+} x \ln x \quad \to 0(-\infty) \\
&= \lim_{x\to 0+} \frac{\ln x}{\frac{1}{x}} \quad \begin{matrix}\to -\infty \\ \to +\infty\end{matrix} \\
&= \lim_{x\to 0+} \frac{\frac{1}{x}}{-\frac{1}{x^2}} \quad \begin{matrix}\to +\infty \\ \to -\infty\end{matrix} \\
&= \lim_{x\to 0+} (-x) = 0.
\end{aligned}$$

We now have, not the limit we want, but the logarithm of that limit. Thus

$$\lim_{x\to 0+} x^x = e^0 = 1.$$

Example 2

Evaluate $\lim_{x \to +\infty} x^{1/x}$.

This has the form ∞^0. Thus,

$$\begin{aligned}
\ln \lim_{x \to +\infty} x^{1/x} &= \lim_{x \to +\infty} \ln x^{1/x} \\
&= \lim_{x \to +\infty} \frac{1}{x} \ln x \quad \to 0(+\infty) \\
&= \lim_{x \to +\infty} \frac{\ln x}{x} \quad \begin{matrix} \to +\infty \\ \to +\infty \end{matrix} \\
&= \lim_{x \to +\infty} \frac{\frac{1}{x}}{1} = \frac{0}{1} = 0.
\end{aligned}$$

Thus,

$$\lim_{x \to +\infty} x^{1/x} = e^0 = 1.$$

Example 3

Evaluate $\lim_{x \to 0} (1 + x)^{1/x}$.

This has the form 1^∞. Thus

$$\begin{aligned}
\ln \lim_{x \to 0} (1 + x)^{1/x} &= \lim_{x \to 0} \ln (1 + x)^{1/x} \\
&= \lim_{x \to 0} \frac{1}{x} \ln (1 + x) \quad \to \infty \cdot 0 \\
&= \lim_{x \to 0} \frac{\ln (1 + x)}{x} \quad \begin{matrix} \to 0 \\ \to 0 \end{matrix} \\
&= \lim_{x \to 0} \frac{\frac{1}{1 + x}}{1} = 1.
\end{aligned}$$

Thus,

$$\lim_{x \to 0} (1 + x)^{1/x} = e^1 = e.$$

Let us recall that e was defined to be this limit (see page 263). Thus, the above is not a proof that this limit exists.

It might appear that 0^∞ is also an indeterminate form. Actually a limit of the form $0^{(+\infty)}$ is always 0, while one of the form $0^{(-\infty)}$ is always $+\infty$. However, they can be handled in the same way as the indeterminate forms above. Let us consider

$$\lim_{x \to a} [f(x)]^{g(x)},$$

where

$$\lim_{x \to a} f(x) = 0 \quad \text{and} \quad \lim_{x \to a} g(x) = +\infty.$$

Then

$$\begin{aligned}\ln \lim_{x\to a} [f(x)]^{g(x)} &= \lim_{x\to a} \ln [f(x)]^{g(x)} \\ &= \lim_{x\to a} g(x) \ln f(x) \quad \to (+\infty)(-\infty) \\ &= -\infty\end{aligned}$$

and

$$\begin{aligned}\lim_{x\to a} [f(x)]^{g(x)} &= \lim_{x\to a} e^{\ln[f(x)]^{g(x)}} \quad \to e^{-\infty} \\ &= 0.\end{aligned}$$

The form $0^{(-\infty)}$ can be shown to give $+\infty$ in the same way.

Problems

Evaluate the limits in Problems 1–24.

1. $\lim_{x\to 0+} x^{x^2}$.
2. $\lim_{x\to 0+} x^{\sin x}$.
3. $\lim_{x\to 0+} x^{\tan x}$.
4. $\lim_{x\to 0} (1 + ax)^{1/x}$.
5. $\lim_{x\to +\infty} \left(1 + \frac{1}{x}\right)^x$.
6. $\lim_{x\to +\infty} \left(1 + \frac{1}{x^2}\right)^x$.
7. $\lim_{x\to \pi/2-} (\sin x)^{\tan x}$.
8. $\lim_{x\to 0+} (\sin x)^{\tan x}$.
9. $\lim_{x\to \pi/2-} (\tan x)^{\cos x}$.
10. $\lim_{x\to +\infty} (\ln x)^{1/x}$.
11. $\lim_{x\to +\infty} (1 + e^{-x})^{1/x}$.
12. $\lim_{x\to 1+} (\ln x)^{x-1}$.
13. $\lim_{x\to 0} (e^x + x)^{1/x}$.
14. $\lim_{x\to 0+} (-\ln x)^x$.
15. $\lim_{x\to 0+} x^{\ln x}$.
16. $\lim_{x\to 0+} \left(\frac{1}{x}\right)^{\tan x}$.
17. $\lim_{x\to 1} x^{1/(1-x)}$.
18. $\lim_{x\to 0+} (\cot x)^{\sin x}$.
19. $\lim_{x\to +\infty} (1 + x)^{1/x}$.
20. $\lim_{x\to 0+} x^{1/\ln \sin x}$.
21. $\lim_{x\to 0} (\cos ax)^{b/x}$.
22. $\lim_{x\to 0} (\cos ax)^{b/x^2}$.
23. $\lim_{x\to 0} (1 - x)^{1/x}$.
24. $\lim_{x\to 0+} x^{1/\ln x}$.
25. Show that a limit of the form $0^{(-\infty)}$ always gives $+\infty$.

Infinite Series

19.1

Sequences and Series

An infinite series is simply an indicated sum of infinitely many terms. But, with this seemingly simple statement, come many questions. What is meant by the sum of infinitely many numbers? Can we always add infinitely many numbers to get a sum? Can we ever add infinitely many numbers? In order to answer these questions we must define more carefully what it is we are talking about.

Let us start with an idea that logically precedes that of a series, namely, a sequence.

Definition

A ***sequence*** *is a function whose domain is the set of all integers equal to or greater than a particular integer N. The functional values are called the* ***terms*** *of the sequence.*

In most cases the domain is the set of all positive integers; however, it is often convenient to have some other domain. One that is frequently used is the set of all non-negative integers; in this case, the first term corresponds to $n = 0$, the second to $n = 1$, and so on. Occasionally it is convenient to have as domain all integers equal to or greater than 2; in this case, the first term corresponds to $n = 2$, the second to $n = 3$, and so on. Let us consider a few examples of sequences.

Example 1

Discuss $f(n) = 2n - 1$, $n = 1, 2, 3, \ldots$.

The given function is a sequence. The terms of this sequence are the numbers we get by replacing n by 1, 2, 3, and so forth, in turn. Thus, the terms are

$$1, 3, 5, 7, 9, \ldots.$$

Instead of using the notation $f(n)$ for the value of the nth term, we shall normally use the notation s_n. Thus, in this notation, the sequence is $\{s_n\}$ where

$$s_n = 2n - 1, \quad n = 1, 2, 3, \ldots,$$

Example 2

Find the first four terms of the sequence $\{s_n\}$ where

$$s_n = (n-1)^2, \quad n = 2, 3, 4, \ldots.$$

The first four terms are s_2, s_3, s_4, and s_5:, which are 1, 4, 9, and 16.

The two forms

$$s_n = (n-1)^2, \quad n = 2, 3, 4, \ldots$$

and

$$1, 4, 9, 16, \ldots$$

are called the generator form and the expanded form, respectively. Sometimes it is more convenient to express the sequence in the expanded form as the following example demonstrates.

Example 3

Express $1, -1, 1, -1, 1, -1, \ldots$ in generator form.

Actually this form does not give a clear-cut definition of the sequence, since it does not state the association between the integers and the numbers 1 and -1. When a sequence is given in the expanded form it is assumed that the first number given is s_1, the second is s_2, and so on. Thus

$$s_1 = 1, s_2 = -1, s_3 = 1, \text{ etc.},$$

and

$$s_n = \begin{cases} 1 & \text{if } n \text{ is odd,} \\ -1 & \text{if } n \text{ is even.} \end{cases}$$

Let us now consider limits of sequences. Because the domain of a sequence is a set of integers, no number is a limit point of the domain. Thus we cannot have limits of the form

$$\lim_{n \to a} s_n,$$

where a is a real number. Furthermore, there is a smallest integer in the domain; so we cannot have limits of the form

$$\lim_{n \to -\infty} s_n.$$

The only limit that can possibly exist is one of the form

$$\lim_{n \to +\infty} s_n .$$

Thus, when we talk of the limit of a sequence, we mean the limit as $n \to +\infty$.

Definition

The sequence $\{s_n\}$ ***converges*** *means that*

$$\lim_{n \to +\infty} s_n$$

exists. The sequence **diverges** *means that it does not converge, or*

$$\lim_{n \to +\infty} s_n$$

does not exist. (*Remember that*

$$\lim_{n \to +\infty} s_n = +\infty \quad \textit{and} \quad \lim_{n \to +\infty} s_n = -\infty$$

are special cases of nonexistence.)

The three examples of sequences which we have seen all diverge, because

$$\lim_{n \to +\infty} (2n - 1) = +\infty, \qquad \lim_{n \to +\infty} (n - 1)^2 = +\infty,$$

and, if

$$s_n = \begin{cases} 1 & \text{if } n \text{ is odd,} \\ -1 & \text{if } n \text{ is odd,} \end{cases}$$

then

$$\lim_{n \to +\infty} s_n$$

does not exist (although it is not the special kind of nonexistence we have seen in the two previous cases). Let us consider the sequence

$$\frac{1}{2}, \frac{3}{4}, \frac{7}{8}, \frac{15}{16}, \ldots, \quad \text{or} \quad \left\{1 - \frac{1}{2^n}\right\}.$$

Since

$$\lim_{n \to +\infty} \left(1 - \frac{1}{2^n}\right) = 1,$$

this sequence converges to the number 1. This is illustrated graphically in Figure 19.1.

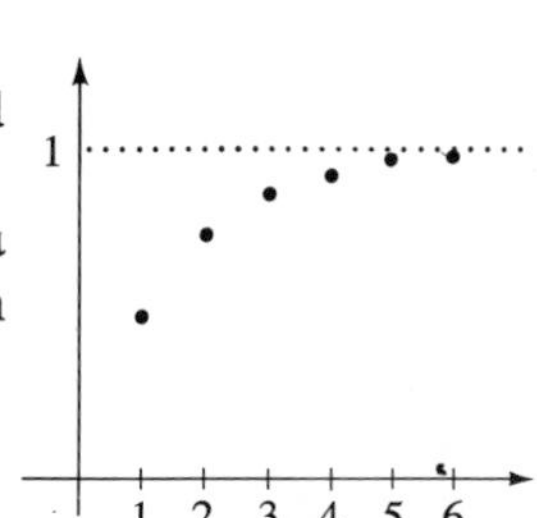

Figure 19.1

Let us return to our primary interest—the series. First a word on notation. We have already used the sigma notation to represent sums. Thus

$$\sum_{n=1}^{5} \frac{1}{n} = \frac{1}{1} + \frac{1}{2} + \frac{1}{3} + \frac{1}{4} + \frac{1}{5}.$$

Let us extend this to an infinite sum.

$$\sum_{n=1}^{\infty} \frac{1}{n} = \frac{1}{1} + \frac{1}{2} + \frac{1}{3} + \cdots \quad \text{(without end)},$$

or, more generally,

$$\sum_{n=1}^{\infty} a_n = a_1 + a_2 + a_3 + \cdots \quad \text{(without end)}.$$

Of course, the values of n need not start with 1—they can start with 0 or 2 or any other number.

Definition

A series is an expression of the form

$$\sum_{n=N}^{\infty} a_n,$$

where N is a given integer and $\{a_n\}$ is a given sequence.

This, of course, is in accord with our idea of a series as an infinite sum. Let us now consider what it means to add infinitely many numbers. For simplicity we shall consider a series of the form

$$\sum_{n=1}^{\infty} a_n,$$

where n begins with 1. This is often abbreviated to $\sum a_n$. Other cases can be considered in exactly the same way.

Definition

If we have the series

$$\sum_{n=1}^{\infty} a_n = a_1 + a_2 + a_3 + \cdots,$$

and if we write

$$\begin{aligned} s_1 &= a_1 \\ s_2 &= a_1 + a_2 \\ s_3 &= a_1 + a_2 + a_3 \\ &\vdots \\ s_n &= a_1 + a_2 + a_3 + \cdots + a_n \\ &\vdots \end{aligned}$$

then the sequence $\{s_n\}$ is called the ***sequence of partial sums****. If $\{s_n\}$ converges to the number S, then $\sum a_n$ is said to* ***converge*** *to S and S is called the* ***sum*** *of the series. If $\{s_n\}$ diverges, then $\sum a_n$ is said to* ***diverge****.*

Example 4

Does the series

$$\sum_{n=1}^{\infty} \frac{1}{2^n} = \frac{1}{2} + \frac{1}{4} + \frac{1}{8} + \cdots$$

converge or diverge? If it converges, to what number does it converge?

We must consider the sequence $\{s_n\}$ of partial sums

$$s_1 = \frac{1}{2}, \quad s_2 = \frac{3}{4}, \quad s_3 = \frac{7}{8}, \ldots, \quad s_n = 1 - \frac{1}{2^n}, \ldots.$$

Since

$$\lim_{n\to+\infty} s_n = \lim_{n\to+\infty} \left(1 - \frac{1}{2^n}\right) = 1,$$

the original series converges to 1.

Example 5

Does the series

$$1 - 1 + 1 - 1 + 1 - 1 + \cdots$$

converge or diverge? If it converges, to what number does it converge?

The sequence $\{s_n\}$ of partial sums is

$$s_1 = 1, \quad s_2 = 0, \quad s_3 = 1, \quad s_4 = 0, \ldots, \quad s_n = \begin{cases} 1 & \text{if } n \text{ is even,} \\ 0 & \text{if } n \text{ is odd.} \end{cases}$$

So $\lim_{n\to+\infty} s_n$ does not exist. Thus the original series diverges.

Let us now consider another relationship between the partial sums and the individual terms.

Theorem 19.1

If the series $\sum a_n$ converges, then

$$\lim_{n\to+\infty} a_n = 0.$$

Before giving a proof of this theorem, let us emphasize that the limit we are considering is *not* the limit of the sequence $\{s_n\}$ of partial sums, but rather the limit of the sequence $\{a_n\}$ of the terms of the series. Thus, the theorem says that if

$$s_1, s_2, s_3, \cdots \to s \qquad (s \text{ a real number}),$$

then

$$a_1, a_2, a_3 \cdots \to 0.$$

Proof

$$a_n = s_n - s_{n-1}.$$

Since $\sum a_n$ converges,

$$\lim_{n \to +\infty} s_n = s \quad \text{and} \quad \lim_{n \to +\infty} s_{n-1} = s.$$

Thus

$$\begin{aligned} \lim_{n \to +\infty} a_n &= \lim_{n \to +\infty} (s_n - s_{n-1}) \\ &= \lim_{n \to +\infty} s_n - \lim_{n \to +\infty} s_{n-1} \\ &= s - s = 0. \end{aligned}$$

The following theorem is a direct consequence of Theorem 19.1.

Theorem 19.2

If

$$\lim_{n \to +\infty} a_n \neq 0,$$

then the series $\sum a_n$ *diverges.*

The proof is left to the student. The application of Theorem 19.2 to Example 5 shows that the series

$$1 - 1 + 1 - 1 + 1 - 1 + \cdots$$

diverges, since the sequence

$$1, -1, 1, -1, 1, -1, \ldots$$

clearly does not converge to 0.

A word of warning: The converse of this theorem is not true. If the limit of the sequence of terms is zero, that is no guarantee that $\sum a_n$ converges. The following example proves this.

Example 6

Show that the series

$$\sum_{n=1}^{\infty} \frac{1}{n} = 1 + \frac{1}{2} + \frac{1}{3} + \frac{1}{4} + \cdots$$

diverges. This is called the *harmonic series.*

Let us group the terms of the series in order to make it easier to consider certain ones of the partial sums.

$$1 + \frac{1}{2} + \left(\frac{1}{3} + \frac{1}{4}\right) + \left(\frac{1}{5} + \frac{1}{6} + \frac{1}{7} + \frac{1}{8}\right) + \left(\frac{1}{9} + \cdots + \frac{1}{16}\right) + \cdots.$$

Now, since $1/3 > 1/4$,

$$\frac{1}{3}+\frac{1}{4} > 2\cdot\frac{1}{4} = \frac{1}{2}.$$

Since 1/5, 1/6, 1/7, and 1/8 are all at least as big as 1/8, their sum is greater than $4\cdot(1/8) = 1/2$. Similarly $1/9 + \cdots + 1/16 > 1/2$, and so forth. Thus,

$$\begin{aligned}
s_1 &> 1\cdot\frac{1}{2},\\
s_2 &> 2\cdot\frac{1}{2},\\
s_4 &> 3\cdot\frac{1}{2},\\
s_8 &> 4\cdot\frac{1}{2},\\
s_{16} &> 5\cdot\frac{1}{2},\\
&\vdots\\
s_{(2^{n-1})} &> n\cdot\frac{1}{2},\\
&\vdots
\end{aligned}$$

and

$$\lim_{n\to+\infty} s_n = \lim_{n\to+\infty} s_{2^{n-1}} = +\infty.$$

The series diverges even though $a_n \to 0$ as $n \to +\infty$.

The preceding argument indicates that, no matter how large a number we choose, there is a partial sum of this series that is greater than that number. For instance, if we choose the number $100 = 200\cdot(1/2)$, then the 2^{199}-th partial sum is greater than 100. If we choose $1000 = 2000\cdot(1/2)$, then the 2^{1999}-th partial sum exceeds it. This seems rather incredible when considering that the terms of the series are small to begin with and getting smaller as we go out. Things aren't always what they seem when we are dealing with infinite series.

Let us conclude this section with a simple theorem that is more self-evident.

Theorem 19.3

If $\sum a_n$ and $\sum b_n$ are convergent series and c is a number, then

$$\sum ca_n,\ \sum (a_n + b_n),\quad \text{and}\quad \sum (a_n - b_n)$$

are convergent and

$$\sum ca_n = c\sum a_n,\quad \sum (a_n + b_n) = \sum a_n + \sum b_n,\quad \text{and}\quad \sum (a_n - b_n) = \sum a_n - \sum b_n.$$

This follows directly from a consideration of partial sums. The details are left to the student.

Problems

In Problems 1–6, give the first four terms of the series.

1. $\sum_{n=1}^{\infty} \frac{1}{3^n}$.

2. $\sum_{n=1}^{\infty} \frac{1}{n^2}$.

3. $\sum_{n=1}^{\infty} \frac{1}{n(n+1)}$.

4. $\sum_{n=1}^{\infty} \frac{n+1}{n(n+2)}$.

5. $\sum_{n=1}^{\infty} \frac{(-1)^n}{n^2+1}$.

6. $\sum_{n=1}^{\infty} \frac{(-1)^n}{n!}$.

In Problems 7–12, give the series in generator form.

7. $1+4+7+10+\cdots$.

8. $\frac{1}{10}+\frac{1}{100}+\frac{1}{1000}+\cdots$.

9. $1\cdot 2+3\cdot 4+5\cdot 6+7\cdot 8+\cdots$.

10. $1+2+4+8+\cdots$.

11. $1\cdot 2-2\cdot 2^2+3\cdot 2^3-\cdots$.

12. $1\cdot 3-2\cdot 4+3\cdot 5-\cdots$.

In Problems 13–20, indicate whether the sequence converges or diverges. If it converges, to what number does it converge?

13. $\frac{1}{2}, \frac{1}{4}, \frac{1}{8}, \frac{1}{16}, \cdots$.

14. $1, \frac{1}{2}, \frac{1}{3}, \frac{1}{4}, \cdots$.

15. $1, -\frac{1}{2}, \frac{1}{3}, -\frac{1}{4}, \cdots$.

16. $\frac{1}{2}, -\frac{3}{4}, \frac{7}{8}, -\frac{15}{16}, \cdots$.

17. $s_n = \frac{n}{n+1}$.

18. $s_n = \frac{n}{n^2+1}$.

19. $s_n = \frac{(-1)^n n}{n+2}$.

20. $s_n = \frac{4n(4n+2)}{(4n+1)(4n+3)}$.

In Problems 21–30, indicate whether the series converges or diverges. If it converges, to what number does it converge?

21. $\frac{1}{1\cdot 2}+\frac{1}{2\cdot 3}+\frac{1}{3\cdot 4}+\cdots+\frac{1}{n(n+1)}+\cdots$.

22. $\frac{1}{1\cdot 2}-\frac{1}{2\cdot 3}-\frac{1}{3\cdot 4}-\cdots-\frac{1}{n(n+1)}-\cdots$.

23. $\frac{1}{3}+\frac{1}{9}+\frac{1}{27}+\cdots+\frac{1}{3^n}+\cdots$.

24. $\frac{1}{4}+\frac{1}{16}+\frac{1}{64}+\cdots+\frac{1}{4^n}+\cdots$.

25. $1-2+3-4+\cdots+(-1)^{n+1}n+\cdots$.

26. $\frac{1}{2}+\frac{2}{3}+\frac{3}{4}+\cdots+\frac{n}{n+1}+\cdots$.

27. $\frac{1}{2}+\frac{1}{3}+\frac{1}{2^2}+\frac{1}{3^2}+\frac{1}{2^3}+\frac{1}{3^3}+\cdots$.

28. $\frac{1}{2}-\frac{1}{3}+\frac{1}{2^2}-\frac{1}{3^2}+\frac{1}{2^3}-\frac{1}{3^3}+\cdots$.

29. $\frac{1}{2}+\frac{1}{4}+\frac{1}{6}+\frac{1}{8}+\cdots+\frac{1}{2n}+\cdots$.

30. $\frac{1}{1\cdot 2}+\frac{3}{2\cdot 5}+\frac{5}{5\cdot 10}+\frac{7}{10\cdot 17}+\cdots+\frac{2n-1}{[(n-1)^2+1](n^2+1)}+\cdots$.

31. Prove Theorem 19.2.

32. Prove Theorem 19.3.

33. Show that if $\sum_{n=1}^{\infty} a_n$ converges, then $\sum_{n=N}^{\infty} a_n$, where $N \geq 1$, converges.

34. Show that if $\sum_{n=N}^{\infty} a_n$, where $N \geq 1$, converges, then $\sum_{n=1}^{\infty} a_n$ converges.

19.2

Geometric Series and p-Series

In this section we shall consider two special types of series: the geometric series and the p-series. The following theorem will be helpful.

Theorem 19.4

If $\{s_n\}$ is a sequence of positive numbers such that $s_{n+1} > s_n$ for every integer n and there is a number k such that $s_n \leq k$ for every integer n, then $\{s_n\}$ converges.

Proof

Let $S = \{x \mid x \geq s_n$ for every integer $n\}$. This set is not empty, since k is in it. Let u be the smallest number in S (the existence of such a number u is a characteristic of the real numbers). Now let us show that

$$\lim_{n\to+\infty} s_n = u.$$

Let ϵ be a positive number. Assume that

$$s_n \leq u - \epsilon$$

for every positive integer n. Then $u - \epsilon$ is in S. But $u - \epsilon < u$, contradicting the statement that u is the smallest number in S. Thus the assumption is wrong, and there is a number N such that $s_N > u - \epsilon$. If $n > N$, then $s_n > s_N > u - \epsilon$ and $s_n < u$. Thus there is a number N such that, if $n > N$, $|s_n - u| < \epsilon$; and $\{s_n\}$ converges to u.

A geometric series is one of the form

$$a + ar + ar^2 + \cdots + ar^{n-1} + \cdots,$$

in which each term is found by multiplying the previous one by a constant r. Let us consider the nth partial sum

$$\begin{aligned} s_n &= a + ar + ar^2 + \cdots + ar^{n-1} \\ &= a(1 + r + r^2 + \cdots + r^{n-1}) \\ &= \frac{a(1 + r + r^2 + \cdots + r^{n-1})(1 - r)}{1 - r} \quad \text{(provided } r \neq 1\text{)} \\ &= \frac{a(1 - r^n)}{1 - r}. \end{aligned}$$

If $|r| < 1$, then

$$\lim_{n\to+\infty} r^n = 0 \quad \text{and} \quad \lim_{n\to+\infty} s_n = \frac{a}{1 - r}.$$

If $|r| > 1$, then, neither $\lim_{n\to+\infty} r^n$ nor $\lim_{n\to+\infty} s_n$ exists. If $|r| = 1$, we cannot use the formula for s_n; but it is clear from a consideration of the original series that if $a \neq 0$, the series diverges.

Theorem 19.5

The geometric series given by

$$a + ar + ar^2 + \cdots + ar^{n-1} + \cdots, \quad a \neq 0,$$

converges to $a/(1-r)$ *if* $|r| < 1$ *and diverges if* $|r| \geq 1$.

Example 1

Indicate whether the series

$$1 + \frac{1}{5} + \frac{1}{25} + \frac{1}{125} + \cdots$$

converges or diverges. If it converges, to what number does it converge?

This is clearly a geometric series with $a = 1$ and $r = 1/5$. Since $r = 1/5$, the series converges and it converges to the number

$$\frac{a}{1-r} = \frac{1}{1-1/5} = \frac{1}{4/5} = \frac{5}{4}.$$

Example 2

Give 0.232323... as a quotient of two integers.

$$0.232323\ldots = 0.23 + 0.0023 + 0.000023 + \cdots$$

This is a geometric series with $a = 0.23$ and $r = 0.01$. It converges to

$$\frac{a}{1-r} = \frac{0.23}{1-0.01} = \frac{0.23}{0.99} = \frac{23}{99}.$$

This can easily be checked by division.

The second series we want to consider here is the p-series, which is of the form

$$\sum_{n=1}^{\infty} \frac{1}{n^p} = \frac{1}{1^p} + \frac{1}{2^p} + \frac{1}{3^p} + \cdots.$$

We have already seen (Example 6 of the previous section) an example of the p-series. That is the harmonic series

$$1 + \frac{1}{2} + \frac{1}{3} + \cdots,$$

for which $p = 1$. We have seen that this series diverges.

Theorem 19.6

If p *is a real number, then the* p*-series*

$$\sum_{n=1}^{\infty} \frac{1}{n^p} = \frac{1}{1^p} + \frac{1}{2^p} + \frac{1}{3^p} + \cdots$$

converges if $p > 1$ *and diverges if* $p \leq 1$.

Proof

Let us first consider the case in which $p > 1$. Suppose we group the terms of the series in the following way (see Note):

$$1 + \left(\frac{1}{2^p} + \frac{1}{3^p}\right) + \left(\frac{1}{4^p} + \frac{1}{5^p} + \frac{1}{6^p} + \frac{1}{7^p}\right) + \left(\frac{1}{8^p} + \cdots + \frac{1}{15^p}\right) + \cdots.$$

Now

$$\frac{1}{2^p} + \frac{1}{3^p} < 2 \cdot \frac{1}{2^p} = \frac{1}{2^{p-1}}$$

$$\frac{1}{4^p} + \frac{1}{5^p} + \frac{1}{6^p} + \frac{1}{7^p} < 4 \cdot \frac{1}{4^p} = \frac{1}{4^{p-1}}$$

$$\frac{1}{8^p} + \frac{1}{9^p} + \cdots + \frac{1}{15^p} < 8 \cdot \frac{1}{8^p} = \frac{1}{8^{p-1}},$$

and so forth. Thus the terms of this series (each group considered as a single term) are less than or equal to the terms of the series

$$1 + \frac{1}{2^{p-1}} + \frac{1}{4^{p-1}} + \frac{1}{8^{p-1}} + \cdots = 1 + \frac{1}{2^{p-1}} + \frac{1}{(2^{p-1})^2} + \frac{1}{(2^{p-1})^3} + \cdots.$$

But the last series is a geometric series with

$$r = \frac{1}{2^{p-1}} < 1;$$

it converges. Since the terms of the (grouped) p-series are less than or equal to the corresponding terms of a convergent series, then the partial sums of the (grouped) p-series are less than or equal to those of the convergent series. Since the p-series is a series of positive terms, the sequence of partial sums is an increasing one and, by Theorem 19.4, it must converge.

We have already proved in the previous section that the p-series diverges if $p = 1$. Suppose now that $p < 1$. Then

$$n^p \leq n \quad \text{and} \quad \frac{1}{n^p} \geq \frac{1}{n}.$$

Thus the partial sums of the p-series with $p < 1$ are all equal to or greater than the corresponding partial sums of the harmonic series (p-series with $p = 1$). Since

$$\lim_{n \to +\infty} s_n = +\infty,$$

where s_n is the nth partial sum of the harmonic series, the same is true of the partial sums of the p-series. Thus the p-series diverges.

Note: When we group the terms of the series, we are replacing the original series,

$$\sum_{n=1}^{\infty} a_n$$

with sequence $\{s_n\}$ of partial sums, by the series

$$\sum_{n=1}^{\infty} b_n,$$

where

$$b_1 = a_1,$$
$$b_2 = a_2 + a_3,$$
$$b_3 = a_4 + a_5 + a_6 + a_7,$$

and so forth. The latter series has the sequence $\{t_n\}$ of partial sums where

$$t_1 = s_1, \quad t_2 = s_3, \quad t_3 = s_7, \quad \text{etc.}$$

Since, in this case, the sequence $\{s_n\}$ of partial sums is an increasing one,

$$\lim_{n\to+\infty} t_n = \lim_{n\to+\infty} s_n.$$

This is not necessarily the case if the original series is not a series of positive terms.

It might be noted that, if $p > 1$, the theorem asserts that the p-series converges. However, it does not tell us to what number it converges.

It frequently happens that we can easily determine that a series converges, but we do not know to what number it converges. The latter question is far more difficult.

Example 3

Determine whether

$$1 + \frac{1}{\sqrt{2}} + \frac{1}{\sqrt{3}} + \cdots$$

converges or diverges.

This is a p-series with $p = 1/2$. It diverges.

19.3

The Comparison Test

The series of the preceding section lead up to our first test for convergence or divergence—the comparison test.

Theorem 19.7

(*Comparison test*) *If $\sum a_n$ is a series of positive terms, $\sum b_n$ is a convergent series of positive terms, and $a_n \le b_n$ for all n, then $\sum a_n$ converges; if $\sum b_n$ is a divergent series of positive terms and $a_n \ge b_n$ for all n, then $\sum a_n$ diverges.*

Proof

Let us consider the first case. Let $\{s_n\}$ and $\{t_n\}$ be the sequences of partial sums of $\sum a_n$ and $\sum b_n$, respectively. Since $a_n \le b_n$ for every integer n, $s_n \le t_n$ for every n. But

$$\lim_{n\to+\infty} t_n = t.$$

Since $\sum b_n$ is a series of positive terms converging to t, $t_n \le t$ for every n. Thus $s_n \le t_n \le t$ for every n and, by Theorem 19.4, $\sum a_n$ converges.

Suppose now that $\sum b_n$ diverges and $a_n \ge b_n$. Assume that $\sum a_n$ converges. By the first part, $\sum b_n$ converges; but this is a contradiction. Thus $\sum a_n$ diverges.

It must be emphasized that $\sum a_n$ and $\sum b_n$ are series of *positive* terms. Neither part of Theorem 19.7 would hold without that restriction (see Problems 31 and 32).

Let us also note that the terms of the series being tested must be less than or equal to those of a convergent series or greater than or equal to those of a divergent series. Getting the terms less than or equal to those of a divergent series or greater than or equal to those of a convergent series tells us nothing about the series.

Example 1

Test for convergence

$$\frac{1}{1\cdot 2}+\frac{1}{2\cdot 3}+\cdots+\frac{1}{n(n+1)}+\cdots.$$

In making a comparison, let us consider the nth term and see if we can simplify it in the proper way.

$$\frac{1}{n(n+1)}=\frac{1}{n^2+n}<\frac{1}{n^2}.$$

But

$$\sum_{n=1}^{\infty}\frac{1}{n^2}$$

is a p-series with $p>1$; it converges. Thus, the original also converges.

Example 2

Test for convergence

$$\frac{1}{1\cdot 1}+\frac{1}{2\cdot 3}+\frac{1}{3\cdot 5}+\cdots+\frac{1}{n(2n-1)}+\cdots.$$

Suppose we try the same sort of thing that we did in Example 1:

$$\frac{1}{n(2n-1)}=\frac{1}{2n^2-n}>\frac{1}{2n^2}.$$

But the series

$$\sum_{n=1}^{\infty}\frac{1}{2n^2}=\frac{1}{2}\sum_{n=1}^{\infty}\frac{1}{n^2}$$

is convergent. The combination of $>$ and convergence tells us nothing. Let us try to reverse the inequality. In the situation above, we simplified

$$\frac{1}{2n^2-n}$$

by throwing away the $-n$. This made the new denominator bigger and the new fraction smaller. In order to reverse this situation, let us replace $2n^2-n$ by an expression that is smaller (or, at least, never bigger).

$$\frac{1}{n(2n-1)}=\frac{1}{2n^2-n}\leq\frac{1}{2n^2-n^2}=\frac{1}{n^2}.$$

Now the situation is much better.

$$\sum_{n=1}^{\infty} \frac{1}{n^2}$$

converges and

$$\frac{1}{2n^2 - n} \leq \frac{1}{n^2}$$

for every positive integer n. By the comparison test, the original series converges.

Example 3

Test for convergence

$$\sum_{n=1}^{\infty} \frac{1}{n+1}.$$

Let us try the above process again:

$$\frac{1}{n+1} < \frac{1}{n}.$$

But

$$\sum_{n=1}^{\infty} \frac{1}{n} \text{ diverges.}$$

A false start. Let us try

$$\frac{1}{n+1} > \frac{1}{n+n} = \frac{1}{2n}.$$

Now

$$\sum_{n=1}^{\infty} \frac{1}{2n} = \frac{1}{2} \sum_{n=1}^{\infty} \frac{1}{n}$$

must diverge (if $\sum 1/2n$ converges, then, by Theorem 19.3, so does $\sum 1/n$). Thus the original diverges.

Example 4

Test for convergence

$$\frac{1}{1 \cdot 2} + \frac{1}{2 \cdot 2^2} + \frac{1}{3 \cdot 2^3} + \cdots + \frac{1}{n \cdot 2^n} + \cdots.$$

Again

$$\frac{1}{n \cdot 2^n} < \frac{1}{n}.$$

But $\sum 1/n$ diverges. Let us try again:

$$\frac{1}{n \cdot 2^n} < \frac{1}{2^n}.$$

Now $\sum_{n=1}^{\infty} 1/2^n$ converges, since it is a geometric series with $r = 1/2$. Thus the original converges.

With some experience, a proper type of simplification will become more obvious and you will avoid the false starts we ran into above.

Problems

In Problems 1–8, express the given repeating decimal as a quotient of two integers.

1. 0.1111 . . . .
2. 0.424242 . . . .
3. 0.143143143 . . . .
4. 0.131313 . . . .
5. 0.9999 . . . .
6. 0.316931693169 . . . .
7. 1.242424 . . . .
8. 2.35121212 . . . .

In Problems 9–30, test for convergence.

9. $\frac{1}{2}+\frac{1}{5}+\frac{1}{10}+\cdots+\frac{1}{n^2+1}+\cdots.$
10. $1+\frac{1}{4}+\frac{1}{9}+\cdots+\frac{1}{n^2}+\cdots.$
11. $1+\frac{1}{4}+\frac{1}{16}+\cdots+\frac{1}{4^{n-1}}+\cdots.$
12. $1+\frac{1}{\sqrt[3]{2}}+\frac{1}{\sqrt[3]{3}}+\cdots+\frac{1}{\sqrt[3]{n}}+\cdots.$
13. $\frac{1}{2}+\frac{2}{3}+\frac{3}{4}+\cdots+\frac{n}{n+1}+\cdots.$
14. $\frac{1}{\ln 2}+\frac{1}{\ln 3}+\frac{1}{\ln 4}+\cdots+\frac{1}{\ln (n+1)}+\cdots.$
15. $\frac{1}{2}+\frac{1}{2^2}+\frac{1}{2^3}+\cdots+\frac{1}{2^n}+\cdots.$
16. $\frac{1}{1\cdot 3}+\frac{1}{2\cdot 3^2}+\frac{1}{3\cdot 3^3}+\cdots+\frac{1}{n\cdot 3^n}+\cdots.$
17. $1+\frac{1}{2!}+\frac{1}{3!}+\cdots+\frac{1}{n!}+\cdots.$
18. $1+\frac{2!}{2^2}+\frac{3!}{3^2}+\cdots+\frac{n!}{n^2}+\cdots.$
19. $\frac{1}{1\cdot 3}+\frac{1}{2\cdot 4}+\frac{1}{3\cdot 5}+\cdots+\frac{1}{n(n+2)}+\cdots.$
20. $\frac{1}{2\cdot 2}+\frac{2}{3\cdot 2^2}+\frac{3}{4\cdot 2^3}+\cdots+\frac{n}{(n+1)2^n}+\cdots.$
21. $\sum_{n=1}^{\infty}\frac{1}{(n+1)(n+3)}.$
22. $\sum_{n=1}^{\infty}\frac{1}{(n+1)(n+2)}.$
23. $\sum_{n=1}^{\infty}\frac{2n}{2n+1}.$
24. $\sum_{n=1}^{\infty}\frac{2n}{(n+1)(n+2)}.$
25. $\sum_{n=1}^{\infty}\frac{n}{(n+1)(n+2)(n+3)}.$
26. $\sum_{n=1}^{\infty}\frac{n+3}{n(n+1)(n+2)}.$
27. $\sum_{n=2}^{\infty}\frac{n+1}{n\ln n}.$
28. $\sum_{n=1}^{\infty}\frac{1}{e^n}.$
29. $\sum_{n=1}^{\infty}\frac{1}{\sqrt{n(n+1)}}.$
30. $\sum_{n=1}^{\infty}\frac{1}{n^n}.$
31. Give an example of a series $\sum a_n$ and a convergent series $\sum b_n$ of positive terms such that $a_n \le b_n$ for all n but $\sum a_n$ is divergent.
32. Give an example of a series $\sum a_n$ of positive terms and a divergent series $\sum b_n$ such that $a_n \ge b_n$ for all b but $\sum a_n$ is convergent.

19.4

The Ratio and Integral Tests

While the comparison test can determine convergence or divergence for many series, it is a difficult, or impossible test for many others. Let us consider some other methods of testing series.

Theorem 19.8

(*Ratio test*) *If* $\sum a_n$ *is a series of positive terms and*

$$r = \lim_{n \to +\infty} \frac{a_{n+1}}{a_n},$$

and if

(1) $r < 1$, *then the series converges,*
(2) $r > 1$ (*including* $r = +\infty$), *then the series diverges,*
(3) $r = 1$, *the test fails.*

Proof

Suppose $r < 1$; let v be a number such that $r < v < 1$ and let $\epsilon = v - r$. By the definition of a limit, there is a number N such that, if $n > N$, then

$$\left| \frac{a_{n+1}}{a_n} - r \right| < \epsilon,$$

$$-\epsilon < \frac{a_{n+1}}{a_n} - r < \epsilon,$$

$$r - \epsilon < \frac{a_{n+1}}{a_n} < r + \epsilon = v.$$

Suppose $M > N$. Then

$$\frac{a_{M+1}}{a_M} < v, \qquad a_{M+1} < va_M,$$

$$\frac{a_{M+2}}{a_{M+1}} < v, \qquad a_{M+2} < va_{M+1} < v^2 a_M,$$

$$\frac{a_{M+3}}{a_{M+2}} < v, \qquad a_{M+3} < va_{M+2} < v^3 a_M,$$

and so forth. Let us consider the series

$$\sum_{n=1}^{\infty} v^n a_M = a_M \sum_{n=1}^{\infty} v^n.$$

Since $v < 1$, this series converges. By the comparison test, the series

$$a_{M+1} + a_{M+2} + a_{M+3} + \cdots$$

also converges, and thus $\sum a_n$ converges (see Problem 34, page 464).

Suppose now that $r > 1$. Let $\epsilon = r - 1$. Again, by the definition of a limit, there is a number N such that, if $n > N$, then

$$\left| \frac{a_{n+1}}{a_n} - r \right| < \epsilon.$$

Then

$$-\epsilon < \frac{a_{n+1}}{a_n} - r < \epsilon,$$

$$1 = r - \epsilon < \frac{a_{n+1}}{a_n} < r + \epsilon.$$

Thus, $a_{n+1} > a_n$ for all $n > N$. Therefore,

$$\lim_{n \to +\infty} a_n \neq 0,$$

and the series diverges.

To show that the test fails when $r = 1$, we need merely note that $r = 1$ for

$$\sum_{n=1}^{\infty} \frac{1}{n} \quad \text{and} \quad \sum_{n=1}^{\infty} \frac{1}{n^2},$$

while the first series diverges and the second converges.

Example 1

Test for convergence

$$\sum_{n=1}^{\infty} \frac{n}{3^n}.$$

$$\begin{aligned} \lim_{n \to +\infty} \frac{a_{n+1}}{a_n} &= \lim_{n \to +\infty} \frac{(n+1)/3^{n+1}}{n/3^n} \\ &= \lim_{n \to +\infty} \frac{n+1}{3n} \\ &= \frac{1}{3} < 1. \end{aligned}$$

The series converges.

The ratio test is especially useful in handling expressions involving factorials.

Example 2

Test for convergence $\sum_{n=1}^{\infty} 2^n/n!$.

$$\begin{aligned} \lim_{n \to +\infty} \frac{a_{n+1}}{a_n} &= \lim_{n \to +\infty} \frac{2^{n+1}/(n+1)!}{2^n/n!} \\ &= \lim_{n \to +\infty} \frac{2}{n+1} \\ &= 0 < 1. \end{aligned}$$

The series converges.

Recall that if $r > 1$, then the limit of the sequence of terms is not zero. Thus the ratio test indicates divergence only when the terms do not tend to zero—it is not a sensitive test for divergence. Actually, as we shall see in Section 19.6, this insensitivity is an advantage.

We see that the ratio test is a very simple one to use—when it works. However, the examples above might give one a false sense of confidence in this test. There are many series for which the test fails. If it does, we simply have to fall back on the comparison test or the integral test, which follows.

Theorem 19.9

(Integral test) *If* $\sum_{n=1}^{\infty} a_n$ *is a series of positive terms and* f *is a continuous function such that* $f(n) = a_n$ *for all integers* n *and* f *is decreasing for all* $x > 1$, *then*

(1) $\sum_{n=1}^{\infty} a_n$ *converges if* $\int_1^{+\infty} f(x)\,dx$ *exists, and*

(2) $\sum_{n=1}^{\infty} a_n$ *diverges if* $\int_1^{+\infty} f(x)\,dx$ *does not exist.*

Proof

Suppose the integral exists. In Figure 19.2(a) the first rectangle has height a_1 and width 1. Thus its area is a_1. Similarly the areas of the other rectangles are $a_2, a_3, a_4 \ldots$. Thus, from the Figure, we see that

$$\int_1^n f(x)\,dx > a_2 + a_3 + \cdots + a_n,$$

or

$$a_1 + \int_1^n f(x)\,dx > a_1 + a_2 + a_3 + \cdots + a_n = s_n.$$

Thus,

$$\begin{aligned}\lim_{n \to +\infty} \left[a_1 + \int_1^n f(x)\,dx \right] &= a_1 + \lim_{n \to +\infty} \int_1^n f(x)\,dx \\ &= a_1 + \int_1^{+\infty} f(x)\,dx \\ &\geq \lim_{n \to +\infty} s_n.\end{aligned}$$

Since the first limit exists, the last one must also, and the series converges.

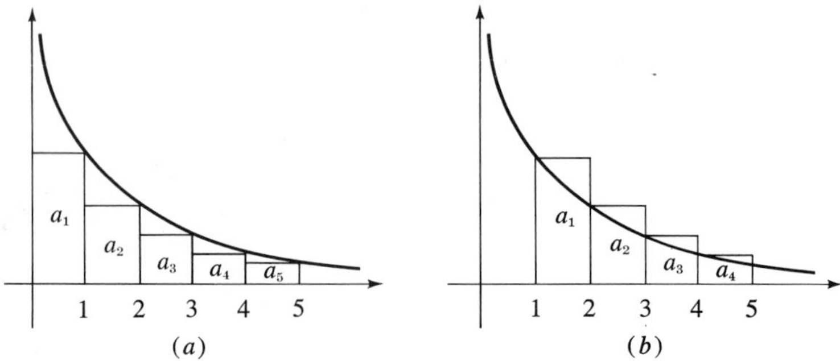

Figure 19.2

Now suppose that the integral does not exist. A similar consideration of Figure 19.2(b) gives

$$\int_1^n f(x)\,dx < a_1 + a_2 + \cdots + a_{n-1} = s_{n-1}.$$

and

$$\lim_{n\to+\infty} \int_1^n f(x)\,dx \le \lim_{n\to+\infty} s_{n-1} = \lim_{n\to+\infty} s_n.$$

If we assume that the series converges, then the last limit exists and the first must also. But the first limit is the integral which does not exist, giving a contradiction. The series must diverge.

It might be noted that if the series were given by

$$\sum_{n=2}^{\infty} a_n,$$

then the integral would be

$$\int_2^{+\infty} f(x)\,dx.$$

Example 3

Test for convergence

$$\sum_{n=1}^{\infty} \frac{1}{n^2+1}.$$

The function f is given by

$$f(x) = \frac{1}{x^2+1}.$$

Let us see where this function is increasing and where it is decreasing.

$$f'(x) = \frac{-2x}{(x^2+1)^2}.$$

Since $f'(x)$ is negative for all positive values of x, f is decreasing for all positive values of x and, thus, for all x greater than 1.

$$\begin{aligned}\int_1^{+\infty} \frac{dx}{x^2+1} &= \lim_{n\to+\infty} \int_1^n \frac{dx}{x^2+1} \\ &= \lim_{n\to+\infty} \operatorname{Arctan} x \Big|_1^n \\ &= \lim_{n\to+\infty} \left(\operatorname{Arctan} n - \frac{\pi}{4}\right) \\ &= \frac{\pi}{2} - \frac{\pi}{4} = \frac{\pi}{4}.\end{aligned}$$

Since the integral exists, the series converges.

Example 4

Test for convergence $\sum_{n=1}^{\infty} \frac{n}{n^2+1}$.

The function f is given by

$$f(x) = \frac{x}{x^2+1}.$$

Now that we have this function, let us see where it is increasing and where decreasing.

$$f'(x) = \frac{1-x^2}{(x^2+1)^2}.$$

The derivative is 0 at $x = 1$ and negative for $x > 1$. Thus, f is decreasing for all $x > 1$.
Now

$$\begin{aligned}\int_1^{+\infty} \frac{x\,dx}{x^2+1} &= \lim_{n\to+\infty} \int_1^n \frac{x\,dx}{x^2+1} \\ &= \lim_{n\to+\infty} \frac{1}{2}\ln(x^2+1)\Big|_1^n \\ &= \lim_{n\to+\infty} \left[\frac{1}{2}\ln(n^2+1) - \frac{1}{2}\ln 2\right] \\ &= +\infty.\end{aligned}$$

The series diverges.

It might be noted that the theorem still holds if we can merely find some number N such that f is decreasing for all $x > N$ (see Problem 34, page 464).

Problems

In Problems 1–10, test for convergence by the ratio test. Use another test only if the ratio test fails.

1. $\sum_{n=1}^{\infty} \frac{n+1}{n!}$.
2. $\sum_{n=1}^{\infty} \frac{n+1}{n \cdot 2^n}$.
3. $\sum_{n=1}^{\infty} \frac{2^n}{3^{n+1}}$.
4. $\sum_{n=1}^{\infty} \frac{2^{n+1}}{3^n}$.
5. $\sum_{n=1}^{\infty} \frac{4^n}{n!}$.
6. $\sum_{n=1}^{\infty} \frac{n!}{1 \cdot 3 \cdot 5 \cdots (2n-1)}$.
7. $\sum_{n=1}^{\infty} \frac{3^n}{n \cdot 2^n}$.
8. $\sum_{n=1}^{\infty} \frac{3^n}{n^2 \cdot 2^n}$.
9. $\sum_{n=1}^{\infty} \frac{2 \cdot 4 \cdot 6 \cdots 2n}{1 \cdot 3 \cdot 5 \cdots (2n-1)}$.
10. $\sum_{n=1}^{\infty} \frac{n!}{(2n)!}$.

In Problems 11–20, test for convergence by the integral test.

11. $\sum_{n=1}^{\infty} \frac{1}{n^p} \ (p > 1)$.

12. $\sum_{n=1}^{\infty} \frac{1}{n^p} \ (p < 1)$.

13. $\sum_{n=1}^{\infty} \frac{\ln n}{n}$.

14. $\sum_{n=2}^{\infty} \frac{1}{n \ln n}$.

15. $\sum_{n=1}^{\infty} \frac{1}{n(n+1)}$.

16. $\sum_{n=1}^{\infty} \frac{1}{2n+1}$.

17. $\sum_{n=1}^{\infty} \frac{n}{e^n}$.

18. $\sum_{n=1}^{\infty} \frac{n^2}{e^n}$.

19. $\sum_{n=1}^{\infty} \frac{n+1}{n^2}$.

20. $\sum_{n=1}^{\infty} \frac{n+1}{n^3}$.

In Problems 21–30, test for convergence by any test.

21. $\sum_{n=1}^{\infty} \frac{1}{2^n+1}$.

22. $\sum_{n=1}^{\infty} \frac{1}{2^n-1}$.

23. $\sum_{n=1}^{\infty} \frac{n(n+2)}{(n+1)(n+3)}$.

24. $\sum_{n=1}^{\infty} \frac{1}{n^2(n+1)}$.

25. $\sum_{n=1}^{\infty} \frac{n}{(n+1)^2(n+2)}$.

26. $\sum_{n=1}^{\infty} \frac{\sqrt{n}}{(n+1)^2}$.

27. $\sum_{n=1}^{\infty} \frac{2n-1}{2^n}$.

28. $\sum_{n=1}^{\infty} \frac{1 \cdot 3 \cdot 5 \cdots (2n-1)}{2 \cdot 5 \cdot 8 \cdots (3n-1)}$.

29. $\sum_{n=1}^{\infty} \frac{n^n}{n!}$.

30. $\sum_{n=1}^{\infty} \frac{2^n}{n^2+1}$.

19.5

Alternating Series

In the past three sections we have been dealing exclusively with series of positive terms. Of course, series in which the terms are all negative are handled in exactly the same way. We now turn to series of both positive and negative terms. By far the most frequently encountered series of this type is the alternating series, in which the terms are alternately positive and negative. Testing for convergence of an alternating series is relatively easy in certain cases.

Theorem 19.10

(*Alternating series test*) *If $\sum a_n$ is an alternating series and if*

$$|a_{n+1}| < |a_n| \quad \text{and} \quad \lim_{n \to +\infty} |a_n| = 0,$$

then $\sum a_n$ converges; furthermore if s denotes the sum of the series and s_n the n-th partial sum, then

$$|s - s_n| < |a_{n+1}|.$$

Proof

We shall prove only the first part of this theorem; the second part is left to the student. In proving the first part, we shall consider the case in which $a_1 > 0$ Let us consider an even-numbered partial sum.

$$\begin{aligned} s_n &= (a_1 + a_2) + (a_3 + a_4) + \cdots + (a_{n-1} + a_n) \\ &= a_1 + (a_2 + a_3) + (a_4 + a_5) + \cdots + (a_{n-2} + a_{n-1}) + a_n . \end{aligned}$$

Since $a_1 > 0$, $a_2 < 0$, and $|a_2| < a_1$,

$$a_1 + a_2 > 0.$$

Similarly, $a_3 + a_4 > 0, \ldots, a_{n-1} + a_n > 0$. Thus $s_n > 0$. Again, since $a_2 < 0$, $a_3 > 0$, and $a_3 < |a_2|$,

$$a_2 + a_3 < 0.$$

Similarly, $a_4 + a_5 < 0, \ldots, a_{n-2} + a_{n-1} < 0$; and, finally, $a_n < 0$. Thus $0 < s_n < a_1$. Let us consider the sequence

$$s_2, s_4, s_6, \ldots$$

of even-numbered partial sums. Since all sums are positive and less than a_1 and since they form an increasing sequence, it follows from Theorem 19.4 that they have a limit s: that is,

$$\lim_{\substack{n \text{ even} \\ n \to +\infty}} s_n = s,$$

Now let us consider the odd-numbered partial sums:

$$\begin{aligned} \lim_{\substack{n \text{ even} \\ n \to +\infty}} s_{n+1} &= \lim_{\substack{n \text{ even} \\ n \to +\infty}} (s_n + a_{n+1}) \\ &= \lim_{\substack{n \text{ even} \\ n \to +\infty}} s_n + \lim_{\substack{n \text{ even} \\ n \to +\infty}} a_{n+1} \\ &= s + 0 = s. \end{aligned}$$

Thus

$$\lim_{n \to +\infty} s_n = s,$$

and the series converges. The case in which $a_1 < 0$ is left to the student.

Example 1

Test for convergence

$$\sum_{n=1}^{\infty} \frac{(-1)^{n+1}}{n} = 1 - \frac{1}{2} + \frac{1}{3} - \frac{1}{4} + \cdots.$$

This is an alternating series in which

$$|a_{n+1}| = \frac{1}{n+1} < \frac{1}{n} = |a_n|$$

and

$$\lim_{n \to +\infty} |a_n| = \lim_{n \to +\infty} \frac{1}{n} = 0.$$

The series converges.

Of course, the series

$$\sum_{n=1}^{\infty} \frac{1}{n} = 1 + \frac{1}{2} + \frac{1}{3} + \frac{1}{4} + \cdots$$

has already been shown to diverge, even though

$$a_{n+1} < a_n \quad \text{and} \quad \lim_{n \to +\infty} a_n = 0.$$

Example 2

Test for convergence

$$1 - \frac{1}{2} + \frac{1}{2} - \frac{1}{4} + \frac{1}{3} - \frac{1}{8} + \frac{1}{4} - \frac{1}{16} + \cdots.$$

Although this is an alternating series with

$$\lim_{n \to +\infty} |a_n| = 0,$$

we cannot conclude from Theorem 19.10 that the series converges, because

$$|a_{n+1}| < |a_n|$$

is *not* true for all n.

If we consider the positive and negative terms separately, we see that the series of negative terms converges to -1, while the series of positive terms diverges; that is, no matter how large a number we choose, there is some partial sum that exceeds it. Thus if M is a number, there is a partial sum of the series of positive terms exceeding $M+1$. Since the corresponding partial sum of the negative terms is greater than -1 (all partial sums of negative terms are greater than -1), the partial sum of both positive and negative terms is greater than M. Thus, the series diverges.

Sometimes we find not only that a given alternating series converges, but also that the corresponding series of positive terms converges. Since series of this type have special properties, we want to single them out.

Definition

The series $\sum a_n$ of positive and negative terms ***converges absolutely*** *means that $\sum |a_n|$ converges. If $\sum a_n$ converges but $\sum |a_n|$ diverges, $\sum a_n$ is said to* ***converge conditionally***.

The series

$$\sum_{n=1}^{\infty} \frac{(-1)^{n+1}}{n}$$

of Example 1 converges conditionally, since it converges but the series of absolute values diverges. On the other hand,

$$\sum_{n=1}^{\infty} \frac{(-1)^{n+1}}{2^n}$$

converges absolutely, since the series of absolute values converges.

The following theorems give the relations between convergence and absolute convergence.

Theorem 19.11

If the series $\sum a_n$ converges absolutely, then it converges.

Proof

Let $\{s_n\}$ denote the sequence of partial sums of $\sum a_n$ and let $\{t_n\}$ denote the sequence of partial sums of $\sum |a_n|$. Furthermore, for each n, let u_n denote the sum of the positive terms of s_n and let $-v_n$ denote the sum of the negative terms (note that v_n is positive). Then

$$s_n = u_n - v_n \quad \text{and} \quad t_n = u_n + v_n .$$

Since it is given that $\sum |a_n|$ is convergent,

$$\lim_{n \to +\infty} t_n = \lim_{n \to +\infty} (u_n + v_n) = t.$$

But

$$u_1 \leq u_2 \leq u_3 \ldots .$$

Thus $\{u_n\}$ is a sequence of positive terms (except perhaps for the first few terms, which may be 0) all of which are less than t. Thus it converges to some number u. Similarly, $\{v_n\}$ converges to some number v; and $\{s_n\}$ must converge to $u - v$.

Theorem 19.12

If $\sum a_n$ diverges, then $\sum |a_n|$ diverges.

Proof

Assume that $\sum |a_n|$ converges. Then, by Theorem 19.11, $\sum a_n$ converges, contradicting our hypothesis. Thus $\sum |a_n|$ diverges.

There is no such term as absolute divergence. Theorem 19.12 tells us that if a series is divergent, the corresponding series of absolute values is also divergent. We do not need a special term to indicate that both diverge—simply saying that the series diverges is enough.

Let us consider some properties of absolutely convergent series.

Theorem 19.13

If $\sum a_n$ converges absolutely, then the series of all the positive terms converges, as does the series of all the negative terms.

The proof of this theorem is contained within the proof of Theorem 19.11. Note that this conclusion is not true for all convergent series. The series

$$\sum_{n=1}^{\infty} \frac{(-1)^{n+1}}{n} = 1 - \frac{1}{2} + \frac{1}{3} - \frac{1}{4} - \cdots$$

converges (conditionally), but neither

$$1 + \frac{1}{3} + \frac{1}{5} + \cdots = \sum_{n=1}^{\infty} \frac{1}{2n-1}$$

nor

$$-\frac{1}{2} - \frac{1}{4} - \frac{1}{6} - \cdots = \sum_{n=1}^{\infty} \frac{-1}{2n}$$

converges. The converse of this theorem is also true.

Theorem 19.14

If $\sum a_n$ is a series for which the series of positive terms and the series of negative terms both converge, then $\sum a_n$ converges absolutely.

The proof is left to the student. This theorem is useful in testing alternating series for which Theorem 19.10 cannot be used.

Example 3

Test for convergence

$$\frac{1}{2} - \frac{1}{3} + \frac{1}{4} - \frac{1}{9} + \frac{1}{8} - \frac{1}{27} + \cdots.$$

Theorem 19.10 cannot be used here, since the condition $|a_{n+1}| < |a_n|$ for all n is not satisfied; but the two series

$$\sum_{n=1}^{\infty} \frac{1}{2^n} \quad \text{and} \quad \sum_{n=1}^{\infty} \frac{-1}{3^n}$$

converge. By Theorem 19.14, the original series converges absolutely and thus converges.

Theorem 19.15

If $\sum a_n$ is an absolutely convergent series converging to s, then any series $\sum b_n$ formed by rearranging the terms of $\sum a_n$ also converges to s.

We shall not give a proof of this theorem. Perhaps you think that a proof is unnecessary, since the conclusion appears to be obvious. Furthermore, you may wonder why we have the condition that $\sum a_n$ is absolutely convergent—surely *any* convergent series can be rearranged in *any* way and converge to the same number. If that is what you are thinking, you are wrong. Incredible as it may seem, it is sometimes possible to take an infinite set of numbers, add them in one order to get one sum, then add them in a second order and get a different sum! Let us see how.

We have already seen that the series

$$\sum_{n=1}^{\infty} \frac{(-1)^{n+1}}{n} = 1 - \frac{1}{2} + \frac{1}{3} - \frac{1}{4} + \frac{1}{5} - \frac{1}{6} + \cdots$$

converges conditionally. Furthermore, neither

$$1+\frac{1}{3}+\frac{1}{5}+\frac{1}{7}+\cdots \quad \text{nor} \quad -\frac{1}{2}-\frac{1}{4}-\frac{1}{6}-\frac{1}{8}-\cdots$$

converges. This is very important. No matter how large a number we name, there is some partial sum of

$$1+\frac{1}{3}+\frac{1}{5}+\frac{1}{7}+\cdots$$

which exceeds that number. Furthermore, if we delete the first n terms, for *any* number n, the same can be said for the resulting series. A similar statement can be made for the series of negative terms.

By grouping the terms of the original series in the following two ways,

$$\left(1-\frac{1}{2}\right)+\left(\frac{1}{3}-\frac{1}{4}\right)+\left(\frac{1}{5}-\frac{1}{6}\right)+\cdots=1-\left(\frac{1}{2}-\frac{1}{3}\right)-\left(\frac{1}{4}-\frac{1}{5}\right)-\left(\frac{1}{6}-\frac{1}{7}\right)-\cdots,$$

we see that the sum s of the original series is positive but less than 1 (actually $s = \ln 2 = 0.693\ldots$). Now, let us rearrange these same terms to converge to 1.

Suppose we take positive terms (beginning with 1 and going in descending order) until the partial sum is greater than 1:

$$1+\frac{1}{3}.$$

Now let us take negative terms until the partial sum is less than 1:

$$1+\frac{1}{3}-\frac{1}{2}.$$

Let us continue with the positive terms until the partial sum is greater than 1:

$$1+\frac{1}{3}-\frac{1}{2}+\frac{1}{5}.$$

Again with negative terms:

$$1+\frac{1}{3}-\frac{1}{2}+\frac{1}{5}-\frac{1}{4}.$$

Continuing, we have

$$1+\frac{1}{3}-\frac{1}{2}+\frac{1}{5}-\frac{1}{4}+\frac{1}{7}+\frac{1}{9}-\frac{1}{6}+\frac{1}{11}+\frac{1}{13}-\frac{1}{8}+\cdots.$$

Because of the previously mentioned characteristics of the series of positive terms and negative terms, we know that this process can be carried on indefinitely.

Since the terms we are using tend toward 0 as we go, we see that the difference between 1 and the partial sums tends toward 0. Thus, the series converges to 1.

Perhaps you feel that, because we seem to be using up the positive terms faster than the negative ones, we shall deplete them while some negative ones remain. But there is no danger in that happening, since we have an infinite supply and we use only finitely many at each step. No matter what number of the original series we consider, it must appear somewhere in the rearrangement.

The same argument can be used to find a rearrangement converging to any preassigned number we want. In fact, the series can be rearranged to converge to any number, positive or negative, or to diverge in either direction!

Problems

In Problems 1–20, test for convergence and absolute convergence.

1. $\sum_{n=1}^{\infty} \frac{(-1)^n}{2n}$.

2. $\sum_{n=1}^{\infty} \frac{(-1)^n}{2n+1}$.

3. $\sum_{n=1}^{\infty} \frac{(-1)^{n-1}}{n^2}$.

4. $\sum_{n=1}^{\infty} \frac{(-1)^{n+1}}{n^2+1}$.

5. $\sum_{n=1}^{\infty} \frac{(-1)^{n-1}}{\sqrt{n}}$.

6. $\sum_{n=1}^{\infty} \frac{(-1)^n}{n\sqrt{n}}$.

7. $\sum_{n=2}^{\infty} \frac{(-1)^{n+3}}{\ln n}$.

8. $\sum_{n=2}^{\infty} \frac{(-1)^{n+2}}{n \ln n}$.

9. $\sum_{n=1}^{\infty} \frac{(-1)^n}{2^n}$.

10. $\sum_{n=1}^{\infty} \frac{(-1)^n}{n!}$.

11. $\sum_{n=1}^{\infty} \frac{(-1)^{n+1}n!}{2^n}$.

12. $\sum_{n=1}^{\infty} \frac{(-1)^{n-1}n^2}{2^n}$.

13. $\sum_{n=2}^{\infty} \frac{(-1)^{n+1}n}{\ln n}$.

14. $\sum_{n=1}^{\infty} \frac{(-1)^n n!}{n^2 \cdot 2^n}$.

15. $\sum_{n=1}^{\infty} \frac{(-1)^n(2n+1)}{n^2}$.

16. $\sum_{n=1}^{\infty} \frac{(-1)^n(n+1)}{n\sqrt{n}}$.

17. $\sum_{n=1}^{\infty} \frac{(-1)^{n+1}n}{e^n}$.

18. $\sum_{n=1}^{\infty} (-1)^{n-1} \frac{1 \cdot 3 \cdot 5 \ldots (2n-1)}{1 \cdot 4 \cdot 7 \ldots (3n-2)}$.

19. $\sum_{n=1}^{\infty} \frac{\cos \pi n}{n}$.

20. $\sum_{n=1}^{\infty} \frac{\sin n}{n^2}$.

21. Prove the second part of Theorem 19.10.

In Problems 22–25, use the second part of Theorem 19.10 to approximate the sum of the series to the nearest 0.1.

22. $\sum_{n=1}^{\infty} \frac{(-1)^{n-1}}{n^2}$.

23. $\sum_{n=1}^{\infty} \frac{(-1)^{n+1}}{n}$.

24. $\sum_{n=1}^{\infty} \frac{(-1)^n}{n^2+1}$.

25. $\sum_{n=1}^{\infty} \frac{(-1)^{n+1}n}{(n+1)^2}$.

26. Prove the first part of Theorem 19.10 for the case in which $a_1 < 0$.

27. Show that the terms of the series

$$\sum_{n=1}^{\infty} \frac{(-1)^{n+1}}{n}$$

can be rearranged so that the resulting series converges to 0.

28. Show that the terms of the series

$$\sum_{n=1}^{\infty} \frac{(-1)^{n+1}}{n}$$

can be rearranged so that the resulting series converges to 2.

29. Show that the terms of the series

$$\sum_{n=1}^{\infty} \frac{(-1)^{n+1}}{n}$$

can be rearranged so that the resulting series diverges to $+\infty$.

30. Prove Theorem 19.14.

19.6

Series of Functions

Let us now consider series in which the terms, instead of being constants, are functions of x—that is, $\sum f_n(x)$. A special case of this is the power series

$$\sum_{n=0}^{\infty} a_n(x-a)^n,$$

where the a_n's are constants. There is a notational difficulty here when $x = a$. In that case, we have

$$\sum_{n=0}^{\infty} a_n \cdot 0^n = a_0 \cdot 0^0 + a_1 \cdot 0^1 + a_2 \cdot 0^2 + \cdots.$$

Of course all terms beyond the first are 0. But what is the first term? We have already seen that 0^0 is undefined, and a limit in that form is indeterminate. Since the first term is a_0 for any other value of x, we shall also take it to be a_0 when $x = a$. A more accurate, but more cumbersome, notation is

$$a_0 + \sum_{n=1}^{\infty} a_n(x-a)^n.$$

For each value of x we have a series of constants, which either converges or diverges. Our problem is to find all values of x for which the series converges. The problem is simple enough for a given value of x; we simply need to substitute for x to find the series of constants and test it for convergence by the tests of the previous sections. Unfortunately, we cannot rely upon this method to find all values of x for which the series converges. To complicate matters further, some values of x give series of positive terms, while others give alternating series. This however, can be overcome by taking absolute values and determining the values of x for which the series converges absolutely. The ratio test is generally the simplest test to use on series of functions. Let us consider it in some detail.

Suppose

$$\lim_{n\to+\infty} \left| \frac{f_{n+1}(x)}{f_n(x)} \right| = r(x).$$

The values of x for which $r(x) < 1$ are values for which the series converges absolutely. There is no problem here, for, if the series converges absolutely, it converges. Now the values of x for which $r(x) > 1$ are those for which the series of absolute values diverges. But what is to prevent the series from converging conditionally? The answer is "the insensitivity of the ratio test." We have already seen (page 473) that, if $r > 1$, not only does the series (in this case the series of absolute values) diverge; the terms of the series do not even tend to zero. Now, if the absolute values of the terms do not tend to zero, the terms themselves cannot. Thus, the original series diverges. The only problem we have is with those values of x for which $r = 1$. But there are usually only finitely many such values (often two), and they can be checked individually. Let us consider some examples.

Example 1

Find all values of x for which $\sum_{n=0}^{\infty} x^n$ converges.

Using the ratio test, we have

$$\lim_{n\to+\infty} \frac{|x^{n+1}|}{|x^n|} = \lim_{n\to+\infty} |x| = |x|.$$

Now the original series converges absolutely for all x for which

$$|x| < 1$$

and diverges for all x for which

$$|x| > 1.$$

The only values of x in question are $x = \pm 1$. When $x = 1$, the series is

$$1 + 1 + 1 + 1 + \cdots,$$

which obviously diverges. When $x = -1$, the series is

$$-1 + 1 - 1 + 1 - \cdots,$$

which also diverges. Thus the original series converges for

$$-1 < x < 1.$$

Example 2

Find all values of x for which

$$\sum_{n=1}^{\infty} \frac{x^n}{n} \text{ converges.}$$

$$\lim_{n\to+\infty} \left| \frac{x^{n+1}/(n+1)}{x^n/n} \right| = \lim_{n\to+\infty} \left| \frac{n}{n+1} x \right| = |x|.$$

Again it converges for $|x| < 1$ or $-1 < x < 1$. Let us check the end points. When $x = 1$, the series is

$$\sum_{n=1}^{\infty} \frac{1}{n},$$

which diverges. When $x = -1$, it is

$$\sum_{n=1}^{\infty} \frac{(-1)^n}{n},$$

which converges. Thus the series converges for

$$-1 \leq x < 1.$$

Example 3

Find all values of x for which

$$\sum_{n=0}^{\infty}\left(\frac{x}{2}\right)^n \text{ converges.}$$

$$\lim_{n\to+\infty}\left|\frac{(x/2)^{n+1}}{(x/2)^n}\right| = \lim_{n\to+\infty}\left|\frac{x}{2}\right| = \left|\frac{x}{2}\right|.$$

The series converges when $|x/2| < 1$ or $|x| < 2$, or $-2 < x < 2$. When $x = 2$, we have $1 + 1 + 1 + \cdots$, which diverges. When $x = -2$, we have $-1 + 1 - 1 + \cdots$, which also diverges. Thus the series converges if and only if

$$-2 < x < 2.$$

Example 4

Find all values of x for which

$$\sum_{n=0}^{\infty}\frac{x^n}{n!} \text{ converges.}$$

$$\lim_{n\to+\infty}\left|\frac{x^{n+1}/(n+1)!}{x^n/n!}\right| = \lim_{n\to+\infty}\left|\frac{x}{n+1}\right| = 0.$$

Since $r < 1$ for *any* choice of x, this series converges for every real number x.

Example 5

Find all values of x for which

$$\sum_{n=0}^{\infty} n!\, x^n \text{ converges.}$$

$$\lim_{n\to+\infty}\left|\frac{(n+1)!\, x^{n+1}}{n!\, x^n}\right| = \lim_{n\to+\infty}|(n+1)x| = \begin{cases} 0 & \text{if } x = 0, \\ +\infty & \text{if } x \neq 0. \end{cases}$$

Thus the series converges if and only if $x = 0$.

Examples 4 and 5 give the extremes of convergence ranges. We always have the trivial case of convergence when all the terms (or all but one) are zero, which occurs in any of the above cases when $x = 0$. There is no other value that gives convergence in Example 5.

Example 6

Find all values of x for which

$$\sum_{n=0}^{\infty}\frac{n}{2^n}(x-1)^n$$

converges.

$$\lim_{n\to+\infty}\left|\frac{(n+1)(x-1)^{n+1}/2^{n+1}}{n(x-1)^n/2^n}\right| = \lim_{n\to+\infty}\left|\frac{(n+1)(x-1)}{2n}\right| = \left|\frac{x-1}{2}\right|.$$

The series converges if

$$\left|\frac{x-1}{2}\right| < 1,$$
$$|x-1| < 2,$$
$$-2 < x-1 < 2,$$

or

$$-1 < x < 3.$$

When $x = 3$, we have

$$\sum_{n=1}^{\infty} \frac{n \cdot 2^n}{2^n} = \sum_{n=1}^{\infty} n,$$

which diverges. When $x = -1$, we have

$$\sum_{n=1}^{\infty} \frac{n(-2)^n}{2^n} = \sum_{n=1}^{\infty} (-1)^n n,$$

which also diverges. Thus the series converges if and only if $-1 < x < 3$.

It might be noted that, in checking for convergence at the end points of the interval, one test cannot work—the ratio test. The work done in finding the interval was an attempt at the ratio test, and it was found to fail at the end points.

Problems

Find all values of x for which the series converges.

1. $\sum_{n=0}^{\infty} \frac{x^n}{n+1}$.
2. $\sum_{n=1}^{\infty} nx^n$.
3. $\sum_{n=1}^{\infty} \frac{nx^n}{n+1}$.
4. $\sum_{n=1}^{\infty} \frac{nx^n}{(n+1)^2}$.
5. $\sum_{n=1}^{\infty} \frac{nx^n}{2^n}$.
6. $\sum_{n=1}^{\infty} \frac{n^2x^n}{2^n}$.
7. $\sum_{n=1}^{\infty} \frac{(-1)^n x^n}{n \cdot 2^n}$.
8. $\sum_{n=0}^{\infty} \frac{2^n x^n}{3^n}$.
9. $\sum_{n=1}^{\infty} \frac{n(n+1)x^n}{5^n}$.
10. $\sum_{n=1}^{\infty} n^2 2^n x^n$.
11. $\sum_{n=1}^{\infty} n^2(x-2)^n$.
12. $\sum_{n=1}^{\infty} (-2)^n(x+1)^n$.
13. $\sum_{n=0}^{\infty} \frac{(x+4)^n}{2^n}$.
14. $\sum_{n=1}^{\infty} \frac{(x+4)^n}{n\, 2^n}$.
15. $\sum_{n=1}^{\infty} \frac{(x+4)^n}{n^2 \cdot 2^n}$.
16. $\sum_{n=0}^{\infty} n!(x-2)^n$.
17. $\sum_{n=1}^{\infty} \frac{n \cdot 2^n(x-1)^n}{n+1}$.
18. $\sum_{n=1}^{\infty} \frac{n(2x-3)^n}{(n+1)^2}$.
19. $\sum_{n=1}^{\infty} \frac{(x+1)^n}{n^n}$.
20. $\sum_{n=1}^{\infty} \frac{(x-2)^n}{2 \cdot 5 \cdot 8 \cdots (3n-1)}$.
21. $\sum_{n=1}^{\infty} \frac{(x+4)^n}{n(n+1)}$.
22. $\sum_{n=1}^{\infty} \frac{n!}{1 \cdot 3 \cdot 5 \cdots (2n-1)} x^n$.
23. $\sum_{n=1}^{\infty} \frac{1}{nx^n}$.
24. $\sum_{n=1}^{\infty} \frac{2^n}{nx^n}$.

19.7

Taylor's Series

Let us now consider the problem of expanding a function to give a power series,

$$f(x) = \sum_{n=0}^{\infty} a_n(x-a)^n.$$

In order to determine the coefficients a_n, let us first *assume* that $f(x)$ has a power-series expansion for a given value of a. Let us further assume that all derivatives of f exist in some interval containing a and that term-by-term differentiation is valid. Thus

$$\begin{aligned}
f(x) &= a_0 + a_1(x-a) + a_2(x-a)^2 + a_3(x-a)^3 + \cdots,\\
f'(x) &= a_1 + 2a_2(x-a) + 3a_3(x-a)^2 + 4a_4(x-a)^3 + \cdots,\\
f''(x) &= 1 \cdot 2a_2 + 2 \cdot 3a_3(x-a) + 3 \cdot 4a_4(x-a)^2 + \cdots,\\
f'''(x) &= 1 \cdot 2 \cdot 3a_3 + 2 \cdot 3 \cdot 4a_4(x-a) + 3 \cdot 4 \cdot 5a_5(x-a)^2 + \cdots,\\
f^{(4)}(x) &= 1 \cdot 2 \cdot 3 \cdot 4a_4 + 2 \cdot 3 \cdot 4 \cdot 5a_5(x-a) + 3 \cdot 4 \cdot 5 \cdot 6a_6(x-a)^2 + \cdots.
\end{aligned}$$

Now when $x = a$, we have

$$\begin{aligned}
f(a) &= a_0,\\
f'(a) &= a_1,\\
f''(a) &= 2!a_2,\\
f'''(a) &= 3!a_3,\\
f^{(4)}(a) &= 4!a_4,
\end{aligned}$$

and so forth, or

$$\begin{aligned}
a_0 &= f(a)/0!,\\
a_1 &= f'(a)/1!,\\
a_2 &= f''(a)/2!,\\
a_3 &= f'''(a)/3!,\\
a_4 &= f^{(4)}(a)/4!,\\
&\vdots\\
a_n &= f^{(n)}(a)/n!,\\
&\vdots
\end{aligned}$$

Theorem 19.16

If f has a power series expansion in powers of $x - a$ and all derivatives of f exist in some interval containing a and if term-by-term differentiation is valid then

$$f(x) = \sum_{n=0}^{\infty} \frac{f^{(n)}(a)}{n!}(x-a)^n$$

for all x in the interval. This series is called the ***Taylor's series*** *for f about a.*

Example 1

Expand e^x in a Taylor's series about 0. Determine all values of x for which it converges.

$$\begin{aligned} f(x) &= e^x, & f(0) &= e^0 = 1; \\ f'(x) &= e^x, & f'(0) &= e^0 = 1; \\ f''(x) &= e^x, & f''(0) &= e^0 = 1; \\ &\vdots & &\vdots \end{aligned}$$

$$\begin{aligned} e^x &= \frac{1}{0!}x^0 + \frac{1}{1!}x^1 + \frac{1}{2!}x^2 + \frac{1}{3!}x^3 + \cdots \\ &= 1 + x + \frac{x^2}{2!} + \frac{x^3}{3!} + \cdots. \end{aligned}$$

By Example 4 of the previous section, this series converges for all real numbers x.

Example 2

Expand $\sin x$ in a Taylor's series about $\pi/2$. Determine all values of x for which it converges.

$$\begin{aligned} f(x) &= \sin x, & f(\pi/2) &= 1; \\ f'(x) &= \cos x, & f'(\pi/2) &= 0; \\ f''(x) &= -\sin x, & f''(\pi/2) &= -1; \\ f'''(x) &= -\cos x, & f'''(\pi/2) &= 0; \\ f^{(4)}(x) &= \sin x, & f^{(4)}(\pi/2) &= 1; \\ &\vdots & &\vdots \end{aligned}$$

$$\begin{aligned} \sin x &= \frac{1}{0!}(x-\pi/2)^0 + \frac{0}{1!}(x-\pi/2)^1 - \frac{1}{2!}(x-\pi/2)^2 \\ &\quad + \frac{0}{3!}(x-\pi/2)^3 + \frac{1}{4!}(x-\pi/2)^4 + \cdots \\ &= 1 - \frac{(x-\pi/2)^2}{2!} + \frac{(x-\pi/2)^4}{4!} - \frac{(x-\pi/2)^6}{6!} + \cdots \\ &= \sum_{n=0}^{\infty} (-1)^n \frac{(x-\pi/2)^{2n}}{(2n)!}. \end{aligned}$$

$$\lim_{n\to+\infty}\left|\frac{(x-\pi/2)^{2n+2}/(2n+2)!}{(x-\pi/2)^{2n}/(2n)!}\right| = \lim_{n\to+\infty}\left|\frac{(x-\pi/2)^2}{(2n+1)(2n+2)}\right| = 0.$$

This series converges for all x.

Example 3

Expand $\ln x$ in a Taylor's series about 1. Determine all values of x for which it converges.

$$\begin{aligned} f(x) &= \ln x, & f(1) &= 0; \\ f'(x) &= 1/x, & f'(1) &= 1; \\ f''(x) &= -1/x^2, & f''(1) &= -1; \\ f'''(x) &= 2!/x^3, & f'''(1) &= 2!; \\ f^{(4)}(x) &= -3!/x^4, & f^{(4)}(1) &= -3!; \\ &\vdots & &\vdots \end{aligned}$$

$$\ln x = \frac{0}{0!}(x-1)^0 + \frac{1}{1!}(x-1)^1 - \frac{1}{2!}(x-1)^2 + \frac{2!}{3!}(x-1)^3 - \frac{3!}{4!}(x-1)^4 + \cdots$$

$$= (x-1) - \frac{(x-1)^2}{2} + \frac{(x-1)^3}{3} - \frac{(x-1)^4}{4} + \cdots$$

$$= \sum_{n=1}^{\infty} (-1)^{n+1} \frac{(x-1)^n}{n}.$$

$$\lim_{n\to+\infty} \left| \frac{(x-1)^{n+1}/(n+1)}{(x-1)^n/n} \right| = \lim_{n\to+\infty} \left| \frac{n}{n+1}(x-1) \right| = |x-1|.$$

Thus, it converges if

$$|x-1| < 1$$
$$-1 < x-1 < 1$$
$$0 < x < 2.$$

When $x = 0$, the series is

$$-1 - \frac{1}{2} - \frac{1}{3} - \frac{1}{4} - \cdots,$$

which diverges. When $x = 2$, the series is

$$1 - \frac{1}{2} + \frac{1}{3} - \frac{1}{4} + \cdots,$$

which converges. Thus, the series converges if

$$0 < x \leq 2.$$

Problems

In Problems 1–14, expand the function in a Taylor's series about the given value of a. Determine all values of x for which it converges.

1. $f(x) = e^x, \quad a = 1.$
2. $f(x) = \sin x, \quad a = 0.$
3. $f(x) = \cos x, \quad a = 0.$
4. $f(x) = \sin x, \quad a = \pi/4.$
5. $f(x) = \cos x, \quad a = \pi/6.$
6. $f(x) = 1/x, \quad a = 1.$
7. $f(x) = \dfrac{1}{x^2+1}, \quad a = 0.$
8. $f(x) = \text{Arctan}\, x, \quad a = 0.$
9. $f(x) = \sinh x, \quad a = 0.$
10. $f(x) = \cosh x, \quad a = 0.$
11. $f(x) = \dfrac{1}{1-x}, \quad a = 0.$
12. $f(x) = \dfrac{1}{(x+1)^2}, \quad a = 0.$
13. $f(x) = x^3 + x^2 - 2x + 1, \quad a = 1.$
14. $f(x) = x^4 - 2x^2 - 1, \quad a = 1.$

In Problems 15–20, expand in a Taylor's series about the given value of a.

15. $f(x) = \tan x, \quad a = 0.$
16. $f(x) = \text{Arcsin}\, x, \quad a = 0.$
17. $f(x) = \dfrac{1}{x^2+1}, \quad a = 1.$
18. $f(x) = \sqrt{x}, \quad a = 1.$
19. $f(x) = \dfrac{1}{\sqrt{x}}, \quad a = 1.$
20. $f(x) = \sin 2x, \quad a = 0.$
21. Expand $1/(x+1)$ in powers of x. Divide $1 + x$ into 1. Repeat for $1/(1-x)$. What does this suggest about the number of power-series expansions of a function about a given number a?

22. Prove that there is only one power-series expansion of a given function about the number a.
23. Expand $\sin u$ in powers of u. If $u = x^2$, what is the result? Expand $\sin x^2$ in powers of x. Compare.
24. Expand e^u in powers of u. If $u = x^2$, what is the result? Expand e^{x^2} in powers of x. Compare.
25. Expand $\sin x$ in powers of x. Differentiate the resulting series term by term. Compare with the expansion of $\cos x$.
26. Expand $1/(1 + x^2)$ in powers of x. Integrate the resulting series term by term. Compare with the expansion of Arctan x. Do you expect the same results in any case? Explain your answer.
27. Expand $(1 + x)^n$ (n not an integer) in powers of x. Use the result to express $(a + b)^n$ as an infinite series.

19.8

Remainder Theorems

In the previous section, we showed how to find a Taylor's series from a given function. By previous methods, we can determine the values of x for which a given Taylor's series converges. But even if we have a Taylor's series determined by a given function f and we know that the series converges for some number x, we have no guarantee that the series converges to $f(x)$. In order to settle this problem, we now consider finite series with remainders.

Theorem 19.17

If f is a function such that $f^{(n+1)}(x)$ exists for all x in an interval containing the number a, then, for all x in that interval,

$$f(x) = f(a) + \frac{f'(a)}{1!}(x-a) + \frac{f''(a)}{2!}(x-a)^2 + \cdots + \frac{f^{(n)}(a)}{n!}(x-a)^n + R_n,$$

where

$$R_n = \int_a^x \frac{(x-t)^n}{n!} f^{(n+1)}(t)\,dt.$$

Proof

Let us consider

$$\int_a^x f'(t)\,dt = f(t)\Big|_a^x = f(x) - f(a).$$

Now we evaluate this integral by parts.

$$u = f'(t), \qquad v' = 1,$$
$$u' = f''(t), \qquad v = t - x.$$

Remember that we can use any constant of integration we choose when we integrate v'. In this connection x is a constant, since the original integral is with respect to t.

$$\begin{aligned}\int_a^x f'(t)\,dt &= (t-x)f'(t)\Big|_a^x - \int_a^x (t-x)f''(t)\,dt\\ &= -(a-x)f'(a) - \int_a^x (t-x)f''(t)\,dt\\ &= (x-a)f'(a) - \int_a^x (t-x)f''(t)\,dt.\end{aligned}$$

Repeating, we have

$$u = f''(t), \qquad v' = (t-x),$$

$$u' = f'''(t), \qquad v = \frac{(t-x)^2}{2}.$$

$$\begin{aligned}\int_a^x f'(t)\,dt &= (x-a)f'(a) - \left[\frac{(t-x)^2}{2}f''(t)\right]\Big|_a^x + \int_a^x \frac{(t-x)^2}{2}f'''(t)\,dt\\ &= (x-a)f'(a) + \frac{(a-x)^2}{2}f''(a) + \int_a^x \frac{(t-x)^2}{2}f'''(t)\,dt\\ &= (x-a)f'(a) + \frac{(x-a)^2}{2}f''(a) + \int_a^x \frac{(t-x)^2}{2}f'''(t)\,dt.\end{aligned}$$

After integration by parts n times, we have

$$\begin{aligned}\int_a^x f'(t)\,dt &= (x-a)f'(a) + \frac{(x-a)^2}{2!}f''(a) + \frac{(x-a)^3}{3!}f'''(a) + \cdots\\ &\quad + \frac{(x-a)^n}{n!}f^{(n)}(a) + \int_a^x (-1)^n\frac{(t-x)^n}{n!}f^{(n+1)}(t)\,dt\\ &= (x-a)f'(a) + \frac{(x-a)^2}{2!}f''(a) + \frac{(x-a)^3}{3!}f'''(a) + \cdots\\ &\quad + \frac{(x-a)^n}{n!}f^{(n)}(a) + \int_a^x \frac{(x-t)^n}{n!}f^{(n+1)}(t)\,dt.\end{aligned}$$

Replacing $\int_a^x f'(t)\,dt$ by $f(x) - f(a)$, we have the result we want.

When we approximate the series by s_n, we know that, for a particular a and a given value of x, the error committed is exactly

$$R_n = \int_a^x \frac{(x-t)^n}{n!}f^{(n+1)}(t)\,dt.$$

Unfortunately, this form of the remainder is rather difficult to use. There are many different forms for R_n; we should like to consider one that is especially easy to use. Before considering it, however, we need to make some preliminary observations.

We should like to apply the extended mean-value theorem to R_n, but it will help to restate it in a slightly different form. Since, by Theorem 10.6, differentiability implies continuity, we can replace "continuous on $[a, b]$" and "differentiable on (a, b)" by the single condition "differentiable on $[a, b]$."

Theorem 17.6 (restatement)

If f and g are functions such that

(1) $f'(x)$ and $g'(x)$ exist for all x in $[a, b]$ and
(2) $g'(x) \neq 0$ for each x in (a, b),

then there is a number x_0 between a and b such that

$$\frac{f(b) - f(a)}{g(b) - g(a)} = \frac{f'(x_0)}{g'(x_0)}.$$

Now we still have something of a problem. The extended mean-value theorem is given in terms of functions and their derivatives, but R_n is given in terms of an integral. Let us then put the extended mean-value theorem into an integral form. Suppose we let

$$F(x) = f'(x) \quad \text{and} \quad G(x) = g'(x).$$

Then

$$\int_a^b F(x)\,dx = \int_a^b f'(x)\,dx = f(x)\Big|_a^b = f(b) - f(a).$$

Similarly,

$$\int_a^b G(x)\,dx = g(b) - g(a).$$

Theorem 19.18

(*Integral form of the extended mean-value theorem*) *If F and G are functions such that*

(1) $F(x)$ and $G(x)$ exist for all x in $[a, b]$ and
(2) $G(x) \neq 0$ for each x in (a, b),

then there is a number x_0 between a and b such that

$$\frac{\displaystyle\int_a^b F(x)\,dx}{\displaystyle\int_a^b G(x)\,dx} = \frac{F(x_0)}{G(x_0)}.$$

Now we are in a position to express R_n in another form.

Theorem 19.19

(*Lagrange's form of the remainder*) *If R_n is the remainder of Theorem 19.17, then there is a number c between x and a such that*

$$R_n = \frac{(x - a)^{n+1}}{(n + 1)!} f^{(n+1)}(c).$$

Proof

Suppose we let

$$F(t) = \frac{(x-t)^n}{n!} f^{(n+1)}(t) \quad \text{and} \quad G(t) = \frac{(x-t)^n}{n!}$$

(note that x is regarded as a constant here). Under the conditions of Theorem 19.17, $F(t)$ and $G(t)$ exist for all t in $[a, x]$. Furthermore $G(t) \neq 0$ for any t in (a, x). Thus, by the integral form of the extended mean-value theorem, we have

$$\frac{\int_a^x \frac{(x-t)^n}{n!} f^{(n+1)}(t)\, dt}{\int_a^x \frac{(x-t)^n}{n!}\, dt} = \frac{\frac{(x-c)^n}{n!} f^{(n+1)}(c)}{\frac{(x-c)^n}{n!}} = f^{(n+1)}(c).$$

Since

$$\int_a^x \frac{(x-t)^n}{n!}\, dt = -\left.\frac{(x-t)^{n+1}}{(n+1)!}\right|_a^x = \frac{(x-a)^{n+1}}{(n+1)!},$$

it follows that

$$R_n = \int_a^x \frac{(x-t)^n}{n!} f^{(n+1)}(t)\, dt = \frac{(x-a)^{n+1}}{(n+1)!} f^{(n+1)}(c).$$

Example 1

Find the Taylor's series expansion for $f(x) = e^x$ in powers of x. Find the values of x for which it converges. Find the values of x for which it converges to $f(x)$.

From Example 1 of the last section, the Taylor's series expansion is

$$\sum_{i=0}^{\infty} \frac{x^i}{i!},$$

and it converges for all x. By Theorem 19.19

$$R_n = \frac{x^{n+1}}{(n+1)!} e^c, \text{ where } 0 < c < x.$$

Since

$$\lim_{n \to +\infty} R_n = \lim_{n \to +\infty} \frac{x^{n+1}}{(n+1)!} e^c = 0,$$

the difference between e^x and the nth partial sum of the series approaches zero as n approaches $+\infty$, no matter what number x represents. Thus the series converges to $f(x)$ for all values of x.

Example 2

Find the Taylor's series expansion for

$$f(x) = \begin{cases} e^{-1/x2} & \text{if } x \neq 0, \\ 0 & \text{if } x = 0. \end{cases}$$

Find the values of x for which it converges. Find the values of x for which it converges to $f(x)$.

By the definition of the derivative, $f^{(n)}(0) = 0$. Thus every term of the Taylor's series expansion is 0. Obviously this series converges for all x. But $f(x) = 0$ if and only if $x = 0$. Thus it converges to $f(x)$ only when $x = 0$.

In addition to the theoretical applications mentioned above, these remainder theorems have some very practical applications. If we are interested in a numerical value like $e^{0.1}$ or sin 2°, we can approximate it by a series. Why approximate? The series gives us the exact value, doesn't it? The reason becomes apparent when one attempts to carry it out. From a practical point of view, we cannot add infinitely many numbers. We know that the infinite sum does exist and that it is the number we want, but we must approximate it with some partial sum. As soon as we begin doing this we must consider the error committed in discarding many of the terms. We would be rather unhappy to find, for instance, that we were throwing away more than we were keeping. Thus, we now consider the remainder after the nth partial sum.

Example 3

Approximate $e^{0.1}$ by s_4; what is a maximum value of the error involved?

$$e^x = 1 + x + \frac{x^2}{2!} + \frac{x^3}{3!} + \cdots,$$

$$s_4 = 1 + 0.1 + \frac{(0.1)^2}{2!} + \frac{(0.1)^3}{3!} + \frac{(0.1)^4}{4!}$$

$$= 1.1051708333\ldots,$$

$$R_4 = \frac{(0.1-0)^5}{5!}e^c, \quad \text{where } 0 < c < 0.1,$$

$$< \frac{(0.1)^5}{5!} 2 < 0.0000002.$$

Thus, an approximation of $e^{0.1}$, accurate to six decimal places, is 1.105171.

Example 4

Approximate sin 2° accurate to four decimal places.

$$\sin x = x - \frac{x^3}{3!} + \frac{x^5}{5!} - \cdots,$$

$$x = 2° = 0.0349\ldots \text{(radians)}.$$

Let us first see how many terms are needed for the desired accuracy.

$$R_n = \frac{x^{n+1}}{(n+1)!} f^{(n+1)}(c), \quad \text{where } 0 < c < 0.0349\ldots.$$

Since $f(x) = \sin x$, the derivatives are either $\pm \sin x$ or $\pm \cos x$.
In any case, $f^{(n+1)}(c) < 1$. Thus,

$$R_n < \frac{x^{n+1}}{(n+1)!} \doteq \frac{(0.0349)^{n+1}}{(n+1)!}.$$

We want to choose n big enough that $R_n < 0.00005$. At this point, it is a matter of trial and error to see how big n should be. We see that

$$R_2 < \frac{.035^3}{3!} \doteq 0.00004.$$

Thus we want s_2 which is simply x or

$$\sin 2^\circ \doteq 0.0349 \text{ to four-decimal-place accuracy.}$$

Example 5

Find sin 65° accurate to four decimal places.

Let us proceed as in Example 4.

$$\sin x = x - \frac{x^3}{3!} + \frac{x^5}{5!} \cdots,$$

$$x = 65^\circ = 1.13446\ldots,$$

$$R_n = \frac{x^{n+1}}{(n+1)!} f^{(n+1)}(c), \quad \text{where } 0 < c < 1.13446,$$

$$< \frac{(1.14)^{n+1}}{(n+1)!}.$$

A few trials show that $n = 8$ is sufficiently large. Thus,

$$\sin 65^\circ \doteq \sin 1.13446$$

$$\doteq 1.13446 - \frac{1.13446^3}{3!} + \frac{1.13446^5}{5!} - \frac{1.13446^7}{7!}$$

$$\doteq 0.9063.$$

This problem is considerably more tedious than the other two, since we have to raise 1.13446 to the third, fifth, and seventh powers. Let us alter the procedure slightly. Since 65° is rather near $60^\circ = \pi/3$, let us expand $\sin x$ in powers of $x - \pi/3$.

$$\sin x = \frac{\sqrt{3}}{2} + \frac{1}{2}(x - \pi/3) - \frac{\sqrt{3}}{2 \cdot 2!}(x - \pi/3)^2 - \frac{1}{2 \cdot 3!}(x - \pi/3)^3 + \cdots,$$

$$x = 65^\circ \doteq 1.13446,$$

$$x - \pi/3 \doteq 1.13446 - 1.04720 = 0.08726,$$

$$R_n = \frac{(x - \pi/3)^{n+1}}{(n+1)!} f^{(n+1)}(c), \quad \text{where } \pi/3 < c < 1.13446,$$

$$< \frac{0.09^{n+1}}{(n+1)!}.$$

A few trials show that $n = 3$ is sufficiently large. Thus

$$\sin 65^\circ \doteq \sin 1.13446$$

$$\doteq \frac{\sqrt{3}}{2} + \frac{1}{2}(0.08726) - \frac{\sqrt{3}}{2 \cdot 2!}(0.08726)^2 - \frac{1}{2 \cdot 3!}(0.08726)^3$$

$$\doteq 0.9063.$$

In general, we want to choose a as a convenient number as near x as possible.

It might be noted that the method used here for determining the values of $e^{0.1}$, sin 2°, and sin 65° is the method used in constructing the tables given in this book and others.

Problems

In Problems 1–10, approximate the given number by s_n of Taylor's series with $a = 0$. What is a maximum value of the error involved?

1. $e^{0.2}$, $n = 2$.
2. e, $n = 2$.
3. $\sin 5°$, $n = 4$.
4. $\sin 10°$, $n = 4$.
5. $\cos 5°$, $n = 4$.
6. $\cos 10°$, $n = 4$.
7. $\sinh 1$, $n = 4$.
8. $\cosh 1$, $n = 4$.
9. $\tan 5°$, $n = 4$.
10. Arctan 0.5, $n = 4$.

In Problems 11–22, give the value of the number by using a Taylor's series about the given value of a and with the given error.

11. $e^{0.2}$; $a = 0$, $R_n < 0.00001$.
12. e^2; $a = 0$, $R_n < 0.00005$.
13. $\sin 5°$; $a = 0$, $R_n < 0.00005$.
14. $\sin 15°$; $a = 0$, $R_n < 0.00005$.
15. $\cos 35°$; $a = 0$, $R_n < 0.00005$.
16. $\cos 35°$; $a = \pi/6$, $R_n < 0.00005$.
17. $\sin 35°$; $a = \pi/6$, $R_n < 0.00005$.
18. $\tan 10°$; $a = 0$, $R_n < 0.0001$.
19. $\tan 40°$; $a = \pi/4$, $R_n < 0.0001$.
20. Arctan 0.1; $a = 0$, $R_n < 0.0001$.
21. $\ln 2$; $a = 1$, $R < 0.1$.
22. $\ln 0.3$; $a = 1$, $R < 0.1$.

19.9

Differentiation and Integration of Series

In the last section we saw one application of series—numerical approximation of transcendental functions. A second important application has to do with the differentiation and integration of power series. It is based upon the following two theorems.

Theorem 19.20

If the series $f(x) = \sum_{n=0}^{\infty} a_n(x-a)^n$ *converges for* $|x - a| < R$, *then*

$$\sum_{n=1}^{\infty} na_n(x-a)^{n-1}$$

also converges for $|x - a| < R$ *and*

$$f'(x) = \sum_{n=1}^{\infty} na_n(x-a)^{n-1}.$$

Theorem 19.21

If the series $f(x) = \sum_{n=0}^{\infty} a_n(x-a)^n$ *converges for* $|x - a| < R$, then

$$\sum_{n=0}^{\infty} \frac{a_n}{n+1}(x-a)^{n+1}$$

converges for $|x - a| < R$ *and*

$$\int f(x)\,dx = C + \sum_{n=0}^{\infty} \frac{a_n}{n+1}(x-a)^{n+1}.$$

In other words, these two theorems say that a power series can be differentiated and integrated term by term to give a series that is the derivative or integral, respectively, of the function represented by the original series. We shall not prove either of these theorems, as the proofs* are beyond the scope of this book.

Example 1

Use the Taylor's series expansion for $\sin x$ to find the series for $\cos x$.

As we have already seen,

$$\sin x = x - \frac{x^3}{3!} + \frac{x^5}{5!} - \frac{x^7}{7!} + \cdots.$$

By differentiation, we have

$$\cos x = 1 - \frac{x^2}{2!} + \frac{x^4}{4!} - \frac{x^6}{6!} + \cdots.$$

We could get the same result by integration.

$$-\cos x = C + \frac{x^2}{2!} - \frac{x^4}{4!} + \frac{x^6}{6!} - \cdots,$$

$$\cos x = -C - \frac{x^2}{2!} + \frac{x^4}{4!} - \frac{x^6}{6!} + \cdots.$$

Since $\cos 0 = 1$, we see that $-C = 1$ and

$$\cos x = 1 - \frac{x^2}{2!} + \frac{x^4}{4!} - \frac{x^6}{6!} + \cdots.$$

Example 2

Use the Taylor's series expansion for $1/(1+x)$ to find the series for $\ln(1+x)$.

By dividing or by using the formula for the sum of a geometric series, we have

$$\frac{1}{1+x} = 1 - x + x^2 - x^3 + \cdots,$$

for $|x| < 1$.

Integrating, we get

$$\ln(1+x) = C + x - \frac{x^2}{2} + \frac{x^3}{3} - \frac{x^4}{4} + \cdots.$$

When $x = 0$, we get $\ln 1 = C$, or $C = 0$. Thus

$$\ln(1+x) = x - \frac{x^2}{2} + \frac{x^3}{3} - \frac{x^4}{4} + \cdots,$$

for $|x| < 1$.

* For proofs of these theorems see Walter Rudin, *Principles of Mathematical Analysis* (2nd ed.) (New York, McGraw-Hill, 1964) pp.137–141.

The previous examples illustrated different ways of doing some things which we could already do. Let us now see a very important application of series.

Example 3

Evaluate $\int \sin x^2\, dx$.

As noted on page 366, we have as yet had no method of integrating this expression. Let us see how it can be done by series.

$$\sin u = u - \frac{u^3}{3!} + \frac{u^5}{5!} - \frac{u^7}{7!} + \cdots.$$

By letting $u = x^2$ (see Problem 23, page 491), we have

$$\sin x^2 = x^2 - \frac{x^6}{3!} + \frac{x^{10}}{5!} - \frac{x^{14}}{7!} + \cdots.$$

Now

$$\int \sin x^2\, dx = C + \frac{x^3}{3} - \frac{x^7}{7 \cdot 3!} + \frac{x^{11}}{11 \cdot 5!} - \frac{x^{15}}{15 \cdot 7!} + \cdots.$$

A problem that was impossible by former methods is quite simple now. Perhaps you are a little disappointed by the answer—you want the series expressed in finite terms. But, as noted on page 366, it cannot be given in finite terms—the answer can *only* be given as a series. This is not an unusual situation. Many functions can be given only in terms of infinite series. Actually, the functions we have studied in previous chapters represent only a small class of special functions.

Problems

In Problems 1–10, use the Taylor's series expansion of $f(x)$ to get the one for $g(x)$.

1. $f(x) = \dfrac{-1}{1+x},\ g(x) = \dfrac{1}{(1+x)^2}.$
2. $f(x) = \dfrac{1}{1-x},\ g(x) = \dfrac{1}{(1-x)^2}.$
3. $f(x) = \cos x,\ g(x) = \sin x.$
4. $f(x) = \sinh x,\ g(x) = \cosh x.$
5. $f(x) = \dfrac{1}{1+x^2},\ g(x) = \text{Arctan } x.$
6. $f(x) = \dfrac{1}{1-x^2},\ g(x) = \tanh^{-1} x.$
7. $f(x) = \dfrac{1}{\sqrt{1-x^2}},\ g(x) = \text{Arcsin } x.$
8. $f(x) = \dfrac{1}{\sqrt{1+x^2}},\ g(x) = \sinh^{-1} x.$
9. $f(x) = \tan x,\ g(x) = \ln \cos x.$
10. $f(x) = \dfrac{1}{1-x^2},\ g(x) = \ln \dfrac{1+x}{1-x}.$
11. Use the identity

$$\sin^2 x = \frac{1 - \cos 2x}{2}$$

to find the Taylor's series expansion of $f(x) = \sin^2 x$.

12. Use the identity

$$\cos^2 x = \frac{1 + \cos 2x}{2}$$

to find the Taylor's series expansion of $f(x) = \cos^2 x$.

In Problems 13–18, use series to carry out the integration.

13. $\int \cos x^2 \, dx.$ Know Taylor series For cos u

14. $\int \frac{\sin x}{x} \, dx.$

15. $\int \frac{\cos x}{x} \, dx.$

16. $\int e^{-x^2} \, dx.$

17. $\int \sqrt{1 + x^3} \, dx.$

18. $\int \frac{dx}{\sqrt{1 - x^3}}.$

In Problems 19–22, use series to evaluate the limit.

19. $\lim_{x \to 0} \frac{\sin x}{x}.$

20. $\lim_{x \to 0} \frac{1 - \cos x}{\sin x}.$

21. $\lim_{x \to 0} \frac{e^x - 1}{\sin x}.$

22. $\lim_{x \to 0} \frac{e^x - e^{-x} - 2x}{x - \sin x}.$

Solid Analytic Geometry

20.1

Introduction: The Distance and Point-of-Division Formulas

Up to now we have been dealing almost exclusively with plane figures. The only exceptions have been solids that are generated from plane figures by circles, squares, and so forth. Let us now consider solid figures more generally.

Forming the bridge between the algebra and geometry is a set of three *axes* concurrent at a point (the origin). The only requirement is that these three lines not be coplanar—that is, that they not all lie in the same plane. The only case we shall consider is the one in which the axes are mutually perpendicular. The three axes, labeled x, y, and z, with a scale on each, determine a set of three numbers associated uniquely with any point in space. Since any pair of intersecting lines determines a plane, the three pairs of axes determine three *coordinate planes*, which we shall call the *xy plane*, the *xz plane*, and the *yz plane*. These planes separate space into eight *octants*. Although we shall not number all of them, the one in which all three coordinates are positive is called the *first octant*. Note that points of the xy plane have z coordinate 0, points of the xz plane have y coordinate 0, and points of the yz plane have x coordinate 0. Similarly, points of the x axis have y and z coordinates 0, and so on. Of course the origin has all of these coordinates 0.

The two basic geometric representatives of the axes are given in Figure 20.1; (a) shows a *right-hand system*, while (b) shows a *left-hand system*. Graphs of equations in the two systems are mirror images of each other. Since we shall normally represent space by a right-hand system, the axes will usually appear in the positions indicated in (a).

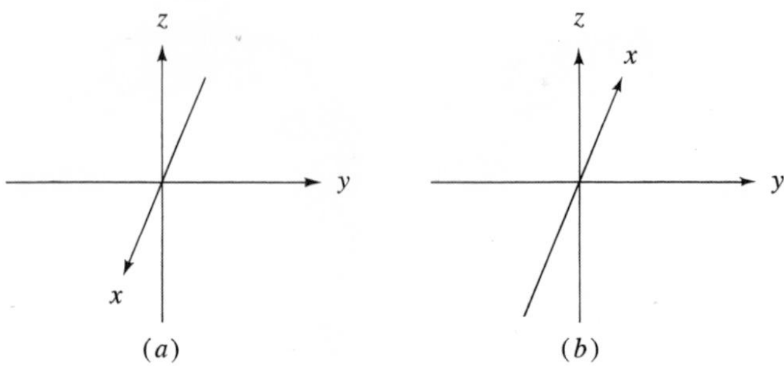

Figure 20.1

Many of the formulas of solid analytic geometry are simple extensions of plane analytic geometry. The one that follows is an example.

Theorem 20.1

The distance between two points (x_1, y_1, z_1) *and* (x_2, y_2, z_2) *is*

$$d = \sqrt{(x_1 - x_2)^2 + (y_1 - y_2)^2 + (z_1 - z_2)^2}.$$

The proof, which requires a double application of the Theorem of Pythagoras, is left to the student. Of course, if the line joining the two points is on or parallel to one of the coordinate planes, at least one of the three terms of this formula is zero, and it reduces to the plane case. Similarly, if the line joining the points is on or parallel to one of the axes, at least two terms are zero and the distance is the absolute value of the difference between the coordinates of the remaining pair.

Example 1

Find the distance between $(1, -2, 5)$ and $(-3, 6, 4)$.

$$\begin{aligned} d &= \sqrt{(x_1 - x_2)^2 + (y_1 - y_2)^2 + (z_1 - z_2)^2} \\ &= \sqrt{(1+3)^2 + (-2-6)^2 + (5-4)^2} \\ &= \sqrt{16 + 64 + 1} \\ &= \sqrt{81} \\ &= 9. \end{aligned}$$

Another easy extension from two dimensions is the point-of-division formula.

Theorem 20.2

If $P_1 = (x_1, y_1, z_1)$ *and* $P_2 = (x_2, y_2, z_2)$ *and* P *is a point such that* $r = P_1P/P_1P_2$, *then the coordinates of* P *are*

$$\begin{aligned} x &= x_1 + r(x_2 - x_1), \\ y &= y_1 + r(y_2 - y_1), \\ z &= z_1 + r(z_2 - z_1). \end{aligned}$$

Again the proof is similar to the one for the two-dimensional case, and it is left to the student.

Example 2

Find the point 1/3 of the way from $(-2, 4, 1)$ to $(4, 1, 7)$

$$x = x_1 + r(x_2 - x_1) = -2 + \frac{1}{3}(4 + 2) = 0,$$

$$y = y_1 + r(y_2 - y_1) = 4 + \frac{1}{3}(1 - 4) = 3,$$

$$z = z_1 + r(z_2 - z_1) = 1 + \frac{1}{3}(7 - 1) = 3.$$

The desired point is $(0, 3, 3)$.

The following theorem is a direct corollary of the point-of-division formulas.

Theorem 20.3

If $P_1 = (x_1, y_1, z_1)$ and $P_2 = (x_2, y_2, z_2)$, then the coordinates of the midpoint of the segment P_1P_2 are

$$x = \frac{x_1 + x_2}{2}, \qquad y = \frac{y_1 + y_2}{2}, \qquad z = \frac{z_1 + z_2}{2}.$$

Example 3

Find the midpoint of the segment with ends $(4, -3, 1)$ and $(-2, 5, 3)$.

$$x = \frac{x_1 + x_2}{2} = \frac{4 - 2}{2} = 1,$$

$$y = \frac{y_1 + y_2}{2} = \frac{-3 + 5}{2} = 1,$$

$$z = \frac{z_1 + z_2}{2} = \frac{1 + 3}{2} = 2.$$

Problems

In Problems 1–10, find the distance between the pair of points given.

1. $(2, 5, 0), (-3, 1, 3)$.
2. $(4, -2, 1), (2, 2, -3)$.
3. $(5, 4, -1), (2, 0, -1)$.
4. $(2, 5, 3), (-2, 4, -1)$.
5. $(-5, 0, 2), (4, 1, -5)$.
6. $(-2, 5, 1), (-2, 8, 4)$.
7. $(3, -1, 4), (3, 4, 4)$.
8. $(2, 5, 0), (5, 5, 0)$.
9. $(4, 7, -1), (3, -1, 3)$.
10. $(5, 2, 3), (4, 5, -1)$.

In Problems 11–16, find the point P such that $AP/AB = r$.

11. $A = (4, 3, -2)$, $B = (-5, 0, 4)$, $r = 2/3$.
12. $A = (5, 2, 3)$, $B = (-5, 7, -2)$, $r = 2/5$.
13. $A = (-2, 0, 1)$, $B = (10, 8, 5)$, $r = 1/4$.
14. $A = (5, 5, 3)$, $B = (2, -4, 0)$, $r = 1/3$.
15. $A = (3, 1, 5)$, $B = (-3, 4, 2)$, $r = 2$.
16. $A = (-2, 5, 1)$, $B = (4, -1, 2)$, $r = 3/2$.

In Problems 17–20, find the midpoint of segment AB.

17. $A = (5, -2, 3)$, $B = (-3, 4, 7)$.
18. $A = (4, 3, 5)$, $B = (-2, -1, 2)$.
19. $A = (-3, 2, 0)$, $B = (5, 4, 3)$.
20. $A = (4, 3, -1)$, $B = (4, 8, -3)$.
21. Given $A = (5, -2, 3)$, $P = (6, 0, 0)$, and $AP/AB = 1/3$, find B.
22. Given $B = (-4, 14, 4)$, $P = (-1, 8, -4)$, and $AP/AB = 2/5$, find A.
23. Given $B = (6, 0, 9)$, $P = (4, 1, 6)$, and $AP/AB = 3/4$, find A.
24. Given $A = (5, 3, -2)$, $P = (1, 5, 2)$, and $AP/AB = 2/3$, find B.

In Problems 25–28, find the unknown quantity.

25. $A = (5, 1, 0)$, $B = (1, y, 2)$, $AB = 6$.
26. $A = (-2, 4, 3)$, $B = (x, -4, 2)$, $AB = 9$.
27. $A = (x, 4, -2)$, $B = (-x, -6, 3)$, $AB = 15$.
28. $A = (x, x, 5)$, $B = (-1, -2, 0)$, $AB = 5\sqrt{2}$.
29. The point $(-1, 5, 2)$ is a distance 6 from the midpoint of the segment joining $(1, 3, 2)$ and $(x, -1, 6)$. Find x.
30. The point $(1, -2, 9)$ is a distance $5\sqrt{5}$ from the midpoint of the segment joining $(1, y, 2)$ and $(5, -1, 6)$. Find y.
31. Prove Theorem 20.1.
32. Prove Theorem 20.2.
33. Prove Theorem 20.3.

20.2

Direction Angles, Direction Cosines, and Direction Numbers

In plane analytic geometry, we used the inclination and slope to give the direction of a line. The corresponding terms in solid analytic geometry are direction angles and direction cosines. Let us first consider a line containing the origin and arbitrarily assign a direction to it; that is, we shall let one direction be positive and the opposite direction be negative, as we have done with the axes. We shall designate by α the smallest angle measured from the positive end of the x axis to the positive end of the line (we have not given any meaning for negative angles in space). Similarly, β is the angle determined in the same way by the line and the y axis, and γ is the angle determined by the line and the z axis (see Figure 20.2). The set $\{\alpha, \beta, \gamma\}$ is called the set of *direction angles* for the directed line. Note that the angle α is *not necessarily* in one of the coordinate planes; it is in the plane determined by the line and the x axis. Similar statements hold for β and γ. Note also that a direction angle cannot be greater than 180°.

Just as the inclination of a line in the plane is relatively inconvenient, the set of direction angles of a line in space is rather inconvenient. Somewhat easier to deal with are the direction cosines.

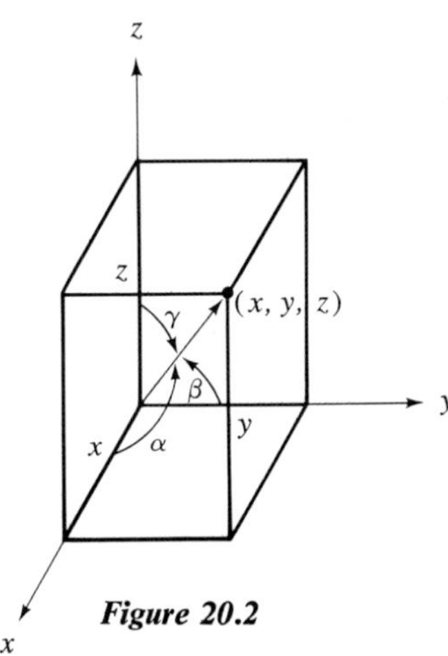

Figure 20.2

Definition

If $\{\alpha, \beta, \gamma\}$ is the set of direction angles for a directed line, then $\{l, m, n\}$, where $l =$ $\cos \alpha$, $m = \cos \beta$, and $n = \cos \gamma$, is the set of ***direction cosines*** *for that directed line.*

If (x, y, z) is a point on the positive end of the line (see Figure 20.2), then

$$l = \cos \alpha = \frac{x}{\rho}, \qquad m = \cos \beta = \frac{y}{\rho}, \qquad n = \cos \gamma = \frac{z}{\rho},$$

where $\rho = \sqrt{x^2 + y^2 + z^2}$. It is this relation to the coordinates of a point on the line which allows us to prove the next theorem.

Theorem 20.4

If $\{l, m, n\}$ is a set of direction cosines for a directed line through the origin, then

$$l^2 + m^2 + n^2 = 1.$$

From the relations above, we have

$$\begin{aligned} l^2 + m^2 + n^2 &= \frac{x^2}{\rho^2} + \frac{y^2}{\rho^2} + \frac{z^2}{\rho^2} \\ &= \frac{x^2 + y^2 + z^2}{\rho^2} \\ &= 1. \end{aligned}$$

Note that every line has two sets of direction angles and two sets of direction cosines corresponding to the two possible directions on the line. It is easily seen that if $\{l, m, n\}$ is one set of direction cosines for a line, then the other is $\{-l, -m, -n\}$.

For most purposes, an even more convenient set of numbers is a set of direction numbers for a line.

Definition

If $\{l, m, n\}$ is a set of direction cosines for a line, then any set $\{a, b, c\}$ such that $a = kl$, $b = km$, and $c = kn$ for some nonzero number k is called a set of ***direction numbers*** *for that line.*

Given a set of direction numbers for a line, we can easily find the two sets of direction cosines (and thus direction angles) from it by use of Theorem 20.4.

Example 1

Find the two sets of direction angles for a line if $\{1, 2, 2\}$ is a set of direction numbers.

Since the three numbers given are a number k times the direction cosines, we have

$$kl = 1, \qquad km = 2, \qquad kn = 2;$$

$$k^2l^2 + k^2m^2 + k^2n^2 = 1 + 4 + 4 = 9,$$

$$k^2(l^2 + m^2 + n^2) = 9,$$

$$k^2 = 9 \quad \text{(by Theorem 20.4)},$$

$$k = \pm 3.$$

Thus, the two possible sets of direction cosines are $\{1/3, 2/3, 2/3\}$ and $\{-1/3, -2/3, -2/3\}$, and they give approximate direction angles $\{71°, 48°, 48°\}$ and $\{109°, 132°, 132°\}$, respectively.

Example 2

If the line of Example 1 is directed below the xy plane, find the set of direction angles for it.

From Example 1 we know that the direction angles are either $\{71°, 48°, 48°\}$ or $\{109°, 132°, 132°\}$. Since the line is directed below the xy plane, the angle γ from the z axis to the line is obtuse. Thus, the set of direction angles is

$$\{109°, 132°, 132°\}.$$

Up to now we have considered only lines through the origin. Now we want to consider a directed line which does not contain the origin. Let us choose a point $P_1 = (x_1, y_1, z_1)$ on this line and consider new axes containing P_1 and parallel to the original axes. In effect, we are translating the axes, but we shall still continue to represent points in the original coordinate system. Let $P_2 = (x_2, y_2, z_2)$ be a point on the positive side of P_1 and on the given line. Now we have

$$l = \frac{x_2 - x_1}{\rho}, \qquad m = \frac{y_2 - y_1}{\rho}, \qquad n = \frac{z_2 - z_1}{\rho},$$

where $\rho = \sqrt{(x_2 - x_1)^2 + (y_2 - y_1)^2 + (z_2 - z_1)^2}$. We see that the previous situation, with the line containing the origin, is only a special case of this one.

Since a set of direction numbers can be found by multiplying the three direction cosines by any nonzero real number, one set of direction numbers is $\{x_2 - x_1, y_2 - y_1, z_2 - z_1\}$. This allows us to find a set of direction numbers directly from a pair of points on the line without first finding direction cosines.

Example 3

Find a set of direction numbers for the line through $(1, 5, -2)$ and $(4, 3, 1)$.

$$a = x_2 - x_1 = 4 - 1 = 3,$$
$$b = y_2 - y_1 = 3 - 5 = -2,$$
$$c = z_2 - z_1 = 1 + 2 = 3.$$

The desired set of direction numbers is $\{3, -2, 3\}$. Of course, any nonzero multiple of these numbers will also be a set of direction numbers.

Example 4

Suppose a line has direction numbers $\{2, -4, 1\}$ and contains the point $(1, 3, 4)$. Find another point on the line.

We simply reverse the process of Example 3 as follows. From the equations

$$a = x_2 - x_1, \qquad b = y_2 - y_1, \qquad c = z_2 - z_1,$$

we get

$$x_2 = x_1 + a, \qquad y_2 = y_1 + b, \qquad z_2 = z_1 + c.$$

Thus,

$$x_2 = 1 + 2 = 3,$$
$$y_2 = 3 - 4 = -1,$$
$$z_2 = 4 + 1 = 5,$$

which gives the point $(3, -1, 5)$.

Perhaps you feel a bit uneasy about the preceding example. How do we know that, of all possible sets of direction numbers, the one we were given is *that* one—that is, the set of direction numbers determined by the method of Example 3? The answer is simple—all of them are. Here is the reason. No matter what pair of points we choose on a line, we must get one of the two possible sets of direction cosines. Taking one of those two sets, we can get from it any set of direction numbers by multiplying by the proper number k. In particular, if we take a set of direction cosines for the line of Example 4 and multiply it by the proper number k, we get the direction numbers $\{2, -4, 1\}$. Now there are two points on the line at a distance $|k|$ from the point $(1, 3, 4)$. By choosing the proper one of those two points, we see that that point, together with $(1, 3, 4)$ would give the direction numbers $\{2, -4, 1\}$. Of course, this argument could be repeated for any point and set of direction numbers.

It might be noted that we could, say, double the direction numbers of Example 4 to give another set of direction numbers, $\{4, -8, 2\}$. This, together with the point $(1, 3, 4)$, gives the point $(5, -5, 6)$, which is also on the line. This could be repeated indefinitely to get as many points on the line as we choose.

20.3

Parallel and Perpendicular Lines

It is clear that if two lines are parallel and directed the same way, they must have the same set of direction angles and, thus, the same set of direction cosines. If they are parallel and have opposite directions, their direction angles are supplementary and one set of direction cosines is the negative of the other. Thus, any set of direction numbers for one line is proportional to a set of direction numbers for the other. Furthermore, this chain of reasoning can be reversed to show that if two lines have proportional sets of direction numbers, they are parallel.

Theorem 20.5

Two lines are parallel if and only if sets of direction numbers for the two lines are proportional.

The situation is not so simple for the case in which the lines are perpendicular. First of all, there is some question as to what it means to say that two lines are perpendicular. Two nonparallel lines need not intersect. Nevertheless we would like to consider some lines to be perpendicular even though they do not intersect. Two lines are said to be *perpendicular* if the lines parallel to them containing the origin are perpendicular. This now makes it relatively easy to relate perpendicularity to direction cosines. Suppose two lines with direction cosines, $\{l_1, m_1, n_1\}$ and $\{l_2, m_2, n_2\}$, are perpendicular. Then the two lines containing the origin and parallel to them are perpendicular. These lines through the origin have the same sets of direction cosines as the original two lines. Suppose $P_1: (x_1, y_1, z_1)$ is a point different from the origin on the first line and $P_2: (x_2, y_2, z_2)$ is a point different from the origin on the second (see Figure 20.3). By the Theorem of Pythagoras,

$$\begin{aligned}\rho_1^2 + \rho_2^2 &= (x_1 - x_2)^2 + (y_1 - y_2)^2 + (z_1 - z_2)^2 \\ &= (\rho_1 l_1 - \rho_2 l_2)^2 + (\rho_1 m_1 - \rho_2 m_2)^2 + (\rho_1 n_1 - \rho_2 n_2)^2 \\ &= \rho_1^2(l_1^2 + m_1^2 + n_1^2) - 2\rho_1\rho_2(l_1 l_2 + m_1 m_2 + n_1 n_2) + \rho_2^2(l_2^2 + m_2^2 + n_2^2) \\ &= \rho_1^2 - 2\rho_1\rho_2(l_1 l_2 + m_1 m_2 + n_1 n_2) + \rho_2^2.\end{aligned}$$

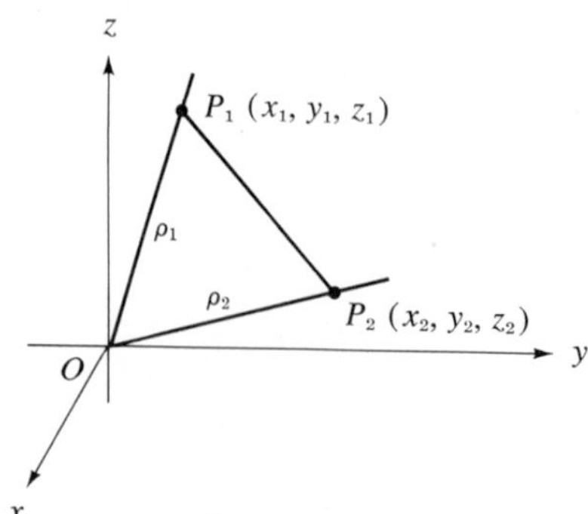

Figure 20.3

Thus

$$0 = -2\rho_1\rho_2(l_1l_2 + m_1m_2 + n_1n_2).$$

Since neither P_1 nor P_2 is the origin, neither ρ_1 nor ρ_2 is zero. Thus

$$l_1l_2 + m_1m_2 + n_1n_2 = 0.$$

Furthermore, since direction numbers are multiples of direction cosines, a similar relation holds for direction numbers;

$$a_1a_2 + b_1b_2 + c_1c_2 = 0.$$

Again, the argument is reversible, as the following theorem states.

Theorem 20.6

Two lines with direction numbers $\{a_1, b_1, c_1\}$ and $\{a_2, b_2, c_2\}$ are perpendicular if and only if

$$a_1a_2 + b_1b_2 + c_1c_2 = 0.$$

Problems

In Problems 1–6, find the set of direction angles for the directed line described.

1. Direction numbers $\{1, 4, 8\}$; directed to the right of the xz plane.
2. Direction numbers $\{4, -4, 2\}$; directed to the right of the xz plane.
3. Direction numbers $\{1, 2, -4\}$; directed behind the yz plane.
4. Direction numbers $\{2, -1, -3\}$; directed above the xy plane.
5. Direction numbers $\{1, 1, 1\}$; directed behind the yz plane.
6. Direction numbers $\{1, -1, 0\}$; directed to the right of the xz plane.

In Problems 7–12, find a set of direction numbers for the lines containing the two given points.

7. $(1, 4, 3)$ and $(5, 2, -1)$.
8. $(2, 0, -4)$ and $(-1, 2, 3)$.
9. $(2, 2, 1)$ and $(0, 0, 3)$.
10. $(3, 5, -2)$ and $(-1, 4, 4)$.
11. $(0, 0, 0)$ and $(5, 1, -2)$.
12. $(-1, 4, 5)$ and $(3, -4, 0)$.

In Problems 13–18, find two more points on the line.

13. Direction numbers $\{1, 5, 2\}$; containing $(2, 3, -1)$.
14. Direction numbers $\{1, 4, 0\}$; containing $(-2, 1, 1)$.
15. Direction numbers $\{2, 1, 2\}$; containing $(1, 3, 3)$.
16. Direction numbers $\{1, 1, 1\}$; containing $(2, 4, -1)$.
17. Direction numbers $\{4, 0, -1\}$; containing $(1, 3, -1)$.
18. Direction numbers $\{4, 4, 3\}$; containing $(-4, -4, -3)$.
19. Give the direction angles and direction cosines for the coordinate axes with their usual directions.
20. Give a set of formulas for finding all points on the line described in Example 3. (Consider the last paragraph in Section 20.2.)

In Problems 21–30, two lines are described by a pair of points on each. Indicate whether the lines are parallel, perpendicular, coincident or none of these.

21. (3, 4, 1), (4, 8, −1); (2, 3, −5), (0, −5, −1).
22. (2, 1, 5), (3, 3, −1); (4, 2, 10), (1, −4, 5).
23. (4, 1, −4), (3, 2, 1); (4, 1, −4), (11, 3, −3).
24. (4, 2, −1), (7, 6, 2); (5, 10, 3), (−4, −2, −6).
25. (2, 1, 4), (4, −3, 12); (1, 3, 0), (6, −7, 20).
26. (4, 5, 1), (3, 2, −4); (4, 1, 2), (5, −1, 3).
27. (2, 3, 1), (4, −2, 2); (1, 0, 3), (3, −3, 1).
28. (3, 1, 4), (4, 3, 3); (5, 5, 2), (0, −5, 7).
29. (2, 1, 3), (5, −1, 1); (3, 4, −1), (5, 3, 3).
30. (4, 4, −3), (1, 3, −1); (2, 1, 5), (8, 3, 1).

20.4

The Line

We have seen that, given a set of direction numbers for a line and one point on that line, we can find another simply by adding. Furthermore, we can find other sets of direction numbers by taking a multiple of the original set. Thus if the point given is (x_0, y_0, z_0) and the set of direction numbers given is $\{a, b, c\}$, then any point (x, y, z) such that

$$x = x_0 + at,$$
$$y = y_0 + bt,$$
$$z = z_0 + ct,$$

where t is a real number, is on the given line. Furthermore, if (x, y, z) is a point on the line different from (x_0, y_0, z_0), then a set of direction numbers for the line is $\{x - x_0, y - y_0, z - z_0\}$. These must be a multiple of the given set of direction numbers $\{a, b, c\}$; that is, for some t,

$$x - x_0 = at,$$
$$y - y_0 = bt,$$
$$z - z_0 = ct.$$

These equations hold not only for every point on the line different from (x_0, y_0, z_0) but also for (x_0, y_0, z_0). Thus a point is on the given line if and only if it satisfies the set of equations given above.

Theorem 20.7

A parametric representation of the line containing (x_0, y_0, z_0) and having direction numbers $\{a, b, c\}$ is

$$x = x_0 + at, \qquad y = y_0 + bt, \qquad z = z_0 + ct.$$

Example 1

Find a parametric representation for the line containing (1, 3, -2) and having direction numbers $\{3, 2, -1\}$.

$$x = 1 + 3t, \qquad y = 3 + 2t, \qquad z = -2 - t.$$

Example 2

Find a parametric representation of the line containing (4, 2, -1) and (0, 2, 3).

A set of direction numbers is $\{4 - 0, 2 - 2, -1 - 3\} = \{4, 0, -4\}$. Thus the line is

$$x = 4 + 4t, \qquad y = 2, \qquad z = -1 - 4t.$$

Once we have the direction numbers we may use them with either of the two given points. Thus, another representation is

$$x = 4s, \qquad y = 2, \qquad z = 3 - 4s.$$

Although this does not look much like the first representation, it is easily seen that they are the same. For instance, $t = 0$ gives the point (4, 2, -1), as does $s = 1$; $t = -1$ gives the point (0, 2, 3), as does $s = 0$, and so forth.

In fact,

$$\begin{aligned} x &= 4 + 4t & y &= 2, & z &= -1 - 4t \\ &= 4(t + 1) & & & &= 3 - 4 - 4t \\ &= 4s, & & & &= 3 - 4(t + 1) \\ & & & & &= 3 - 4s, \end{aligned}$$

where $s = t + 1$. Thus, whatever point we get using a value of t can be found by choosing $s = t + 1$.

A simpler set of direction numbers can also be found. Since the ones we have are all multiples of 4, we can multiply through by 1/4 to get another set of direction numbers, $\{1, 0, -1\}$. Using these with the first point gives

$$x = 4 + u, \qquad y = 2, \qquad z = -1 - u.$$

Again, we see that $4t = u$, so the two representations are equivalent.

Perhaps you wonder what is needed to be able to say that two parametric representations are equivalent. If a value of t and another of s both give the same point, then, for those values of t and s, the three coordinates must be equal. Eliminating x, y, and z between the two parametric representations gives three equations in t and s (in some of these, the parameters may both be absent, as they are in the representation of y here). If all give the same result when they are solved for one parameter in terms of the other and if the domain and range are the same, then the representations are equivalent.

Suppose we eliminate the parameter in the representation given by Theorem 20.7. If none of the direction numbers is zero, we can solve each equation for t and set them equal to each other. This gives

$$\frac{x - x_0}{a} = \frac{y - y_0}{b} = \frac{z - z_0}{c}.$$

Actually, this is just a shorter way of writing the three equations

$$\frac{x - x_0}{a} = \frac{y - y_0}{b},$$

$$\frac{y - y_0}{b} = \frac{z - z_0}{c},$$

$$\frac{x - x_0}{a} = \frac{z - z_0}{c}.$$

But these three equations are not independent—the last can be found from the first two. Let us discard it and consider only the first two, which, as we shall see in the next section, represent planes. Any point that satisfies both equations is on both planes and, therefore on the intersection of the two planes, which is a line. Thus this representation of a line gives it as the intersection of two planes. It might be noted that the equation we discarded is also a plane containing the same line.

What, now, if one of the direction numbers is zero. Let us suppose that $a = 0$. Then the line in parametric form is

$$x = x_0, \qquad y = y_0 + bt, \qquad z = z_0 + ct.$$

We do not have to eliminate the parameter from the first equation—it is already gone. By eliminating t between the last two equations as before, we have

$$\frac{y - y_0}{b} = \frac{z - z_0}{c}.$$

This, together with $x = x_0$ (or $x - x_0 = 0$) gives the line as the intersection of two planes.

If two of the direction numbers are zero, we have two equations in which the parameter is missing. The parameter in the third equation cannot be eliminated, because there is no second equation with which to combine it. But it is not necessary to eliminate it! The two equations without the parameter already give us the necessary two planes.

Theorem 20.8

If a line contains the point (x_0, y_0, z_0) *and has direction numbers* $\{a, b, c\}$, *then it can be represented by*

(a)
$$\frac{x - x_0}{a} = \frac{y - y_0}{b} = \frac{z - z_0}{c}$$

if none of the direction numbers is zero;

(b)
$$x - x_0 = 0 \quad \textit{and} \quad \frac{y - y_0}{b} = \frac{z - z_0}{c}$$

if $a = 0$ *and neither* b *nor* c *is zero (similar results follow if* $b = 0$ *or* $c = 0$*);*

(c)
$$x - x_0 = 0 \quad \textit{and} \quad y - y_0 = 0$$

if $a = 0$ *and* $b = 0$ *(again, similar results follow for some other pair of direction numbers equaling zero).*

Example 3

Find a representation as the intersection of two planes of the line containing $(4, 1, -2)$ and having direction numbers $\{1, 3, -2\}$.

$$\frac{x-4}{1} = \frac{y-1}{3} = \frac{z+2}{-2}.$$

Example 4

Find a representation as the intersection of two planes for the line containing $(4, 1, 3)$ and $(2, 1, -2)$.

A set of direction numbers is $\{4-2, 1-1, 3+2\} = \{2, 0, 5\}$. Since $b = 0$, we have (using the first point)

$$\frac{x-4}{2} = \frac{z-3}{5} \quad \text{and} \quad y - 1 = 0.$$

Example 5

Find the point of intersection (if any) of the lines

$$x = 3 + 2t, \quad y = 2 - t, \quad z = 5 + t$$

and

$$x = -3 - s, \quad y = 7 + s, \quad z = 16 + 3s.$$

Let us assume that there is a point of intersection. Then there is a value of t and a value of s which yield the same values of x, y, and z. For these particular values of t and s, we have

$$\begin{aligned} x &= 3 + 2t = -3 - s, \\ y &= 2 - t = 7 + s, \\ z &= 5 + t = 16 + 3s \end{aligned}$$

or

$$2t + s = -6, \qquad t + s = -5, \qquad t - 3s = 11.$$

If we solve the first pair simultaneously, we get

$$t = -1 \qquad \text{and} \qquad s = -4.$$

We see that they also satisfy the third equation. Thus there is a point of intersection which corresponds to $t = -1$ (or $s = -4$). It is $(1, 3, 4)$.

It might be noted that there are three possibilities. One is the situation in which there is a value of t and a value of s satisfying all three of the equations in t and s, as above. This results in a single point of intersection. In a second possibility, there is no value for t or s satisfying all three of the equations; that is, the values of t and s that satisfy the first two equations fail to satisfy the third. Thus, there is no point of intersection. The third possibility is that any two of the three equations in t and s are dependent; that is, any pair of values for t and s that satisfies one of them, satisfies all three. In this case we have two different representations for the same line (see the discussion following Example 2).

Problems

In Problems 1–16, represent the given line in parametric form and as the intersection of two planes.

1. Containing (5, 1, 3); direction numbers {3, −2, 4}.
2. Containing (2, −4, 2); direction numbers {2, 3, 1}.
3. Containing (5, −2, 1); direction numbers {4, 1, −2}.
4. Containing (2, 0, 3); direction numbers {4, −1, 3}.
5. Containing (1, 1, 1); direction numbers {2, 0, 1}.
6. Containing (1, 0, 5); direction numbers {3, 1, 0}.
7. Containing (4, 4, 1); direction numbers {0, 0, 1}.
8. Containing (3, 1, 2); direction numbers {1, 0, 0}.
9. Containing (4, 0, 5) and (2, 3, 1).
10. Containing (3, 3, 1) and (4, 0, 2).
11. Containing (8, 4, 1) and (−2, 0, 3).
12. Containing (−4, 2, 0) and (3, 1, 2).
13. Containing (5, 1, 3) and (5, 2, 4).
14. Containing (2, 2, 4) and (1, 2, 7).
15. Containing (1, −2, 3) and (1, 4, 3).
16. Containing (2, 4, −5) and (5, 4, −5).

In Problems 17–24, find the point of intersection (if any) of the given lines.

17. $x = 4 + t,\ y = -8 - 2t,\ z = 12t;\quad x = 3 + 2s,\ y = -1 + s,\ z = -3 - 3s.$
18. $x = 2 - t,\ y = 3 + 2t,\ z = 4 + t;\quad x = 1 + t,\ y = -2 + t,\ z = 5 - 4t.$
19. $x = 3 + t,\ y = 4 - 2t,\ z = 1 + 5t;\quad x = 5 - t,\ y = 3 + 2t,\ z = 8 + 4t.$
20. $x = 3 - t,\ y = 5 + 3t,\ z = -1 - 4t;\quad x = 8 + 2s,\ y = -6 - 4s,\ z = 5 + s.$
21. $\dfrac{x-2}{1} = \dfrac{y-3}{-2} = \dfrac{z+1}{1};\quad \dfrac{x-3}{2} = \dfrac{y-1}{-4} = \dfrac{z}{2}.$
22. $\dfrac{x-5}{1} = \dfrac{y+2}{-2} = \dfrac{z-3}{5};\quad \dfrac{x-4}{-2} = \dfrac{y-2}{1} = \dfrac{z-4}{3}.$
23. $\dfrac{x-3}{1} = \dfrac{y+3}{-4},\ z + 1 = 0;\quad \dfrac{x}{-2} = \dfrac{y-2}{1} = \dfrac{z-3}{4}.$
24. $\dfrac{x-2}{1} = \dfrac{y-3}{-2} = \dfrac{z}{4};\quad x - 4 = 0,\ \dfrac{y-2}{1} = \dfrac{z-3}{-1}.$

In Problems 25–30, indicate whether the two given lines are parallel, perpendicular, coincident, or none of these.

25. $x = 3 + 5t,\ y = -1 - 2t,\ z = 4 + t;\quad x = 3,\ y = 4 + 2s,\ z = -2 + 4s.$
26. $x = 4 - t,\ y = 3 + 2t,\ z = 1 + t;\quad x = 1 + 2t,\ y = 4 - 4t,\ z = 3 - 2t.$
27. $x = 2 + t,\ y = 5 - 3t,\ z = 1 + 4t;\quad x = 4 - t,\ y = 2 + 2t,\ z = 3t.$
28. $\dfrac{x-2}{1} = \dfrac{y-5}{-3} = \dfrac{z+1}{2};\quad \dfrac{x-4}{-3} = \dfrac{y+1}{9} = \dfrac{z-3}{-6}.$
29. $\dfrac{x+3}{1} = \dfrac{y-4}{3} = \dfrac{z+2}{-2};\quad \dfrac{x-5}{-3} = \dfrac{y+3}{-9} = \dfrac{z-1}{6}.$
30. $\dfrac{x-1}{2} = \dfrac{z+3}{4},\ y - 5 = 0;\quad \dfrac{x+2}{6} = \dfrac{y-5}{3} = \dfrac{z}{2}.$
31. Give equations for each of the coordinates axes.

20.5

The Plane

Suppose we are given a plane in space and a line l perpendicular to the plane and containing the origin O. Suppose this line intersects the plane at the point Q (see Figure 20.4). If $Q \neq O$, let the direction from O to Q be the positive direction of l; if $Q = O$, the positive direction can be assigned arbitrarily. If $\{\alpha, \beta, \gamma\}$ is a set of direction angles for the directed line l and p is the length of OQ, then the coordinates of Q are $(p \cos \alpha, p \cos \beta, p \cos \gamma)$. Let P: (x, y, z) be a point different from Q in the given plane. A set of direction numbers for the line PQ is $\{x - p \cos \alpha, y - p \cos \beta, z - p \cos \gamma\}$; a set of direction numbers for l is the set of direction cosines themselves $\{\cos \alpha, \cos \beta, \cos \gamma\}$. Since l and PQ are perpendicular,

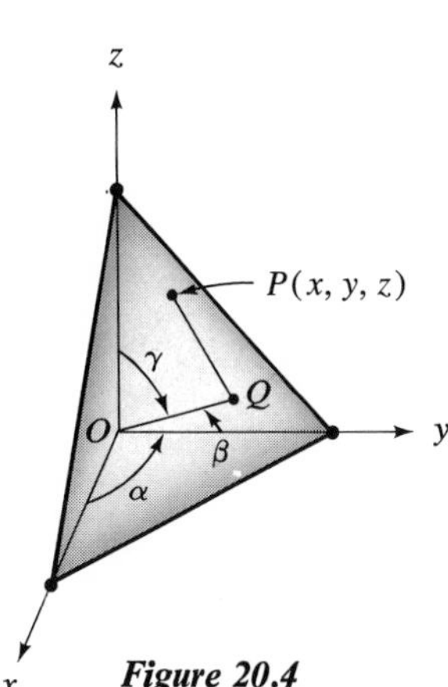

Figure 20.4

$$\cos \alpha\,(x - p \cos \alpha) + \cos \beta\,(y - p \cos \beta) + \cos \gamma\,(z - p \cos \gamma) = 0$$
$$x \cos \alpha + y \cos \beta + z \cos \gamma - p(\cos^2 \alpha + \cos^2 \beta + \cos^2 \gamma) = 0$$
$$x \cos \alpha + y \cos \beta + z \cos \gamma - p = 0.$$

If $P = Q$, we see by substitution that its coordinates also satisfy this equation. Thus the coordinates of every point in the plane satisfy the last equation. If we reverse the steps, the last equation represents the plane with which we started.

Theorem 20.9

If a line perpendicular to a plane has direction angles $\{\alpha, \beta, \gamma\}$ and p is the distance from the origin to the plane, then a point is in the plane if and only if it satisfies the equation

$$x \cos \alpha + y \cos \beta + z \cos \gamma - p = 0.$$

This form for the equation of a plane is called the *normal form*. Compare it with the normal form for a line (see Problem 37, page 33; and Problem 25, page 311).

Theorem 20.10

Any plane can be represented by an equation of the form

$$Ax + By + Cz + D = 0,$$

where $\{A, B, C\}$ is a set of direction numbers for a line normal to (that is, perpendicular to) the plane. Conversely, an equation of the above form (where A, B, and C are not all zero) represents a plane with $\{A, B, C\}$ a set of direction numbers for a normal line.

The first part follows directly from Theorem 20.9, since any plane can be represented by an equation in normal form. If we are given an equation of the form

$$Ax + By + Cz + D = 0,$$

where A, B, and C are not all zero, let us multiply through by the constant

$$k = \frac{\pm 1}{\sqrt{A^2 + B^2 + C^2}},$$

where the sign is chosen opposite the sign of D. The coefficients of x, y, and z form a set of direction cosines,

$$\left\{\frac{\pm A}{\sqrt{A^2 + B^2 + C^2}}, \frac{\pm B}{\sqrt{A^2 + B^2 + C^2}}, \frac{\pm C}{\sqrt{A^2 + B^2 + C^2}}\right\},$$

for some line, since the sum of their squares is 1 (see Problem 39). The resulting equation is, therefore, the normal form of a plane. Since the coefficients are a nonzero multiple of the set of direction cosines above, they are a set of direction numbers for the normal line.

Theorem 20.11

A point is on a plane containing (x_1, y_1, z_1) and perpendicular to a line with direction numbers $\{A, B, C\}$ if and only if it satisfies the equation

$$A(x - x_1) + B(y - y_1) + C(z - z_1) = 0.$$

The proof is left to the student.

Example 1

Sketch $x + 2y + 3z = 6$ and find its distance from the origin.

A simple way to sketch a plane is to find its three intercepts and identify its intersections with the coordinate planes. This has been done in Figure 20.5. To find its distance from the origin, we must put the equation into normal form by dividing through by $\sqrt{1^2 + 2^2 + 3^2} = \sqrt{14}$;

$$\frac{1}{\sqrt{14}}x + \frac{2}{\sqrt{14}}y + \frac{3}{\sqrt{14}}z - \frac{6}{\sqrt{14}} = 0.$$

The desired distance is $6/\sqrt{14}$.

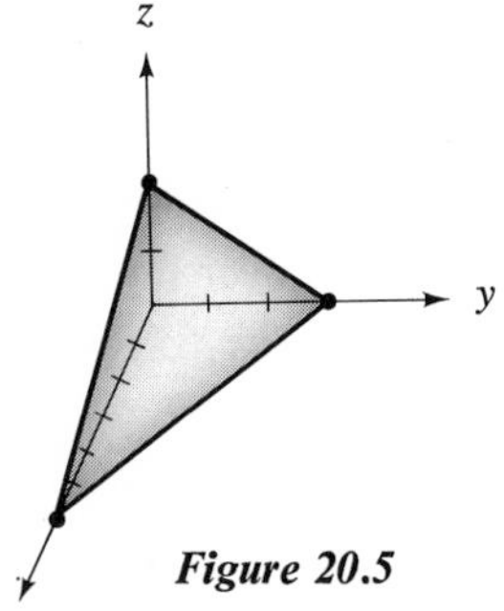

Figure 20.5

Example 2

Find the distance between the parallel planes

$$x - 2y + 2z = 3 \quad \text{and} \quad x - 2y + 2z = 12.$$

Let us put them into normal form by dividing through by $\sqrt{1^2+(-2)^2+2^2} = 3$:

$$\frac{1}{3}x - \frac{2}{3}y + \frac{2}{3}z - 1 = 0,$$

$$\frac{1}{3}x - \frac{2}{3}y + \frac{2}{3}z - 4 = 0.$$

They are at distances 1 and 4 from the origin, respectively, and both are on the same side. Thus, the distance between them is the difference 3.

Example 3

Find the equation of the plane containing $(1, 3, -2)$ and perpendicular to the line through $(2, 5, 1)$ and $(0, 1, -3)$.

A set of direction numbers for the given line is $\{2, 4, 4\}$ or $\{1, 2, 2\}$. Thus the desired plane is

$$1(x-1) + 2(y-3) + 2(z+2) = 0,$$
$$x + 2y + 2z - 3 = 0.$$

Example 4

Find the equation of the plane containing the two lines

$$x = 1, \quad y = 3 + 2t, \quad z = 4 + t$$

and

$$x = 1 + 4s, \quad y = 3 + 2s, \quad z = 4 + 2s.$$

These lines clearly intersect at $(1, 3, 4)$. Since both lines are in the plane, any line perpendicular to the plane is perpendicular to both of them. If $\{a, b, c\}$ is a set of direction numbers for a normal line, then

$$2b + c = 0,$$
$$4a + 2b + 2c = 0.$$

Clearly $a = b = c = 0$ is one solution, but these cannot be direction numbers. Let us try to find another solution. If we subtract the first equation from the second, we have

$$4a + c = 0.$$

Arbitrarily assigning the value $a = 1$, we get $c = -4$ and $b = 2$. Thus $\{1, 2, -4\}$ is a set of direction numbers for the normal line. Using this set with the point $(1, 3, 4)$ we have

$$1(x-1) + 2(y-3) - 4(z-4) = 0,$$
$$x + 2y - 4z + 9 = 0.$$

A second method of solving is to take three noncollinear points in the plane and find the plane containing them. One point is $(1, 3, 4)$. By letting $t = 1$, we get $(1, 5, 5)$. By letting $s = 1$, we get $(5, 5, 6)$. If the desired plane is

$$Ax + By + Cz + D = 0,$$

then we have

$$A + 3B + 4C + D = 0,$$
$$A + 5B + 5C + D = 0,$$
$$5A + 5B + 6C + D = 0.$$

We now have three equations but four unknowns. This can be reduced to two equations in three unknowns and finally to one equation in two unknowns. Again, by arbitrarily assigning a value to one of them, we can find the other three. Substituting these into

$$Ax + By + Cz + D = 0$$

we get

$$x + 2y - 4z + 9 = 0.$$

Example 5

Find the distance between the point (5, 1, 3) and the line $x = 3$, $y = 7 + t$, $z = 1 + t$.

Of course the distance we seek is the minimum, or perpendicular, distance. This leads quite naturally to two methods of solution.

To find the perpendicular distance we first find the plane containing the given point and perpendicular to the given line.

$$0(x - 5) + 1(y - 1) + 1(z - 3) = 0,$$
$$y + z - 4 = 0.$$

Now the distance we want is the distance between the given point and the point of intersection of the given line with the plane we have just found. Substituting the x, y, and z of the line into the equation of the plane, we have

$$(7 + t) + (1 + t) - 4 = 0,$$
$$t = -2.$$

Thus the point of intersection is (3, 5, -1) and the desired distance is

$$s = \sqrt{(5 - 3)^2 + (1 - 5)^2 + (3 + 1)^2} = 6.$$

An alternate method is to solve as a minimum value problem. The distance from (5, 1, 3) to a point (x, y, z) on the given line is

$$\begin{aligned} s &= \sqrt{(x - 5)^2 + (y - 1)^2 + (z - 3)^2} \\ &= \sqrt{(3 - 5)^2 + [(7 + t) - 1]^2 + [(1 + t) - 3]^2} \\ &= \sqrt{2t^2 + 8t + 44} \end{aligned}$$

$$s^2 = 2t^2 + 8t + 44;$$

$$\frac{d}{dt}(s^2) = 4t + 8 = 0,$$

$$t = -2,$$

$$s = \sqrt{2(-2)^2 + 8(-2) + 44} = 6.$$

Example 6

Find the distance between the lines $x = 1 + 2t$, $y = 3 + 3t$, $z = -2 + t$ and $x = 4 + 2s$, $y = 2 + 2s$, $z = -1 - s$.

As always, we want the minimum, or perpendicular distance—that is, the distance along a line which is perpendicular to both of the given lines. The direction numbers $\{a, b, c\}$ must satisfy the equations

$$2a + 3b + c = 0,$$
$$2a + 2b - c = 0.$$

Adding, we have

$$4a + 5b = 0.$$

Thus one such set of direction numbers is $\{5, -4, 2\}$. The plane perpendicular to such a line and containing the point $(1, 3, -2)$ of the first line has equation

$$5(x-1) - 4(y-3) + 2(z+2) = 0,$$
$$5x - 4y + 2z + 11 = 0.$$

Similarly the plane containing $(4, 2, -1)$ and perpendicular to a line with direction numbers $\{5, -4, 2\}$ is

$$5(x-4) - 4(y-2) + 2(z+1) = 0,$$
$$5x - 4y + 2z - 10 = 0.$$

Note that these two planes are parallel, and they contain the given lines. The desired distance is the distance between these planes:

$$d = \frac{11 - (-10)}{\sqrt{5^2 + (-4)^2 + 2^2}} = \frac{21}{3\sqrt{5}} = \frac{7}{\sqrt{5}}.$$

Problems

In Problems 1–6, sketch the plane and find its distance from the origin.

1. $2x + 3y + z = 6$.
2. $3x - y + z = 9$.
3. $2x + y - 4z + 4 = 0$.
4. $x - y - 4z = 8$.
5. $x + 2y = 3$.
6. $y - 5 = 0$.

In Problems 7–12, find the distance between the parallel planes.

7. $2x - y + 2z = 9, \quad 2x - y + 2z = -12$.
8. $x - 4y - 2z = 5, \quad x - 4y - 2z = 10$.
9. $3x + y - 4z = 3, \quad 6x + 2y - 8z = -5$.
10. $x + y + 4z = 6, \quad 2x + 2y + 8z = 9$.
11. $x + 2y = 6, \quad x + 2y = 1$.
12. $x - y - z = 4, \quad 2x - 2y - 2z = -3$.

In Problems 13–30, find an equation(s) of the plane(s) satisfying the given conditions.

13. Containing $(4, 1, -3)$ and perpendicular to the line $x = 2 + 3t$, $y = 4 - t$, $z = 3 - 2t$.
14. Containing $(3, 2, 5)$ and perpendicular to the line $x = 1 + t$, $y = 3t$, $z = 4 + t$.
15. Containing $(3, 5, 1)$ and parallel to $3x - 4y + 2z = 3$.
16. Containing $(4, -1, 2)$ and parallel to $x + y - 2z = 4$.
17. Parallel to $3x + y - 4z + 2 = 0$ and twice as far from the origin.
18. Parallel to $5x - 2y + z - 2 = 0$ and equally distant from the origin but on the opposite side of the origin.
19. Parallel to $2x + y - z = 4$ and at a distance 2 from it.
20. Perpendicular to $x = 1 - t$, $y = 2 + 3t$, $z = 4 + t$ and at a distance 4 from the origin.
21. Containing $(1, 4, 2)$, $(2, 3, -1)$, and $(5, 0, 2)$.
22. Containing $(3, 1, -4)$, $(2, 3, 1)$, and $(7, 4, -2)$.
23. Containing $x = 4 + t$, $y = 2 - t$, $z = 1 + 2t$ and $x = 4 - 3s$, $y = 2 + 2s$, $z = 1 - s$.
24. Containing $x = 2 + 2t$, $y = -1 + t$, $z = 4 - t$ and $x = 2 - s$, $y = -1 - 2s$, $z = 4 + 3s$.
25. Containing $(4, 1, 2)$ and $x = 4 - t$, $y = 1 + 2t$, $z = 3 - t$.

26. Containing $(-2, 3, -4)$ and $x = 1 + t,\ y = 3 - 2t,\ z = -2 + t$.
27. Containing $x = 3 + 2t,\ y = 4 - t,\ z = 1 + t$ and $x = -1 + 2s,\ y = 3 - s,\ z = 4 + s$.
28. Containing $x = 4 + t,\ y = 2t,\ z = 5$ and $x = 1 + s,\ y = 3 + 2s,\ z = -2$.
29. Containing $(1, 5, -2)$ and perpendicular to $3x + 2y - z + 1 = 0$ and $x - y + 2z = 0$.
30. Containing $(3, 0, -4)$ and perpendicular to $2x - 5y + z = 1$ and $x - 2y - z = 3$.

In Problems 31–34, find the distance between the point and line given.

31. $(1, 3, -2)$; $x = 4,\ y = -3 + 4t,\ z = 11 + 5t$.
32. $(4, 3, 3)$; $x = 2 + 2t,\ y = 5 - 5t,\ z = -1 - t$.
33. $(2, 4, -1)$; $x = 5 + t,\ y = -2 + 3t,\ z = 3 + t$.
34. $(-1, 0, 5)$; $\dfrac{x-2}{2} = \dfrac{y-1}{1} = \dfrac{z+2}{3}$.

In Problems 35–38, find the distance between the two given lines.

35. $x = 4 + 3t,\ y = 3 + 2t,\ z = -3 - 4t$; $x = 2 + s,\ y = 1 + 2s,\ z = 2 + 2s$.
36. $x = -3 + t,\ y = 4 - 2t,\ z = -3 - t$; $x = -3 + 3s,\ y = -1 - s,\ z = 1 - s$.
37. $\dfrac{x-4}{2} = \dfrac{y+1}{-2}\dfrac{z-1}{-5}$; $\dfrac{x-3}{2} = \dfrac{y-1}{-2} = \dfrac{z-2}{-5}$.
38. $\dfrac{x-2}{1} = \dfrac{y-2}{-2} = \dfrac{z-2}{-5}$; $\dfrac{x-5}{1} = \dfrac{z-3}{-1}$, $y - 1 = 0$.
39. Show that if $A^2 + B^2 + C^2 = 1$, then $\{A, B, C\}$ is a set of direction cosines for some line. (*Hint:* Consider the point (A, B, C) together with the origin.)
40. Prove Theorem 20.11.

20.6

Distance between a Point and a Plane; Angles between Lines or Planes

---

The normal form for a plane is a very natural one for finding the distance between a point and a plane. Suppose we have a plane

$$Ax + By + Cz + D = 0$$

and a point (x_1, y_1, z_1) (See Figure 20.6). The plane parallel to the given plane and containing (x_1, y_1, z_1) is

$$A(x - x_1) + B(y - y_1) + C(z - z_1) = 0$$

or

$$Ax + By + Cz - (Ax_1 + By_1 + Cz_1) = 0.$$

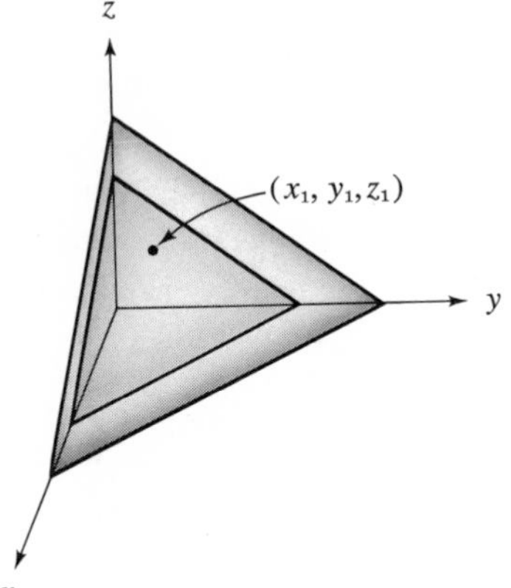

Figure 20.6

Putting both of these planes in normal form, we have

$$\frac{Ax + By + Cz + D}{\sqrt{A^2 + B^2 + C^2}} = 0$$

and

$$\frac{Ax + By + Cz - (Ax_1 + By_1 + Cz_1)}{\sqrt{A^2 + B^2 + C^2}} = 0.$$

The distance between these planes is the absolute value of the difference between their constant terms.

$$d = \frac{|Ax_1 + By_1 + Cz_1 + D|}{\sqrt{A^2 + B^2 + C^2}}.$$

Theorem 20.12

The distance between the point (x_1, y_1, z_1) and the plane $Ax + By + Cz + D = 0$ is

$$d = \frac{|Ax_1 + By_1 + Cz_1 + D|}{\sqrt{A^2 + B^2 + C^2}}.$$

Example 1

Find the distance between $(3, -4, 1)$ and $x - 2y + 2z + 4 = 0$.

$$\begin{aligned} d &= \frac{|Ax_1 + By_1 + Cz_1 + D|}{\sqrt{A^2 + B^2 + C^2}}. \\ &= \frac{|1 \cdot 3 - 2(-4) + 2 \cdot 1 + 4|}{\sqrt{1^2 + (-2)^2 + 2^2}} \\ &= \frac{17}{3}. \end{aligned}$$

Suppose we have a pair of directed lines and want to find the angle between them. First of all, we need to define what we mean by "the angle between them," especially considering that nonparallel lines need not intersect.

Definition

*The **angle of intersection** of two directed lines is the angle between the positive ends of two lines through the origin which are parallel to and directed in the same way as the given lines.*

Now let us proceed to find the angle of intersection. Suppose we have directed lines L_1 and L_2 with direction cosines $\{l_1, m_1, n_1\}$ and $\{l_2, m_2, n_2\}$, respectively. The lines K_1 and K_2 parallel to and directed in the same way as L_1 and L_2, respectively, and containing the origin have the same sets of direction cosines, respectively. Let $P_1: (x_1, y_1, z_1)$ and $P_2: (x_2, y_2, z_2)$ be points on the positive ends of K_1 and K_2, respectively (see Figure 20.7). Using the law of cosines on triangle OP_1P_2, we have

$$\overline{P_1P_2}^2 = \overline{OP_1}^2 + \overline{OP_2}^2 - 2\overline{OP_1}\,\overline{OP_2}\cos\theta;$$

$$(x_1 - x_2)^2 + (y_1 - y_2)^2 + (z_1 - z_2)^2 = x_1^2 + y_1^2 + z_1^2 + x_2^2 + y_2^2 + z_2^2 \\ -2\sqrt{x_1^2 + y_1^2 + z_1^2}\sqrt{x_2^2 + y_2^2 + z_2^2}\cos\theta;$$

$$\cos\theta = \frac{x_1x_2 + y_1y_2 + z_1z_2}{\sqrt{x_1^2 + y_1^2 + z_1^2}\sqrt{x_2^2 + y_2^2 + z_2^2}}.$$

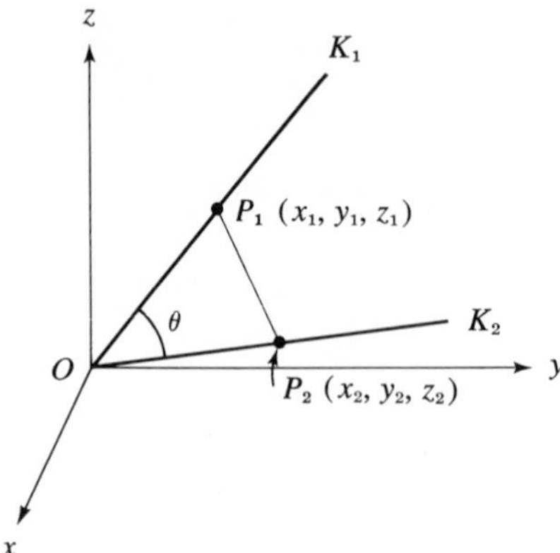

Figure 20.7

Letting $\rho_1 = \sqrt{x_1^2 + y_1^2 + z_1^2}$ and $\rho_2 = \sqrt{x_2^2 + y_2^2 + z_2^2}$, we have

$$\begin{aligned}\cos\theta &= \frac{x_1}{\rho_1}\frac{x_2}{\rho_2} + \frac{y_1}{\rho_1}\frac{y_2}{\rho_2} + \frac{z_1}{\rho_1}\frac{z_2}{\rho_2} \\ &= l_1 l_2 + m_1 m_2 + n_1 n_2 .\end{aligned}$$

Theorem 20.13

If θ is the angle between two directed lines with direction cosines $\{l_1, m_1, n_1\}$ and $\{l_2, m_2, n_2\}$, then

$$\cos\theta = l_1 l_2 + m_1 m_2 + n_1 n_2 .$$

Example 2

Find the angle between two directed lines having direction cosines {1/3, −2/3, 2/3} and {−4/9, −1/9, 8/9}.

$$\begin{aligned}\cos\theta &= l_1 l_2 + m_1 m_2 + n_1 n_2 \\ &= \frac{1}{3}\left(-\frac{4}{9}\right) + \left(-\frac{2}{3}\right)\left(-\frac{1}{9}\right) + \frac{2}{3}\cdot\frac{8}{9} \\ &= \frac{14}{27} \doteq 0.5185; \\ \theta &\doteq 59°.\end{aligned}$$

Example 3

Find the acute angle between the lines $x = 2 - 3t$, $y = 4 + t$, $z = t$ and $x = 3 + s$, $y = 1 - s$, $z = 2 + 2s$.

A set of direction numbers for the first line is {−3, 1, 1} giving $\{-3/\sqrt{11}, 1/\sqrt{11}, 1/\sqrt{11}\}$ as a set of direction cosines. For the second line we have direction numbers {1, −1, 2} and direction cosines $\{1/\sqrt{6}, -1/\sqrt{6}, 2/\sqrt{6}\}$. In each case the direction cosines represent one of two possible sets, the other being the negative of the first. Thus

$$\begin{aligned}\cos\theta &= \pm(l_1l_2 + m_1m_2 + n_1n_2)\\ &= \pm\left(\frac{-3}{\sqrt{11}}\cdot\frac{1}{\sqrt{6}} + \frac{1}{\sqrt{11}}\cdot\frac{-1}{\sqrt{6}} + \frac{1}{\sqrt{11}}\cdot\frac{2}{\sqrt{6}}\right)\\ &= \frac{2}{\sqrt{66}} \doteq 0.2462\\ \theta &\doteq 14^\circ.\end{aligned}$$

The choice of signs for $\cos\theta$ is determined by the fact that we want the cosine of the acute angle and that is positive.

A special case of Theorem 20.13 follows.

Theorem 20.14

Two lines with direction numbers $\{a_1, b_1, c_1\}$ and $\{a_2, b_2, c_2\}$ are perpendicular if and only if

$$a_1a_2 + b_1b_2 + c_1c_2 = 0.$$

Proof

Suppose the two lines are perpendicular. Then

$$\begin{aligned}a_1a_2 + b_1b_2 + c_1c_2 &= (k_1l_1)(k_2l_2) + (k_1m_1)(k_2m_2) + (k_1n_1)(k_2n_2)\\ &= k_1k_2(l_1l_2 + m_1m_2 + n_1n_2)\\ &= k_1k_2\cos 90^\circ\\ &= 0.\end{aligned}$$

If, on the other hand, we are given

$$a_1a_2 + b_1b_2 + c_1c_2 = 0,$$

then

$$l_1l_2 + m_1m_2 + n_1n_2 = 0$$

and $\theta = 90^\circ$.

Example 4

Show that $x = 1 + t$, $y = 2 - 2t$, $z = 3 + 4t$ and $x = 4 - 8s$, $y = 1 - 2s$, $z = 2 + s$ are perpendicular.

Direction numbers for the two lines are $\{1, -2, 4\}$ and $\{-8, -2, 1\}$. Thus,

$$\begin{aligned}a_1a_2 + b_1b_2 + c_1c_2 &= 1(-8) - 2(-2) + 4\cdot 1\\ &= 0,\end{aligned}$$

and the lines are perpendicular.

Let us now consider an angle of intersection of two planes. Again there is a question of definition.

Definition

An ***angle between two planes*** *is an angle between their normal lines.*

With this definition, the problem is reduced to a familiar one. We have made no attempt to define *the* angle between two planes but only *an* angle. The particular one desired must be specified in the problem.

Example 5

Find the acute angle between the planes $2x + y - z + 3 = 0$ and $4x - y + z + 1 = 0$.

The two normal lines have direction numbers $\{2, 1, -1\}$ and $\{4, -1, 1\}$ and direction cosines $\{2/\sqrt{6}, 1/\sqrt{6}, -1/\sqrt{6}\}$ and $\{4/3\sqrt{2}, -1/3\sqrt{2}, 1/3\sqrt{2}\}$. Thus

$$\cos\theta = \pm\left(\frac{2}{\sqrt{6}}\frac{4}{3\sqrt{2}} + \frac{1}{\sqrt{6}}\frac{-1}{3\sqrt{2}} + \frac{-1}{\sqrt{6}}\frac{1}{3\sqrt{2}}\right)$$

$$= \frac{6}{6\sqrt{3}} = \frac{\sqrt{3}}{3} \doteq 0.5773$$

$$\theta \doteq 55°.$$

Again, the sign was chosen because the given angle is acute.

Planes are parallel or perpendicular if and only if their normal lines are parallel or perpendicular, respectively. Thus the conditions are basically the same.

Theorem 20.15

The planes $A_1x + B_1y + C_1z + D_1 = 0$ *and* $A_2x + B_2y + C_2z + D_2 = 0$ *are parallel if and only if* $\{A_1, B_1, C_1\}$ *and* $\{A_2, B_2, C_2\}$ *are proportional; they are perpendicular if and only if* $A_1A_2 + B_1B_2 + C_1C_2 = 0$.

Problems

In Problems 1–8, find the distance between the plane and point given.

1. $2x - 4y + 4z + 3 = 0$; $(1, 3, -2)$.
2. $4x + y - 8z + 1 = 0$; $(2, 0, 3)$.
3. $x + y - 2z - 4 = 0$; $(3, 3, 1)$.
4. $2x - y + z + 5 = 0$; $(1, 0, 2)$.
5. $x + 3y + z - 2 = 0$; $(2, 1, -3)$.
6. $x - 2y + 4 = 0$; $(2, 2, 4)$.
7. $x + z - 5 = 0$; $(3, 3, 1)$.
8. $y + 7 = 0$; $(1, 3, 1)$.
9. If the distance between $(1, 4, z)$ and $8x - y + 4z - 3 = 0$ is 1, find z.
10. If the distance between $(2, y, 3)$ and $4x - 4y + 2z - 5 = 0$ is 3/2, find y.

In Problems 11–18, find the angle described.

11. The angle between the lines with direction cosines

$$\{1/\sqrt{26}, 3/\sqrt{26}, 4/\sqrt{26}\} \text{ and } \{3/\sqrt{26}, -1/\sqrt{26}, 4/\sqrt{26}\}.$$

12. The angle between the lines with direction cosines
$$\{1/\sqrt{41}, -2/\sqrt{41}, 6/\sqrt{41}\} \text{ and } \{4/\sqrt{41}, 5/\sqrt{41}, 0\}.$$
13. The acute angle between $x = 2t$, $y = 3t$, $z = -t$ and $x = 4t$, $y = -t$, $z = 2t$.
14. The obtuse angle between $x = 1 - 2t$, $y = 3 + t$, $z = 4t$, and $x = 2 + t$, $y = 3 - 2t$, $z = 1 + 3t$.
15. The angle between $x = 2 + t$, $y = 3 - 2t$, $z = 2 - t$ and $x = 4 - t$, $y = 2 + t$, $z = 2t$, both directed upward.
16. The angle between $x = 3 - t$, $y = 4 - 2t$, $z = -1 - t$ and $x = t$, $y = -4 + t$, $z = 2 + t$, both directed to the right.
17. The acute angle between $2x + y - z - 1 = 0$ and $x + y - 3z + 4 = 0$.
18. The obtuse angle between $x - y + z - 4 = 0$ and $2x + y + z = 0$.

In Problems 19–28, indicate whether the given lines (planes) are parallel, perpendicular, coincident, or none of these.

19. $x = 2 - t$, $y = 3 + t$, $z = -1 - 2t$; $x = 4 + t$, $y = 6t$, $z = -1 + 2t$.
20. $x = 2 + t$, $y = -1 - 2t$, $z = 2 + 3t$; $x = 1 + 2t$, $y = 4 - 4t$, $z = -2 + 6t$.
21. $\dfrac{x-2}{3} = \dfrac{y+1}{-2} = \dfrac{z-4}{2}$; $\dfrac{x}{2} = \dfrac{y-1}{4} = \dfrac{z+2}{1}$.
22. $\dfrac{x}{4} = \dfrac{y-1}{3} = \dfrac{z+2}{1}$; $\dfrac{x+1}{-2} = \dfrac{y+2}{1} = \dfrac{z-4}{5}$.
23. $2x + y - 4z + 2 = 0$; $6x + 3y + 4 = 0$.
24. $x - y - 5z + 1 = 0$; $2x + y - z = 0$.
25. $2x - y - 3z + 1 = 0$; $4x - 2y - 6z - 3 = 0$.
26. $3x + y - 4z + 1 = 0$; $5x - 3y + 3z - 1 = 0$.
27. $4x - 2y + z - 5 = 0$; $5x + 7y - 6z + 2 = 0$.
28. $2x - y + 3z - 1 = 0$; $4x - 2y + 6z - 2 = 0$.

20.7

Cylinders and Spheres

We now turn our attention to more complex surfaces, beginning with the cylinder. A cylinder is formed by a line (generatrix) moving along a curve (directrix) while remaining parallel to a fixed line. If the generatrix is parallel to one of the coordinate axes, the equation of the cylinder is quite simple.

Theorem 20.16

An equation of the form
$$f(x, y) = 0$$
is a cylinder with generatrix parallel to the z axis and directrix $f(x, y) = 0$ in the xy plane. Similar statements hold when one of the other variables is absent.

It is a simple matter to see why this is so. If $x = x_0$ and $y = y_0$ satisfies the equation $f(x, y) = 0$, then any point of the form (x_0, y_0, z), for *any* choice of z, is on the surface. But this is a line parallel to the z axis. Thus any point on the curve $f(x, y) = 0$ in the xy plane determines a line parallel to the z axis in space. The result is then a cylinder.

Example 1

Sketch $x^2 + y^2 = 4$.

The surface is a cylinder with generatrix parallel to the z axis and directrix a circle in the xy plane. A portion of the cylinder is given in Figure 20.8.

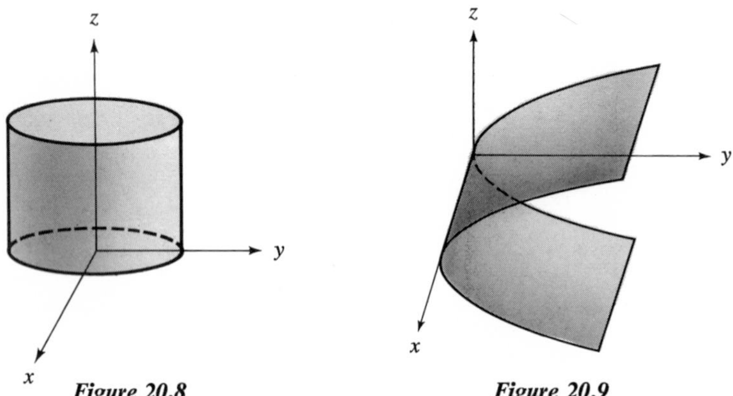

Figure 20.8

Figure 20.9

Example 2

Sketch $y = z^2$.

The surface is a cylinder with generatrix parallel to (or on) the x axis and directrix a parabola in the yz plane. A portion of the cylinder is given in Figure 20.9.

Another relatively simple surface is the sphere. The following theorems concerning the sphere are analogous to those for a circle and are proved in much the same way.

Theorem 20.17

A point (x, y, z) is on the sphere of radius r and center at (h, k, l) if and only if it satisfies the equation

$$(x - h)^2 + (y - k)^2 + (z - l)^2 = r^2.$$

Theorem 20.18

Any sphere can be represented by an equation of the form

$$Ax^2 + Ay^2 + Az^2 + Gx + Hy + Iz + J = 0,$$

where $A \neq 0$.

Theorem 20.19

An equation of the form

$$Ax^2 + Ay^2 + Az^2 + Gx + Hy + Iz + J = 0,$$

where $A \neq 0$, *represents a sphere, a point, or no locus.*

The proofs are left to the student.

Example 3

Give an equation for the sphere with center $(1, 3, -2)$ and radius 3.

By Theorem 20.17, the equation is

$$(x-1)^2 + (y-3)^2 + (z+2)^2 = 9$$

or

$$x^2 + y^2 + z^2 - 2x - 6y + 4z + 5 = 0.$$

Example 4

Describe the locus of $x^2 + y^2 + z^2 + 2x - 4y - 8z + 5 = 0$.

Let us put the equation into the form of Theorem 20.17 by completing squares.

$$\begin{aligned} x^2 + 2x \qquad + y^2 - 4y \qquad + z^2 - 8z \qquad &= -5, \\ x^2 + 2x + 1 + y^2 - 4y + 4 + z^2 - 8z + 16 &= -5 + 1 + 4 + 16, \\ (x+1)^2 + (y-2)^2 + (z-4)^2 &= 16. \end{aligned}$$

This represents a sphere with center $(-1, 2, 4)$ and radius 4.

Example 5

Describe the locus of

$$2x^2 + 2y^2 + 2z^2 - 2x + 6y - 4z + 7 = 0.$$

$$x^2 + y^2 + z^2 - x + 3y - 2z + \frac{7}{2} = 0,$$

$$x^2 - x \qquad + y^2 + 3y \qquad + z^2 - 2z \qquad = -\frac{7}{2},$$

$$x^2 - x + \frac{1}{4} + y^2 + 3y + \frac{9}{4} + z^2 - 2z + 1 = -\frac{7}{2} + \frac{1}{4} + \frac{9}{4} + 1,$$

$$\left(x - \frac{1}{2}\right)^2 + \left(y + \frac{3}{2}\right)^2 + (z-1)^2 = 0.$$

The equation represents the point $\left(\frac{1}{2}, -\frac{3}{2}, 1\right)$.

Problems

In Problems 1–10, sketch the given surface.

1. $y^2 + z^2 = 1$.
2. $x^2 + z^2 = 4$.
3. $y = x^2$.
4. $x^2 - z^2 = 1$.
5. $xy = 4$.
6. $x^2 + z^2 + 2x = 0$.
7. $z = 4 - y^2$.
8. $x = \sin z$.
9. $y = \ln x$.
10. $z = e^y$.

In Problems 11–20, identify the equation as representing a sphere, a point, or no locus. If it is a sphere, give its center and radius. If it is a point give its coordinates.

11. $x^2 + y^2 + z^2 - 2x + 4z - 4 = 0$.
12. $x^2 + y^2 + z^2 + 6x - 10y + 2z + 19 = 0$.
13. $x^2 + y^2 + z^2 - 8x + 4y - 10z + 46 = 0$.
14. $x^2 + y^2 + z^2 + 6x - 8y - 2z + 22 = 0$.
15. $2x^2 + 2y^2 + 2z^2 + 2x - 6y + 4z - 1 = 0$.
16. $2x^2 + 2y^2 + 2z^2 - 2x + 2y - 10z + 13 = 0$.
17. $9x^2 + 9y^2 + 9z^2 - 6x + 6y + 12z - 2 = 0$.
18. $3x^2 + 3y^2 + 3z^2 + 4x - 2y - 8z + 7 = 0$.
19. $4x^2 + 4y^2 + 4z^2 - 8x - 4y + 16z + 21 = 0$.
20. $6x^2 + 6y^2 + 6z^2 - 6x - 4y - 3z = 0$.

In Problems 21–28, find an equation(s) in the general form of the sphere(s) described.

21. Center $(4, 1, -2)$ and radius 3.
22. Center $(3, 1, 1)$ and containing the origin.
23. Center $(2, 4, 7)$ and tangent to $4x - 8y + z = 1$.
24. Center $(4, 1, -3)$ and tangent to $2x - y - 2z = 4$.
25. Tangent to $x - 3y + 4z + 23 = 0$ with radius $\sqrt{26}$.
26. Tangent to $x + 2y + 2z - 17 = 0$ with radius 3.
27. Containing $(3, 1, -1)$, $(2, 5, 2)$, $(-3, 0, 1)$, and $(-1, 0, 0)$.
28. Containing $(4, 1, 0)$, $(-2, -1, 0)$, $(0, 2, 1)$, and $(1, 1, 1)$.
29. Prove Theorem 20.17.
30. Prove Theorem 20.18.
31. Prove Theorem 20.19.

20.8

Quadric Surfaces

In the plane, a second-degree equation represents a parabola, ellipse, hyperbola, or a degenerate case of one of them. There are far more variations in space, where we have seen that certain cylinders and the sphere are represented by second-degree equations.

The *ellipsoid* (see Figure 20.10) is represented by an equation of the form

$$\frac{x^2}{a^2} + \frac{y^2}{b^2} + \frac{z^2}{c^2} = 1.$$

Its traces in the coordinate planes are ellipses (or circles). We have already seen a special case of this, in which $a = b = c$. In that case, we have a sphere. There are two other special cases. One is the *prolate spheroid.* Here, two of the denominators are equal and both are less than the third. It has the shape of a football and may be generated by rotating an ellipse about its major axis. The other case is the *oblate spheroid,* in which two of the denominators are equal and both greater than the third. It has the shape of a doorknob and may be generated by rotating an ellipse about its minor axis.

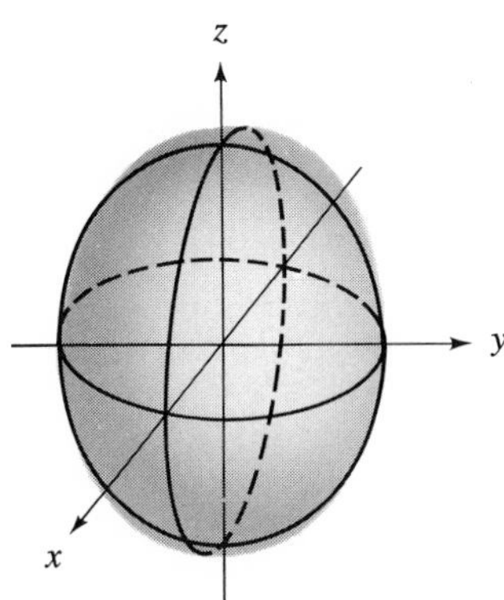

Figure 20.10

The *hyperboloid of one sheet* (see Figure 20.11) is represented by an equation of the form

$$\frac{x^2}{a^2} + \frac{y^2}{b^2} - \frac{z^2}{c^2} = 1.$$

Its traces in the xz plane and yz plane are hyperbolas; in the xy plane, it is an ellipse. If $a = b$, it may be generated by rotating a hyperbola about its conjugate axis.

The *hyperboloid of two sheets* (see Figure 20.12) is represented by an equation of the form

$$\frac{x^2}{a^2} - \frac{y^2}{b^2} - \frac{z^2}{c^2} = 1.$$

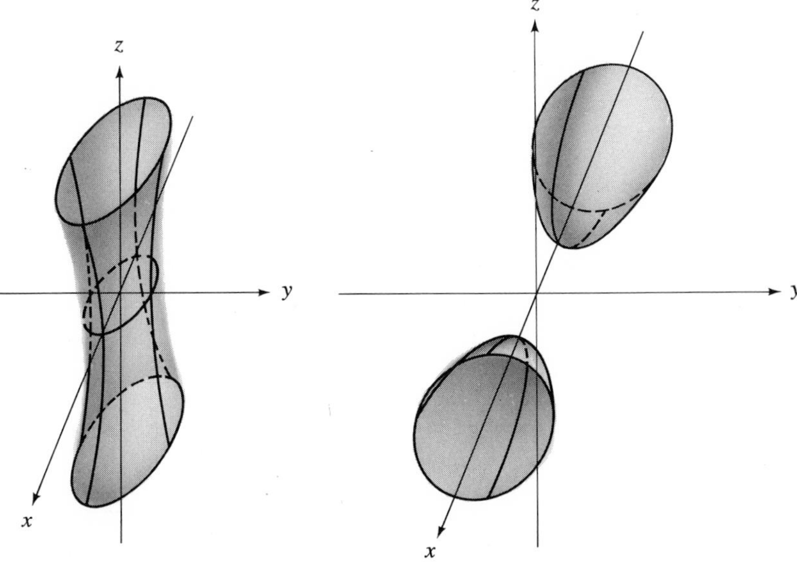

Figure 20.11 *Figure 20.12*

Its traces in the xy plane and xz plane are hyperbolas. It has no trace in the yz plane; however, if $|x| > a$, its intersection with a plane parallel to the yz plane is an ellipse. If $b = c$, it may be generated by rotating a hyperbola about its transverse axis.

The *elliptic paraboloid* (see Figure 20.13) is represented by an equation of the form

$$\frac{x^2}{a^2} + \frac{y^2}{b^2} = \frac{z}{c}.$$

Its traces in the xz plane and yz plane are parabolas. Its trace in the xy plane is a single point. If $c > 0$, then its intersection with a plane parallel to and above the xy plane is an ellipse; below the xy plane there is no intersection. This situation is reversed if $c < 0$. In Figure 20.13 $c > 0$. If $a = b$, the elliptic paraboloid is generated by rotating a parabola about its axis.

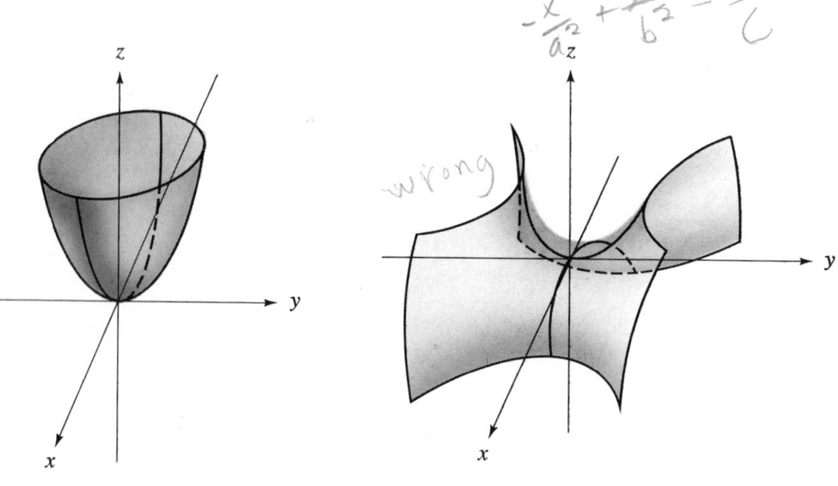

Figure 20.13 *Figure 20.14*

The *hyperbolic paraboloid* (see Figure 20.14) is represented by an equation of the form

$$\frac{x^2}{a^2} - \frac{y^2}{b^2} = \frac{z}{c}.$$

Its traces in the xz plane and yz plane are parabolas, one opening upward and the other down. Its trace in the xy plane is a pair of lines intersecting at the origin (a degenerate hyperbola). Its intersection with a plane parallel to the xy plane is a hyperbola. If $c > 0$, those hyperbolas above the xy plane have the transverse axis parallel to the x axis, while those below have it parallel to the y axis. If $c < 0$, this situation is reversed. In Figure 20.14, $c < 0$.

The *elliptic cone* (see Figure 20.15) is represented by an equation of the form

$$\frac{x^2}{a^2} + \frac{y^2}{b^2} - \frac{z^2}{c^2} = 0.$$

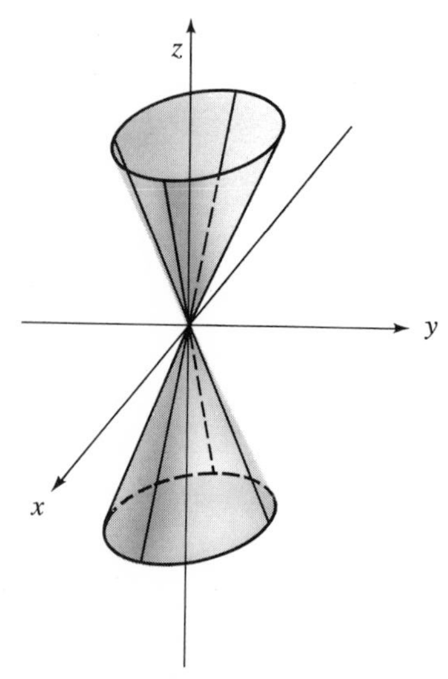

Figure 20.15

Its trace in the xz plane is a pair of lines intersecting at the origin. Its trace in the yz plane is also a pair of lines intersecting at the origin. Its trace in the xy plane is a single point at the origin. Its intersection with a plane parallel to the xy plane is an ellipse. If $a = b$, it is a circular cone.

Example 1

Describe and sketch

$$9x^2 + 9y^2 - 4z^2 = 36.$$

Dividing by 36, we have a hyperboloid of one sheet in the standard form:

$$\frac{x^2}{4} + \frac{y^2}{4} - \frac{z^2}{9} = 1.$$

Since the denominators of the x^2 and y^2 terms are equal, the trace in the xy plane, as well as in any plane parallel to it, is a circle. The surface is given in Figure 20.16.

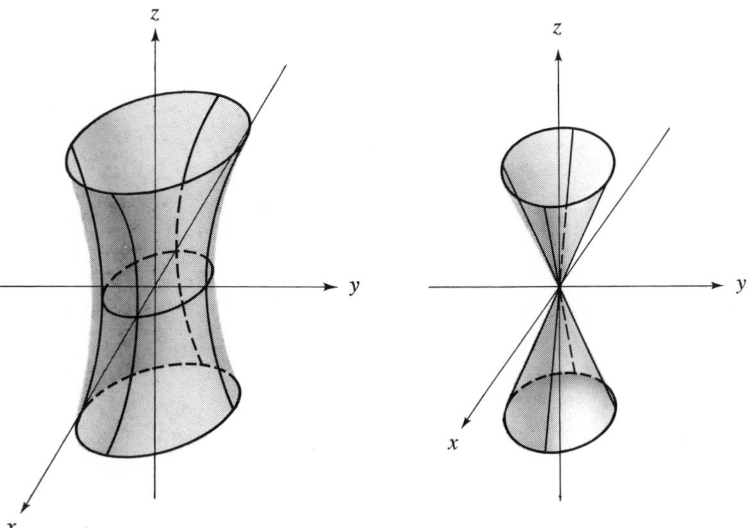

Figure 20.16 *Figure 20.17*

Example 2

Describe and sketch

$$9x^2 + 9y^2 - 4z^2 = 0.$$

Again dividing by 36, we have

$$\frac{x^2}{4} + \frac{y^2}{4} - \frac{z^2}{9} = 0,$$

which is a circular cone with its axis the z axis. The cone is given in Figure 20.17.

If the given equation does not fit any of these forms, determine its traces in the coordinate planes and planes parallel to them in order to have some idea of the shape.

Problems

Describe and sketch the following.

1. $36x^2 + 9y^2 + 4z^2 = 36.$
2. $4x^2 + 9y^2 + 9z^2 = 36.$
3. $x - y^2 - z^2 = 0.$
4. $4x^2 + 4y^2 - z^2 + 16 = 0.$
5. $x^2 - y^2 + z^2 = 0.$
6. $x^2 - y - z^2 = 0.$
7. $x^2 + 2y + z^2 = 0.$
8. $x^2 - 4y^2 - 4z^2 = 0.$
9. $25x^2 - 4y^2 + 25z^2 + 100 = 0.$
10. $16x^2 - 9y^2 - 9z^2 + 144 = 0.$
11. $x^2 + 4y - z^2 = 0.$
12. $25x^2 + 16y^2 + 25z^2 = 400.$
13. $36x^2 - 9y^2 + 16z^2 + 144 = 0.$
14. $16x^2 - 9y + 16z^2 = 0.$
15. $16x^2 - 9y^2 - 9z^2 = 0.$
16. $36x^2 - 4y - 9z^2 = 0.$
17. $9x^2 - 36y^2 + 16z^2 + 144 = 0.$
18. $x^2 + y^2 - 4z = 0.$
19. $x^2 + y^2 - 4z^2 = 4.$
20. $x^2 + y^2 + 4z^2 = 4.$
21. $x^2 - y^2 - 9z = 0.$
22. $9x^2 - y^2 - z^2 = 9.$
23. $9x^2 - y^2 - z^2 = 0.$
24. $x^2 + y^2 + 2z = 0.$
25. $25x^2 - 4y^2 + 25z^2 = 100.$

20.9

Cylindrical and Spherical Coordinates

Here we look at two other coordinate systems in space that are useful. The first of these is called a *cylindrical coordinate system.* In this system, a point P with projection Q on the xy plane (see Figure 20.18) is represented by (r, θ, z), where (r, θ) is a polar representation of Q and z is the (directed) distance of P from the xy plane. The relations between rectangular and cylindrical coordinates are the same as the relations between rectangular and polar coordinates; that is,

$$x = r\cos\theta, \qquad y = r\sin\theta, \qquad z = z$$

or

$$r = \pm\sqrt{x^2 + y^2}, \qquad \theta = \arctan\frac{y}{x}, \qquad z = z.$$

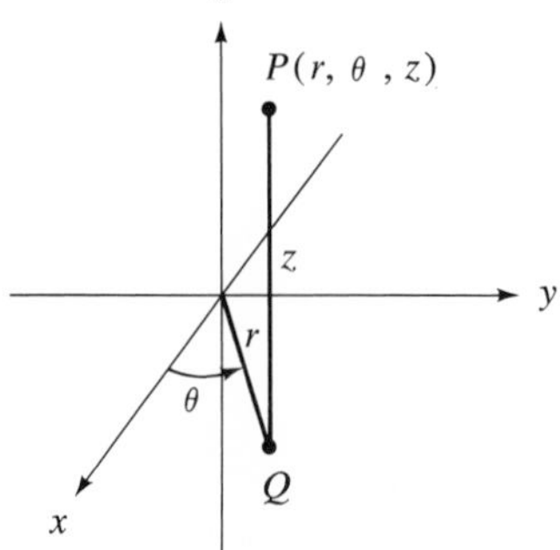

Figure 20.18

Example 1

Express (4, 30°, −2) in rectangular coordinates.

$$x = r\cos\theta = 4\cos 30° = 4\cdot\frac{\sqrt{3}}{2} = 2\sqrt{3},$$

$$y = r\sin\theta = 4\sin 30° = 4\cdot\frac{1}{2} = 2,$$

$$z = -2.$$

Thus, the point is $(2\sqrt{3}, 2, -2)$.

Example 2

Express (2, 2, 4) in cylindrical coordinates.

$$r = \pm\sqrt{x^2+y^2} = \pm\sqrt{8} = \pm 2\sqrt{2},$$

$$\theta = \arctan\frac{y}{x} = \arctan 1 = 45° + 180°\cdot n,$$

$$z = 4.$$

There are two choices for r and infinitely many for θ. The choices we make are not independent of each other—the choice of one of them puts restrictions on the other. If we choose θ to be 45° (or any first-quadrant angle), we must choose $r = 2\sqrt{2}$; if we choose θ to be 225° (or any third-quadrant angle), we must choose $r = -2\sqrt{2}$. Thus, two possible representations are

$$(2\sqrt{2}, 45°, 4) = (-2\sqrt{2}, 225°, 4).$$

Example 3

Express $x + y + z = 1$ in cylindrical coordinates.

Substituting $x = r\cos\theta$ and $y = r\sin\theta$, we have

$$r\cos\theta + r\sin\theta + z = 1.$$

Example 4

Express $r = z\sin\theta$ in rectangular coordinates.

Multiplying both sides by r, we have

$$r^2 = z\cdot r\sin\theta, \qquad x^2 + y^2 = yz.$$

Another useful system for representing points in space uses *spherical coordinates.* In this system, a point is represented by (ρ, θ, φ), where ρ is the distance of the point from the origin, θ has the same meaning as in cylindrical coordinates, and φ is the angle between the positive end of the z axis and the segment joining the origin to the given point (see Figure 20.19). Since φ is undirected, it is never negative. Furthermore

$$0^\circ \le \varphi \le 180^\circ.$$

Likewise, we restrict ρ: $\rho \ge 0$.

From Figure 20.19, we see that $OQ = \rho \sin \varphi$. Thus

$$x = OQ \cos \theta = \rho \sin \varphi \cos \theta,$$
$$y = OQ \sin \theta = \rho \sin \varphi \sin \theta,$$
$$z = \rho \cos \varphi.$$

We can easily see from these that

$$\rho^2 = x^2 + y^2 + z^2.$$

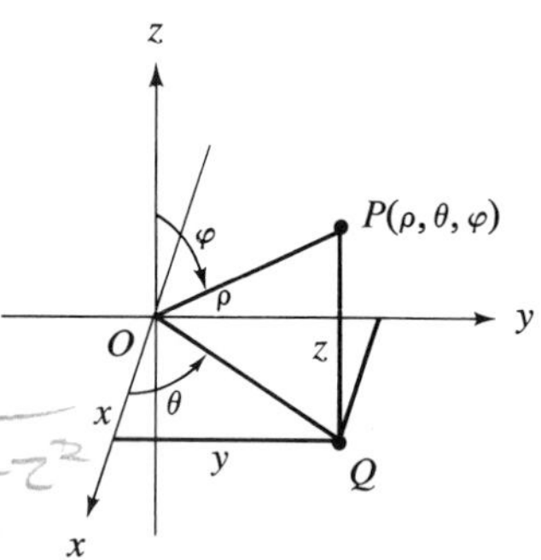

Figure 20.19

Example 5

Express (2, 30°, 120°) in rectangular coordinates.

$$\begin{aligned} x &= \rho \sin \varphi \cos \theta \\ &= 2 \sin 120^\circ \cdot \cos 30^\circ \\ &= 2 \cdot \frac{\sqrt{3}}{2} \cdot \frac{\sqrt{3}}{2} = \frac{3}{2}, \\ y &= \rho \sin \varphi \sin \theta \\ &= 2 \sin 120^\circ \sin 30^\circ \\ &= 2 \cdot \frac{\sqrt{3}}{2} \cdot \frac{1}{2} = \frac{\sqrt{3}}{2}, \\ z &= \rho \cos \varphi \\ &= 2 \cos 120^\circ \\ &= 2\left(-\frac{1}{2}\right) = -1. \end{aligned}$$

Thus the point is $(3/2, \sqrt{3}/2, -1)$.

Example 6

Express $(\sqrt{3}, \sqrt{3}, -\sqrt{2})$ in spherical coordinates.

$$\begin{aligned} \rho^2 &= x^2 + y^2 + z^2 \\ &= 3 + 3 + 2 = 8, \\ \rho &= 2\sqrt{2}; \\ z &= \rho \cos \varphi, \\ -\sqrt{2} &= 2\sqrt{2} \cos \varphi, \\ \cos \varphi &= -\frac{1}{2}, \\ \varphi &= 120^\circ; \end{aligned}$$

$$x = \rho \sin \varphi \cos \theta,$$

$$\sqrt{3} = 2\sqrt{2} \cdot \frac{\sqrt{3}}{2} \cos \theta,$$

$$\cos \theta = \frac{1}{\sqrt{2}},$$

$$\theta = 45°.$$

The point is $(2\sqrt{2}, 45°, 120°)$.

Example 7

Express $x^2 + y^2 - z^2 = 0$ in spherical coordinates.

$$\begin{aligned}
\rho^2 \sin^2 \varphi \cos^2 \theta + \rho^2 \sin^2 \varphi \sin^2 \theta - \rho^2 \cos^2 \varphi &= 0, \\
\rho^2[\sin^2 \varphi(\cos^2 \theta + \sin^2 \theta) - \cos^2 \varphi] &= 0, \\
\rho^2(\sin^2 \varphi - \cos^2 \varphi) &= 0, \\
\sin^2 \varphi - \cos^2 \varphi = 0 \quad &\text{or} \quad \rho = 0; \\
\cos 2\varphi &= 0, \\
2\varphi &= 90°, 270° \\
\varphi &= 45°, 135°.
\end{aligned}$$

Thus, we have $\varphi = 45°$, $\varphi = 135°$, and $\rho = 0$. $\varphi = 45°$ gives the top half of the cone, $\varphi = 135°$ gives the bottom half, and $\rho = 0$ gives a single point—the origin. Since $\rho = 0$ is included in both of the others, we may drop it. The final result is

$$\varphi = 45° \quad \text{and} \quad \varphi = 135°.$$

Example 8

Express $\rho^2 \sin \varphi \cos \varphi \cos \theta = 1$ in rectangular coordinates.

$$\begin{aligned}
\rho^2 \sin \varphi \cos \varphi \cos \theta &= 1, \\
(\rho \sin \varphi \cos \theta)(\rho \cos \varphi) &= 1, \\
xz &= 1.
\end{aligned}$$

Problems

1. The following points are given in cylindrical coordinates. Express them in rectangular coordinates.

   a. $(2, 45°, 1)$, b. $(3, 2\pi/3, -2)$,
   c. $(1, 0°, 2)$, d. $(0, \pi/4, -3)$.

2. The following points are given in rectangular coordinates. Express them in cylindrical coordinates.

   a. $(1, 1, 3)$, b. $(0, 2, -2)$,
   c. $(-1, \sqrt{3}, 4)$, d. $(-2\sqrt{3}, -2, 3)$.

3. The following points are given in spherical coordinates. Express them in rectangular coordinates.

   a. $(3, 45°, 30°)$, b. $(1, \pi/6, 0)$,
   c. $(1, 90°, 45°)$, d. $(2, 5\pi/6, 3\pi/4)$.

4. The following points are given in rectangular coordinates. Express them in spherical coordinates.

   a. $(2, 2, 0)$, b. $(2, 1, -2)$,
   c. $(2, -\sqrt{3}, 4)$, d. $(1, 1, \sqrt{2})$.

5. The following points are given in cylindrical coordinates. Express them in spherical coordinates.

   a. $(3, 30°, 4)$, b. $(2, \pi/4, -2)$,
   c. $(0, 45°, 3)$, d. $(2, \pi/2, -4)$.

6. The following points are given in spherical coordinates. Express them in cylindrical coordinates.

   a. $(4, 45°, 30°)$, b. $(2, 2\pi/3, \pi/2)$,
   c. $(2, 210°, 135°)$, d. $(3, \pi/6, 2\pi/3)$.

In Problems 7–14, express the given equations in cylindrical and spherical coordinates.

7. $x^2 + y^2 = 4$.
8. $x^2 + y^2 + z^2 = 4$.
9. $x^2 + y^2 = z$.
10. $x^2 - y^2 = z$.
11. $x^2 - y^2 - z^2 = 1$.
12. $x^2 - y^2 + z^2 = 1$.
13. $x^2 + y^2 - z^2 = 1$.
14. $4x^2 + 9y^2 + 9z^2 = 1$.

In Problems 15–22, express the given equations in rectangular coordinates.

15. $z = r^2 \sin 2\theta$.
16. $z = r^2 \cos 2\theta$.
17. $z = r^2$.
18. $z = 1 + \sin \theta$.
19. $\rho \sin \varphi \tan \varphi \sin 2\theta = 2$.
20. $\rho \sin \varphi = 1$.
21. $\rho = \sin \varphi \cos \theta$.
22. $\rho^2 \sin \varphi \cos \varphi = 1$.

Vectors in the Plane and in Space

21.1

Directed Line Segments and Vectors

Vectors, which have direction as well as magnitude, are very important in physics and engineering. Furthermore, their use can considerably simplify geometric problems, especially in solid analytic geometry. One reason vectors are so useful is the wide range of interpretations they may be given. Since we are interested mainly in the geometric applications, vectors will be introduced geometrically by means of directed line segments.

Suppose A and B are points (not necessarily different) in space. The directed line segment from A to B is represented by $\overrightarrow{AB}$. B is called the *head* and A the *tail* of this segment. Two directed line segments $\overrightarrow{AB}$ and $\overrightarrow{CD}$ are *equivalent*, $\overrightarrow{AB} \equiv \overrightarrow{CD}$, (1) if both are of length zero or (2), if both have the same positive length, both lie on the same or parallel lines, and both are directed in the same way (see Figure 21.1 in which $\overrightarrow{AB} \equiv \overrightarrow{CD}$ and $\overrightarrow{EF} \equiv \overrightarrow{GH}$). With this information, you can easily prove the following theorem.

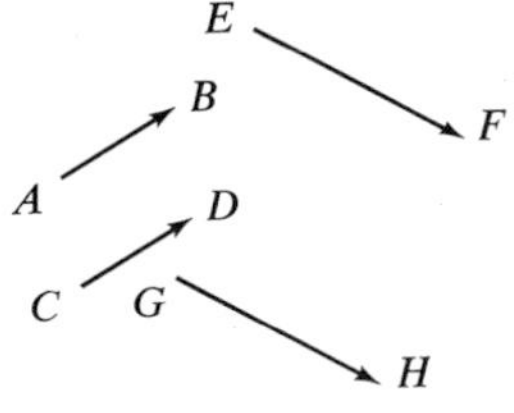

Figure 21.1

Theorem 21.1

(a) $\overrightarrow{AB} \equiv \overrightarrow{AB}$ *for any directed line segment* $\overrightarrow{AB}$;

(b) *if* $\overrightarrow{AB} \equiv \overrightarrow{CD}$, *then* $\overrightarrow{CD} \equiv \overrightarrow{AB}$;

(c) *if* $\overrightarrow{AB} \equiv \overrightarrow{CD}$ *and* $\overrightarrow{CD} \equiv \overrightarrow{EF}$, *then* $\overrightarrow{AB} \equiv \overrightarrow{EF}$.

Now let us choose an arbitrary directed line segment $\overrightarrow{AB}$. Let M_1 be the set of all directed line segments equivalent to $\overrightarrow{AB}$. Now let us choose another segment $\overrightarrow{CD}$ not in M_1 and let M_2 be the set of all directed line segments equivalent to $\overrightarrow{CD}$. Proceeding in this way, we can partition the set of all directed line segments into a collection of subsets no two of which have any element in common. These subsets are what we call *vectors*. Thus, a vector is a certain set of mutually equivalent directed line segments.

Definition

The set of all directed line segments equivalent to a given directed line segment is a ***vector*** $\mathbf{v}$. *Any member of that set is a* ***representative*** *of* $\mathbf{v}$. *The set of all directed line segments equivalent to one of length zero is called the* ***zero vector***, $\mathbf{0}$.

It might be noted that a vector has magnitude (length) and direction, but not position. Any representative of a given vector has not only magnitude and direction but also position. Let us now consider how vectors may be combined.

Definition

Suppose $\mathbf{u}$ *and* $\mathbf{v}$ *are vectors. Let* $\overrightarrow{AB}$ *be a representative of* $\mathbf{u}$. *Let* $\overrightarrow{BC}$ *be that representative of* $\mathbf{v}$ *with tail at B. The* ***sum*** $\mathbf{u} + \mathbf{v}$ *of* $\mathbf{u}$ *and* $\mathbf{v}$ *is the vector* $\mathbf{w}$, *having* $\overrightarrow{AC}$ *as a representative.*

Since the sum of two vectors is given in terms of representatives of those vectors, the question remains, "Is the sum well defined—that is, is it independent of the representatives used?" Theorem 21.1 and the congruence of triangles easily shows that the sum is well defined.

It might be noted that this definition is equivalent to the well-known parallelogram law for the addition of vectors (see Figure 21.2). Let us observe that the figures given here represent vectors graphically by means of representative directed line segments. In Figure 21.2 the vector $\mathbf{u}$ is represented by two equivalent directed line segments, both of which are labeled $\mathbf{u}$.

The definition of addition of vectors can easily be extended to subtraction.

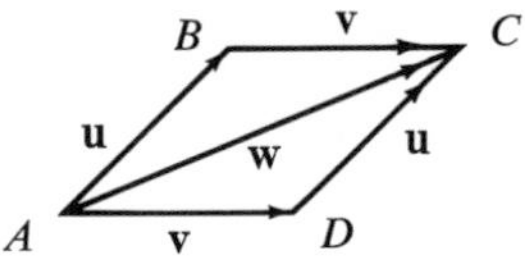

Figure 21.2

Definition

If $\mathbf{u}$ *and* $\mathbf{v}$ *are vectors, then* $\mathbf{u} - \mathbf{v}$ *is the vector* $\mathbf{w}$ *such that* $\mathbf{u} = \mathbf{v} + \mathbf{w}$.

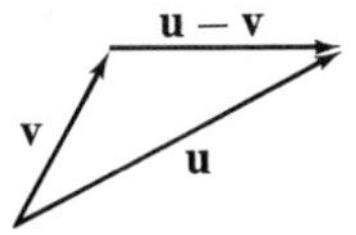

Figure 21.3

This is represented graphically in Figure 21.3.

We shall use the word *scalar* for number. A scalar has magnitude but not direction. Thus

Definition

If $\mathbf{v}$ *is a vector, then* $|\mathbf{v}|$ *is the length of any representative of* $\mathbf{v}$. *It is called the* ***absolute value*** *or* ***length*** *of* $\mathbf{v}$.

Note that the absolute value of a vector is not a vector, but a scalar.

Definition

If k *is a scalar and* $\mathbf{v}$ *a vector, then* $k\mathbf{v}$ *is a vector whose length is* $|k| \cdot |\mathbf{v}|$ *and whose direction is the same as or opposite to the direction of* $\mathbf{v}$, *according to whether* k *is positive or negative. It is called a scalar multiple of* $\mathbf{v}$.

Figure 21.4 gives several examples of scalar multiples of the vector $\mathbf{v}$.

Let us take note of the fact that we are not adding and multiplying ordinary numbers; thus it is not obvious that the rules of ordinary arithmetic hold—they must be proved from the given definitions.

Theorem 21.2

The following properties hold for arbitrary vectors $\mathbf{u}$, $\mathbf{v}$, *and* $\mathbf{w}$ *and arbitrary scalars* a *and* b.

(a) $\mathbf{u} + \mathbf{v} = \mathbf{v} + \mathbf{u}$.
(b) $\mathbf{u} + (\mathbf{v} + \mathbf{w}) = (\mathbf{u} + \mathbf{v}) + \mathbf{w}$.
(c) $(ab)\mathbf{v} = a(b\mathbf{v})$.
(d) $(a + b)\mathbf{v} = a\mathbf{v} + b\mathbf{v}$.
(e) $\mathbf{v} + \mathbf{0} = \mathbf{v}$.
(f) $0\mathbf{v} = \mathbf{0}$.
(g) $a\mathbf{0} = \mathbf{0}$.
(h) $|a\mathbf{v}| = |a| \cdot |\mathbf{v}|$.
(i) $|\mathbf{u} + \mathbf{v}| \leq |\mathbf{u}| + |\mathbf{v}|$.
(j) $a(\mathbf{u} + \mathbf{v}) = a\mathbf{u} + a\mathbf{v}$.

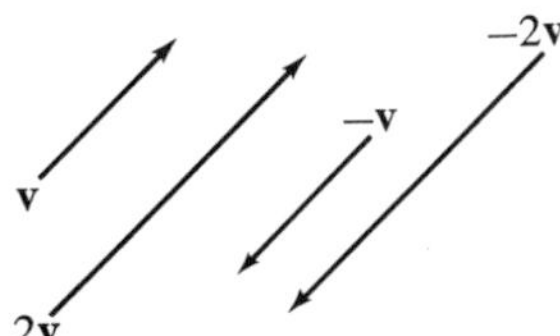

Figure 21.4

If we form the scalar multiple of the vector $\mathbf{v}$ and the scalar $1/|\mathbf{v}|$, the result is easily seen to be the unit vector (that is, the vector of length 1) in the direction of $\mathbf{v}$. It is usually written

$$\frac{\mathbf{v}}{|\mathbf{v}|}.$$

Of special interest are the unit vectors along the axes.

Definition

If $O = (0, 0, 0)$, $X = (1, 0, 0)$, $Y = (0, 1, 0)$ and $Z = (0, 0, 1)$, then the vectors represented by $\overrightarrow{OX}$, $\overrightarrow{OY}$, and $\overrightarrow{OZ}$ are denoted by $\mathbf{i}$, $\mathbf{j}$, and $\mathbf{k}$, respectively.

Theorem 21.3

Every vector in the xy plane can be written in the form

$$a\mathbf{i} + b\mathbf{j}.$$

Every vector in space can be written in the form

$$a\mathbf{i} + b\mathbf{j} + c\mathbf{k}.$$

The numbers a and b (and c) are called the ***components*** *of the vector.*

Proof

Let us consider the proof for the two-dimensional case only. Suppose we have a vector $\mathbf{v}$ in the plane. Let us consider the representative of $\mathbf{v}$ with its tail at the origin O (see Figure 21.5). The head is at P: (a, b). Let us project P onto both axes, giving points A:$(a, 0)$ and B: $(0, b)$. Since $\overrightarrow{OA}$ represents a vector of length $|a|$ that is either in the direction of $\mathbf{i}$ or in the opposite direction, depending upon whether a is positive or negative, it represents $a\mathbf{i}$. Similarly $\overrightarrow{OB}$ represents $b\mathbf{j}$. It is clear that $\mathbf{v} = a\mathbf{i} + b\mathbf{j}$.

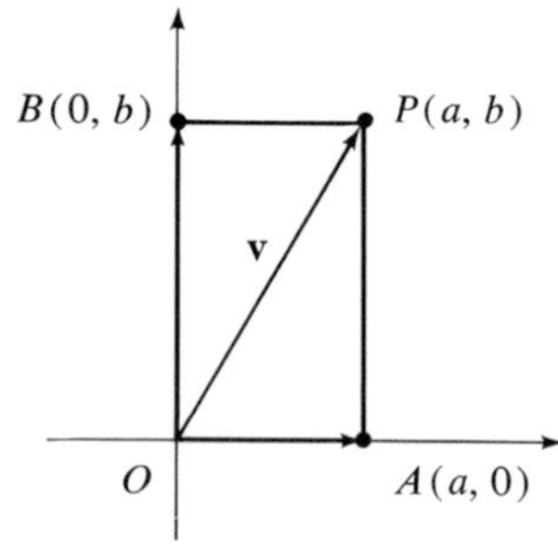

Figure 21.5

Theorem 21.4

If $\overrightarrow{AB}$, where $A = (x_1, y_1)$ and $B = (x_2, y_2)$, represents a vector $\mathbf{v}$ in the xy plane, then $\mathbf{v} = (x_2 - x_1)\mathbf{i} + (y_2 - y_1)\mathbf{j}$; if $\overrightarrow{AB}$, where $A = (x_1, y_1, z_1)$ and $B = (x_2, y_2, z_2)$, represents a vector $\mathbf{v}$ in space, then $\mathbf{v} = (x_2 - x_1)\mathbf{i} + (y_2 - y_1)\mathbf{j} + (z_2 - z_1)\mathbf{k}$.

Proof

Again let us prove only the two-dimensional case. Let C be the point (x_2, y_1) (see Figure 21.6). Then

$$\mathbf{v} = \mathbf{u} + \mathbf{w},$$

where $\mathbf{u}$ is represented by $\overrightarrow{AC}$ and $\mathbf{w}$ by $\overrightarrow{CB}$. Since $\mathbf{u}$ is of length $|x_2 - x_1|$ and is in either the same or the opposite direction as **i**, depending upon whether $x_2 - x_1$ is positive or negative, it follows that $\mathbf{u} = (x_2 - x_1)\mathbf{i}$. Similarly $\mathbf{w} = (y_2 - y_1)\mathbf{j}$. Thus

$$\mathbf{v} = (x_2 - x_1)\mathbf{i} + (y_2 - y_1)\mathbf{j}.$$

The proof of the three-dimensional case is similar.

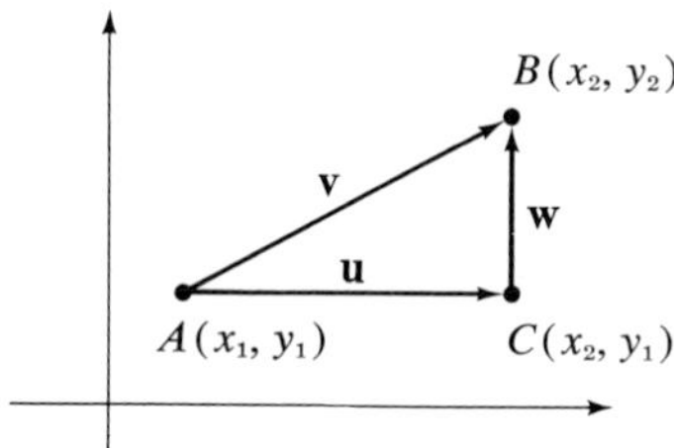

Figure 21.6

Example 1

Find the vector in the plane represented by the directed line segment from $(3, -2)$ to $(-1, 5)$.

$$\begin{aligned}\mathbf{v} &= (x_2 - x_1)\mathbf{i} + (y_2 - y_1)\mathbf{j}\\ &= (-1 - 3)\mathbf{i} + (5 + 2)\mathbf{j}\\ &= -4\mathbf{i} + 7\mathbf{j}.\end{aligned}$$

The coefficients of **i**, **j**, and **k** in Theorem 21.4 are a set of direction numbers for the line through (x_1, y_1, z_1) and (x_2, y_2, z_2), as the following theorem states.

Theorem 21.5

A vector directed along a line with direction numbers $\{a, b, c\}$ *is* $\mathbf{v} = a\mathbf{i} + b\mathbf{j} + c\mathbf{k}$.

A vector "directed along a line" is one having representatives on or parallel to that line. This theorem gives only one of many vectors along the given line, and there is no indication which of the two directions on the line is represented by the resulting vector. The proof of this theorem is left to the student.

Example 2

Find a vector directed along the line

$$\frac{x-2}{1} = \frac{y+3}{4} = \frac{z-1}{2}.$$

Since a set of direction numbers for this line is $\{1, 4, 2\}$, such a vector is $\mathbf{v} = \mathbf{i} + 4\mathbf{j} + 2\mathbf{k}$.

Theorem 21.6

$$(a_1\mathbf{i} + b_1\mathbf{j} + c_1\mathbf{k}) + (a_2\mathbf{i} + b_2\mathbf{j} + c_2\mathbf{k}) = (a_1 + a_2)\mathbf{i} + (b_1 + b_2)\mathbf{j} + (c_1 + c_2)\mathbf{k};$$
$$(a_1\mathbf{i} + b_1\mathbf{j} + c_1\mathbf{k}) - (a_2\mathbf{i} + b_2\mathbf{j} + c_2\mathbf{k}) = (a_1 - a_2)\mathbf{i} + (b_1 - b_2)\mathbf{j} + (c_1 - c_2)\mathbf{k};$$
$$d(a\mathbf{i} + b\mathbf{j} + c\mathbf{k}) = da\mathbf{i} + db\mathbf{j} + dc\mathbf{k};$$
$$|a\mathbf{i} + b\mathbf{j}| = \sqrt{a^2 + b^2};$$
$$|a\mathbf{i} + b\mathbf{j} + c\mathbf{k}| = \sqrt{a^2 + b^2 + c^2}.$$

The proof is left to the student.

Example 3

If $\mathbf{u} = 3\mathbf{i} - \mathbf{j} + 2\mathbf{k}$ and $\mathbf{v} = 4\mathbf{i} + \mathbf{j} - \mathbf{k}$, find $\mathbf{u} + \mathbf{v}$, $\mathbf{u} - \mathbf{v}$, $3\mathbf{u}$ and $|\mathbf{u}|$.

$$\mathbf{u} + \mathbf{v} = (3 + 4)\mathbf{i} + (-1 + 1)\mathbf{j} + (2 - 1)\mathbf{k} = 7\mathbf{i} + \mathbf{k},$$
$$\mathbf{u} - \mathbf{v} = (3 - 4)\mathbf{i} + (-1 - 1)\mathbf{j} + (2 + 1)\mathbf{k} = \mathbf{i} - 2\mathbf{j} + 3\mathbf{k},$$
$$3\mathbf{u} = 3 \cdot 3\mathbf{i} + 3(-1)\mathbf{j} + 3 \cdot 2\mathbf{k} = 9\mathbf{i} - 3\mathbf{j} + 6\mathbf{k},$$
$$|\mathbf{u}| = \sqrt{3^2 + (-1)^2 + 2^2} = \sqrt{14}.$$

Problems

In Problems 1–8, give in component form the vector $\mathbf{v}$ that is represented by $\overrightarrow{AB}$.

1. $A = (4, 3)$, $B = (-2, 1)$.
2. $A = (2, 5)$, $B = (0, 1)$.
3. $A = (-3, 2)$, $B = (4, 3)$.
4. $A = (-2, 4)$, $B = (0, 4)$.
5. $A = (1, -2, 3)$, $B = (0, 3, -1)$.
6. $A = (0, 2, 5)$, $B = (1, 4, -2)$.
7. $A = (-3, 2, 4)$, $B = (1, -1, 2)$.
8. $A = (4, -3, 1)$, $B = (0, 5, 3)$.

In Problems 9–16, give the unit vector in the direction of $\mathbf{v}$.

9. $\mathbf{v} = 3\mathbf{i} - \mathbf{j}$.
10. $\mathbf{v} = 2\mathbf{i} + 4\mathbf{j}$.
11. $\mathbf{v} = -\mathbf{i} + 2\mathbf{j}$.
12. $\mathbf{v} = 3\mathbf{j}$.
13. $\mathbf{v} = \mathbf{i} + 2\mathbf{j} - \mathbf{k}$.
14. $\mathbf{v} = 3\mathbf{i} - \mathbf{j} + 2\mathbf{k}$.
15. $\mathbf{v} = -\mathbf{i} + 2\mathbf{j} - 3\mathbf{k}$.
16. $\mathbf{v} = 4\mathbf{k}$.

In Problems 17–28, find the end points of the representative $\overrightarrow{AB}$ of $\mathbf{v}$ from the given information.

17. $\mathbf{v} = 3\mathbf{i} - \mathbf{j}$, $A = (1, 4)$.
18. $\mathbf{v} = 2\mathbf{i} + 3\mathbf{j}$, $A = (-1, 3)$.
19. $\mathbf{v} = -\mathbf{i} + 2\mathbf{j}$, $B = (4, 2)$.
20. $\mathbf{v} = 2\mathbf{i} - 4\mathbf{j}$, $B = (0, 3)$.
21. $\mathbf{v} = 3\mathbf{i} + 5\mathbf{j}$, $(4, 1)$ is the midpoint of AB.
22. $\mathbf{v} = 4\mathbf{i} - 6\mathbf{j}$, $(2, 5)$ is the midpoint of AB.
23. $\mathbf{v} = \mathbf{i} - \mathbf{j} + 2\mathbf{k}$, $A = (5, 1, 2)$.
24. $\mathbf{v} = 2\mathbf{i} + \mathbf{j} - 3\mathbf{k}$, $A = (-2, 0, 3)$.
25. $\mathbf{v} = 3\mathbf{i} - \mathbf{j} + 2\mathbf{k}$, $B = (4, 2, -1)$.
26. $\mathbf{v} = 2\mathbf{i} + 2\mathbf{j} - \mathbf{k}$, $B = (1, 1, 1)$.

27. $\mathbf{v} = \mathbf{i} + \mathbf{j} + \mathbf{k}$, (2, 0, 3) is the midpoint of AB.
28. $\mathbf{v} = 2\mathbf{i} - \mathbf{j} + 3\mathbf{k}$, (0, −2, 1) is the midpoint of AB.
29. If $\mathbf{u} = 3\mathbf{i} - \mathbf{j}$ and $\mathbf{v} = \mathbf{i} + 2\mathbf{j}$, find $\mathbf{u} + \mathbf{v}$. Draw a diagram showing $\mathbf{u}$, $\mathbf{v}$ and $\mathbf{u} + \mathbf{v}$.
30. If $\mathbf{u} = 2\mathbf{i} + 3\mathbf{j}$ and $\mathbf{v} = 2\mathbf{i} - \mathbf{j}$, find $\mathbf{u} + \mathbf{v}$. Draw a diagram showing $\mathbf{u}$, $\mathbf{v}$ and $\mathbf{u} + \mathbf{v}$.
31. If $\mathbf{u} = \mathbf{i} - \mathbf{j}$ and $\mathbf{v} = 2\mathbf{i} + 2\mathbf{j}$, find $\mathbf{u} - \mathbf{v}$. Draw a diagram showing $\mathbf{u}$, $\mathbf{v}$ and $\mathbf{u} - \mathbf{v}$.
32. If $\mathbf{u} = 3\mathbf{i} + \mathbf{j}$ and $\mathbf{v} = 2\mathbf{i}$, find $\mathbf{u} - \mathbf{v}$. Draw a diagram showing $\mathbf{u}$, $\mathbf{v}$ and $\mathbf{u} - \mathbf{v}$.
33. If $\mathbf{u} = \mathbf{i} - 3\mathbf{j}$ and $\mathbf{v} = 2\mathbf{i} + 4\mathbf{j}$, find $2\mathbf{u} + \mathbf{v}$. Draw a diagram showing $\mathbf{u}$, $\mathbf{v}$ and $2\mathbf{u} + \mathbf{v}$.
34. If $\mathbf{u} = 4\mathbf{i} + \mathbf{j} - \mathbf{k}$ and $\mathbf{v} = \mathbf{i} + 2\mathbf{j} + \mathbf{k}$, find $\mathbf{u} + \mathbf{v}$ and $\mathbf{u} - \mathbf{v}$.
35. If $\mathbf{u} = 3\mathbf{i} - \mathbf{j} + 2\mathbf{k}$ and $\mathbf{v} = 2\mathbf{i} - 2\mathbf{j} + \mathbf{k}$, find $\mathbf{u} + \mathbf{v}$ and $\mathbf{u} - \mathbf{v}$.
36. If $\mathbf{u} = \mathbf{i} - \mathbf{j} + 3\mathbf{k}$ and $\mathbf{v} = 2\mathbf{i} + \mathbf{j} - 2\mathbf{k}$, find $2\mathbf{u} - \mathbf{v}$.
37. If $\mathbf{u} = 2\mathbf{i} - 3\mathbf{j} + \mathbf{k}$ and $\mathbf{v} = 4\mathbf{i} - \mathbf{j} - 2\mathbf{k}$, find $3\mathbf{u} + 2\mathbf{v}$.
38. Prove Theorem 21.1.
39. Prove Theorem 21.2.
40. Prove the three-dimensional case of Theorem 21.3.
41. Prove the three-dimensional case of Theorem 21.4.
42. Prove Theorem 21.5.
43. Prove Theorem 21.6.
44. Show that the sum of two vectors is well defined (see the paragraph following the definition of the sum).

21.2

The Dot Product

In the previous section we considered the sums and differences of pairs of vectors, but the only product we considered was the scalar multiple—the product of a scalar and a vector. We did not consider the product of two vectors. There are two different products for a pair of vectors, the dot product and the cross product. We shall consider the dot product in this section and the cross product in the next. But first, let us consider the angle between two vectors.

Definition

The ***angle between two nonzero vectors*** $\mathbf{u}$ *and* $\mathbf{v}$ *is the smallest non-negative angle between the positive ends of representatives of* $\mathbf{u}$ *and* $\mathbf{v}$ *having their tails at the origin.*

This is basically the same as the angle between two directed lines given on page 521, and the similarity provides a relatively easy proof of the following theorem.

Theorem 21.7

If $\mathbf{u} = a_1\mathbf{i} + b_1\mathbf{j} + c_1\mathbf{k}$ *and* $\mathbf{v} = a_2\mathbf{i} + b_2\mathbf{j} + c_2\mathbf{k}$ ($\mathbf{u} \neq \mathbf{0}$ *and* $\mathbf{v} \neq \mathbf{0}$) *and if* θ *is the angle between them, then*

$$\cos\theta = \frac{a_1a_2 + b_1b_2 + c_1c_2}{|\mathbf{u}|\,|\mathbf{v}|}.$$

Proof

A set of direction numbers for a line determined by **u** is $\{a_1, b_1, c_1\}$. Since

$$|\mathbf{u}| = \sqrt{a_1^2 + b_1^2 + c_1^2},$$

the set of direction cosines for the directed line determined by **u** is $\{a_1/|\mathbf{u}|, b_1/|\mathbf{u}|, c_1/|\mathbf{u}|\}$. Similarly, the set of direction cosines for the directed line determined by **v** is $\{a_2/|\mathbf{v}|, b_2/|\mathbf{v}|, c_2/|\mathbf{v}|\}$. Thus, by Theorem 20.12,

$$\begin{aligned}\cos\theta &= l_1 l_2 + m_1 m_2 + n_1 n_2 \\ &= \frac{a_1}{|\mathbf{u}|}\cdot\frac{a_2}{|\mathbf{v}|} + \frac{b_1}{|\mathbf{u}|}\cdot\frac{b_2}{|\mathbf{v}|} + \frac{c_1}{|\mathbf{u}|}\cdot\frac{c_2}{|\mathbf{v}|} \\ &= \frac{a_1 a_2 + b_1 b_2 + c_1 c_2}{|\mathbf{u}|\,|\mathbf{v}|}.\end{aligned}$$

Example 1

Find the cosine of the angle between $\mathbf{v} = 3\mathbf{i} - 2\mathbf{j} + 2\mathbf{k}$ and $\mathbf{u} = 4\mathbf{i} - \mathbf{k}$.

$$\begin{aligned}\cos\theta &= \frac{a_1 a_2 + b_1 b_2 + c_1 c_2}{|\mathbf{u}|\,|\mathbf{v}|} \\ &= \frac{3\cdot 4 - 2\cdot 0 + 2(-1)}{\sqrt{9+4+4}\,\sqrt{16+0+1}} \\ &= \frac{10}{17}.\end{aligned}$$

The dot product is closely related to $\cos\theta$.

Definition

If $\mathbf{u} = a_1\mathbf{i} + b_1\mathbf{j} + c_1\mathbf{k}$ *and* $\mathbf{v} = a_2\mathbf{i} + b_2\mathbf{j} + c_2\mathbf{k}$, *then the* ***dot product*** (***scalar product, inner product***) *of* **u** *and* **v** *is*

$$\mathbf{u}\cdot\mathbf{v} = a_1 a_2 + b_1 b_2 + c_1 c_2 .$$

Note that the dot product of two vectors is *not* another vector; it is a scalar.

Example 2

Find the dot product of

$$\mathbf{u} = 3\mathbf{i} - 2\mathbf{j} + 4\mathbf{k} \quad \text{and} \quad \mathbf{v} = \mathbf{i} + \mathbf{j} - 2\mathbf{k}.$$

$$\begin{aligned}\mathbf{u}\cdot\mathbf{v} &= 3\cdot 1 - 2\cdot 1 + 4(-2) \\ &= -7.\end{aligned}$$

Let us now consider some applications of the dot product.

Theorem 21.8

The vectors **u** *and* **v** *(not both* **0***) are orthogonal (perpendicular) if and only if* $\mathbf{u} \cdot \mathbf{v} = 0$ *(the zero vector is taken to be orthogonal to every other vector).*

This follows directly from Theorem 21.7 and the definition of the dot product. Thus we have a simple test for the orthogonality (perpendicularity) of two vectors. As we shall see later, orthogonality of vectors is an important concept.

Example 3

Determine whether or not $\mathbf{u} = 2\mathbf{i} - \mathbf{j} + \mathbf{k}$ and $\mathbf{v} = \mathbf{i} + 2\mathbf{j} - \mathbf{k}$ are orthogonal.

$$\begin{aligned} \mathbf{u} \cdot \mathbf{v} &= 2 \cdot 1 - 1 \cdot 2 + 1(-1) \\ &= -1. \end{aligned}$$

They are not orthogonal since $\mathbf{u} \cdot \mathbf{v} \neq 0$.

Again there is the question of whether or not the dot product of vectors has the same properties as the product of numbers. The definition itself shows one difference, in that the dot product of two vectors is not itself a vector. While there are other differences, let us first note the similarities.

Theorem 21.9

If **u**, **v** *and* **w** *are vectors then*

$$\begin{aligned} \mathbf{u} \cdot \mathbf{v} &= \mathbf{v} \cdot \mathbf{u}, \\ (\mathbf{u} + \mathbf{v}) \cdot \mathbf{w} &= \mathbf{u} \cdot \mathbf{w} + \mathbf{v} \cdot \mathbf{w}. \end{aligned}$$

This is easily proved from the definitions. The proof is left to the student. It might be noted that the dot product of three vectors $\mathbf{u} \cdot \mathbf{v} \cdot \mathbf{w}$ is meaningless, since the dot product of any pair of them is a scalar.

Theorem 21.10

If **u** *and* **v** *are vectors and* θ *is the angle between them, then*

$$\begin{aligned} \mathbf{u} \cdot \mathbf{v} &= |\mathbf{u}|\ |\mathbf{v}| \cos \theta, \\ \mathbf{v} \cdot \mathbf{v} &= |\mathbf{v}|^2. \end{aligned}$$

The proof is left to the student. We might note some special cases of this theorem. If **u** and **v** are orthogonal, $\theta = 90°$ and $\mathbf{u} \cdot \mathbf{v} = 0$, as we have seen before. If **u** and **v** are parallel, $\theta = 0°$ or $\theta = 180°$ and $\mathbf{u} \cdot \mathbf{v} = \pm|\mathbf{u}| \cdot |\mathbf{v}|$.

The projection of one vector upon another is determined by the angle between them or the dot product.

Definition

The ***projection*** *of* **u** *on* **v** $(\mathbf{v} \neq \mathbf{0})$ *is a vector* **w** *such that if* $\overrightarrow{AB}$ *is a representative of* **u** *and* $\overrightarrow{CD}$ *is a representative of* **v**, *then a representative of* **w** *is a directed line segment* $\overrightarrow{EF}$ *such that* $EF \perp AE$, $AE \perp CD$, *and* $BF \perp CD$ *(see Figure* 21.7).

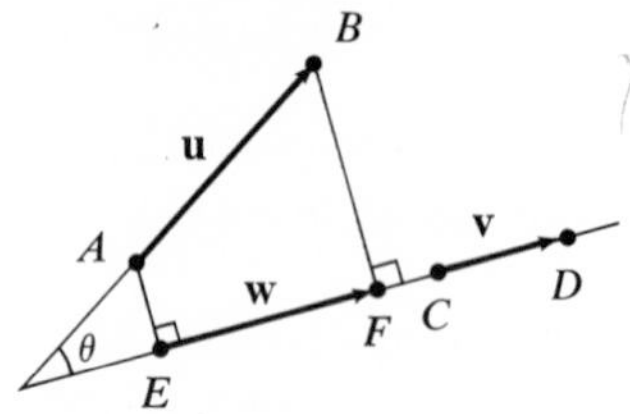

Figure 21.7

The projection of **u** on **v** is defined in terms of representatives of these vectors. Thus we again have the question of whether or not the projection is well defined. Theorem 21.1 and the congruence of triangles show that the projection of **u** on **v** is independent of the representatives considered.

Theorem 21.11

If **w** *is the projection of* **u** *on* **v** *and* θ *is the angle between* **u** *and* **v**, *then*

$$|\mathbf{w}| = \frac{|\mathbf{u} \cdot \mathbf{v}|}{|\mathbf{v}|}.$$

Proof

We can see from Figure 21.7, that

$$\begin{aligned} |\mathbf{w}| &= |\mathbf{u}|\ |\cos\theta| \\ &= \frac{|\mathbf{u}|\ |\mathbf{v}|\ |\cos\theta|}{|\mathbf{v}|} \\ &= \frac{|\mathbf{u} \cdot \mathbf{v}|}{|\mathbf{v}|} \qquad \text{(by Theorem 21.10).} \end{aligned}$$

Example 4

Find the projection **w** of $\mathbf{u} = 3\mathbf{i} - \mathbf{j} + 2\mathbf{k}$ on $\mathbf{v} = \mathbf{i} + \mathbf{j} - 3\mathbf{k}$.

By Theorem 21.11,

$$\begin{aligned} |\mathbf{w}| &= \frac{|\mathbf{u} \cdot \mathbf{v}|}{|\mathbf{v}|} \\ &= \frac{|-4|}{\sqrt{11}} \\ &= \frac{4}{\sqrt{11}}. \end{aligned}$$

Since **w** and **v** have the same (or opposite) directions, there is a number c such that

$$\begin{aligned} \mathbf{w} &= c\mathbf{v} \\ &= c\mathbf{i} + c\mathbf{j} - 3c\mathbf{k} \end{aligned}$$

Thus $|\mathbf{w}| = \dfrac{4}{\sqrt{11}} = \sqrt{11c^2}$

$$c = \pm\frac{4}{11}.$$

Since $\mathbf{u} \cdot \mathbf{v}$ is negative, $\cos\theta$ is negative. Thus $\theta > 90°$ and $\mathbf{w}$ and $\mathbf{v}$ have opposite directions. Thus $c = -4/11$ and

$$\mathbf{w} = -\frac{4}{11}\mathbf{i} - \frac{4}{11}\mathbf{j} + \frac{12}{11}\mathbf{k}.$$

Problems

In Problems 1–8, find the angle θ between the given vectors.

1. $\mathbf{u} = 3\mathbf{i} - \mathbf{j}$, $\mathbf{v} = \mathbf{i} + 2\mathbf{j}$.
2. $\mathbf{u} = 4\mathbf{i} + \mathbf{j}$, $\mathbf{v} = \mathbf{i} + 2\mathbf{j}$.
3. $\mathbf{u} = -\mathbf{i} + 2\mathbf{j}$, $\mathbf{v} = 2\mathbf{i} + \mathbf{j}$.
4. $\mathbf{u} = \mathbf{i} + \mathbf{j}$, $\mathbf{v} = 2\mathbf{i} - \mathbf{j}$.
5. $\mathbf{u} = 2\mathbf{i} - \mathbf{j} + \mathbf{k}$, $\mathbf{v} = \mathbf{i} + \mathbf{j} - \mathbf{k}$.
6. $\mathbf{u} = 3\mathbf{i} + 2\mathbf{j} - \mathbf{k}$, $\mathbf{v} = \mathbf{i} - \mathbf{j} + 2\mathbf{k}$.
7. $\mathbf{u} = 2\mathbf{i} - 2\mathbf{j} + 3\mathbf{k}$, $\mathbf{v} = 4\mathbf{i} + \mathbf{j} + \mathbf{k}$.
8. $\mathbf{u} = \mathbf{i} + \mathbf{j} - 3\mathbf{k}$, $\mathbf{v} = 2\mathbf{i} + 4\mathbf{j} + \mathbf{k}$.

In Problems 9–16, find $\mathbf{u} \cdot \mathbf{v}$ and indicate whether or not $\mathbf{u}$ and $\mathbf{v}$ are orthogonal.

9. $\mathbf{u} = \mathbf{i} - \mathbf{j}$, $\mathbf{v} = 2\mathbf{i} + \mathbf{j}$.
10. $\mathbf{u} = 2\mathbf{i} + \mathbf{j}$, $\mathbf{v} = \mathbf{i} - 2\mathbf{j}$.
11. $\mathbf{u} = 3\mathbf{i} + 2\mathbf{j}$, $\mathbf{v} = 2\mathbf{i} - \mathbf{j}$.
12. $\mathbf{u} = 2\mathbf{i} - 4\mathbf{j}$, $\mathbf{v} = 2\mathbf{i} + \mathbf{j}$.
13. $\mathbf{u} = \mathbf{i} - \mathbf{j} + 2\mathbf{k}$, $\mathbf{v} = 3\mathbf{i} + 4\mathbf{j} + \mathbf{k}$.
14. $\mathbf{u} = \mathbf{i} + \mathbf{j} + \mathbf{k}$, $\mathbf{v} = 2\mathbf{i} - 3\mathbf{j} + \mathbf{k}$.
15. $\mathbf{u} = 2\mathbf{i} - 3\mathbf{j} + \mathbf{k}$, $\mathbf{v} = 3\mathbf{i} + \mathbf{j} - 3\mathbf{k}$.
16. $\mathbf{u} = 4\mathbf{i} + 2\mathbf{k}$, $\mathbf{v} = \mathbf{i} + \mathbf{j} - 2\mathbf{k}$.

In Problems 17–24, find the projection of $\mathbf{u}$ on $\mathbf{v}$.

17. $\mathbf{u} = 2\mathbf{i} - \mathbf{j}$, $\mathbf{v} = \mathbf{i} + \mathbf{j}$.
18. $\mathbf{u} = \mathbf{i} - 3\mathbf{j}$, $\mathbf{v} = 2\mathbf{i} + \mathbf{j}$.
19. $\mathbf{u} = 2\mathbf{i} + 4\mathbf{j}$, $\mathbf{v} = \mathbf{i} - 2\mathbf{j}$.
20. $\mathbf{u} = 4\mathbf{i} + \mathbf{j}$, $\mathbf{v} = 2\mathbf{i} + \mathbf{j}$.
21. $\mathbf{u} = \mathbf{i} - \mathbf{j} + 2\mathbf{k}$, $\mathbf{v} = 2\mathbf{i} + \mathbf{j} + \mathbf{k}$.
22. $\mathbf{u} = 2\mathbf{i} - 3\mathbf{j} + \mathbf{k}$, $\mathbf{v} = \mathbf{i} + 2\mathbf{j} + 4\mathbf{k}$.
23. $\mathbf{u} = 2\mathbf{i} + \mathbf{j} - 3\mathbf{k}$, $\mathbf{v} = 4\mathbf{i} - 2\mathbf{j} + \mathbf{k}$.
24. $\mathbf{u} = 3\mathbf{i} - \mathbf{j} + \mathbf{k}$, $\mathbf{v} = 2\mathbf{i} + 2\mathbf{j} - 3\mathbf{k}$.

In Problems 25–36, determine the value(s) of a so that the given conditions are satisfied.

25. $\mathbf{u} = 3\mathbf{i} - \mathbf{j}$, $\mathbf{v} = \mathbf{i} + a\mathbf{j}$, $\mathbf{u}$ and $\mathbf{v}$ are perpendicular.
26. $\mathbf{u} = \mathbf{i} + \mathbf{j}$, $\mathbf{v} = 3\mathbf{i} - a\mathbf{j}$, $\mathbf{u}$ and $\mathbf{v}$ are perpendicular.
27. $\mathbf{u} = \mathbf{i} - 2\mathbf{j}$, $\mathbf{v} = a\mathbf{i} + \mathbf{j}$, $\mathbf{u}$ and $\mathbf{v}$ are parallel.
28. $\mathbf{u} = a\mathbf{i} - \mathbf{j}$, $\mathbf{v} = 2\mathbf{i} + a\mathbf{j}$, $\mathbf{u}$ and $\mathbf{v}$ are parallel.
29. $\mathbf{u} = a\mathbf{i} + 2\mathbf{j}$, $\mathbf{v} = \mathbf{i} - \mathbf{j}$, the angle between $\mathbf{u}$ and $\mathbf{v}$ is $\pi/3$.
30. $\mathbf{u} = 3\mathbf{i} - a\mathbf{j}$, $\mathbf{v} = 2\mathbf{i} + \mathbf{j}$, the angle between $\mathbf{u}$ and $\mathbf{v} = \pi/4$.
31. $\mathbf{u} = 4\mathbf{i} + \mathbf{j} - \mathbf{k}$, $\mathbf{v} = 2\mathbf{i} + a\mathbf{j} - \mathbf{k}$, $\mathbf{u}$ and $\mathbf{v}$ are perpendicular.
32. $\mathbf{u} = 2\mathbf{i} - \mathbf{j} + 3\mathbf{k}$, $\mathbf{v} = a\mathbf{i} + \mathbf{j} - \mathbf{k}$, $\mathbf{u}$ and $\mathbf{v}$ are perpendicular.
33. $\mathbf{u} = \mathbf{i} + \mathbf{j} + \mathbf{k}$, $\mathbf{v} = a\mathbf{i} - \mathbf{j} + 2\mathbf{k}$, $\mathbf{u}$ and $\mathbf{v}$ are parallel.
34. $\mathbf{u} = a\mathbf{i} + a\mathbf{j} - \mathbf{k}$, $\mathbf{v} = 2\mathbf{i} + \mathbf{j} - 3\mathbf{k}$, $\mathbf{u}$ and $\mathbf{v}$ are parallel.
35. $\mathbf{u} = 2\mathbf{i} + \mathbf{j} + 3\mathbf{k}$, $\mathbf{v} = a\mathbf{i} - \mathbf{j} + \mathbf{k}$, the angle between $\mathbf{u}$ and $\mathbf{v}$ is $2\pi/3$.
36. $\mathbf{u} = \mathbf{i} - \mathbf{j} + 2\mathbf{k}$, $\mathbf{v} = 4\mathbf{i} + a\mathbf{j} - \mathbf{k}$, the angle between $\mathbf{u}$ and $\mathbf{v}$ is $\pi/6$.

In Problems 37–40, let $\mathbf{u}$ be represented by $\overrightarrow{AB}$, $\mathbf{v}$ by $\overrightarrow{AC}$ and $\mathbf{w}$ by $\overrightarrow{BC}$. Find the projections of $\mathbf{v}$ and $\mathbf{w}$ on $\mathbf{u}$.

37. $A = (0, 0)$, $B = (1, 4)$, $C = (2, -1)$.
38. $A = (2, 3)$, $B = (-3, -1)$, $C = (4, 2)$.
39. $A = (4, 1, 2)$, $B = (3, -1, -1)$, $C = (0, 2, 3)$.
40. $A = (2, 0, 4)$, $B = (5, 5, 3)$, $C = (3, 5, 8)$.
41. Prove Theorem 21.8.
42. Prove Theorem 21.9.
43. Prove Theorem 21.10.

21.3

The Cross Product

Let us now look at the other product of two vectors—the cross product.

Definition

If $\mathbf{u} = a_1\mathbf{i} + b_1\mathbf{j} + c_1\mathbf{k}$ *and* $\mathbf{v} = a_2\mathbf{i} + b_2\mathbf{j} + c_2\mathbf{k}$, *then the* ***cross product (vector product, outer product)*** *of* **u** *and* **v** *is*

$$\mathbf{u} \times \mathbf{v} = (b_1c_2 - c_1b_2)\mathbf{i} + (c_1a_2 - a_1c_2)\mathbf{j} + (a_1b_2 - b_1a_2)\mathbf{k}.$$

Some obvious questions arise. Why do we want to define a cross product this way? What is it good for? What are its properties? In some ways, all answers are the same. We define the cross product in this way to establish some interesting properties that are useful for certain applications. In a way, this is approaching the problem backward. It would be more logical to define the cross product of two vectors as that one having the desired properties and then show that such a vector must take the form given. The reason for our way of doing it is that it is by far the simpler approach. Before looking at some properties, let us consider a simpler form for the cross product.

Theorem 21.12

If $\mathbf{u} = a_1\mathbf{i} + b_1\mathbf{j} + c_1\mathbf{k}$ *and* $\mathbf{v} = a_2\mathbf{i} + b_2\mathbf{j} + c_2\mathbf{k}$, *then*

$$\mathbf{u} \times \mathbf{v} = \begin{vmatrix} \mathbf{i} & \mathbf{j} & \mathbf{k} \\ a_1 & b_1 & c_1 \\ a_2 & b_2 & c_2 \end{vmatrix}.$$

This theorem follows directly from the definition.

Example 1

If $\mathbf{u} = 3\mathbf{i} + \mathbf{j} - 2\mathbf{k}$ and $\mathbf{v} = \mathbf{i} + 2\mathbf{j} + \mathbf{k}$, find $\mathbf{u} \times \mathbf{v}$ and $\mathbf{v} \times \mathbf{u}$.

$$\mathbf{u} \times \mathbf{v} = \begin{vmatrix} \mathbf{i} & \mathbf{j} & \mathbf{k} \\ 3 & 1 & -2 \\ 1 & 2 & 1 \end{vmatrix} = 5\mathbf{i} - 5\mathbf{j} + 5\mathbf{k},$$

$$\mathbf{v} \times \mathbf{u} = \begin{vmatrix} \mathbf{i} & \mathbf{j} & \mathbf{k} \\ 1 & 2 & 1 \\ 3 & 1 & -2 \end{vmatrix} = -5\mathbf{i} + 5\mathbf{j} - 5\mathbf{k}.$$

Note that $\mathbf{u} \times \mathbf{v} \neq \mathbf{v} \times \mathbf{u}$!

Again we are not multiplying numbers; there is no reason to assume that the cross product of two vectors has the same properties as the product of two numbers. We have already seen one difference in Example 1. The cross product has the following properties.

Theorem 21.13

If **u**, **v** *and* **w** *are vectors and a is a scalar, then*

(*a*) $\mathbf{u} \times \mathbf{v} = -\mathbf{v} \times \mathbf{u}$;
(*b*) $\mathbf{u} \times (\mathbf{v} + \mathbf{w}) = \mathbf{u} \times \mathbf{v} + \mathbf{u} \times \mathbf{w}$;
(*c*) $\mathbf{u} \times \mathbf{0} = \mathbf{0} \times \mathbf{u} = \mathbf{0}$;
(*d*) *if* $\mathbf{u} = a\mathbf{v}$, *then* $\mathbf{u} \times \mathbf{v} = \mathbf{0}$;
(*e*) $(\mathbf{u} \times \mathbf{v}) \cdot \mathbf{w} = \mathbf{u} \cdot (\mathbf{v} \times \mathbf{w})$.

This follows from the definition of the cross product. The proof is left to the student. It might be noted that the definition was stated in terms of three-dimensional vectors. In fact, we must have a three-dimensional vector space, for $\mathbf{u} \times \mathbf{v}$ is not in the plane determined by **u** and **v**.

Theorem 21.14

If **u** *and* **v** *are nonzero vectors, then* $\mathbf{u} \times \mathbf{v}$ *is perpendicular to both* **u** *and* **v**.

Proof

$$\begin{aligned} \mathbf{u} \cdot (\mathbf{u} \times \mathbf{v}) &= (\mathbf{u} \times \mathbf{u}) \cdot \mathbf{v} && \text{(why?)} \\ &= \mathbf{0} \cdot \mathbf{v} && \text{(why?)} \\ &= 0. && \text{(why?)} \end{aligned}$$

Thus **u** and $\mathbf{u} \times \mathbf{v}$ are perpendicular. A similar argument shows that $\mathbf{u} \times \mathbf{v}$ and **v** are perpendicular.

This property of the cross product gives us its principal use. Certain problems in three-dimensional analytic geometry that were relatively difficult without the use of the cross product are easier now.

Example 2

Find an equation of the plane containing the two lines

$$x = 1, \quad y = 3 + 2t, \quad z = 4 + t$$

and

$$x = 1 + 4s, \quad y = 3 + 2s, \quad z = 4 + 2s$$

(this is the same as Example 4, page 517).

The two lines intersect at (1, 3, 4). All we need is a set of direction numbers of a line perpendicular to the plane. But any line perpendicular to the desired plane is perpendicular to any line in that plane. This suggests the use of the cross product. Vectors directed along the given lines are

$$\mathbf{u} = 2\mathbf{j} + \mathbf{k} \quad \text{and} \quad \mathbf{v} = 4\mathbf{i} + 2\mathbf{j} + 2\mathbf{k}.$$

$\mathbf{u} \times \mathbf{v} = 2\mathbf{i} + 4\mathbf{j} - 8\mathbf{k}$. Thus, $\{2, 4, -8\}$ is one set of direction numbers for the desired line; $\{1, 2, -4\}$ is a simpler set. Thus, the desired plane is

$$1(x - 1) + 2(y - 3) - 4(z - 4) = 0,$$

or

$$x + 2y - 4z + 9 = 0.$$

Example 3

Find an equation of the plane containing (1, 4, 3) and parallel to

$$\frac{x-1}{2}=\frac{y+3}{1}=\frac{z-2}{4} \quad \text{and} \quad \frac{x+2}{3}=\frac{y-4}{2}=\frac{z+1}{-2}.$$

Again, vectors along the two given lines are

$$\mathbf{u}=2\mathbf{i}+\mathbf{j}+4\mathbf{k} \quad \text{and} \quad \mathbf{v}=3\mathbf{i}+2\mathbf{j}-2\mathbf{k}.$$

$\mathbf{u}\times\mathbf{v}=-10\mathbf{i}+16\mathbf{j}+\mathbf{k}$ is perpendicular to both of them; thus it is perpendicular to the plane we want. The plane is

$$-10(x-1)+16(y-4)+1(z-3)=0,$$

or

$$10x-16y-z+57=0.$$

Example 4

Find the distance between the lines

$$x=1-4t, \quad y=2+t, \quad z=3+2t$$

and

$$x=2+s, \quad y=2-2s, \quad z=4-s.$$

The desired distance is to be measured along a line perpendicular to both of the given lines. Again, vectors along the given lines are $\mathbf{u}=-4\mathbf{i}+\mathbf{j}+2\mathbf{k}$ and $\mathbf{v}=\mathbf{i}-2\mathbf{j}-\mathbf{k}$. Thus the distance is to be measured along $\mathbf{u}\times\mathbf{v}=3\mathbf{i}-2\mathbf{j}+7\mathbf{k}$. The point A: (1, 2, 3) is on the first line, and B: (2, 2, 4) is on the second. The vector represented by $\overrightarrow{AB}$ is $\mathbf{w}=\mathbf{i}+\mathbf{k}$. We want a vector whose representatives are all perpendicular to both of the given lines and with one representative having its head on one line and its tail on the other. All of the representatives of $\mathbf{u}\times\mathbf{v}$ are perpendicular to both lines and one of the representatives of $\mathbf{w}$ has its end points on the given lines. Thus, the projection of $\mathbf{w}$ on $\mathbf{u}\times\mathbf{v}$ has the desired properties and its length is the distance between the given lines.

$$\frac{\mathbf{w}\cdot(\mathbf{u}\times\mathbf{v})}{|\mathbf{u}\times\mathbf{v}|}=\frac{1\cdot 3+0(-2)+1\cdot 7}{\sqrt{9+4+49}}=\frac{10}{\sqrt{62}}.$$

Up to this point we have been dealing exclusively with the direction of $\mathbf{u}\times\mathbf{v}$. Its length also has some interesting properties.

Theorem 21.15

If $\mathbf{u}$ *and* $\mathbf{v}$ *are vectors and* θ *is the angle between them, then*

$$|\mathbf{u}\times\mathbf{v}|=|\mathbf{u}|\,|\mathbf{v}|\sin\theta.$$

Proof

Since $\cos\theta=\mathbf{u}\cdot\mathbf{v}/(|\mathbf{u}|\,|\mathbf{v}|)$ by Theorem 21.10,

$$|\mathbf{u}|\,|\mathbf{v}|\sin\theta=|\mathbf{u}|\,|\mathbf{v}|\sqrt{1-\cos^2\theta} \qquad \text{(See Note 1.)}$$

$$=|\mathbf{u}|\,|\mathbf{v}|\sqrt{1-\frac{(\mathbf{u}\cdot\mathbf{v})^2}{|\mathbf{u}|^2|\mathbf{v}|^2}}$$

$$=\sqrt{|\mathbf{u}|^2|\mathbf{v}|^2-(\mathbf{u}\cdot\mathbf{v})^2}.$$

If we let $\mathbf{u} = a_1\mathbf{i} + b_1\mathbf{j} + c_1\mathbf{k}$ and $\mathbf{v} = a_2\mathbf{i} + b_2\mathbf{j} + c_2\mathbf{k}$, then

$$|\mathbf{u}|\ |\mathbf{v}| \sin\theta = \sqrt{(a_1^2 + b_1^2 + c_1^2)(a_2^2 + b_2^2 + c_2^2) - (a_1a_2 + b_1b_2 + c_1c_2)^2}$$

$$= \sqrt{(b_1c_2 - c_1b_2)^2 + (c_1a_2 - a_1c_2)^2 + (a_1b_2 - b_1a_2)^2} \qquad \text{(See Note 2.)}$$

$$= |\mathbf{u} \times \mathbf{v}|.$$

Note 1: By the definition of the angle between two vectors, $0° \leq \theta \leq 180°$; and $\sin\theta \geq 0$.

Note 2: The algebra here is routine but tedious. It is left to the student.

Note the similarity between this theorem and the first part of Theorem 21.10. One consequence of this theorem is given in Problem 30.

Problems

In Problems 1–6, find $\mathbf{u} \times \mathbf{v}$.

1. $\mathbf{u} = 3\mathbf{i} - \mathbf{j} + 4\mathbf{k}$, $\mathbf{v} = 2\mathbf{i} + \mathbf{j} + \mathbf{k}$.
2. $\mathbf{u} = \mathbf{i} + \mathbf{j} + \mathbf{k}$, $\mathbf{v} = 2\mathbf{i} - \mathbf{j} - 4\mathbf{k}$.
3. $\mathbf{u} = 2\mathbf{i} + 3\mathbf{j} - \mathbf{k}$, $\mathbf{v} = -\mathbf{i} + 2\mathbf{j}$.
4. $\mathbf{u} = 4\mathbf{i} + 2\mathbf{j}$, $\mathbf{v} = 3\mathbf{i} - \mathbf{j}$.
5. $\mathbf{u} = 3\mathbf{i} + \mathbf{k}$, $\mathbf{v} = -\mathbf{i} + \mathbf{j}$.
6. $\mathbf{u} = 2\mathbf{i} + \mathbf{j} - \mathbf{k}$, $\mathbf{v} = -\mathbf{i} - \mathbf{j} + 3\mathbf{k}$.

In Problems 7–20, find an equation of the plane described.

7. Containing (4, 1, 2), (2, −1, 1), and (3, 0, 4).
8. Containing (2, 2, 3), (−1, 4, 1), and (0, 1, 2).
9. Containing $x = 2 + t$, $y = 3 - 2t$, $z = -t$ and $x = 2 - 2s$, $y = 3 + s$, $z = -s$.
10. Containing $x = 3 + 4t$, $y = 1 - t$, $z = 3$ and $x = 3 - 2s$, $y = 1 + 2s$, $z = 3 - s$.
11. Containing $x = 4 + t$, $y = -1 + 2t$, $z = 2t$ and $x = 2 + s$, $y = 4 + 2s$, $z = 1 + 2s$.
12. Containing $x = 2 + 2t$, $y = 3 - t$, $z = -1 + t$ and $x = 4 + 2s$, $y = 2 - s$, $z = 4 + s$.
13. Containing (3, 2, 1) and parallel to $x = 1 - 2t$, $y = 3 + t$, $z = 4 - t$ and $x = 2 + s$, $y = -1 + 2s$, $z = 3 - s$.
14. Containing (4, −1, 0) and parallel to $x = 3 + t$, $y = 2 - t$, $z = 2t$ and $x = 4$, $y = 2 + s$, $z = -1 + s$.
15. Containing (2, 1, 4) and (4, 0, 3) and parallel to $x = 3 - t$, $y = 1 + t$, $z = 2t$.
16. Containing (0, 4, −1) and (2, 0, 5) and parallel to $x = 1 + t$, $y = 2 - t$, $z = -2 + 3t$.
17. Containing (1, 0, 4) and perpendicular to $x - y + z + 2 = 0$ and $2x + y - z + 5 = 0$.
18. Containing (4, 1, 1) and perpendicular to $2x - 3y + z = 0$ and $x + y - 2z + 1 = 0$.
19. Containing (2, 0, 1) and (3, 3, 2) and perpendicular to $4x + y - 3 = 0$.
20. Containing (4, 4, 2) and (−1, 3, 1) and perpendicular to $3x - 4y + z - 2 = 0$.

In Problems 21–24, find an equation of the line described.

21. Containing (3, 1, 4) and parallel to $x - y + 2z - 1 = 0$ and $2x + y - z + 3 = 0$.
22. Containing (4, 4, 1) and parallel to $2x - y - z + 2 = 0$ and $3x + y - z - 4 = 0$.
23. Containing (2, 0, 5) and perpendicular to and containing a point of $x = 4 + t$, $y = 3 - 2t$, $z = 1 + t$.
24. Containing (1, 1, 2) and perpendicular to and containing a point of $x = 1 - t$, $y = 2 + 2t$, $z = 4t$.

In Problems 25–28, find the distance between the given lines.

25. $x = 1 + t$, $y = -2 + 3t$, $z = 4 + t$ and $x = 2 - s$, $y = 3 + 2s$, $z = 1 + s$.
26. $x = 2 + t$, $y = 1 - t$, $z = 4t$ and $x = 2 + s$, $y = 4 - 2s$, $z = 1 + 3s$.

27. $x = 1 + t$, $y = 1 - 5t$, $z = 2 + t$ and $x = 4 + s$, $y = 5 + 2s$, $z = -3 + 4s$.
28. $x = 2 + t$, $y = -4 + t$, $z = 1 - 3t$ and $x = 3 - s$, $y = 4 + 2s$, $z = 2 + s$.
29. Use the method of Example 4 to find the distance between
$$Ax + By + Cz + D = 0 \text{ and } (x_1, y_1, z_1).$$
30. Suppose the vectors **u** and **v** are represented by $\overrightarrow{AB}$ and $\overrightarrow{AC}$, respectively. Show that the area of $\triangle ABC$ is $\frac{1}{2}|\mathbf{u} \times \mathbf{v}|$. (*Hint*: Use Theorem 21.15.)

In Problems 31–34, use the result of Problem 30 to find the area of triangles with the given vertices.

31. (1, 0, 4), (2, −1, 2), (4, 4, 1).
32. (3, −2, 1), (−1, 2, 0), (4, 4, 2).
33. (2, 4, 3), (1, 0, 1), (−2, 2, 4).
34. (4, 2) (3, −1), (−1, 0).
35. Prove Theorem 21.13.
36. Complete the proof of Theorem 21.14.

21.4

Vector Functions and Their Derivatives

A *vector function* of a real variable is simply a set of ordered pairs $(t, \mathbf{f}(t))$, of which the first term is a real number and the second a vector. It is represented in the following way:
$$\mathbf{f}(t) = f_1(t)\mathbf{i} + f_2(t)\mathbf{j} + f_3(t)\mathbf{k}.$$
Of course, if $f_3(t)$ is identically zero, the vector is only two-dimensional.

Recall that, in graphing vectors, we graph only representatives. Thus, in graphing vector functions, let us graph representatives of the vectors, each having its tail at the origin. Thus,
$$\mathbf{f}(t) = t\mathbf{i} + t^2\mathbf{j}$$
has the graphical representation shown in Figure 21.8(a). Normally we shall omit the directed line segments and show only their heads, as in Figure 21.8(b). Thus, the result is equivalent to graphing the curve represented parametrically by
$$x = t, \qquad y = t^2.$$

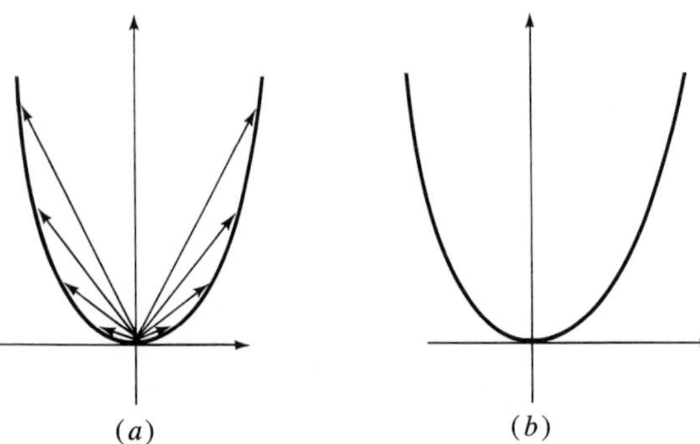

Figure 21.8

Example 1

Graph $\mathbf{f}(t) = \cos t\mathbf{i} + \sin t\mathbf{j} + t\mathbf{k}$.

This has a three-dimensional graph which is equivalent to

$$x = \cos t, \qquad y = \sin t, \qquad z = t.$$

The result is the spiral shown in Figure 21.9.

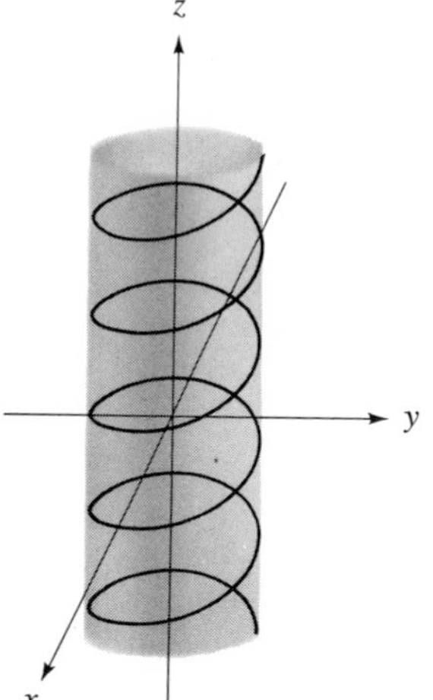

Figure 21.9

Limits for vector functions can be defined in terms of limits for the components.

Definition

If $\mathbf{f}(t) = f_1(t)\mathbf{i} + f_2(t)\mathbf{j} + f_3(t)\mathbf{k}$, *then*

$$\lim_{t\to a} \mathbf{f}(t) = \left[\lim_{t\to a} f_1(t)\right]\mathbf{i} + \left[\lim_{t\to a} f_2(t)\right]\mathbf{j} + \left[\lim_{t\to a} f_3(t)\right]\mathbf{k}.$$

Now the derivative is defined as it was for real-valued functions.

Definition

$$\mathbf{f}'(t) = \lim_{h\to 0} \frac{\mathbf{f}(t+h) - \mathbf{f}(t)}{h}.$$

Theorem 21.16

If $\mathbf{f}(t) = f_1(t)\mathbf{i} + f_2(t)\mathbf{j} + f_3(t)\mathbf{k}$, *then*

$$\mathbf{f}'(t) = f_1'(t)\mathbf{i} + f_2'(t)\mathbf{j} + f_3'(t)\mathbf{k}.$$

It is a simple matter to show that this theorem follows from the definition of a derivative. The proof is left to the student.

Example 2

Find the derivative of $\mathbf{f}(t) = t^2\mathbf{i} + (2t+1)\mathbf{j} + (2t-1)\mathbf{k}$.

$$\mathbf{f}'(t) = 2t\mathbf{i} + 2\mathbf{j} + 2\mathbf{k}.$$

The derivative of a vector function at a particular value of t is another vector with representatives on or parallel to the tangent to the graph of the original function at the given value of t. This is seen by a graphical consideration of the definition of the derivative.

Problems

In Problems 1–10, sketch the graph of the given vector function.

1. $\mathbf{f}(t) = (t-1)\mathbf{i} + t^2\mathbf{j}$.
2. $\mathbf{f}(t) = (t^2+1)\mathbf{i} + (t^2-1)\mathbf{j}$.
3. $\mathbf{f}(t) = t^2\mathbf{i} + t^3\mathbf{j}$.
4. $\mathbf{f}(t) = (3t+1)\mathbf{i} + (t^3-1)\mathbf{j}$.

5. $\mathbf{f}(t) = \cos t\mathbf{i} + \sin t\mathbf{j}$.
6. $\mathbf{f}(t) = t^2\mathbf{i} + e^t\mathbf{j}$.
7. $\mathbf{f}(t) = t\mathbf{i} + t\mathbf{j} + t\mathbf{k}$.
8. $\mathbf{f}(t) = (2t+1)\mathbf{i} + (t-1)\mathbf{j} + t\mathbf{k}$.
9. $\mathbf{f}(t) = (t-1)\mathbf{i} + t^2\mathbf{j} + t\mathbf{k}$.
10. $\mathbf{f}(t) = \cos t\mathbf{i} + \sin t\mathbf{j} + \tan t\mathbf{k}$.

In Problems 11–16, find $\mathbf{f}'(a)$. Sketch $\mathbf{f}(t)$ and $\mathbf{f}'(a)$.

11. $\mathbf{f}(t) = t\mathbf{i} + t^3\mathbf{j}$, $a = 1$.
12. $\mathbf{f}(t) = t^3\mathbf{i} + t^2\mathbf{j}$, $a = 2$.
13. $\mathbf{f}(t) = (t+1)\mathbf{i} + (t^2-1)\mathbf{j}$, $a = 2$.
14. $\mathbf{f}(t) = \cos t\mathbf{i} + \sin t\mathbf{j}$, $a = 0$.
15. $\mathbf{f}(t) = t\mathbf{i} + t^2\mathbf{j} + (t^2+1)\mathbf{k}$, $a = 1$.
16. $\mathbf{f}(t) = \cos t\mathbf{i} + \sin t\mathbf{j} + e^t\mathbf{k}$, $a = 0$.

In Problems 17–28, find $\mathbf{f}'(t)$ and $\mathbf{f}''(t)$.

17. $\mathbf{f}(t) = t\mathbf{i} + (t^2-1)\mathbf{j}$.
18. $\mathbf{f}(t) = (t+1)\mathbf{i} + (t^2+1)\mathbf{j}$.
19. $\mathbf{f}(t) = t^2\mathbf{i} + t^3\mathbf{j}$.
20. $\mathbf{f}(t) = (t^4+1)\mathbf{i} + (t^4-1)\mathbf{j}$.
21. $\mathbf{f}(t) = \cos t\mathbf{i} + \sin t\mathbf{j}$.
22. $\mathbf{f}(t) = \cosh t\mathbf{i} + \sinh t\mathbf{j}$.
23. $\mathbf{f}(t) = t\mathbf{i} + t^2\mathbf{j} - t^3\mathbf{k}$.
24. $\mathbf{f}(t) = (t^2+1)\mathbf{i} + (t^2-1)\mathbf{j} + t^2\mathbf{k}$.
25. $\mathbf{f}(t) = (t^2+1)\mathbf{i} + (t^3-1)\mathbf{j} + t^4\mathbf{k}$.
26. $\mathbf{f}(t) = (t^2-4)\mathbf{i} + (t^3-1)\mathbf{j} + (t+2)\mathbf{k}$.
27. $\mathbf{f}(t) = \ln t\mathbf{i} + \dfrac{1}{t}\mathbf{j} + \dfrac{1}{t^2}\mathbf{k}$.
28. $\mathbf{f}(t) = t\mathbf{i} + \sin t\mathbf{j} + \cos t\mathbf{k}$.
29. If $\mathbf{f}(t) = (t^2+1)\mathbf{i} + (t^2-1)\mathbf{j}$, find $\dfrac{d}{dt}[\mathbf{f}(t)\cdot\mathbf{f}'(t)]$.
30. If $\mathbf{f}(t) = t\mathbf{i} + t^2\mathbf{j} + t^3\mathbf{k}$, find $\dfrac{d}{dt}[\mathbf{f}(t)\cdot\mathbf{f}'(t)]$.
31. If $\mathbf{f}(t) = t\mathbf{i} + e^t\mathbf{j}$, find $\dfrac{d}{dt}|\mathbf{f}(t)|$.
32. If $\mathbf{f}(t) = t^2\mathbf{i} - t^3\mathbf{j}$, find $\dfrac{d}{dt}|\mathbf{f}(t)|$.
33. Prove Theorem 21.16.
34. Prove that if $f(t) = \mathbf{u}(t)\cdot\mathbf{v}(t)$, then $f'(t) = \mathbf{u}(t)\cdot\mathbf{v}'(t) + \mathbf{u}'(t)\cdot\mathbf{v}(t)$.
35. Prove that if $\mathbf{f}(t) = \mathbf{u}(t)\times\mathbf{v}(t)$, then $\mathbf{f}'(t) = \mathbf{u}(t)\times\mathbf{v}'(t) + \mathbf{u}'(t)\times\mathbf{v}(t)$.

21.5

Vector Velocity and Acceleration

As noted earlier, velocity is a vector having both magnitude and direction. Up to now we have used the scalar speed and the vector velocity interchangeably, since we were dealing only with rectilinear motion. Let us now consider curvilinear motion. Suppose a particle is moving along a curve represented parametrically by

$$x = x(t), \quad y = y(t), \quad z = z(t).$$

Suppose further that at time t the particle is at $(x(t), y(t), z(t))$. This can be represented vectorially by

$$\mathbf{r}(t) = x(t)\mathbf{i} + y(t)\mathbf{j} + z(t)\mathbf{k}.$$

Now we define velocity and acceleration.

Definition

If $\mathbf{r}(t) = x(t)\mathbf{i} + y(t)\mathbf{j} + z(t)\mathbf{k}$ *represents the position of a particle at time t, then the* ***velocity*** *at time t is the vector*

$$\mathbf{v}(t) = \mathbf{r}'(t)$$

and the ***acceleration*** *at time t is the vector*

$$\mathbf{a}(t) = \mathbf{r}''(t).$$

This is basically the same thing that we encountered with rectilinear motion; the only difference is that we are dealing with vector functions here instead of the real-valued functions we have had in the past. The two situations are tied together by the following.

Definition

If $\mathbf{r}(t) = x(t)\mathbf{i} + y(t)\mathbf{j} + z(t)\mathbf{k}$ *represents the position of a particle at time t, then the* ***speed*** *at time t is*

$$\frac{ds}{dt} = |\mathbf{r}'(t)| = |\mathbf{v}(t)|$$

and the ***rate of change of speed*** *is*

$$\frac{d^2s}{dt^2} = \frac{d}{dt}|\mathbf{r}'(t)| = \frac{d}{dt}|\mathbf{v}(t)|.$$

The speed, which is defined above as the absolute value of the velocity, is equivalent to the absolute value of the rectilinear velocity that we have already considered. Let us see how. Since the distance covered by a moving particle is the length of the arc traversed, we want to concern ourselves here with arc length. You will recall that in two dimensions, arc length is given by

$$s = \int_a^b \sqrt{\left(\frac{dx}{dt}\right)^2 + \left(\frac{dy}{dt}\right)^2}\, dt.$$

This can easily be extended to three dimensions, to get

$$s = \int_a^b \sqrt{\left(\frac{dx}{dt}\right)^2 + \left(\frac{dy}{dt}\right)^2 + \left(\frac{dz}{dt}\right)^2}\, dt.$$

Now if we take the limits of integration to be 0 and t_0, instead of a and b, we see that s (which is now a function of t_0) is the length of the arc traversed between time 0 and time t_0.

$$s(t_0) = \int_0^{t_0} \sqrt{\left(\frac{dx}{dt}\right)^2 + \left(\frac{dy}{dt}\right)^2 + \left(\frac{dz}{dt}\right)^2}\, dt.$$

Thus, $s(t_0)$ represents the distance traversed in a given time t_0. The speed is the rate of change of this distance, or ds/dt_0. Differentiating $s(t_0)$, we have

$$\frac{ds}{dt_0} = \sqrt{\left(\frac{dx}{dt_0}\right)^2 + \left(\frac{dy}{dt_0}\right)^2 + \left(\frac{dz}{dt_0}\right)^2}$$

$$= \left|\frac{d\mathbf{r}(t_0)}{dt}\right| = |\mathbf{r}'(t_0)|,$$

or

$$\frac{ds}{dt} = |\mathbf{r}'(t)|.$$

This is exactly the way the speed was defined. Thus, this definition is consistent with our former idea of speed.

Example 1

A particle moves along a path according to the equation $\mathbf{r}(t) = \cos t\mathbf{i} + \sin t\mathbf{j}$ Find the velocity, acceleration, speed, and rate of change of speed at $t = \pi/4$. Graph the path of the particle and give a graphical representation of $\mathbf{v}$ and $\mathbf{a}$ at $t = \pi/4$.

$$\mathbf{r}(t) = \cos t\mathbf{i} + \sin t\mathbf{j},$$

$$\mathbf{v}(t) = -\sin t\mathbf{i} + \cos t\mathbf{j},$$

$$\mathbf{a}(t) = -\cos t\mathbf{i} - \sin t\mathbf{j},$$

$$\frac{ds}{dt} = |\mathbf{v}(t)| = \sqrt{\sin^2 t + \cos^2 t} = 1,$$

$$\frac{d^2s}{dt^2} = 0.$$

At $t = \pi/4$,

$$\mathbf{r}(t) = \cos\frac{\pi}{4}\mathbf{i} + \sin\frac{\pi}{4}\mathbf{j} = \frac{1}{\sqrt{2}}\mathbf{i} + \frac{1}{\sqrt{2}}\mathbf{j},$$

$$\mathbf{v}(t) = -\sin\frac{\pi}{4}\mathbf{i} + \cos\frac{\pi}{4}\mathbf{j} = -\frac{1}{\sqrt{2}}\mathbf{i} + \frac{1}{\sqrt{2}}\mathbf{j},$$

$$\mathbf{a}(t) = -\cos\frac{\pi}{4}\mathbf{i} - \sin\frac{\pi}{4}\mathbf{j} = -\frac{1}{\sqrt{2}}\mathbf{i} - \frac{1}{\sqrt{2}}\mathbf{j},$$

$$\frac{ds}{dt} = 1,$$

$$\frac{d^2s}{dt^2} = 0.$$

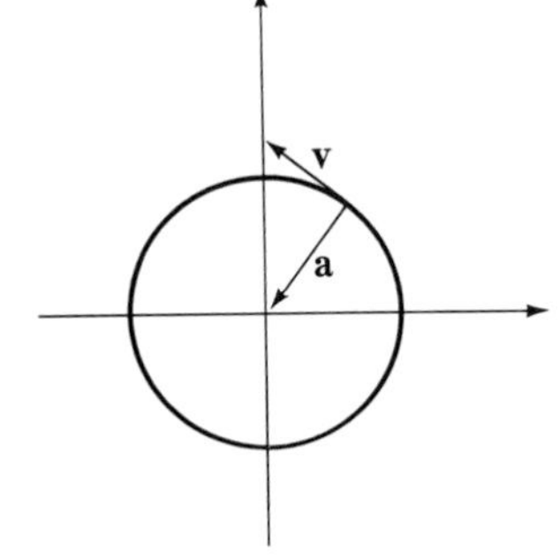

Figure 21.10

The path of the particle is a circle of radius 1 as shown in Figure 21.10. The velocity and acceleration are represented by directed line segments having their tails at $(\sqrt{1}/2, \sqrt{1}/2)$, which is the position of the particle at $t = \pi/4$.

Note that, while the speed is a constant, the velocity is not, since the particle is always changing direction. Similarly the rate of change of the speed is zero, but the acceleration is not. Note that the particle is always accelerating toward the center of the circle.

Example 2

A particle moves along a path according to the equation $\mathbf{r}(t) = t\mathbf{i} + t^2\mathbf{j} + \frac{2}{3}t^3\mathbf{k}$. Find $\mathbf{v}$, $\mathbf{a}$, ds/dt and d^2s/dt^2.

$$\mathbf{r}(t) = t\mathbf{i} + t^2\mathbf{j} + \frac{2}{3}t^3\mathbf{k}$$

$$\mathbf{v} = \mathbf{i} + 2t\mathbf{j} + 2t^2\mathbf{k}$$

$$\mathbf{a} = 2\mathbf{j} + 4t\mathbf{k}$$

$$\frac{ds}{dt} = |\mathbf{v}| = \sqrt{1 + 4t^2 + 4t^4} = 1 + 2t^2$$

$$\frac{d^2s}{dt^2} = 4t$$

It can be seen by both of these examples that, while the absolute value of the velocity is the speed, the absolute value of the acceleration is *not* the rate of change of speed.

Problems

In Problems 1–14, a particle moves along a path according to the equation given. Find $\mathbf{v}$, $\mathbf{a}$, ds/dt, and d^2s/dt^2 at the given value of t. Sketch the path of the particle and give a graphical representation of $\mathbf{v}$ and $\mathbf{a}$ at the given value of t.

1. $\mathbf{r}(t) = t\mathbf{i} + t^2\mathbf{j}$, $t = 1$.
2. $\mathbf{r}(t) = (t + 1)\mathbf{i} + (t^2 - 1)\mathbf{j}$, $t = 0$.
3. $\mathbf{r}(t) = (t^2 + 1)\mathbf{i} + (t^2 - 1)\mathbf{j}$, $t = 1$.
4. $\mathbf{r}(t) = t^2\mathbf{i} + (t^2 + t)\mathbf{j}$, $t = 2$.
5. $\mathbf{r}(t) = t\mathbf{i} + t^3\mathbf{j}$, $t = 1$.
6. $\mathbf{r}(t) = (t + 1)\mathbf{i} - t^3\mathbf{j}$, $t = 0$.
7. $\mathbf{r}(t) = (t^2 - 1)\mathbf{i} + (t^4 - 1)\mathbf{j}$, $t = -1$.
8. $\mathbf{r}(t) = (t^3 - 1)\mathbf{i} + (t^2 - 1)\mathbf{j}$, $t = 1$.
9. $\mathbf{r}(t) = t\mathbf{i} + \frac{1}{t}\mathbf{j}$, $t = 1$.
10. $\mathbf{r}(t) = t^2\,\mathbf{i} + \frac{1}{t^2}\mathbf{j}$, $t = 1$.
11. $\mathbf{r}(t) = \cos 2t\mathbf{i} + \sin 2t\mathbf{j}$, $t = \frac{\pi}{2}$.
12. $\mathbf{r}(t) = \cosh t\mathbf{i} + \sinh t\mathbf{j}$, $t = 0$.
13. $\mathbf{r}(t) = t\mathbf{i} + e^t\mathbf{j}$, $t = 1$.
14. $r(t) = t\mathbf{i} + \ln t\mathbf{j}$, $t = 1$.

In Problems 15–22, a particle moves along a path according to the equation given. Find $\mathbf{v}$, $\mathbf{a}$, ds/dt, and d^2s/dt^2.

15. $\mathbf{r}(t) = t\mathbf{i} - (t + 1)\mathbf{j} + t^2\mathbf{k}$.
16. $\mathbf{r}(t) = \mathbf{i} + (t - 1)\mathbf{j} + (t^2 + 1)\mathbf{k}$.
17. $\mathbf{r}(t) = t^2\mathbf{i} + (1 - t)\mathbf{j} + t\mathbf{k}$.
18. $\mathbf{r}(t) = \sqrt{2}t\mathbf{i} + \sqrt{t}\mathbf{j} + \frac{4}{3}t^{3/2}\mathbf{k}$.
19. $\mathbf{r}(t) = \cos t\mathbf{i} + \sin t\mathbf{j} + t\mathbf{k}$.
20. $\mathbf{r}(t) = \frac{1}{2}e^{2t}\mathbf{i} + \sqrt{2}e^t\mathbf{j} + t\mathbf{k}$.
21. $\mathbf{r}(t) = \frac{1}{t}\mathbf{i} + \sqrt{2}t\mathbf{j} + \frac{1}{3}t^3\mathbf{k}$.
22. $\mathbf{r}(t) = \frac{1}{2}t^2\mathbf{i} + \sqrt{2}t\mathbf{j} + \ln t\mathbf{k}$.

Partial Derivatives

22.1

Functions of Several Variables

Although we considered functions of several variables in Chapter 4, our considerations there were largely notational. Let us now move on to those things that are of some importance in calculus.

Definition

$\lim\limits_{\substack{x \to a \\ y \to b}} f(x, y) = L$ *means that*

(*a*) *if* δ *is a positive number, then there is a number pair* (x, y) *of the domain of* f *such* that $|x - a| < \delta$ and $|y - b| < \delta$, *and* $|x - a|$ *and* $|y - b|$ *are not both* 0, *and*

(*b*) *if* ϵ *is a positive number, then there is a positive number* δ *such that*

$$|f(x, y) - L| < \epsilon$$

whenever $|x - a| < \delta$ *and* $|y - b| < \delta$ *and* $|x - a|$ *and* $|y - b|$ *are not both* 0.

The geometric interpretation of this definition is given in Figure 22.1. The first part says that there is a number pair of the domain of f which is "close" to but not equal to (a, b)—"close" in this case meaning within a square of side 2δ, sides parallel to the x and y axes, and center at (a, b). The second part says that if we take a pair of horizontal planes with (a, b, L) between them, then there is a square of the type given above such that every point of the graph whose projection on the xy plane is inside the square, but not at its center, is between the horizontal planes.

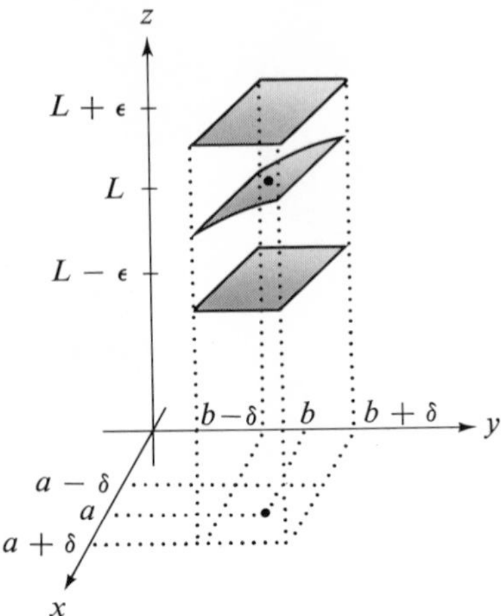

Figure 22.1

Note the similarity between this definition and the definition of a limit of a function of one variable. Of course, a similar definition holds for a function of three or more variables, although there is no graphical representation. Continuity is defined analogously.

Definition

If f is a real-valued function of two real variables, then f is **continuous** *at the point (a, b) of the domain of f means that if ϵ is a positive number, then there is a positive number δ such that*

$$|f(x, y) - f(a, b)| < \epsilon$$

whenever $|x - a| < \delta$ and $|y - b| < \delta$.

We can see, by their similarity, the relationship between these two definitions; limits of continuous functions can be found by substitution provided the point in question is a limit point of the domain of the function.

22.2

The Partial Derivative

Now we consider two derivatives, which we call partial derivatives, of a function of two variables.

Definition

If $z = f(x, y)$, then the **partial derivative** *of z with respect to x at (x, y) is*

$$\frac{\partial z}{\partial x} = \lim_{h \to 0} \frac{f(x+h, y) - f(x, y)}{h}$$

if this limit exists. The partial derivative of z with respect to y at (x, y) *is*

$$\frac{\partial z}{\partial y} = \lim_{h \to 0} \frac{f(x, y+h) - f(x, y)}{h}$$

if this limit exists.

Note that when the partial derivative of z is taken with respect to x, the y is unchanged in the two terms of the numerator; similarly the x is unchanged when the partial derivative is with respect to y. This suggests a very simple way of finding partial derivatives. When finding a partial derivative with respect to x, we simply differentiate, with y being regarded as a constant; similarly we find a partial derivative with respect to y by regarding x as a constant and differentiating with respect to the variable y.

Example 1

If $z = x^2 + xy$, find $\partial z/\partial x$ and $\partial z/\partial y$.

Regarding y as a constant, we have

$$\frac{\partial z}{\partial x} = 2x + y.$$

Regarding x as a constant, we have

$$\frac{\partial z}{\partial y} = x.$$

Of course, if we want a partial derivative at a particular point of the graph, we merely substitute its coordinates into the result.

Let us consider a graphical interpretation of partial derivatives. Suppose z is a function of x and y and we are considering the partial derivative of z with respect to x at the point (x_1, y_1, z_1). Since y is taken to be a constant and an ordinary derivative is taken with respect to x, this is graphically equivalent to considering the intersection of the plane $y = y_1$ with the surface $z = f(x, y)$ (see Figure 22.2) and then finding the slope of the curve that is the intersection of this plane and the original surface.

Exactly the same type of definition holds for functions of n variables.

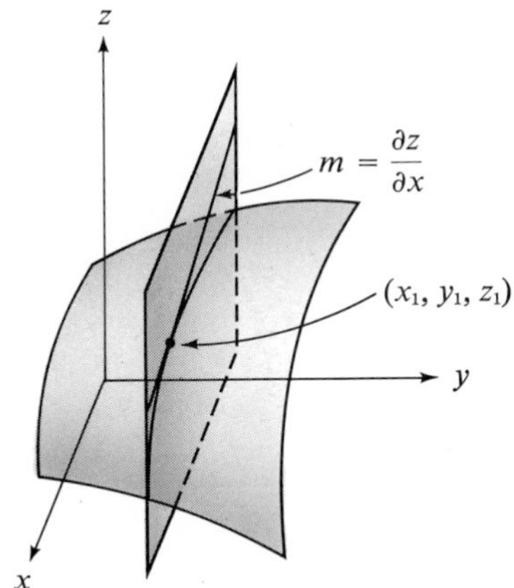

Figure 22.2

Definition

If $z = f(x_1, x_2, x_3, \ldots, x_n)$*, then*

$$\frac{\partial z}{\partial x_i} = \lim_{h \to 0} \frac{f(x_1, \ldots, x_i + h, \ldots x_n) - f(x_1, \ldots, x_i, \ldots x_n)}{h}$$

if this limit exists.

Again, $\partial z/\partial x_i$ is found by looking upon all variables but z and x_i as constants and finding an ordinary derivative. The only difference here is that if we go beyond a total of three variables, there is no easily visualized graphical interpretation, since more than three dimensions would be required.

Example 2

If $w = x^2y + y^2z - z^2x$, find $\partial w/\partial x$, $\partial w/\partial y$ and $\partial w/\partial z$.

$$\frac{\partial w}{\partial x} = 2xy - z^2,$$

$$\frac{\partial w}{\partial y} = x^2 + 2yz,$$

$$\frac{\partial w}{\partial z} = y^2 - 2zx.$$

There are several different types of notation used in connection with partial derivatives. If $z = f(x_1, x_2, \ldots, x_n)$, then the partial derivative of z (or f) with respect to x_i is denoted by

$$\frac{\partial z}{\partial x_i}, \quad z_{x_i}, \quad z_i, \quad D_{x_i} z \quad D_i z,$$

$$\frac{\partial f}{\partial x_i}, \quad f_{x_i}, \quad f_i, \quad D_{x_i} f \quad D_i f.$$

Each has its advantages and disadvantages, but all are used interchangeably; so you must learn all of them.

Just as with ordinary derivatives, it is possible to take a second, third, etc., partial derivative of a function. But there are more of them, since the second partial need not be with respect to the same variable as the first. For instance, if $z = f(x, y)$, we can take second partials, both with respect to x, both with respect to y, first with respect to x and then y, or first with respect to y and then x. The notation is as follows: both with respect to x:

$$\frac{\partial^2 z}{\partial x^2} = z_{xx} = z_{11} = D_{11} z,$$

both with respect to y:

$$\frac{\partial^2 z}{\partial y^2} = z_{yy} = z_{22} = D_{22} z,$$

first with respect to x and then y:

$$\frac{\partial^2 z}{\partial y\, \partial x} = z_{xy} = z_{12} = D_{12} z,$$

and first with respect to y and then x:

$$\frac{\partial^2 z}{\partial x\, \partial y} = z_{yx} = z_{21} = D_{21}z.$$

Example 3

Find all second partials of $z = x^2 - 2xy + 2y^2$.

$$\frac{\partial z}{\partial x} = 2x - 2y \qquad \frac{\partial z}{\partial y} = -2x + 4y$$

$$\frac{\partial^2 z}{\partial x^2} = 2, \quad \frac{\partial^2 z}{\partial y\, \partial x} = -2, \quad \frac{\partial^2 z}{\partial x\, \partial y} = -2, \quad \frac{\partial^2 z}{\partial y^2} = 4.$$

It might be noted that, in this case,

$$\frac{\partial^2 z}{\partial y\, \partial x} = \frac{\partial^2 z}{\partial x\, \partial y}.$$

Actually there is a large class of functions for which this is true, and it includes most of the functions with which we shall be dealing.

Theorem 22.1

If f is a function such that

$$\frac{\partial^2 z}{\partial y\, \partial x} \quad \text{and} \quad \frac{\partial^2 z}{\partial x\, \partial y}$$

are both continuous, then

$$\frac{\partial^2 z}{\partial y\, \partial x} = \frac{\partial^2 z}{\partial x\, \partial y}.$$

Problems

In Problems 1–14, find $\partial z/\partial x$ and $\partial z/\partial y$.

1. $z = x^2 + y^2$.
2. $z = x^2 - 2xy$.
3. $z = \dfrac{x}{y}$.
4. $z = \dfrac{x + y}{x - y}$.
5. $z = \sqrt{xy}$.
6. $z = (x^2 + y)^2$.
7. $z = (x - 2y)^3$.
8. $z = x + y + e^{xy}$.
9. $z = \dfrac{x^2 + y^2}{x^2 - y^2}$.
10. $z = \sin x \cos y$.
11. $z = \ln(x^2 + y^2)$.
12. $z = \ln \sin xy$.
13. $z = e^{x \sin y}$.
14. $z = x \sin y - y \sin x$.

In Problems 15–22, find $\partial z/\partial x$ and $\partial z/\partial y$ at the point indicated.

15. $z = x^2 - y^2$, (1, 1, 0).

16. $z = x + \dfrac{y^2}{x}$, (1, 2, 5).

17. $z = xy - y^3$, (2, −1, −1).

18. $z = \dfrac{x - 2y}{2x + y}$, (1, −1, 3).

19. $z = x \sin y$, (2, $\pi/2$, 2).

20. $z = e^{x/y}$, (2, 1, e^2).

21. $z = \tan xy$, ($\pi/2$, 1/2, 1).

22. $z = e^{\sin xy}$, (4, 0, 1).

In Problems 23–28, find $\partial w/\partial x$, $\partial w/\partial y$ and $\partial w/\partial z$.

23. $w = xyz$.

24. $w = x \sin yz$.

25. $w = x^2y^2 + y^3 + y^2z^2$.

26. $w = \dfrac{x^2 + y^2}{y^2 + z^2}$.

27. $w = x^2 + y^2$.

28. $w = xe^{y/z}$.

In Problems 29–36, find $\partial^2 z/\partial x^2$, $\partial^2 z/\partial y\, \partial x$, $\partial^2 z/\partial x\, \partial y$, and $\partial^2 z/\partial y^2$.

29. $z = x^3 - 3x^2y + y^3$.

30. $z = \dfrac{y}{x}$.

31. $z = \dfrac{1}{(x + y)^2}$.

32. $z = \sin x \cos y$.

33. $z = e^x \tan y$.

34. $z = \ln (x^3 + y^3)$.

35. $z = \dfrac{\sin x}{y}$.

36. $z = \dfrac{\sin xy}{xy}$.

22.3

The Chain Rule

Suppose that $z = f(x, y)$, $x = F(t)$, and $y = G(t)$. It then follows that z is a function of t, $z = f(F(t), G(t))$, and we can consider the derivative of z with respect to t.

$$\frac{dz}{dt} = \lim_{h\to 0} \frac{f(F(t+h), G(t+h)) - f(F(t), G(t))}{h}$$

$$= \lim_{h\to 0} \left[\frac{f(F(t+h), G(t+h)) - f(F(t), G(t+h))}{h} + \frac{f(F(t), G(t+h)) - f(F(t), G(t))}{h}\right] \qquad \text{(See Note 1)}$$

$$= \lim_{h\to 0} \left[\frac{f(F(t+h), G(t+h)) - f(F(t), G(t+h))}{F(t+h) - F(t)} \frac{F(t+h) - F(t)}{h} + \frac{f(F(t), G(t+h)) - f(F(t), G(t))}{G(t+h) - G(t)} \frac{G(t+h) - G(t)}{h}\right]. \qquad \text{(See Note 2)}$$

Substituting $i = F(t+h) - F(t)$ and $j = G(t+h) - G(t)$, we have

$$\frac{dz}{dt} = \lim_{\substack{h\to 0\\ i\to 0\\ j\to 0}} \left[\frac{f(F(t)+i, G(t)+j) - f(F(t), G(t)+j)}{i}\,\frac{F(t+h)-F(t)}{h}\right.$$

$$\left. + \frac{f(F(t), G(t)+j) - f(F(t),G(t))}{j}\,\frac{G(t+h)-G(t)}{h}\right] \qquad \text{(See Note 3)}$$

$$= \lim_{\substack{h\to 0\\ i\to 0\\ j\to 0}} \left[\frac{f(x+i, y+j) - f(x, y+j)}{i}\,\frac{F(t+h)-F(t)}{h}\right.$$

$$\left. + \frac{f(x, y+j) - f(x, y)}{j}\,\frac{G(t+h)-G(t)}{h}\right]$$

$$= \frac{\partial z}{\partial x}\cdot\frac{dx}{dt} + \frac{\partial z}{\partial y}\cdot\frac{dy}{dt}. \qquad \text{(See Notes 4 and 5)}$$

Note 1: We have added and subtracted $f(F(t), G(t+h))$—in order to make the expression look a little more like a partial derivative, in which the second variable $G(t+h)$ remains unchanged while the first changes from $F(t+h)$ to $F(t)$. This is the old policy of putting in what we want and compensating to give equality.

Note 2: We want the denominator to be the difference between $F(t+h)$ and $F(t)$ in the first expression and $G(t+h)$ and $G(t)$ in the second. Again, we put them in and compensate. One problem arises at this point; we must be sure that $F(t+h) - F(t)$ and $G(t+h) - G(t)$ are not zero. Let us consider how this may be done with the function F. Suppose there is an interval (a, b) containing t such that $F'(x) \neq 0$ for any x in (a, b) except possibly $x = t$. Let us choose h small enough so that $t + h$ is in this interval. Applying the mean-value theorem for the interval $[t, t+h]$ (or $[t+h, t]$ if $h < 0$), we see that there is a number t_0 between t and $t+h$ such that

$$F'(t_0) = \frac{F(t+h) - F(t)}{h}.$$

Since $F'(t_0) \neq 0$

$$F(t+h) - F(t) \neq 0.$$

A similar argument can be used to show $G(t+h) - G(t) \neq 0$. For the case in which there is no such interval (a, b), see Note 5.

Note 3: Assuming F and G to be differentiable functions, we know that they are continuous. Thus as h approaches 0,

$$i = F(t+h) - F(t) \to 0 \quad \text{and} \quad j = G(t+h) - G(t) \to 0.$$

Note 4: Since $y = G(t)$ is continuous, we see that

$$\lim_{\substack{i\to 0\\ j\to 0}} \frac{f(x+i, y+j) - f(x, y+j)}{i} = \lim_{i\to 0} \frac{f(x+i, y) - f(x, y)}{i} = \frac{\partial f}{\partial x} = \frac{\partial z}{\partial x}.$$

Note 5: Suppose there is no interval (a, b) containing t such that $F'(x) \neq 0$ for any x in (a, b). Then for every number h, there is a number t_0 between t and $t + h$ such that $F'(t_0) = 0$. If F' is continuous at t, then

$$\frac{dx}{dt} = F'(t) = \lim_{s \to t} F'(s) = 0.$$

But for every number h, there is a number t_1 between t and $t + h$ such that $F(t_1) = F(t)$; if this were not so, then, by the mean-value theorem, $F'(x) \neq 0$ for any x between t and $t + h$. Thus,

$$\lim_{h \to 0} \frac{f(F(t+h), G(t+h)) - f(F(t), G(t+h))}{h}$$
$$= \lim_{t_1 \to t} \frac{f(F(t_1), G(t_1)) - f(F(t), G(t_1))}{h}$$
$$= \lim_{t_1 \to t} \frac{0}{t} = 0.$$

Thus

$$\lim_{h \to 0} \frac{f(F(t+h), G(t+h)) - f(F(t), G(t+h))}{h} = \frac{\partial z}{\partial x} \cdot \frac{dx}{dt}.$$

Theorem 22.2

If $z = f(x, y)$, $x = F(t)$, and $y = G(t)$, and if $\partial z/\partial x$ and $\partial z/\partial y$ exist, and dx/dt and dy/dt are continuous, then

$$\frac{dz}{dt} = \frac{\partial z}{\partial x} \cdot \frac{dx}{dt} + \frac{\partial z}{\partial y} \cdot \frac{dy}{dt}.$$

Example 1

If $z = x^2 + y^2$, $x = \sin t$ and $y = e^t$, find dz/dt.

$$\begin{aligned} \frac{dz}{dt} &= \frac{\partial z}{\partial x}\frac{dx}{dt} + \frac{\partial z}{\partial y}\frac{dy}{dt} \\ &= 2x \cdot \cos t + 2y \cdot e^t \\ &= 2(x \cos t + ye^t). \end{aligned}$$

By substituting $x = \sin t$ and $y = e^t$, we can express the result entirely in terms of t.

$$\frac{dz}{dt} = 2(\sin t \cos t + e^{2t}).$$

Of course, this derivative could also be found by substituting first and then differentiating.

$$\begin{aligned} z &= x^2 + y^2 \\ &= \sin^2 t + e^{2t} \\ \frac{dz}{dt} &= 2 \sin t \cos t + 2e^{2t}. \end{aligned}$$

Theorem 22.2 is especially useful when we do not know what all of the functions are. This theorem can be extended in many ways. Perhaps the most obvious is the case in which z is a function of three or more variables, each of which is a function of t.

Theorem 22.3

If $z = f(x_1, x_2, \ldots, x_n)$ and $x_i = g_i(t)$, $i = 1, 2, \ldots, n$, and if all partial derivatives of z exist, and dx_i/dt is continuous, $i = 1, 2, \ldots, n$, then

$$\frac{dz}{dt} = \sum_{i=1}^{\infty} \frac{\partial f}{\partial x_i} \frac{dx_i}{dt}.$$

A special case of Theorem 22.2 follows.

Theorem 22.4

If $z = f(x, y)$ and $y = g(x)$ and if $\partial z/\partial x$ and $\partial z/\partial y$ exist and dy/dx is continuous, then

$$\frac{dz}{dx} = \frac{\partial z}{\partial x} + \frac{\partial z}{\partial y} \cdot \frac{dy}{dx}.$$

Example 2

If $z = x^2 + xy + y^2$ and $y = \sin x$, find dz/dx.

$$\frac{dz}{dx} = \frac{\partial z}{\partial x} + \frac{\partial z}{\partial y} \cdot \frac{dy}{dx} = (2x + y) + (x + 2y)\cos x.$$

Again, this expression can be put entirely in terms of x, or it could be found by substituting $y = \sin x$ first and differentiating in the ordinary way.

Note the distinction between $\partial z/\partial x$ and dz/dx. $\partial z/\partial x$ is determined by the original function $z = f(x, y)$, where x and y are assumed to be two independent variables. The fact that $y = g(x)$ puts an additional restriction upon x and y does not enter into consideration when one is finding $\partial z/\partial x$ or $\partial z/\partial y$. This restriction *is* taken into account when finding dz/dx.

Just as Theorem 22.2, in which z is a function of two variables, can be extended to give Theorem 22.3, in which z is a function of n variables, it can also be extended from the case in which x and y are functions of a single variable t to the case in which x and y are functions of m variables. Let us consider one special case here.

Theorem 22.5

If $z = f(x, y)$, $x = F(u, v)$, and $y = G(u, v)$ and if $\partial z/\partial x$ and $\partial z/\partial y$ exist, and $\partial x/\partial u$, $\partial x/\partial v$, $\partial y/\partial u$, and $\partial y/\partial v$ are continuous, then

$$\frac{\partial z}{\partial u} = \frac{\partial z}{\partial x} \cdot \frac{\partial x}{\partial u} + \frac{\partial z}{\partial y} \cdot \frac{\partial y}{\partial u}$$

and

$$\frac{\partial z}{\partial v} = \frac{\partial z}{\partial x} \cdot \frac{\partial x}{\partial v} + \frac{\partial z}{\partial y} \cdot \frac{\partial y}{\partial v}.$$

The proof of this theorem is analogous to the proof of Theorem 22.2.

Example 3

If $z = x^2 - y^3$, $x = u + v$, and $y = u - v$, find $\partial z/\partial u$ and $\partial z/\partial v$.

$$\frac{\partial z}{\partial u} = \frac{\partial z}{\partial x} \cdot \frac{\partial x}{\partial u} + \frac{\partial z}{\partial y} \cdot \frac{\partial y}{\partial u}$$

$$= 2x \cdot 1 - 3y^2 \cdot 1$$

$$= 2x - 3y^2.$$

A question that arises is, "How do we know when to use a partial derivative and when to use an ordinary derivative?" It is simply a matter of noting whether the function in question is a function of one variable or more than one. For instance, in Theorem 22.5, z is a function of the two variables x and y. Thus we want the partial derivatives

$$\frac{\partial z}{\partial x} \quad \text{and} \quad \frac{\partial z}{\partial y}.$$

Again, both x and y are functions of the two variables u and v. We again want partial derivatives

$$\frac{\partial x}{\partial u}, \quad \frac{\partial x}{\partial v}, \quad \frac{\partial y}{\partial u}, \quad \frac{\partial y}{\partial v}.$$

Finally, if the x and y in $z = f(x, y)$ are by replaced $F(u, v)$ and $G(u, v)$, we have $z = f(F(u, v), G(u, v))$, which is still a function of two variables. Thus, we still want partial derivatives,

$$\frac{\partial z}{\partial u} \quad \text{and} \quad \frac{\partial z}{\partial v}.$$

Problems

In Problems 1–24, use the theorems of this section to find the required derivatives.

1. $z = xy$, $x = 2t + 1$, $y = \sin t$; find dz/dt.
2. $z = x^2y$, $x = t^2 + 1$, $y = e^t$; find dz/dt.
3. $z = x/y$, $x = t \sin t$, $y = \cos t$; find dz/dt.
4. $z = x^3 - y$, $x = te^t$, $y = \sin t$; find dz/dt.
5. $w = x^2 + y^2 + z^2$, $x = t + 1$, $y = t$, $z = t - 1$; find dw/dt.
6. $w = \dfrac{x^2 + y^2}{z}$, $x = t - 2$, $y = t^2 - 1$, $z = t^2 + 1$; find dw/dt.
7. $w = x^2y + y^2z + z^2x$, $x = \sin t$, $y = \cos t$, $z = \tan t$; find dw/dt.
8. $w = z(x^2 + y)$, $x = e^t$, $y = e^{-t}$, $z = t$; find dw/dt.
9. $z = x^2 + y^2$, $x = u^2 + v^2$, $y = u^2 - v^2$; find $\partial z/\partial u$ and $\partial z/\partial v$.
10. $z = \dfrac{x}{y}$, $x = u \sin v$, $y = v \cos u$; find $\partial z/\partial u$ and $\partial z/\partial v$.

11. $z = xy$, $x = u^2 + v^2$, $y = \dfrac{u}{v}$; find $\partial z/\partial u$ and $\partial z/\partial v$.
12. $z = x^2y$, $x = 2u + v$, $y = 2v - u$; find $\partial z/\partial u$ and $\partial z/\partial v$.
13. $w = x^2 + y^2 + z^2$, $x = u^2 + v^2$, $y = u^2 - v^2$, $z = uv$; find $\partial w/\partial u$ and $\partial w/\partial v$.
14. $w = xyz$, $x = u + v$, $y = u - v$, $z = 2u + 3v$; find $\partial w/\partial u$ and $\partial w/\partial v$.
15. $w = 2x + 3y - z$, $x = u \sin v$, $y = v \sin u$, $z = \sin u \sin v$; find $\partial w/\partial u$ and $\partial w/\partial v$.
16. $w = xy + yz + zx$, $x = u + v$, $y = 2u + v$, $z = u - 2v$; find $\partial w/\partial u$ and $\partial w/\partial v$.
17. $w = xyz$, $x = tuv$, $y = \dfrac{t}{u}$, $z = \dfrac{u}{v}$; find $\partial w/\partial t$, $\partial w/\partial u$, and $\partial w/\partial v$.
18. $w = 2x + y - z$, $x = t^2 + u^2$, $y = u^2 + v^2$, $z = v^2 + t^2$; find $\partial w/\partial t$, $\partial w/\partial u$, and $\partial w/\partial v$.
19. $v = xy + zw$, $x = st$, $y = s + t$, $z = \dfrac{s}{t}$, $w = s - t$; find $\partial v/\partial s$ and $\partial v/\partial t$.
20. $v = 2x + y - z + 3w$, $x = t \sin t$, $y = \dfrac{\sin t}{t}$, $z = t \cos t$, $w = \dfrac{\cos t}{t}$; find dv/dt.
21. $z = x^2 + y^2$, $y = x \sin x$; find dz/dx.
22. $z = xy$, $y = e^x \sin x$; find dz/dx.
23. $z = 2x - y$, $y = xe^x$; find dz/dx.
24. $z = \dfrac{x}{y}$, $y = x + \sin x$; find dz/dx.
25. If $z = f(x, y)$, $x = r \cos \theta$, and $y = r \sin \theta$, find $\partial z/\partial r$ and $\partial z/\partial \theta$.
26. If $z = f(r, \theta)$, $r = \sqrt{x^2 + y^2}$, and $\theta = \text{Arctan}\, \dfrac{y}{x}$, find $\partial z/\partial x$ and $\partial z/\partial y$.
27. If $w = f(x, y, z)$, $x = \rho \sin \varphi \cos \theta$, $y = \rho \sin \varphi \sin \theta$, and $z = \rho \cos \varphi$, find $\partial w/\partial \rho$, $\partial w/\partial \varphi$, and $\partial w/\partial \theta$.
28. Prove Theorem 22.4.

22.4

Implicit Functions

We first considered derivatives of implicit functions in Chapter 5. Now we shall reconsider them in the light of partial derivatives and go on to consider more complicated cases. An expression of the form

$$F(x, y) = 0$$

determines y as a function (or combination of functions) of x, $y = f(x)$. Thus, F is indirectly a function of x. Let us take the derivative of both sides with respect to x. Assuming that the derivatives in question exist, then by Theorem 22.4,

$$\frac{\partial F}{\partial x} + \frac{\partial F}{\partial y} \cdot \frac{dy}{dx} = 0.$$

Solving for dy/dx, we have

$$\frac{dy}{dx} = -\frac{\partial F/\partial x}{\partial F/\partial y}.$$

Theorem 22.6

If $F(x, y) = 0$, $\partial F/\partial x$ and $\partial F/\partial y$ both exist, and $\partial F/\partial y \neq 0$, then dy/dx exists and

$$\frac{dy}{dx} = -\frac{\partial F/\partial x}{\partial F/\partial y}.$$

Example 1

If $x^2 + y^2 = 4$, find dy/dx.

First of all, the equation can be written in the form

$$x^2 + y^2 - 4 = 0.$$

$$\frac{dy}{dx} = -\frac{\partial F/\partial x}{\partial F/\partial y} = -\frac{x}{y}.$$

If we compare this example with what we did on pages 82–83, we see that the procedures are essentially the same. In effect, we were deriving this formula every time we needed it in Chapter 5. Let us consider a somewhat more difficult case. Suppose

$$F(x, y, z) = 0.$$

The equation again determines one of the three variables, say z, as a function of the other two.

$$z = f(x, y).$$

So we can find $\partial z/\partial x$ and $\partial z/\partial y$. Suppose we first take the derivative of both sides of $F(x, y, z) = 0$ with respect to x, remembering that $z = f(x, y)$ and x and y are independent.

$$\frac{\partial F}{\partial x} \cdot \frac{\partial x}{\partial x} + \frac{\partial F}{\partial y}\frac{\partial y}{\partial x} + \frac{\partial F}{\partial z}\frac{\partial z}{\partial x} = 0.$$

Of course $\partial x/\partial x = 1$. Since x and y are taken to be independent, $\partial y/\partial x = 0$, and the above equation can be simplified to

$$\frac{\partial F}{\partial x} + \frac{\partial F}{\partial z}\frac{\partial z}{\partial x} = 0.$$

Solving for $\partial z/\partial x$, we have

$$\frac{\partial z}{\partial x} = -\frac{\partial F/\partial x}{\partial F/\partial z}.$$

By a similar argument, we could show that

$$\frac{\partial z}{\partial y} = -\frac{\partial F/\partial y}{\partial F/\partial z}.$$

Theorem 22.7

If $F(x, y, z) = 0$, the three partial derivatives of F exist, and $\partial F/\partial z \neq 0$, then $\partial z/\partial x$ and $\partial z/\partial y$ exist and

$$\frac{\partial z}{\partial x} = -\frac{\partial F/\partial x}{\partial F/\partial z}, \qquad \frac{\partial z}{\partial y} = -\frac{\partial F/\partial y}{\partial F/\partial z}.$$

Example 2

If $x^2y + y^2z + z^2x = 0$, find $\partial z/\partial x$ and $\partial z/\partial y$.

$$\frac{\partial z}{\partial x} = -\frac{\partial F/\partial x}{\partial F/\partial z} = -\frac{2xy + z^2}{y^2 + 2zx},$$

$$\frac{\partial y}{\partial z} = -\frac{\partial F/\partial y}{\partial F/\partial z} = -\frac{x^2 + 2yz}{y^2 + 2zx}.$$

Actually, there is no particular reason to consider z as a function of x and y; we can think of any one of the three as a function of the other two. There are six possible derivatives we can consider:

$$\frac{\partial z}{\partial x} = -\frac{\partial F/\partial x}{\partial F/\partial z}, \qquad \frac{\partial z}{\partial y} = -\frac{\partial F/\partial y}{\partial F/\partial z},$$

$$\frac{\partial y}{\partial x} = -\frac{\partial F/\partial x}{\partial F/\partial y}, \qquad \frac{\partial y}{\partial z} = -\frac{\partial F/\partial z}{\partial F/\partial y},$$

$$\frac{\partial x}{\partial y} = -\frac{\partial F/\partial y}{\partial F/\partial x}, \qquad \frac{\partial x}{\partial z} = -\frac{\partial F/\partial z}{\partial F/\partial x}.$$

As an aid to the memory, we might note that, except for the minus sign, the quotients behave as if the partial derivatives were fractions. There is another way of looking at the expressions which will carry over to other, more complicated situations. Suppose, for instance, that we want to find $\partial y/\partial x$ from the equation $F(x, y, z) = 0$. We must then consider y to be a function of x and z, $y = f(x, z)$. In effect, this says that x and z are two independent variables and that y is the dependent variable. In that case, $\partial F/\partial y$, the derivative with respect to this one dependent variable, must be in the denominator. The numerator is found by replacing the y in the denominator by x, since we are looking for $\partial y/\partial x$. This scheme works in all of the cases listed. However, you are warned not to draw any far-reaching conclusions from the above discussion—it is only a device to aid the memory. This result holds for an equation of any number of variables.

Let us now consider a somewhat more complicated situation. Suppose we have the two equations in x, y, and z

$$F(x, y, z) = 0,$$

$$G(x, y, z) = 0.$$

Suppose further that one of the variables, say z, can be eliminated to give a single equation, $H(x, y) = 0$ in x and y, and that we can solve for y as a function of x, that is, $y = f(x)$. Then we could consider dy/dx.

Suppose we try to find dy/dx without first finding $y = f(x)$. We begin by taking the partial derivatives of both equations with respect to x. By Theorem 22.4 (extended to three variables), we have

$$\frac{\partial F}{\partial x} + \frac{\partial F}{\partial y}\frac{dy}{dx} + \frac{\partial F}{\partial z}\cdot\frac{dz}{dx} = 0,$$

$$\frac{\partial G}{\partial x} + \frac{\partial G}{\partial y}\cdot\frac{dy}{dx} + \frac{\partial G}{\partial z}\cdot\frac{dz}{dx} = 0$$

or

$$\frac{\partial F}{\partial y}\cdot\frac{dy}{dx} + \frac{\partial F}{\partial z}\cdot\frac{dz}{dx} = -\frac{\partial F}{\partial x},$$

$$\frac{\partial G}{\partial y}\cdot\frac{dy}{dx} + \frac{\partial G}{\partial z}\cdot\frac{dz}{dx} = -\frac{\partial G}{\partial x}.$$

We now have two simultaneous equations in dy/dx and dz/dx. Solving by determinants, we have

$$\frac{dy}{dx} = \frac{\begin{vmatrix} -\dfrac{\partial F}{\partial x} & \dfrac{\partial F}{\partial z} \\[2ex] -\dfrac{\partial G}{\partial x} & \dfrac{\partial G}{\partial z} \end{vmatrix}}{\begin{vmatrix} \dfrac{\partial F}{\partial y} & \dfrac{\partial F}{\partial z} \\[2ex] \dfrac{\partial G}{\partial y} & \dfrac{\partial G}{\partial z} \end{vmatrix}} = -\frac{\begin{vmatrix} \dfrac{\partial F}{\partial x} & \dfrac{\partial F}{\partial z} \\[2ex] \dfrac{\partial G}{\partial x} & \dfrac{\partial G}{\partial z} \end{vmatrix}}{\begin{vmatrix} \dfrac{\partial F}{\partial y} & \dfrac{\partial F}{\partial z} \\[2ex] \dfrac{\partial G}{\partial y} & \dfrac{\partial G}{\partial z} \end{vmatrix}}$$

and

$$\frac{dz}{dx} = \frac{\begin{vmatrix} \dfrac{\partial F}{\partial y} & -\dfrac{\partial F}{\partial x} \\[2ex] \dfrac{\partial G}{\partial y} & -\dfrac{\partial G}{\partial x} \end{vmatrix}}{\begin{vmatrix} \dfrac{\partial F}{\partial y} & \dfrac{\partial F}{\partial z} \\[2ex] \dfrac{\partial G}{\partial y} & \dfrac{\partial G}{\partial z} \end{vmatrix}} = -\frac{\begin{vmatrix} \dfrac{\partial F}{\partial y} & \dfrac{\partial F}{\partial x} \\[2ex] \dfrac{\partial G}{\partial y} & \dfrac{\partial G}{\partial x} \end{vmatrix}}{\begin{vmatrix} \dfrac{\partial F}{\partial y} & \dfrac{\partial F}{\partial z} \\[2ex] \dfrac{\partial G}{\partial y} & \dfrac{\partial G}{\partial z} \end{vmatrix}}.$$

This result is often abbreviated to

$$\frac{dy}{dx} = -\frac{\dfrac{\partial(F, G)}{\partial(x, z)}}{\dfrac{\partial(F, G)}{\partial(y, z)}}, \qquad \frac{dz}{dx} = -\frac{\dfrac{\partial(F, G)}{\partial(y, x)}}{\dfrac{\partial(F, G)}{\partial(y, z)}}.$$

Theorem 22.8

If

$$F(x, y, z) = 0 \quad \textit{and} \quad G(x, y, z) = 0$$

and if all partial derivatives of both functions exist and

$$\frac{\partial(F, G)}{\partial(y, z)} \neq 0,$$

then dy/dx and dz/dx both exist and

$$\frac{dy}{dx} = -\frac{\dfrac{\partial(F, G)}{\partial(x, z)}}{\dfrac{\partial(F, G)}{\partial(y, z)}}, \qquad \frac{dz}{dx} = -\frac{\dfrac{\partial(F, G)}{\partial(y, x)}}{\dfrac{\partial(F, G)}{\partial(y, z)}},$$

where

$$\frac{\partial(F, G)}{\partial(y, z)} = \begin{vmatrix} \dfrac{\partial F}{\partial y} & \dfrac{\partial F}{\partial z} \\ \dfrac{\partial G}{\partial y} & \dfrac{\partial G}{\partial z} \end{vmatrix}.$$

Before we apply this theorem, some comments upon the final form are in order. When we have two equations, there must be two dependent variables. As already noted, we can imagine z to be eliminated between the two equations, with the result being solved for y as a function of x. Similarly, we can imagine y to be eliminated, with the result being solved for z as a function of x. Thus, both y and z are dependent variables, since both are functions of the single independent variable x. Of course, there are other combinations; for instance, x and z might be the dependent variables and y the independent variable, and so forth.

Now suppose we want to find dy/dx. How do we know which are the dependent variables and which the independent variable? When we see dy/dx, we know immediately that y must be a function of x. Thus y is a dependent variable and x an independent variable. Since two equations are given, there must be a second dependent variable—it must be z. So y and z are the two dependent variables, and the denominator must be

$$\frac{\partial(F, G)}{\partial(y, z)},$$

by the scheme we have already described. Since we want dy/dx, we replace the y of the denominator by x to get the proper expression for the numerator. Thus

$$\frac{dy}{dx} = -\frac{\dfrac{\partial(F, G)}{\partial(x, z)}}{\dfrac{\partial(F, G)}{\partial(y, z)}}.$$

While the order of the y and z of the denominator is quite arbitrary, we must simply substitute without changing the order if we are to get the proper expression for the numerator. If the order were reversed, we would not get the correct expression, but rather its negative.

Example 3

If $x^2 + y^2 + z^2 = 4$ and $xyz = 1$, find dy/dx.

The two equations are

$$F: x^2 + y^2 + z^2 - 4 = 0,$$
$$G: xyz - 1 = 0.$$

Therefore,

$$\frac{dy}{dx} = -\frac{\dfrac{\partial(F, G)}{\partial(x\ z)}}{\dfrac{\partial(F, G)}{\partial(y, z)}} = -\frac{\begin{vmatrix} \dfrac{\partial F}{\partial x} & \dfrac{\partial F}{\partial z} \\ \dfrac{\partial G}{\partial x} & \dfrac{\partial G}{\partial z} \end{vmatrix}}{\begin{vmatrix} \dfrac{\partial F}{\partial y} & \dfrac{\partial F}{\partial z} \\ \dfrac{\partial G}{\partial y} & \dfrac{\partial G}{\partial z} \end{vmatrix}} = -\frac{\begin{vmatrix} 2x & 2z \\ yz & xy \end{vmatrix}}{\begin{vmatrix} 2y & 2z \\ xz & xy \end{vmatrix}}$$

$$= -\frac{2x^2y - 2yz^2}{2xy^2 - 2xz^2} = -\frac{y(x^2 - z^2)}{x(y^2 - z^2)}.$$

This procedure can be extended to two equations in four, five, six, or more variables, as well as to three equations in four or more variables. In setting up the expression for the desired derivative, remember that the number of equations equals the number of dependent variables. An additional problem arises when the number of variables exceeds the number of equations by more than one. To see how, suppose we have the two equations

$$F(w, x, y, z) = 0,$$
$$G(w, x, y, z) = 0$$

and we are asked to find $\partial y/\partial x$. Now we know that, if we are to talk about $\partial y/\partial x$, then y must be a function of x and some other variable. Thus y is a dependent variable and x is independent. But what of the other two variables? Which is the second dependent variable and which is independent? There is no way of determining it from the information given. The problem, as stated, is ambiguous—there are two possible answers, depending upon whether we take w or z to be the second dependent variable.

In order to avoid this ambiguity, we shall use the following notation:

$$\left(\frac{\partial y}{\partial x}\right)_w,$$

which is read: the partial derivative of y with respect to x, w held constant. It implies that w, as well as x, is an independent variable. Thus

$$\left(\frac{\partial y}{\partial x}\right)_w = -\frac{\dfrac{\partial(F, G)}{\partial(x, z)}}{\dfrac{\partial(F, G)}{\partial(y, z)}}.$$

Example 4

If $w^2 + x^2 + y^2 + z^2 = 4$ and $wxyz = 1$ find $(\partial z/\partial y)_x$.

$$F\colon w^2 + x^2 + y^2 + z^2 - 4 = 0,$$

$$G\colon wxyz - 1 = 0.$$

$$\left(\frac{\partial z}{\partial y}\right)_x = -\frac{\dfrac{\partial(F, G)}{\partial(w, y)}}{\dfrac{\partial(F, G)}{\partial(w, z)}} = -\frac{\begin{vmatrix} \dfrac{\partial F}{\partial w} & \dfrac{\partial F}{\partial y} \\ \dfrac{\partial G}{\partial w} & \dfrac{\partial G}{\partial y} \end{vmatrix}}{\begin{vmatrix} \dfrac{\partial F}{\partial w} & \dfrac{\partial F}{\partial z} \\ \dfrac{\partial G}{\partial w} & \dfrac{\partial G}{\partial z} \end{vmatrix}} = -\frac{\begin{vmatrix} 2w & 2y \\ xyz & wxz \end{vmatrix}}{\begin{vmatrix} 2w & 2z \\ xyz & wxy \end{vmatrix}}$$

$$= -\frac{2w^2xz - 2xy^2z}{2w^2xy - 2xyz^2} = -\frac{z(w^2 - y^2)}{y(w^2 - z^2)}.$$

Example 5

If $u^2 + v^2 = 1$, $x^2 + y^2 = 1$, and $u + v + x + y = 0$, find dy/du.

$$\begin{aligned} &F\colon\ u^2 + v^2 \qquad\qquad\quad - 1 = 0, \\ &G\colon\ \qquad\qquad x^2 + y^2 - 1 = 0, \\ &H\colon\ u + v + x + y \qquad\ \ = 0. \end{aligned}$$

Since there are three equations, there are three dependent variables. Since we want dy/du, u is the one independent variable. Thus,

$$\frac{dy}{du} = -\frac{\dfrac{\partial(F, G, H)}{\partial(v, x, u)}}{\dfrac{\partial(F, G, H)}{\partial(v, x, y)}} = -\frac{\begin{vmatrix} \dfrac{\partial F}{\partial v} & \dfrac{\partial F}{\partial x} & \dfrac{\partial F}{\partial u} \\ \dfrac{\partial G}{\partial v} & \dfrac{\partial G}{\partial x} & \dfrac{\partial G}{\partial u} \\ \dfrac{\partial H}{\partial v} & \dfrac{\partial H}{\partial x} & \dfrac{\partial H}{\partial u} \end{vmatrix}}{\begin{vmatrix} \dfrac{\partial F}{\partial v} & \dfrac{\partial F}{\partial x} & \dfrac{\partial F}{\partial y} \\ \dfrac{\partial G}{\partial v} & \dfrac{\partial G}{\partial x} & \dfrac{\partial G}{\partial y} \\ \dfrac{\partial H}{\partial v} & \dfrac{\partial H}{\partial x} & \dfrac{\partial H}{\partial y} \end{vmatrix}} = -\frac{\begin{vmatrix} 2v & 0 & 2u \\ 0 & 2x & 0 \\ 1 & 1 & 1 \end{vmatrix}}{\begin{vmatrix} 2v & 0 & 0 \\ 0 & 2x & 2y \\ 1 & 1 & 1 \end{vmatrix}}$$

$$= -\frac{4xv - 4xu}{4xv - 4yv} = -\frac{x(v - u)}{v(x - y)}.$$

Problems

In Problems 1–27, find the required derivative(s).

1. $x^3 - 3x^2y + y^3 = 4$; find dy/dx.
2. $x^2 - 2xy - y^2 = 1$; find dy/dx.
3. $x + \sqrt{xy} + y = 1$; find dy/dx.
4. $(x^2 + y)^2 + y = 2$; find dy/dx.
5. $\sin xy + x = 1$; find dy/dx.
6. $e^{xy} + y^2 + 1 = 0$; find dy/dx.
7. $x^2 + y^2 + z^2 = 4$; find $\partial y/\partial x$ and $\partial y/\partial z$.
8. $x^2 - xyz + z^2 = 2$; find $\partial y/\partial x$ and $\partial y/\partial z$.
9. $xy + yz + zx = 1$; find $\partial x/\partial z$ and $\partial x/\partial y$.
10. $x^3 - y^3 - z^3 = 4$; find $\partial x/\partial y$ and $\partial x/\partial z$.
11. $\sin xy + \sin yz = 1$; find $\partial x/\partial y$ and $\partial x/\partial z$.
12. $(x + y)^2 = (y - z)^3$; find $\partial y/\partial x$ and $\partial y/\partial z$.
13. $x^2 - y^2 + 2z^2 = w$; find $\partial z/\partial x$.
14. $(x + y)^2 + (y - z)^2 = w$; find $\partial z/\partial y$.
15. $u^2 - v^2 = x + y + z$; find $\partial x/\partial u$ and $\partial x/\partial v$.
16. $(u + v)^2 - (x + y + z)^2 = 1$; find $\partial u/\partial x$ and $\partial u/\partial y$.
17. $x^2 + y^2 + z^2 = 4$, $x + y + z = 1$; find dy/dx.
18. $x^2 + y^2 = 1$, $y^2 + z^2 = 1$; find dy/dz.
19. $2x + y - z = 3$, $x^2 + y^2 - z^2 = 1$; find dx/dy.
20. $x - y + z = 1$, $x^3 - y^3 = 4$; find dz/dx.
21. $x^2 = y$, $y^2 = z$; find dy/dx.
22. $x^2 - y^2 = 1$, $x + y + z + w = 1$; find $(\partial y/\partial x)_w$.
23. $x + y + z = 1$, $y^2 + z^2 = w$; find $(\partial w/\partial x)_y$.
24. $u - 2v + x + 2y - z = 0$, $u^2 + v^2 + x^2 + y^2 + z^2 = 4$; find $(\partial u/\partial x)_{y,z}$.
25. $w + x + y + z = 1$, $w^2 + x^2 + y^2 + z^2 = 4$, $wxyz = 2$; find dy/dx.
26. $x = r\cos\theta$, $y = r\sin\theta$; find $(\partial r/\partial\theta)_x$ and $(\partial r/\partial\theta)_y$.
27. $x = r\cos\theta$, $y = r\sin\theta$, $z = t$; find $(\partial y/\partial t)_{r,\theta}$.
28. If $z = xy$ and $u = x + y$ and $v = x - y$, find $(\partial z/\partial u)_v$.
29. If $z = x/y$ and $u = 2x + y$ and $v = x - 2y$, find $(\partial z/\partial v)_u$.
30. If $z = f(x, y)$, $x = r\cos\theta$, and $y = r\sin\theta$, show that

$$\left(\frac{\partial z}{\partial r}\right)_\theta^2 + \frac{1}{r^2}\left(\frac{\partial z}{\partial \theta}\right)_r^2 = \left(\frac{\partial z}{\partial x}\right)_y^2 + \left(\frac{\partial z}{\partial y}\right)_x^2.$$

22.5

The Total Differential

Recall that when dealing with a function of one variable, $y = f(x)$, we let dx be a new independent variable and we defined $dy = f'(x)\,dx$. Now we should like to consider differentials for a function of two variables, $z = f(x, y)$. We shall let dx and dy be a pair of new variables that are independent of x, y, and each other.

Definition

If $z = f(x, y)$ and both partial derivatives of z exist, then the **total differential**, *dz, of z is*

$$dz = \frac{\partial f}{\partial x}\,dx + \frac{\partial f}{\partial y}\,dy.$$

There is nothing said about dx, dy, or dz being "small." As we shall see, differentials have some important applications when dx and dy are small, but there is no reason to assume that dx and dy are *always* small.

Example 1

Find dz if $z = x^2 - xy$.

$$dz = \frac{\partial z}{\partial x}\,dx + \frac{\partial z}{\partial y}\,dy$$

$$= (2x - y)\,dx - x\,dy.$$

Of course, the same type of definition holds for functions of three or more variables.

Example 2

Find dw if $w = x^3 - x^2y + y^2z$.

$$dw = \frac{\partial w}{\partial x}\,dx + \frac{\partial w}{\partial y}\,dy + \frac{\partial w}{\partial z}\,dz$$

$$= (3x^2 - 2xy)\,dx + (2yz - x^2)\,dy + y^2\,dz.$$

22.6

Approximation by Differentials

We used the differential dy to approximate Δy when $dx = \Delta x$ was small and $y = f(x)$. Now if Δx and Δy represent errors in x and y, respectively, and $z = f(x, y)$, then we write

$$\Delta z = f(x + \Delta x, y + \Delta y) - f(x, y).$$

Now suppose we take $dx = \Delta x$ and $dy = \Delta y$. What is the relationship between dz and Δz?

$$\begin{aligned}
\lim_{\substack{\Delta x \to 0 \\ \Delta y \to 0}} \Delta z &= \lim_{\substack{\Delta x \to 0 \\ \Delta y \to 0}} [f(x + \Delta x, y + \Delta y) - f(x, y)] \\
&= \lim_{\substack{\Delta x \to 0 \\ \Delta y \to 0}} \{[f(x + \Delta x, y + \Delta y) - f(x, y + \Delta y)] + [f(x, y + \Delta y) - f(x, y)]\} \\
&= \lim_{\substack{\Delta x \to 0 \\ \Delta y \to 0}} \left\{\frac{f(x + \Delta x, y + \Delta y) - f(x, y + \Delta y)}{\Delta x} dx + \frac{f(x, y + \Delta y) - f(x, y)}{\Delta y} dy\right\} \\
&= \lim_{\substack{dx \to 0 \\ dy \to 0}} \left(\frac{\partial z}{\partial x} dx + \frac{\partial z}{\partial y} dy\right) \\
&= \lim_{\substack{dx \to 0 \\ dy \to 0}} dz.
\end{aligned}$$

Thus if $dx = \Delta x$ and $dy = \Delta y$, then the smaller Δx and Δy get, the closer Δz gets to dz. It appears then that we can use dz to "approximate" Δz, provided dx and dy are "small." Of course, the same holds for functions of three or more variables.

Example 1

The sides of a rectangle are measured and found to be 4.00 in. and 6.50 in., with a maximum error of 0.02 in. in each case. What is the area of the rectangle and what is the maximum error in the area?

$$\begin{aligned}
x &= 4.00, \quad |dx| \leq 0.02, \\
y &= 6.50, \quad |dy| \leq 0.02, \\
A &= xy \\
&= (4.00)(6.50) \\
&= 26 \text{ in.}^2, \\
|dA| &= |y\, dx + x\, dy| \\
&\leq |y|\,|dx| + |x|\,|dy| \\
&\leq (6.50)(0.02) + (4.00)(0.02) \\
&= 0.21 \text{ in.}^2.
\end{aligned}$$

The value of $|\triangle A|$ is

$$\begin{aligned}
|\triangle A| &\leq (4.02)(6.52) - (4.00)(6.50) \\
&= 0.2102 \text{ in.}^2.
\end{aligned}$$

We see that $|dA|$ is very nearly $|\triangle A|$.

Example 2

The volume of a cone is found by measuring the diameter and height. If the diameter is 4.12 ± 0.02 in. and the height is 6.21 ± 0.03 in., find the volume and the maximum error in volume.

$$r = 2.06 \text{ in.,} \qquad |dr| \leq 0.01 \text{ in.,}$$
$$h = 6.21 \text{ in.,} \qquad |dh| \leq 0.03 \text{ in.,}$$

$$\begin{aligned} V &= \frac{1}{3}\pi r^2 h \\ &= \frac{1}{3}(3.14)(2.06)^2(6.21) \\ &= 27.6 \text{ in.}^3, \\ |dV| &= \left|\frac{\partial V}{dr}\,dr + \frac{\partial V}{\partial h}\,dh\right| \\ &\leq \left|\frac{\partial V}{\partial r}\right| |dr| + \left|\frac{\partial V}{\partial h}\right| |dh| \\ &= \left|\frac{2}{3}\pi rh\right|\left|dr\right| + \left|\frac{1}{3}\pi r^2\right|\left|dh\right| \\ &= \frac{2}{3}(3.14)(2.06)(6.21)(0.01) + \frac{1}{3}(3.14)(2.06)^2(0.03) \\ &= 0.40 \text{ in.}^3. \end{aligned}$$

Problems

In Problems 1–16, find *df*.

1. $f(x, y) = x^3 - y^3$.
2. $f(x, y) = xy$.
3. $f(x, y) = x^2y + xy^2$.
4. $f(x, y) = x \sin y$.
5. $f(x, y) = x + y + e^{xy}$.
6. $f(x, y) = \dfrac{x}{y}$.
7. $f(x, y) = \dfrac{x + y}{xy}$.
8. $f(x, y) = \dfrac{\sin (x + y)}{xy}$.
9. $f(x, y, z) = x^2 + y^2 + z^2$.
10. $f(x, y, z) = xyz$.
11. $f(x, y, z) = x \sin y + y \sin z$.
12. $f(x, y, z) = x^2yz - y^2z + z^2$.
13. $f(x, y, z) = e^{xy} + \sin yz$.
14. $f(x, y, z) = \dfrac{x + y + z}{xyz}$.
15. $f(x, y, z, w) = x^2 + 2yz + w^2$.
16. $f(x, y, z, w) = x^3y - y^2z^2 + zw^3$.
17. The volume of a cylinder is determined by measuring the diameter and height. The diameter is 5.21 ± 0.04 in., and the height 7.32 ± 0.05 in. Find the volume and the maximum error in the volume.
18. Find the total surface area and the maximum error in the area of the cylinder of Problem 17.
19. The sides of a box are measured and found to be $4.00 \times 3.00 \times 6.00$ in. Find the maximum error in the volume if the maximum error in any of the three measurements is 0.01 in.
20. The density D of an object is given by $D = M/V$, where M is the mass and V the volume of the object. A certain object is found to have mass 439.81 g and volume 25.34 ml. What is the density? If the maximum error in measuring the mass is ± 0.01 g and the maximum error in measuring the volume is ± 0.05 ml, find the maximum error in the density.

21. The two legs of a right triangle are measured and found to be 4.00 ± 0.02 in. and 6.00 ± 0.02. Find the hypotenuse and the maximum error of the hypotenuse.
22. The angle of elevation of the top of a building is $23°00'00''$ when measured from a point 100 ft away. If the maximum error in measuring the angle is $30''$ and the maximum error in measuring the distance is 0.1 ft, what is the maximum error in the height of the building?
23. The angle of elevation of the top of a hill is $21°00'00''$ and the distance to the top of the hill is 500 ft. If the maximum error in measuring the angle is $30''$ and the maximum error in measuring the distance is 0.3 ft, find the maximum error in determining the height of the hill.
24. In determining the molecular weight of a low-boiling liquid by the Victor Meyer method, the ideal gas formula,

$$PV = nRT,$$

is used. The number of moles n of the liquid is represented by w/M, where w is the weight of the liquid and M the molecular weight. Thus

$$M = \frac{wRT}{PV},$$

where w is the weight of the liquid in grams, T is the temperature of the vapor in degrees absolute, P is the pressure in atmospheres, V the volume in liters, and R is the ideal gas constant 0.082054. The following data are taken:

$T = 370.00 \pm 0.04°$,

$w = 0.05000 \pm 0.00001$ g,

$P = 0.9605 \pm 0.0001$ atm,

$V = 0.06070 \pm 0.00002$ l.

Find M and the maximum error in M.

22.7

Directional Derivatives

We have already noted that, if $z = f(x, y)$, then $\partial z/\partial x$ represents the slope of the graph found by taking a vertical cross section parallel to the x axis (see Figure 22.2). Similarly $\partial z/\partial y$ is the slope of the graph found by taking a vertical cross section parallel to the y axis. These are just special cases of a more general type of derivative—the directional derivative.

Suppose we consider the direction of a vertical plane to be represented by a unit vector $\mathbf{v}$ (see Figure 22.3(*a*)) in the xy plane, making an angle θ with the positive x axis. First of all, $\mathbf{v}$ can be expressed in the form

$$\mathbf{v} = \cos\theta\mathbf{i} + \sin\theta\mathbf{j}.$$

A vector of length h and having the same direction as $\mathbf{v}$ is

$$h\mathbf{v} = h\cos\theta\mathbf{i} + h\sin\theta\mathbf{j},$$

with tail at (x, y) and head at $(x + h\cos\theta, y + h\sin\theta)$.

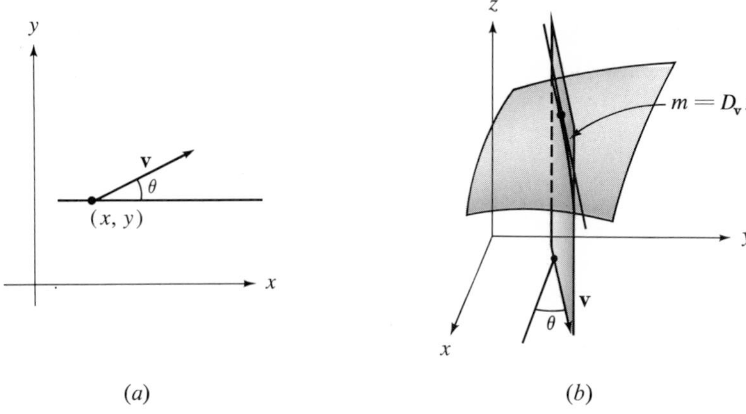

(a) (b)

Figure 22.3

Definition

If $z = f(x, y)$ *and* $\mathbf{v}$ *is the unit vector* $\cos\theta\mathbf{i} + \sin\theta\mathbf{j}$, *then the directional derivative of z in the direction of* $\mathbf{v}$ *is*

$$D_{\mathbf{v}}\, z = \lim_{h\to 0} \frac{f(x + h\cos\theta,\ y + h\sin\theta) - f(x, y)}{h}$$

if this limit exists.

Example 1

If $z = x^2 + y^2$ and $\mathbf{v}$ is the unit vector making an angle 30° with the x axis, find $D_{\mathbf{v}}\, z$.

$$\begin{aligned} D_{\mathbf{v}}\, z &= \lim_{h\to 0} \frac{f(x + h\cos 30^\circ,\ y + h\sin 30^\circ) - f(x, y)}{h} \\ &= \lim_{h\to 0} \frac{f\left(x + \frac{\sqrt{3}}{2}h,\ y + \frac{1}{2}h\right) - f(x, y)}{h} \\ &= \lim_{h\to 0} \frac{\left(x + \frac{\sqrt{3}}{2}h\right)^2 + \left(y + \frac{1}{2}h\right)^2 - (x^2 + y^2)}{h} \\ &= \lim_{h\to 0} \frac{x^2 + \sqrt{3}\,hx + \frac{3}{4}h^2 + y^2 + hy + \frac{1}{4}h^2 - x^2 - y^2}{h} \\ &= \lim_{h\to 0} (\sqrt{3}\,x + y + h) \\ &= \sqrt{3}\,x + y. \end{aligned}$$

The amount of work involved in finding a directional derivative by means of the definition is relatively great—compare it with the problem of finding the two partial derivatives. Since the partial derivatives are so easy to find, it would simplify the problem considerably if we could relate the directional derivative to the partial derivatives. Before doing so, we might note that the two partial derivatives are special cases of the directional derivative. When $\theta = 0$,

$$\begin{aligned} D_{\mathbf{v}} z &= \lim_{h \to 0} \frac{f(x + h \cos 0,\, y + h \sin 0) - f(x, y)}{h} \\ &= \lim_{h \to 0} \frac{f(x + h,\, y) - f(x, y)}{h} \\ &= \frac{\partial z}{\partial x}. \end{aligned}$$

Similarly, when $\theta = \pi/2$,

$$\begin{aligned} D_{\mathbf{v}} z &= \lim_{h \to 0} \frac{f\left(x + h \cos \frac{\pi}{2},\, y + h \sin \frac{\pi}{2}\right) - f(x, y)}{h} \\ &= \lim_{h \to 0} \frac{f(x, y + h) - f(x, y)}{h} \\ &= \frac{\partial z}{\partial y}. \end{aligned}$$

Now let us consider the relationship between the directional derivative and the two partial derivatives.

Theorem 22.9

If $z = f(x, y)$, and if $\partial z/\partial x$ and $\partial z/\partial y$ both exist and $\mathbf{v} = \cos \theta \mathbf{i} + \sin \theta \mathbf{j}$, then

$$D_{\mathbf{v}} z = \frac{\partial z}{\partial x} \cos \theta + \frac{\partial z}{\partial y} \sin \theta.$$

Proof

Let us consider the function g such that

$$g(s) = f(x + s \cos \theta,\, y + s \sin \theta),$$

where x, y, and θ are taken to be constants.

Let us take the derivative of $g(s)$ at $s = 0$ by two different methods. Using the chain rule, we have

$$\begin{aligned} g'(s) &= f_1(x + s \cos \theta,\, y + s \sin \theta) \cdot \frac{d}{ds}(x + s \cos \theta) \\ &\quad + f_2(x + s \cos \theta,\, y + s \sin \theta) \cdot \frac{d}{ds}(y + s \sin \theta) \qquad \text{(See Note.)} \\ &= f_1(x + s \cos \theta,\, y + s \sin \theta) \cdot \cos \theta \\ &\quad + f_2(x + s \cos \theta,\, y + s \sin \theta) \cdot \sin \theta; \end{aligned}$$

$$g'(0) = f_1(x, y) \cdot \cos\theta + f_2(x, y) \cdot \sin\theta$$
$$= \frac{\partial z}{\partial x} \cos\theta + \frac{\partial z}{\partial y} \sin\theta.$$

Now, using the definition of a derivative, we have

$$g'(0) = \lim_{h \to 0} \frac{f[x + (0 + h)\cos\theta, y + (0 + h)\sin\theta] - f[x + 0 \cdot \cos\theta, y + 0 \sin\theta]}{h}$$
$$= \lim_{h \to 0} \frac{f(x + h\cos\theta, y + h\sin\theta) - f(x, y)}{h}$$
$$= D_{\mathbf{v}} z.$$

Thus

$$D_{\mathbf{v}} z = \frac{\partial z}{\partial x} \cos\theta + \frac{\partial z}{\partial y} \sin\theta.$$

Note: The symbol $f_1(x + s\cos\theta, y + s\sin\theta)$ means the partial derivative of $f(x + s\cos\theta, y + s\sin\theta)$ with respect to $x + s\cos\theta$ (see page 562, where this notation was introduced). Note that this is the only convenient notation for this derivative.

Example 2

Use Theorem 22.9 to find the directional derivative of Example 1.

$$D_{\mathbf{v}} z = \frac{\partial z}{\partial x} \cos\theta + \frac{\partial z}{\partial y} \sin\theta$$
$$= 2x \cdot \cos 30^\circ + 2y \sin 30^\circ$$
$$= 2x \cdot \frac{\sqrt{3}}{2} + 2y \cdot \frac{1}{2}$$
$$= \sqrt{3}\, x + y.$$

Let us extend the preceding definition to functions of three variables. Recall that a unit vector in three dimensions is represented by its direction cosines:

$$\mathbf{v} = \cos\alpha\mathbf{i} + \cos\beta\mathbf{j} + \cos\gamma\mathbf{k}.$$

Definition

If $w = f(x, y, z)$ and $\mathbf{v}$ is the unit vector

$$\cos\alpha\mathbf{i} + \cos\beta\mathbf{j} + \cos\gamma\mathbf{k},$$

then the directional derivative in the direction of $\mathbf{v}$ is

$$D_{\mathbf{v}} w = \lim_{h \to 0} \frac{f(x + h\cos\alpha, y + h\cos\beta, z + h\cos\gamma) - f(x, y, z)}{h}$$

if this limit exists.

An argument similar to the one used for Theorem 22.9 proves the following theorem.

Theorem 22.10

If $w = f(x, y, z)$, *and* $\partial w/\partial x$, $\partial w/\partial y$, $\partial w/\partial z$ *all exist, and*

$$\mathbf{v} = \cos\alpha\mathbf{i} + \cos\beta\mathbf{j} + \cos\gamma\mathbf{k},$$

then

$$D_{\mathbf{v}}\, w = \frac{\partial w}{\partial x}\cos\alpha + \frac{\partial w}{\partial y}\cos\beta + \frac{\partial w}{\partial z}\cos\gamma.$$

The form of the conclusions of Theorem 22.9 and Theorem 22.10 suggests the dot product of two vectors. One of these vectors is $\mathbf{v}$. The other is called the gradient of f and is represented by

$$\mathbf{grad}\, f(x, y) = \frac{\partial f}{\partial x}\mathbf{i} + \frac{\partial f}{\partial y}\mathbf{j}$$

or

$$\mathbf{grad}\, f(x, y, z) = \frac{\partial f}{\partial x}\mathbf{i} + \frac{\partial f}{\partial y}\mathbf{j} + \frac{\partial f}{\partial z}\mathbf{k}.$$

With this, we see that

$$D_{\mathbf{v}} f = \mathbf{grad}\, f \cdot \mathbf{v}.$$

The gradient plays an important role in vector analysis and has some interesting properties. One of these is given below.

Theorem 22.11

The maximum value of the directional derivative $D_{\mathbf{v}} f$ *at a given point is* $|\mathbf{grad}\, f|$; *its direction is the same as that of* $\mathbf{grad}\, f$.

Proof

We shall consider only the two-dimensional case here. If

$$\mathbf{v} = \cos\theta\mathbf{i} + \sin\theta\mathbf{j},$$

then

$$D_{\mathbf{v}} f = \frac{\partial f}{\partial x}\cos\theta + \frac{\partial f}{\partial y}\sin\theta = g(\theta),$$

and

$$g'(\theta) = -\frac{\partial f}{\partial x}\sin\theta + \frac{\partial f}{\partial y}\cos\theta.$$

In order to have a maximum, we let $g'(\theta) = 0$. Thus

$$\frac{\partial f}{\partial x}\sin\theta = \frac{\partial f}{\partial y}\cos\theta,$$

$$\frac{\sin\theta}{\cos\theta} = \frac{\partial f/\partial y}{\partial f/\partial x},$$

$$\tan\theta = \frac{\partial f/\partial y}{\partial f/\partial x}.$$

From Figure 22.4, we have

$$\sin\theta = \frac{\dfrac{\partial f}{\partial y}}{\sqrt{\left(\dfrac{\partial f}{\partial x}\right)^2 + \left(\dfrac{\partial f}{\partial y}\right)^2}},$$

$$\cos\theta = \frac{\dfrac{\partial f}{\partial x}}{\sqrt{\left(\dfrac{\partial f}{\partial x}\right)^2 + \left(\dfrac{\partial f}{\partial y}\right)^2}}.$$

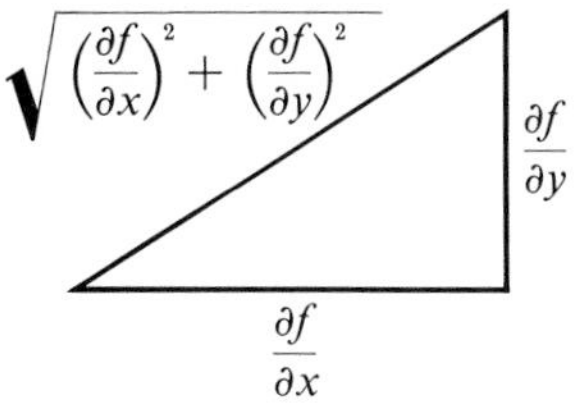

$\sqrt{\left(\dfrac{\partial f}{\partial x}\right)^2 + \left(\dfrac{\partial f}{\partial y}\right)^2}$ $\dfrac{\partial f}{\partial y}$ $\dfrac{\partial f}{\partial x}$

Figure 22.4

(The positive square root gives the maximum we want; the negative gives a minimum.) Substituting these into the expression for $D_{\mathbf{v}} f$, we have

$$D_{\mathbf{v}} f = \sqrt{\left(\frac{\partial f}{\partial x}\right)^2 + \left(\frac{\partial f}{\partial y}\right)^2} = |\mathbf{grad}\, f|.$$

Let us now find the angle α between $\mathbf{grad}\, f$ and the x axis, represented by the vector $\mathbf{v}$.

By Theorem 21.7,

$$\cos\alpha = \frac{\dfrac{\partial f}{\partial x}\cdot 1 + \dfrac{\partial f}{\partial y}\cdot 0}{|\mathbf{grad}\, f|\ |\mathbf{i}|}$$

$$= \frac{\dfrac{\partial f}{\partial x}}{\sqrt{\left(\dfrac{\partial f}{\partial x}\right)^2 + \left(\dfrac{\partial f}{\partial y}\right)^2}} = \cos\theta.$$

Definition

*The **normal derivative** df/dn at a given point is the maximum directional derivative at that point.*

Example 3

Find the normal derivative of $z = x^2 + y^2$ and the vector $\mathbf{v}$ to which it corresponds.

$$\mathbf{grad}\, z = \frac{\partial z}{\partial x}\mathbf{i} + \frac{\partial z}{\partial y}\mathbf{j} = 2x\mathbf{i} + 2y\mathbf{j},$$

$$\frac{df}{dn} = |\mathbf{grad}\, z| = \sqrt{4x^2 + 4y^2} = 2\sqrt{x^2 + y^2},$$

$$\mathbf{v} = \frac{\mathbf{grad}\, z}{|\mathbf{grad}\, z|} = \frac{2x\mathbf{i} + 2y\mathbf{j}}{2\sqrt{x^2 + y^2}} = \frac{x\mathbf{i} + y\mathbf{j}}{\sqrt{x^2 + y^2}}.$$

Problems

In Problems 1–10, find the directional derivative for the given vector.

1. $z = x^2 + xy$, $\mathbf{v} = \dfrac{1}{\sqrt{2}}\mathbf{i} + \dfrac{1}{\sqrt{2}}\mathbf{j}$.

2. $z = x^3 + xy + y^3$, $\mathbf{v} = \dfrac{\sqrt{3}}{2}\mathbf{i} - \dfrac{1}{2}\mathbf{j}$.

3. $z = \dfrac{x}{y}$, $\mathbf{v} = -\dfrac{1}{\sqrt{2}}\mathbf{i} + \dfrac{1}{\sqrt{2}}\mathbf{j}$.

4. $z = \dfrac{x+y}{xy}$, $\mathbf{v} = \dfrac{3}{\sqrt{10}}\mathbf{i} + \dfrac{1}{\sqrt{10}}\mathbf{j}$.

5. $z = x^3 - y + 1$, $\mathbf{v} = \dfrac{\sqrt{2}}{\sqrt{3}}\mathbf{i} - \dfrac{1}{\sqrt{3}}\mathbf{j}$.

6. $z = e^{xy}$, $\mathbf{v} = \dfrac{1}{2}\mathbf{i} - \dfrac{\sqrt{3}}{2}\mathbf{j}$.

7. $w = x^2 + y^2 + z^2$, $\mathbf{v} = \dfrac{1}{2}\mathbf{i} + \dfrac{1}{2}\mathbf{j} - \dfrac{1}{\sqrt{2}}\mathbf{k}$.

8. $w = xyz$, $\mathbf{v} = \dfrac{1}{3}\mathbf{i} - \dfrac{2}{3}\mathbf{j} + \dfrac{2}{3}\mathbf{k}$.

9. $w = x - y^2 + z^3$, $\mathbf{v} = \dfrac{2}{\sqrt{10}}\mathbf{i} - \dfrac{1}{\sqrt{10}}\mathbf{j} - \dfrac{1}{\sqrt{2}}\mathbf{k}$.

10. $w = \dfrac{x + 2y - z}{xy}$, $\mathbf{v} = \dfrac{1}{2\sqrt{2}}\mathbf{i} + \dfrac{1}{2}\mathbf{j} - \dfrac{\sqrt{5}}{2\sqrt{2}}\mathbf{k}$.

In Problems 11–20, find the directional derivative for the given vector at the given point.

11. $z = x + y^2$, $\mathbf{v} = \dfrac{1}{2}\mathbf{i} + \dfrac{\sqrt{3}}{2}\mathbf{j}$; (1, 2, 5).

12. $z = x^2 - 2y^2$, $\mathbf{v} = -\dfrac{1}{\sqrt{2}}\mathbf{i} - \dfrac{1}{\sqrt{2}}\mathbf{j}$; (0, 1, −2).

13. $z = x^3 + xy^2$, $\mathbf{v} = \dfrac{2}{\sqrt{13}}\mathbf{i} + \dfrac{3}{\sqrt{13}}\mathbf{j}$; (1, 1, 2).

14. $z = (x + y)^2$, $\mathbf{v} = \dfrac{1}{\sqrt{5}}\mathbf{i} - \dfrac{2}{\sqrt{5}}\mathbf{j}$; (1, −1, 0).

15. $z = (2x + 3y)^2$, $\mathbf{v} = \dfrac{1}{2}\mathbf{i} + \dfrac{\sqrt{3}}{2}\mathbf{j}$; (−1, 1, 1).

16. $z = xy^3$, $\mathbf{v} = \dfrac{4}{\sqrt{17}}\mathbf{i} + \dfrac{1}{\sqrt{17}}\mathbf{j}$; (1, 1, 1).

17. $w = xy + yz$, $\mathbf{v} = \dfrac{1}{\sqrt{14}}\mathbf{i} + \dfrac{3}{\sqrt{14}}\mathbf{j} + \dfrac{2}{\sqrt{14}}\mathbf{k}$; (1, 2, 1, 4).

18. $w = x^2 - (y + z)^2$, $\mathbf{v} = \dfrac{1}{\sqrt{6}}\mathbf{i} - \dfrac{2}{\sqrt{6}}\mathbf{j} + \dfrac{1}{\sqrt{6}}\mathbf{k}$; (2, 1, 1, 0).

19. $w = \dfrac{x + y}{y + z}$, $\mathbf{v} = \dfrac{1}{\sqrt{3}}\mathbf{i} + \dfrac{1}{\sqrt{3}}\mathbf{j} - \dfrac{1}{\sqrt{3}}\mathbf{k}$; (1, 1, 1, 1).

20. $w = \dfrac{xy}{z}$, $\mathbf{v} = \dfrac{3}{4}\mathbf{i} - \dfrac{1}{4}\mathbf{j} + \dfrac{\sqrt{6}}{4}\mathbf{k}$; (2, 1, −1, −2).

In Problems 21–30, find the normal derivative and the corresponding unit vector.

21. $z = x^2 - y$.

22. $z = x^3y$.

23. $z = x^3 - y^2$.

24. $z = \dfrac{x}{y}$.

25. $w = x^2 + y^2 + z^2$.

26. $w = xyz$.

27. $z = x^2 - 2y^2$ at (2, 1, 2).

28. $z = xy + 1$ at (1, 1, 2).

29. $w = x^2y + yz$ at (1, 0, 2, 0).

30. $w = xy - yz$ at (1, 1, −1, 2).

31. The temperature of a metal plate is given by the formula

$$T = 50 - 5x - 10y + xy, \quad |x| \le 2, \ |y| \le 2.$$

What is the temperature at (1, 1)? In what direction must one go in order to have the temperature increase fastest?

32. The electric potential on a plate is distributed according to the formula

$$E = 20 - 4x - 5y + xy, \ |x| \leq 5, \ |y| \leq 4.$$

A particle moves along the plate in such a way that the electric potential is always increasing as rapidly as possible. Assuming that it starts at (5, 4), describe its path.

22.8

Tangent Plane and Normal Line to a Surface

Just as the derivative of $y = f(x)$ allowed us to find the equation of a line tangent to $y = f(x)$, the partial derivatives of $z = f(x, y)$ allow us to find the equation of a plane tangent to $z = f(x, y)$. Again we have the problem of determining what is meant by the plane tangent to a surface at a given point. Since we know what a tangent line to a curve is, let us define a tangent plane in terms of it. Suppose we consider a vertical plane containing (x_0, y_0, z_0). The intersection of this plane with the surface $z = f(x, y)$ is a curve (see Figure 22.5). It seems reasonable that the tangent line to this curve lies in the plane tangent to the surface at (x_0, y_0, z_0). As a tentative definition, we might say that the tangent plane to the surface $z = f(x, y)$ at (x_0, y_0, z_0) is the plane containing all such tangent lines. Of course, there is the question of whether or not all of these lines lie in a single plane. Let us assume for the time being that they do (we shall prove it later).

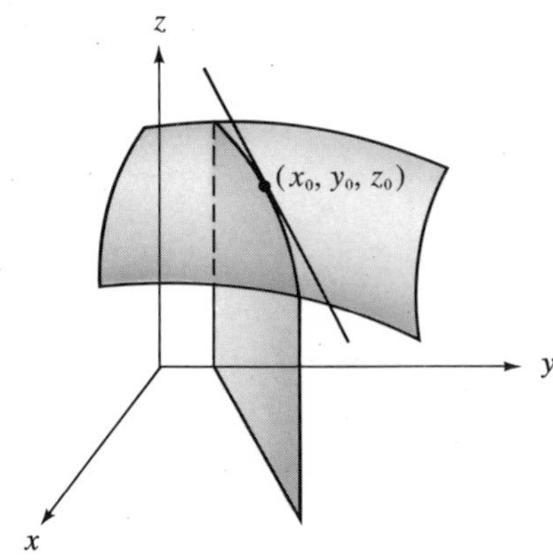

Figure 22.5

Let us now consider the two simplest such vertical planes—those parallel to the xz plane and the yz plane. Now $\partial z/\partial x$ evaluated at (x_0, y_0, z_0), which we represent by

$$\left.\frac{\partial z}{\partial x}\right|_{(x_0, y_0, z_0)},$$

gives the slope of the line tangent to the curve determined by $z = f(x, y)$ and the plane $y = y_0$. Similarly,

$$\left.\frac{\partial z}{\partial y}\right|_{(x_0, y_0, z_0)}$$

gives the slope of the line tangent to the curve determined by $z = f(x, y)$ and $x = x_0$. Now we have the slopes of two lines in the desired plane; we want a set of direction numbers for a line perpendicular to the plane. In order to do this, let us find vectors along the two lines. For the line in the plane $y = y_0$, we have the vector

$$\mathbf{v} = 1 \cdot \mathbf{i} + 0 \cdot \mathbf{j} + \frac{\partial z}{\partial x}\mathbf{k}$$

(see Figure 22.6). We abbreviate the notation for the partial derivative evaluated at (x_0, y_0, z_0) to simply $\partial z/\partial x$—it is understood that it is evaluated at (x_0, y_0, z_0). Similarly, the vector along the line in the plane $x = x_0$ is

$$\mathbf{u} = 0 \cdot \mathbf{i} + 1 \cdot \mathbf{j} + \frac{\partial z}{\partial y}\mathbf{k}.$$

Now a vector perpendicular to both of these is the cross product $\mathbf{u} \times \mathbf{v}$.

$$\mathbf{u} \times \mathbf{v} = \begin{vmatrix} \mathbf{i} & \mathbf{j} & \mathbf{k} \\ 0 & 1 & \dfrac{\partial z}{\partial y} \\ 1 & 0 & \dfrac{\partial z}{\partial x} \end{vmatrix} = \frac{\partial z}{\partial x}\mathbf{i} + \frac{\partial z}{\partial y}\mathbf{j} - 1 \cdot \mathbf{k}.$$

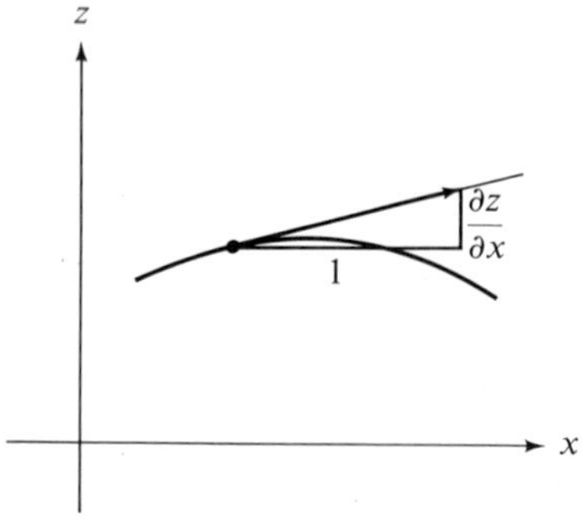

Figure 22.6

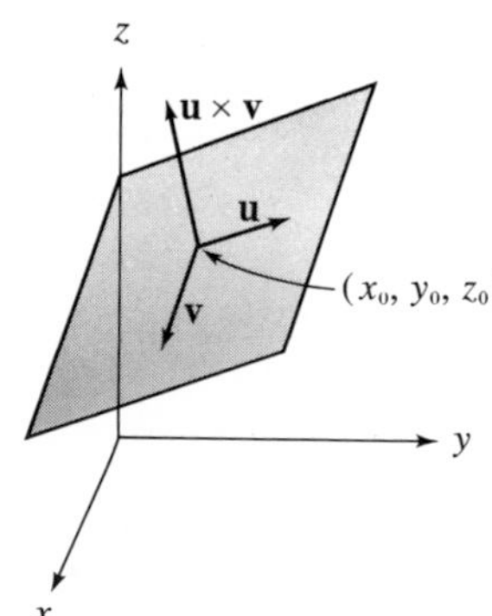

Figure 22.7

The components of this vector give a set of direction numbers for a line perpendicular to the desired plane (see Figure 22.7). Using them, together with the point (x_0, y_0, z_0) in the plane, we have the tangent plane.

$$\left.\frac{\partial z}{\partial x}\right|_{(x_0, y_0, z_0)} (x - x_0) + \left.\frac{\partial z}{\partial y}\right|_{(x_0, y_0, z_0)} (y - y_0) - (z - z_0) = 0.$$

This plane was found using only two tangent lines. There is still the question of whether or not this plane contains *all* the tangent lines through (x_0, y_0, z_0). Suppose we consider the derivative in the direction of the vector

$$\cos\theta\mathbf{i} + \sin\theta\mathbf{j}$$

(see Figure 22.8). The slope of the tangent line is given by

$$\left.\frac{\partial z}{\partial x}\right|_{(x_0, y_0, z_0)} \cos\theta + \left.\frac{\partial z}{\partial y}\right|_{(x_0, y_0, z_0)} \sin\theta.$$

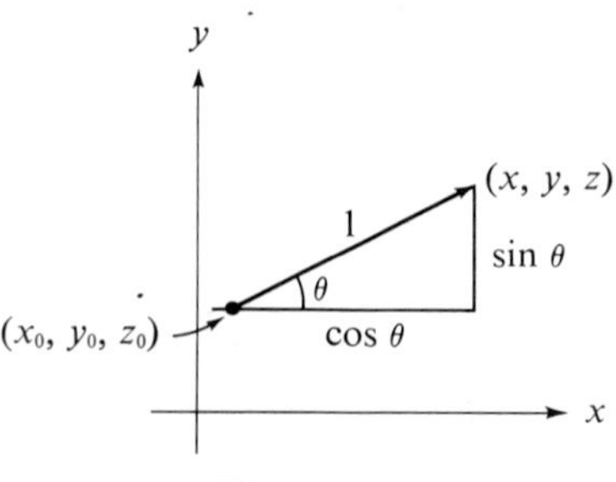

Figure 22.8

The coordinates of the point (x, y, z) of Figure 22.8 are

$$\left(x_0 + \cos\theta,\ y_0 + \sin\theta,\ z_0 + \left.\frac{\partial z}{\partial x}\right|_{(x_0, y_0, z_0)} \cos\theta + \left.\frac{\partial z}{\partial y}\right|_{(x_0, y_0, z_0)} \sin\theta\right).$$

It is a simple matter to see that this point—and thus the entire tangent line—is in the tangent plane.

Theorem 22.12

If $z = f(x, y)$ and both partial derivatives of z exist at (x_0, y_0, z_0), then the plane tangent at (x_0, y_0, z_0) to the surface represented by $z = f(x, y)$ is

$$\left.\frac{\partial z}{\partial x}\right|_{(x_0, y_0, z_0)} (x - x_0) + \left.\frac{\partial z}{\partial y}\right|_{(x_0, y_0, z_0)} (y - y_0) - (z - z_0) = 0$$

and the normal line is

$$\frac{x - x_0}{\left.\dfrac{\partial z}{\partial x}\right|_{(x_0, y_0, z_0)}} = \frac{y - y_0}{\left.\dfrac{\partial z}{\partial y}\right|_{(x_0, y_0, z_0)}} = \frac{z - z_0}{-1}.$$

Example 1

Find equations of the tangent plane and normal line to $z = x^2 + y^2$ at $(1, 1, 2)$.

$$\left.\frac{\partial z}{\partial x}\right|_{(1,1,2)} = \left.2x\right|_{(1,1,2)} = 2,$$

$$\left.\frac{\partial z}{dy}\right|_{(1,1,2)} = \left.2y\right|_{(1,1,2)} = 2.$$

The desired plane is

$$2(x-1) + 2(y-1) - (z-2) = 0,$$

$$2x + 2y - z - 2 = 0,$$

and the normal line is

$$\frac{x-1}{2} = \frac{y-1}{2} = \frac{z-2}{-1}.$$

Suppose the surface is given in the form $F(x, y, z) = 0$. By using implicit differentiation, we have

$$\frac{\partial z}{\partial x} = -\frac{\partial F/\partial x}{\partial F/\partial z} \quad \text{and} \quad \frac{\partial z}{\partial y} = -\frac{\partial F/\partial y}{\partial F/\partial z}.$$

Substituting into the equation of the plane given in Theorem 22.12 gives the following theorem.

Theorem 22.13

If $F(x, y, z) = 0$ and all partial derivatives of F exist, then the plane tangent at (x_0, y_0, z_0) to the surface determined by $F(x, y, z) = 0$ is

$$\left.\frac{\partial F}{\partial x}\right|_{(x_0, y_0, z_0)}(x - x_0) + \left.\frac{\partial F}{\partial y}\right|_{(x_0, y_0, z_0)}(y - y_0) + \left.\frac{\partial F}{\partial z}\right|_{(x_0, y_0, z_0)}(z - z_0) = 0$$

and the normal line is

$$\frac{x - x_0}{\left.\frac{\partial F}{\partial x}\right|_{(x_0, y_0, z_0)}} = \frac{y - y_0}{\left.\frac{\partial F}{\partial y}\right|_{(x_0, y_0, z_0)}} = \frac{z - z_0}{\left.\frac{\partial F}{\partial z}\right|_{(x_0, y_0, z_0)}}$$

It might be noted that Theorem 22.12 is a special case of this last one.

Example 2

Find equations of the tangent plane and normal line to

$$\frac{x^2}{4} + \frac{y^2}{4} + \frac{z^2}{9} = 1$$

at $(1, -1, 3/\sqrt{2})$.

$$\left.\frac{\partial F}{\partial x}\right|_{(1, -1, 3/\sqrt{2})} = \left.\frac{x}{2}\right|_{(1, -1, 3/\sqrt{2})} = \frac{1}{2},$$

$$\left.\frac{\partial F}{\partial y}\right|_{(1, -1, 3/\sqrt{2})} = \left.\frac{y}{2}\right|_{(1, -1, 3/\sqrt{2})} = -\frac{1}{2},$$

$$\left.\frac{\partial F}{\partial z}\right|_{(1, -1, 3/\sqrt{2})} = \left.\frac{2z}{9}\right|_{(1, -1, 3/\sqrt{2})} = \frac{2\sqrt{2}}{3}.$$

Thus the tangent plane is

$$\frac{1}{2}(x - 1) - \frac{1}{2}(y + 1) + \frac{2\sqrt{2}}{3}\left(z - \frac{3}{\sqrt{2}}\right) = 0$$

$$3x - 3y + 4\sqrt{2}\,z - 18 = 0,$$

and the normal line is

$$\frac{x - 1}{1/2} = \frac{y + 1}{-1/2} = \frac{x - 3/\sqrt{2}}{2\sqrt{2}/3}.$$

22.9

Tangent Line to a Curve

The only convenient representation of a curve in space is the parametric form (or the vector form, which is equivalent to it). We saw an example of this in Section 21.4, where we graphed

$$\mathbf{f}(t) = \cos t\mathbf{i} + \sin t\mathbf{j} + t\mathbf{k},$$

which we noted is equivalent to

$$x = \cos t, \qquad y = \sin t, \qquad z = t.$$

We also noted there that the derivative of a vector function is another vector tangent to the curve representing the vector function. This gives us a simple way of finding an equation of the line tangent to a curve in space. If

$$\mathbf{f}(t) = x(t)\mathbf{i} + y(t)\mathbf{j} + z(t)\mathbf{k},$$

then

$$\mathbf{f}'(t) = x'(t)\mathbf{i} + y'(t)\mathbf{j} + z'(t)\mathbf{k}$$

is tangent to the curve represented by $f(t)$. Therefore, $\{x'(t_0), y'(t_0), z'(t_0)\}$ is a set of direction numbers for the tangent line at $(x(t_0), y(t_0), z(t_0))$.

Theorem 22.14

If $x(t)$, $y(t)$, and $z(t)$ are differentiable at $t = t_0$ and $x_0 = x(t_0)$, $y_0 = y(t_0)$, and $z_0 = z(t_0)$, then the line tangent to

$$x = x(t), \quad y = y(t), \quad z = z(t)$$

at $t = t_0$ is

$$\frac{x - x_0}{x'(t_0)} = \frac{y - y_0}{y'(t_0)} = \frac{z - z_0}{z'(t_0)}.$$

Example

Find an equation of the line tangent to $x = \cos t$, $y = \sin t$, $z = t$ at $t = \pi$.

$$\begin{aligned} &x_0 = \cos \pi = -1, \qquad y_0 = \sin \pi = 0, \qquad z_0 = \pi, \\ &x' = -\sin t = -\sin \pi = 0, \\ &y' = \cos t = \cos \pi = -1, \\ &z' = 1. \end{aligned}$$

The line is

$$x + 1 = 0, \qquad \frac{y}{-1} = \frac{z - \pi}{1}.$$

In parametric form, it is

$$x = -1, \qquad y = -t, \qquad z = \pi + t.$$

Problems

In Problems 1–16, find equations for the tangent plane and normal line to the given surface at the indicated point.

1. $z = x^2 - y^2$ at (2, 1, 3).
2. $z = xy$ at (2, 1, 2).
3. $z = \dfrac{x^2}{4} + y^2$ at (2, 2, 5).
4. $z = x^2 - xy$ at (2, 1, 2).
5. $z = \dfrac{x + y}{xy}$ at (1, 1, 2).
6. $z = xy - x - 2y + 2$ at (1, 2, −1).
7. $z = x^3 - y^2$ at (1, 1, 0).
8. $z = xy^2$ at (2, 1, 2).
9. $x^2 + y^2 + z^2 = 9$ at (1, 2, 2).
10. $z^2 = x^2 + y^2$ at (3, 4, 5).
11. $x^2 + y^2 - z^2 = 4$ at (2, 3, 3).
12. $x^2 - y^2 - z^2 = 9$ at (9, 6, −6).
13. $xy + yz = 4$ at (1, 2, 1).
14. $xyz + x + y + z = -3$ at (1, −2, 2).
15. $x = y^2 + z^2$ at (5, 1, 2).
16. $y = x^2 - z^2$ at (5, 3, 4).

In Problems 17–24, find equations for the line tangent to the curve at the given point.

17. $x = \cos t$, $y = \sin t$, $z = t$; at $t = 0$.
18. $x = 4 \cos t$, $y = 3 \sin t$, $z = t$; at $t = \pi/2$.
19. $x = t^2$, $y = t + 1$, $z = t - 1$; at $t = 0$.
20. $x = t^2 + 1$, $y = t^2 - 1$, $z = t$; at $t = 2$.
21. $x = t^3$, $y = t^2$, $z = 1/t$; at $t = 1$.
22. $x = t^2 - 1$, $y = t^3 + 1$, $z = 2t$; at $t = 3$.
23. $x = 2t + 1$, $y = \sin t$, $z = \cos t$; at $t = \pi$.
24. $x = e^t$, $y = \ln t$, $z = t$; at $t = 1$.
25. Show that the two surfaces $f(x, y, z) = 0$ and $g(x, y, z) = 0$ intersect orthogonally if and only if
$$\frac{\partial f}{\partial x} \cdot \frac{\partial g}{\partial x} + \frac{\partial f}{\partial y} \cdot \frac{\partial g}{\partial y} + \frac{\partial f}{\partial z} \cdot \frac{\partial g}{\partial z} = 0.$$
26. Use the result of Problem 25 to show that $xyz^2 = 1$ and $x^2 + y^2 - z^2 = 1$ intersect orthogonally.
27. Show that the plane tangent to
$$\frac{x^2}{a^2} + \frac{y^2}{b^2} + \frac{z^2}{c^2} = 1$$
at (x_0, y_0, z_0) is
$$\frac{xx_0}{a^2} + \frac{yy_0}{b^2} + \frac{zz_0}{c^2} = 1.$$
(Compare this with Problem 24, page 184.)
28. Show that the plane tangent to
$$\frac{x^2}{a^2} + \frac{y^2}{b^2} - \frac{z^2}{c^2} = 1$$
at (x_0, y_0, z_0) is
$$\frac{xx_0}{a^2} + \frac{yy_0}{b^2} - \frac{zz_0}{c^2} = 1.$$
(Compare this with Problem 31, page 193.)

22.10

Maxima and Minima

One of the principal applications of ordinary derivatives is the determination of relative maxima and minima. This application can be extended to relative maxima and minima of functions of two variables by the use of partial derivatives. If $z = f(x, y)$ and $\partial z/\partial x$ and $\partial z/\partial y$ exist, it is clear that, in order to have a relative maximum or minimum, we must have a horizontal tangent plane. Thus both partial derivatives must be zero, which condition is enough for determining critical points.

Unfortunately, the use of second derivatives to determine whether we have a relative maximum, minimum, or neither is a relatively complicated process. For instance, the fact that

$$\frac{\partial^2 z}{\partial x^2} < 0 \quad \text{and} \quad \frac{\partial^2 z}{\partial y^2} < 0$$

is not enough to guarantee that we have a relative maximum. An important consideration in the determination of relative maxima and minima is the determinant

$$D = \begin{vmatrix} \dfrac{\partial^2 z}{\partial x^2} & \dfrac{\partial^2 z}{\partial y\,\partial x} \\ \dfrac{\partial^2 z}{\partial x\,\partial y} & \dfrac{\partial^2 z}{\partial y^2} \end{vmatrix} = \frac{\partial^2 z}{\partial x^2} \cdot \frac{\partial^2 z}{\partial y^2} - \left(\frac{\partial^2 z}{\partial y\,\partial x}\right)^2.$$

(Assuming that we are dealing with a function with continuous second partial derivatives, we can replace $\partial^2 z/\partial x\,\partial y$ by $\partial^2 z/\partial y\,\partial x$.)

Theorem 22.15

If $z = f(x, y)$, all second partial derivatives are continuous, $\partial z/\partial x = \partial z/\partial y = 0$ at (a, b), and

(a) if $D > 0$, $\partial^2 z/\partial x^2 > 0$ and $\partial^2 z/\partial y^2 > 0$ at (a, b), then (a, b) is a relative minimum;
(b) if $D > 0$, $\partial^2 z/\partial x^2 < 0$ and $\partial^2 z/\partial y^2 < 0$ at (a, b), then (a, b) is a relative maximum;
(c) if $D < 0$ at (a, b), then (a, b) is neither a relative maximum nor a relative minimum;
(d) if $D = 0$ at (a, b), the test fails.

We shall not give a proof of this theorem, since it involves some rather sophisticated ideas that we have not considered. We can make a few observations, however. If $\partial^2 z/\partial x^2$ and $\partial^2 z/\partial y^2$ have opposite signs, their product is negative and $D < 0$. Thus if $D > 0$, then $\partial^2 z/\partial x^2$ and $\partial^2 z/\partial y^2$ are either both positive or both negative. However, it is possible for $\partial^2 z/\partial x^2$ and $\partial^2 z/\partial y^2$ to have the same signs and have $D < 0$; the implication cannot be reversed.

Example 1

Test $z = x^2 + y^2$ for relative maxima and minima.

$$\frac{\partial z}{\partial x} = 2x, \qquad \frac{\partial z}{\partial y} = 2y.$$

Setting both derivatives equal to zero, we get the critical point (0, 0).

$$\frac{\partial^2 z}{\partial x^2} = 2, \qquad \frac{\partial^2 z}{\partial y^2} = 2, \qquad \frac{\partial^2 z}{\partial y\, \partial x} = 0;$$

$$D = 2 \cdot 2 - 0^2 = 4.$$

At $x = 0$, $y = 0$ (or at any other point, since all three of the second partial derivatives are constant),

$$D > 0, \qquad \frac{\partial^2 z}{\partial x^2} > 0, \qquad \frac{\partial^2 z}{\partial y^2} > 0.$$

Thus we have a relative minimum at the origin. This result agrees with our previous notions of this curve (see Figure 20.13, page 530).

Example 2

Test $z = x^2 - y^2$ for relative maxima and minima.

$$\frac{\partial z}{\partial x} = 2x, \qquad \frac{\partial z}{\partial y} = -2y.$$

We again have the critical point (0, 0).

$$\frac{\partial^2 z}{\partial x^2} = 2, \qquad \frac{\partial^2 z}{\partial y^2} = -2; \qquad \frac{\partial^2 z}{\partial y \partial x} = 0;$$

$$D = 2(-2) - 0^2 = -4.$$

Since $D < 0$, we have neither a relative maximum nor a relative minimum. The given surface is a hyperbolic paraboloid (see Figure 20.14, page 530), which is saddle shaped. For this reason, critical points that are neither relative maxima nor minima are sometimes referred to as "saddle points."

Example 3

Test $z = x^3 + y^3 - 3xy$ for relative maxima and minima.

$$\frac{\partial z}{\partial x} = 3x^2 - 3y, \qquad \frac{\partial z}{\partial y} = 3y^2 - 3x.$$

Setting both equal to zero and solving simultaneously, we have

$$3x^2 - 3y = 0 \quad \text{or} \quad y = x^2,$$
$$3y^2 - 3x = 0 \quad \text{or} \quad x = y^2.$$

Thus

$$x = x^4,$$
$$x^4 - x = 0,$$
$$x(x^3 - 1) = 0;$$
$$x = 0 \quad \text{or} \quad x = 1.$$

Thus we have the two critical points (0, 0) and (1, 1).

$$\frac{\partial^2 z}{\partial x^2} = 6x, \qquad \frac{\partial^2 z}{\partial y^2} = 6y, \qquad \frac{\partial^2 z}{\partial y\, \partial x} = -3,$$

and

$$D = 6x \cdot 6y - (-3)^2 = 36xy - 9.$$

At (0, 0), $D = -9$ and (0, 0) is a saddle point. At (1, 1), $D = 27$, $\partial^2 z/\partial x^2 = 6$, and $\partial^2 z/\partial y^2 = 6$; and (1, 1) is a relative minimum.

Example 4

Find three positive numbers x, y, and z such that $x + y + z = 12$ and x^2yz is a maximum.

$$\begin{aligned} M &= x^2yz, \quad \text{where } x + y + z = 12, \\ &= x^2y(12 - x - y) \\ &= 12x^2y - x^3y - x^2y^2, \end{aligned}$$

$$\frac{\partial M}{\partial x} = 24xy - 3x^2y - 2xy^2 = xy(24 - 3x - 2y),$$

$$\frac{\partial M}{\partial y} = 12x^2 - x^3 - 2x^2y = x^2(12 - x - 2y).$$

Neither $x = 0$ nor $y = 0$ gives a maximum value for M. Thus we have

$$\begin{aligned} 24 - 3x - 2y = 0 \quad &\text{or} \quad 3x + 2y = 24, \\ 12 - x - 2y = 0 \quad &\text{or} \quad x + 2y = 12. \end{aligned}$$

Solving simultaneously, we have

$$x = 6, \quad y = 3, \quad z = 3.$$

It is clear from the given conditions that this must give a maximum although the second derivative test may be used.

Problems

In Problems 1–16, find all critical points and test for relative maxima and minima.

1. $z = x^2 + y^2 - 2x + 4y - 2.$
2. $z = x^2 + 4y^2 + x + 8y + 1.$
3. $z = x^2 - 2y^2 + 2x + 4y - 1.$
4. $z = x^2 + 2xy - y^2.$
5. $z = x^2 + 4xy + y^2 + 6x + 1.$
6. $z = 2x^2 + xy + y^2 + 2x - 3y + 2.$
7. $z = x^3 + y^3 + 3xy.$
8. $z = x^3 + y^3 - 3x^2 - 6y^2 + 9x.$
9. $z = x^3 - x^2 + y^2 - x + 2y + 2.$
10. $z = 2y^3 + x^2 - y^2 - 4x - 4y + 1.$
11. $z = x^2y + xy^2 - 3xy.$
12. $z = x^3 + x^2y + y^2 - 4y + 2.$
13. $z = x^2 + xy + y^2 - x - 2y + 1.$
14. $z = 3x^3 - xy^2 + y.$
15. $z = xy + \dfrac{1}{x} + \dfrac{8}{y}.$
16. $z = 3(x + y)^3 + (x - y)^2 - (x + y).$
17. Find three positive numbers x, y, and z such that $x + y + z = 25$ and x^2y^2z is a maximum.
18. Find three positive numbers x, y, and z such that $x + y + z = k$ and $x^ay^bz^c$ is a maximum.
19. Find the volume of the largest rectangular parallelepiped which can be inscribed in

$$\frac{x^2}{1} + \frac{y^2}{4} + \frac{z^2}{9} = 1.$$

20. Find the volume of the largest rectangular parallelopiped which can be inscribed in

$$\frac{x^2}{a^2}+\frac{y^2}{b^2}+\frac{z^2}{c^2}=1.$$

21. Find the shortest distance from (1, 3, 4) to $2x-y+z=1$.
22. Find the shortest distance from (x_1, y_1, z_1) to $Ax+By+Cz+D=0$.
23. Find the volume of the largest rectangular parallelepiped in the first octant with three faces in the coordinate planes and a vertex on

$$2x+y+z=4.$$

24. Find the volume of the largest rectangular parallelepiped in the first octant with three faces in the coordinate planes and a vertex on

$$\frac{x}{a}+\frac{y}{b}+\frac{z}{c}=1 \quad (a, b, c>0).$$

22.11

Constrained Maxima and Minima

Quite often we are called upon to maximize or minimize $w=f(x, y, z)$ subject to the condition that $g(x, y, z)=0$. When presented with a problem of this type in the past, we solved $g(x, y, z)$ for one of the variables, say z, in terms of the others, $z=G(x, y)$, and substituted into the other equation, to get

$$w=f(x, y, G(x, y))=F(x, y).$$

Thus the critical values were found by setting the two partial derivatives equal to zero:

$$\frac{\partial F}{\partial x}=0, \qquad \frac{\partial F}{\partial y}=0.$$

Unfortunately, this procedure is often tedious and sometimes impossible. In such cases, another method—called the method of Lagrangian multipliers, after Joseph Lagrange—can be used.

In order to find the critical values of

$$f(x, y, z)$$

subject to the constraint

$$g(x, y, z)=0,$$

we introduce a new variable λ, which gives

$$F(x, y, z, \lambda)=f(x, y, z)+\lambda g(x, y, z).$$

Although we shall not do so here, it can be shown that the critical values of f and F correspond. Thus we have

$$\frac{\partial f}{\partial x}+\lambda\frac{\partial g}{\partial x}=0,$$

$$\frac{\partial f}{\partial y} + \lambda \frac{\partial g}{\partial y} = 0,$$

$$\frac{\partial f}{\partial z} + \lambda \frac{\partial g}{\partial z} = 0,$$

$$g(x, y, z) = 0.$$

Solving these four equations for x, y, and z gives the desired critical values.

The Lagrangian method can be extended to a function with two or more constraining equations. It has the disadvantage of giving us critical points only. It does not tell us whether we have a relative maximum, minimum, or neither. Fortunately, this can often be determined from the physical situation for stated problems.

Example 1

Find the minimum value of $w = x^2 + y^2 + z^2$ subject to the condition $x + y + z = 1$.

From $u = x^2 + y^2 + z^2 + \lambda(x + y + z - 1)$, we get

$$\frac{\partial u}{\partial x} = 2x + \lambda = 0,$$

$$\frac{\partial u}{\partial y} = 2y + \lambda = 0,$$

$$\frac{\partial u}{\partial z} = 2z + \lambda = 0,$$

$$\frac{\partial u}{\partial \lambda} = x + y + z - 1 = 0.$$

The first three give us $x = y = z$. Substituting into the last equation, we have

$$x = y = z = \frac{1}{3} \quad \text{and} \quad w = \frac{1}{3}.$$

Example 2

Find the maximum value of $w = xy + z$ subject to the condition that

$$x^2 + y^2 + z^2 = 1.$$

$$u = xy + z + \lambda(x^2 + y^2 + z^2 - 1),$$

$$\frac{\partial u}{\partial x} = y + 2\lambda x = 0,$$

$$\frac{\partial u}{\partial y} = x + 2\lambda y = 0,$$

$$\frac{\partial u}{\partial z} = 1 + 2\lambda z = 0,$$

$$\frac{\partial u}{\partial \lambda} = x^2 + y^2 + z^2 - 1 = 0.$$

The first three equations give

$$\begin{aligned} y^2z + 2\lambda xyz &= 0, \\ x^2z + 2\lambda xyz &= 0, \\ xy + 2\lambda xyz &= 0, \end{aligned}$$

or

$$y^2z = x^2z = xy.$$

From the first equality, $y^2z = x^2z$, we get either $z = 0$ or $x^2 = y^2$. If $z = 0$, then

$$\frac{\partial u}{\partial z} = 1 + 2\lambda z = 1 \neq 0.$$

Thus $x^2 = y^2$, or $x = \pm y$.

If $x = y$, then	If $x = -y$, then
$x^2z = xy = x^2$	$x^2z = xy = -x^2$
and	and
$x = 0$ or $z = 1$.	$x = 0$ or $z = -1$.

Actually, both equalities hold in each case, because if we start with $x = 0$, we get $z = \pm 1$, while if we start with $z = 1$ or $z = -1$, we get $x = y = 0$. Thus, the critical values are (0, 0, 1) and (0, 0, -1). Clearly, the maximum corresponds to (0, 0, 1), which gives

$$w = xy + z = 0 \cdot 0 + 1 = 1.$$

Example 3

Find the point of $x + 2y - z = 3$ which is nearest the origin.

The distance from a point (x, y, z) in the plane to the origin is

$$d = \sqrt{x^2 + y^2 + z^2}.$$

Since d cannot be negative, it is a minimum whenever $d^2 = u$ is a minimum. Thus we want to minimize

$$u = x^2 + y^2 + z^2$$

under the condition

$$x + 2y - z = 3.$$

Using Lagrangian multipliers, we have

$$w = x^2 + y^2 + z^2 + \lambda(x + 2y - z - 3),$$

$$\frac{\partial w}{\partial x} = 2x + \lambda = 0, \quad \text{or} \quad \lambda = -2x,$$

$$\frac{\partial w}{\partial y} = 2y + 2\lambda = 0, \quad \text{or} \quad \lambda = -y,$$

$$\frac{\partial w}{\partial z} = 2z - \lambda = 0, \quad \text{or} \quad \lambda = 2z,$$

$$\frac{\partial w}{\partial \lambda} = x + 2y - z - 3 = 0.$$

Thus

$$-2x = -y = 2z$$

or

$$y = 2x \quad \text{and} \quad z = -x.$$

Substituting into $x + 2y - z - 3 = 0$, we have

$$6x = 3, \quad \text{or} \quad x = 1/2.$$

The desired point is $(1/2, 1, -1/2)$.

Example 4

Find the minimum value of $w = x^2 + y^2 + z^2$ subject to the conditions

$$x + y + 2z = 12 \quad \text{and} \quad x - 3y - 2z = -16.$$

$$u = x^2 + y^2 + z^2 + \lambda(x + y + 2z - 12) + \mu(x - 3y - 2z + 16),$$

$$\frac{\partial u}{\partial x} = 2x + \lambda + \mu = 0,$$

$$\frac{\partial u}{\partial y} = 2y + \lambda - 3\mu = 0,$$

$$\frac{\partial u}{\partial z} = 2z + 2\lambda - 2\mu = 0,$$

$$\frac{\partial u}{\partial \lambda} = x + y + 2z - 12 = 0,$$

$$\frac{\partial u}{\partial \mu} = x - 3y - 2z + 16 = 0.$$

Eliminating λ and μ from the first three equations, we have $x + y - z = 0$. Solving this together with the last two equations we have $x = 1$, $y = 3$, $z = 4$. Thus the minimum value of w is

$$w = 1^2 + 3^2 + 4^2 = 26.$$

Problems

Use Lagrangian multipliers to find the desired critical points.

1. Find the maximum value of $w = x + y + z$ subject to the condition $x^2 + y^2 + z^2 = 4$.
2. Find the minimum value of $w = x^2 + y^2 + z^2$ subject to the condition $xyz = 1$.
3. Find the maximum value of $w = xyz$ subject to the condition $x^2 + y^2 + z^2 = 1$.
4. Find the minimum value of $w = x^2 + y^2 + z^2$ subject to the condition $2x - y + 3z = 6$.
5. Find the minimum value of $w = 2x^2 + y^2 + z^2$ subject to the condition $x + 2y - 4z = 8$.
6. Find the minimum value of $w = x^2 + 3y^2 + 2z^2$ subject to the condition $2x - 3y + 5z = 1$.
7. Find the minimum value of $w = x^4 + y^4 + z^4$ subject to the condition $x + y + z = 1$.
8. Find the minimum value of $w = x^4 + y^4 + z^4$ subject to the condition $2x - 3y + 6z = 6$.
9. Find the maximum value of $w = xyz$ subject to the condition $x^2 + 2y^2 + z^2 = 2$.
10. Find the maximum value of $w = xyz$ subject to the condition $2x^2 + y^2 + 4z^2 = 4$.

11. Find the maximum value of $w = xyz$ subject to the condition $x^3 + y^3 + z^3 = 24$.
12. Find the maximum value of $w = x^3 + yz^2$ subject to the condition $x^2 + y^2 + z^2 = 1$.
13. Find the minimum value of $w = x^2 + y^2 + z^2$ subject to the conditions $x + 2y - z = 2$ and $2x - y - z = 2$.
14. Find the minimum value of $w = x^2 + y^2 + z^2$ subject to the conditions $x - y + z = 1$ and $2x + y + 3z = 6$.
15. Find the minimum value of $w = x^2 + y^2 + z^2$ subject to the conditions $x + 3y - z = 6$ and $2x + 2y + z = 2$.
16. Find the maximum value of $w = xyz$ subject to the conditions $x + y + z = 2$ and $x - y - z = 1$.
17. Find the point of $-x^2 - z^2 + y = 2$ nearest the origin.
18. Find the point of $x^2 - y^2 - (z - 4)^2 = 1$ nearest the origin.
19. Find the volume of the largest rectangular parallelepiped that can be inscribed in $4x^2 + 9y^2 + 36z^2 = 36$.
20. Find the volume of the largest rectangular parallelepiped that can be inscribed in

$$\frac{x^2}{a^2} + \frac{y^2}{b^2} + \frac{z^2}{c^2} = 1.$$

21. Find the volume of the largest rectangular parallelepiped in the first octant which has three faces in the coordinate planes and a vertex on

$$x + 2y + z = 2.$$

22. Find the volume of the largest rectangular parallelepiped in the first octant which has three faces in the coordinate planes and a vertex on

$$\frac{x}{a} + \frac{y}{b} + \frac{z}{c} = 1 \quad (a, b, c, > 0).$$

Multiple Integrals

23.1

The Double Integral

Let us recall that in defining the integral, we first considered a subdivision

$$a = x_0, x_1, x_2, x_3, \ldots, x_n = b$$

of the interval $[a, b]$; then for each subinterval $[x_{i-1}, x_i]$ we selected any number x_i^* such that

$$x_{i-1} \leq x_i^* \leq x_i;$$

finally, we defined

$$\int_a^b f(x)\, dx = \lim_{\|s\| \to 0} \sum_{i=1}^{n} f(x_i^*)(x_i - x_{i-1}),$$

where $\|s\|$ is the norm of the subdivision—that is, the length of the longest subinterval. The result was a close—but not exact—correspondence to the area of the region "under the curve."

Let us now increase the number of dimensions by one. We shall consider as our model the volume "under a surface." This, of course, brings up the question "What is volume?" While we might be able to answer this question for certain special types of solids that can be given in terms of a single integral, we cannot yet answer this question in general. We shall make the following assumptions about volume:

(1) the volume of a solid is a non-negative number;
(2) if S_1 and S_2 are congruent solids, then their volumes are equal;

(3) if $S = S_1 \cup S_2$, where S_1 and S_2 have only boundary points in common, then the volume of S is the sum of the volumes of S_1 and S_2.

In addition, we shall define the volume of a rectangular parallelepiped to be the product of the length, width, and height. Now suppose we have a bounded region R (see Figure 23.1) in the xy plane and f is a function that is bounded, continuous, and non-negative for all points in R. Let us subdivide R by a set of horizontal and vertical lines—not necessarily evenly spaced—forming a set of rectangles covering R. Suppose we consider only those rectangles which lie entirely inside R and number them from 1 to n. For each of these rectangles, let us choose a point on or inside it. Thus we have a set

$$\{R_1, R_2, R_3, \ldots, R_n\}$$

of rectangles, each lying entirely inside the given region R, and a set

$$\{(x_1^*, y_1^*), (x_2^*, y_2^*), (x_3^*, y_3^*), \ldots, (x_n^*, y_n^*)\}$$

of points such that

$$(x_i^*, y_i^*) \text{ is in } R_i.$$

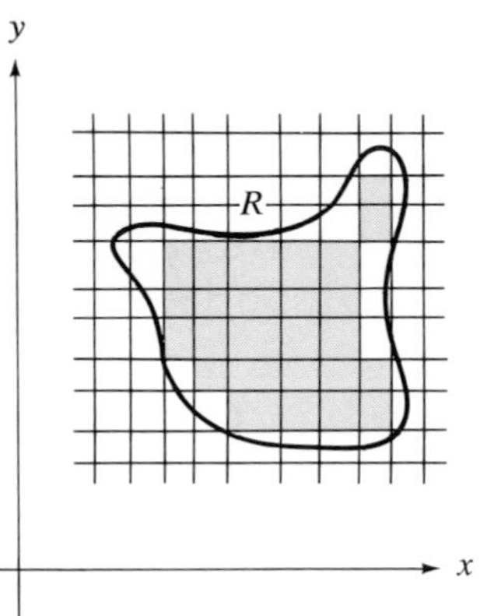

Figure 23.1

Now, for each rectangle R_i, let us consider a rectangular parallelepiped having base R_i with area A_i and height $f(x_i^*, y_i^*)$. The sum of the volumes of all such parallelepipeds,

$$\sum_{i=1}^{n} f(x_i^*, y_i^*)A_i,$$

gives an approximation of the volume under the surface. As our subdivision gets finer (both dimensions of the rectangles approach zero), the approximations get better. The limit of these approximating sums is what we shall call the volume under the surface.

In order to say exactly what is meant by the subdivision getting finer, let us define the norm of the subdivision $\|S\|$ to be the length of the longest diagonal of all rectangles having a point in common with R.

Definition

*If f is bounded and continuous in a bounded plane region R and if S is a subdivision of R with (x_i^*, y_i^*) in R_i, then the **double integral** of f over R is*

$$\iint_R f(x, y)\, dA = \lim_{\|s\| \to 0} \sum_{i=1}^{n} f(x_i^*, y_i^*)A_i,$$

*provided this limit exists. If it exists, f is **integrable** over R.*

Of course, while the definition is inspired by volume, it gives the volume "under the surface" only when $f(x, y) \geq 0$ for all (x, y) in R. Since the following theorems are intuitively obvious from our idea of a double integral, we do not give proofs.

Theorem 23.1

If f is integrable over R and c is a real number, then

$$\iint_R cf(x, y)\, dA = c \iint_R f(x, y)\, dA.$$

Theorem 23.2

If f and g are both integrable over R, then

$$\iint_R [f(x, y) + g(x, y)]\, dA = \iint_R f(x, y)\, dA + \iint_R g(x, y)\, dA.$$

Theorem 23.3

If f is integrable over R and $R = R_1 \cup R_2$, where R_1 and R_2 have only boundary points in common, then

$$\iint_R f(x, y)\, dA = \iint_{R_1} f(x, y)\, dA + \iint_{R_2} f(x, y)\, dA.$$

Single integrals are difficult to evaluate by means of the definition. Double integrals are even more difficult. Let us see what can be done to simplify matters. In particular, since we can now evaluate many single integrals rather easily, let us try to put the double integral in terms of a combination of single integrals. Suppose we consider a vertical line intersecting R at x (see Figure 23.2). Assuming that its intersection with R is an interval, we subdivide this interval and consider a sum of the form

$$\sum_{i=1}^{n} f(x, y_i^*)\, \Delta y_i .$$

The limit of this sum as the norm of the subdivision approaches zero is the integral

$$\int_{g_1(x)}^{g_2(x)} f(x, y)\, dy.$$

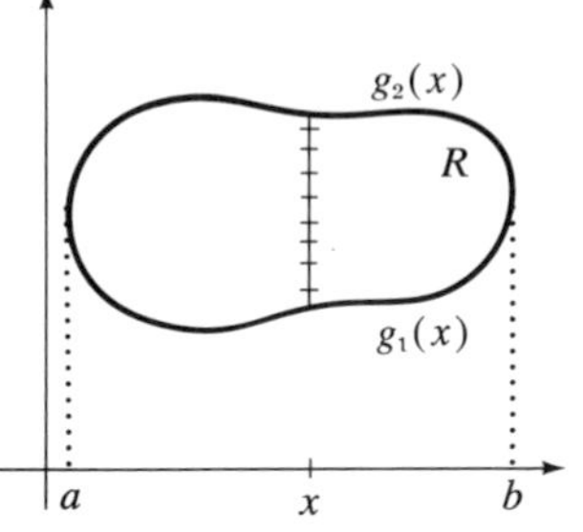

Figure 23.2

Of course the limits of integration are dependent upon the value of x, and, thus, the value of the integral itself is a function of x. If $f(x, y) \geq 0$, this is the cross-sectional area at x. From Section 16.4 we see that the volume is the integral of this function from $x = a$ to $x = b$.

$$\int_a^b \left[\int_{g_1(x)}^{g_2(x)} f(x, y)\, dy \right] dx.$$

Of course, this does not give a volume unless $f(x, y) \geq 0$, but it does give the double integral in any case.

$$\iint_R f(x, y)\, dA = \int_a^b \left[\int_{g_1(x)}^{g_2(x)} f(x, y)\, dy \right] dx.$$

Usually the brackets are omitted:

$$\iint_R f(x, y)\, dA = \int_a^b \int_{g_1(x)}^{g_2(x)} f(x, y)\, dy\, dx.$$

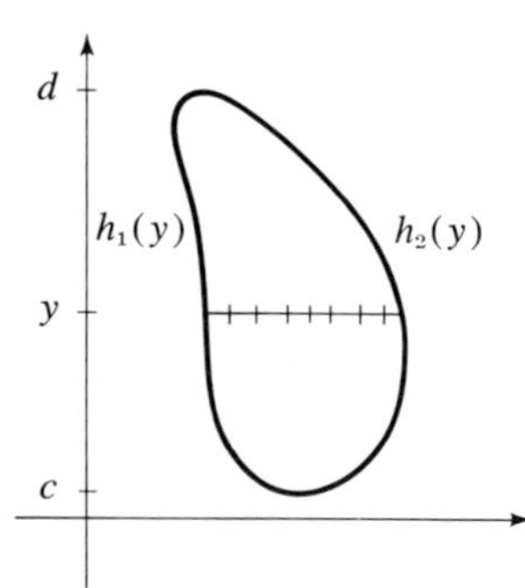

Figure 23.3

The same thing can be done if we reverse the role of x and y, to get

$$\iint_R f(x, y)\, dA = \int_c^d \int_{h_1(y)}^{h_2(y)} f(x, y)\, dx\, dy$$

(see Figure 23.3). These forms are called *iterated integrals.* Thus we may use iterated integrals to evaluate double integrals. The choice between the two forms above is dependent upon the shape of the region R. If R does not lend itself to either of these two forms, it may be necessary to partition it into several regions and use Theorem 23.3.

Example 1

Evaluate

$$\int_0^1 \int_0^{x^2} (x^2 + xy - y^2)\, dy\, dx$$

and describe R.

$$\begin{aligned}\int_0^1 \int_0^{x^2} (x^2 + xy - y^2)\, dy\, dx &= \int_0^1 \left(x^2y + \frac{xy^2}{2} - \frac{y^3}{3}\right)\bigg|_0^{x^2} dx \\ &= \int_0^1 \left(x^4 + \frac{x^5}{2} - \frac{x^6}{3}\right) dx \\ &= \frac{x^5}{5} + \frac{x^6}{12} - \frac{x^7}{21}\bigg|_0^1 \\ &= \frac{1}{5} + \frac{1}{12} - \frac{1}{21} = \frac{33}{140}.\end{aligned}$$

Note that, in carrying out the integration with respect to y, we take the x to be a constant—in keeping with the above discussion. In this sense, multiple integration is like partial differentiation. The region of integration is bounded below by $y = 0$, above by $y = x^2$, and on the left and right by $x = 0$ and $x = 1$. This is shown in Figure 23.4.

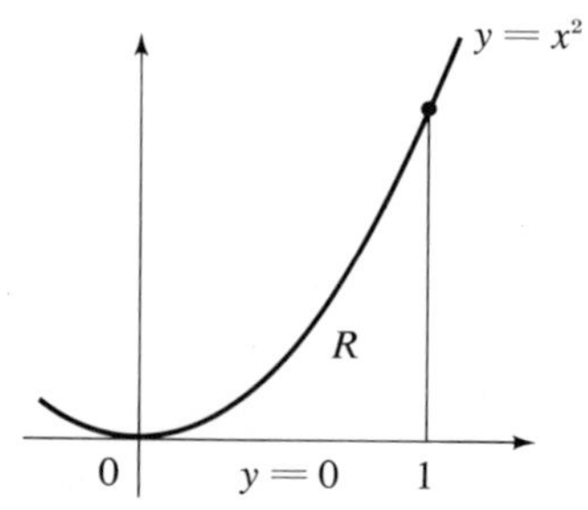

Figure 23.4

Example 2

Evaluate

$$\iint_R (x^2 + y^2)\, dA,$$

where R is the triangle formed by $y = x$, $y = 0$, and $x = 1$.

There are two ways of expressing this double integral as an iterated integral. If R is cut up, as in Figure 23.5(a), we have

$$\iint_R (x^2+y^2)\,dA = \int_0^1 \int_0^x (x^2+y^2)\,dy\,dx$$
$$= \int_0^1 \left(x^2y+\frac{y^3}{3}\right)\Big|_0^x dx$$
$$= \int_0^1 \frac{4x^3}{3}\,dx$$
$$= \frac{x^4}{3}\Big|_0^1 = \frac{1}{3}.$$

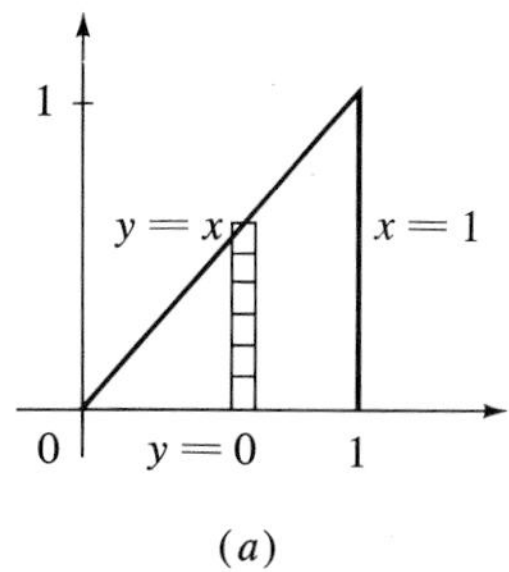

(a)

If R is cut up as in Figure 23.5(b), we have

$$\iint_R (x^2+y^2)\,dA = \int_0^1 \int_y^1 (x^2+y^2)\,dx\,dy$$
$$= \int_0^1 \left(\frac{x^3}{3}+xy^2\right)\Big|_y^1 dy$$
$$= \int_0^1 \left(\frac{1}{3}+y^2-\frac{4y^3}{3}\right) dy$$
$$= \frac{y}{3}+\frac{y^3}{3}-\frac{y^4}{3}\Big|_0^1 = \frac{1}{3}.$$

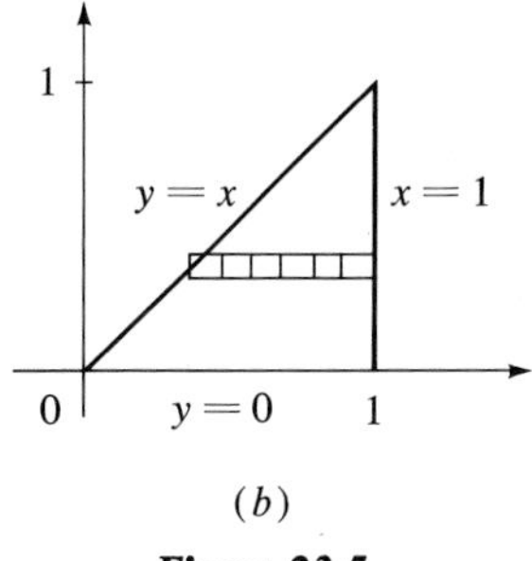

(b)

Figure 23.5

Example 3

Evaluate

$$\iint_R (x^2-xy)\,dA,$$

where R is the region bounded by $y=x$ and $y=3x-x^2$.

The simpler way of setting up the iterated integral is shown graphically in Figure 23.6(a); it gives

$$\iint_R (x^2-xy)\,dA = \int_0^2 \int_x^{3x-x^2} (x^2-xy)\,dy\,dx$$
$$= \int_0^2 \left(x^2y-\frac{xy^2}{2}\right)\Big|_x^{3x-x^2} dx$$
$$= \int_0^2 \left[x^2(3x-x^2)-\frac{x(3x-x^2)^2}{2}-\left(x^3-\frac{x^3}{2}\right)\right] dx$$
$$= \int_0^2 \left(-2x^3+2x^4-\frac{x^5}{2}\right) dx$$
$$= \left(-\frac{x^4}{2}+\frac{2x^5}{5}-\frac{x^6}{12}\right)\Big|_0^2$$
$$= -\frac{8}{15}.$$

Since the result is negative, it cannot be a volume. The reason it is negative is that x^2-xy is negative throughout R.

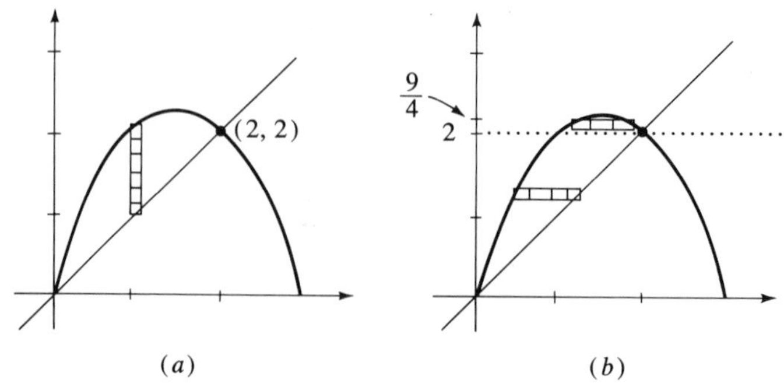

Figure 23.6

An alternate, though more difficult way is illustrated in Figure 23.6(b). Two iterated integrals are needed here, since the horizontal strips sometimes have one end on the parabola and the other on the line and sometimes have both ends on the parabola. Solving the equation $y = 3x - x^2$ for x, we have

$$x = \frac{3 \pm \sqrt{9 - 4y}}{2}.$$

Thus,

$$\iint_R (x^2 - xy)\, dA = \int_0^2 \int_{\frac{3-\sqrt{9-4y}}{2}}^{y} (x^2 - xy)\, dx\, dy + \int_2^{9/4} \int_{\frac{3-\sqrt{9-4y}}{2}}^{\frac{3+\sqrt{9-4y}}{2}} (x^2 - xy)\, dx\, dy.$$

We shall not evaluate these integrals—the work involved is left to your imagination.

Problems

In Problems 1–14, evaluate the given integral and sketch R.

1. $\int_0^1 \int_0^x xy\, dy\, dx.$
2. $\int_0^2 \int_0^{x^2} (x^2 - y^2)\, dy\, dx.$
3. $\int_0^1 \int_0^{1-x} (x^2y + xy^2)\, dy\, dx.$
4. $\int_0^1 \int_{y^2}^{y} (xy + 1)\, dx\, dy.$
5. $\int_0^2 \int_0^1 (x^3 + y^3 - 3xy)\, dx\, dy.$
6. $\int_0^1 \int_{y^3}^{y} (x^2y^2 - 1)\, dx\, dy.$
7. $\int_1^2 \int_y^{y^2} \frac{x}{y}\, dx\, dy.$
8. $\int_1^2 \int_{x^2}^{x^3} (x^2 - xy)\, dy\, dx.$
9. $\int_{-1}^1 \int_{-1}^1 dy\, dx.$
10. $\int_0^1 \int_0^{1-x} x^2\, dy\, dx.$
11. $\int_{-1}^1 \int_{x^2}^1 (x^2 + y^2)\, dy\, dx.$
12. $\int_0^\pi \int_0^1 e^x \sin y\, dx\, dy.$
13. $\int_0^1 \int_0^y e^{x+y}\, dx\, dy.$
14. $\int_0^\pi \int_0^{\sin x} x\, dy\, dx.$

In Problems 15–24, evaluate the given integral.

15. $\iint_R (x^2 - y^2)\, dA$, where R is the region bounded by $x = 0$, $y = 1$, and $y = x$.

16. $\iint_R x^2 y\, dA$, where R is the region bounded by $y = x^2$, $y = 0$, and $x = 2$.

17. $\iint_R (x^3 - y^3)\, dA$, where R is the region bounded by $y = x^3$, $x = 0$, and $y = 1$.

18. $\iint_R (x + y)^2\, dA$, where R is the region bounded by $y = x^3$ and $y = x$.

19. $\iint_R xy\, dA$, where R is the region bounded by $y = x^2$ and $y = x + 2$.

20. $\iint_R xy\, dA$, where R is the region bounded by $y = x^2 - 3x$ and $y = 0$.

21. $\iint_R xy\, dA$, where R is the region bounded by $y = x$ and $y = x^2$.

22. $\iint_R (x + y)\, dA$, where R is the region bounded by $xy = 4$ and $x + y = 5$.

23. $\iint_R (x^2 + y^3)\, dA$, where R is the region bounded by $x = 1$, $x = 3$, $y = 0$, and $y = 4$.

24. $\iint_R dA$, where R is the region bounded by $y = x^2 - 4$ and $y = 8 + 2x - x^2$.

23.2

Volume, Area, and Mass

The definition of the double integral was formulated with volume in mind. Let us consider some examples of this.

Example 1

Find the volume of the ellipsoid

$$\frac{x^2}{4} + \frac{y^2}{9} + \frac{z^2}{1} = 1.$$

First of all, by symmetry, we need only find the volume in the first octant and multiply by 8. The ellipsoid is given in (a) of Figure 23.7, and its projection onto the xy plane is shown in (b). The portion of this projection that lies in the first quadrant is the region R. Suppose the solid is cut by vertical slices parallel to the yz-plane and each of these is cut by slices parallel to the xz plane. A representative

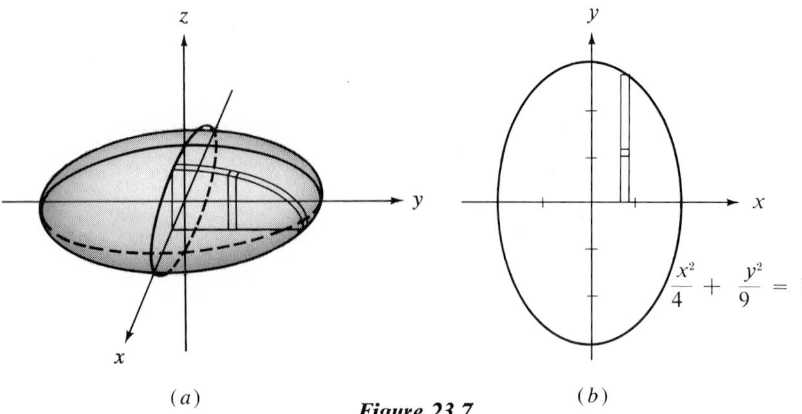

Figure 23.7

of these is given in Figure 23.7. Thus we have

$$\begin{aligned}
V &= 8\int_0^2\int_0^{\frac{3}{2}\sqrt{4-x^2}} z\,dy\,dx \\
&= 8\int_0^2\int_0^{\frac{3}{2}\sqrt{4-x^2}} \sqrt{1-\frac{x^2}{4}-\frac{y^2}{9}}\,dy\,dx \\
&= 8\int_0^2 \frac{1}{2}\left[x\sqrt{1-\frac{x^2}{4}-\frac{y^2}{9}}+3\left(1-\frac{x^2}{4}\right)\operatorname{Arcsin}\frac{2y}{3\sqrt{4-x^2}}\right]\Bigg|_0^{\frac{3}{2}\sqrt{4-x}} dx \\
&= 8\int_0^2 \frac{3\pi}{4}\left(1-\frac{x^2}{4}\right)dx \\
&= 6\pi\left(x-\frac{x^3}{12}\right)\Bigg|_0^2 \\
&= 8\pi.
\end{aligned}$$

Example 2

Find the volume inside $z = x^2 + y^2$ between $z = 0$ and $z = 4$.

Again, by symmetry, we need consider only the portion in the first octant and multiply by 4. The solid is given in (a) of Figure 23.8 and its projection onto the xy plane is shown in (b). Note that this projection corresponds to the widest portion existing when $z = 4$. Again let us take slices parallel to the yz plane and cut each of these into slices parallel to the xz plane. Note from (a) of the figure that the height of the resulting parallelepiped is not the z coordinate of a point on the parabaloid, but rather is $4 - z$. Thus,

$$\begin{aligned}
V &= 4\int_0^2\int_0^{\sqrt{4-x^2}} (4-z)\,dy\,dx \\
&= 4\int_0^2\int_0^{\sqrt{4-x^2}} (4-x^2-y^2)\,dy\,dx \\
&= 4\int_0^2 \left(4y-x^2y-\frac{y^3}{3}\right)\Bigg|_0^{\sqrt{4-x^2}} dx \\
&= 4\int_0^2 \frac{2}{3}(4-x^2)^{3/2}\,dx.
\end{aligned}$$

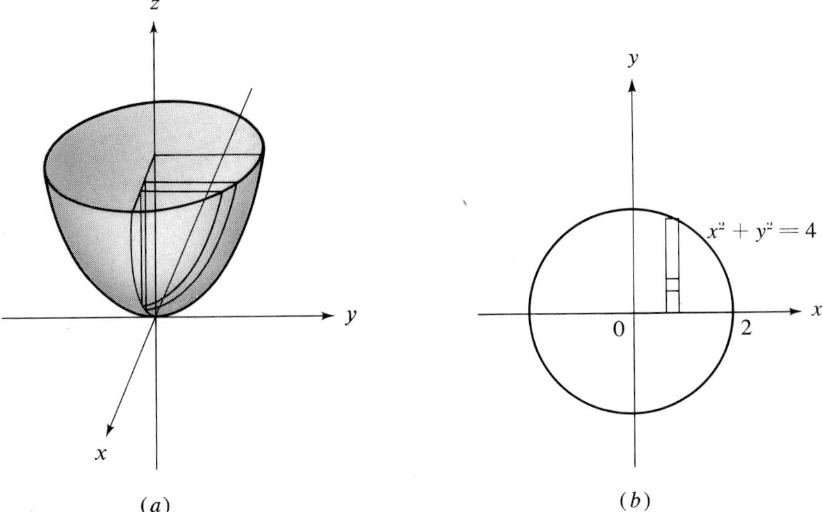

Figure 23.8

Substituting $x = 2 \sin \theta$, we have

$$\begin{aligned} V &= \frac{8}{3}\int_0^{\pi/2} (4 - 4\sin^2\theta)^{3/2}\, 2\cos\theta \, d\theta \\ &= \frac{128}{3}\int_0^{\pi/2} \cos^4\theta \, d\theta \\ &= \frac{32}{3}\int_0^{\pi/2} (1+\cos 2\theta)^2 \, d\theta \\ &= \frac{32}{3}\int_0^{\pi/2} \left(1 + 2\cos 2\theta + \frac{1+\cos 4\theta}{2}\right) d\theta \\ &= \frac{32}{3}\left(\frac{3}{2}\theta + \sin 2\theta + \frac{1}{8}\cos 4\theta\right)\Bigg|_0^{\pi/2} \\ &= 8\pi. \end{aligned}$$

While both of these examples were worked by projecting the solid onto the xy plane, we could make the projection onto any convenient coordinate plane. Both examples could have been done by the methods of Chapter 16, since Example 2 is a solid of revolution and parallel cross sections of Example 1 are all ellipses. However, where the methods of Chapter 16 can only be used for special cases, the use of the double integral is much more general.

Let us now consider the problem of finding area by a double integral. Since the double integral gives volume, it may be difficult to see how we can go back to a two-dimensional figure to find area. In effect, we don't. The area of a plane region is the same as the volume of a cylinder having that region as base and height 1. Thus, we can find an area by finding the volume of the proper cylinder.

Example 3

Find the area of the region bounded by $y = x^2$, $x = 1$, and $y = 0$.

From Figure 23.9, we have

$$\begin{aligned} A &= \int_0^1 \int_0^{x^2} dy\, dx \\ &= \int_0^1 y \Big|_0^{x^2} dx \\ &= \int_0^1 x^2\, dx \\ &= \frac{x^3}{3}\Big|_0^1 \\ &= \frac{1}{3}. \end{aligned}$$

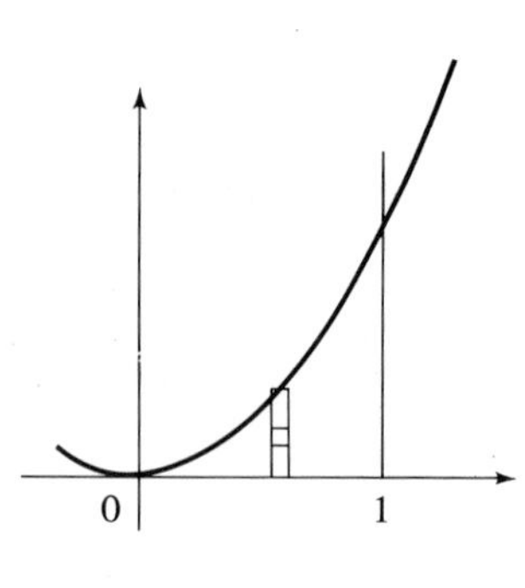

Figure 23.9

Perhaps you feel at this point that we are using a sledge hammer to swat a fly. Why not use a single integral in the example and get the same result with much less effort?

$$\begin{aligned} A &= \int_0^1 y\, dx \\ &= \int_0^1 x^2\, dx \\ &= \frac{x^3}{3}\Big|_0^1 = \frac{1}{3}. \end{aligned}$$

You are quite right. We did more work than necessary—on this particular problem. Suppose, however, that we want the mass of this region and that it does not have uniform density. Since the mass is the product of the area and the density (given in terms of mass per unit *area*), we need merely include the density as a factor of the integral.

Example 4

Find the mass of the region of Example 3 if the density at (x, y) is $1 + x + y$.

$$\begin{aligned} W &= \int_0^1 \int_0^{x^2} (1 + x + y)\, dy\, dx \\ &= \int_0^1 \left(y + xy + \right)\frac{y^2}{2}\Big|_0^{x^2} dx \\ &= \int_0^1 \left(x^2 + x^3 + \frac{x^4}{2}\right) dx \\ &= \frac{x^3}{3} + \frac{x^4}{4} + \frac{x^5}{10}\Big|_0^1 \\ &= \frac{41}{60}. \end{aligned}$$

Problems

In Problems 1–14, use the double integral to find the volume of the given solid.

1. A sphere of radius R.
2. A cone of height h and radius r.
3. The solid bounded by the three coordinate planes and $x + y + z = 1$.
4. The solid bounded by the xz plane, the yz plane, $6x + 2y + 3z = 6$, and $4x + 2y - z = 4$.
5. The solid bounded by $x^2 + y^2 = 4$, $y = z$, and $z = 0$ (one side of the xz plane only).
6. The solid bounded by $x^2 + y^2 - 4x = 0$, $y = z$, and $z = 0$.
7. The solid in the first octant bounded by $x + y = 4$ and $z = xy$.
8. The solid inside $x^2 + y^2 + z^2 = 4$ and above $z = 1$.
9. The solid bounded by the three coordinate planes and $\sqrt{x} + \sqrt{y} + \sqrt{z} = 1$.
10. The portion of the sphere $x^2 + y^2 + z^2 = 9$, that is above $z = 1$.
11. The solid bounded by $y = x^2$, $z = 0$, and $y + z = 2$.
12. The solid bounded by $x^2 + y^2 = 4$ and $x^2 + z^2 = 4$.
13. The solid bounded by $x^2 + y^2 = 1$ and $x^2 + z^2 = 1$.
14. The solid bounded by $z = x^2 + y^2$ and $z = 2$.

In Problems 15–20, find the area of the given region.

15. The region bounded by $y = x^3$, the x axis, and $x = 1$.
16. The region bounded by $y = x^2 - 2x$ and the x axis.
17. The region bounded by $y = x^2$ and $y = x$.
18. The region bounded by $y = x^2$ and $x - y + 2 = 0$.
19. The region bounded by $y = \sin x$ and the x axis between $x = 0$ and $x = \pi$.
20. The region between the x axis and $y = e^x$ to the left of the y axis.

In Problems 21–28, find the mass of the given plane region.

21. The region bounded by $y = x^3$, the x axis, and $x = 1$ with density xy.
22. The region bounded by $y = x^3$, the x axis, and $x = 1$ with density $2 - (x + y)$.
23. The region bounded by $y = 4 - x^2$ and the x axis with density $1 + y$.
24. The region bounded by $y = x^2$ and $y = x$ with density $x^2 + y^2$.
25. The region inside $x^2 + y^2 = 4$ with density $|x| + |y|$.
26. The region inside $x^2 + 4y^2 = 4$ with density $x^2 + y^2$.
27. The region bounded by $y = \sin x$ and the x axis between $x = 0$ and $x = \pi$ with density $|\cos x|$.
28. The region bounded by $y = \sin x$ and the x axis between $x = 0$ and $x = \pi$ with density $x + y$.

23.3

Double Integrals in Polar Coordinates

Suppose the region R is given in polar coordinates. Then, instead of subdividing R by rectangles, we shall use portions of sectors as given in Figure 23.10. Now we want to express dA in terms of dr and $d\theta$. If the dimensions given are

$$\Delta\theta = \theta_i - \theta_{i-1} \quad \text{and} \quad \Delta r = r_j - r_{j-1},$$

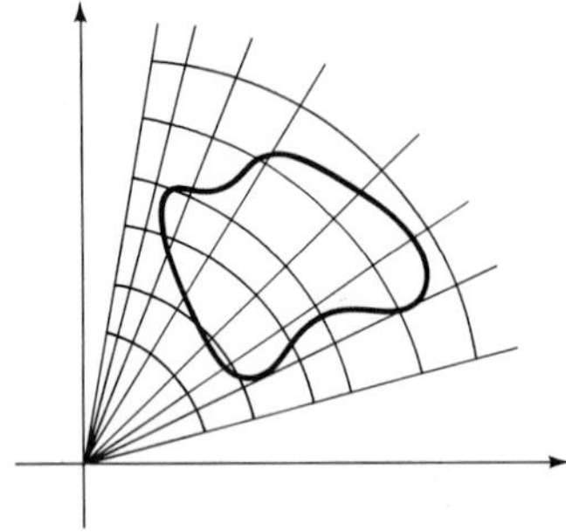

Figure 23.10

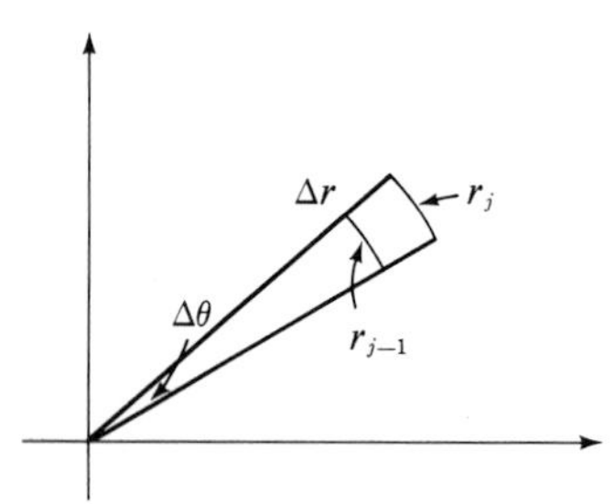

Figure 23.11

(see Figure 23.11), then, as we saw in Section 16.2, the area of the sector with radius r and central angle $\Delta\theta$ is

$$\frac{1}{2} r^2 \, \Delta\theta.$$

The portion of the sector between r_j and r_{j-1} is then

$$\begin{aligned} \frac{1}{2} r_j^2 \, \Delta\theta - \frac{1}{2} r_{j-1}^2 \, \Delta\theta &= \frac{1}{2} (r_j^2 - r_{j-1}^2) \, \Delta\theta \\ &= \frac{1}{2} (r_j + r_{j-1})(r_j - r_{j-1}) \, \Delta\theta \\ &= \frac{r_j + r_{j-1}}{2} \, \Delta r \, \Delta\theta. \end{aligned}$$

In the limit, both Δr and $\Delta\theta$ approach 0. Thus r_j and r_{j-1} approach a common limit r, and

$$\iint_R f(x, y) \, dA = \iint_R f(x, y) r \, dr \, d\theta.$$

Of course $f(x, y)$ must be given in terms of r and θ by

$$x = r \cos\theta \quad \text{and} \quad y = r \sin\theta.$$

Example 1

Find the volume of the solid bounded above by $z = x^2 + y^2$, below by $z = 0$, and on the sides by $r = 1 - \cos\theta$.

Since the solid is symmetric about the xz plane (see Figure 23.12) we can consider just half of it and double the result

$$\begin{aligned} V &= 2 \int_0^{\pi} \int_0^{1-\cos\theta} zr \, dr \, d\theta \\ &= 2 \int_0^{\pi} \int_0^{1-\cos\theta} (x^2 + y^2) r \, dr \, d\theta \\ &= 2 \int_0^{\pi} \int_0^{1-\cos\theta} r^3 \, dr \, d\theta \end{aligned}$$

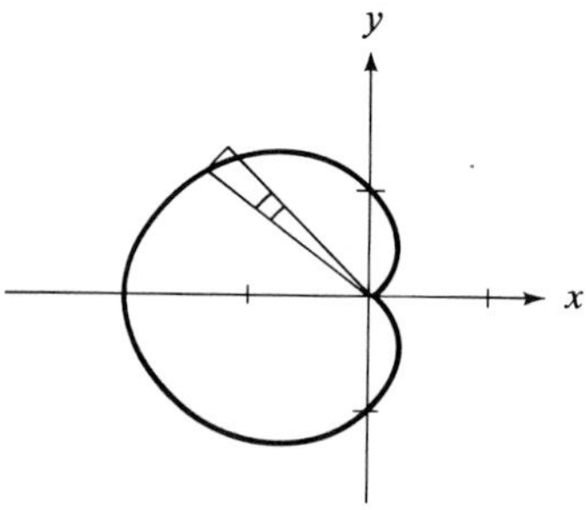

Figure 23.12

$$= 2\int_0^\pi \frac{r^4}{4}\Bigg|_0^{1-\cos\theta} d\theta$$

$$= \frac{1}{2}\int_0^\pi (1-\cos\theta)^4\, d\theta$$

$$= \frac{1}{2}\int_0^\pi (1 - 4\cos\theta + 6\cos^2\theta - 4\cos^3\theta + \cos^4\theta)\, d\theta$$

$$= \frac{1}{2}\int_0^\pi \left[1 - 4\cos\theta + 3(1+\cos 2\theta) - 4(1-\sin^2\theta)\cos\theta + \frac{(1+\cos 2\theta)^2}{4}\right] d\theta$$

$$= \frac{1}{2}\int_0^\pi \left(\frac{17}{4} - 8\cos\theta + \frac{13}{4}\cos 2\theta + 4\sin^2\theta\cos\theta + \frac{1}{4}\cos^2 2\theta\right) d\theta$$

$$= \frac{1}{2}\int_0^\pi \left(\frac{17}{4} - 8\cos\theta + \frac{13}{4}\cos 2\theta + 4\sin^2\theta\cos\theta + \frac{1+\cos 4\theta}{8}\right) d\theta$$

$$= \frac{1}{2}\int_0^\pi \left(\frac{35}{8} - 8\cos\theta + \frac{13}{4}\cos 2\theta + 4\sin^2\theta\cos\theta + \frac{1}{8}\cos 4\theta\right) d\theta$$

$$= \frac{1}{2}\left(\frac{35}{8}\theta - 8\sin\theta + \frac{13}{8}\sin 2\theta + \frac{4}{3}\sin^3\theta + \frac{1}{32}\sin 4\theta\right)\Bigg|_0^\pi$$

$$= \frac{35}{16}\pi.$$

Example 2

Find the mass of the region inside $r = 1 + \sin\theta$ where the density at (r, θ) is r.

We see (Figure 23.13) that the region as well as the density is symmetric about the y axis. Again we may find the mass of half the region and double.

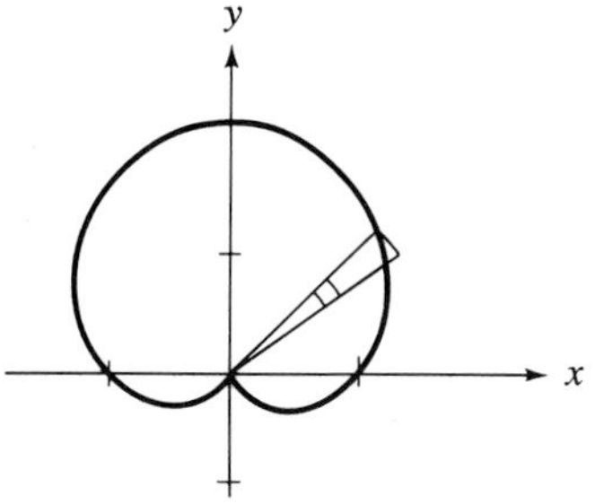

$$W = 2\int_{-\pi/2}^{\pi/2}\int_0^{1+\sin\theta} r\cdot r\, dr\, d\theta$$

$$= 2\int_{-\pi/2}^{\pi/2} \frac{r^3}{3}\Bigg|_0^{1+\sin\theta} d\theta$$

$$= \frac{2}{3}\int_{-\pi/2}^{\pi/2} (1+\sin\theta)^3\, d\theta$$

$$= \frac{2}{3}\int_{-\pi/2}^{\pi/2} (1 + 3\sin\theta + 3\sin^2\theta + \sin^3\theta)\, d\theta$$

Figure 23.13

$$= \frac{2}{3}\int_{-\pi/2}^{\pi/2} \left[1 + 3\sin\theta + \frac{3}{2}(1-\cos 2\theta) + (1-\cos^2\theta)\sin\theta\right] d\theta$$

$$= \frac{2}{3}\int_{-\pi/2}^{\pi/2} \left(\frac{5}{2} + 4\sin\theta - \frac{3}{2}\cos 2\theta - \cos^2\theta\sin\theta\right) d\theta$$

$$= \frac{2}{3}\left(\frac{5}{2}\theta - 4\cos\theta - \frac{3}{4}\sin 2\theta + \frac{1}{3}\cos^3\theta\right)\Bigg|_{-\pi/2}^{\pi/2}$$

$$= \frac{2}{3}\left[\frac{5\pi}{4} - \left(-\frac{5\pi}{4}\right)\right]$$

$$= \frac{5\pi}{3}.$$

Even if the problem is given entirely in terms of rectangular coordinates, it is sometimes easier to integrate if polar coordinates are used.

Example 3

Find the volume of the solid inside $x^2 + y^2 + z^2 = 4$ and $x^2 + y^2 = 1$.

In cylindrical coordinates the surfaces are $z = \pm\sqrt{4 - r^2}$ and $r = 1$.

$$\begin{aligned} V &= 8 \int_0^{\pi/2} \int_0^1 \sqrt{4 - r^2}\, r\, dr\, d\theta \\ &= -4 \int_0^{\pi/2} \int_0^1 \sqrt{4 - r^2}(-2r)\, dr\, d\theta \\ &= -4 \int_0^{\pi/2} \frac{2}{3}(4 - r^2)^{3/2} \Big|_0^1 d\theta \\ &= -4 \int_0^{\pi/2} \frac{2}{3}(3^{3/2} - 8)\, d\theta \\ &= -\frac{8}{3}(3\sqrt{3} - 8)\, \theta \Big|_0^{\pi/2} \\ &= \frac{4\pi}{3}(8 - 3\sqrt{3}). \end{aligned}$$

Problems

In Problems 1–8, find the volume of the given solid.

1. The solid bounded above by $z = 3$, below by $z = 0$, and on the sides by $r = \sin\theta$.
2. The solid bounded above by $z = x$, below by $z = 0$, and on the sides by $r = \cos\theta$.
3. The solid bounded above by $z = \sqrt{x^2 + y^2}$, below by $z = 0$, and on the sides by $r = 1 + \sin\theta$.
4. The solid bounded above by $z = 1 - (x^2 + y^2)$, below by $z = 0$, and on the sides by $r = \sin\theta$.
5. The solid bounded above by $z = 1 + x^2 + y^2$, below by $z = 0$, and on the sides by $r = \sin 2\theta$.
6. The solid bounded above by $z = 1 + x^2 + y^2$, below by $z = 1 - x^2 - y^2$, and on the sides by $r = \cos\theta$.
7. The solid bounded above by $z = \sqrt{x^2 + y^2}$, below by $z = -\sqrt{x^2 + y^2}$, and on the sides by $r = \sin 3\theta$.
8. The solid bounded above by $z = x^2 + y^2$, below by $z = -\sqrt{x^2 + y^2}$, and on the sides by $r = \cos 4\theta$.

In Problems 9–16, find the mass of the given region.

9. Inside $r = 1 + \sin\theta$ with density $|r|$ at (r, θ).
10. Inside $r = 1 + \sin\theta$ with density $|\sin\theta|$ at (r, θ).
11. Inside $r = \cos\theta$ with density $\sin^2\theta$ at (r, θ).
12. Inside $r = \sin\theta$ with density r^2 at (r, θ).
13. Inside $r = \sin 2\theta$ with density $|\sin 2\theta|$ at (r, θ).

14. Inside $r = \cos 2\theta$ with density $|r|$ at (r, θ).
15. Inside $r = \sin^2 \theta$ with density $1 + |r|$ at (r, θ).
16. Inside $r^2 = \sin \theta$ with density r^2 at (r, θ).

In Problems 17–24, use polar coordinates to find the given volume.

17. Inside $x^2 + y^2 = 1$ and bounded by $z = 0$ and $z = 4$.
18. Inside $x^2 + y^2 = 1$ and bounded by $z = 0$ and $z = x^2 + y^2$.
19. Inside $x^2 + y^2 = 1$ and $x^2 + y^2 + z^2 = 9$.
20. Inside $x^2 + y^2 = 1$ and $y^2 + z^2 = 1$.
21. Inside $x^2 + y^2 + z^2 = 1$ and above $x^2 + y^2 = z^2$.
22. Inside $x^2 + y^2 - 2x = 0$ and bounded by $z = 0$ and $z = y$.
23. Inside $x^2 + y^2 - 2x = 0$ and bounded by $z^2 = x^2 + y^2$.
24. Inside $x^2 + y^2 - 2y = 0$ and bounded by $z = 0$ and $z = x^2 + y^2$.

23.4

Centers of Gravity and Moments of Inertia

Of course the double integral can be used in the determination of centers of gravity and moments of inertia. We merely have to make the proper subdivision and recall the meaning of the first and second moments. In order to set up the integral for a first moment of a plane region, we set up the integral for the mass and include a factor for the (directed) distance from the element of area to the axis in question. If we are dealing with a second moment, that distance is squared.

Example 1

Find the center of gravity of the region bounded by $y = x^2$, the x axis, and $x = 1$ if the density at (x, y) is $x + y$.

From Figure 23.14, we have

$$\begin{aligned} W &= \int_0^1 \int_0^{x^2} (x + y)\, dy\, dx \\ &= \int_0^1 \left(xy + \frac{y^2}{2}\right)\Bigg|_0^{x^2} dx \\ &= \int_0^1 \left(x^3 + \frac{x^4}{2}\right) dx \\ &= \left(\frac{x^4}{4} + \frac{x^5}{10}\right)\Bigg|_0^1 \\ &= \frac{7}{20}. \end{aligned}$$

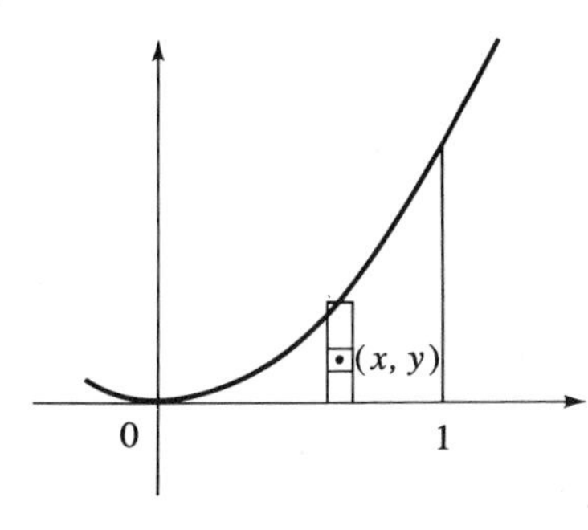

Figure 23.14

Since, in the limit, the element of area shrinks to the point (x, y), we have the following moments.

$$\begin{aligned} M_x &= \int_0^1 \int_0^{x^2} y(x+y)\,dy\,dx \\ &= \int_0^1 \left(\frac{xy^2}{2} + \frac{y^3}{3}\right)\Big|_0^{x^2} dx \\ &= \int_0^1 \left(\frac{x^5}{2} + \frac{x^6}{3}\right) dx \\ &= \left(\frac{x^6}{12} + \frac{x^7}{21}\right)\Big|_0^1 \\ &= \frac{11}{84}. \end{aligned}$$

$$\begin{aligned} M_y &= \int_0^1 \int_0^{x^2} x(x+y)\,dy\,dx \\ &= \int_0^1 \left(x^2y + \frac{xy^2}{2}\right)\Big|_0^{x^2} dx \\ &= \int_0^1 \left(x^4 + \frac{x^5}{2}\right) dx \\ &= \left(\frac{x^5}{5} + \frac{x^6}{12}\right)\Big|_0^1 \\ &= \frac{17}{60}. \end{aligned}$$

$$\bar{x} = \frac{M_y}{W} = \frac{17/60}{7/20} = \frac{17}{21}, \qquad \bar{y} = \frac{M_x}{W} = \frac{11/84}{7/20} = \frac{55}{147}.$$

Example 2

Find the moment of inertia and radius of gyration of the region of Example 1 about the y axis.

$$\begin{aligned} I_y &= \int_0^1 \int_0^{x^2} x^2(x+y)\,dy\,dx \\ &= \int_0^1 \left(x^3y + \frac{x^2y^2}{2}\right)\Big|_0^{x^2} dx \\ &= \int_0^1 \left(x^5 + \frac{x^6}{2}\right) dx \\ &= \left(\frac{x^6}{6} + \frac{x^7}{14}\right)\Big|_0^1 \\ &= \frac{5}{21}, \end{aligned}$$

$$I_y = WR_y^2,$$

$$R_y = \sqrt{\frac{I_y}{W}} = \sqrt{\frac{5/21}{7/20}} = \sqrt{\frac{100}{147}} = \frac{10}{7\sqrt{3}}.$$

Example 3

Find the moment of inertia and radius of gyration of the region of Example 1 about the z axis.

The distance from the point (x, y) to the z axis is $\sqrt{x^2+y^2}$. Thus

$$
\begin{aligned}
I_z &= \int_0^1 \int_0^{x^2} (x^2+y^2)(x+y)\,dy\,dx \\
&= \int_0^1 \left(x^3y + \frac{x^2y^2}{2} + \frac{xy^3}{3} + \frac{y^4}{4}\right)\Bigg|_0^{x^2} dx \\
&= \int_0^1 \left(x^5 + \frac{x^6}{2} + \frac{x^7}{3} + \frac{x^8}{4}\right) dx \\
&= \left(\frac{x^6}{6} + \frac{x^7}{14} + \frac{x^8}{24} + \frac{x^9}{36}\right)\Bigg|_0^1 \\
&= \frac{155}{504}, \\
I_z &= WR_z^2, \\
R_z &= \sqrt{\frac{I_z}{W}} = \sqrt{\frac{155/504}{7/20}} = \frac{5\sqrt{31}}{21\sqrt{2}}.
\end{aligned}
$$

Let us recall that first moments for solids are taken about planes rather than lines. Thus we set up integrals for first moments by setting up the integral for the mass and include a factor for the (directed) distance from the center of gravity of the element of volume to the plane in question.

Example 4

Find the center of gravity of the solid inside $x^2+y^2=1$ and between $z=0$ and $z=1-x$.

The solid is given in (a) of Figure 23.15. We see by symmetry that $\bar{y}=0$. Thus, we need to find only two of the three moments. The projection of the solid onto the xy plane is given in (b). From this we have

$$
\begin{aligned}
V &= 2\int_{-1}^1 \int_0^{\sqrt{1-x^2}} z\,dy\,dx \\
&= 2\int_{-1}^1 \int_0^{\sqrt{1-x^2}} (1-x)\,dy\,dx \\
&= 2\int_{-1}^1 (1-x)\sqrt{1-x^2}\,dx.
\end{aligned}
$$

Substituting $x = \sin\theta$, we have

$$
\begin{aligned}
V &= 2\int_{-\pi/2}^{\pi/2} (1-\sin\theta)\cos^2\theta\,d\theta \\
&= \int_{-\pi/2}^{\pi/2} (1-\cos 2\theta - 2\sin\theta\cos^2\theta)\,d\theta \\
&= \theta - \frac{1}{2}\sin 2\theta + \frac{2}{3}\cos^3\theta\Bigg|_{-\pi/2}^{\pi/2} \\
&= \pi.
\end{aligned}
$$

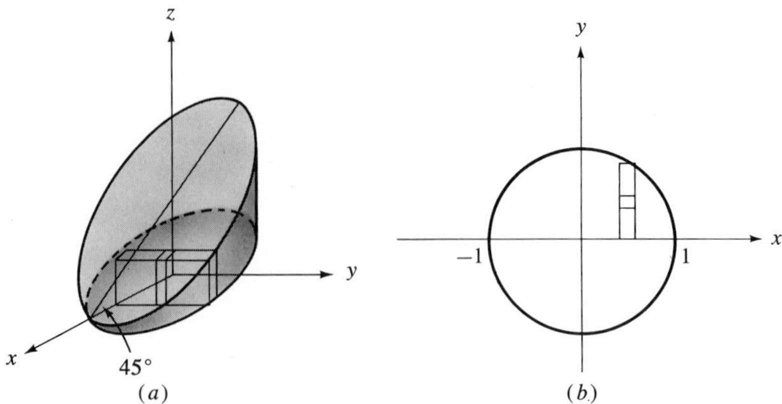

Figure 23.15

From (a) of the figure, we see that the element of volume is a vertical solid strip. Its center of gravity is at the geometric center of this strip or at $(x, y, z/2)$ where (x, y, z) is a point of the plane $z = 1 - x$.

$$M_{yz} = 2\int_{-1}^{1}\int_{0}^{\sqrt{1-x^2}} x(1 - x)\,dy\,dx$$

$$= 2\int_{-1}^{1} (x - x^2)\sqrt{1 - x^2}\,dx.$$

Again substituting $x = \sin\theta$, we have

$$M_{yz} = 2\int_{-\pi/2}^{\pi/2} (\sin\theta - \sin^2\theta)\cos^2\theta\,d\theta$$

$$= \int_{-\pi/2}^{\pi/2} \left[2\sin\theta\cos^2\theta - \frac{1}{2}(1 - \cos^2 2\theta)\right] d\theta$$

$$= \int_{-\pi/2}^{\pi/2} \left[2\sin\theta\cos^2\theta - \frac{1}{2} + \frac{1}{4}(1 + \cos 4\theta)\right] d\theta$$

$$= \int_{-\pi/2}^{\pi/2} \left[2\sin\theta\cos^2\theta - \frac{1}{4} + \frac{1}{4}\cos 4\theta\right] d\theta$$

$$= -\frac{2}{3}\cos^3\theta - \frac{1}{4}\theta + \frac{1}{16}\sin 4\theta \Big|_{-\pi/2}^{\pi/2}$$

$$= -\frac{\pi}{4};$$

$$M_{xy} = 2\int_{-1}^{1}\int_{0}^{\sqrt{1-x^2}} \frac{z^2}{2}\,dy\,dx$$

$$= \int_{-1}^{1}\int_{0}^{\sqrt{1-x^2}} (1 - x)^2\,dy\,dx$$

$$= \int_{-1}^{1} (1 - x)^2\sqrt{1 - x^2}\,dx.$$

Again substituting $x = \sin\theta$, we have

$$M_{xy} = \int_{-\pi/2}^{\pi/2} (1 - \sin\theta)^2 \cos^2\theta \, d\theta$$

$$= \int_{-\pi/2}^{\pi/2} (\cos^2\theta - 2\sin\theta\cos^2\theta + \sin^2\theta\cos^2\theta)\, d\theta$$

$$= \int_{-\pi/2}^{\pi/2} \left[\frac{1}{2}(1 + \cos 2\theta) - 2\sin\theta\cos^2\theta + \frac{1}{4}(1 - \cos^2 2\theta)\right] d\theta$$

$$= \int_{-\pi/2}^{\pi/2} \left[\frac{3}{4} + \frac{1}{2}\cos 2\theta - 2\sin\theta\cos^2\theta - \frac{1}{8}(1 + \cos 4\theta)\right] d\theta$$

$$= \int_{-\pi/2}^{\pi/2} \left(\frac{5}{8} + \frac{1}{2}\cos 2\theta - 2\sin\theta\cos^2\theta - \frac{1}{8}\cos 4\theta\right) d\theta$$

$$= \frac{5}{8}\theta + \frac{1}{4}\sin 2\theta + \frac{2}{3}\cos^3\theta - \frac{1}{32}\sin 4\theta \Big|_{-\pi/2}^{\pi/2}$$

$$= \frac{5}{8}\pi;$$

$$\bar{x} = \frac{M_{yz}}{V} = \frac{-\pi/4}{\pi} = -\frac{1}{4},$$

$$\bar{y} = 0,$$

$$\bar{z} = \frac{M_{xy}}{V} = \frac{5\pi/8}{\pi} = \frac{5}{8}.$$

Second moments for solids are moments about lines. Moreover, since we are not dealing with centers of gravity, the solid strip should be parallel to the line. Thus, if the moment of inertia is the moment about the z axis (or a line parallel to it), we must use solid strips parallel to the z axis—that is, vertical strips; if we want the moment about the y axis, we must use solid strips parallel to the y axis, and so on.

Example 5

Find the moment of inertia and radius of gyration of the solid of Example 4 about the z axis. The density is one.

First, we must cut up the solid in such a way that all points of the resulting slice are the same distance from the z axis. The vertical strips of Example 4 are the proper ones for the moment of inertia about the z axis or any line parallel to it. Thus, we have

$$I_z = 2\int_{-1}^{1}\int_{0}^{\sqrt{1-x^2}} (x^2 + y^2) z \, dy\, dx$$

$$= 2\int_{-1}^{1}\int_{0}^{\sqrt{1-x^2}} (x^2 + y^2)(1 - x)\, dy\, dx$$

$$= 2\int_{-1}^{1} (1 - x)\left(x^2 y + \frac{y^3}{3}\right)\Big|_{0}^{\sqrt{1-x^2}} dx$$

$$= \frac{2}{3}\int_{-1}^{1} (1 - x)(2x^2 + 1)\sqrt{1 - x^2}\, dx.$$

Substituting $x = \sin\theta$, we have

$$
\begin{aligned}
I_z &= \frac{2}{3}\int_{-\pi/2}^{\pi/2} (1 - \sin\theta)(2\sin^2\theta + 1)\cos^2\theta\, d\theta \\
&= \frac{2}{3}\int_{-\pi/2}^{\pi/2} (-2\sin^3\theta\cos^2\theta + 2\sin^2\theta\cos^2\theta - \sin\theta\cos^2\theta + \cos^2\theta)\, d\theta \\
&= \frac{2}{3}\int_{-\pi/2}^{\pi/2} \left[-2\sin\theta(1 - \cos^2\theta)\cos^2\theta + \frac{1}{2}(1 - \cos^2 2\theta) - \sin\theta\cos^2\theta \right.\\
&\qquad \left. + \frac{1}{2}(1 + \cos 2\theta)\right] d\theta \\
&= \frac{2}{3}\int_{-\pi/2}^{\pi/2} \left[-3\sin\theta\cos^2\theta + 2\sin\theta\cos 4\theta + 1 - \frac{1}{4}(1 + \cos 4\theta) + \frac{1}{2}\cos 2\theta\right] d\theta \\
&= \frac{2}{3}\int_{-\pi/2}^{\pi/2} \left[-3\sin\theta\cos^2\theta + 2\sin\theta\cos^4\theta + \frac{3}{4} - \frac{1}{4}\cos 4\theta + \frac{1}{2}\cos 2\theta\right] d\theta \\
&= \frac{2}{3}\left(\cos^3\theta - \frac{2}{5}\cos^5\theta + \frac{3}{4}\theta - \frac{1}{16}\sin 4\theta + \frac{1}{4}\sin 2\theta\right)\Bigg|_{-\pi/2}^{\pi/2} \\
&= \frac{\pi}{2};
\end{aligned}
$$

$$R_z = \sqrt{\frac{I_z}{V}} = \sqrt{\frac{\pi/2}{\pi}} = \frac{1}{\sqrt{2}}.$$

Problems

In Problems 1–8, find the center of gravity of the given region.

1. The region bounded by $y = x^2$, the x axis, and $x = 1$ with density xy at (x, y).
2. The region in the first quadrant bounded by $y = x^2$, the y axis, and $y = 1$ with density xy at (x, y).
3. The region in the first quadrant bounded by $y = x^2$, the y axis, and $y = 1$ with density $x + y$ at (x, y).
4. The region bounded by $y = x^3$, the x axis, and $x = 1$ with density $x + y$ at (x, y).
5. The region bounded by $y = x^3$, the x axis, and $x = 1$ with density $2 - x - y$ at (x, y).
6. The region bounded by $y = x^2$ and $y = x$ with density x^2y at (x, y).
7. The region bounded by $y = x^2$ and $x + y = 2$ with density $|xy|$ at (x, y).
8. The region bounded by $y = x^2$ and $8y = 16 - x^2$ with density $1 + |x| + |y|$ at (x, y).

In Problems 9–14, find the moment of inertia and radius of gyration of the given region about the given line.

9. The region bounded by $y = x^2$, the x axis, and $x = 1$ with density xy; about the y axis.
10. The region in the first quadrant bounded by $y = x^2$, the y axis, and $y = 1$ with density $x + y$; about the x axis.
11. The region in the first quadrant bounded by $y = x^2$, the y axis, and $y = 1$ with density $x + y$; about the z axis.
12. The region bounded by $y = x^3$, the x axis, and $x = 1$ with density xy; about the x axis.
13. The region bounded by $y = x^3$, the x axis, and $x = 1$ with density $x + y$; about the y axis.
14. The region bounded by $y = x^2$ and $y = x$ with density $x + y$; about the z axis.

In Problems 15–18, find the center of gravity of the given solid.

15. The solid bounded by $y = x^2$, $y = 1$, $z = 0$, and $z = 1 + y$.
16. The solid bounded by $y = x$, $y = x^2$, $z = 0$, and $z = 1 + x + y$.
17. The solid bounded by $x^2 + y^2 = 1$, $z = 0$, and $x + y + z = 2$.
18. The solid bounded by $x^2 + y^2 = 1$, $z = 0$, and $z = 1 - x^2$.

In Problems 19–22, find the moment of inertia and radius of gyration of the given solid about the given line. The density is one.

19. The solid bounded by the coordinate planes and $x + y + z = 1$; about the z axis.
20. The solid bounded by the coordinate planes and $x + 2y + z = 4$; about the x axis.
21. The solid bounded by $z = 1 - y^2$, $x = 1 - y^2$, $z = 0$, and $x = 0$; about the x axis.
22. The solid of Example 4; about the y axis.

23.5

Triple Integrals, Volume and Mass

Let us consider another method of determining the volume of a bounded solid. Instead of considering the projection of the solid onto a coordinate plane and subdividing that projection with two sets of lines, suppose we subdivide the solid itself with three sets of planes parallel to the three coordinate axes. This gives a set of rectangular parallelepipeds. Suppose we number from 1 to n all of the parallelepipeds lying entirely inside the given solid S. The volume V_i of the ith parallelepiped is assumed to be the product of its three dimensions. The sum of the V_i's,

$$\sum_{i=1}^{n} V_i,$$

gives an approximation of the volume of the solid. The norm $\|s\|$ of the subdivision s is taken to be the length of the longest diagonal of the n parallelepipeds determined by the subdivision and the solid S. The volume of S is then taken to be the limit of the approximating sum as $\|s\|$ approaches zero. This gives the triple integral:

$$\iiint_S dV = \lim_{\|s\| \to 0} \sum_{i=1}^{n} V_i.$$

In most cases, we shall be interested, not in volume—which can be found by a double integral—but in something related to volume, like mass or moments. Therefore, we shall consider triple integrals of some real-valued function f which is bounded and continuous on S. We choose a point (x_i^*, y_i^*, z_i^*) on or inside the ith parallelepiped and consider the sum of the products,

$$\sum_{i=1}^{n} f(x_i^*, y_i^*, z_i^*)V_i.$$

The limit of this sum is the triple integral of f over S:

$$\iiint_S f(x, y, z)\,dV = \lim_{\|s\| \to 0} \sum_{i=1}^{n} f(x_i^*, y_i^*, z_i^*)V_i.$$

Triple integrals are very difficult to evaluate by this definition. But the process can again be simplified by considering iterated integrals, as we did with the double integral. This time we repeat the process a third time, in the direction of the z axis. Thus we have

$$\iiint_S dV = \int_a^b \int_{f(x)}^{g(x)} \int_{F(x,y)}^{G(x,y)} dz\,dy\,dx.$$

Example 1

Evaluate $\displaystyle\int_0^1 \int_0^{x^2} \int_{x+y}^{x^2+y^2} dz\,dy\,dx.$

$$\begin{aligned}\int_0^1 \int_0^{x^2} \int_{x+y}^{x^2+y^2} dz\,dy\,dx &= \int_0^1 \int_0^{x^2} z\Big|_{x+y}^{x^2+y^2} dy\,dx \\ &= \int_0^1 \int_0^{x^2} (x^2 + y^2 - x - y)\,dy\,dx \\ &= \int_0^1 \left(x^2 y + \frac{y^3}{3} - xy - \frac{y^2}{2}\right)\Big|_0^{x^2} dx \\ &= \int_0^1 \left(x^4 + \frac{x^6}{3} - x^3 - \frac{x^4}{2}\right) dx \\ &= \frac{x^5}{10} + \frac{x^7}{21} - \frac{x^4}{4}\Big|_0^1 \\ &= -\frac{43}{420}.\end{aligned}$$

You might be a little alarmed that the result in the example is negative, when the triple integral is supposed to represent a volume. As in the case of the single and double integrals, the triple integral can be used for other things besides volumes.

Example 2

Find the volume of the solid inside $x^2 + y^2 = 1$ and $x^2 + z^2 = 1$.

The solid is the intersection of the two cylinders given in Figure 23.16. Since it is symmetric about all three coordinate axes, we need only find the volume in the first octant and multiply by eight. Let us consider the projection of the solid onto one of the coordinate planes—say the xy plane. This is given in (b) of Figure 23.16. Cutting by planes, first parallel to the yz plane, then parallel to the xz plane, and finally to the xy plane, we have

$$V = 8 \int_0^1 \int_0^{\sqrt{1-x^2}} \int_0^{\sqrt{1-x^2}} dz\,dy\,dx.$$

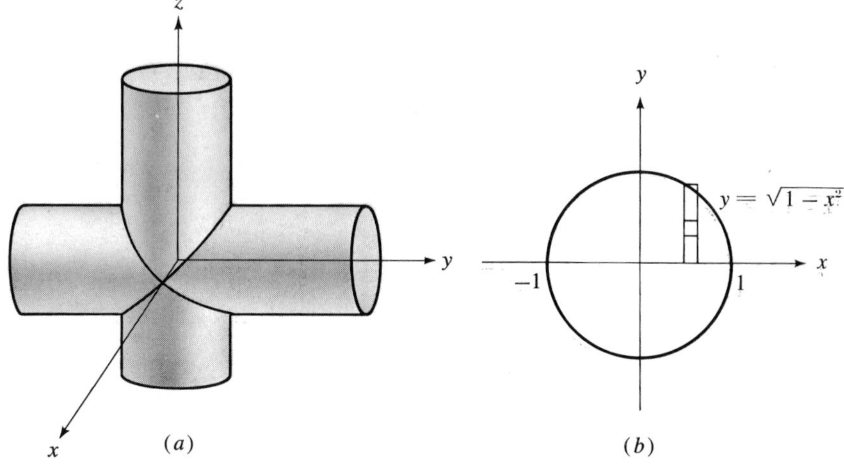

Figure 23.16

The upper limits are found by solving $x^2 + y^2 = 1$ for y and $x^2 + z^2 = 1$ for z.

$$V = 8\int_0^1 \int_0^{\sqrt{1-x^2}} \sqrt{1-x^2}\, dy\, dx$$

$$= 8\int_0^1 (1 - x^2)\, dx$$

$$= 8\left(x - \frac{x^3}{3}\right)\Big|_0^1$$

$$= \frac{16}{3}.$$

If we had used a double integral in the last example, we would have had

$$V = 8\int_0^1 \int_0^{\sqrt{1-x^2}} \sqrt{1-x^2}\, dy\, dx,$$

which is what we had after the first integration. We see that in this instance there is no advantage in using a triple integral. Then what can a triple integral do that a double integral cannot do just as easily? A triple integral is especially useful in finding the mass of a solid that is not of uniform density. In that case, we simply have the same integral that we had for volume with the density as an additional factor.

Example 3

Find the mass of the solid of Example 2 if the density is $|xyz|$.

We again have symmetry about all three axes, not only with respect to the solid itself, but also with respect to the density. Thus we have the same mass in all eight octants and we need to consider only the first. In that octant, xyz is always positive and $|xyz| = xyz$. Thus,

$$W = 8\int_0^1 \int_0^{\sqrt{1-x^2}} \int_0^{\sqrt{1-x^2}} xyz\, dz\, dy\, dx$$

$$= 4\int_0^1 \int_0^{\sqrt{1-x^2}} xyz^2 \Big|_0^{\sqrt{1-x^2}} dy\, dx$$

$$= 4\int_0^1 \int_0^{\sqrt{1-x^2}} x(1-x^2)y\, dy\, dx$$

$$= 2\int_0^1 x(1-x^2)y^2 \Big|_0^{\sqrt{1-x^2}} dx$$

$$= 2\int_0^1 x(1-x^2)^2\, dx$$

$$= -\frac{1}{3}(1-x^2)^3 \Big|_0^1$$

$$= \frac{1}{3}.$$

Problems

In Problems 1–8, evaluate the integral.

1. $\int_0^2 \int_0^x \int_0^{x+y} x\, dz\, dy\, dx.$
2. $\int_0^1 \int_1^y \int_1^{y+z} x\, dx\, dz\, dy.$
3. $\int_1^2 \int_0^{z^2} \int_0^{xz} z^2\, dy\, dx\, dz.$
4. $\int_{-1}^1 \int_0^y \int_0^{yz} yz\, dx\, dz\, dy.$
5. $\int_0^1 \int_{-x}^x \int_{-x}^x (x+z)\, dy\, dz\, dx.$
6. $\int_0^1 \int_0^{\sqrt{1-y^2}} \int_0^y xz\, dz\, dx\, dy.$
7. $\int_1^2 \int_{-z}^z \int_0^{\sqrt{y^2+z^2}} 2x\, dx\, dy\, dz.$
8. $\int_0^1 \int_{-x}^x \int_x^{x+z} (x+z)\, dy\, dz\, dx.$

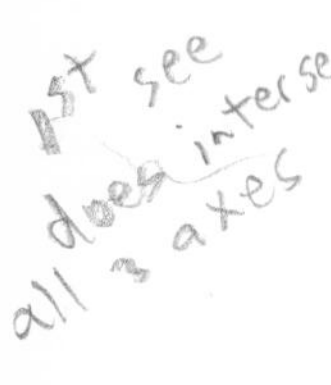

In Problems 9–16, use a triple integral to find the volume of the given solid.

9. The solid bounded by the three coordinate planes and $2x - y + 3z = 6$.
10. The solid bounded by $x^2 + y^2 = 1$, $z = 0$, and $x + y + 4z = 4$.
11. The solid bounded by $x^2 + 4y^2 = 4$, $z = 0$, and $x + y + 4z = 4$.
12. The solid bounded by $x^2 + 4y^2 = 4$, $z = 0$, and $z = 1 - y^2$.
13. The solid inside $x^2 + y^2 + z^2 = 4$.
14. The solid inside $\frac{x^2}{a^2} + \frac{y^2}{b^2} + \frac{z^2}{c^2} = 1$.
15. The solid bounded by $y = x$, $y = x^2$, $z = 0$ and $z = x + y$.
16. The solid bounded by $y = x^2$, $y = 0$, $x = 1$, and $z = 0$ and $z = x^2 + y^2$.

In Problems 17–24, find the mass of the given solid.

17. The unit cube lying in the first octant with three faces in the coordinate planes and with density xyz.

18. The cube of Problem 17 with density $x + y + z$.
19. The solid bounded by $x^2 + y^2 = 1$, $z = 0$, and $z = 1$ with density $|xyz|$.
20. The solid inside $x^2 + y^2 = 1$ and $x^2 + z^2 = 1$ with density $|z|$.
21. The solid inside $x^2 + y^2 = 1$ and $y^2 + z^2 = 1$ with density $|y|$.
22. The solid bounded by $y = x^2$, $z = 0$, and $y + z = 1$ with density $|x|$.
23. The solid bounded by the coordinate planes and $x + y + z = 1$ with density $1 - x - y$.
24. The solid bounded by the coordinate planes and $x + 2y + 3z = 6$ with density $x + y + z$.

23.6

Centers of Gravity and Moments of Inertia

Triple integrals can also be used to determine centers of gravity and moments of inertia. The triple integral's advantage over the double integral occurs when the solid is not of uniform density. To obtain the triple iterated integral for first and second moments, we set up the integral for mass and include a factor for the distance (raised to the first or second powers for first and second moments, respectively) from the element of mass to the line or plane in question.

Example 1

Find the center of gravity of the solid bounded by $y = x^2$, $y = 0$, $x = 1$, $z = 0$ and $z = x + y$ with density $x + y + z$ at (x, y, z).

The solid, shown in Figure 23.17(a), is first cut up by planes parallel to the yz plane, then by planes parallel to the xz plane, and finally by planes parallel to the xy plane. The projection onto the xy plane is given in (b) of the figure.

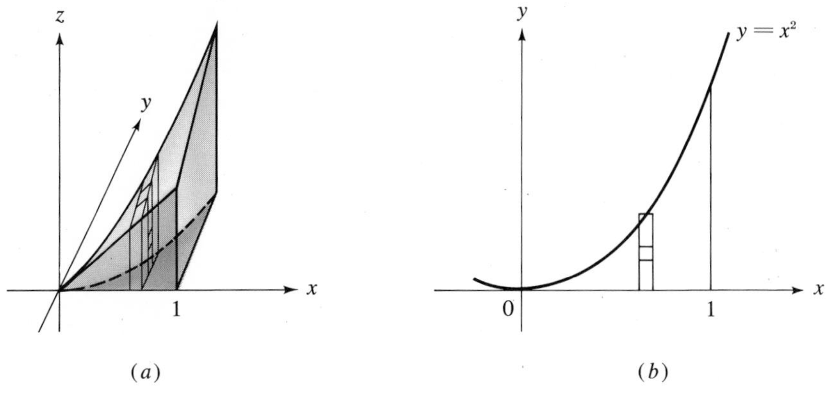

Figure 23.17

From these two figures, we have

$$W = \int_0^1 \int_0^{x^2} \int_0^{x+y} (x + y + z)\, dz\, dy\, dx$$

$$= \int_0^1 \int_0^{x^2} \left[(x + y)z + \frac{z^2}{2}\right]\Bigg|_0^{x+y} dy\, dx$$

$$= \int_0^1 \int_0^{x^2} \frac{3}{2}(x + y)^2\, dy\, dx$$

$$= \int_0^1 \frac{1}{2}(x + y)^3\Bigg|_0^{x^2} dx$$

$$= \int_0^1 \left[\frac{1}{2}(x + x^2)^3 - \frac{1}{2}x^3\right] dx$$

$$= \frac{1}{2}\int_0^1 (3x^4 + 3x^5 + x^6)\, dx$$

$$= \frac{1}{2}\left(\frac{x^5}{5} + \frac{x^6}{2} + \frac{x^7}{7}\right)\Bigg|_0^1$$

$$= \frac{87}{140};$$

$$M_{yz} = \int_0^1 \int_0^{x^2} \int_0^{x+y} x(x + y + z)\, dz\, dy\, dx$$

$$= \int_0^1 \int_0^{x^2} \frac{3}{2}x(x + y)^2\, dy\, dx$$

$$= \frac{1}{2}\int_0^1 (3x^5 + 3x^6 + x^7)\, dx$$

$$= \frac{1}{2}\left(\frac{x^6}{2} + \frac{3x^7}{7} + \frac{x^8}{8}\right)\Bigg|_0^1$$

$$= \frac{59}{112};$$

$$M_{xz} = \int_0^1 \int_0^{x^2} \int_0^{x+y} y(x + y + z)\, dz\, dy\, dx$$

$$= \int_0^1 \int_0^{x^2} \frac{3}{2}y(x + y)^2\, dy\, dx$$

$$= \frac{3}{2}\int_0^1 \int_0^{x^2} (x^2y + 2xy^2 + y^3)\, dy\, dx$$

$$= \frac{3}{2}\int_0^1 \left(\frac{x^2y^2}{2} + \frac{2xy^3}{3} + \frac{y^4}{4}\right)\Bigg|_0^{x^2} dx$$

$$= \frac{3}{2}\int_0^1 \left(\frac{x^6}{2} + \frac{2x^7}{3} + \frac{x^8}{4}\right) dx$$

$$= \frac{3}{2}\left(\frac{x^7}{14} + \frac{x^8}{12} + \frac{x^9}{36}\right)\Bigg|_0^1$$

$$= \frac{23}{84};$$

$$\begin{aligned}
M_{xy} &= \int_0^1 \int_0^{x^2} \int_0^{x+y} z(x+y+z)\,dz\,dy\,dx \\
&= \int_0^1 \int_0^{x^2} \left[(x+y)\frac{z^2}{2} + \frac{z^3}{3}\right]\Bigg|_0^{x+y} dy\,dx \\
&= \int_0^1 \int_0^{x^2} \frac{5}{6}(x+y)^3\,dy\,dx \\
&= \int_0^1 \frac{5}{24}(x+y)^4\Bigg|_0^{x^2} dx \\
&= \frac{5}{24}\int_0^1 (4x^5 + 6x^6 + 4x^7 + x^8)\,dx \\
&= \frac{5}{24}\left(\frac{2x^6}{3} + \frac{6x^7}{7} + \frac{x^8}{2} + \frac{x^9}{9}\right)\Bigg|_0^1 \\
&= \frac{1345}{3024};
\end{aligned}$$

$$\bar{x} = \frac{M_{yz}}{W} = \frac{59/112}{87/140} = \frac{295}{348};$$

$$\bar{y} = \frac{M_{xz}}{W} = \frac{23/84}{87/140} = \frac{115}{261};$$

$$\bar{z} = \frac{M_{xy}}{W} = \frac{1345/3024}{87/140} = \frac{6725}{10{,}266}.$$

Example 2

Find the moment of inertia and radius of gyration of the solid of Example 1 about the z axis.

The distance of a point (x, y, z) from the z axis is $\sqrt{x^2 + y^2}$. Thus,

$$\begin{aligned}
I_z &= \int_0^1 \int_0^{x^2} \int_0^{x+y} (x^2+y^2)(x+y+z)\,dz\,dy\,dx \\
&= \int_0^1 \int_0^{x^2} \frac{3}{2}(x^2+y^2)(x+y)^2\,dy\,dx \\
&= \frac{3}{2}\int_0^1 \int_0^{x^2} (x^4 + 2x^3y + 2x^2y^2 + 2xy^3 + y^4)\,dy\,dx \\
&= \frac{3}{2}\int_0^1 \left(x^4y + x^3y^2 + \frac{2x^2y^3}{3} + \frac{xy^4}{2} + \frac{y^5}{5}\right)\Bigg|_0^{x^2} dx \\
&= \frac{3}{2}\int_0^1 \left(x^6 + x^7 + \frac{2x^8}{3} + \frac{x^9}{2} + \frac{x^{10}}{5}\right) dx \\
&= \frac{3}{2}\left(\frac{x^7}{7} + \frac{x^8}{8} + \frac{2x^9}{27} + \frac{x^{10}}{20} + \frac{x^{11}}{55}\right)\Bigg|_0^1 \\
&= \frac{26{,}867}{55{,}440};
\end{aligned}$$

$$R_z = \sqrt{\frac{I_z}{W}} = \sqrt{\frac{26{,}867/55{,}440}{87/140}} = \frac{1}{6}\sqrt{\frac{26{,}867}{957}}.$$

Sometimes a triple integral is simpler to evaluate than a double integral, even when the solid is of uniform density. Recall that when we used a double integral to obtain a moment of inertia, we found that the element of volume had to be parallel to the axis in question, so that all points of it would be the same distance from that axis. Since the element of mass used to set up the triple iterated integral is a cube, rather than the solid strip used for the double iterated integral, the cubical element shrinks to a point in the limit. Thus, there is no need to consider the question of having the element of mass parallel to a certain axis.

Example 3

Find the moment of inertia about the x axis of the solid of Example 4, Section 23.4. The density is one.

If we consider cuts parallel to the xy plane (Figure 23.15), we have

$$W = 2\int_{-1}^{1}\int_{0}^{\sqrt{1-x^2}}\int_{0}^{1-x} dz\,dy\,dx = \pi;$$

$$\begin{aligned}
I_x &= 2\int_{-1}^{1}\int_{0}^{\sqrt{1-x^2}}\int_{0}^{1-x} (y^2+z^2)\,dz\,dy\,dx \\
&= 2\int_{-1}^{1}\int_{0}^{\sqrt{1-x^2}} \frac{z}{3}(3y^2+z^2)\Big|_{0}^{1-x} dy\,dx \\
&= \frac{2}{3}\int_{-1}^{1}\int_{0}^{\sqrt{1-x^2}} (1-x)[3y^2+(1-x)^2]\,dy\,dx \\
&= \frac{2}{3}\int_{-1}^{1} (1-x)[y^3+(1-x)^2y]\Big|_{0}^{\sqrt{1-x^2}} dx \\
&= \frac{4}{3}\int_{-1}^{1} (1-x)^2\sqrt{1-x^2}\,dx.
\end{aligned}$$

Letting $x = \sin\theta$, we have

$$\begin{aligned}
I_x &= \frac{4}{3}\int_{-\pi/2}^{\pi/2} (1-\sin\theta)^2\cos^2\theta\,d\theta \\
&= \frac{4}{3}\int_{-\pi/2}^{\pi/2} (\cos^2\theta - 2\sin\theta\cos^2\theta + \sin^2\theta\cos^2\theta)\,d\theta \\
&= \frac{4}{3}\int_{-\pi/2}^{\pi/2} \left[\frac{1}{2}(1+\cos 2\theta) - 2\sin\theta\cos^2\theta + \frac{1}{4}(1-\cos^2 2\theta)\right] d\theta \\
&= \frac{4}{3}\int_{-\pi/2}^{\pi/2} \left[\frac{3}{4} + \frac{1}{2}\cos 2\theta - 2\sin\theta\cos^2\theta - \frac{1}{8}(1+\cos 4\theta)\right] d\theta \\
&= \frac{4}{3}\int_{-\pi/2}^{\pi/2} \left(\frac{5}{8} + \frac{1}{2}\cos 2\theta - 2\sin\theta\cos^2\theta - \frac{1}{8}\cos 4\theta\right) d\theta \\
&= \frac{4}{3}\left(\frac{5}{8}\theta + \frac{1}{4}\sin 2\theta + \frac{2}{3}\cos^3\theta - \frac{1}{32}\sin 4\theta\right)\Big|_{-\pi/2}^{\pi/2} \\
&= \frac{5\pi}{6};
\end{aligned}$$

$$R_x = \sqrt{\frac{I_x}{W}} = \sqrt{\frac{5\pi/6}{\pi}} = \sqrt{\frac{5}{6}}.$$

Problems

In Problems 1–8, find the center of gravity of the given solid.

1. The unit cube in the first octant with three faces in the coordinate planes and with density xyz.
2. The solid of Problem 1 with density $x + y + z$.
3. The solid bounded by $x = 0$, $x = 1$, $y = 0$, $y = 1$, $z = 0$, and $z = xy$ with density xyz.
4. The solid bounded by $y = 0$, $y = x$, $x = 1$, $z = 0$, and $z = xy$ with density z.
5. The solid inside $x^2 + y^2 = 1$ and between $z = 0$ and $z = 1$ with density $|xyz|$.
6. The portion of the solid of Problem 5 which lies in the first octant.
7. The solid inside $x^2 + y^2 = 1$ and between $z = 0$ and $z = x^2 + y^2$ with density $|y|$.
8. The solid in the first octant inside $x^2 + y^2 = 1$ and between $z = 0$ and $z = xy$ with density x.

In Problems 9–16, find the moment of inertia and radius of gyration of the given solid about the given axis.

9. The solid of Problem 1; about the z axis.
10. The solid of Problem 1; about the x axis.
11. The solid bounded by $y = x$, $y = x^2$, $z = 0$, and $z = xy$ with density 1; about the y axis.
12. The solid bounded by $x = 0$, $x = 1$, $y = 0$, $y = 1$, $z = 0$, and $z = x^2y^2$ with density 2; about the z axis.
13. The solid bounded by $y = 0$, $y = x^2$, $x = 1$, $z = 0$, and $z = x$ with density 4; about the x axis.
14. The solid inside $x^2 + y^2 = 4$, above $z = 0$ and below $z = y$ with density 1; about the x axis.
15. The solid of Problem 14 with density $|x|$; about the x axis.
16. The solid in the first octant inside $x^2 + y^2 = 1$, above $z = 0$ and below $z = x^2 + y^2$ with density y; about the z axis.

Appendix A Absolute Values and Inequalities

A.1 Inequalities

Definition

If a and b are real numbers, $a < b$ *means there is a positive number c such that* $a + c = b$*;* $a > b$ *means* $b < a$*.*

Thus $3 < 4$, since $3 + 1 = 4$; $-2 < 6$, since $-2 + 8 = 6$; $-4 < -1$, since $-4 + 3 = -1$.

Theorem A.1

If $a < b$ *and* $b < c$*, then* $a < c$*.*

Proof

If $a < b$ and $b < c$, then there are positive numbers d and e such that $a + d = b$ and $b + e = c$. Thus,

$$a + d + e = b + e = c.$$

Since d and e are both positive, $d + e$ is positive and $a < c$.

Theorem A.2

If $a < b$*, then* $a + c < b + c$*.*

Proof

If $a < b$, there is a positive number d such that

$$a + d = b.$$

Then

$$a + c + d = b + c \quad \text{or} \quad a + c < b + c.$$

Theorem A.3

If $a < b$ *and* $c > 0$*, then* $ac < bc$*; if* $a < b$ *and* $c < 0$*, then* $ac > bc$*.*

Proof

If $a < b$, then there is a positive number d such that

$$a + d = b.$$

Thus,

$$ac + dc = bc.$$

If c is positive, then dc is positive and

$$ac < bc.$$

If c is negative, then dc is negative and

$$ac = bc + (-dc) \quad \text{and} \quad ac > bc.$$

Similar theorems can be stated using $a > b$. The above theorems allow us to solve inequalities much as we do equations.

Example 1

Solve $3x - 2 < x + 4$.

$$\begin{aligned} 3x - 2 &< x + 4, \\ 2x - 2 &< 4, && \text{(adding } -x \text{ to both sides)} \\ 2x &< 6, && \text{(adding 2 to both sides)} \\ x &< 3. && \text{(multiplying both sides by 1/2)} \end{aligned}$$

Example 2

Solve $-x - 3 < 2x + 6$.

$$\begin{aligned} -x - 3 &< 2x + 6, \\ -3x - 3 &< 6, \\ -3x &< 9, \\ x &> -3. \end{aligned}$$

Note that the last step involved multiplying both sides by $-1/3$, which reversed the inequality.

Definition

If a and b are numbers, $a \leq b$ means $a < b$ or $a = b$; $a \geq b$ means $a > b$ or $a = b$.

The solution of inequalities involving $\leq$ or $\geq$ is basically the same as for strict inequalities or equations.

Example 3

Solve $4x - 3 \leq x - 6$.

$$\begin{aligned} 4x - 3 &\leq x - 6, \\ 3x - 3 &\leq -6, \\ 3x &\leq -3, \\ x &\leq -1. \end{aligned}$$

Definition

If a, b, and c are real numbers, $a < b < c$ means $a < b$ and $b < c$.

With this definition, two inequalities can be solved at once in some cases.

Example 4

Solve $1 < 2x + 5 < 7$.

$$1 < 2x + 5 < 7,$$
$$-4 < 2x < 2,$$
$$-2 < x < 1.$$

Sometimes these double inequalities must be solved as two separate problems.

Example 5

Solve $x - 5 < 3x + 1 < -x + 2$.

$$\begin{aligned} x - 5 &< 3x + 1, \\ -2x - 5 &< 1, \\ -2x &< 6, \\ x &> -3, \\ -3 &< x; \end{aligned} \qquad \begin{aligned} 3x + 1 &< -x + 2, \\ 4x + 1 &< 2, \\ 4x &< 1, \\ x &< \frac{1}{4}; \end{aligned}$$

$$-3 < x < \frac{1}{4}.$$

Example 6

Solve $\dfrac{2x+1}{x-1} < 1$.

We have a special problem here that did not occur in the previous cases. We should like to multiply both sides by $x - 1$, but we do not know whether $x - 1$ is positive or negative. Let us consider two cases.

Case I $x - 1 > 0$ or $x > 1$:

$$\frac{2x+1}{x-1} < 1,$$
$$2x + 1 < x - 1,$$
$$x + 1 < -1,$$
$$x < -2.$$

Now we have $x < -2$ provided $x > 1$. Of course, x cannot satisfy both of these inequalities. Case *I* gives no solution.

Case II $x - 1 < 0$ or $x < 1$:

$$\frac{2x+1}{x-1} < 1,$$
$$2x + 1 > x - 1,$$
$$x > -2.$$

Now we have $x > -2$, provided $x < 1$. Thus the solution is

$$-2 < x < 1.$$

Problems

In Problems 1–24, solve the given inequalities.

1. $2x+5<3$.
2. $4x+1<2x$.
3. $3x-5<4$.
4. $4x-2<x+1$.
5. $2x+2\leq x-4$.
6. $3x+1\leq 4x+4$.
7. $4x-3>2x+2$.
8. $3x-5>x-2$.
9. $3x+1\geq 2x+2$.
10. $2x-4\geq -x+2$.
11. $-2<x+1<2$.
12. $-3<x-4<3$.
13. $1\leq 2x+1\leq 4$.
14. $3\leq 4x-3\leq 5$.
15. $2x-8<x-1<2x-4$.
16. $3x-5<2x-3<4x-3$.
17. $2x-1\leq x+4\leq 3x+1$.
18. $3x\leq x+4\leq 2x+5$.
19. $\dfrac{2x-5}{x-2}<1$.
20. $\dfrac{x-4}{x+1}<2$.
21. $\dfrac{2x+1}{x-4}\leq 1$.
22. $\dfrac{4x-5}{x+3}\leq 1$.
23. $\dfrac{x-1}{x+1}<1$.
24. $\dfrac{1}{x}<\dfrac{1}{x+1}$.
25. Show that if $0<a<b$, then $1/a>1/b$.
26. Show that if $a<b<0$, then $1/a>1/b$.
27. Show that if $a<0<b$, then $1/a<1/b$.
28. Show that if $a<b$ and $c<d$, then $a+c<b+d$.

A.2 Absolute Values

The absolute value of a number is defined in the following way.

Definition

$$|x| = \begin{cases} x & \text{if } x\geq 0, \\ -x & \text{if } x<0. \end{cases}$$

Thus $|5| = |-5| = 5$, or $|x| = 5$, implies that $x = \pm 5$.

Example 1

Solve $|x-1|=3$.

$$|x-1|=3,$$
$$x-1=\pm 3,$$
$$x=1\pm 3=4 \text{ or } -2.$$

Example 2

Solve $|x+1|=|2x+3|$.

$$|x+1|=|2x+3|;$$
$$x+1=2x+3, \qquad x+1=-2x-3,$$
$$-x=2, \qquad 3x=-4,$$
$$x=-2. \qquad x=-\frac{4}{3}.$$

Let us now consider the inequality $|x| < a$, where a is a positive number. If $0 \leq x < a$, then $|x| = x < a$. If $-a < x < 0$, then $|x| = -x < a$. Thus $|x| < a$ if $-a < x < a$. Furthermore, if $x \geq a$ or $x \leq -a$, $|x| \nless a$. Thus, $|x| < a$ if and only if $-a < x < a$.

Example 3

Solve $|x-1| < 1$.

$$-1 < x - 1 < 1,$$
$$0 < x < 2.$$

Example 4

Solve $|x-1| > 2$.

$$x - 1 > 2 \quad \text{or} \quad x - 1 < -2,$$
$$x > 2 \quad \text{or} \quad x < -1.$$

The solution *cannot* be put into the form $-1 > x > 2$. The latter means $x < -1$ *and* $x > 2$. Our solution is $x < -1$ *or* $x > 2$.

Example 5

If $|x-2| < 1$ and $f(x) = 2x - 1$, what can be said about $|f(x) - 3|$?

$$\begin{aligned} |f(x) - 3| &= |(2x-1) - 3| \\ &= |2x - 4| \\ &= 2|x-2| \\ &< 2 \cdot 1 = 2. \end{aligned}$$

Thus,

$$|f(x) - 3| < 2.$$

Problems

In Problems 1–24, solve for x.

1. $|x+2| = 5$.
2. $|2x-1| = 3$.
3. $|4x-4| = 1$.
4. $|4-2x| = 3$.
5. $|x-2| = 0$.
6. $|2x-5| = 3$.
7. $|2x+1| = |x-3|$.
8. $|x-4| = |2x-5|$.
9. $\left|\dfrac{x-2}{x+1}\right| = 3$.
10. $\left|\dfrac{4x+2}{x-3}\right| = 1$.
11. $|x+1| = |x-3|$.
12. $|x-5| = |x+2|$.
13. $|x+3| < 1$.
14. $|x-4| < 2$.
15. $|2x+3| < 3$.
16. $|3x-1| < 2$.
17. $|2x-5| \leq 4$.
18. $|x-3| \leq 5$.
19. $|x-4| > 1$.
20. $|2x-3| > 2$.
21. $|3x+1| \geq 4$.
22. $|2x+5| \geq 1$.
23. $|x-2| \leq 0$.
24. $|2x+1| \geq 0$.
25. If $|x-2| < 1$ and $f(x) = x + 1$, what can be said about $|f(x) - 3|$?
26. If $|x+1| < 2$ and $f(x) = x + 4$, what can be said about $|f(x) - 3|$?
27. If $|x-1| < \delta$ and $f(x) = 2x + 1$, what can be said about $|f(x) - 3|$?
28. If $|x-3| < \delta$ and $f(x) = 3x - 1$, what can be said about $|f(x) - 8|$?

A.3 Absolute Values and Inequalities

Let us consider absolute values of sums, differences, products, and quotients.

Theorem A.4

If a and b are real numbers, then

$$|ab| = |a| \cdot |b|$$

$$\left|\frac{a}{b}\right| = \frac{|a|}{|b|}.$$

This theorem is easily proved by considering several cases ($a \geq 0$ or $a < 0$, $b \geq 0$ or $b < 0$).

Theorem A.5

If a and b are numbers, then

$$|a + b| \leq |a| + |b|,$$
$$|a - b| \leq |a| + |b|.$$

Proof

By the definition of absolute value,

$$-|a| \leq a \leq |a| \quad \text{and} \quad -|b| \leq b \leq |b|.$$

Thus

$$-(|a| + |b|) \leq a + b \leq |a| + |b| \quad \text{(see Problem 28, page 634).}$$

By the discussion following Example 2, page 634,

$$|a + b| \leq |a| + |b|.$$

Finally,

$$\begin{aligned} |a - b| &= |a + (-b)| \\ &\leq |a| + |-b| \\ &= |a| + |b|. \end{aligned}$$

Example 1

If $|x| < 1$, what can be said about $|2x + 1|$?

$$\begin{aligned} |2x + 1| &\leq |2x| + |1| \\ &= 2|x| + 1 \\ &< 2 \cdot 1 + 1 = 3. \end{aligned}$$

Thus, $|2x + 1| < 3$.

Example 2

If $|x| \leq 3$, what can be said about $|x^2 + x + 1|$?

$$\begin{aligned} |x^2 + x + 1| &\leq |x^2| + |x| + |1| \\ &= |x|^2 + |x| + 1 \\ &\leq 3^2 + 3 + 1 \\ &= 13. \end{aligned}$$

Thus $|x^2 + x + 1| \leq 13$.

Example 3

Show that if $|x - 1| < \delta$ and $\delta \leq 1$, then $|x^2 - 1| < 3\delta$.

$$\begin{aligned} |x^2 - 1| &= |(x + 1)(x - 1)| \\ &= |x + 1|\ |x - 1|. \end{aligned}$$

We know that $|x - 1| < \delta$. Let us consider $|x + 1|$. Since $|x - 1| < \delta$ and $\delta \leq 1$,

$$\begin{aligned} |x - 1| &< 1, \\ -1 < x - 1 &< 1, \\ 1 < x + 1 &< 3, \\ |x + 1| &< 3. \end{aligned}$$

Thus $|x^2 - 1| = |x + 1||x - 1| < 3\delta$.

Example 4

Show that if $|x - 1| < \delta$ and $\delta \leq 1/2$, then

$$\left|\frac{1}{x} - 1\right| < 2\delta.$$

$$\begin{aligned} \left|\frac{1}{x} - 1\right| &= \left|\frac{1 - x}{x}\right| \\ &= \frac{1}{|x|}\,|x - 1|. \end{aligned}$$

Again we know that $|x - 1| < \delta$. Let us consider $1/|x|$. Since $|x - 1| < \delta$ and $\delta \leq 1/2$,

$$\begin{aligned} |x - 1| &< \frac{1}{2}, \\ -\frac{1}{2} < x - 1 &< \frac{1}{2}, \\ \frac{1}{2} < x &< \frac{3}{2}, \\ 2 > \frac{1}{x} &> \frac{2}{3}, \qquad \text{(See Problem 25, page 634)} \\ \frac{1}{|x|} = \left|\frac{1}{x}\right| &< 2. \end{aligned}$$

Thus $\left|\frac{1}{x} - 1\right| = \frac{1}{|x|}\,|x - 1| < 2\delta$.

Problems

1. If $|x| < 2$, what can be said about $|x^2 + 1|$?
2. If $|x| < 3$, what can be said about $|x^2 - 2x - 3|$?
3. If $|x| < 1$, what can be said about $|x^2 + 2x + 2|$?
4. If $|x| < 2$, what can be said about $|x^3 + x|$?
5. If $|x| < 5$, what can be said about $|x^4 + 4|$?
6. If $|x| < 1$, what can be said about $|x^4 - 2x^3 + x^2 + x|$?
7. If $-1 < x < 2$, what can be said about $|x^2 + x + 1|$?
8. If $-2 < x < 4$, what can be said about $|x^3 + x^2 + x + 1|$?
9. If $-5 < x < 1$, what can be said about $|x^2 - 3|$?
10. If $-3 < x < 2$, what can be said about $|x^3 - x + 1|$?
11. If $|x| < \delta$, show that $|x^2 + 1| < 1 + \delta^2$.
12. If $|x - 2| < \delta$ and $\delta \leq 1$, show that $|x^2 - 4| < 5\delta$.
13. If $|x - 1| < \delta$ and $\delta \leq 1$, show that $|x^2 + x - 2| < 4\delta$.
14. If $|x + 2| < \delta$ and $\delta \leq 1$, show that $|x^2 + x - 2| < 4\delta$.
15. If $|x - 1| < \delta$ and $\delta \leq 2$, show that $|x^3 - 1| < 13\delta$.
16. If $|x - 1| < \delta$ and $\delta \leq 1$, show that $|x^3 - 1| < 7\delta$.
17. If $|x - 1| < \delta$ and $\delta \leq \frac{3}{4}$, show that $\left|\frac{1}{x} - 1\right| < 4\delta$.
18. If $|x - 2| < \delta$ and $\delta \leq 1$, show that $\left|\frac{1}{x} - \frac{1}{2}\right| < \frac{\delta}{2}$.
19. Prove that $|a + b| \geq ||a| - |b||$.

Appendix B Mean-Value Theorem

The proofs of several important theorems were omitted because they required the mean-value theorem. The proofs of these theorems are given here. First, we reiterate the mean-value theorem upon which these proofs are based.

Theorem 17.5

(*Mean-value theorem*) *If a and b are numbers* ($a < b$) *and f is a function such that*
(*a*) *f is continuous on* $[a, b]$, *and*
(*b*) $f'(x)$ *exists for all x in* (a, b), *then there is a number* x_0 *between a and b such that*

$$f'(x_0) = \frac{f(b) - f(a)}{b - a}.$$

B.1 Theorem 5.12

Theorem 5.12

(*See page 88*) *If f and g are functions such that* $f'(x) = g'(x)$ *for all x, then* $f(x) - g(x)$ *is a constant.*

Proof

Let F be the function such that $F(x) = f(x) - g(x)$. Assume that F is not a constant; that is, assume there are two numbers a and b ($a < b$) such that $F(a) \neq F(b)$. Since $f'(x)$ and $g'(x)$ exist for all x, f and g are continuous for all x by Theorem 10.6 (page 234). Thus F is continuous for all x in $[a, b]$ by Theorem 17.2 (page 434), and $F'(x) = f'(x) - g'(x)$ exists for all x in (a, b). By the mean-value theorem, there is a number x_0 between a and b such that

$$F'(x_0) = \frac{F(b) - F(a)}{b - a}.$$

Since $F(a) \neq F(b)$,

$$F'(x_0) \neq 0.$$

Thus

$$f'(x_0) - g'(x_0) \neq 0 \quad \text{and} \quad f'(x_0) \neq g'(x_0),$$

which contradicts our hypothesis. Thus $F(x) = f(x) - g(x)$ is constant.

B.2 Theorem 6.5

Theorem 6.5

(*Page 108*) *If f is a function such that $f'(x) > 0$ for every x on (a, b), then f is increasing on (a, b); if $f'(x) < 0$ for every x on (a, b), then f is decreasing on (a, b).*

Proof

Suppose $f'(x) > 0$ for every x on (a, b). Assume that f is not increasing on (a, b); that is, there is a pair of numbers c and d such that $a < c < d < b$ and $f(c) \geq f(d)$. Since $f'(x)$ exists for all x in $[c, d]$, f is continuous on $[c, d]$. We are given that $f'(x)$ exists for all x in (c, d). By the mean-value theorem, there is a number x_0 between c and d (and thus between a and b) such that

$$f'(x_0) = \frac{f(d) - f(c)}{d - c}.$$

Since $c < d$,

$$d - c > 0;$$

since $f(c) \geq f(d)$,

$$f(d) - f(c) \leq 0.$$

Thus

$$f'(x_0) = \frac{f(d) - f(c)}{d - c} \leq 0,$$

which contradicts the hypothesis that $f'(x) > 0$ for every x on (a, b). Thus, f is increasing on (a, b). A similar argument proves the second part of the theorem.

B.3 Theorem 6.6

Before proving Theorem 6.6, let us define our terms more carefully.

Definition

The graph of $y = f(x)$ is concave upward on (a, b) means that if $a < x_1 < x_2 < x_3 < b$, then $P_2 = (x_2, f(x_2))$ is below the line determined by P_1: $(x_1, f(x_1))$ and P_3: $(x_3, f(x_3))$; it is concave downward if P_2 is above the line determined by P_1 and P_3.

Theorem

If the graph of $y = f(x)$ is concave upward on (a, b) and $a < x_1 < x_2 < x_3 < b$, then

$$\frac{f(x_2) - f(x_1)}{x_2 - x_1} < \frac{f(x_3) - f(x_2)}{x_3 - x_2};$$

if it is concave downward, then

$$\frac{f(x_2) - f(x_1)}{x_2 - x_1} > \frac{f(x_3) - f(x_2)}{x_3 - x_2}.$$

Proof

Suppose the graph of $y = f(x)$ is concave upward on (a, b) and $a < x_1 < x_2 < x_3 < b$. Let $P:(x_2, y)$ be the point on P_1P_3 with abscissa x_2. The slope of P_1P is equal to the slope of PP_3. Thus

$$\frac{y - f(x_1)}{x_2 - x_1} = \frac{f(x_3) - y}{x_3 - x_2}.$$

Since the graph is concave upward on (a, b), P_2 is below P, or $f(x_2) < y$. Thus,

$$\frac{f(x_2) - f(x_1)}{x_2 - x_1} < \frac{y - f(x_1)}{x_2 - x_1} = \frac{f(x_3) - y}{x_3 - x_2} < \frac{f(x_3) - f(x_2)}{x_3 - x_2},$$

which is the desired result. A similar argument proves the second part.

Theorem 6.6

(*Page 113*) *If f is a function such that $f''(x)$ is positive (negative) for all x on (a, b), then the graph of f is concave upward (downward) on (a, b).*

Proof

Suppose $f''(x)$ is positive for all x on (a, b). By Theorem 6.5, f' is increasing on (a, b). Suppose $a < x_1 < x_2 < x_3 < b$. The conditions of the mean-value theorem are satisfied for the function f on $[x_1, x_2]$ as well as for f on $[x_2, x_3]$. Thus there is a number x_4 between x_1 and x_2 such that

$$f'(x_4) = \frac{f(x_2) - f(x_1)}{x_2 - x_1}.$$

Similarly there is a number x_5 between x_2 and x_3 such that

$$f'(x_5) = \frac{f(x_3) - f(x_2)}{x_3 - x_2}.$$

Since $x_1 < x_4 < x_2$ and $x_2 < x_5 < x_3$, it follows that $x_4 < x_5$. But f' is an increasing function on $(a. b)$. Thus

$$f'(x_4) < f'(x_5)$$

or

$$\frac{f(x_2) - f(x_1)}{x_2 - x_1} < \frac{f(x_3) - f(x_2)}{x_3 - x_2}.$$

By the previous theorem, f cannot be concave downward; f cannot be linear, or the above expressions would be equal. Thus, f must be concave upward on (a, b). A similar argument proves that, if $f''(x)$ is negative for all x on (a, b), then the graph is concave downward on (a, b).

B.4 The Fundamental Theorem of Integral Calculus

The statement of the fundamental theorem of integral calculus given on page 153 requires only that the function f be integrable; however it was noted there that f is assumed to be "well-behaved." In Section 10.7 it is noted that we may use the term "continuous" in place of "well-behaved." Thus f is *continuous* on $[a, b]$. This was used in the proof when it was noted that

$$\lim_{h \to 0} m = f(x) \quad \text{and} \quad \lim_{h \to 0} M = f(x).$$

Of course all of this, while intuitively clear, lacks rigor. Furthermore, the existence of the function F is not established in the given proof. The following argument, based upon the mean-value theorem, is a more rigorous proof of the fundamental theorem.

Theorem 8.8

(*Fundamental theorem of integral calculus*): *If f is continuous on the interval* $[a, b]$ *and F is any function such that $F'(x) = f(x)$ for all x in* $[a, b]$, *then*

$$\int_a^b f(x)\,dx = F(b) - F(a).$$

Proof

Suppose the interval $[a, b]$ is subdivided by

$$a = x_0,\ x_1\ x_2,\ \ldots\ x_n = b.$$

Now let us consider the ith subinterval $[x_{i-1}, x_i]$. Since $F'(x)$ exists for all x in $[x_{i-1}, x_i]$, then, by Theorem 10.6 (page 234), F is continuous on $[x_{i-1}, x_i]$. The conditions of the mean-value theorem are satisfied by F. Thus, there is a number x_i^* between x_{i-1} and x_i such that

$$F'(x_i^*) = \frac{F(x_i) - F(x_{i-1})}{x_i - x_{i-1}}.$$

But $F'(x_i^*) = f(x_i^*)$ and $x_i - x_{i-1} = \Delta x_i$. Thus,

$$f(x_i^*)\,\Delta x_i = F(x_i) - F(x_{i-1}),$$

$$\sum_{1=i}^{n} f(x_i^*)\,\Delta x_i = \sum_{i=1}^{n} [F(x_i) - F(x_{i-1})]$$

$$= F(x_n) - F(x_0)$$

$$= F(b) - F(a),$$

and

$$\int_a^b f(x)\,dx = \lim_{\|s\| \to 0} \sum_{i=1}^{n} f(x_i^*)\,\Delta x_i$$

$$= \lim_{\|s\| \to 0} [F(b) - F(a)]$$

$$= F(b) - F(a).$$

This argument assumes that the value of the integral is independent of the choice of x_i^*. A proof of this independence rests upon the notion of uniform continuity, which we have not considered. Thus we shall *assume* the integral to be independent of the choice of the x_i^*.

Appendix C Formulas

C.1 Elementary Algebra

(*1*) *Quadratic formula*

The solutions of the quadratic equation

$$ax^2 + bx + c = 0 \quad (a \neq 0)$$

are

$$x = \frac{-b \pm \sqrt{b^2 - 4ac}}{2a}.$$

(*2*) *Binomial theorem* (*n a positive integer*)

$$(a + b)^n = a^n + na^{n-1}\,b + \frac{n(n-1)}{2!}\,a^{n-2}\,b^2 + \frac{n(n-1)(n-2)}{3!}\,a^{n-3}\,b^3 + \cdots$$

$$+ \frac{n(n-1)(n-2)\cdots(n-r+1)}{r!}\,a^{n-r}\,b^r + \cdots + nab^{n-1} + b^n.$$

(*3*) *Exponents*

$a^m \cdot a^n = a^{m+n}.$

$\frac{a^m}{a^n} = a^{m-n} \quad (a \neq 0).$

$(a^m)^n = a^{mn}.$

$(ab)^n = a^n b^n.$

(*4*) *Logarithms*

$\log_a x + \log_a y = \log_a xy.$

$\log_a x - \log_a y = \log_a \frac{x}{y}.$

$n \log_a x = \log_a x^n.$

$\frac{1}{n} \log_a x = \log_a \sqrt[n]{x}.$

$\log_a x = \frac{\log_b x}{\log_b a}.$

$\log_a 1 = 0, \qquad \log_a a = 1.$

C.2 Trigonometry

(1) *Trigonometric identities*

$$\tan x = \frac{\sin x}{\cos x}, \qquad \cot x = \frac{\cos x}{\sin x},$$

$$\sec x = \frac{1}{\cos x}, \qquad \csc x = \frac{1}{\sin x}.$$

$$\sin^2 x + \cos^2 x = 1.$$
$$\tan^2 x + 1 = \sec^2 x.$$
$$1 + \cot^2 x = \csc^2 x.$$

$$\sin (x + y) = \sin x \cos y + \cos x \sin y.$$
$$\sin (x - y) = \sin x \cos y - \cos x \sin y.$$
$$\cos (x + y) = \cos x \cos y - \sin x \sin y.$$
$$\cos (x - y) = \cos x \cos y + \sin x \sin y.$$

$$\tan (x + y) = \frac{\tan x + \tan y}{1 - \tan x \tan y}.$$

$$\tan (x - y) = \frac{\tan x - \tan y}{1 + \tan x \tan y}.$$

$$\sin 2x = 2 \sin x \cos x.$$
$$\begin{aligned}\cos 2x &= \cos^2 x - \sin^2 x \\ &= 1 - 2 \sin^2 x \\ &= 2 \cos^2 x - 1.\end{aligned}$$

$$\tan 2x = \frac{2 \tan x}{1 - \tan^2 x}.$$

$$\sin \frac{x}{2} = \pm \sqrt{\frac{1 - \cos x}{2}}.$$

$$\cos \frac{x}{2} = \pm \sqrt{\frac{1 + \cos x}{2}}.$$

$$\tan \frac{x}{2} = \pm \sqrt{\frac{1 - \cos x}{1 + \cos x}} = \frac{1 - \cos \mathrm{x}}{\sin x} = \frac{\sin x}{1 + \cos x}.$$

$$\sin x + \sin y = 2 \sin \frac{x + y}{2} \cos \frac{x - y}{2}.$$

$$\sin x - \sin y = 2 \cos \frac{x + y}{2} \sin \frac{x - y}{2}.$$

$$\cos x + \cos y = 2 \cos \frac{x+y}{2} \cos \frac{x-y}{2}.$$

$$\cos x - \cos y = 2 \sin \frac{x+y}{2} \sin \frac{x-y}{2}.$$

(2) ***Triangles*** (***Figure C.1***)

$$\text{Law of sines: } \frac{a}{\sin A} = \frac{b}{\sin B} = \frac{c}{\sin C}.$$

$$\text{Law of cosines: } c^2 = a^2 + b^2 - 2ab \cos C.$$

C.3 Mensuration formulas

(1) Triangle:

$$\text{Area} = \frac{1}{2} bh \quad \text{(Figure C.2).}$$

(2) Parallelogram:

$$\text{Area} = bh \quad \text{(Figure C.3).}$$

(3) Trapezoid:

$$\text{Area} = \frac{1}{2} h(a+b) \quad \text{(Figure C.4).}$$

(4) Circle:

$$\text{Area} = \pi r^2, \qquad \text{Circumference} = 2\pi r \quad \text{(Figure C.5).}$$

(5) Sector:

$$\text{Area} = \frac{1}{2} r^2\theta \quad \text{(Figure C.6).}$$

(6) Ellipse:

$$\text{Area} = \pi ab \quad \text{(Figure C.7).}$$

(7) Right circular cylinder:

$$\text{Volume} = \pi r^2 h;$$
$$\text{Lateral surface} = 2\pi rh;$$
$$\text{Total surface} = 2\pi r(r+h) \quad \text{(Figure C.8).}$$

(8) Right circular cone:

$$\text{Volume} = \frac{1}{3} \pi r^2 h;$$
$$\text{Lateral surface} = \pi rs;$$
$$\text{Total surface} = \pi r(r+s) \quad \text{(Figure C.9).}$$

(9) Sphere:

$$\text{Volume} = \frac{4}{3}\pi r^3; \qquad \text{Surface} = 4\pi r^2 \quad \text{(Figure C.10).}$$

(10) Frustum of a right circular cone:

$$\text{Volume} = \frac{1}{3}\pi h(r_1^2 + r_1 r_2 + r_2^2), \qquad \text{Lateral surface} = \pi s(r_1 + r_2)$$

(Figure C.11).

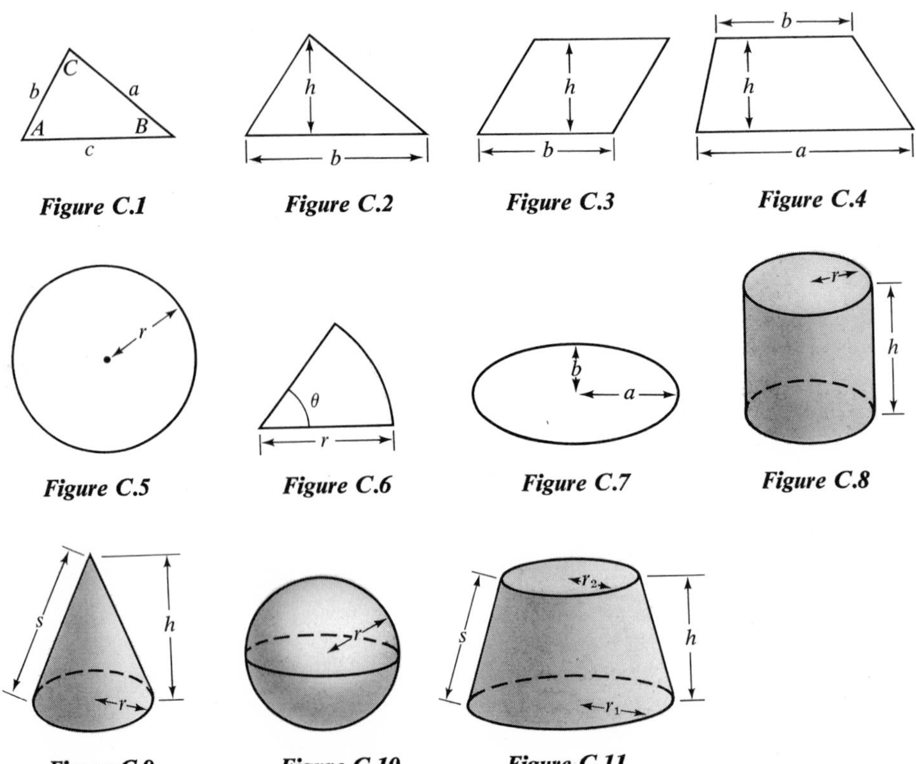

Figure C.1 *Figure C.2* *Figure C.3* *Figure C.4*

Figure C.5 *Figure C.6* *Figure C.7* *Figure C.8*

Figure C.9 *Figure C.10* *Figure C.11*

Appendix D Tables

Table 1 Exponential Functions

x	e^x	e^{-x}	x	e^x	e^{-x}
0.00	1.0000	1.0000	1.5	4.4817	0.2231
0.01	1.0101	0.9901	1.6	4.9530	0.2019
0.02	1.0202	0.9802	1.7	5.4739	0.1827
0.03	1.0305	0.9705	1.8	6.0496	0.1653
0.04	1.0408	0.9608	1.9	6.6859	0.1496
0.05	1.0513	0.9512	2.0	7.3891	0.1353
0.06	1.0618	0.9418	2.1	8.1662	0.1225
0.07	1.0725	0.9324	2.2	9.0250	0.1108
0.08	1.0833	0.9331	2.3	9.9742	0.1003
0.09	1.0942	0.9139	2.4	11.023	0.0907
0.10	1.1052	0.9048	2.5	12.182	0.0821
0.11	1.1163	0.8958	2.6	13.464	0.0743
0.12	1.1275	0.8869	2.7	14.880	0.0672
0.13	1.1388	0.8781	2.8	16.445	0.0608
0.14	1.1503	0.8694	2.9	18.174	0.0550
0.15	1.1618	0.8607	3.0	20.086	0.0498
0.16	1.1735	0.8521	3.1	22.198	0.0450
0.17	1.1853	0.8437	3.2	24.533	0.0408
0.18	1.1972	0.8353	3.3	27.113	0.0369
0.19	1.2092	0.8270	3.4	29.964	0.0334
0.20	1.2214	0.8187	3.5	33.115	0.0302
0.21	1.2337	0.8106	3.6	36.598	0.0273
0.22	1.2461	0.8025	3.7	40.447	0.0247
0.23	1.2586	0.7945	3.8	44.701	0.0224
0.24	1.2712	0.7866	3.9	49.402	0.0202
0.25	1.2840	0.7788	4.0	54.598	0.0183
0.30	1.3499	0.7408	4.1	60.340	0.0166
0.35	1.4191	0.7047	4.2	66.686	0.0150
0.40	1.4918	0.6703	4.3	73.700	0.0136
0.45	1.5683	0.6376	4.4	81.451	0.0123
0.50	1.6487	0.6065	4.5	90.017	0.0111
0.55	1.7333	0.5769	4.6	99.484	0.0101
0.60	1.8221	0.5488	4.7	109.95	0.0091
0.65	1.9155	0.5220	4.8	121.51	0.0082
0.70	2.0138	0.4966	4.9	134.29	0.0074
0.75	2.1170	0.4724	5.0	148.41	0.0067
0.80	2.2255	0.4493	5.5	244.69	0.0041
0.85	2.3396	0.4274	6.0	403.43	0.0025
0.90	2.4596	0.4066	6.5	665.14	0.0015
0.95	2.5857	0.3867	7.0	1096.6	0.0009
1.0	2.7183	0.3679	7.5	1808.0	0.0006
1.1	3.0042	0.3329	8.0	2981.0	0.0003
1.2	3.3201	0.3012	8.5	4914.8	0.0002
1.3	3.6693	0.2725	9.0	8103.1	0.0001
1.4	4.0552	0.2466	10.0	22026	0.00005

Table 2 Common Logarithms

x	0	1	2	3	4	5	6	7	8	9
1.0	.0000	.0043	.0086	.0128	.0170	.0212	.0253	.0294	.0334	.0374
1.1	.0414	.0453	.0492	.0531	.0569	.0607	.0645	.0682	.0719	.0755
1.2	.0792	.0828	.0864	.0899	.0934	.0969	.1004	.1038	.1072	.1106
1.3	.1139	.1173	.1206	.1239	.1271	.1303	.1335	.1367	.1399	.1430
1.4	.1461	.1492	.1523	.1553	.1584	.1614	.1644	.1673	.1703	.1732
1.5	.1761	.1790	.1818	.1847	.1875	.1903	.1931	.1959	.1987	.2014
1.6	.2041	.2068	.2095	.2122	.2148	.2175	.2201	.2227	.2253	.2279
1.7	.2304	.2330	.2355	.2380	.2405	.2430	.2455	.2480	.2504	.2529
1.8	.2553	.2577	.2601	.2625	.2648	.2672	.2695	.2718	.2742	.2765
1.9	.2788	.2810	.2833	.2856	.2878	.2900	.2923	.2945	.2967	.2989
2.0	.3010	.3032	.3054	.3075	.3096	.3118	.3139	.3160	.3181	.3201
2.1	.3222	.3243	.3263	.3284	.3304	.3324	.3345	.3365	.3385	.3404
2.2	.3424	.3444	.3464	.3483	.3502	.3522	.3541	.3560	.3579	.3598
2.3	.3617	.3636	.3655	.3674	.3692	.3711	.3729	.3747	.3766	.3784
2.4	.3802	.3820	.3838	.3856	.3874	.3892	.3909	.3927	.3945	.3962
2.5	.3979	.3997	.4014	.4031	.4048	.4065	.4082	.4099	.4116	.4133
2.6	.4150	.4166	.4183	.4200	.4216	.4232	.4249	.4265	.4281	.4298
2.7	.4314	.4330	.4346	.4362	.4378	.4393	.4409	.4425	.4440	.4456
2.8	.4472	.4487	.4502	.4518	.4533	.4548	.4564	.4579	.4594	.4609
2.9	.4624	.4639	.4654	.4669	.4683	.4698	.4713	.4728	.4742	.4757
3.0	.4771	.4786	.4800	.4814	.4829	.4843	.4857	.4871	.4886	.4900
3.1	.4914	.4928	.4942	.4955	.4969	.4983	.4997	.5011	.5024	.5038
3.2	.5051	.5065	.5079	.5092	.5105	.5119	.5132	.5145	.5159	.5172
3.3	.5185	.5198	.5211	.5224	.5237	.5250	.5263	.5276	.5289	.5302
3.4	.5315	.5328	.5340	.5353	.5366	.5378	.5391	.5403	.5416	.5428
3.5	.5441	.5453	.5465	.5478	.5490	.5502	.5514	.5527	.5539	.5551
3.6	.5563	.5575	.5587	.5599	.5611	.5623	.5635	.5647	.5658	.5670
3.7	.5682	.5694	.5705	.5717	.5729	.5740	.5752	.5763	.5775	.5786
3.8	.5798	.5809	.5821	.5832	.5843	.5855	.5866	.5877	.5888	.5899
3.9	.5911	.5922	.5933	.5944	.5955	.5966	.5977	.5988	.5999	.6010
4.0	.6021	.6031	.6042	.6053	.6064	.6075	.6085	.6096	.6107	.6117
4.1	.6128	.6138	.6149	.6160	.6170	.6180	.6191	.6201	.6212	.6222
4.2	.6232	.6243	.6253	.6263	.6274	.6284	.6294	.6304	.6314	.6325
4.3	.6335	.6345	.6355	.6365	.6375	.6385	.6395	.6405	.6415	.6425
4.4	.6435	.6444	.6454	.6464	.6474	.6484	.6493	.6503	.6513	.6522
4.5	.6532	.6542	.6551	.6561	.6571	.6580	.6590	.6599	.6609	.6618
4.6	.6628	.6637	.6646	.6656	.6665	.6675	.6684	.6693	.6702	.6712
4.7	.6721	.6730	.6739	.6749	.6758	.6767	.6776	.6785	.6794	.6803
4.8	.6812	.6821	.6830	.6839	.6848	.6857	.6866	.6875	.6884	.6893
4.9	.6902	.6911	.6920	.6928	.6937	.6946	.6955	.6964	.6972	.6981
5.0	.6990	.6998	.7007	.7016	.7024	.7033	.7042	.7050	.7059	.7067
5.1	.7076	.7084	.7093	.7101	.7110	.7118	.7126	.7135	.7143	.7152
5.2	.7160	.7168	.7177	.7185	.7193	.7202	.7210	.7218	.7226	.7235
5.3	.7243	.7251	.7259	.7267	.7275	.7284	.7292	.7300	.7308	.7316
5.4	.7324	.7332	.7340	.7348	.7356	.7364	.7372	.7380	.7388	.7396
x	0	1	2	3	4	5	6	7	8	9

Table 2 (*Continued*)

x	0	1	2	3	4	5	6	7	8	9
5.5	.7404	.7412	.7419	.7427	.7435	.7443	.7451	.7459	.7466	.7474
5.6	.7482	.7490	.7497	.7505	.7513	.7520	.7528	.7536	.7543	.7551
5.7	.7559	.7566	.7574	.7582	.7589	.7597	.7604	.7612	.7619	.7627
5.8	.7634	.7642	.7649	.7657	.7664	.7672	.7679	.7686	.7694	.7701
5.9	.7709	.7716	.7723	.7731	.7738	.7745	.7752	.7760	.7767	.7774
6.0	.7782	.7789	.7796	.7803	.7810	.7818	.7825	.7832	.7839	.7846
6.1	.7853	.7860	.7868	.7875	.7882	.7889	.7896	.7903	.7910	.7917
6.2	.7924	.7931	.7938	.7945	.7952	.7959	.7966	.7973	.7980	.7987
6.3	.7993	.8000	.8007	.8014	.8021	.8028	.8035	.8041	.8048	.8055
6.4	.8062	.8069	.8075	.8082	.8089	.8096	.8102	.8109	.8116	.8122
6.5	.8129	.8136	.8142	.8149	.8156	.8162	.8169	.8176	.8182	.8189
6.6	.8195	.8202	.8209	.8215	.8222	.8228	.8235	.8241	.8248	.8254
6.7	.8261	.8267	.8274	.8280	.8287	.8293	.8299	.8306	.8312	.8319
6.8	.8325	.8331	.8338	.8344	.8351	.8357	.8363	.8370	.8376	.8382
6.9	.8388	.8395	.8401	.8407	.8414	.8420	.8426	.8432	.8439	.8445
7.0	.8451	.8457	.8463	.8470	.8476	.8482	.8488	.8494	.8500	.8506
7.1	.8513	.8519	.8525	.8531	.8537	.8543	.8549	.8555	.8561	.8567
7.2	.8573	.8579	.8585	.8591	.8597	.8603	.8609	.8615	.8621	.8627
7.3	.8633	.8639	.8645	.8651	.8657	.8663	.8669	.8675	.8681	.8686
7.4	.8692	.8698	.8704	.8710	.8716	.8722	.8727	.8733	.8739	.8745
7.5	.8751	.8756	.8762	.8768	.8774	.8779	.8785	.8791	.8797	.8802
7.6	.8808	.8814	.8820	.8825	.8831	.8837	.8842	.8848	.8854	.8859
7.7	.8865	.8871	.8876	.8882	.8887	.8893	.8899	.8904	.8910	.8915
7.8	.8921	.8927	.8932	.8938	.8943	.8949	.8954	.8960	.8965	.8971
7.9	.8976	.8982	.8987	.8993	.8998	.9004	.9009	.9015	.9020	.9025
8.0	.9031	.9036	.9042	.9047	.9053	.9058	.9063	.9069	.9074	.9079
8.1	.9085	.9090	.9096	.9101	.9106	.9112	.9117	.9122	.9128	.9133
8.2	.9138	.9143	.9149	.9154	.9159	.9165	.9170	.9175	.9180	.9186
8.3	.9191	.9196	.9201	.9206	.9212	.9217	.9222	.9227	.9232	.9238
8.4	.9243	.9248	.9253	.9258	.9263	.9269	.9274	.9279	.9284	.9289
8.5	.9294	.9299	.9304	.9309	.9315	.9320	.9325	.9330	.9335	.9340
8.6	.9345	.9350	.9355	.9360	.9365	.9370	.9375	.9380	.9385	.9390
8.7	.9395	.9400	.9405	.9410	.9415	.9420	.9425	.9430	.9435	.9440
8.8	.9445	.9450	.9455	.9460	.9465	.9469	.9474	.9479	.9484	.9489
8.9	.9494	.9499	.9504	.9509	.9513	.9518	.9523	.9528	.9533	.9538
9.0	.9542	.9547	.9552	.9557	.9562	.9566	.9571	.9576	.9581	.9586
9.1	.9590	.9595	.9600	.9605	.9609	.9614	.9619	.9624	.9628	.9633
9.2	.9638	.9643	.9647	.9652	.9657	.9661	.9666	.9671	.9675	.9680
9.3	.9685	.9689	.9694	.9699	.9703	.9708	.9713	.9717	.9722	.9727
9.4	.9731	.9736	.9741	.9745	.9750	.9754	.9759	.9763	.9768	.9773
9.5	.9777	.9782	.9786	.9791	.9795	.9800	.9805	.9809	.9814	.9818
9.6	.9823	.9827	.9832	.9836	.9841	.9845	.9850	.9854	.9859	.9863
9.7	.9868	.9872	.9877	.9881	.9886	.9890	.9894	.9899	.9903	.9908
9.8	.9912	.9917	.9921	.9926	.9930	.9934	.9939	.9943	.9948	.9952
9.9	.9956	.9961	.9965	.9969	.9974	.9978	.9983	.9987	.9991	.9996
x	0	1	2	3	4	5	6	7	8	9

Table 3 Natural Logarithms of Numbers

n	$\log_e n$	n	$\log_e n$	n	$\log_e n$
	*	4.5	1.5041	9.0	2.1972
0.1	7.6974	4.6	1.5261	9.1	2.2083
0.2	8.3906	4.7	1.5476	9.2	2.2192
0.3	8.7960	4.8	1.5686	9.3	2.2300
0.4	9.0837	4.9	1.5892	9.4	2.2407
0.5	9.3069	5.0	1.6094	9.5	2.2513
0.6	9.4892	5.1	1.6292	9.6	2.2618
0.7	9.6433	5.2	1.6487	9.7	2.2721
0.8	9.7769	5.3	1.6677	9.8	2.2824
0.9	9.8946	5.4	1.6864	9.9	2.2925
1.0	0.0000	5.5	1.7047	10	2.3026
1.1	0.0953	5.6	1.7228	11	2.3979
1.2	0.1823	5.7	1.7405	12	2.4849
1.3	0.2624	5.8	1.7579	13	2.5649
1.4	0.3365	5.9	1.7750	14	2.6391
1.5	0.4055	6.0	1.7918	15	2.7081
1.6	0.4700	6.1	1.8083	16	2.7726
1.7	0.5306	6.2	1.8245	17	2.8332
1.8	0.5878	6.3	1.8405	18	2.8904
1.9	0.6419	6.4	1.8563	19	2.9444
2.0	0.6931	6.5	1.8718	20	2.9957
2.1	0.7419	6.6	1.8871	25	3.2189
2.2	0.7885	6.7	1.9021	30	3.4012
2.3	0.8329	6.8	1.9169	35	3.5553
2.4	0.8755	6.9	1.9315	40	3.6889
2.5	0.9163	7.0	1.9459	45	3.8067
2.6	0.9555	7.1	1.9601	50	3.9120
2.7	0.9933	7.2	1.9741	55	4.0073
2.8	1.0296	7.3	1.9879	60	4.0943
2.9	1.0647	7.4	2.0015	65	4.1744
3.0	1.0986	7.5	2.0149	70	4.2485
3.1	1.1314	7.6	2.0281	75	4.3175
3.2	1.1632	7.7	2.0412	80	4.3820
3.3	1.1939	7.8	2.0541	85	4.4427
3.4	1.2238	7.9	2.0669	90	4.4998
3.5	1.2528	8.0	2.0794	100	4.6052
3.6	1.2809	8.1	2.0919	110	4.7005
3.7	1.3083	8.2	2.1041	120	4.7875
3.8	1.3350	8.3	2.1163	130	4.8676
3.9	1.3610	8.4	2.1282	140	4.9416
4.0	1.3863	8.5	2.1401	150	5.0106
4.1	1.4110	8.6	2.1518	160	5.0752
4.2	1.4351	8.7	2.1633	170	5.1358
4.3	1.4586	8.8	2.1748	180	5.1930
4.4	1.4816	8.9	2.1861	190	5.2470

* Subtract 10 for $n < 1$. Thus $\log_e 0.1 = 7.6974 - 10 = -2.3026$.

Table 4 Squares, Square Roots, and Prime Factors

No.	Sq.	Sq. Rt.	Factors	No.	Sq.	Sq. Rt.	Factors
1	1	1.000		51	2,601	7.141	$3 \cdot 17$
2	4	1.414	2	52	2,704	7.211	$2^2 \cdot 13$
3	9	1.732	3	53	2,809	7.280	53
4	16	2.000	2^2	54	2,916	7.348	$2 \cdot 3^3$
5	25	2.236	5	55	3,025	7.416	$5 \cdot 11$
6	36	2.449	$2 \cdot 3$	56	3,136	7.483	$2^3 \cdot 7$
7	49	2.646	7	57	3,249	7.550	$3 \cdot 19$
8	64	2.828	2^3	58	3,364	7.616	$2 \cdot 29$
9	81	3.000	3^2	59	3,481	7.681	59
10	100	3.162	$2 \cdot 5$	60	3,600	7.746	$2^2 \cdot 3 \cdot 5$
11	121	3.317	11	61	3,721	7.810	61
12	144	3.464	$2^2 \cdot 3$	62	3,844	7.874	$2 \cdot 31$
13	169	3.606	13	63	3,969	7.937	$3^2 \cdot 7$
14	196	3.742	$2 \cdot 7$	64	4,096	8.000	2^6
15	225	3.873	$3 \cdot 5$	65	4,225	8.062	$5 \cdot 13$
16	256	4.000	2^4	66	4,356	8.124	$2 \cdot 3 \cdot 11$
17	289	4.123	17	67	4,489	8.185	67
18	324	4.243	$2 \cdot 3^2$	68	4,624	8.246	$2^2 \cdot 17$
19	361	4.359	19	69	4,761	8.307	$3 \cdot 23$
20	400	4.472	$2^2 \cdot 5$	70	4,900	8.367	$2 \cdot 5 \cdot 7$
21	441	4.583	$3 \cdot 7$	71	5,041	8.426	71
22	484	4.690	$2 \cdot 11$	72	5,184	8.485	$2^3 \cdot 3^2$
23	529	4.796	23	73	5,329	8.544	73
24	576	4.899	$2^3 \cdot 3$	74	5,476	8.602	$2 \cdot 37$
25	625	5.000	5^2	75	5,625	8.660	$3 \cdot 5^2$
26	676	5.099	$2 \cdot 13$	76	5,776	8.718	$2^2 \cdot 19$
27	729	5.196	3^3	77	5,929	8.775	$7 \cdot 11$
28	784	5.292	$2^2 \cdot 7$	78	6,084	8.832	$2 \cdot 3 \cdot 13$
29	841	5.385	29	79	6,241	8.888	79
30	900	5.477	$2 \cdot 3 \cdot 5$	80	6,400	8.944	$2^4 \cdot 5$
31	961	5.568	31	81	6,561	9.000	3^4
32	1,024	5.657	2^5	82	6,724	9.055	$2 \cdot 41$
33	1,089	5.745	$3 \cdot 11$	83	6,889	9.110	83
34	1,156	5.831	$2 \cdot 17$	84	7,056	9.165	$2^2 \cdot 3 \cdot 7$
35	1,225	5.916	$5 \cdot 7$	85	7,225	9.220	$5 \cdot 17$
36	1,296	6.000	$2^2 \cdot 3^2$	86	7,396	9.274	$2 \cdot 43$
37	1,369	6.083	37	87	7,569	9.327	$3 \cdot 29$
38	1,444	6.164	$2 \cdot 19$	88	7,744	9.381	$2^3 \cdot 11$
39	1,521	6.245	$3 \cdot 13$	89	7,921	9.434	89
40	1,600	6.325	$2^3 \cdot 5$	90	8,100	9.487	$2 \cdot 3^2 \cdot 5$
41	1,681	6.403	41	91	8,281	9.539	$7 \cdot 13$
42	1,764	6.481	$2 \cdot 3 \cdot 7$	92	8,464	9.592	$2^2 \cdot 23$
43	1,849	6.557	43	93	8,649	9.644	$3 \cdot 31$
44	1,936	6.633	$2^2 \cdot 11$	94	8,836	9.695	$2 \cdot 47$
45	2,025	6.708	$3^2 \cdot 5$	95	9,025	9.747	$5 \cdot 19$
46	2,116	6.782	$2 \cdot 23$	96	9,216	9.798	$2^5 \cdot 3$
47	2,209	6.856	47	97	9,409	9.849	97
48	2,304	6.928	$2^4 \cdot 3$	98	9,604	9.899	$2 \cdot 7^2$
49	2,401	7.000	7^2	99	9,801	9.950	$3^2 \cdot 11$
50	2,500	7.071	$2 \cdot 5^2$	100	10,000	10.000	$2^2 \cdot 5^2$

Table 5 Trigonometric Functions

Degrees	Radians	Sin	Cos	Tan	Cot		
0	0.0000	0.0000	1.0000	0.0000		1.5708	90
1	0.0175	0.0175	0.9998	0.0175	57.290	1.5533	89
2	0.0349	0.0349	0.9994	0.0349	28.636	1.5359	88
3	0.0524	0.0523	0.9986	0.0524	19.081	1.5184	87
4	0.0698	0.0698	0.9976	0.0699	14.301	1.5010	86
5	0.0873	0.0872	0.9962	0.0875	11.430	1.4835	85
6	0.1047	0.1045	0.9945	0.1051	9.5144	1.4661	84
7	0.1222	0.1219	0.9925	0.1228	8.1443	1.4486	83
8	0.1396	0.1392	0.9903	0.1405	7.1154	1.4312	82
9	0.1571	0.1564	0.9877	0.1584	6.3138	1.4137	81
10	0.1745	0.1736	0.9848	0.1763	5.6713	1.3963	80
11	0.1920	0.1908	0.9816	0.1944	5.1446	1.3788	79
12	0.2094	0.2079	0.9781	0.2126	4.7046	1.3614	78
13	0.2269	0.2250	0.9744	0.2309	4.3315	1.3439	77
14	0.2443	0.2419	0.9703	0.2493	4.0108	1.3265	76
15	0.2618	0.2588	0.9659	0.2679	3.7321	1.3090	75
16	0.2793	0.2756	0.9613	0.2867	3.4874	1.2915	74
17	0.2967	0.2924	0.9563	0.3057	3.2709	1.2741	73
18	0.3142	0.3090	0.9511	0.3249	3.0777	1.2566	72
19	0.3316	0.3256	0.9455	0.3443	2.9042	1.2392	71
20	0.3491	0.3420	0.9397	0.3640	2.7475	1.2217	70
21	0.3665	0.3584	0.9336	0.3839	2.6051	1.2043	69
22	0.3840	0.3746	0.9272	0.4040	2.4751	1.1868	68
23	0.4014	0.3907	0.9205	0.4245	2.3559	1.1694	67
24	0.4189	0.4067	0.9135	0.4452	2.2460	1.1519	66
25	0.4363	0.4226	0.9063	0.4663	2.1445	1.1345	65
26	0.4538	0.4384	0.8988	0.4877	2.0503	1.1170	64
27	0.4712	0.4540	0.8910	0.5095	1.9626	1.0996	63
28	0.4887	0.4695	0.8829	0.5317	1.8807	1.0821	62
29	0.5061	0.4848	0.8746	0.5543	1.8040	1.0647	61
30	0.5236	0.5000	0.8660	0.5774	1.7321	1.0472	60
31	0.5411	0.5150	0.8572	0.6009	1.6643	1.0297	59
32	0.5585	0.5299	0.8480	0.6249	1.6003	1.0123	58
33	0.5760	0.5446	0.8387	0.6494	1.5399	0.9948	57
34	0.5934	0.5592	0.8290	0.6745	1.4826	0.9774	56
35	0.6109	0.5736	0.8192	0.7002	1.4281	0.9599	55
36	0.6283	0.5878	0.8090	0.7265	1.3764	0.9425	54
37	0.6458	0.6018	0.7986	0.7536	1.3270	0.9250	53
38	0.6632	0.6157	0.7880	0.7813	1.2799	0.9076	52
39	0.6807	0.6293	0.7771	0.8098	1.2349	0.8901	51
40	0.6981	0.6428	0.7660	0.8391	1.1918	0.8727	50
41	0.7156	0.6561	0.7547	0.8693	1.1504	0.8552	49
42	0.7330	0.6691	0.7431	0.9004	1.1106	0.8378	48
43	0.7505	0.6820	0.7314	0.9325	1.0724	0.8203	47
44	0.7679	0.6947	0.7193	0.9657	1.0355	0.8029	46
45	0.7854	0.7071	0.7071	1.0000	1.0000	0.7854	45
		Cos	Sin	Cot	Tan	Radians	Degrees

Answers to Selected Problems

Chapter 1

Section 1.2, page 5

1. $\sqrt{65}$. **3.** 2. **5.** $\sqrt{37}/2$. **7.** $\sqrt{6}$. **9.** $-3, 5$. **11.** 2, 3.
13. Collinear. **15.** Not collinear. **17.** Collinear. **19.** Right triangle.
21. Not a right triangle.
27. $(0, -1)$ inside; $(1, 7)$, $(2, 0)$, $(-5, 7)$, $(-5, -1)$, $(-6, 6)$ on; $(-3, 8)$, $(4, 2)$ outside.

Section 1.3, page 9

1. $(4, 3)$. **3.** $(16/5, -9/5)$. **5.** $(17, 22)$. **7.** $(2, 1)$. **9.** $(7/2, 1)$.
11. $(12, -4)$. **13.** $(0, -7)$. **15.** $(3, 0)$. **17.** $(14/5, 7/5)$. **19.** $(6, -7)$.
21. $(2, -1/2)$. **23.** $7, -9$.

Section 1.5, page 14

1. 5/3, 59°. **3.** 2/3, 34°. **5.** No slope, 90°. **7.** 1, 45°. **9.** Parallel.
11. None. **13.** Coincident. **15.** Perpendicular. **17.** 14/3. **19.** 10/7, 11.
21. 9.

Section 1.6, page 16

1. 135°. **3.** 135°. **5.** 6°. **7.** 12°. **9.** 60°. **11.** 112°.
13. $-7 - 5\sqrt{2}$. **15.** $1 + \sqrt{2}$. **17.** $(128 + \sqrt{17{,}170})/23$. **19.** 37°, 72°, 72°.
21. 1/5.

Section 1.7, page 18

1. **3.** **5.**

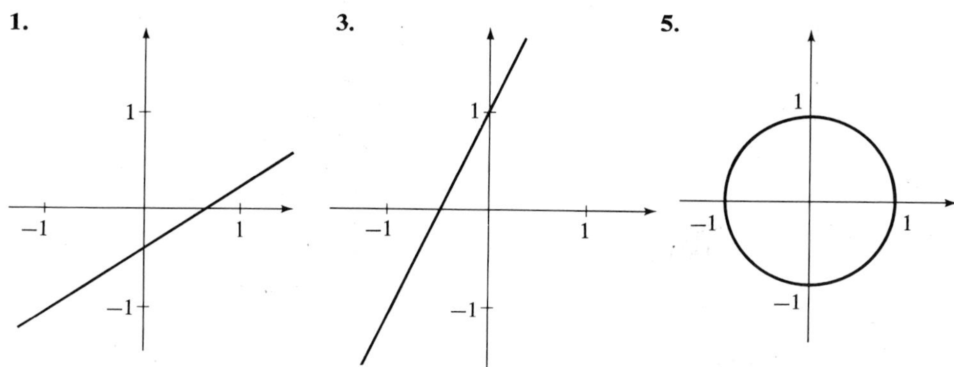

7.

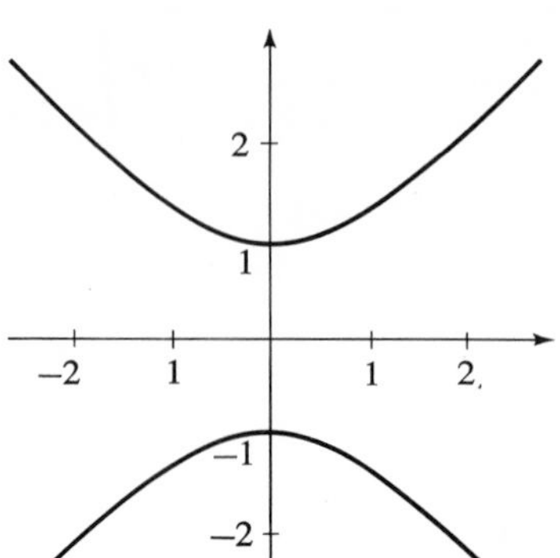

9.

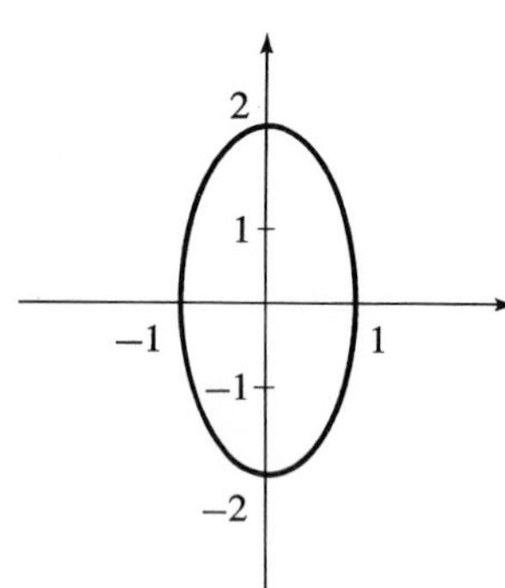

11.

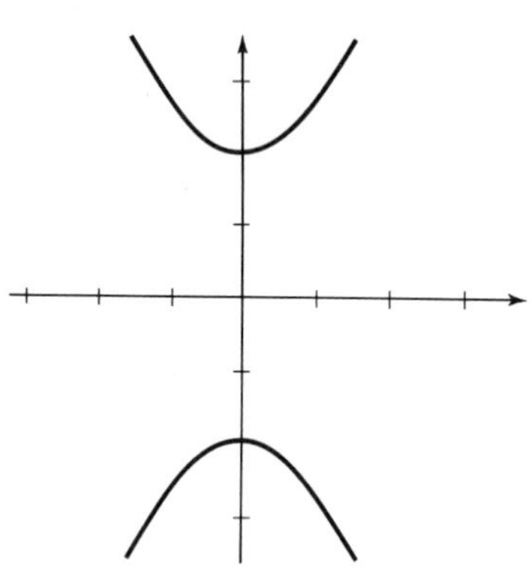

13.

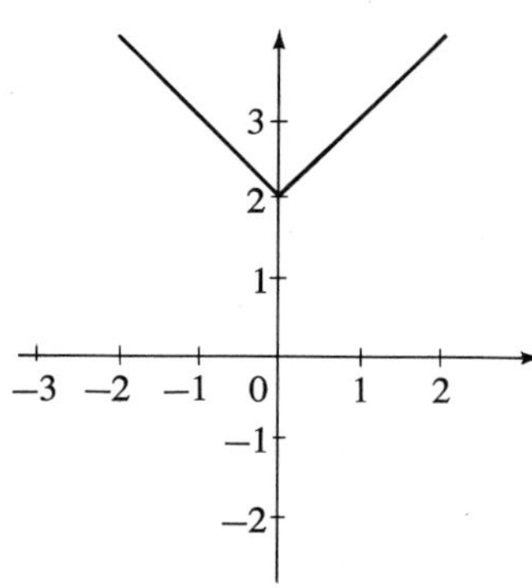

15.

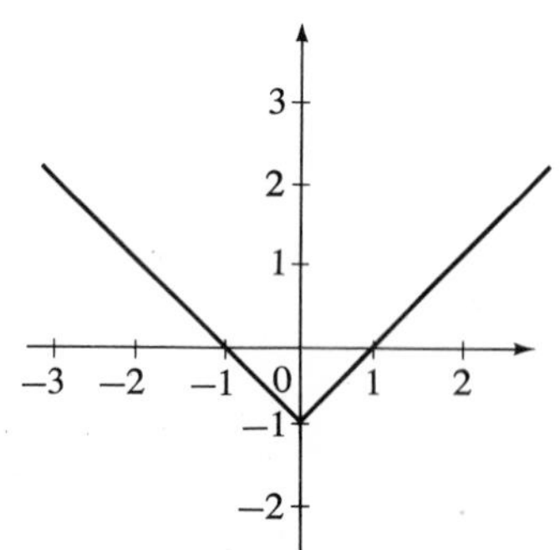

17.

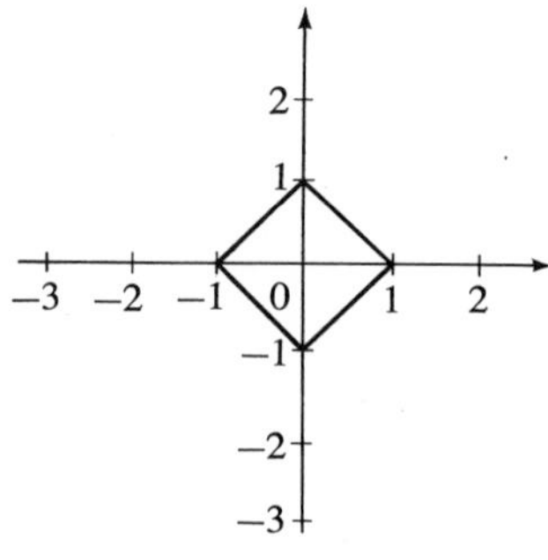

19.

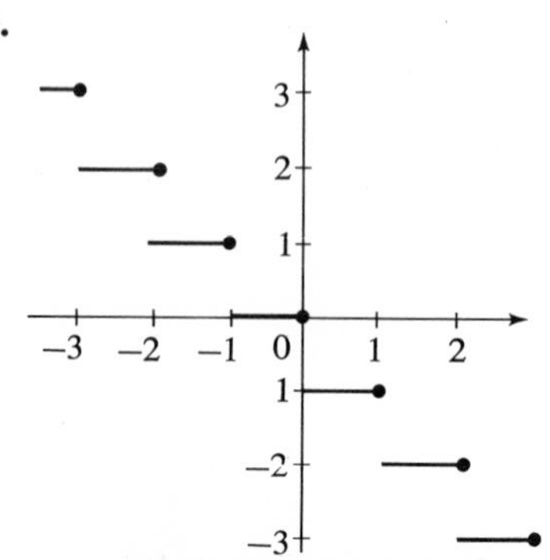

21.

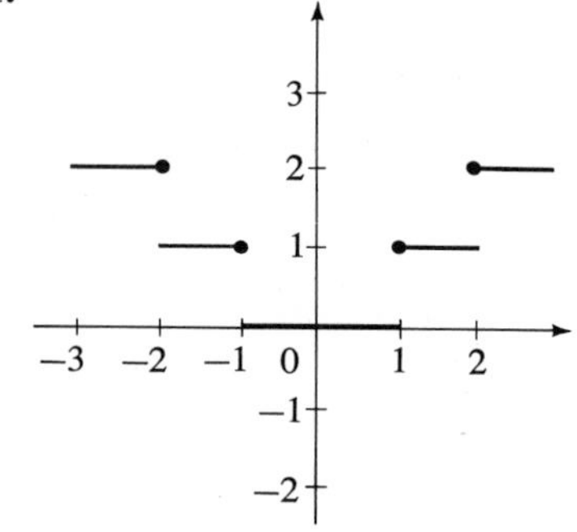

23.

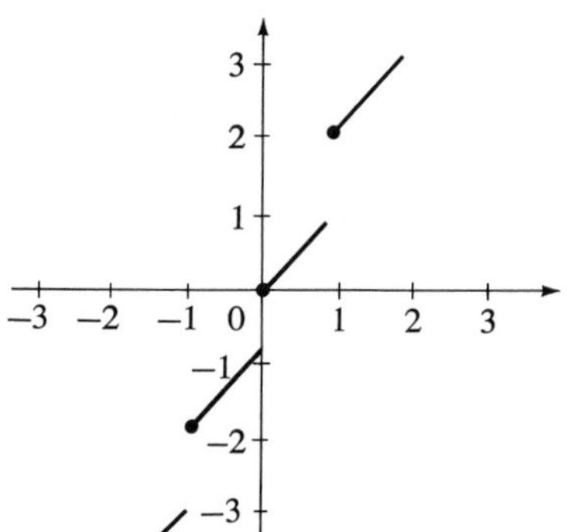

25.

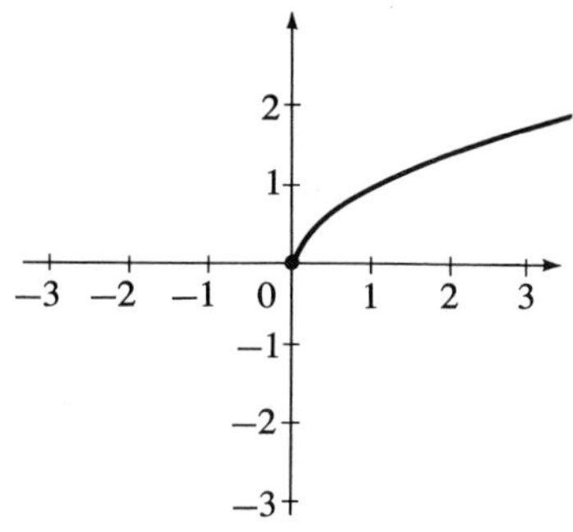

27.

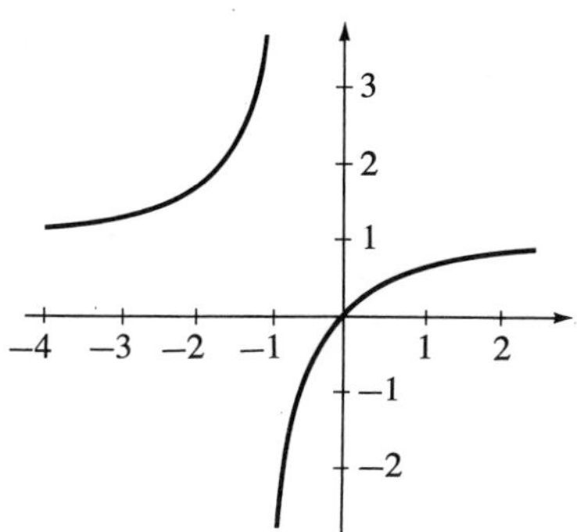

29.

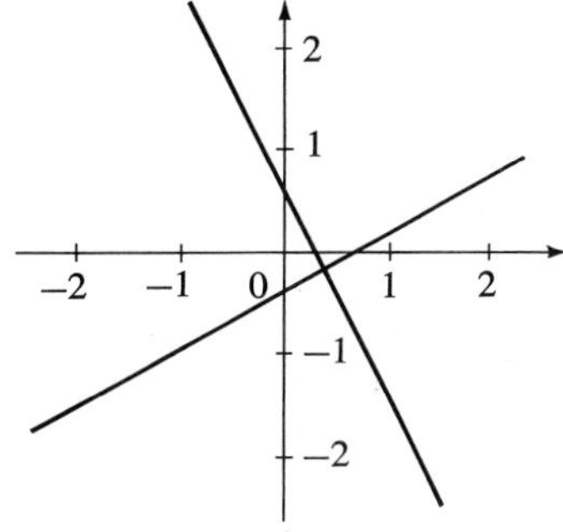

31.

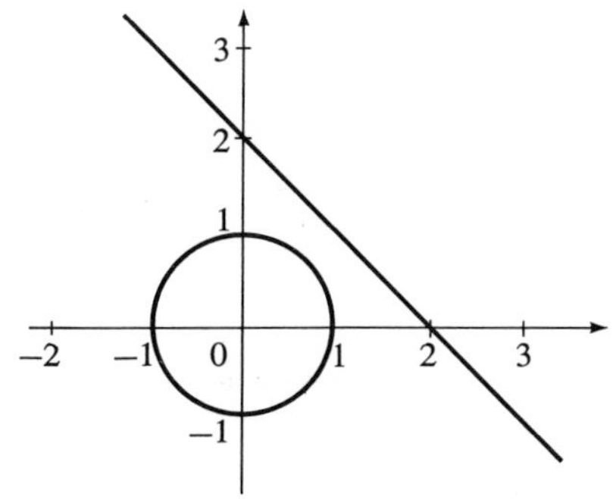

33.

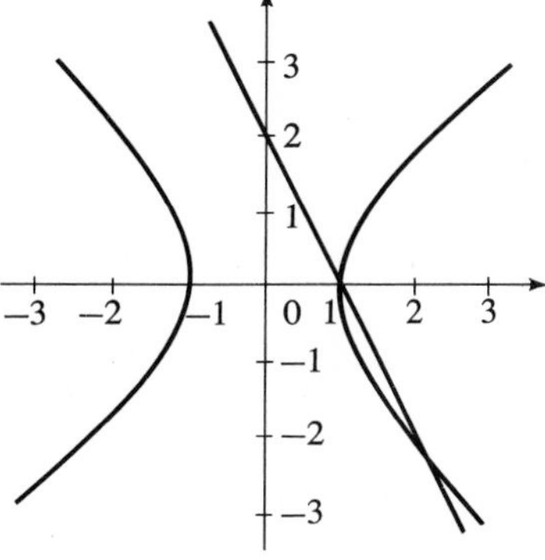

35.

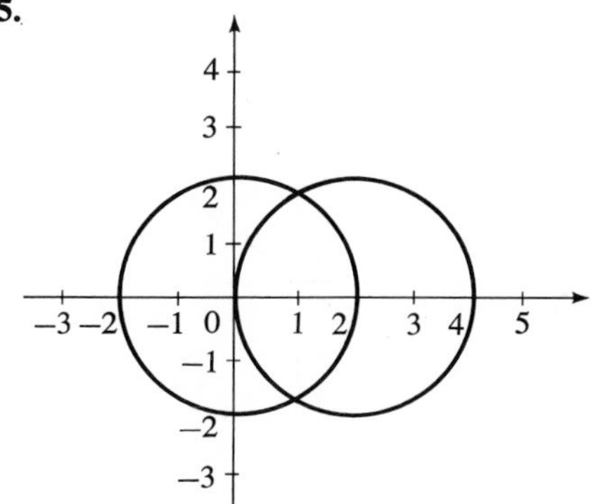

37.

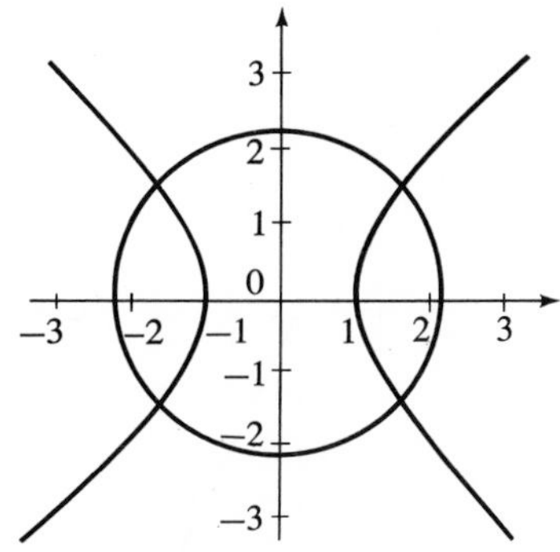

39.

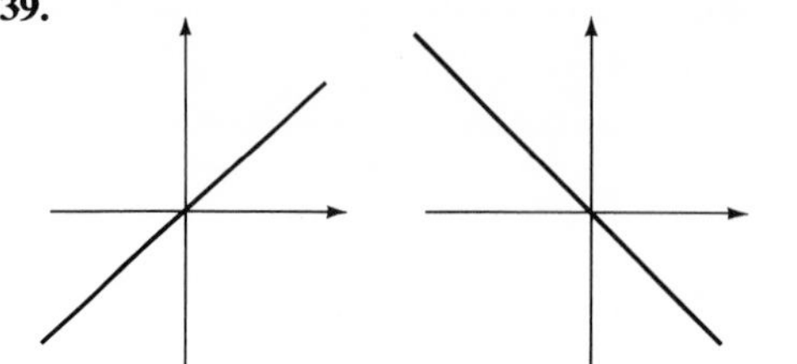

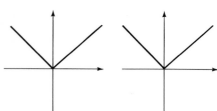

41.

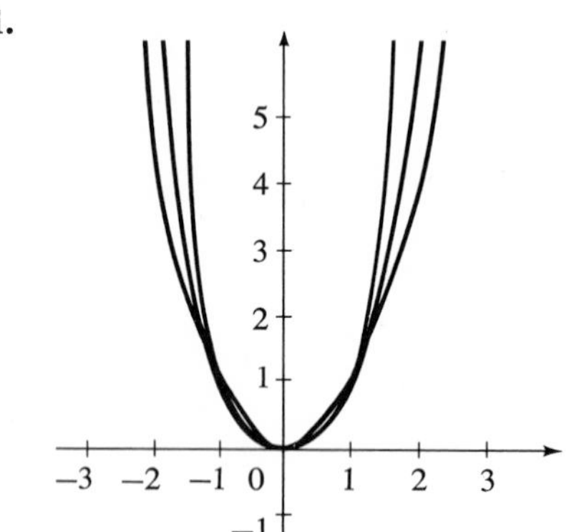

43.

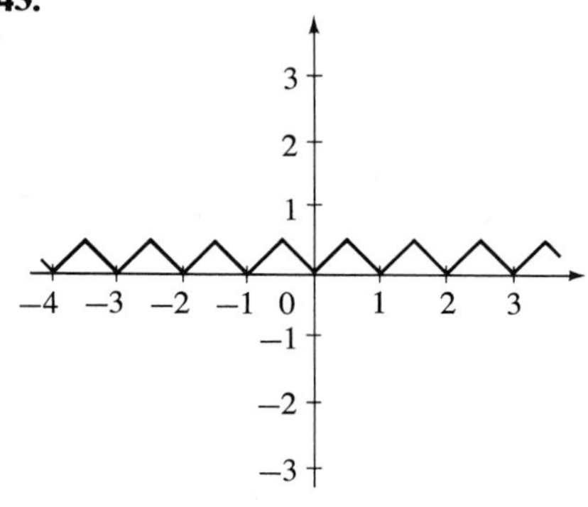

Chapter 2

Section 2.1, page 23

1.

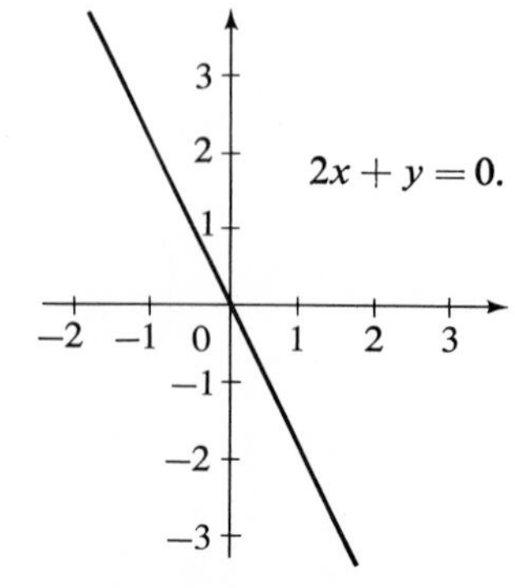

3.

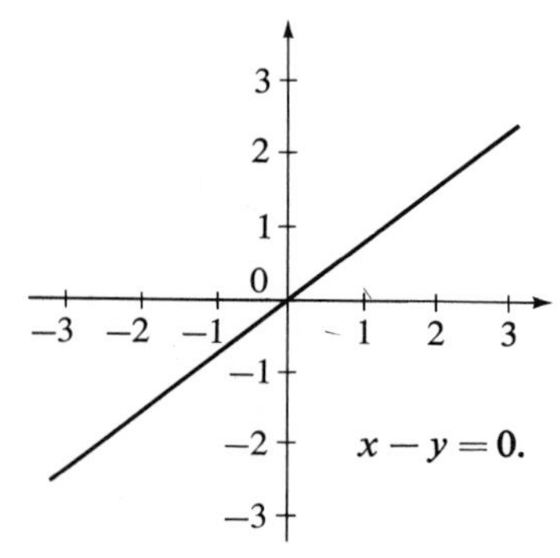

5.

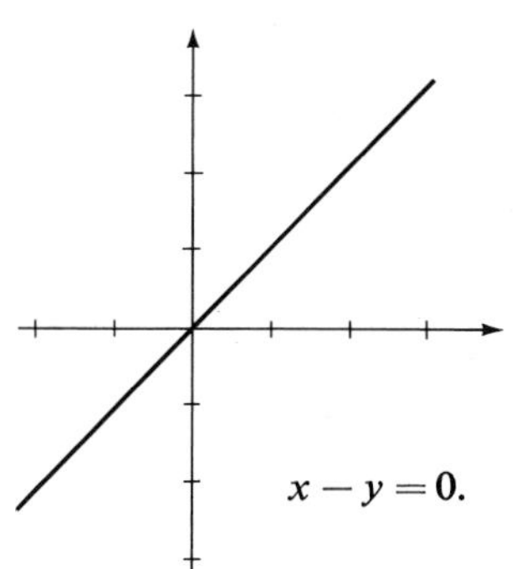

7.

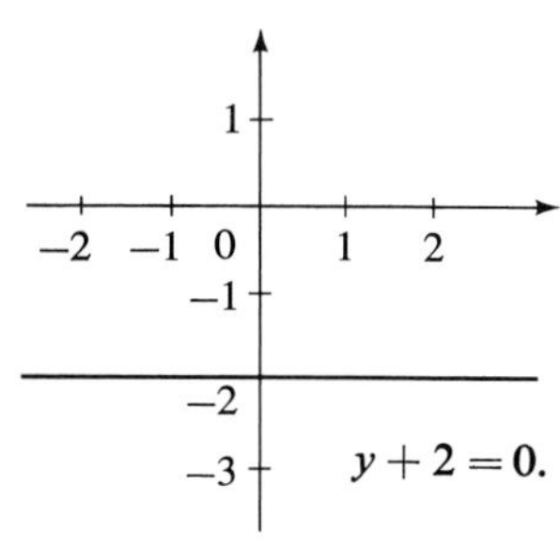

9.

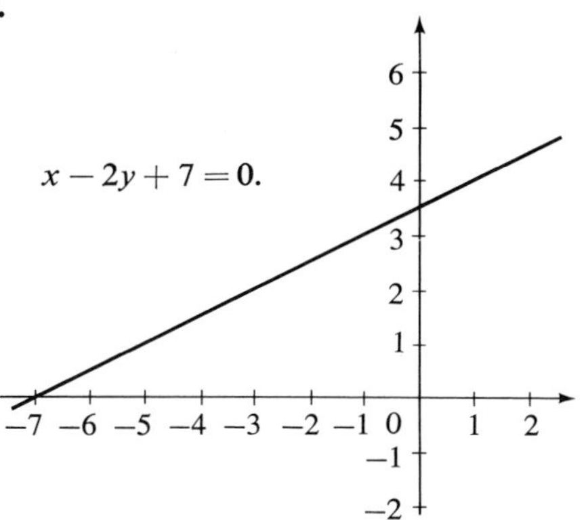

11.

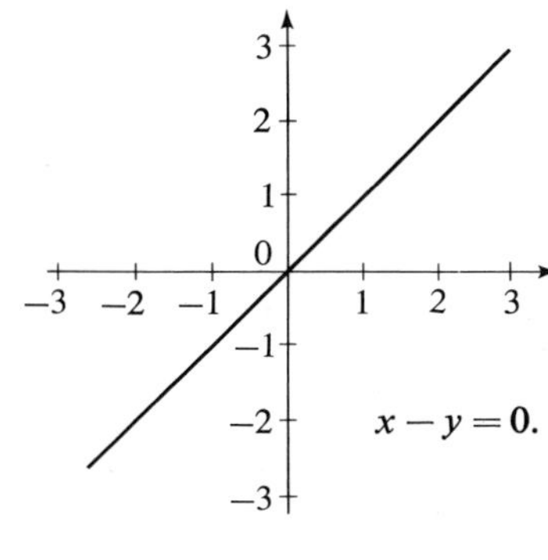

13.

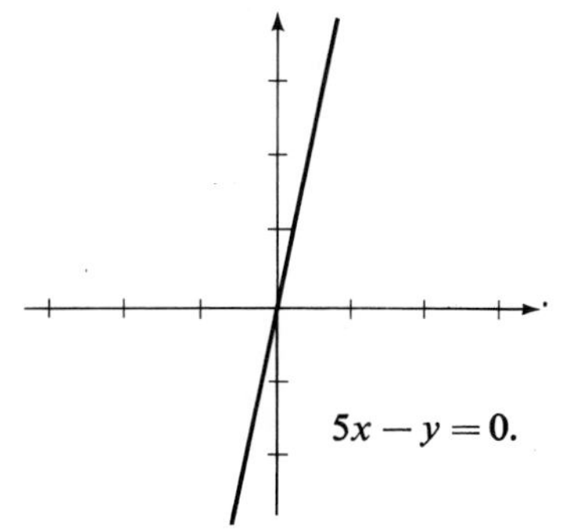

15.

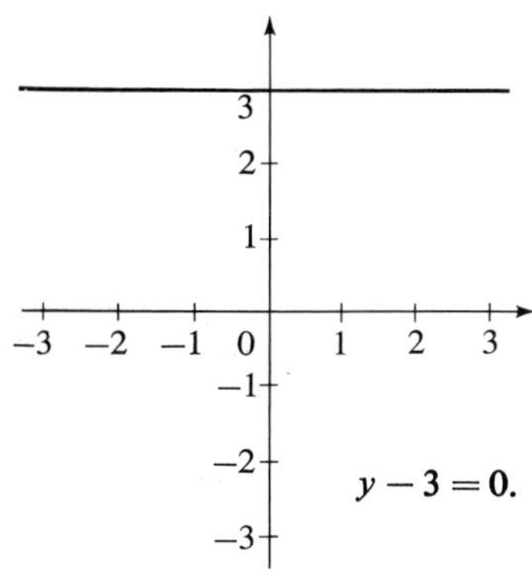

17. $2x + y - 6 = 0$, $x - 2y - 3 = 0$, $3x - y + 1 = 0$.

19. $x - 2y - 3 = 0$, $2x + y - 6 = 0$, $x + 3y - 3 = 0$.

21. $5x - 6y + 2 = 0$, $2x + 9y - 3 = 0$, $7x + 3y - 1 = 0$.

23.

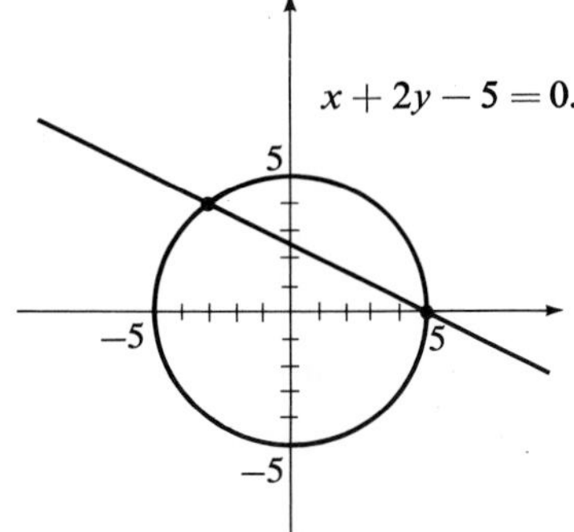

25. $3x - 2y + 5 = 0.$ **29.** $x - 3y + 3 = 0.$

31. $7x - y - 20 = 0,\ 7x - y - 20 = 0.$ **33.** $9C - 5F + 160 = 0.$

Section 2.2, page 27

1.

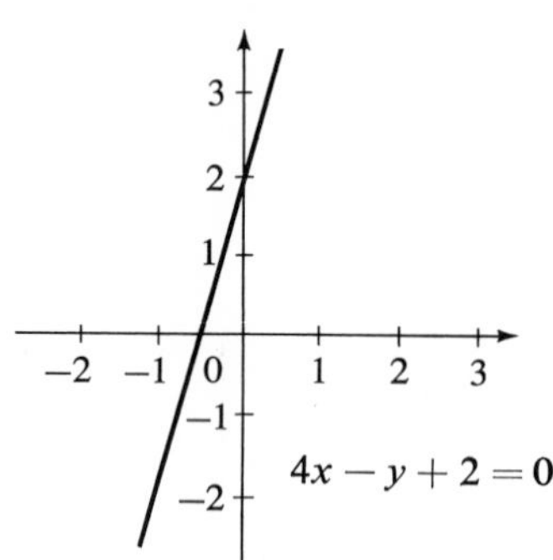

3.

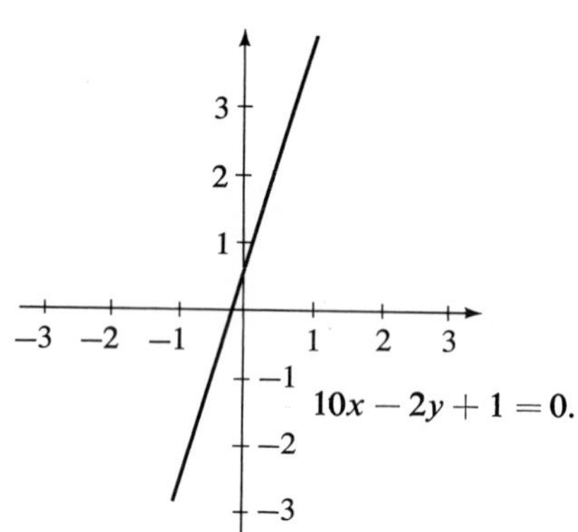

5.

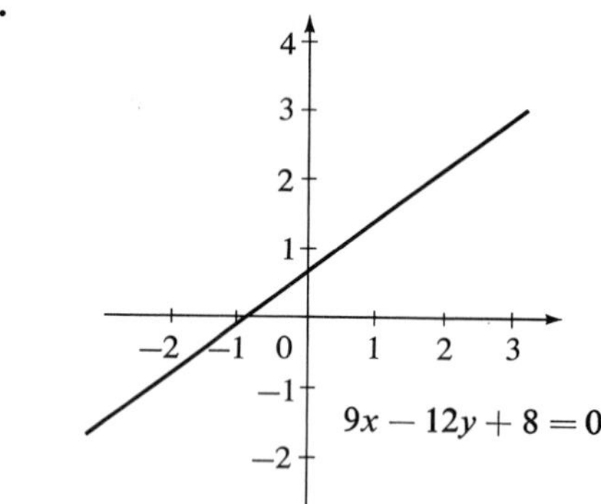

7.

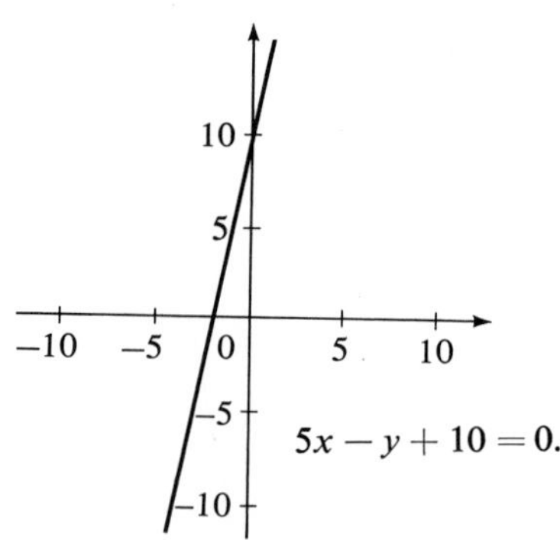

9.

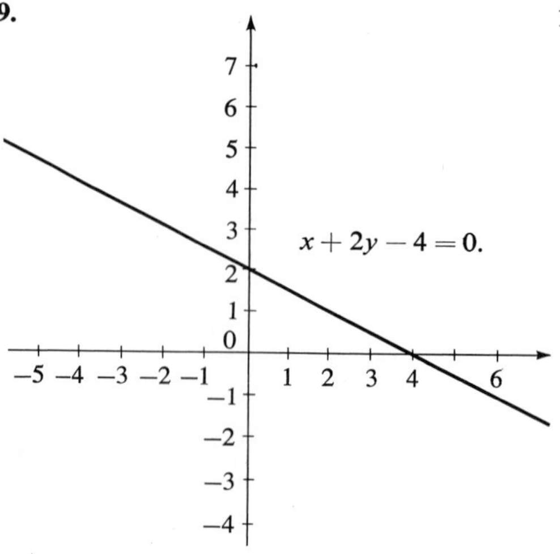

11.

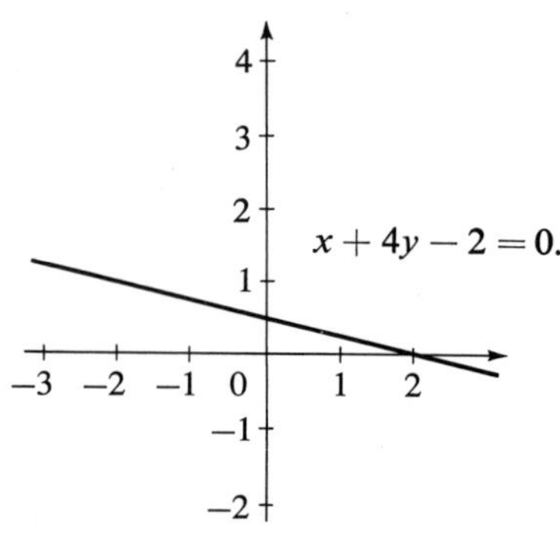

13.

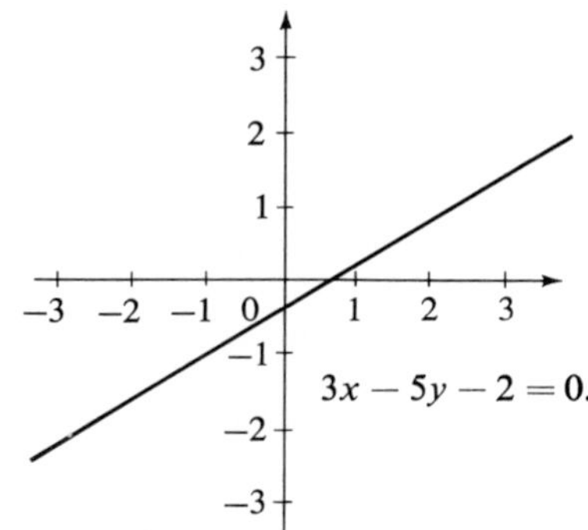

15.

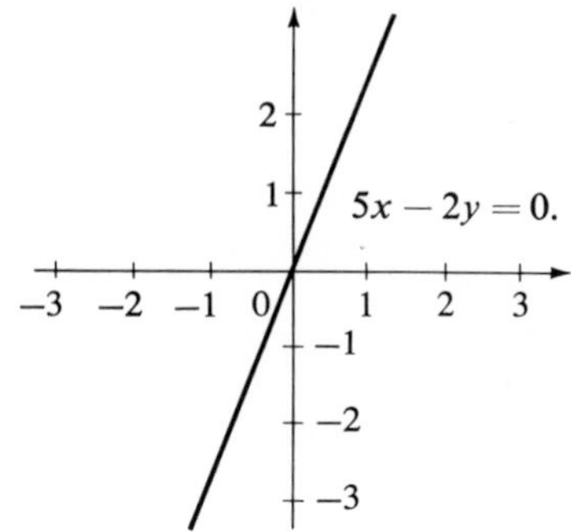

17.

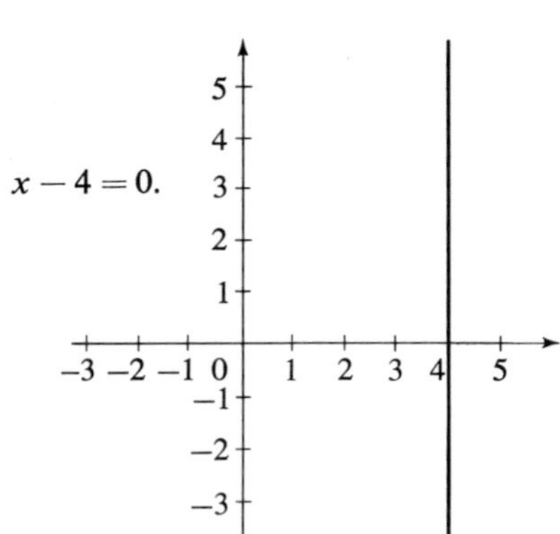

19. $2x - 5y + 11 = 0.$

21. $2x - y - 7 = 0.$

23. $(15/14, -5/14).$

25. $(119/41, 99/41).$

27. $5/2.$

29. $1.$

31.

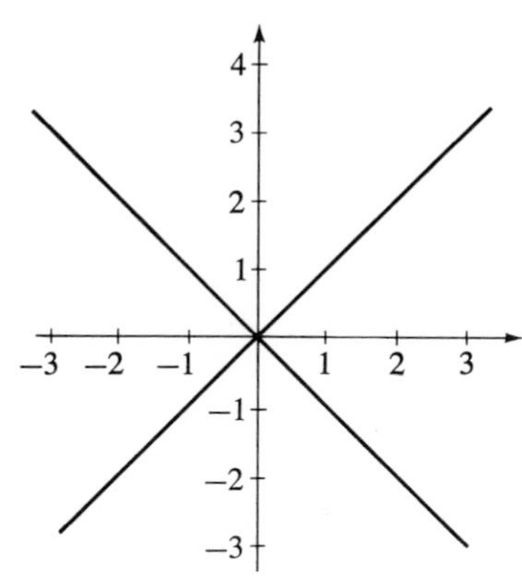

33.

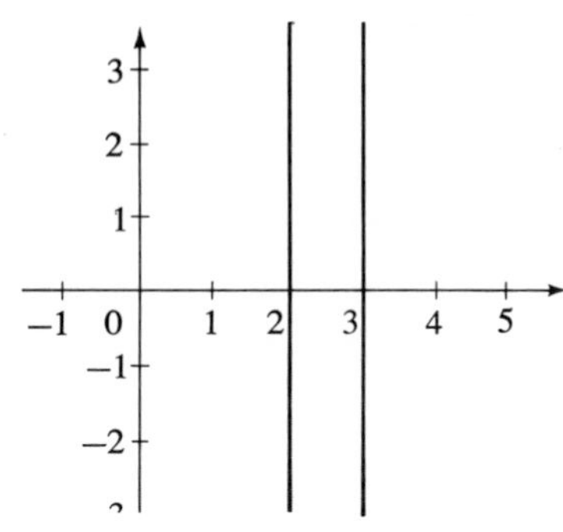

35. 0.0709 Cal Mole^{-1}.

Section 2.3, page 32

1. $\sqrt{2}.$ **3.** $9/\sqrt{41}.$ **5.** $2/5.$ **7.** $18/\sqrt{29}.$ **9.** $10/3.$

11. $13/\sqrt{10}, 26/\sqrt{29}, 26/5.$ **13.** $7x - 7y + 2 = 0.$ **15.** $39x + 13y - 24 = 0.$

17. $2(\sqrt{2} - 1)x - 2y + (4 - 3\sqrt{2}) = 0.$ **19.** $4/\sqrt{29}.$ **21.** $7/2\sqrt{5}.$ **23.** $8/\sqrt{5}.$

25. 13.

27. $(21/10, 31/10), (-9/4, -5/4), (113/30, 31/10), (-9/4, 159/28).$

29. $\pm 3/\sqrt{7}.$ **31.** $\pm 3/2\sqrt{2}.$

Section 2.4, page 36

1. Lines through $(-1, 4)$. Does not include $x = -1$.
3. Lines with x intercept 2. Does not include $x = 2$.
5. All lines through the origin.
7. Lines having both an x intercept and a y intercept. Does not include any line through the origin.
9. Lines containing the point of intersection of $2x + 3y + 1 = 0$ and $4x + 2y - 5 = 0$. Does not include $4x + 2y - 5 = 0$.
11. Lines with y intercept twice the x intercept. Does not include any line through the origin.
13. All lines with y intercept equal to their slope.
15. $\{3x - 5y = k \mid k \text{ real}\}$. **17.** $\{y - 5 = m(x - 2) \mid m \text{ real}\} \cup \{x = 2\}$.
19. $\{3x - 5y + 1 + k(2x + 3y - 7) = 0 \mid k \text{ real}\} \cup \{2x + 3y - 7 = 0\}$.
21. $\{Ax + By = 0 \mid A, B \text{ real}\}$. **23.** $\{Ax + By + C = 0 \mid |6A + C|/\sqrt{A^2 + B^2} = 5\}$.
25. (a) $3x - 5y + 25 = 0$, (b) $5x + 3y - 49 = 0$.
27. (a) $2x + y - 5 = 0$, (b) $x - 2y + 10 = 0$. **29.** $5x - y \pm 3\sqrt{26} = 0$.
31. $15x - 8y - 43 = 0$, $3x - 4y + 1 = 0$. **33.** $11x - 60y - 17 = 0$, $x - 7 = 0$.
35. $16x - 8y - 27 = 0$. **37.** $x - 2y - 10 = 0$, $3x + 2y - 6 = 0$.
39. $x + 2y - 8 = 0$, $9x + 2y - 24 = 0$, $(11 \pm 4\sqrt{7})x - 2y - (16 \pm 8\sqrt{7}) = 0$.
41. $x + y - (4 + 2\sqrt{2}) = 0$.
43. $\sqrt{3}x - y + (6 - 4\sqrt{3}) = 0$, $\sqrt{3}x + y - (6 + 4\sqrt{3}) = 0$.

Chapter 3

Section 3.1, page 42

1. $(x - 1)^2 + (y - 3)^2 = 25$,
$x^2 + y^2 - 2x - 6y - 15 = 0$.

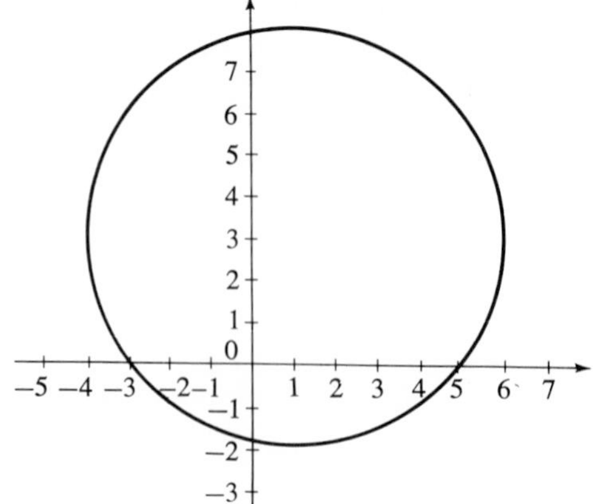

3. $(x - 5)^2 + (y + 2)^2 = 4$,
$x^2 + y^2 - 10x + 4y + 25 = 0$.

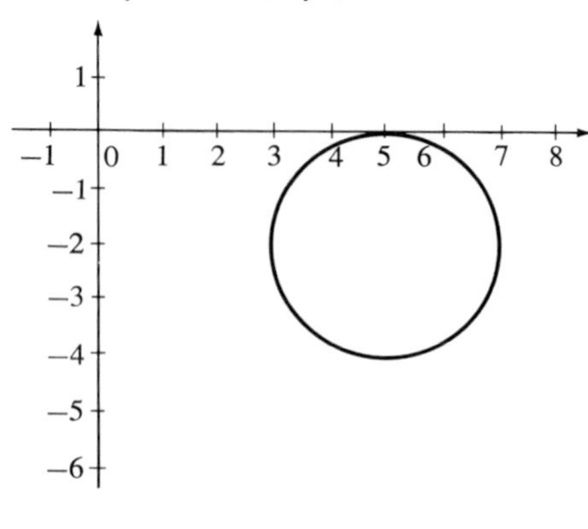

5. $(x - 1/2)^2 + (y + 3/2)^2 = 4,$
$2x^2 + 2y^2 - 2x + 6y - 3 = 0.$

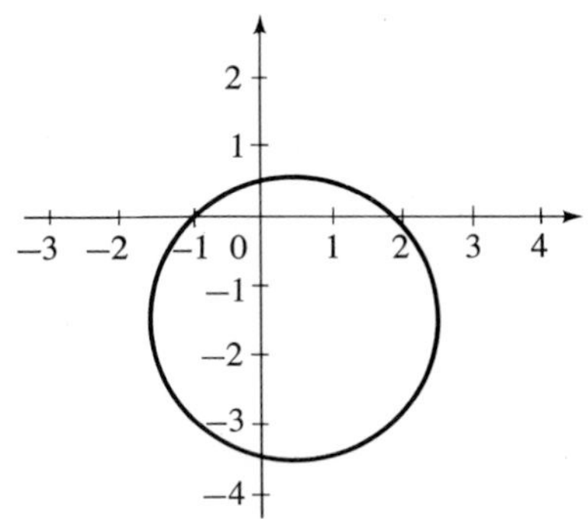

7. $(x - 4)^2 + (y + 2)^2 = 26,$
$x^2 + y^2 - 8x + 4y - 6 = 0.$

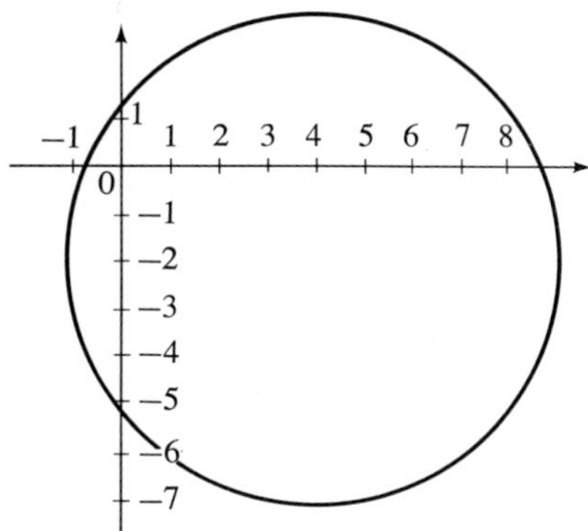

9. $x^2 + (y + 3/2)^2 = 25/4,$
$x^2 + y^2 + 3y - 4 = 0.$

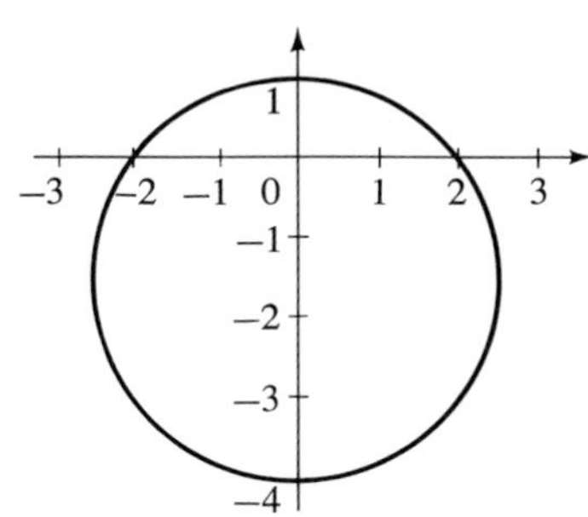

11. $(x - 3)^2 + (y - 3)^2 = 9,$
$x^2 + y^2 - 6x - 6y + 9 = 0.$

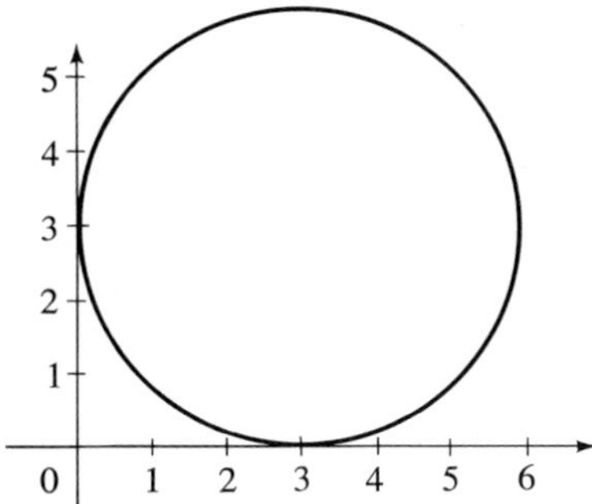

13. $(x - 4)^2 + (y - 1)^2 = 4,$
$x^2 + y^2 - 8x - 2y + 13 = 0.$

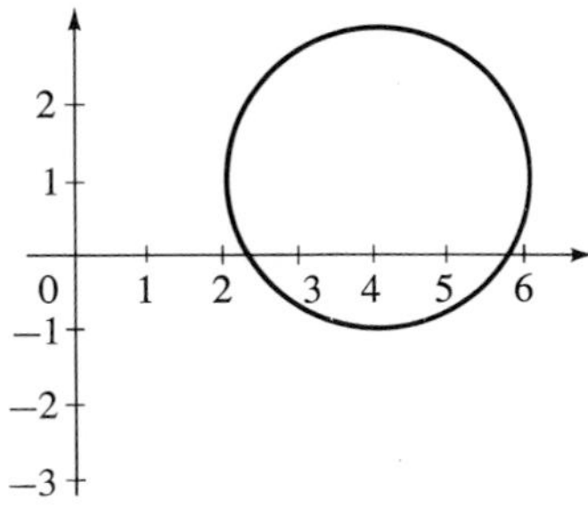

15. $(x - 4)^2 + (y + 4)^2 = 16,$
$x^2 + y^2 - 8x + 8y + 16 = 0.$

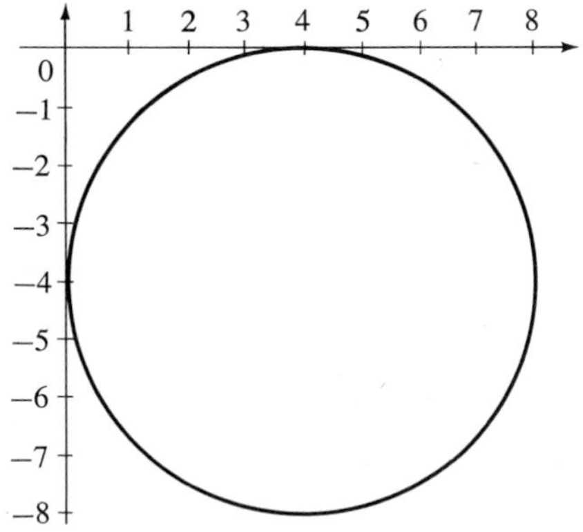

17. $(x-1)^2+(y-2)^2=4;$

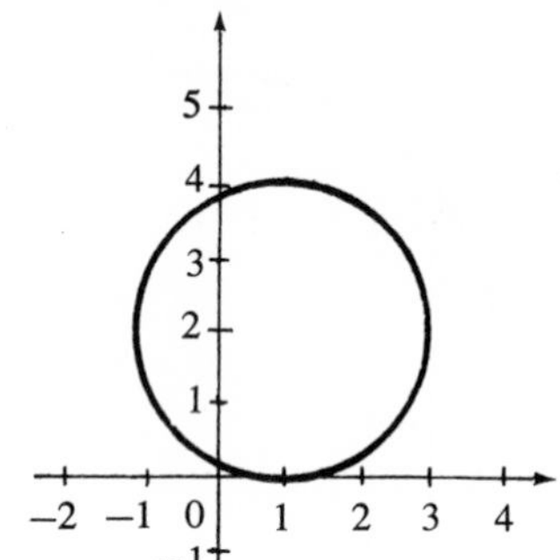

19. $(x+3)^2+y^2=25.$

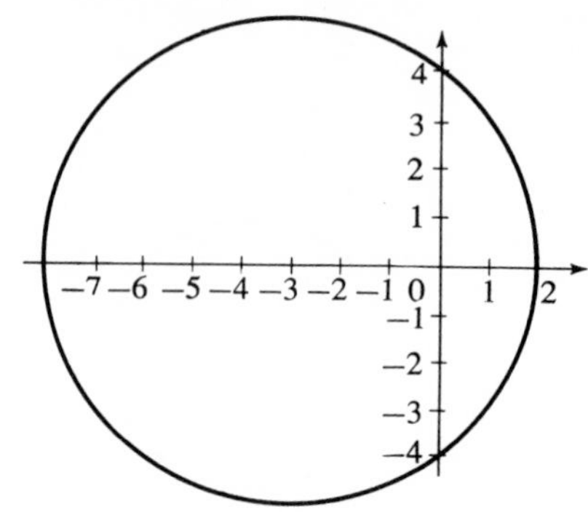

21. $(x-1/2)^2+(y-3/2)^2=9/4.$

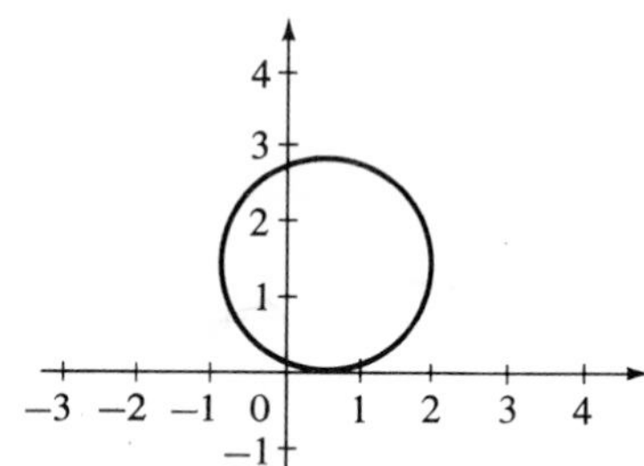

23. $(x-4/5)^2+(y-2/5)^2=25.$

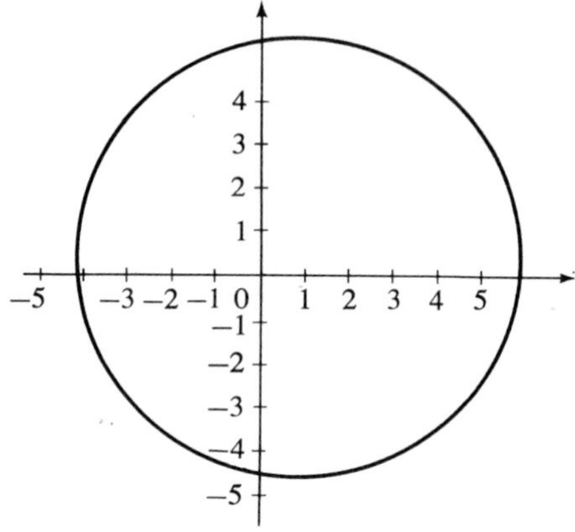

25. $(x-1/3)^2+(y+1)^2=-1/9.$

27. $(x-2/3)^2+(y-1/2)^2=0.$

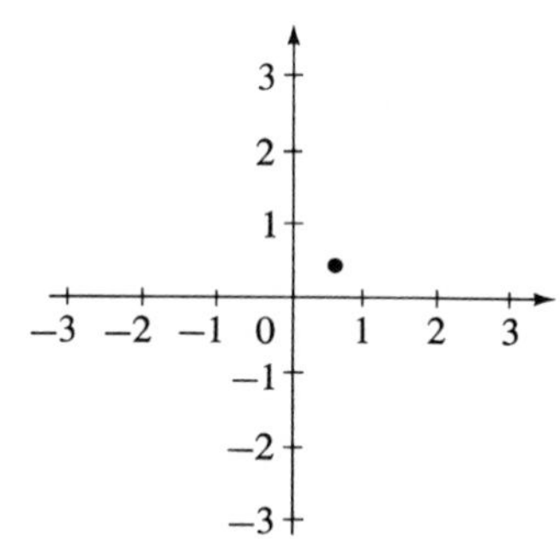

29. $(2,-1),(3,3).$

31. $(1,4),(3,1).$

35. $x+y+1=0.$

39. (a) $D^2+E^2-4AF>0,$
(b) $=0,$
(c) $<0.$

Section 3.2, page 48

1. $3x^2+3y^2-10x-10y-5=0.$ **3.** $5x^2+5y^2+13x-17y-40=0.$

5. $x^2+y^2-13x-y=0.$

7. $x^2+y^2+4x-10y+4=0,\ x^2+y^2-6x+10y+9=0.$

9. $x^2+y^2-4x+8y-5=0.$

11. $2x^2+2y^2+8x+12y+1=0,\ 2x^2+2y^2-12x-48y+81=0.$

13. $x^2 + y^2 - 2x + 6y = 0.$ **15.** $x^2 + y^2 + 4x + 6y - 37 = 0.$
17. $13x^2 + 13y^2 + 4x + 19y - 49 = 0.$
19. $x^2 + y^2 + 6x + 6y + 9 = 0$, $x^2 + y^2 + 6x - 6y + 9 = 0$, $x^2 + y^2 - 6x + 6y + 9 = 0$, $x^2 + y^2 - 6x - 6y + 9 = 0.$
21. $5x^2 + 5y^2 + 52x - 56y + 47 = 0$, $5x^2 + 5y^2 - 32x + 56y - 37 = 0.$
23. $x^2 + y^2 + 4x - 6y - 12 = 0.$ **27.** $x - 3y - 7 \pm 13\sqrt{10} = 0.$
29. $7x^2 + 7y^2 + 26x + 32y - 17 = 0.$ **31.** $3x^2 + 3y^2 - 2x - 10y - 2 = 0.$

Chapter 4, page 55

---

1. Function. **3.** No function. **5.** Function. **7.** Function.
9. No function. **11.** $\{x \mid x \text{ real}, x \leq 0\}$, $\{y \mid y \text{ real}, y \geq 0\}$.
13. $\{x \mid x \text{ real}, x \neq 1\}$, $\{y \mid y \text{ real}, y \neq 0\}$.
15. $\{x \mid x \text{ real}, x \neq \pm 1\}$, $\{y \mid y \text{ real}, y > 0 \text{ or } y \leq -1\}$.
17. $\{x \mid x \text{ real}, x \geq 2\}$, $\{y \mid y \text{ real}, y \geq 0\}$.
19. $\{x \mid x \text{ real and } x \geq 3 \text{ or } x \leq -2\}$, $\{y \mid y \text{ real}, y \geq 0\}$.
21. $\{x \mid x \text{ a positive integer}\}$, $\{y \mid y \text{ a positive integer}\}$.
23. $\{x \mid x \text{ real}, x > 0\}$, $\{y \mid y \text{ real}, y > 0\}$.
25. $\{x \mid x \text{ real}\}$, $\{y \mid y \text{ real}, y < 0 \text{ or } y = 1\}$.
27. $\{x \mid x \text{ real}, x \neq 0\}$, $\{y \mid y \text{ real}, y < 0 \text{ or } y \geq 1\}$.
29. $\{(x, y) \mid x, y \text{ real}\}$, $\{z \mid z \text{ real}, z \geq 0$. **31.** $\{(x, y) \mid x, y \text{ real}, |x| \geq |y|\}$, $\{z \mid z \text{ real}, z \geq 0\}$.
33. $\{(x, y, z) \mid x, y, z \text{ real}\}$, $\{w \mid w \text{ real}, w \geq 0\}$. **35.** $f\colon f(x) = x^2$, $\{x \mid x \text{ real}, 0 \leq x \leq 1\}$.
37. $f\colon f(x) = x - 3$, $\{x \mid x \text{ real}, 0 < x \leq 6\}$. **39.** $f\colon f(x) = x$, $\{0, 1, 2, 3, 4, 5\}$.
41. $f\colon f(x) = 2x$, $\{x \mid x \text{ a positive integer}\}$.
43. $f\colon f(x, y) = x + y$, $\{(x, y) \mid x = 0, 1, 2; y = 0, 1, 2\}$.
45. 3, 5, 13, −3. **47.** −1, does not exist, 1/2, $1/(x + 1)$.
49. 0, 2, $|x|$, $\sqrt{x + h}$; **51.** $y^2 + 1$, $x^2 + 2hx + h^2 + 1$, $2x + h$. **53.** 0, 1/2, 1.
55. 0, $\sin(1/h)$. **57.** 1, 1, 1/2, $1/2y^2$, $1/(x^2 + y^2)$. **59.** 1, −1.

Chapter 5

Section 5.1, page 60

1. −2. **3.** 3. **5.** 7. **7.** 3. **9.** −2. **11.** Does not exist.
13. $4x - y - 4 = 0$, $x + 4y - 18 = 0$. **15.** $8x - y - 12 = 0$, $x + 8y - 34 = 0$.
17. $5x - y - 22 = 0$, $x + 5y + 32 = 0$. **19.** 1, 1, 1, −1, −1, −1, no slope.
21. (2, −4). **23.** 3, 3, 3.

Section 5.2, page 64

1. $4x - 4$. **3.** $8s - 1$. **5.** $-1/(x+1)^2$. **7.** $4q(q^2+2)$. **9.** $1/3x^{2/3}$.
11. 9. **13.** 5, 5/9. **15.** 4. **17.** (0, 0). **19.** (1, −2). **21.** $(\pm 1, \pm 2)$.
23. $3x - y - 2 = 0$. **25.** $9x + y + 2 = 0$. **27.** $(\pm 1/\sqrt{3}, \pm 1/3\sqrt{3})$.
29. 34°, 146° **31.** $3x - y - 3 = 0$.

35.

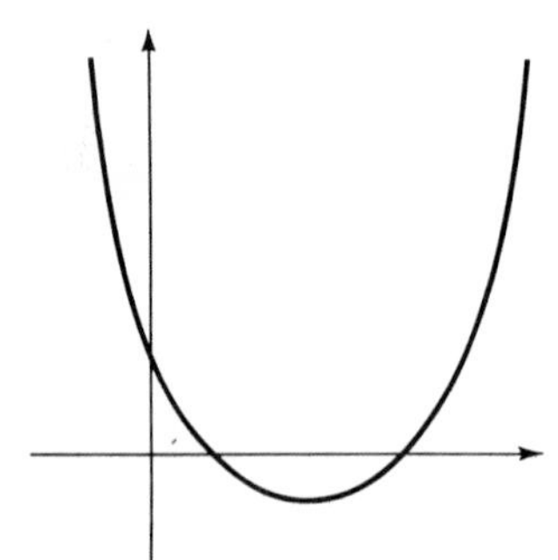

37.

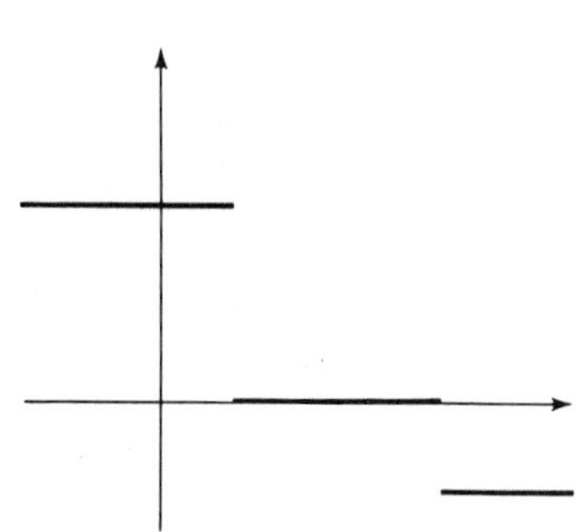

Section 5.3, page 69

1. $6x + 5$. **3.** $5x^4 + 20x^3$. **5.** $35x^4 + 15x^2 + 1$. **7.** $12s^2 - 6s - 12$.
9. $4(x^3 - 2x + 1)$. **11.** $(q^2+1)(5q^2+1)$. **13.** 1. **15.** 36. **17.** 4.
19. (0, 0). **21.** (3, −1), (5, −5). **23.** $5x - y - 1 = 0$. **27.** $3x^2 + 12x + 11$.
29. $4x^3 - 30x^2 + 70x - 50$.

Section 5.4, page 77

1. $-2/x^3$. **3.** $(x^2 - 1)/x^2$. **5.** $(2/3)x^{-1/3}$. **7.** $x(x-2)/(x-1)^2$.
9. $(2t+1)/3t^{4/3}$. **11.** $-4v(v+2)/(v^2 - 2v - 2)^2$.
13. $-4a^{2/3}/3q^{1/3}(q^{2/3} - a^{2/3})^2$. **15.** $(4x^3 + 3x^2 + 3)/x^2$.
17. $(x^4 + 4x^2 + 2x - 1)/(x^2+1)^2$. **19.** $(t^{2/3} - 2t^{1/3} - 3)/3t^2$.
21. $-1/[3\sqrt[6]{x}(\sqrt{x} - \sqrt[3]{x})^2]$. **23.** 1/6. **25.** 32/121. **27.** 5/9
29. (2, 5), (−1, −4). **31.** (0, 0). **33.** $x - 4y + 4 = 0$.

Section 5.5, page 80

1. $4(x+1)^3$. **3.** $20(4x+2)^4$. **5.** $2/\sqrt{4x+2}$. **7.** $2q^2/\sqrt[3]{q^3 - 8}$.
9. $-1/(x+1)^{1/2}(x-1)^{3/2}$. **11.** $(v-3)/3(v+1)^{1/3}(v-1)^{4/3}$.
13. $8/3(2x+1)^{5/3}(2x-1)^{1/3}$. **15.** $1 + 1/2\sqrt{x+1}$. **17.** $3x^5(2 - x^3)/(1 + x^3)^4$.
19. $2/(1-x)^2$. **21.** $-(x^3 + 2x^2 + 12x + 8)/2\sqrt{x+1}(x^2 - 4)^2$. **23.** 24.
25. 28. **27.** 3/4. **29.** 2, 4. **31.** 2, 3, 12/5. **33.** $6x + y - 15 = 0$.
35. $x/|x|$, 1, 1, 1, −1, −1, −1, no derivative.

Section 5.6, page 83

1. −1. **3.** 1/4. **5.** 0. **7.** 3. **9.** $-x^2/y^2$. **11.** $-(y/x)^{1/3}$.
13. $(y/x)^{2/3}$. **15.** $-y/x$. **17.** $y/(y-x)$. **19.** $(1-2y)/(1+2x)$.
21. $-(x^2 + 2xy)/(x^2 + y^2)$. **23.** $x(2x^2 - 2y^2 - 1)/y(2x^2 - 2y^2 + 1)$.
25. $[y + x(x-y)^2]/[x - y(x-y)^2]$. **27.** (1, 0), (1, −4); (−1, −2), (3, −2).
29. $3x - 4y - 18 = 0$. **33.** $3x - 4y + 24 = 0$, $4x + 3y + 7 = 0$.
35. $-4x/9y$.

37. 2, −1, 2, −1, does not exist.

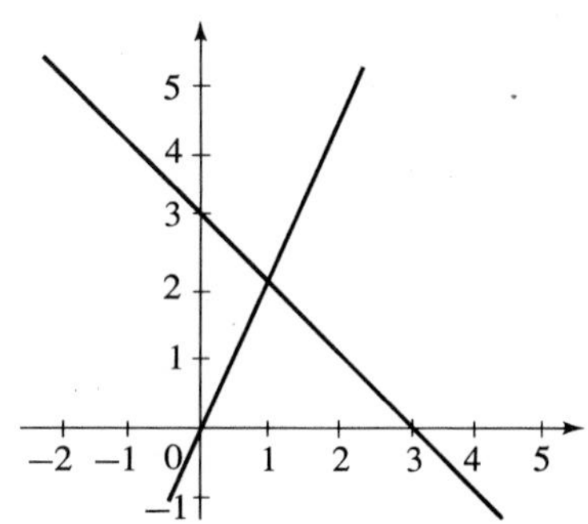

Section 5.7, page 86

1. 6. **3.** 0. **5.** $x^{-5/2}(3-x)/4$. **7.** $24v(5v^2+3)$. **9.** $(6x^2+2)/(x^2-1)^3$.
11. $-16/y^3$. **13.** $2y(y-x)/(2y-x)^3$. **15.** $1/3x^{4/3}y^{1/3}$.
17. $-6(x^2+xy+y^2)/(x+2y)^3$. **19.** 3, 6, 8. **21.** 2, 1/3, −2/9.
23. 9, −12, 32. **25.** 3/4, 25/64. **27.** −1, 4.

31.

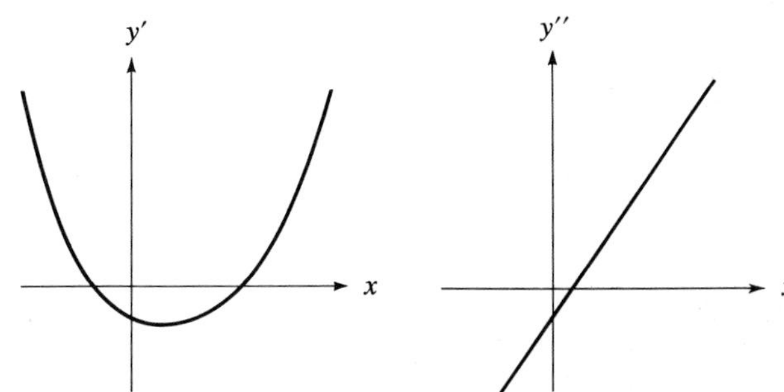

33.

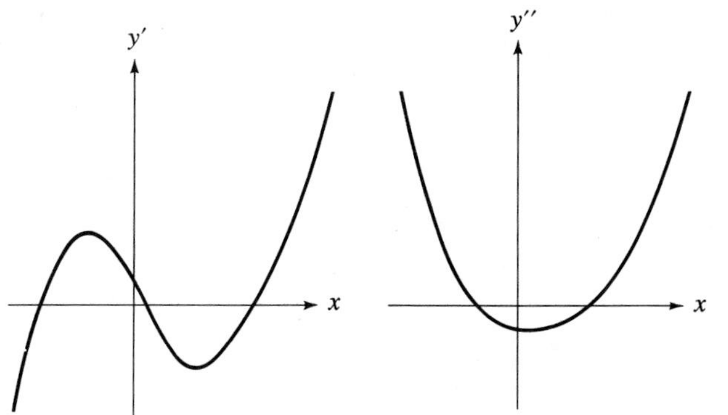

Section 5.8, page 90

1. $2x^4+C$. **3.** $(3/5)x^{5/3}+C$. **5.** $-1/x+C$. **7.** $3x^4-2x^3+3x+C$.
9. $(x^2+1)/x+C$. **11.** $2\sqrt{x}(3x^2+5x+15)/15$. **13.** $x^3/3-x^2+x+C$.
15. x^4+2. **17.** $(3x^{2/3}+1)/2$. **19.** $2x^3+2x^2-3x-17$.
21. $6x^2-9x+7$. **23.** $-3x^2+11x-5$. **25.** x^3+x^2-4x+5.
27. $(4x^{5/2}+35x+21)/15$. **29.** x^3+x-2.

Chapter 6

Section 6.1, page 96

1. (0, 0), (−3, 0). **3.** (1, 0), (−1, 0), (0, −1).
5. (−1/4, 0), (2, 0), (−3/2, 0), (0, −18). **7.** (1, 0), (0, −1).
9. (1/3, 0), (−1/2, 0), (0, 8). **11.** (0, 0). **13.** (3, 0), (0, 9). **15.** None.
17. None. **19.** $x = 1$, $y = 0$. **21.** $x = -3$, $y = 1$. **23.** $x = -1$, $y = 2$.
25. $x = -1$, $x = 3$, $y = 0$. **27.** $y = 1$. **29.** $x = -3/2$, $x = -1$, $y = 0$.
31. $y = 0$. **33.** $y = 0$. **35.** (a) $y = 0$, (b) $y = a_n/b_m$, (c) none.

Section 6.2, page 102

1. y axis. **3.** None. **5.** x axis. **7.** Origin. **9.** Origin.

11.

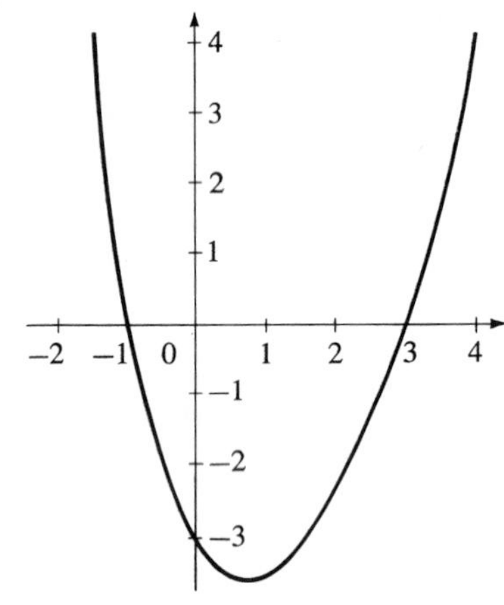

13.

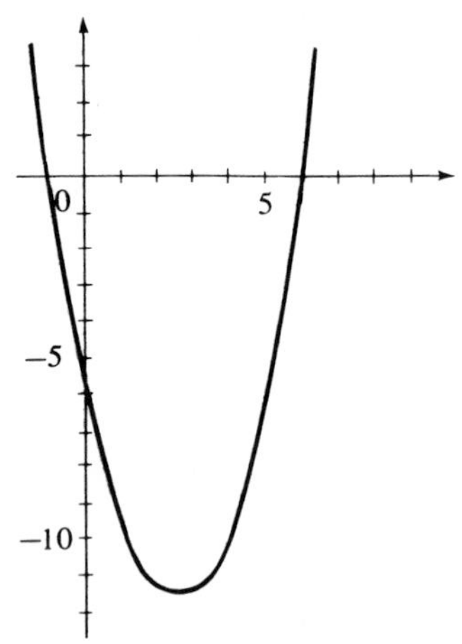

15.

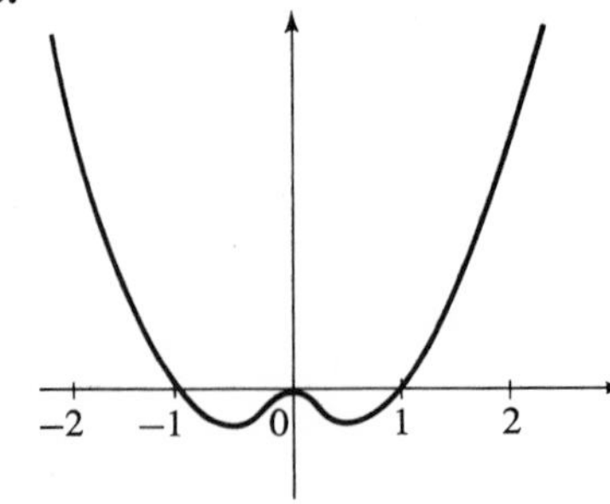

17.

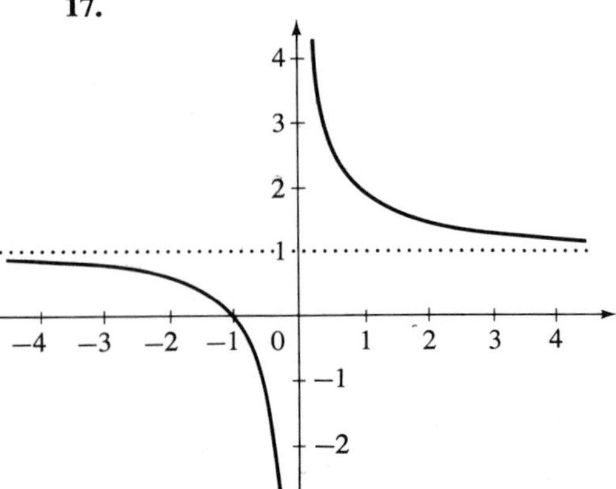

19.

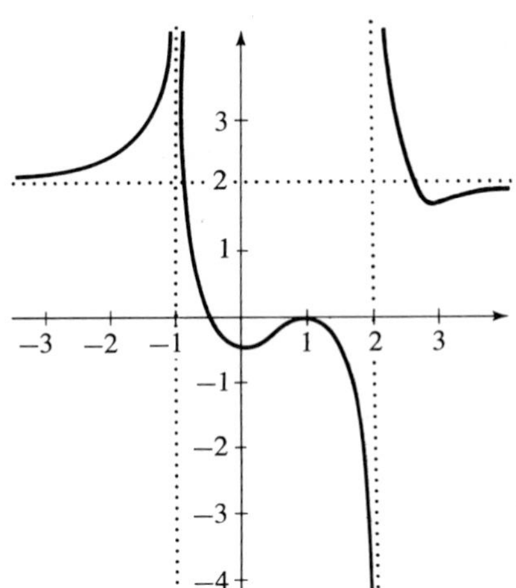

21.

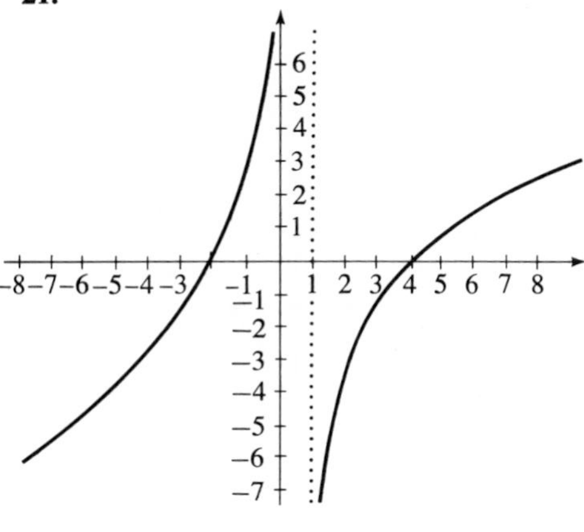

23.

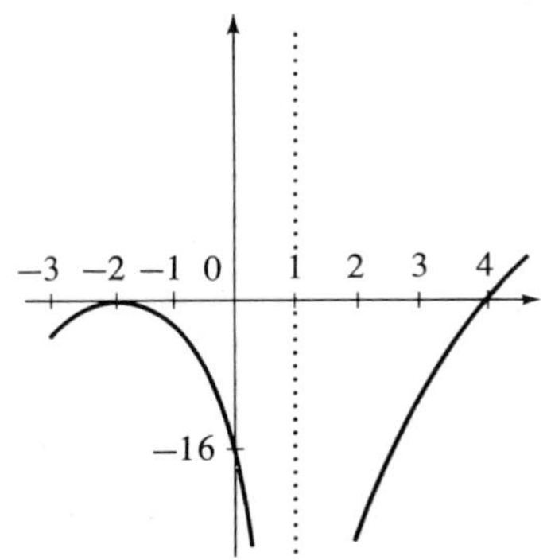

25.

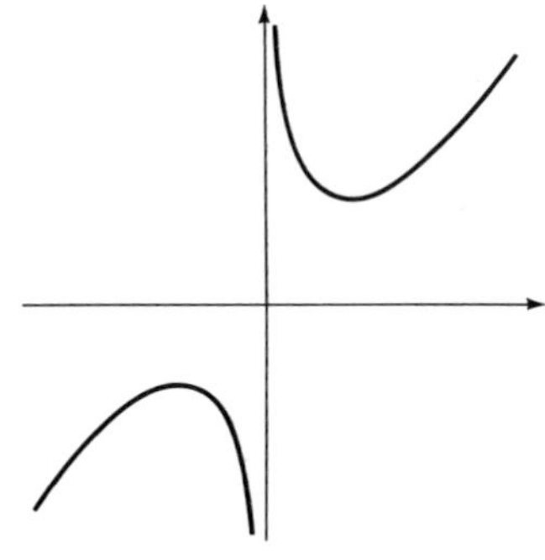

27.

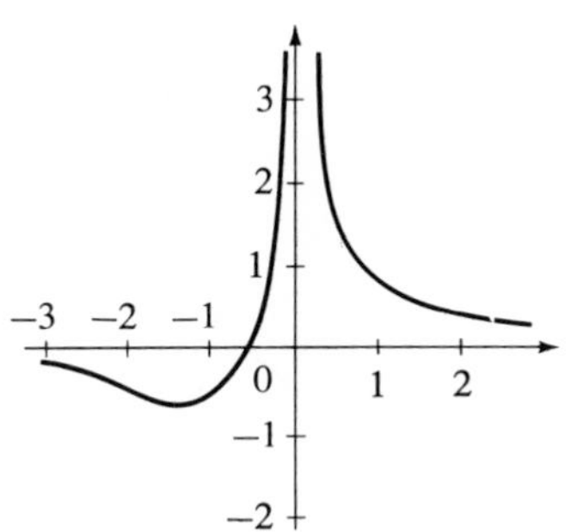

29.

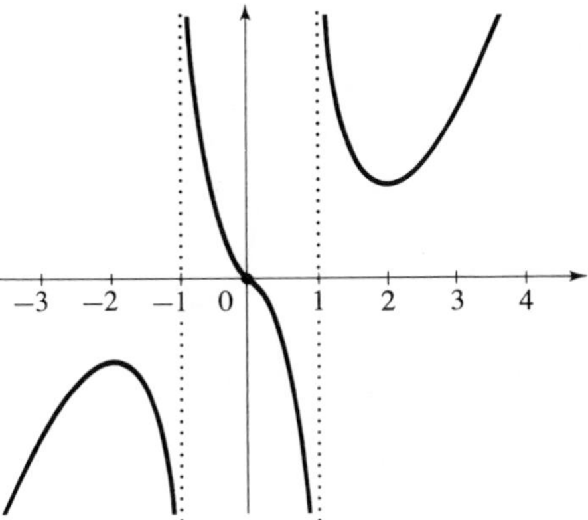

33. Yes.

Section 6.3, page 106

1.

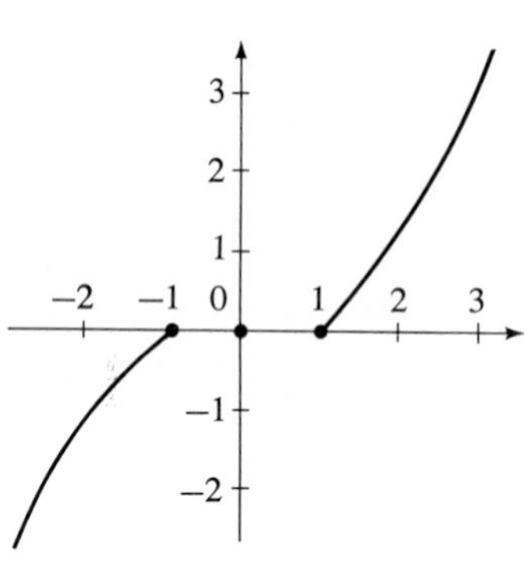

3.

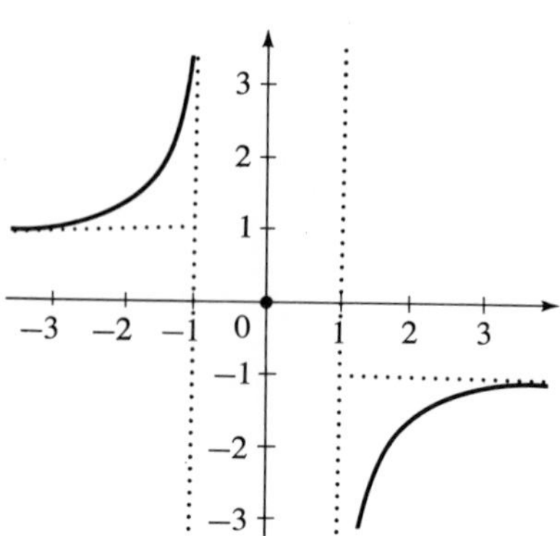

5.

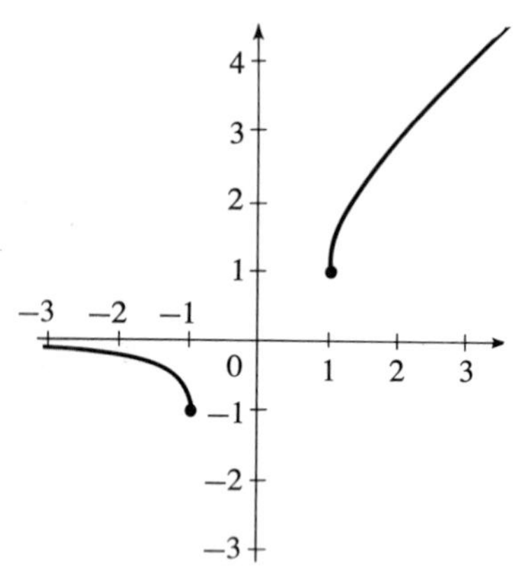

7.

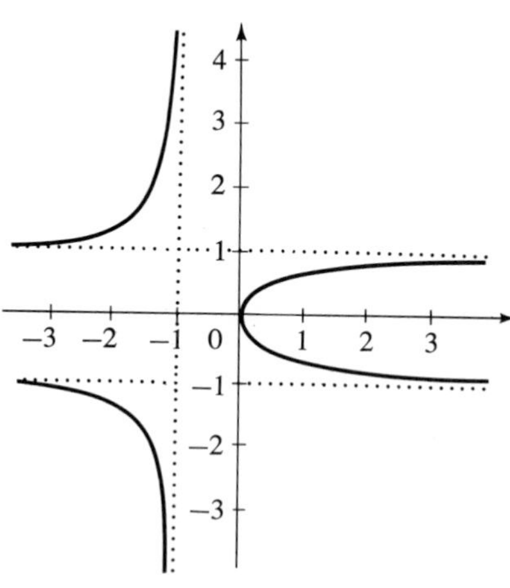

9.

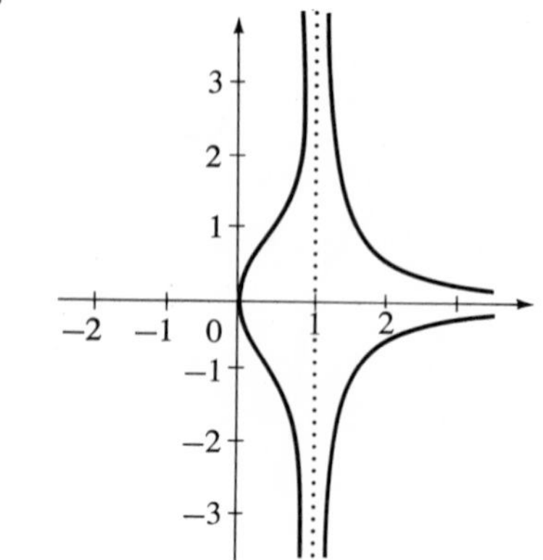

11.

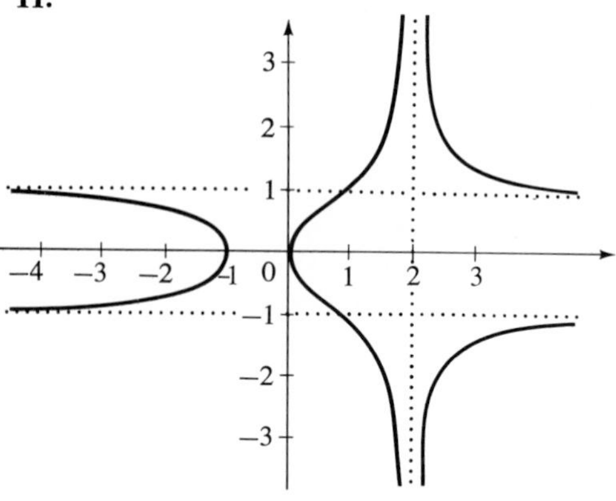

13.

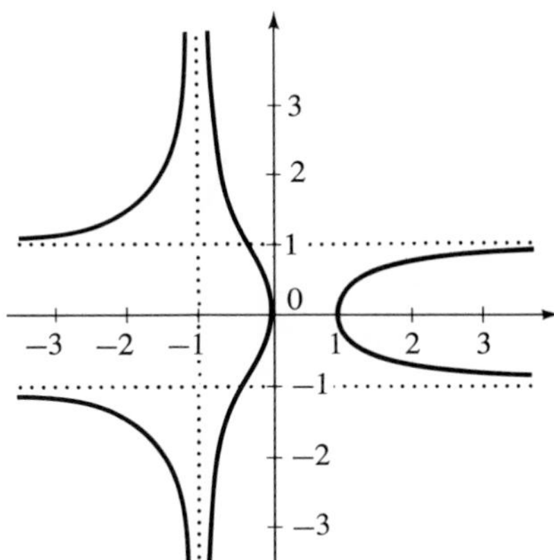

15.

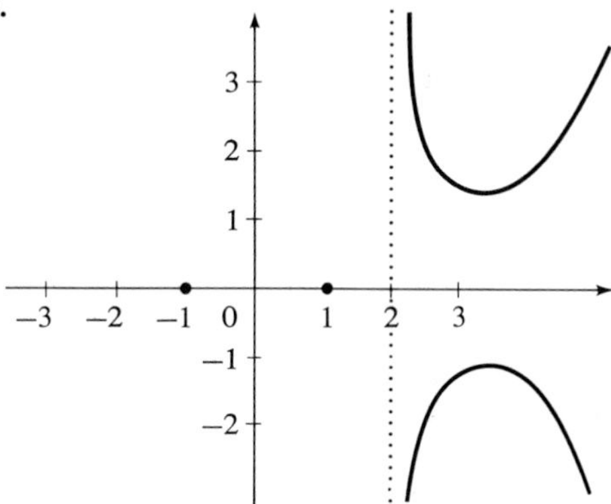

17.

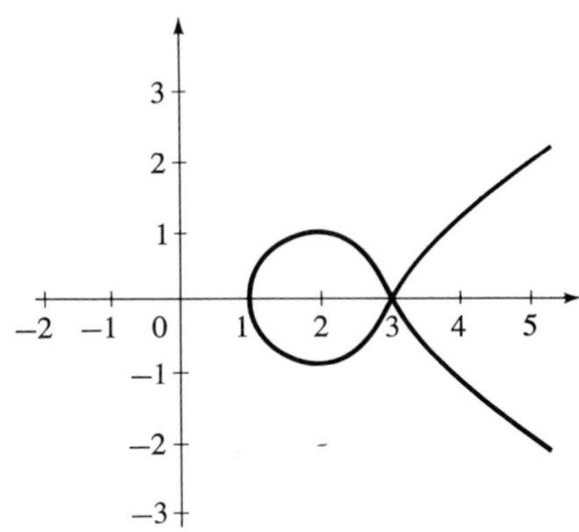

19.

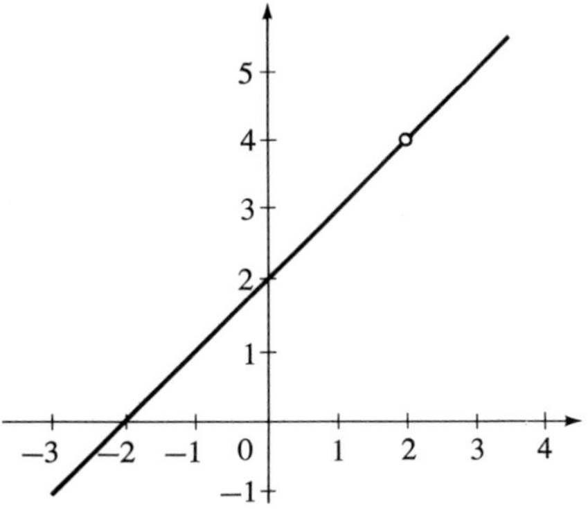

21.

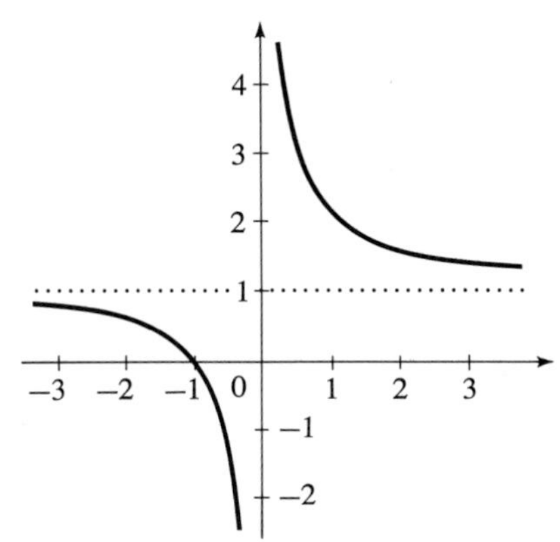

23.

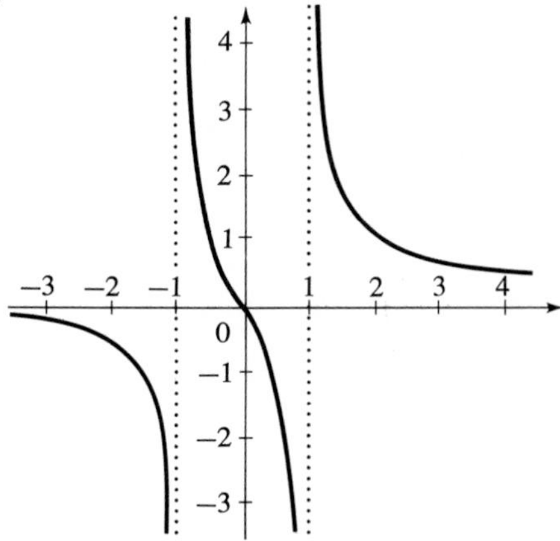

25.

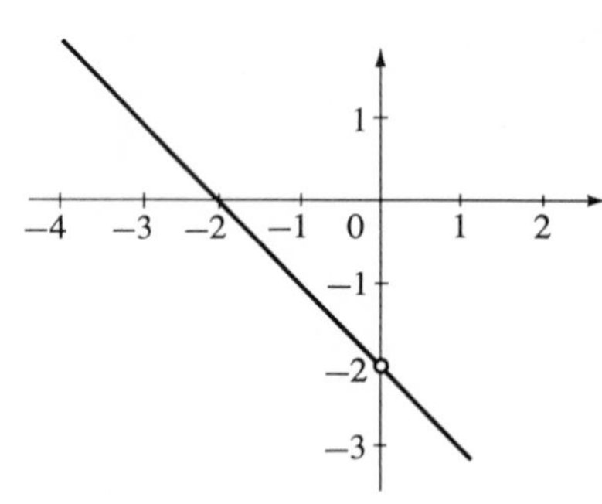

27.

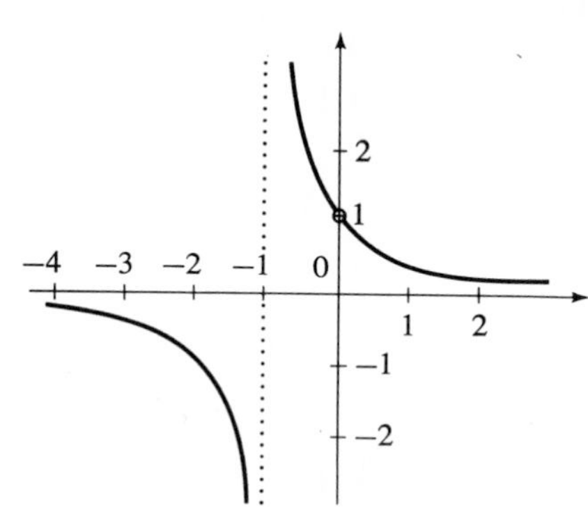

Section 6.4, page 111

1. $(-1, -4)$ min. 3. $(3, 11)$ max. 5. $(0, 1)$ max, $(2, -3)$ min.
7. $(1, 0)$ min, $(-1, 4)$ max. 9. $(-1, -1)$ min, $(0, 0)$ neither.
11. $(0, 16)$ max, $(1, 15)$ neither. 13. None. 15. None. 17. $(0, -1)$ max.
19. $(0, 0)$ neither, $(3, 27/4)$ min. 21. $(-1, 0)$ max, $(1, -4)$ min.
23. $(4, 0)$ min, $(-2, 0)$ neither, $(1, 6561)$ max. 25. $(0, 0)$ neither.
27. $(0, 1)$ min. 29. $(1, 0)$ neither, $(-2, 0)$ max, $(0, -\sqrt[3]{4})$ min.
31. $(0, 0)$ min, $(2, 0)$ min, $(2/3, 8\sqrt[3]{2}/9)$ max. 33. $(0, 0)$ max, $(\pm 1/2\sqrt{2}, -1/4)$ min.

Section 6.5, page 115

1. $(1/2, -25/4)$ min. 3. $(1, -1)$ min, $(-2/3, 98/27)$ max.
5. $(0, 24)$ max, $(-1, 19)$ min, $(2, -8)$ min. 7. $(0, 0)$ max, $(1, -1)$ min.
9. $(0, 0)$ min, $(-2, -4)$ max. 11. $(0, -1)$ max. 13. Concave upward everywhere.
15. $(1, -8)$, concave downward for $x < 1$, concave upward for $x > 1$.
17. $(0, 0)$, $(3, -81)$; concave downward for $0 < x < 3$; concave upward for $x < 0$ and $x > 3$.
19. Concave downward for $x < -1$, concave upward for $x > -1$.
21. $(0, 0)$, $(\sqrt{3}, \sqrt{3}/4)$, $(-\sqrt{3}, -\sqrt{3}/4)$; concave upward for $-\sqrt{3} < x < 0$ and $x > \sqrt{3}$; concave downward for $x < -\sqrt{3}$ and $0 < x < \sqrt{3}$.
23. $(0, 0)$ max, $(4, -32)$ min, $(2, -16)$ point of inflection.
25. $(-1/2, 59/4)$ max, $(3, -71)$ min, $(5/4, -225/8)$ point of inflection.
27. $(1/2, -3/8)$ min. 29. $(0, 0)$ max, $(4, -256)$ min, $(3, -162)$ point of inflection.
31. $(\sqrt{3}, 3\sqrt{3}/2)$ min, $(-\sqrt{3}, -3\sqrt{3}/2)$ max, $(0, 0)$ point of inflection.

Section 6.6, page 118

1. $(0, 0)$ min, $(-4, 32)$ max, $(-2, 16)$ point of inflection.

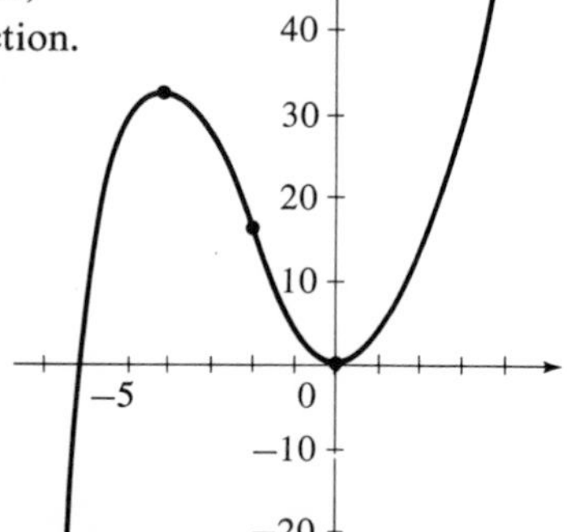

3. $(1, -1)$ min, $(-2/3, 98/27)$ max, $(1/6, 71/54)$ point of inflection.

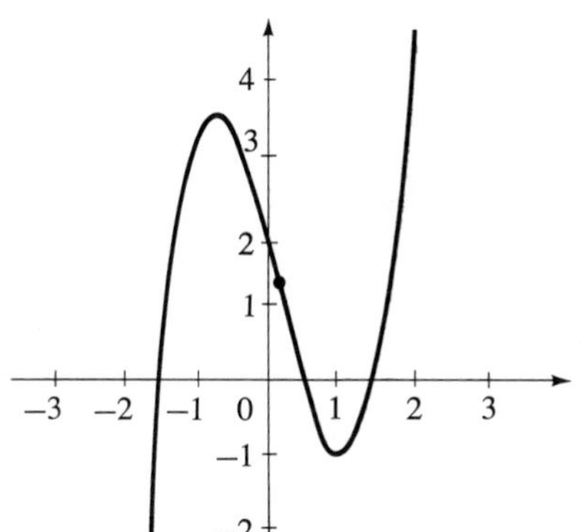

5. $(-1, 0)$ max, $(3/5, -35)$ min, $(3, 0)$, $(1.6, -18.5)$ and $(0.4, -6.3)$ points of inflection.

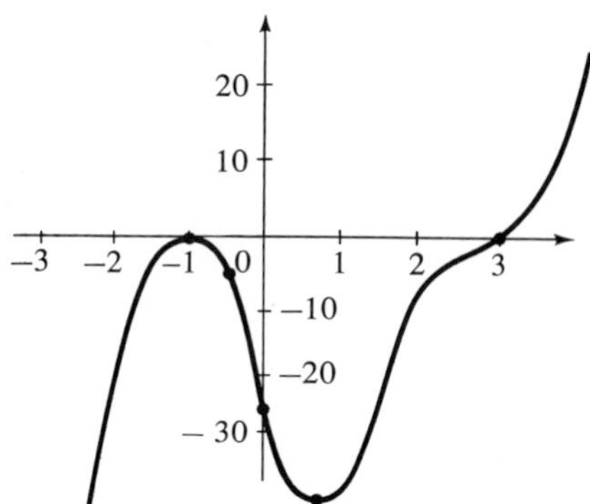

7. $(1.3, -3.2)$ min, $(-0.3, 0.2)$ max, $(1/2, -3/2)$ point of inflection.

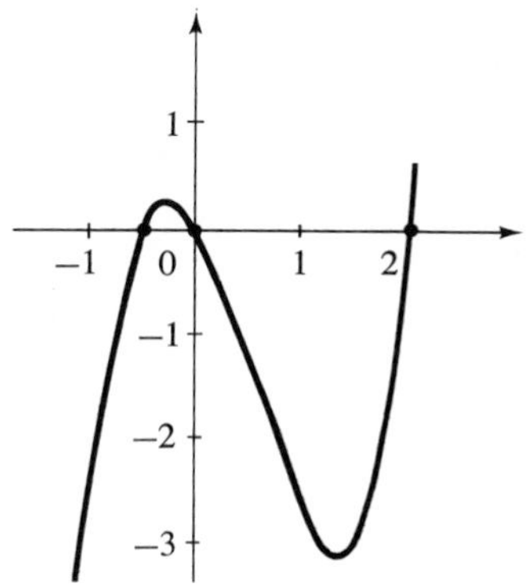

9. $(-3, 0)$ max, $(-1/3, -4\sqrt[3]{4}/3)$ min, $(1, 0)$ point of inflection.

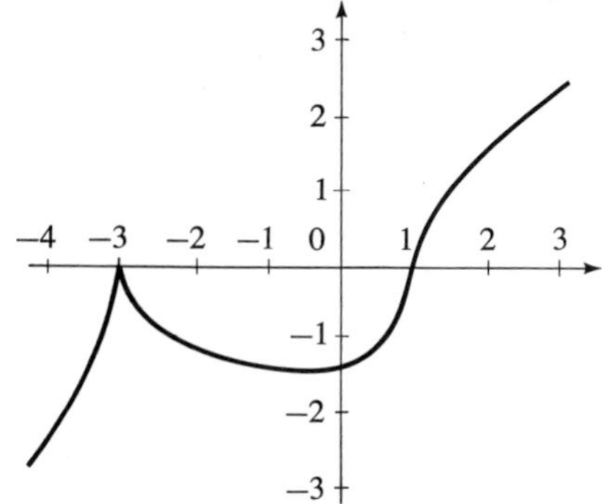

11. $(0, 0)$ max, $(1/3, -2/3\sqrt{3})$ min.

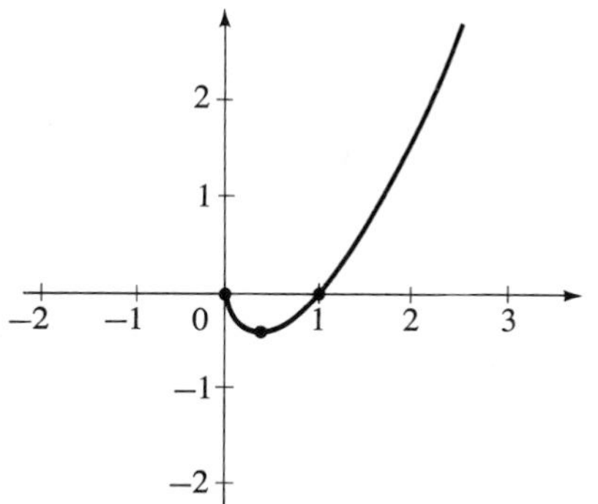

13. $(0, 0)$ min, $(-2, -4)$ max.

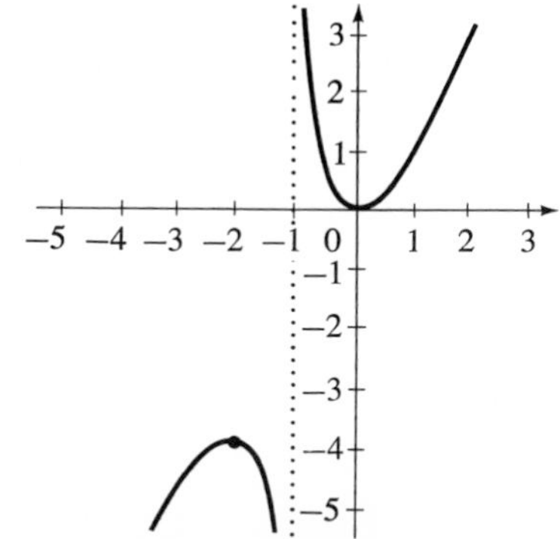

15. $(-1, -2)$ max, $(1, 2)$ min.

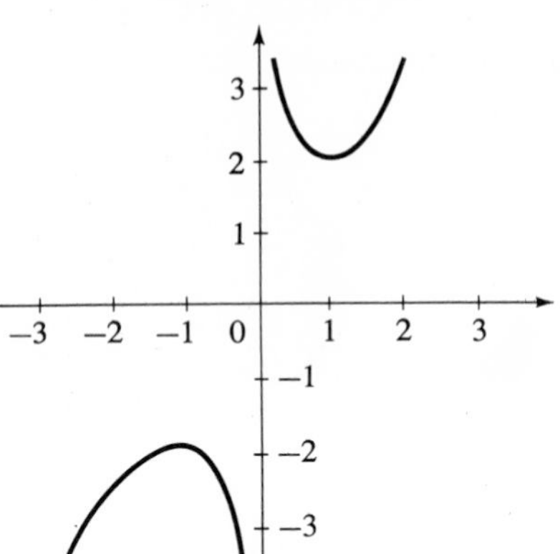

17. None.

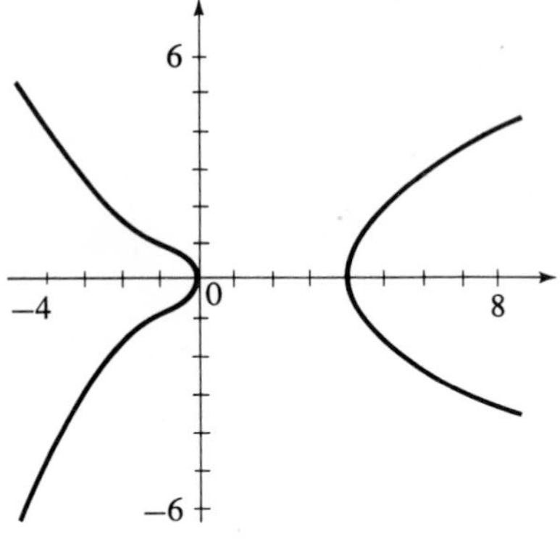

19. $(4, 4\sqrt{2})$ max, $(4, -4\sqrt{2})$ min.

21. $(3/2, 2/3\sqrt{3})$ max, $(3/2, -2/3\sqrt{3})$ min.

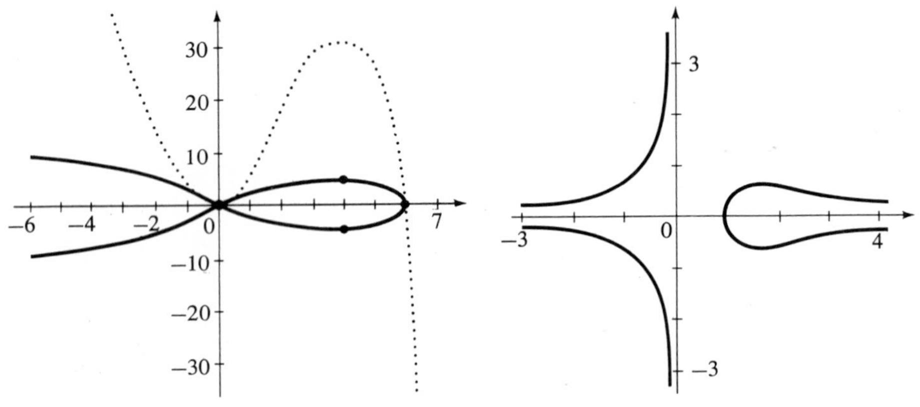

23. $(-1/2, 2/3\sqrt{3})$ max, $(-1/2, -2/3\sqrt{3})$ min.

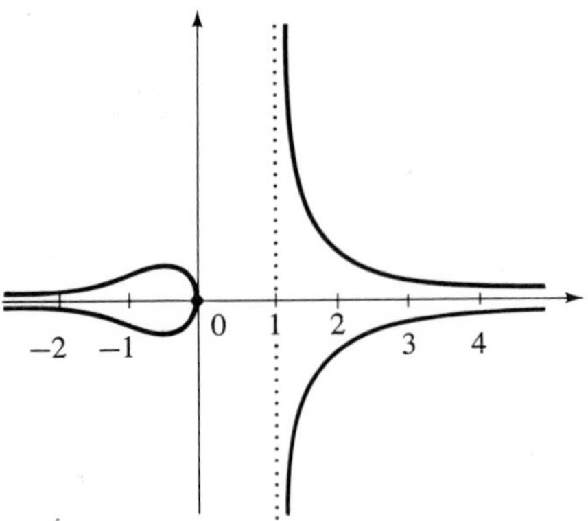

Chapter 7

Section 7.1, page 122

1. $x = y = 24$. **3.** 200 ft of \$1.00 fence, 800 ft of \$.50 fence, \$600. **5.** 2400 ft.
7. Plan b, $1800\sqrt{2}$ ft. **9.** $4\pi R^2H/27$. **11.** $r = R/\sqrt{2}$, $h = R\sqrt{2}$.
13. Base: 20×20 in.; height: 10. **15.** Radius: $\sqrt[3]{V/2\pi}$; height: $\sqrt[3]{4V/\pi}$.
17. Base: $\sqrt{3}R$; height: $3R/2$. **19.** Bases: $2R$ and R; height: $\sqrt{3}\,R/2$.
21. $32/3 \times 8\sqrt{3}$. **23.** $(1, 3)$. **25.** $2P/(4 + \pi) \times 2P(4 + \pi)$.
27. 3 miles down the coast. **29.** 16/3 miles down the coast. **33.** $V/2$.
35. $|Ax_1 + By_1 + C|/\sqrt{A^2 + B^2}$. **37.** $2k/3$. **39.** 12.8 ft.

Section 7.2, page 127

1. 19, 9, 2. **3.** 2, 0, -2. **5.** 15, 32, 48. **7.** 15, 17, 14.
9. 144, 168, 146. **11.** $s = -16t^2 + 64t$. **13.** $s = 2t^3/3 + 16t + 4$.
15. $s = -16t^2 + 128t$. **17.** $s = 2t^2 + t$. **19.** $s = 3t^4 - t^2 + t + 6$.
21. $-v_0$. **23.** $s = -16t^2 + v_0 t + s_0$. **25.** 27/8 ft, 243/128 ft.
27. 44/225, 352 ft/sec (240 mph).

Section 7.3, page 130

1. 1400 in.^{3}/min, 560 in.^{2}/min. **3.** $5\sqrt{3}$ in.^{2}/min. **5.** $2/\sqrt{10\pi}$ in./min.
7. 8/3 ft^2/min, $8\sqrt[3]{\pi/130}/9$ ft^2/min. **9.** -15 mph, $25/\sqrt{2}$ mph. **11.** -0.1 1/min.
13. 0, 4, 8 units/min. **15.** 4, 8 units/min. **17.** $5/4\pi$ ft/min. **19.** 0.48 in/min.

Section 7.4, page 133

1. $3dx$. **3.** $2x\,dx$. **5.** $(3x - 2)x\,dx$. **7.** $-5\,dx/(3x - 2)^2$.
9. $2(1 - x)\,dx/x^3$. **11.** $5(x + 1)(3x - 2)^2(3x + 1)\,dx$. **13.** $(3x - 4)\,dx/2\sqrt{x}$.
15. $x\,dx/(x + 2)^{1/3}(x - 1)^{2/3}$. **17.** $8x(x^2 + 1)^3\,dx$. **19.** $-6(x + 1)^2\,dx/(x - 1)^4$.
21. $x(x^2 + 6x - 4)\,dx/(x + 2)^3$. **23.** $y\,dx/\sqrt{x^2 + 1}$. **25.** $-x\,dx/y$.
27. $(1 - 2x - 2y)\,dx/(1 + 2x + 2y)$. **29.** $(2\sqrt{xy} + y)\,dx/(2\sqrt{xy} - x)$.
31. $y[4(x + y) + (x - y)^3]\,dx/x[4(x + y) - (x - y)^3]$.

Section 7.5, page 137

1. 2.4 in.^{2}. **3.** $\pm 0.03\pi$, $\pm 0.1107\pi$. **5.** $5/9°$. **7.** 40 ± 0.16 ohm.
9. 7.071. **11.** 2.926. **13.** 2.991. **15.** 0.192. **19.** 1%. **21.** 1/3%.

Chapter 8

Section 8.1, page 143

1. $1+8+27+64+125+216+343$. **3.** $-2+0+2+4+6+8$.
5. $1+3+5+7+9+11+13+15$. **7.** $1+8+27+\cdots+(n-1)^3$.
9. $3+5+7+\cdots+(2n+1)$. **11.** $\sum_{i=1}^{10} i$. **13.** $\sum_{i=1}^{11} 2i$. **15.** $\sum_{i=1}^{8} (i^2+i)$.
17. $\sum_{i=1}^{n} (2i-1)$. **19.** $\sum_{i=3}^{n} (i^2+1)$. **21.** Equal. **23.** Not equal. **25.** Equal.
27. Not equal. **29.** $(n+1)(2n+1)/6n^2$. **31.** $(n+1)(1-n)/6n^2$.
33. $(n-1)(2n-1)/6n^2$. **35.** $4(n+1)(2n+1)/3n^2$. **43.** $n(n+1)$, n^2.

Section 8.2, page 148

5. 1/2. **7.** 1/4. **9.** 7/3. **11.** 20. **13.** 1. **15.** 5/6. **17.** 1/6.

Section 8.3, page 151

1. 6. **3.** 0. **5.** 1/4. **7.** 1/3. **9.** −1/6. **11.** 1/4. **13.** 1.
15. 32/3. **17.** 1/12. **19.** 1/2.

Section 8.4, page 155

1. 8/3. **3.** 4. **5.** 10. **7.** 1/12. **9.** 17/12. **11.** 73/6. **13.** 45/4.
15. 2. **17.** 1/2. **19.** 8/3. **21.** 4/3. **23.** 8/5. **25.** 1/3.
27. $2(\sqrt{2}-1)$. **29.** 16/3.

Section 8.5, page 159

1. $(2x-3)^3/3+C$. **3.** $(x^2-x)^2/2+C$. **5.** $(4x-3)^{3/2}/6+C$.
7. $(x^2+4)^3/6+C$. **9.** $x^8/8+4x^6/3+4x^4+C$. **11.** $(x^3+1)^3/9+C$.
13. $(x^{1/3}-1)^6/2+C$. **15.** $(x^{-2}+x)^6/6+C$. **17.** $(3x^2-5)^{4/3}/8+C$.
19. $(x^2+x-1)/(x+1)+C$. **21.** $x^2/2+4x-4/(x+2)+C$. **23.** 32/3.
25. 72. **27.** 1022/9. **29.** −15/8.

Section 8.6, page 162

1. 4/3. **3.** 9/2. **5.** 23/3. **7.** 9/2. **9.** 9/2. **11.** 9/2. **13.** 1/2.
15. 37/12. **17.** 125/24. **19.** 1/12. **21.** 4/3. **23.** 9/2. **25.** 9.

Section 8.7, page 165

1. 9/2 ft lb. **3.** 1/2 ft lb. **5.** 30 ft lb. **7.** 127,000 ft lb.
9. 42,330 ft lb, 56,450 ft lb. **11.** 3674 ft lb, 11,025 ft lb. **13.** 1250 ft lb.
15. 625 ft lb. **17.** 1514 ft lb. **19.** 2515 ft lb.

Section 8.8, page 169

1. 3.344, 3.333, 3.333. **3.** 1.908, 1.867, 1.867. **5.** 1.218, 1.219, 1.219.
7. 1.231, 1.219, 1.219. **9.** 1.509, 1.500, 1.500. **11.** 1.150. **13.** 3.110.

15. 11.983. **17.** 0.771. **19.** 7.734. **21.** 0.307. **23.** 46.20, 45.65.
25. 2.897, 2.901 **27.** 0.859, 0.857.
29. $a = (y_0 - 2y_1 + y_2)/(2h^2)$, $b = (y_2 - y_1)/2h$, $c = y_1$.

Chapter 9

Section 9.2, page 174

1. Axis: x axis, $V(0, 0)$, $F(4, 0)$, D: $x = -4$, lr $= 16$.

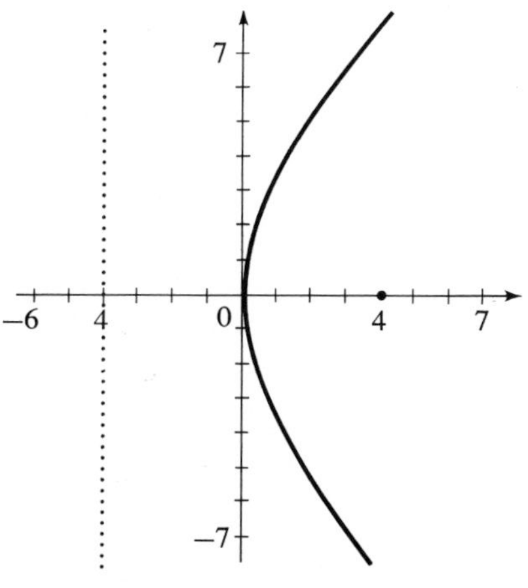

3. Axis: y axis, $V(0, 0)$, $F(0, 1)$, D: $y = -1$, lr $= 4$.

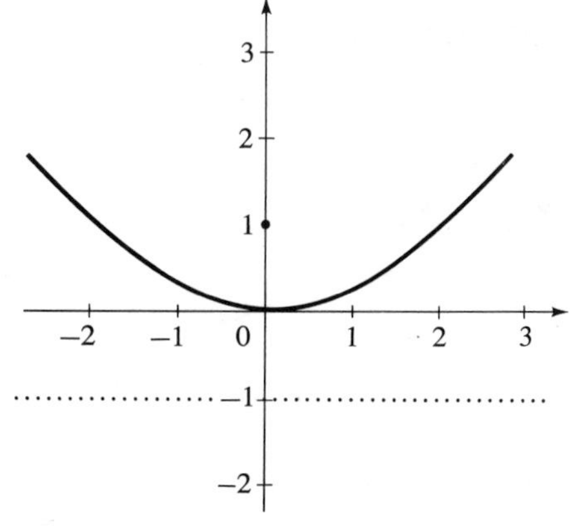

5. Axis: x axis, $V(0, 0)$, $F(5/2, 0)$, D: $x = -5/2$, lr $= 10$.

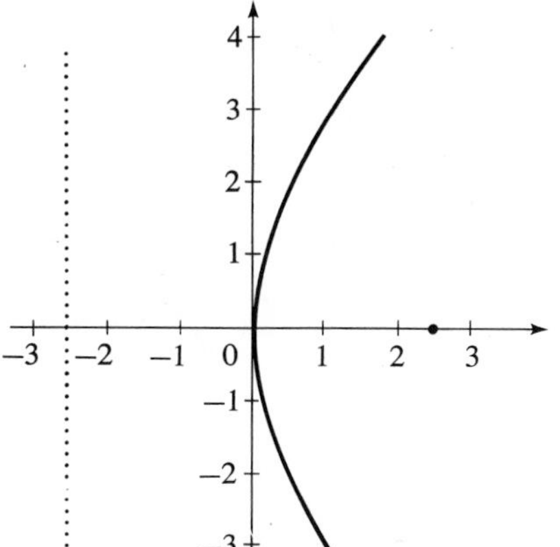

7. Axis: y axis, $V(0, 0)$, $F(0, 5/4)$, D: $y = -5/4$, lr $= 5$.

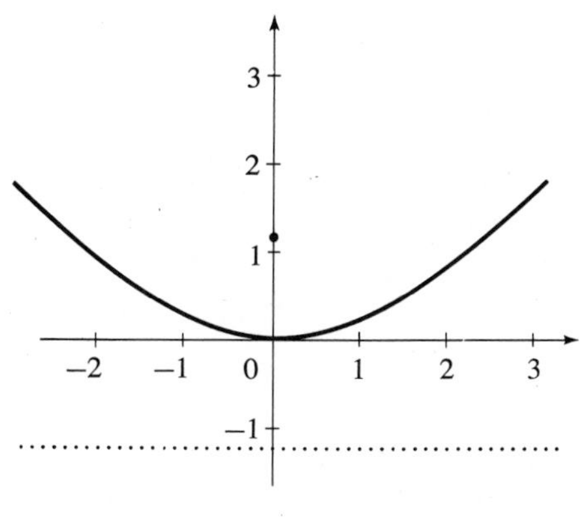

9. Axis: y axis, $V(0, 0)$, $F(0, -1/2)$, D: $y = 1/2$, lr $= 2$.

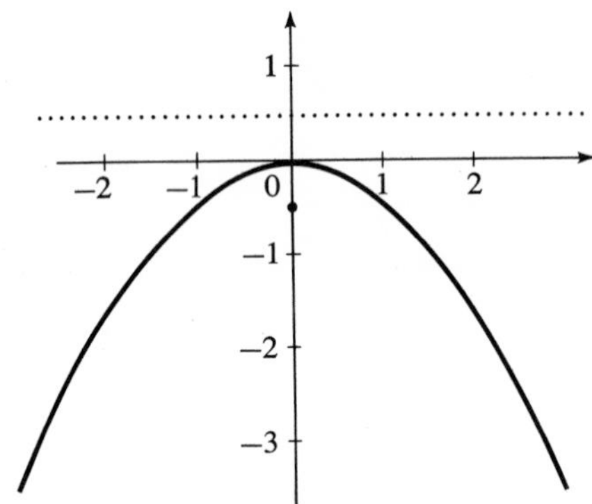

11. $y^2 = 25x$.
13. $y^2 = 5x$, $y^2 = -5x$.
15. $y^2 = -12x$.
17. $x^2 = 4y/3$.
21. $2x + y - 5 = 0$.
23. $2x - y - 6 = 0$.
25. $y = 0$, $2x + y - 8 = 0$.

Section 9.3, page 178

1. Axis: $x = 3$, $V(3, 2)$, $F(3, 4)$, D: $y = 0$, lr $= 8$.

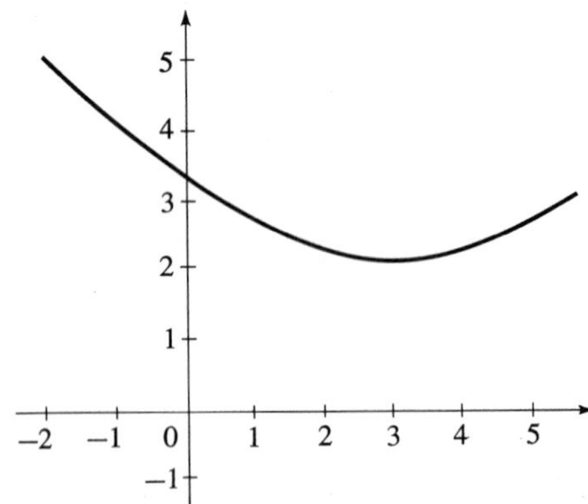

3. Axis: $x = -5$, $V(-5, -2)$, $F(-5, -1/2)$, D: $y = -7/2$, lr $= 6$.

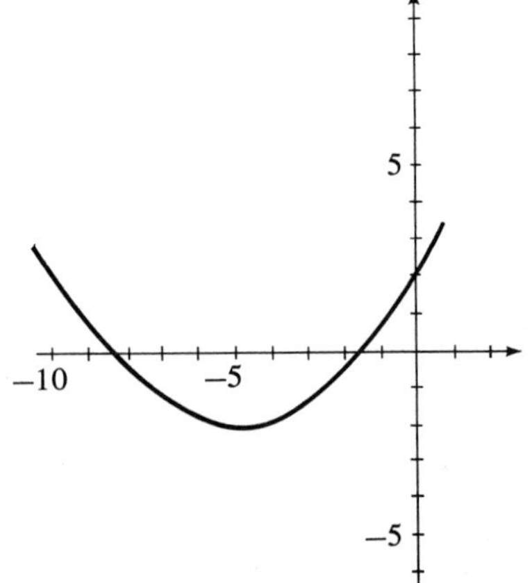

5. Axis: $x = -2$, $V(-2, 1)$, $F(-2, 2)$, D: $y = 0$, lr $= 4$.

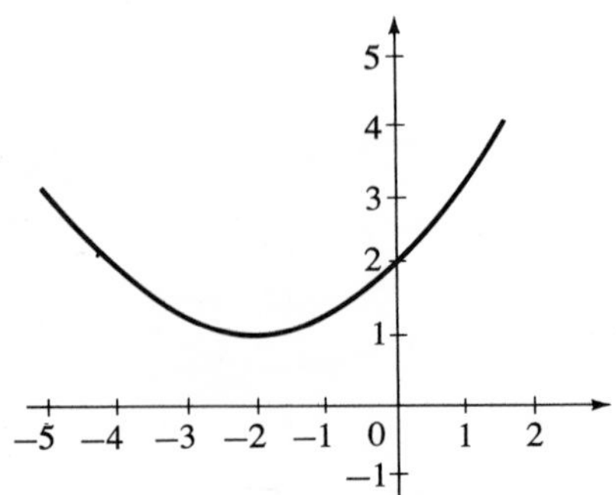

7. Axis: $y = -1$, $V(3, -1)$, $F(13/4, -1)$, D: $x = 11/4$, lr $= 1$.

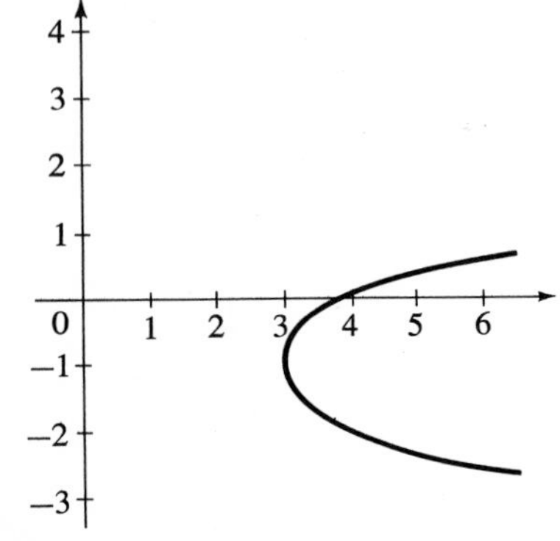

9. Axis: $y = 0$, $V(-2, 0)$, $F(-5/2, 0)$, D: $x = -3/2$, lr $= 2$.

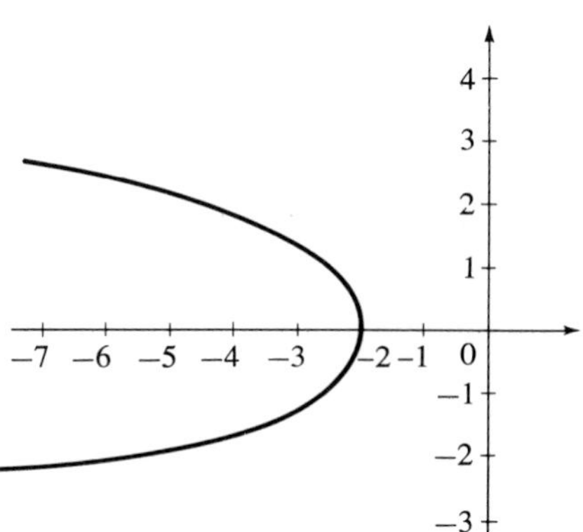

11. No locus.

13. Axis: $y = 2/5$, $V(-3/5, 2/5)$, $F(7/5, 2/5)$, D: $x = -13/5$, lr $= 8$.

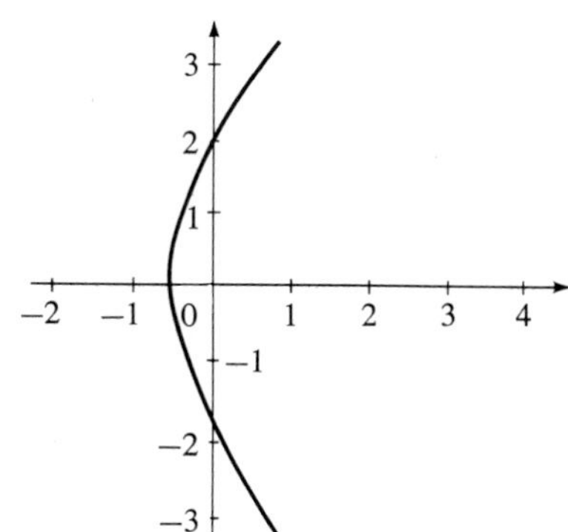

15. Axis: $x = 1/2$, $V(1/2, 1/3)$, $F(1/2, 5/6)$, D: $y = -1/6$, lr $= 2$.

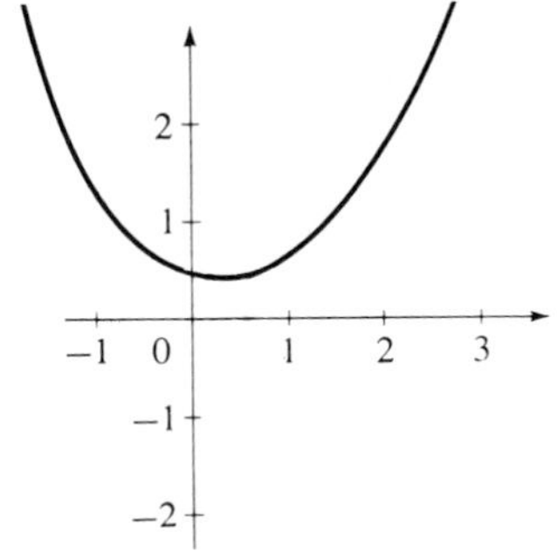

17. $y^2 - 8x - 10y + 33 = 0$.

19. $x^2 - 8x - 12y + 28 = 0$.

21. $y^2 - 8x - 8y = 0$,
$y^2 + 8x - 8y + 32 = 0$.

23. $x^2 - 7x - y + 6 = 0$.

25. $x + 3y - 2 = 0$.

27. $10x + y - 12 = 0$,
$2x + y - 4 = 0$.

Section 9.4, page 183

1. $C(0, 0)$, $V(\pm 13, 0)$, $CV(0, \pm 5)$, $F(\pm 12, 0)$, lr $= 50/13$.

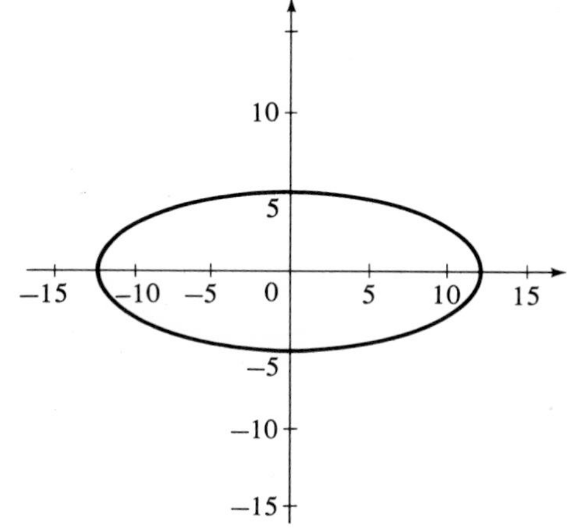

3. $C(0, 0)$, $V(\pm 5, 0)$, $CV(0, \pm 2)$, $F(\pm\sqrt{21}, 0)$, lr $= 8/5$.

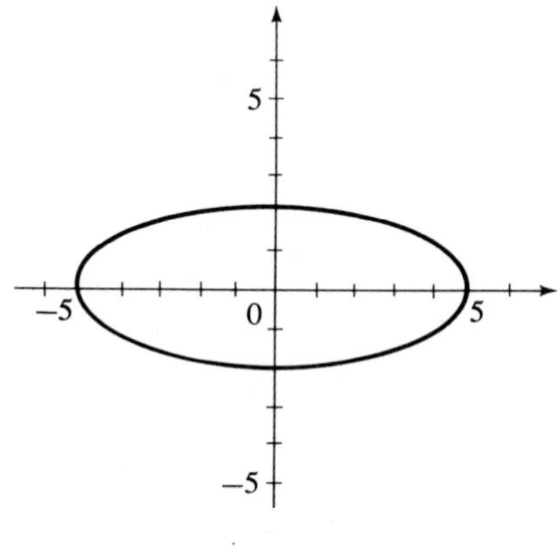

5. $C(0, 0)$, $V(0, \pm 7)$, $CV(\pm 5, 0)$, $F(0, \pm 2\sqrt{6})$, $\text{lr} = 50/7$.

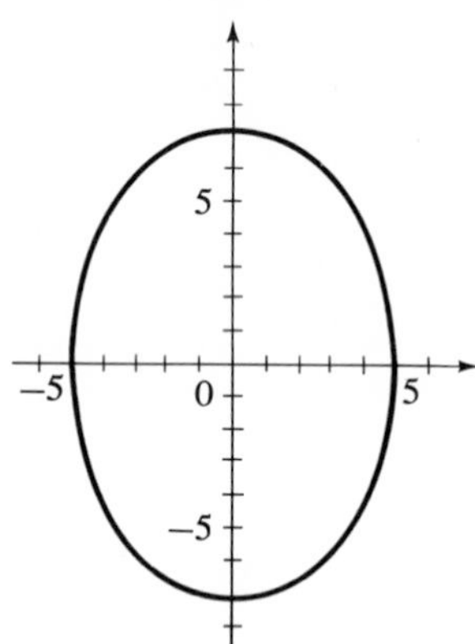

7. $C(0, 0)$, $V(0, \pm 3)$, $CV(\pm 2, 0)$, $F(0, \pm \sqrt{5})$, $\text{lr} = 8/3$.

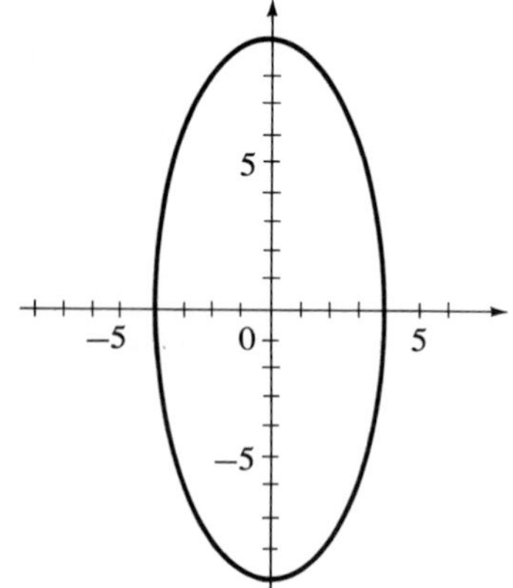

9. $C(0, 0)$, $V(0, \pm 4)$, $CV(\pm 3, 0)$, $F(0, \pm \sqrt{7})$, $\text{lr} = 9/2$.

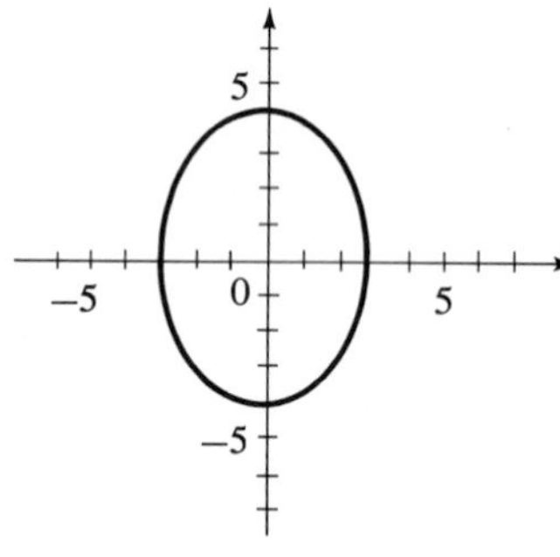

11. $x^2/144 + y^2/169 = 1$.
13. $x^2/25 + y^2/10 = 1$.
15. $x^2/36 + y^2/9 = 1$.
17. $x^2/100 + y^2/64 = 1$.
21. $4x + 3y - 11 = 0$.
23. $x - 4y + 14 = 0$, $11x + 12y - 70 = 0$.
29. 0.0167.

Section 9.5, page 187

1. $C(0, 3)$, $V(\pm 1, 3)$, $CV(0, 3 \pm 1/2)$, $F(\pm \sqrt{3}/2, 3)$, $\text{lr} = 1/2$.

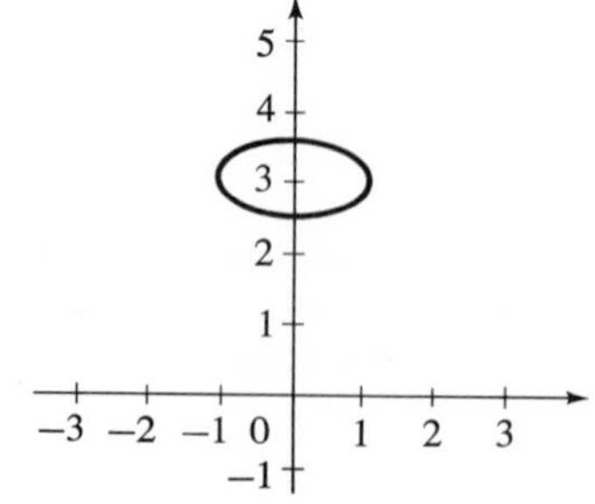

3. $C(-4, 1)$, $V(-4 \pm 5, 1)$, $CV(-4, 1 \pm 3)$, $F(-4 \pm 4, 1)$, $\text{lr} = 18/5$.

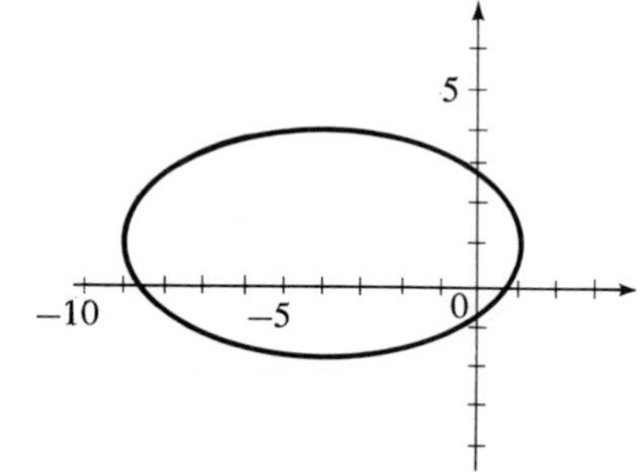

5. $C(-1, -5)$, $V(-1, -5 \pm 4)$, $CV(-1 \pm 2, -5)$, $F(-1, -5 \pm 2\sqrt{3})$, $\text{lr} = 2$.

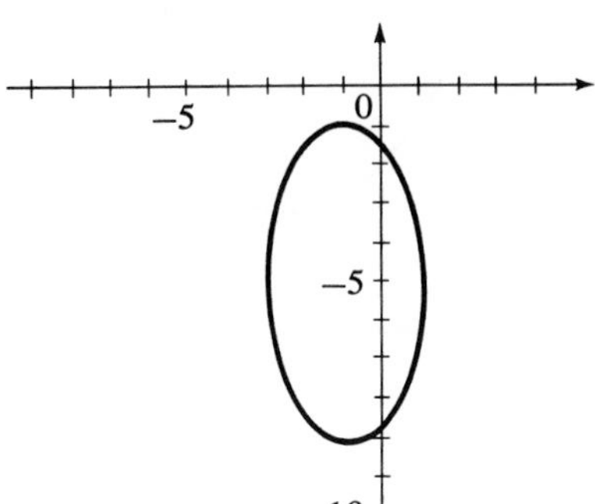

7. $(-4, 3)$.

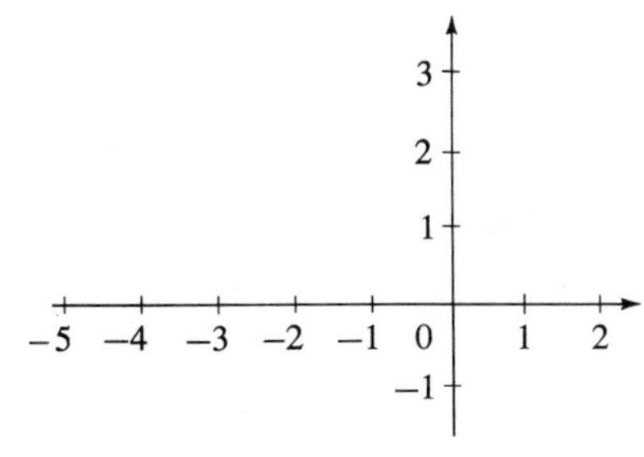

9. $C(-1, 2)$, $V(-1 \pm 3, 2)$, $CV(-1, 2 \pm 2)$, $F(-1 \pm \sqrt{5}, 2)$, $\text{lr} = 8/3$.

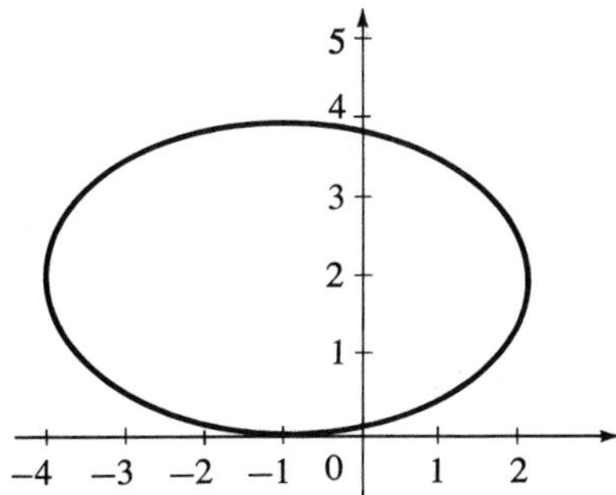

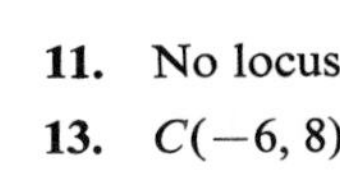

11. No locus.

13. $C(-6, 8)$, $V(-6 \pm 3, 8)$, $CV(-6, 8 \pm 2)$, $F(-6 \pm \sqrt{5}, 8)$, $\text{lr} = 8/3$.

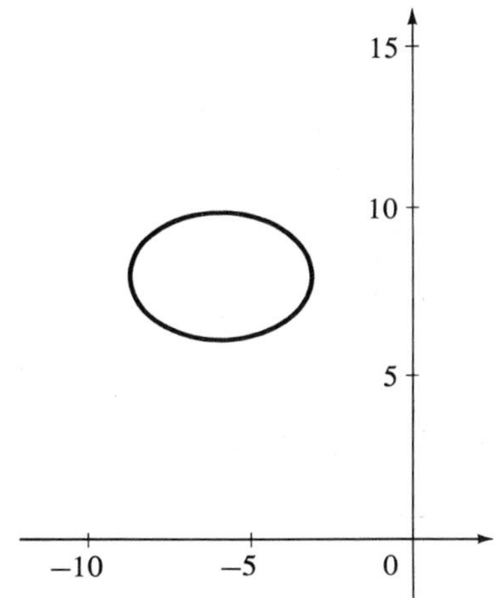

15. $16x^2 + y^2 - 32x + 8y + 16 = 0$. **17.** $4x^2 + y^2 + 8x - 6y - 12 = 0$.
19. $4x^2 + 9y^2 + 16x - 20 = 0$. **21.** $x^2 + 36y^2 - 2x + 216y + 156 = 0$.
23. $16x^2 + 25y^2 - 96x + 50y - 231 = 0$. **25.** $9x^2 + 8y^2 + 54x - 16y - 559 = 0$.
27. $5x + 4y - 9 = 0$. **29.** $3x + 8y + 40 = 0$, $3x - 8y + 24 = 0$.

Section 9.6, page 192

1. $C(0, 0)$, $V(\pm 4, 0)$, $F(\pm 5, 0)$,
A: $y = \pm 3x/4$, $\text{lr} = 9/2$.

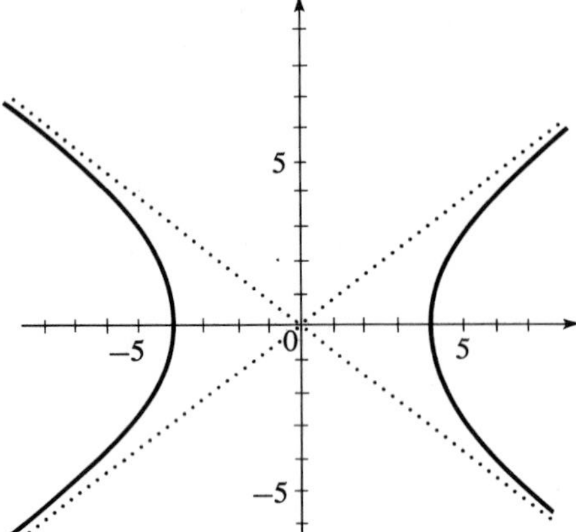

3. $C(0, 0)$, $V(0, \pm 3)$, $F(0, \pm\sqrt{13})$,
A: $y = \pm 3x/2$, $\text{lr} = 8/3$.

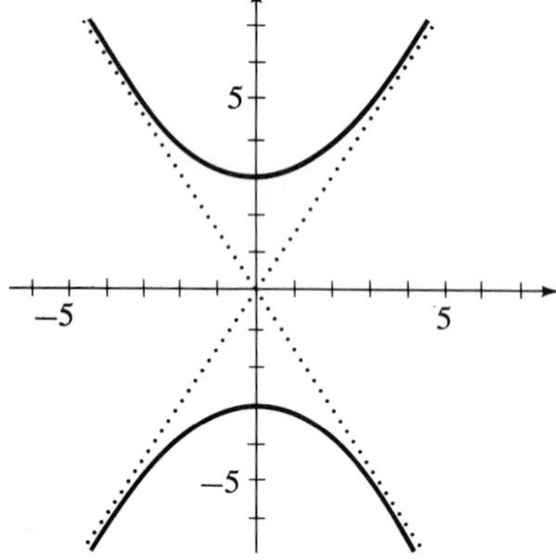

5. $C(0, 0)$, $V(\pm 12, 0)$, $F(\pm 13, 0)$,
A: $y = \pm 5x/12$, $\text{lr} = 25/6$.

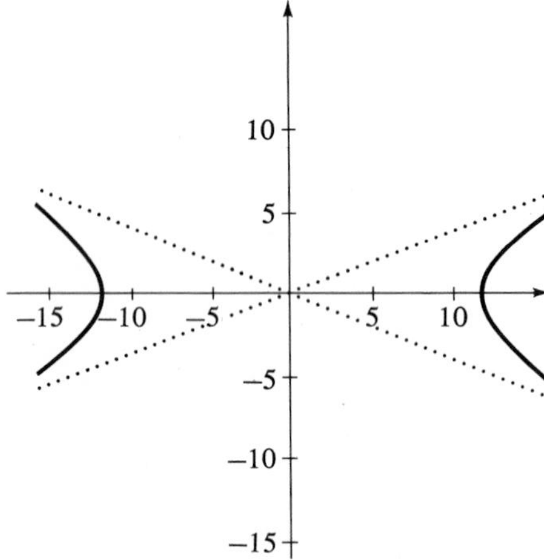

7. $C(0, 0)$, $V(0, \pm 5)$, $F(0, \pm\sqrt{34})$,
A: $y = \pm 5x/3$, $\text{lr} = 18/5$.

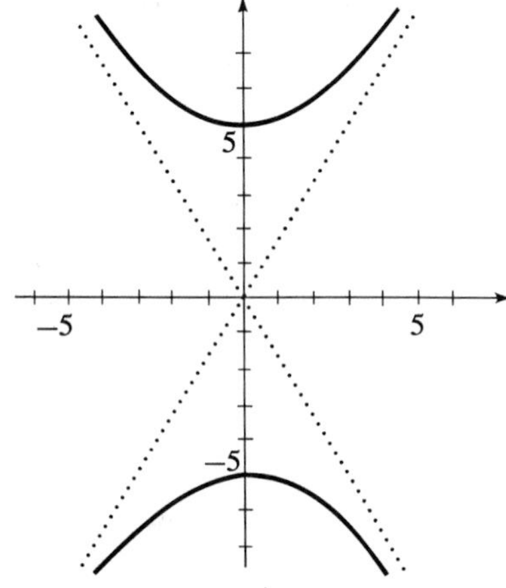

9. $C(0, 0)$, $V(\pm 1, 0)$, $F(\pm\sqrt{5}, 0)$,
A: $y = \pm 2x$, $\text{lr} = 8$.

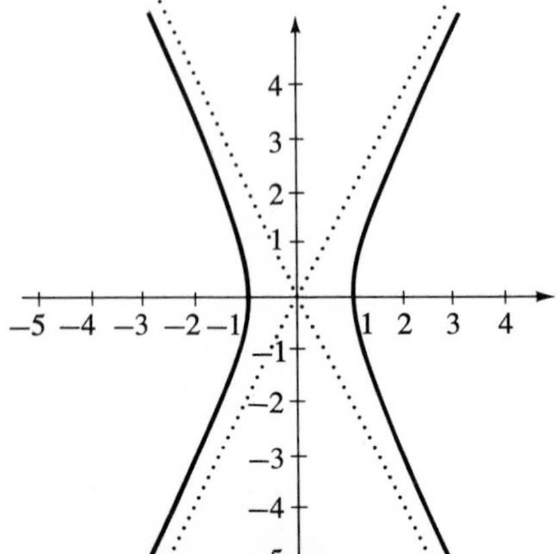

11. $C(0, 0)$, $V(\pm 3, 0)$, $F(\pm 3\sqrt{2}, 0)$,
A: $y = \pm x$, $\text{lr} = 6$.

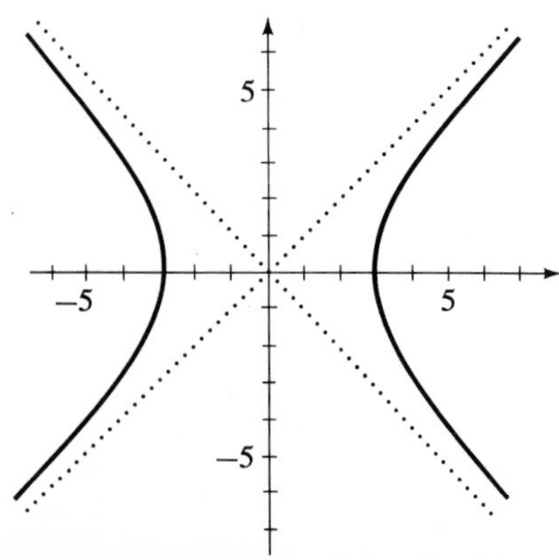

13. $C(0, 0)$, $V(0, \pm 5/2)$, $F(0, \pm \sqrt{34}/2)$,
A: $y = \pm 5x/3$, lr $= 9/5$.

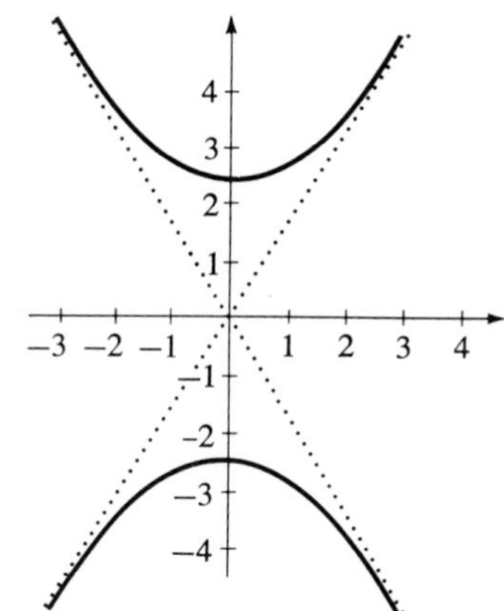

15. $x^2/4 - y^2/12 = 1$.
17. $x^2/36 - y^2/16 = 1$.
19. $16x^2 - 9y^2 = 144$.
21. None.
23. $y^2/9 - x^2/16 = 1$.
25. $x^2/9 - y^2/16 = 1$.
27. $52x - 15y - 144 = 0$.
29. $5x - 4y - 9 = 0$.

Section 9.7, page 195

1. $C(0, 3)$, $V(\pm 3, 3)$, $F(\pm 5, 3)$,
A: $y = 3 \pm 4x/3$, lr $= 32/3$.

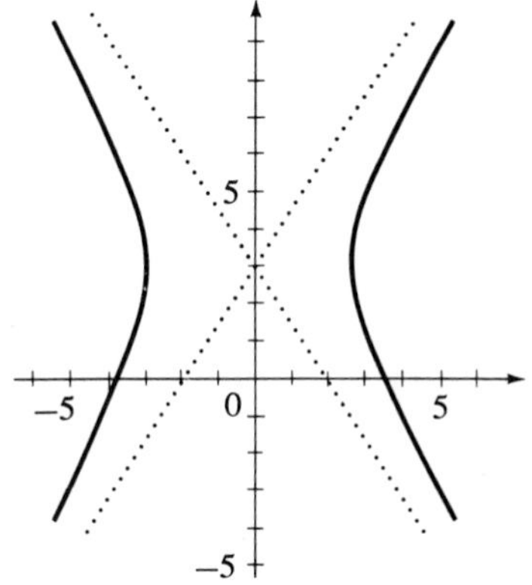

3. $C(5, -1)$, $V(5 \pm 8, -1)$, $F(5 \pm 8\sqrt{2}, -1)$,
A: $y + 1 = \pm(x - 5)$, lr $= 16$.

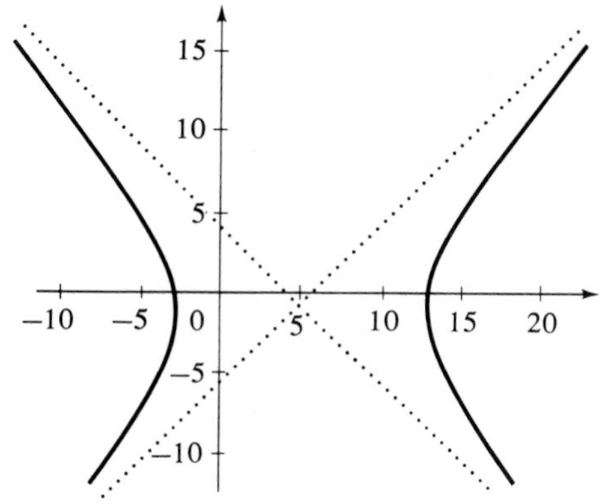

5. $C(-3/2, 1/2)$, $V(-3/2, 1/2 \pm 2)$,
$F(-3/2, 1/2 \pm 2\sqrt{5})$,
A: $y = 1/2 \pm (x + 3/2)/2$, lr $= 16$.

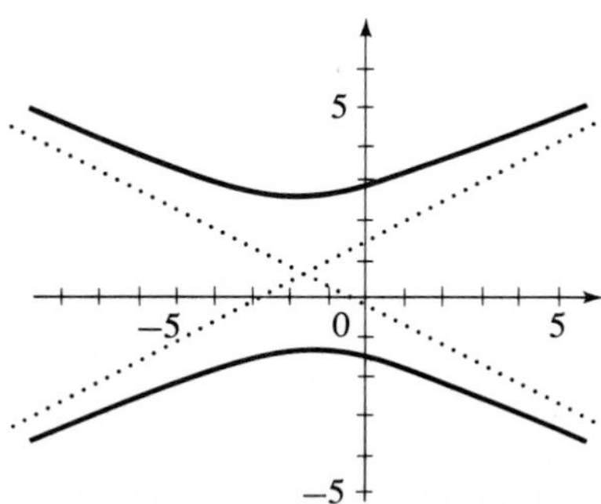

7. $y = -1 \pm 3(x - 2)/2$.

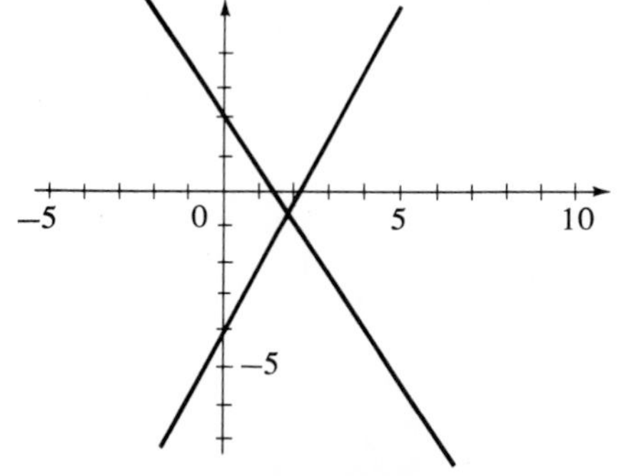

9. $C(1/3, -2/3)$, $V(1/3 \pm 2, -2/3)$, $F(1/3 \pm 2\sqrt{2}, -2/3)$, A: $y = -2/3 \pm (x - 1/3)$, $\text{lr} = 4$.

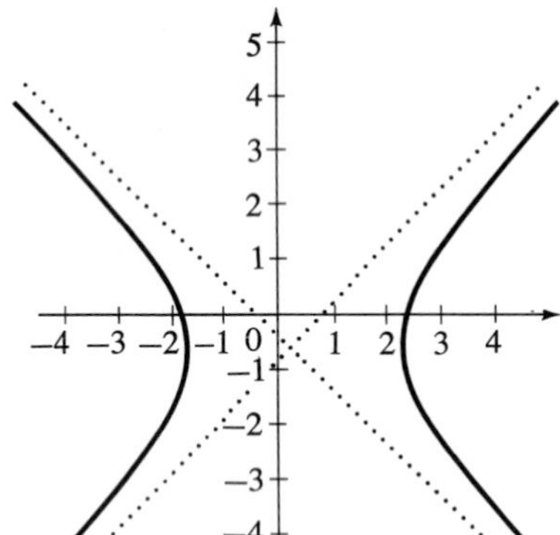

11. $C(-1/3, 1/2)$, $V(-1/3, 1/2 \pm 1)$, $F(-1/3, 1/2 \pm \sqrt{2})$, A: $y - 1/2 = \pm(x + 1/3)$, $\text{lr} = 2$.

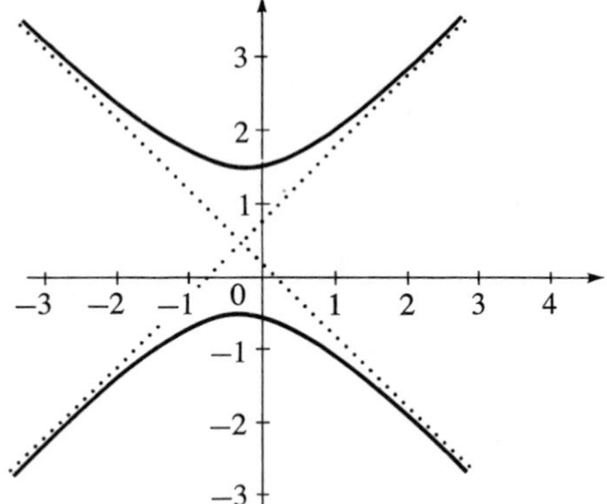

13. $3x^2 - y^2 - 12x + 2y - 1 = 0$. **15.** $9x^2 - 4y^2 - 24x - 8y - 184 = 0$.
17. $4x^2 - 21y^2 - 16x + 210y - 425 = 0$. **19.** $3x^2 - 2y^2 + 3x + 12y + 14 = 0$.
21. $21x^2 - 4y^2 + 42x - 63 = 0$. **23.** $4x^2 - y^2 - 40x + 2y + 63 = 0$.
25. $4x - 7y + 3 = 0$. **27.** $x + y + 4 = 0$, $x - y - 2 = 0$.

Section 9.8, page 199

1. $y'^2 = 4x'$;

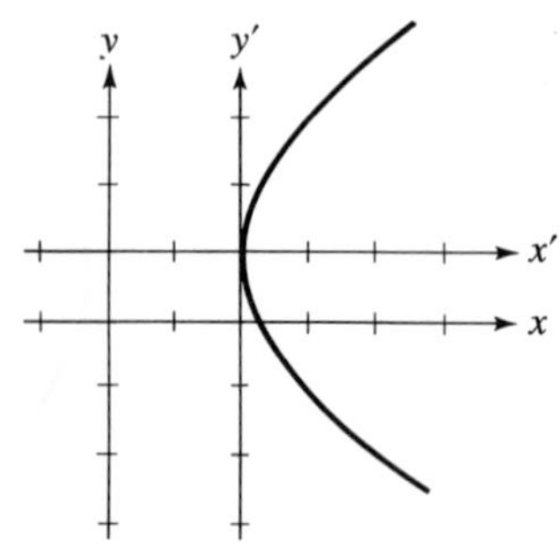

3. $4x'^2 + y'^2 = 16$.

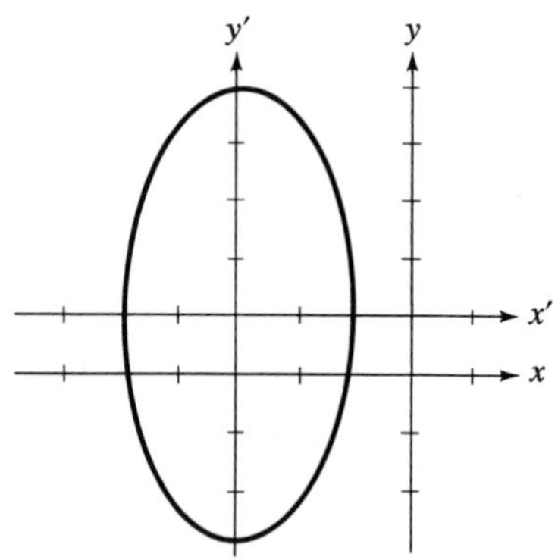

5. $9x'^2 - 4y'^2 = 36$.

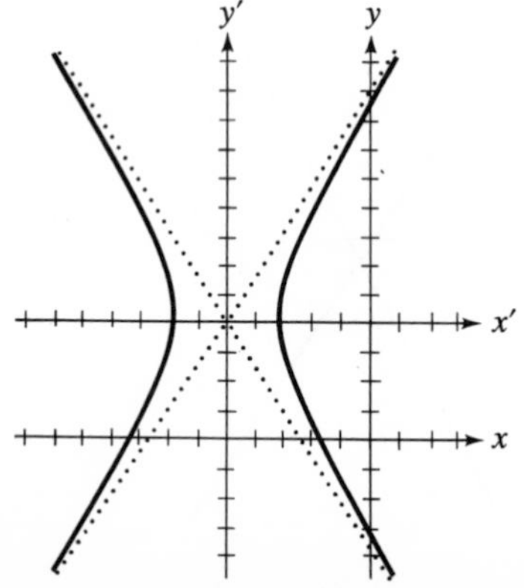

7. $9x'^2 + 4y'^2 = 0$.

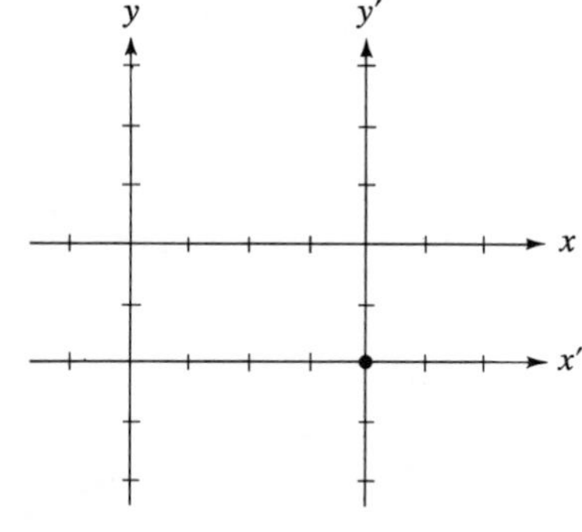

9. $x'^2 = y'$.

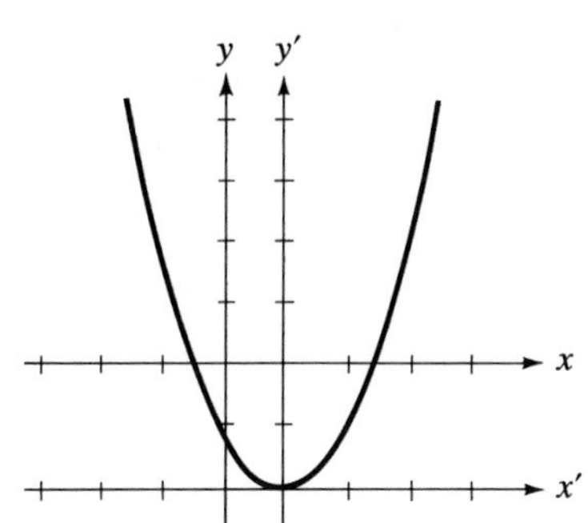

11. $x'^2 - 2x'y' + 4y'^2 - 5 = 0$.
13. $x'^2 + 4x'y' - y'^2 + 1 = 0$.
15. $x'y' + 16 = 0$.
17. $y' = x'^3 - x'$.
19. $y' = x'^4 - 4x'^3 + 6x'^2$.
21. $y' = x'^5 - 2x'^3 + 2x'$.
23. $x'^2y' - 2x'^2 - 4 = 0$.

Section 9.9, page 201

1. $\sqrt{13}x' = 6$.

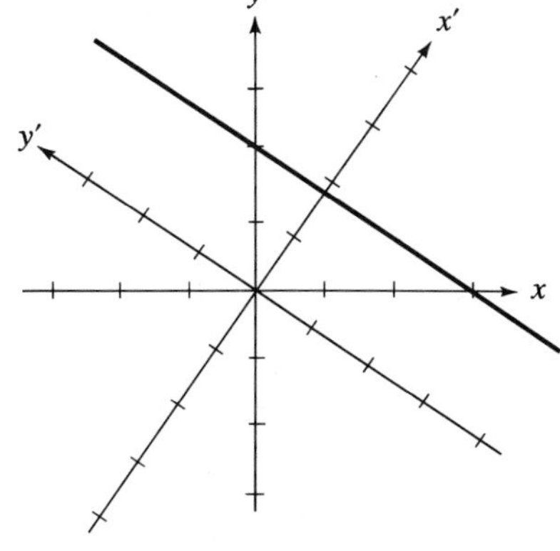

3. $x'^2 - y'^2 = 8$.

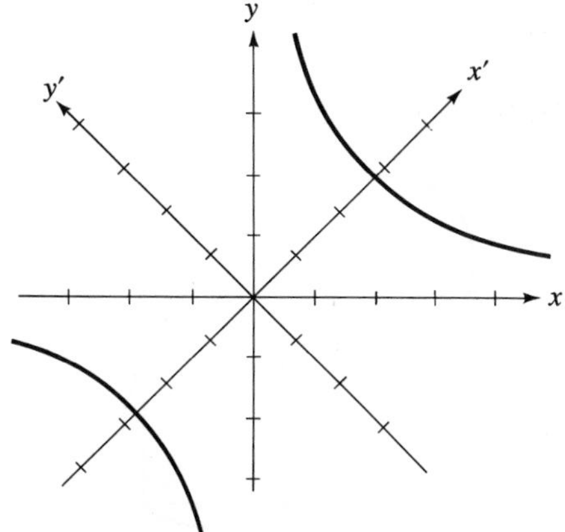

5. $\sqrt{2}y'^2 + x' = 0$.

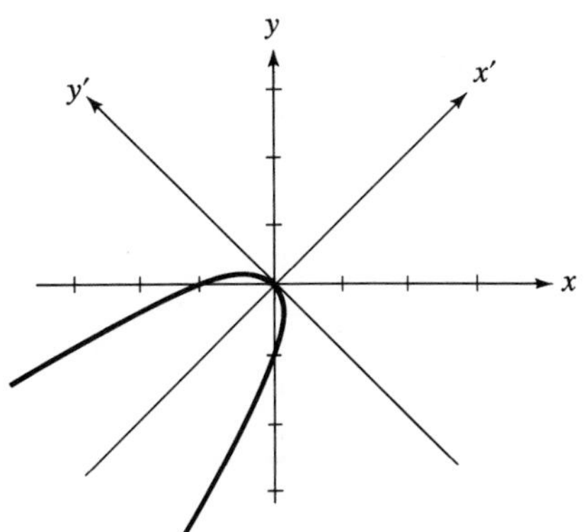

7. $x'^2 - 4y' = 0$.

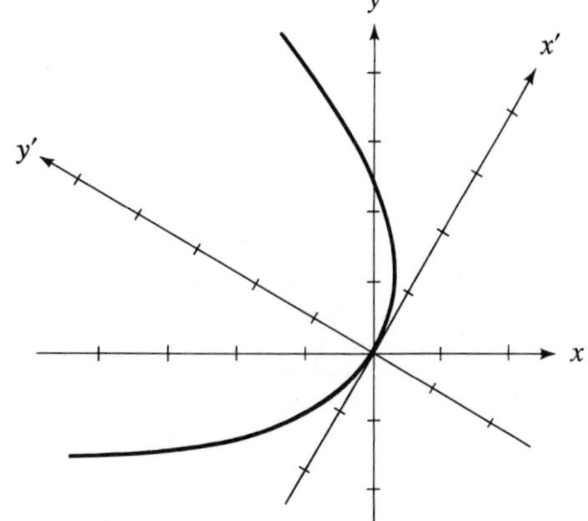

9. $17x'^2 - 9y'^2 = 8.$

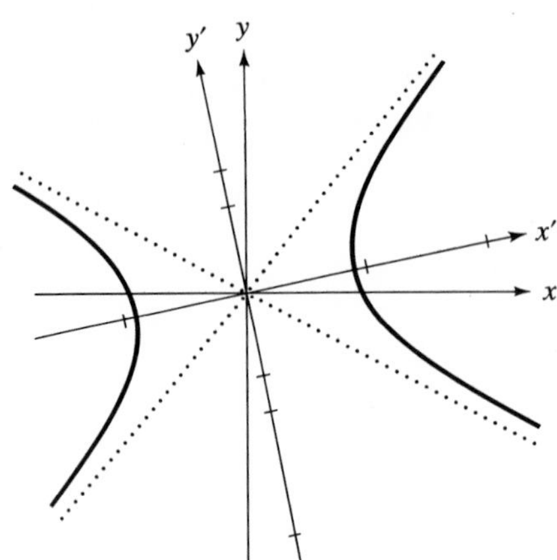

11. $17x'^2 + 7x'y' - 7y'^2 + 20 = 0.$

13. $7x'^2 - 8x'y' + y'^2 - 10 = 0.$

15. $3\sqrt{3}x'^2 - (6 - 8\sqrt{3})x'y' - (8 + 3\sqrt{3})y'^2 - 16 = 0.$

Section 9.10, page 206

1. $3x'^2 + y'^2 - 16y' = 0.$

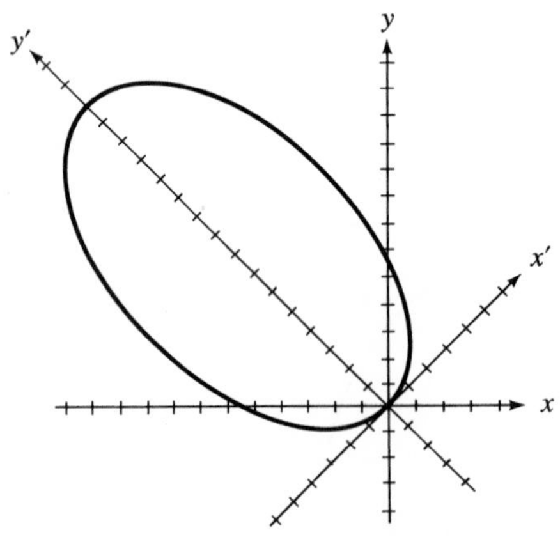

3. $4x'^2 - y'^2 - 16 = 0.$

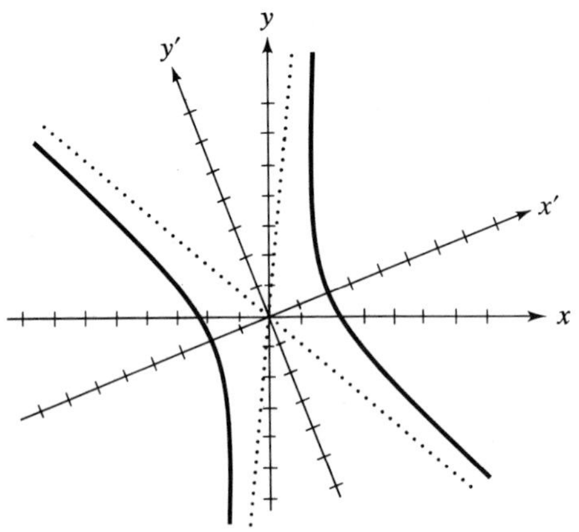

5. $25x'^2 + 4y'^2 = 100.$

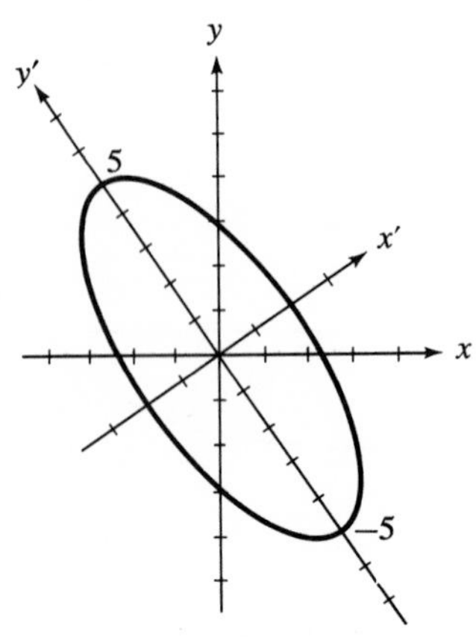

7. $4x'^2 + 9y'^2 - 36 = 0.$

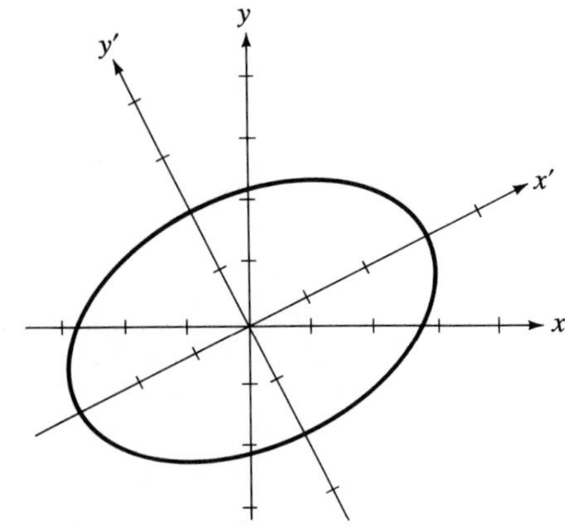

9. $x'^2 + 4x' - 5 = 0.$

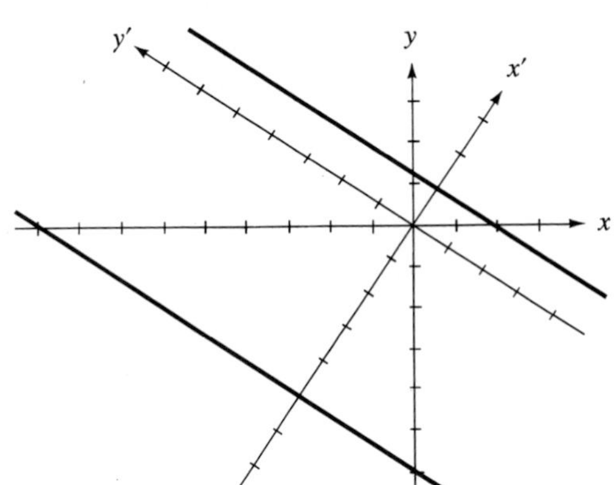

11. $y'^2 - 12x' = 0.$

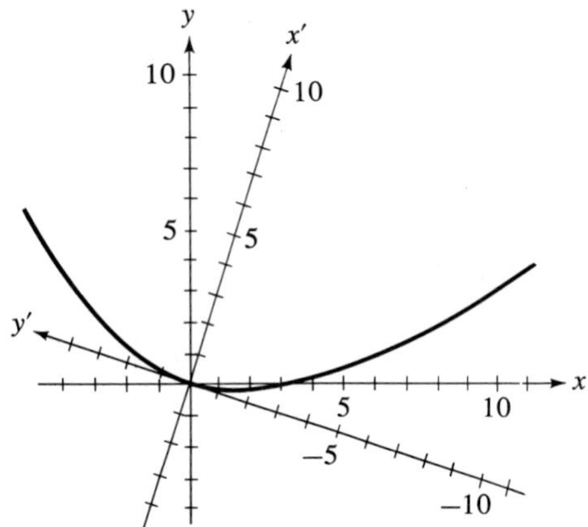

13. $x'^2 - y'^2 + 2x' + 4y' - 4 = 0.$

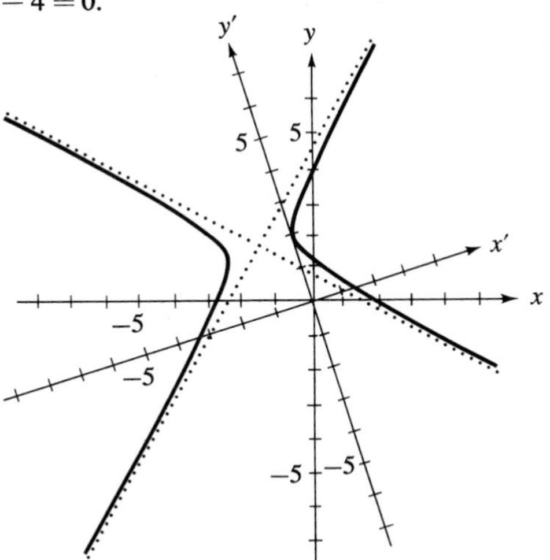

Section 9.11, page 209

1.

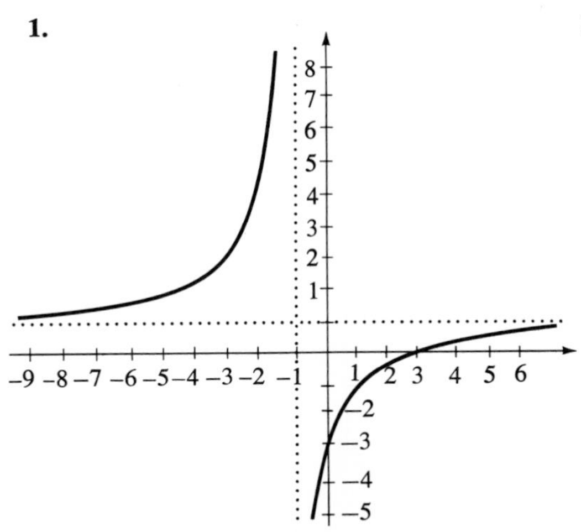

3.

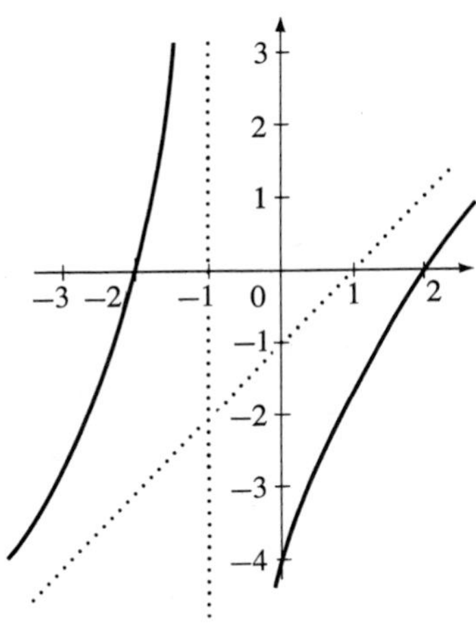

5.

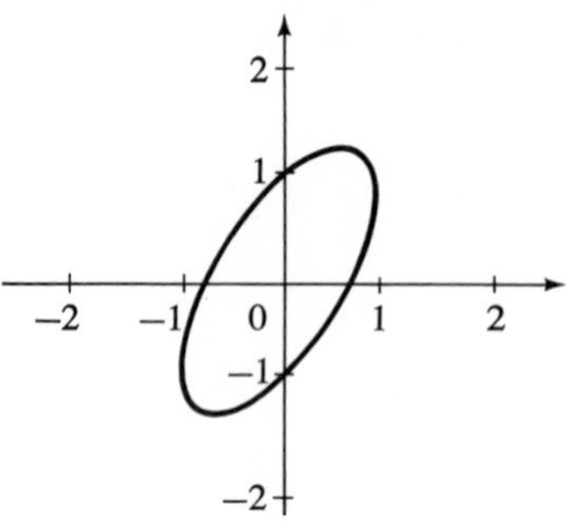

7.

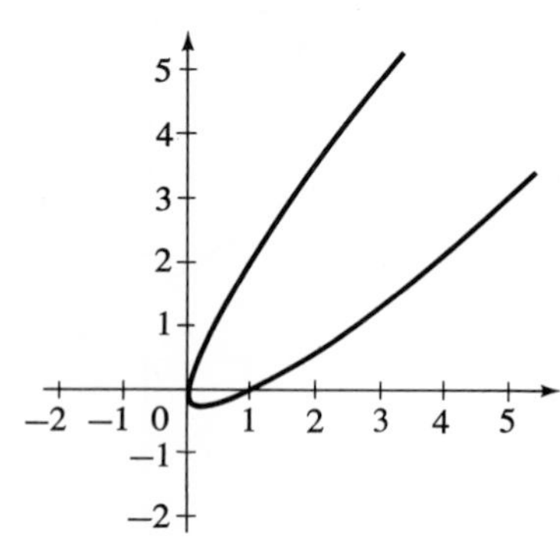

9.

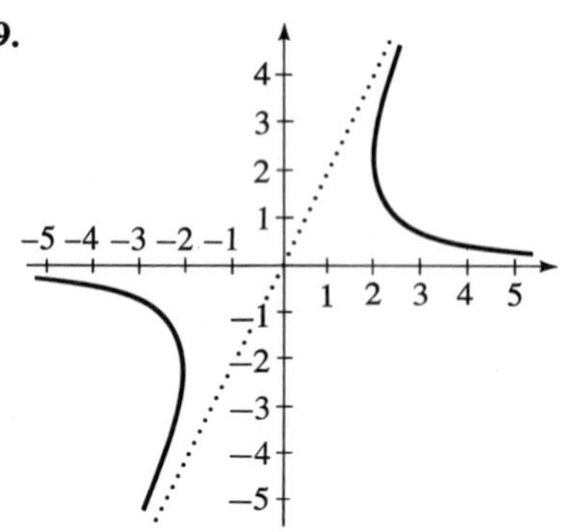

11.

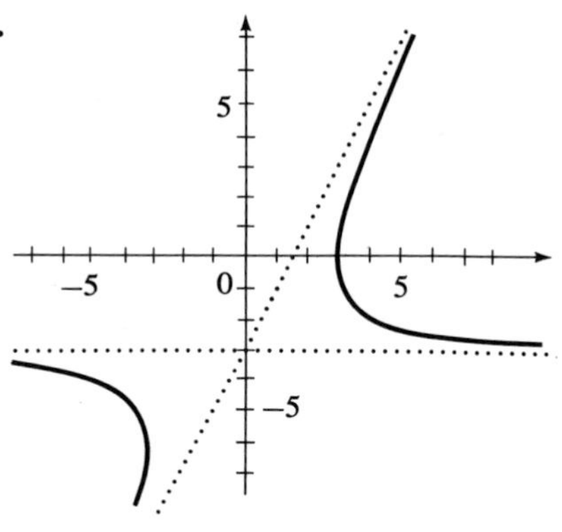

13.

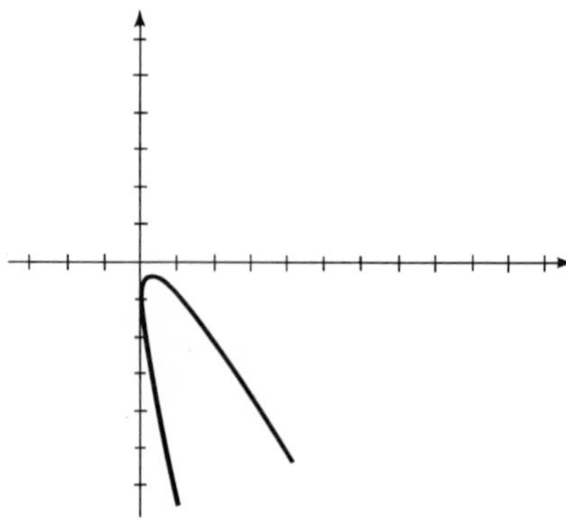

15.

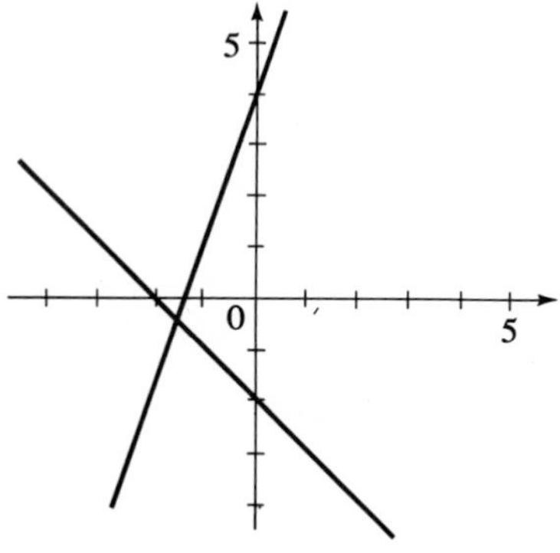

17.

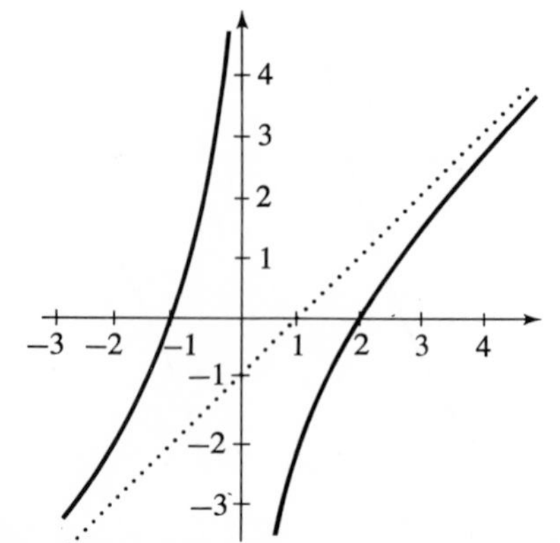

19.

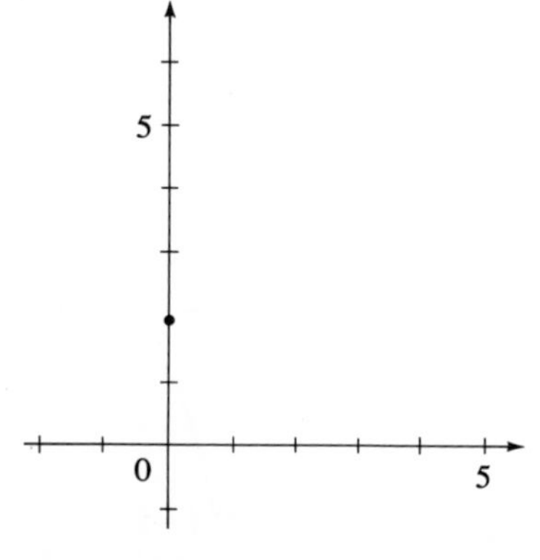

Chapter 10

Section 10.1, page 214

1. $P = A = (0, 0)$. **3.** $P = A = (2, 3)$. **5.** $P = (2, 4)$, no A. **7.** $P = A = (3, 5)$.
9. $P = A = (0, 0)$. **11.** Limit point. **13.** Not a limit point. **15.** Limit point.
17. Limit point. **19.** Limit point. **21.** Not a limit point. **23.** Limit point.
25. Limit point.

Section 10.2, page 217

1. Not satisfied. **3.** Not satisfied. **5.** Satisfied.

Section 10.3, page 220

7. False. **9.** True. **11.** True. **13.** False. **15.** True.

Section 10.4, page 224

13. 2, 0, does not exist. **15.** Does not exist, 0, 0.
17. Does not exist, 0, does not exist.

Section 10.5, page 228

15. False. **17.** True. **19.** True.

Section 10.6, page 231

1. Continuous. **3.** Discontinuous. **5.** Continuous. **7.** Continuous.
9. Continuous. **11.** Discontinuous. **13.** Continuous. **15.** Continuous.
17. Continuous. **19.** Continuous. **21.** Discontinuous, (1, 3).
23. Discontinuous, (1, 0). **25.** Discontinuous everywhere.

Section 10.7, page 235

1. -1. Theorems 10.4 and 10.3. **3.** 2, Theorems 10.4 and 10.3.
5. 4, Theorems 10.4 and 10.3. **7.** -1, Theorems 10.4 and 10.3.
9. $1/(x+1)^2$, Theorems 10.4 and 10.3.

Section 10.8, page 238

1. $f'(x) = \begin{cases} -1 & \text{if } x < 0, \\ 2x & \text{if } x > 0. \end{cases}$ **3.** $f'(x) = \begin{cases} 0 & \text{if } x < 0, \\ 1 & \text{if } x > 0. \end{cases}$ **5.** $f'(x) = 1 \quad \text{if} \quad x \neq 0.$

7. $f'(x) = \begin{cases} -1 & \text{if } x < 0, \\ 0 & \text{if } 0 < x < 1, \\ 2(x-1) & \text{if } 1 \leq x. \end{cases}$ **9.** $f'(x) = \begin{cases} 0 & \text{if } x < 0, \\ 6x & \text{if } 0 \leq x < 1, \\ 0 & \text{if } 1 < x. \end{cases}$

11. Does not exist. **13.** 0.

Chapter 11

Section 11.1, page 242

1. $\pi/4$, $-7\pi/6$, $3\pi/2$, $\pi/6$. **2.** $60°$, $180°$, $135°$, $-90°$.

3.

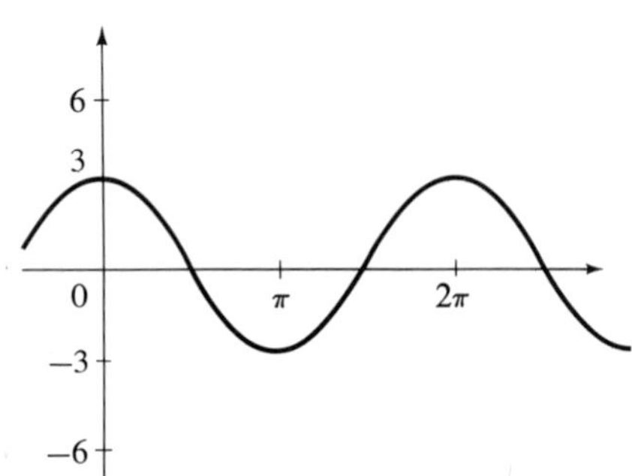

5.

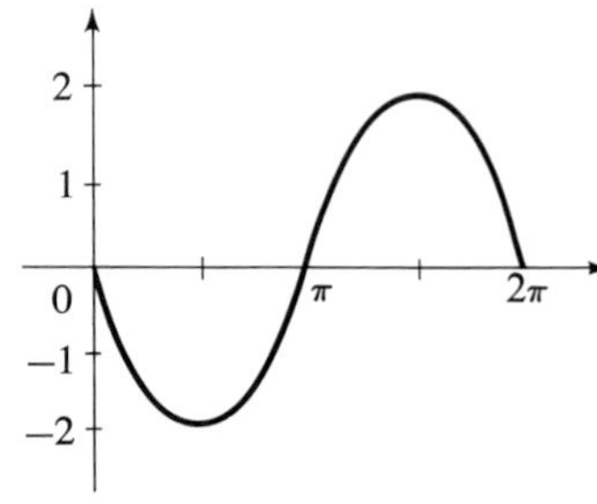

7.

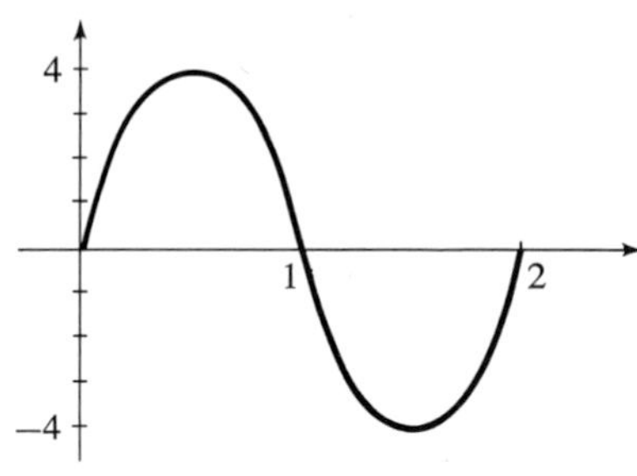

9.

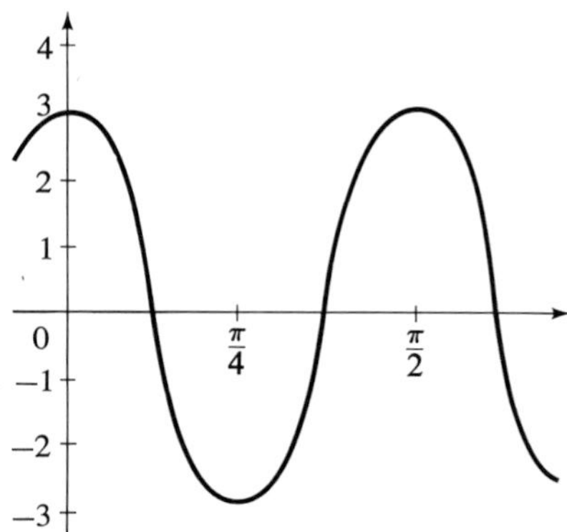

11.

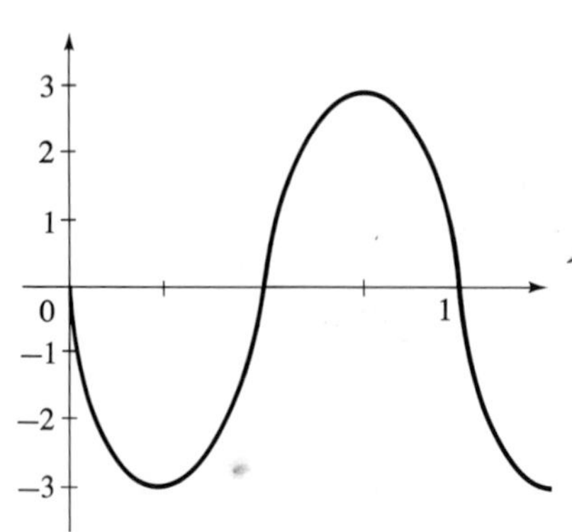

13.

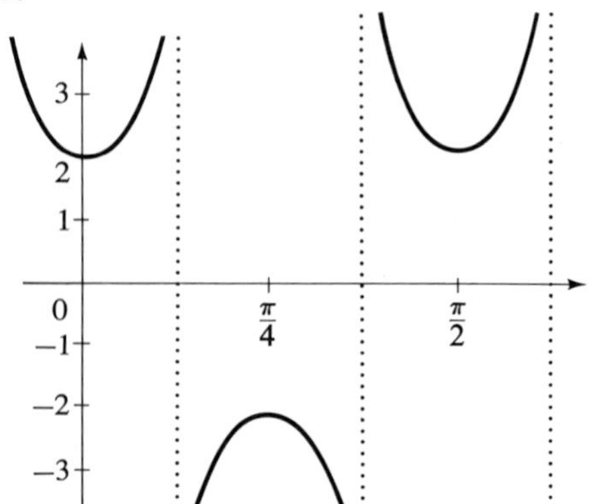

15.

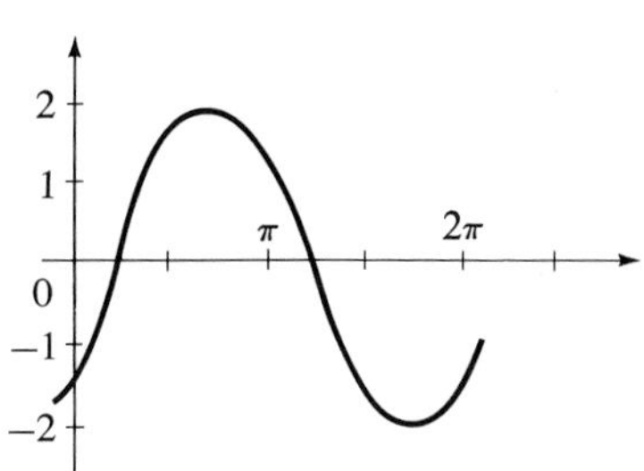

17.

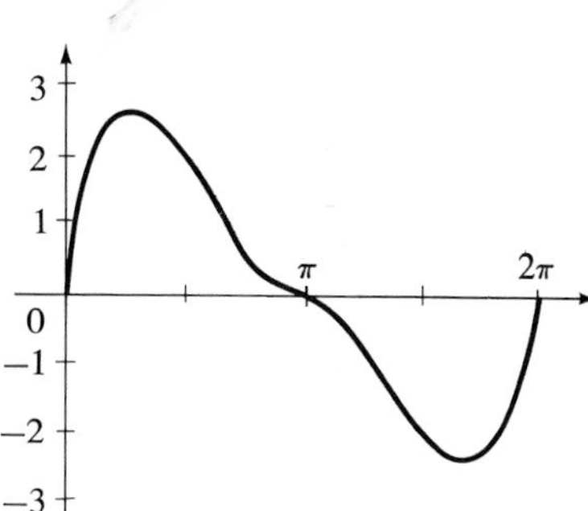

19.

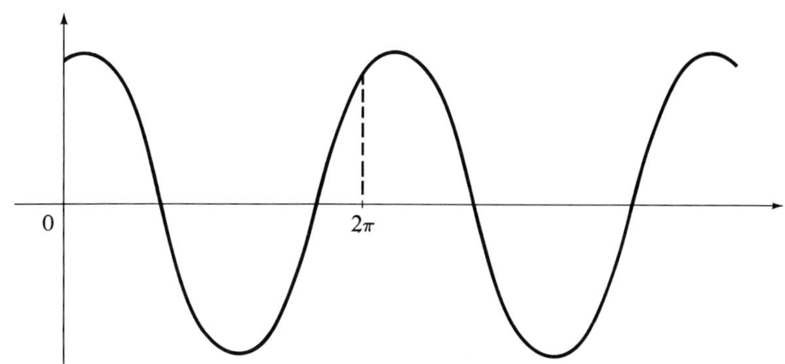

21.

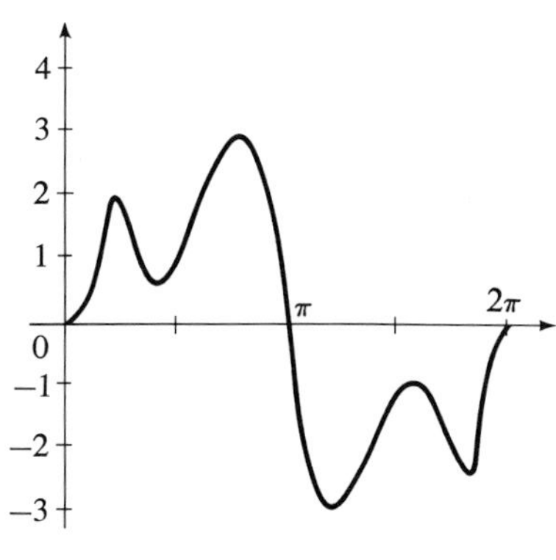

23.

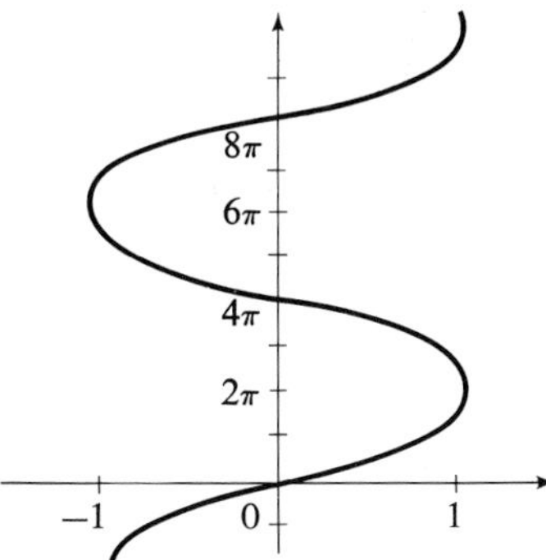

25.

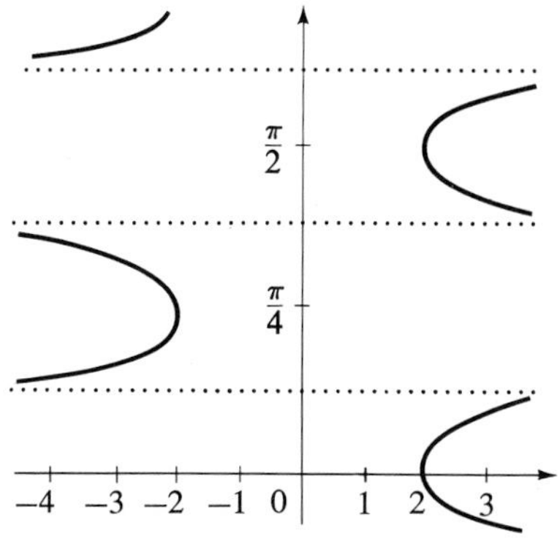

27.

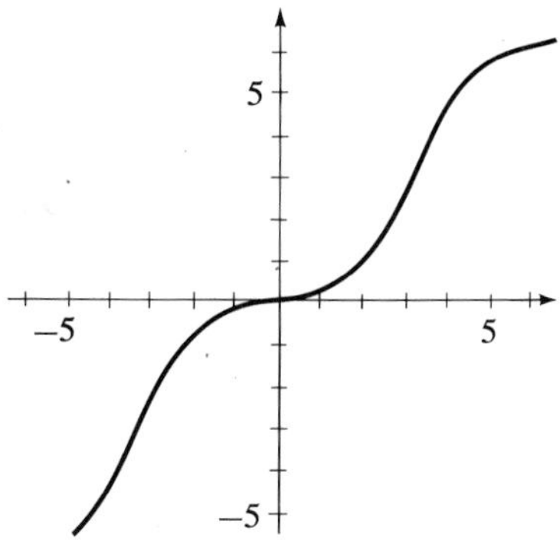

29.

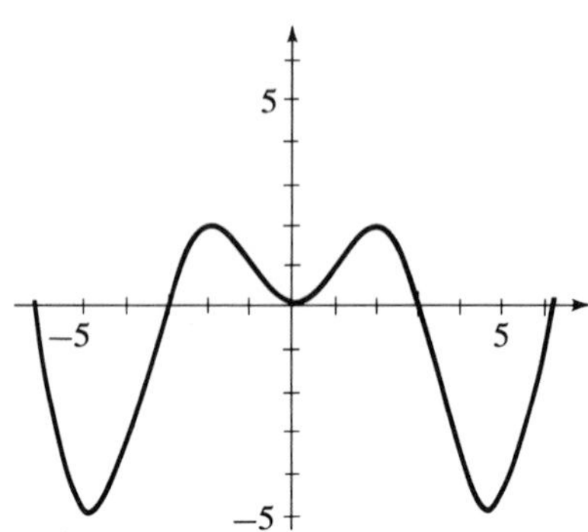

31.

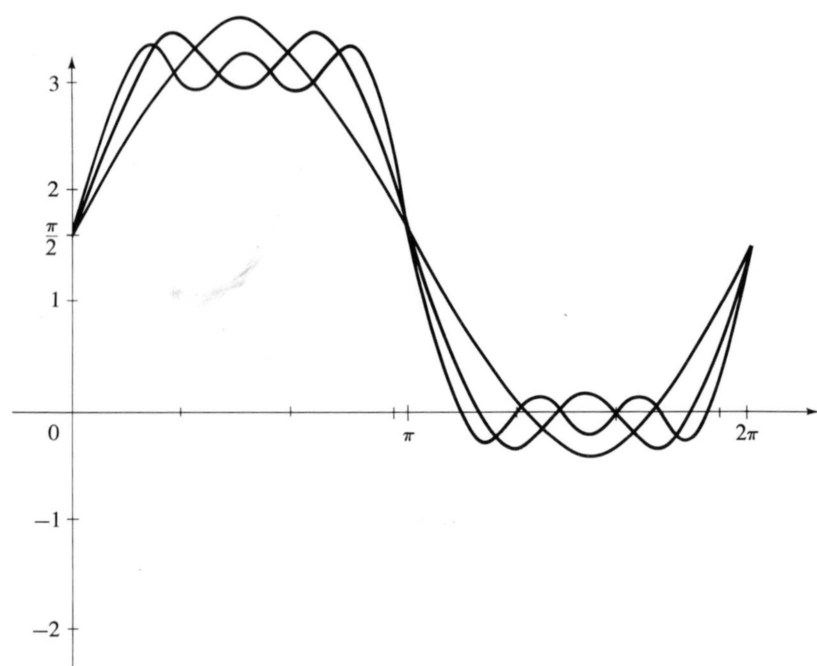

Section 11.2, page 248

1. $2 \cos 2x$. **3.** $3 \sec^2 3x$. **5.** $6 \sin 3x \cos 3x$. **7.** $-6\sqrt{\cot 4x} \csc^2 4x$.
9. $\sec^3 x + \sec x \tan^2 x$. **11.** $2(\cos^2 x - \sin^2 x)$. **13.** 0.
15. $-2 \sin x/(1 - \cos x)^2$. **17.** $(2x \sec^2 2x - \tan 2x)/2x^2$. **19.** $1 + \sec^2 x$.
21. $-\sin x \cos \cos x$. **23.** $(1 - 2\sqrt{2})/\sqrt{2}$. **25.** No value. **27.** -3.
29. $-\cos x/\sin y$. **31.** $-\csc^2(x + y)$.
33. $\sec^2(x - y) + \tan^2(x - y)$. **35.** $3x - 6y + (3\sqrt{3} - \pi) = 0$.

Section 11.3, page 250

1. $-\cos 2\theta/2 + C$. **3.** $-\csc 3x/3 + C$. **5.** $\sec x^3/3 + C$. **7.** $x + \sin^2 x + C$.
9. $-\sin 2x/2 + C$. **11.** $\sin^4 2\theta/8 + C$. **13.** $-\cos^3 x/3 + C$.
15. $2 \tan x + 2 \sec x - x + C$. **17.** $x + 2 \csc x - \cot^3 x/3 + C$.
19. $-2 \cot^{3/2} x/3 + C$. **21.** $1/3$. **23.** $2 - \pi/2$. **25.** 2π.

Section 11.4, page 255

1. $2/\sqrt{1-4x^2}$. **3.** $-1/x\sqrt{9x^2-1}$. **5.** $2/(1+4x^2)$. **7.** $(1-x)/\sqrt{1-x^2}$.
9. $x^2/(1+x^2)$. **11.** $x/(1+x^2)+\text{Arctan}\,x$. **13.** $1/2\sqrt{x-x^2}$.
15. $1/x\sqrt{1-x^2}-\text{Arcsin}\,x/x^2$. **17.** $2x^2/\sqrt{1-x^2}$. **19.** $1/(1-x^2)^{3/2}$.
21. $-1/|x|\sqrt{x^2-1}$. **23.** $x^2/(1-x^2)^{3/2}$. **25.** $2/\sqrt{3}$. **27.** $(\sqrt{3}+2\pi)/3$.
29. $4\sqrt{3}/3-4\pi/9$.

Section 11.5, page 259

1. $\sqrt{1-x^2}+C$. **3.** $(1/2)\text{Arctan}\,x^2+C$. **5.** $(1/3)\text{Arcsin}\,3x+C$.
7. $(1/2)\text{Arctan}\,2x+C$. **9.** $(1/2)\text{Arcsin}(2x+1)+C$. **11.** $\text{Arctan}(x-1)+C$.
13. $\text{Arcsec}(x-2)+C$. **15.** $(1/2)\text{Arctan}(2x+3)+C$. **17.** $\text{Arctan}\sin x+C$.
19. $-\sqrt{1-\tan^2 x}+C$. **21.** $(1/2)\text{Arctan}^2\,x+C$. **23.** $\pi/6$. **25.** $\pi/4$.
27. $\pi/2$. **31.** $\text{Arcsin}(u/a)+C$.

Chapter 12

Section 12.1, page 264

1.

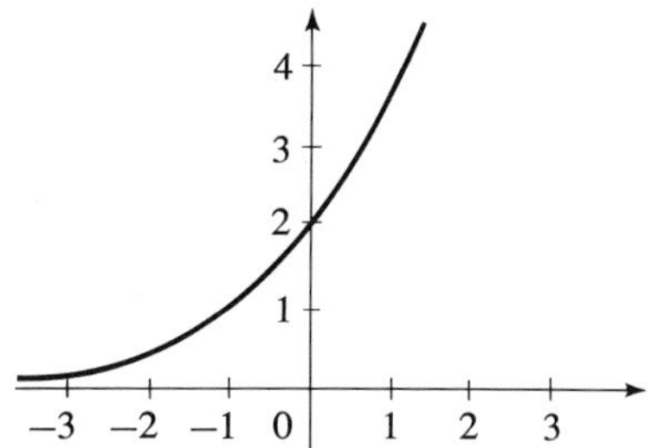

3.

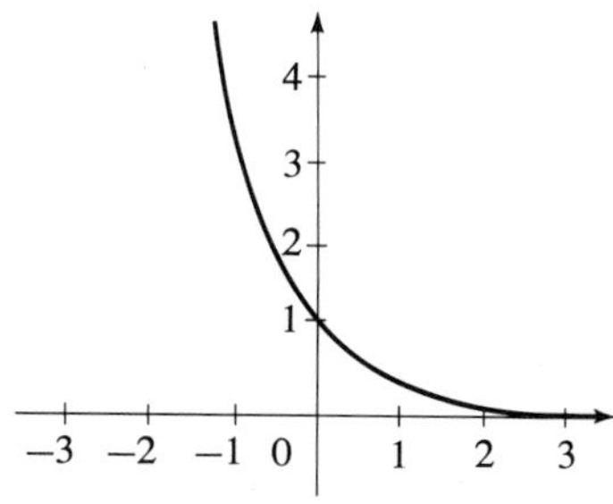

5.

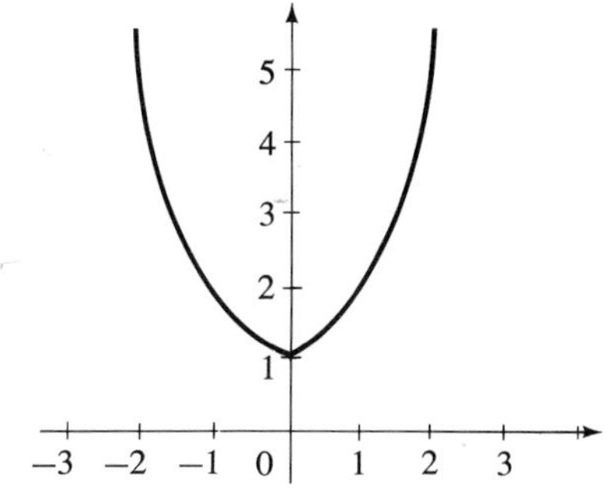

7.

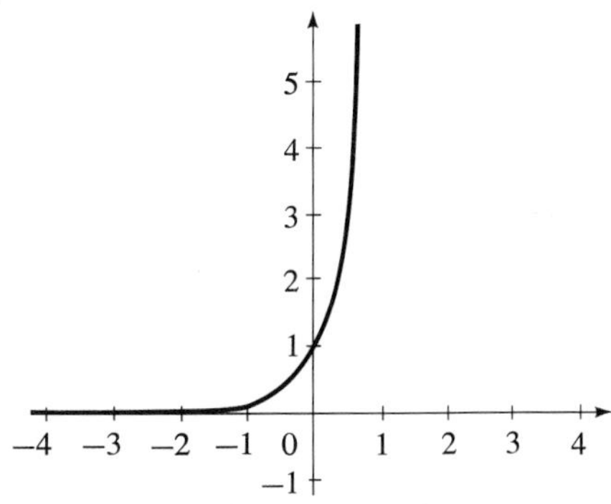

9.

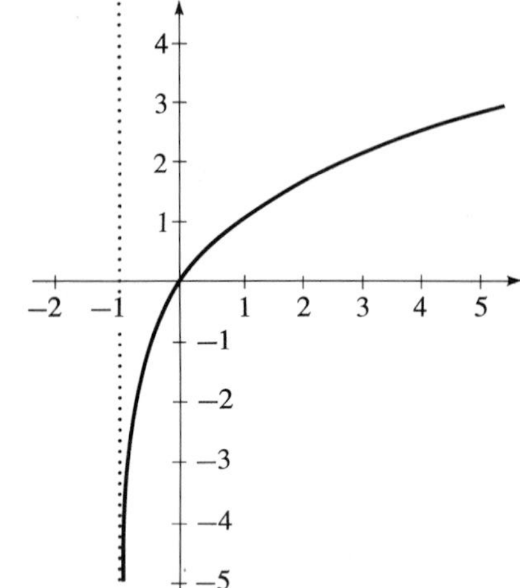

11.

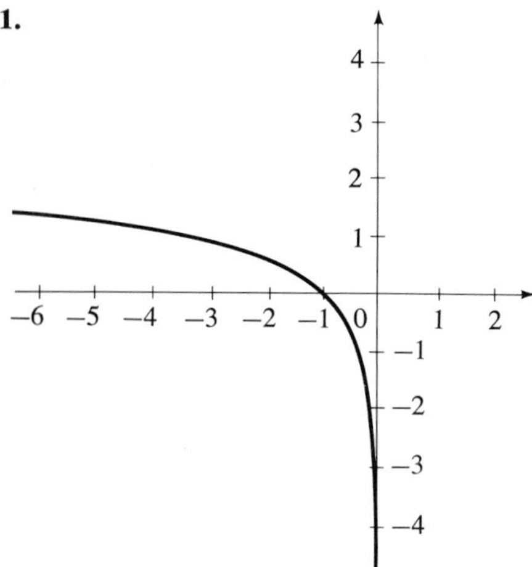

13.

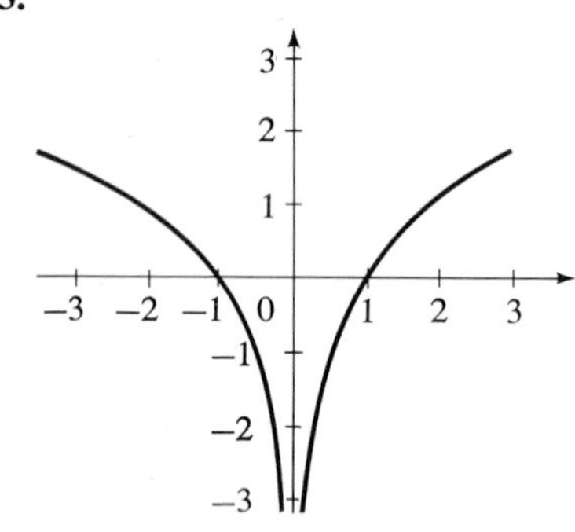

15.

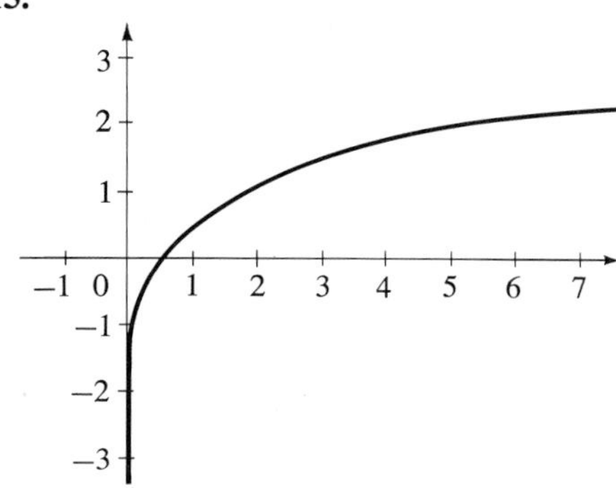

17. $\ln y$. **19.** $1 + 7^y$. **21.** y. **23.** $\log_4 y - 1$. **25.** $9/4$. **27.** $4\sqrt{5}/9$.
29. 27. **31.** $2 \log x + \log(x + 1)$. **33.** $2 \log_5 x + \log_5(x + 3) - \log_5(x - 1)$.
35. $(3/2)\ln(x + 1) + (1/2)\ln(x - 2) - (1/3)\ln(x + 3)$.

Section 12.2, page 268

1. $(\log e)/x$. **3.** $2x/(x^2 + 1)$. **5.** $-1/x$. **7.** $2/(1 - 4x^2)$.
9. $(4 \log_5 e)/(1 - 9x^2)$. **11.** $x + 2x \ln x$. **13.** $(1 - \ln x)/x^2$. **15.** $\cot x$,
17. $(\cos \ln x)/x$. **19.** $1/\sqrt{x^2 - 1}$. **21.** $1/(x \ln x)$. **23.** $(1 + \ln x)/(x \ln x)$.
25. $y \cos x$. **27.** $[y \cos(x + y)]/[1 - y \cos(x + y)]$.
29. $(1 - 2x^2 - 2xy)/(2xy + 2y^2 - 1)$. **31.** $\frac{y}{2}\left(\frac{1}{x} + \frac{1}{x-1} - \frac{1}{x+3}\right)$.
33. $\frac{y}{3}\left(\frac{2}{x} + \frac{4}{x+1} - \frac{1}{x-5}\right)$. **35.** $1/2$. **37.** 1. **39.** -1.

Section 12.3, page 271

1. $3^x \ln 3$. **3.** $(2^{\sqrt{x}} \ln 2)/2\sqrt{x}$. **5.** $2e^{2x+2}$. **7.** $5^{2x^2+3}4x \ln 5$. **9.** $1 + e^x$.
11. $2xe^{x^2}(x^2 + 1)$. **13.** $3^x[3x^2 + (x^3 - 1)\ln 3]$. **15.** $e^x(1 + x \ln x)/x$.
17. $(1 + x)e^x$. **19.** $e^{\tan x} \sec^2 x$. **21.** $x^{x^2+1}(1 + 2 \ln x)$.
23. $(\sin x)^x(x \cot x + \ln \sin x)$. **25.** ye^x. **27.** -1. **29.** $1/(e^y x \ln x)$.
31. e^2. **33.** 0. **35.** $4 \ln 2$. **37.** $u^v\left(\frac{vu'}{u} + v' \ln u\right)$.

Section 12.4, page 274

1. $(1/2)\ln|2x+1|+C.$ **3.** $x^2/2+3x+5\ln|x-1|+C.$ **5.** $-\ln|\cos x|+C.$
7. $\ln(e^x+1)+C.$ **9.** $2\sqrt{x^2+x}+C.$ **11.** $-e^{-x}+C.$ **13.** $e^{\tan x}+C.$
15. $e^x+x-e^{-x}+C.$ **17.** $x^2/2+x+2\ln|x+1|+C.$ **19.** $10^x\log e+C.$
21. $e^x+e^{-x}+C.$ **23.** $x^3-5x^2/2+x-4\ln|x|+C.$ **25.** $\ln 2.$
27. $11/2-\ln 2.$ **29.** $\ln 2.$

Section 12.5, page 278

11. $\cosh x=5/3$, $\tanh x=4/5$, $\coth x=5/4$, $\operatorname{sech} x=3/5$, $\operatorname{csch} x=3/4.$
13. $\sinh x=-5/12$, $\cosh x=13/12$, $\coth x=-13/5$, $\operatorname{sech} x=12/13$, $\operatorname{csch} x=-12/5.$
15. $\cosh x=13/12$, $\tanh x=-5/13$, $\coth x=-13/5$, $\operatorname{sech} x=12/13$, $\operatorname{csch} x=-12/5.$
21. $2x\cosh x^2.$ **23.** $2\operatorname{sech}^2(2x-3).$ **25.** $(-\operatorname{sech}\sqrt{x}\tanh\sqrt{x})/2\sqrt{x}.$
27. $-4\operatorname{csch}^2 x\cot x.$ **29.** $4\sinh x\cosh x.$ **31.** $\sinh x e^{\cosh x}.$
33. $-\sin\sinh x\cosh x.$

Section 12.6, page 282

1. 1.819. **3.** 0.881. **5.** 0.347. **7.** $3/\sqrt{9x^2+6x}.$ **9.** $1/2\sqrt{x+x^2}.$
11. $1/(x-x^3)-(\coth^{-1}x)/x^2.$ **13.** $e^x/(1-e^{2x}).$ **15.** $(1+x)/\sqrt{1+x^2}.$
17. $(2\sinh^{-1}x)/\sqrt{1+x^2}.$ **19.** $2(1+\tanh^{-1}x)/(1-x^2).$

Section 12.7, page 286

1. $(1/2)\sinh(2x+1)+C.$ **3.** $\operatorname{sech}(1/x)+C.$ **5.** $(\sinh^3 x)/3+C.$
7. $-(\operatorname{csch}^4 x)/4+C.$ **9.** $-\tanh^{-1}x+C$ if $|x|<1$, $-\coth^{-1}x+C$ if $|x|>1.$
11. $\sinh^{-1}(x/2)+C.$
13. $-(1/4)\operatorname{csch}^{-1}(x/4)+C$ if $x>0$, $(1/4)\operatorname{csch}^{-1}(x/4)+C$ if $x<0.$
15. $\cosh^{-1}(x+1)+C.$ **17.** $(1/2)\sinh^{-1}(2x+3)+C.$ **19.** $\sinh^{-1}e^x+C.$
21. $\cosh 4-1.$ **23.** $(1/2)\sinh^{-1}1.$ **25.** $\coth^{-1}4-\coth^{-1}2.$
27. $\operatorname{csch}^{-1}(-1)-\operatorname{csch}^{-1}(-2).$ **29.** $\cosh^{-1}e.$

Section 12.8, page 288

1. $x-y=0.$
3. $y-\pi=0.$
5. $2x-y-2=0.$
7. $4\sqrt{2}x-4y+(4-\pi)=0.$
9. $x-y=0.$

11. $(1/e,-1/e)$ min.

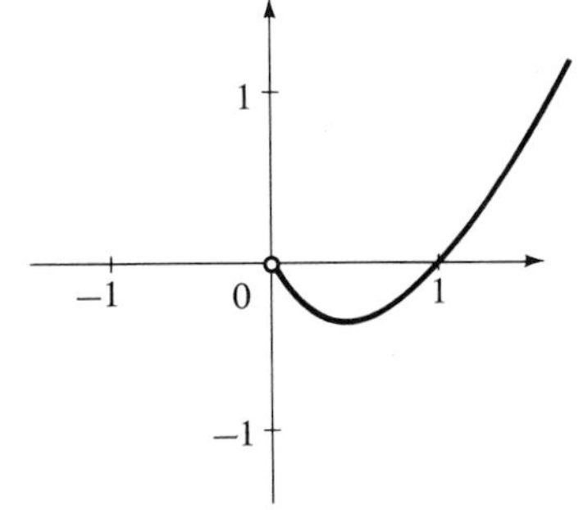

13. $[(1/2)\text{Arctan } 2+n\pi, 2e^{-x}/\sqrt{5}]$ max,
$[(1/2)\text{Arctan } 2+(\pi/2)+n\pi,$
$-2e^{-x}/\sqrt{5}]$ min.

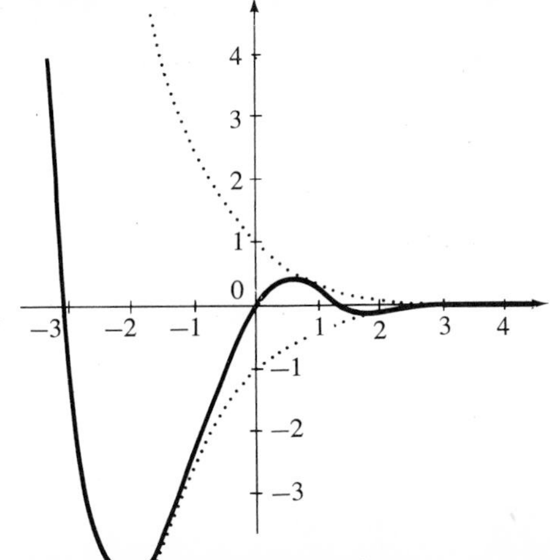

15. $(\ln n\pi, 1)$ max if n even,
$(\ln n\pi, -1)$ min if n odd.

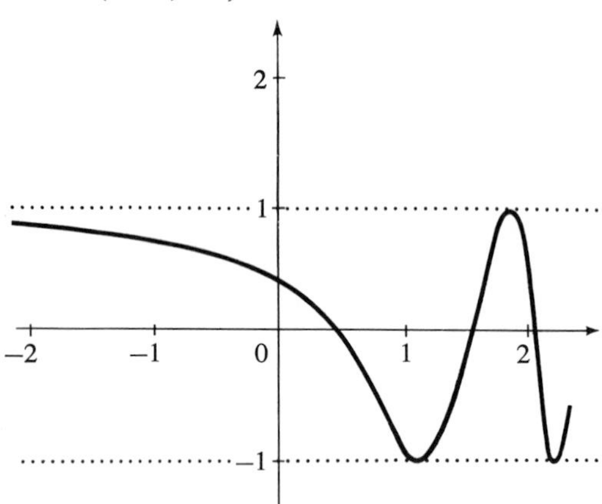

17. $[\text{Arctan}(a/b) + 2\pi n, \sqrt{a^2 + b^2}]$ max,
$[\text{Arctan}(a/b) + (2n + 1)\pi, -\sqrt{a^2 + b^2}]$ min.

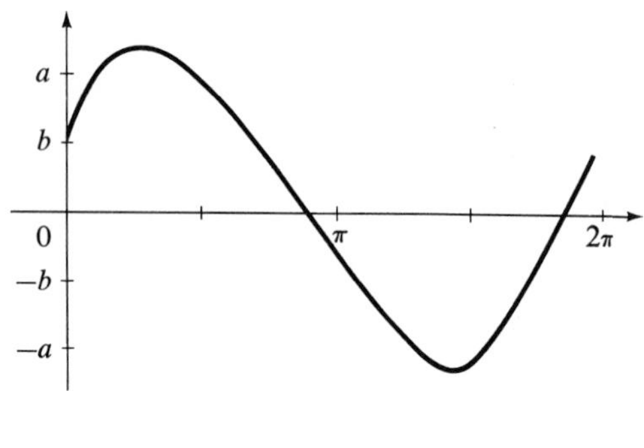

19. $(0, 0)$ min, $(-2, 4/e^2)$ max.

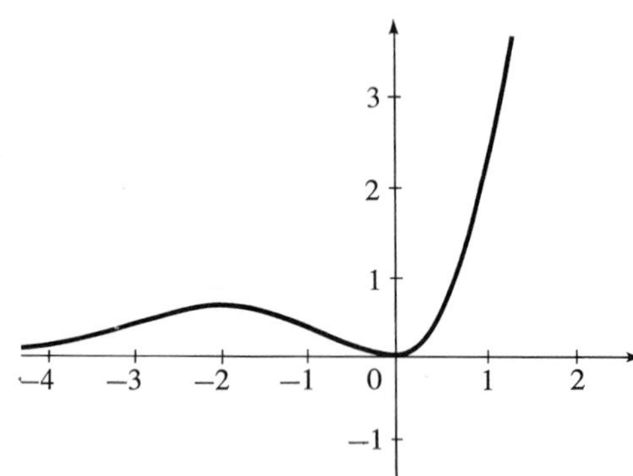

21. $1 - 1/e$.
23. $2 \ln 2 - 1$.
25. $\sinh 1$.
27. $1 - 1/e^k$, 1.
29. 48π mi/min.
31. 625/16 ft.
33. Eye level.

Chapter 13

Section 13.1, page 294

1. $y^2 - x + 2y - 2 = 0$.

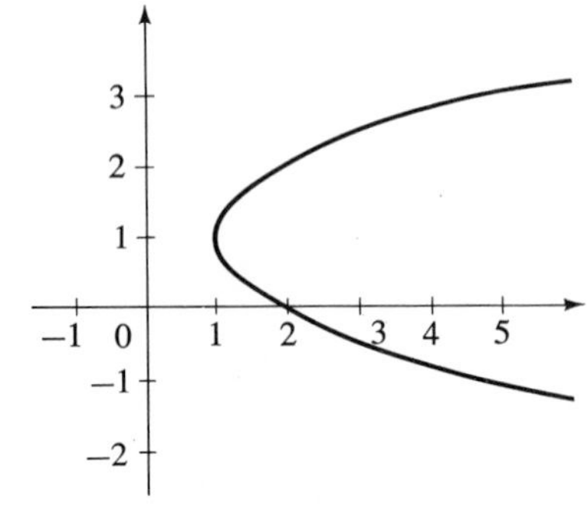

3. $y = x^2 - 1$.

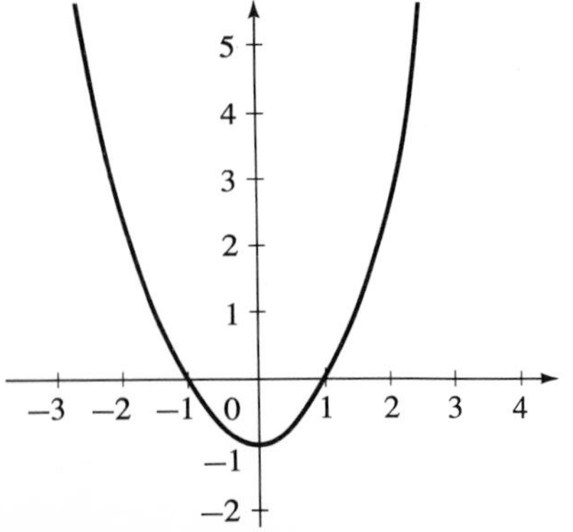

5. $x^2 - 2xy + y^2 - 2x - 2y = 0$.

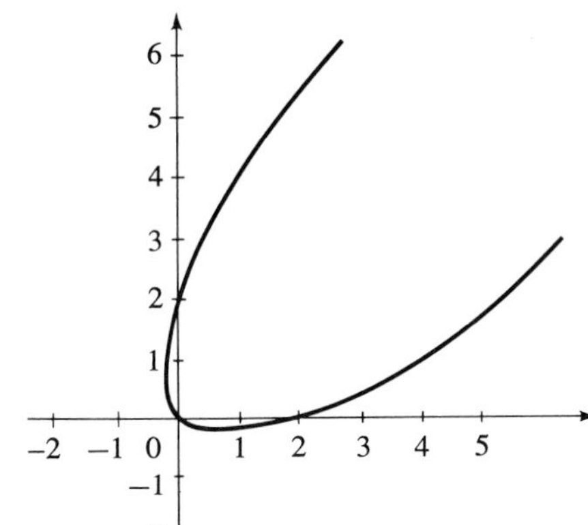

7. $y^3 = x^2$.

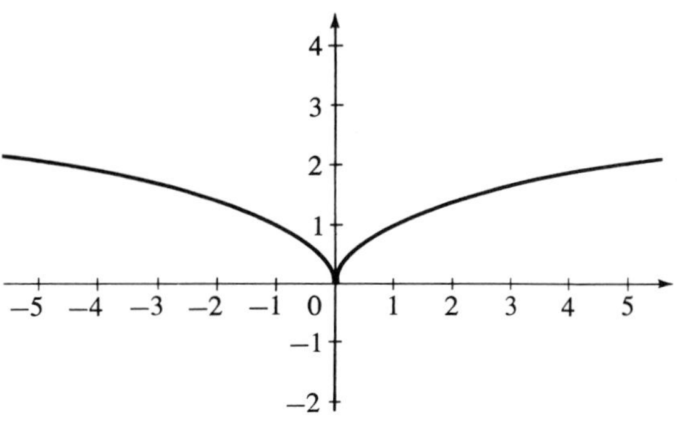

9. $x^2/a^2 + y^2/b^2 = 1$.

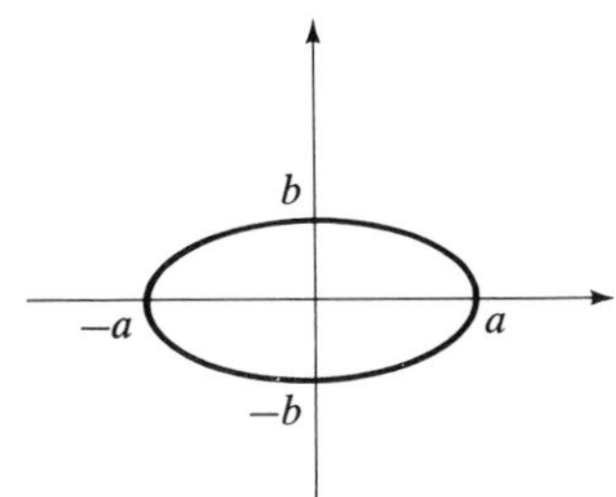

11. $(x - 2)^2 + (y + 1)^2 = 1$.

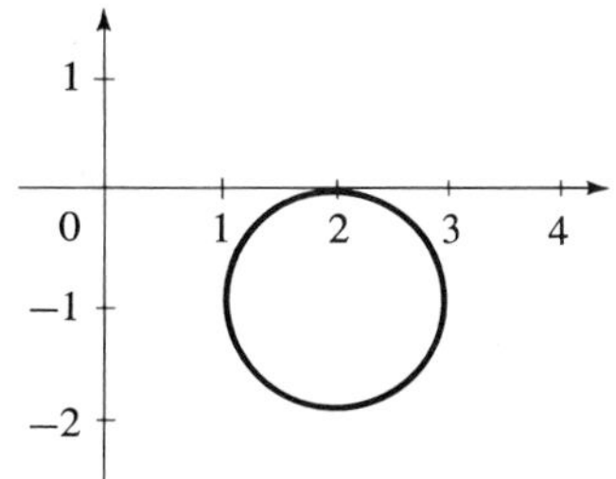

13. $(x - 3)^2 - (y - 2)^2 = 1$.

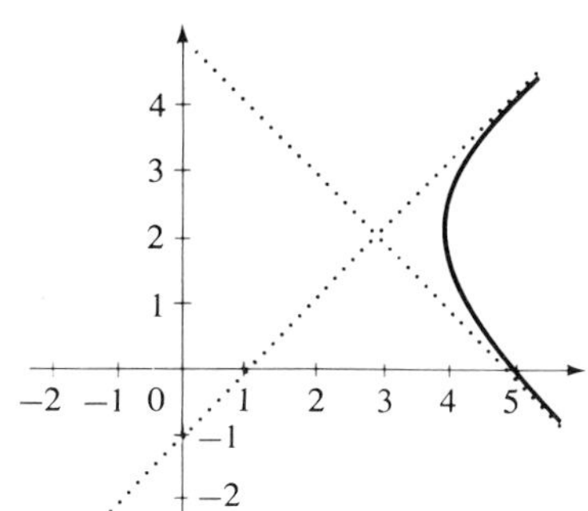

15.

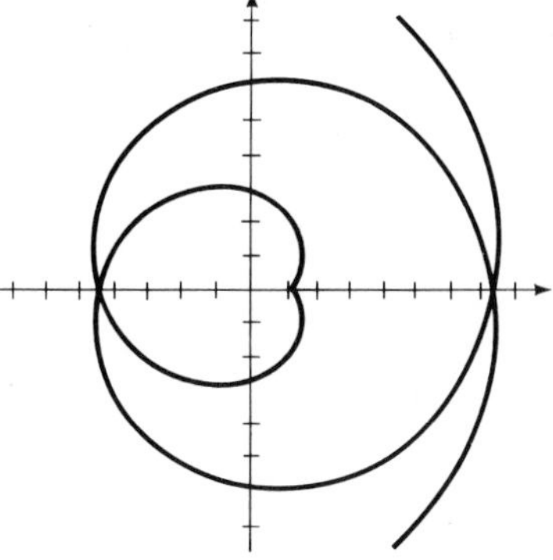

17.

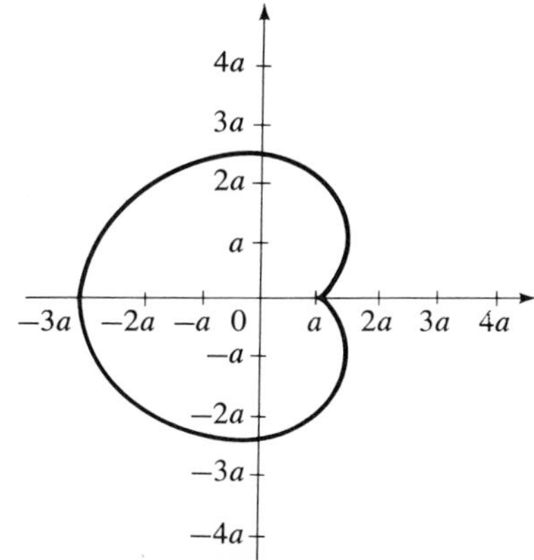

19.

(a)

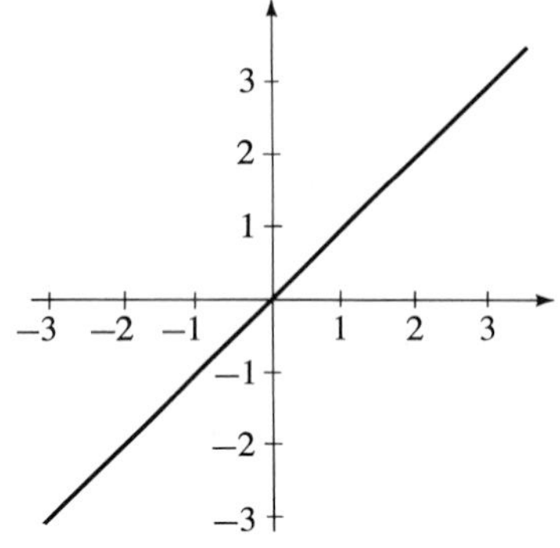

(b)

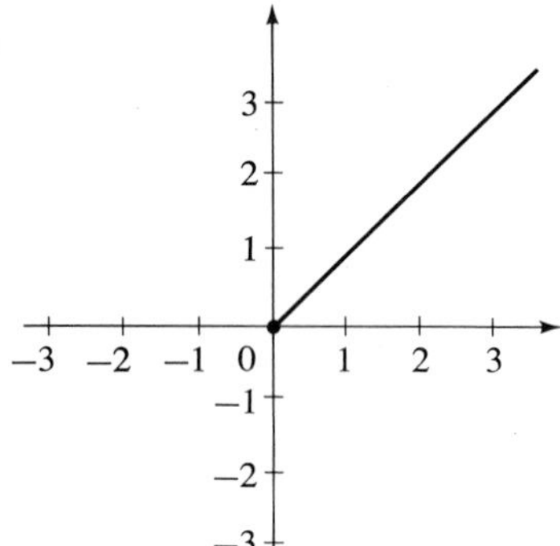

(c)

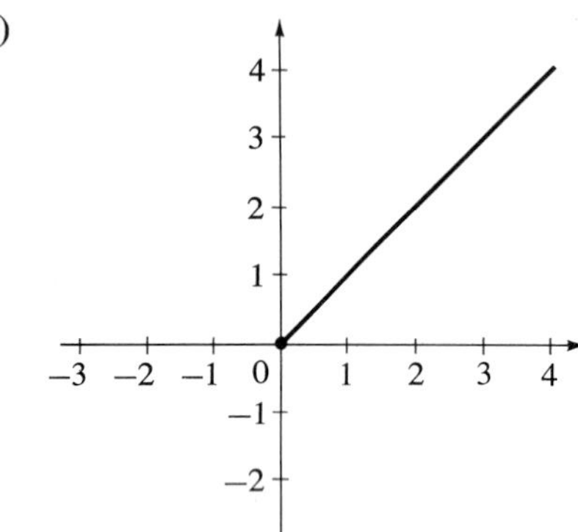

(d)

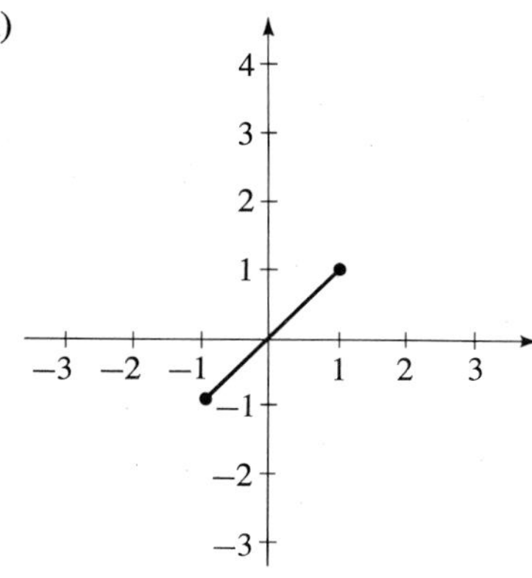

(e)

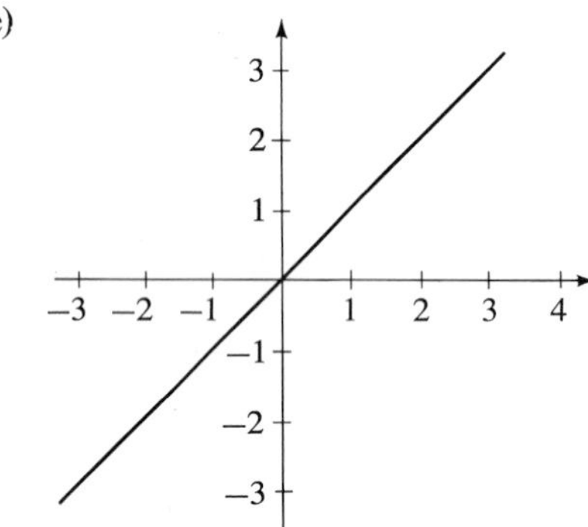

(f)

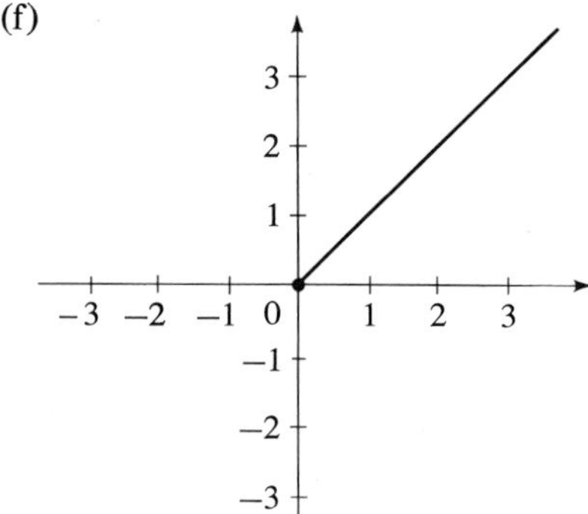

21. $x = v_0 t/\sqrt{2}$, $y = -16t^2 + v_0 t/\sqrt{2} + 10$. **23.** $45°$.
25. $x = a\theta - b \sin \theta$, $y = a - b \cos \theta$.
27. $x = 3a \cos \theta + a \cos 3\theta$, $y = 3a \sin \theta - a \sin 3\theta$.

Section 13.2, page 296

1. $1/(2t + 1)$, $-2/(2t + 1)^3$. **3.** $1/(2t + 1)$, $-2/(2t + 7)^3$.
5. $(2t - 1)/(2t + 1)$, $4/(2t + 1)^3$. **7.** $-\cot t$, $-\csc^3 t$. **9.** $\coth t$, $-\operatorname{csch}^3 t$.
11. 6, 2. **13.** $-2/9$, $-2/729$. **15.** 0, 2. **17.** $3x - y - 1 = 0$.
19. $2x + 3y - 6\sqrt{2} = 0$. **21.** (3, 0), (5, −4). **23.** (4, 0), (0, 2), (−4, 0), (0, −2).
25. $(2n\pi, 0)$, $((2n + 1)\pi, 2)$. **27.** (1, 0), (0, 1), (−1, 0), (0, −1). **29.** (0, 1).

Chapter 14

Section 14.2, page 303

2. (−4, 150°), (−2, 60°), (−1, 30°).

3. (4, 300°), (3, 300°), (0, 0°).

5.

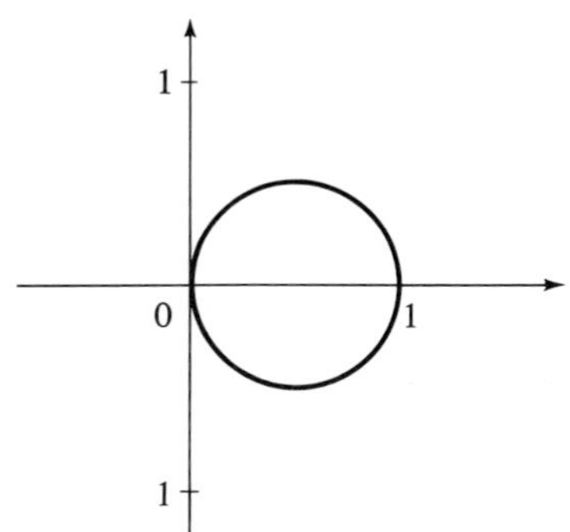

7.

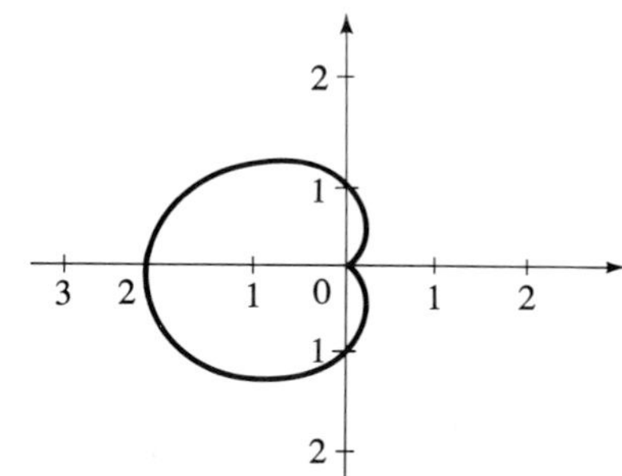

9.

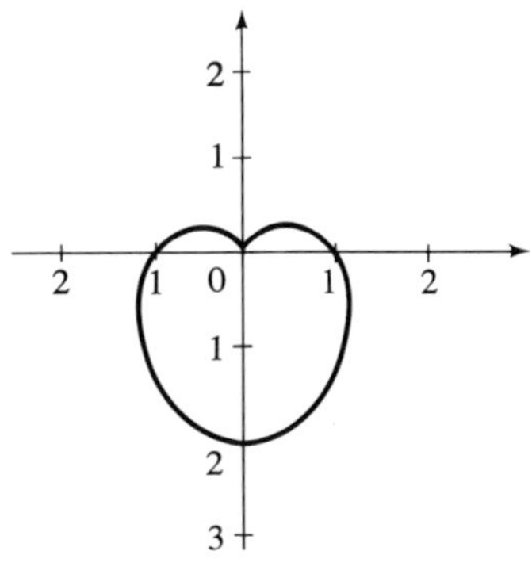

11.

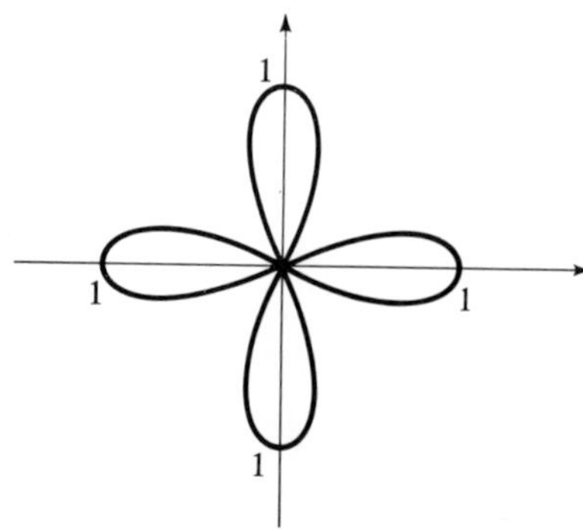

13.

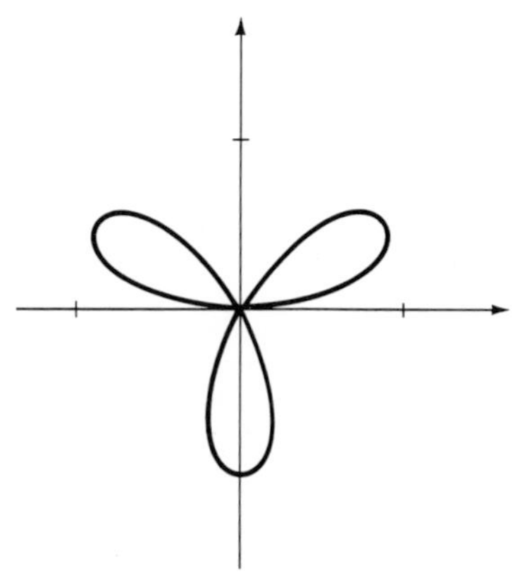

15.

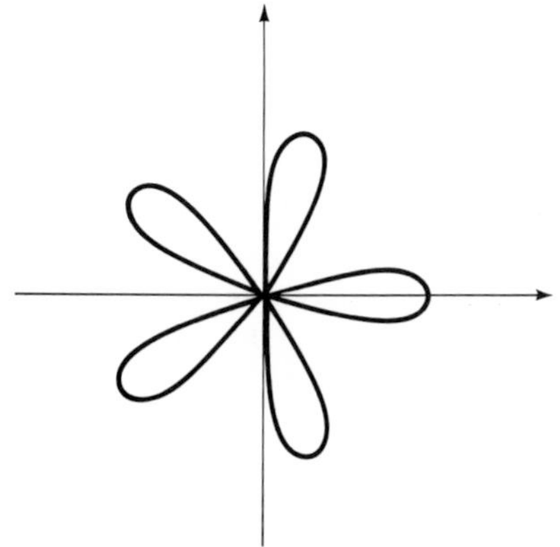

17.

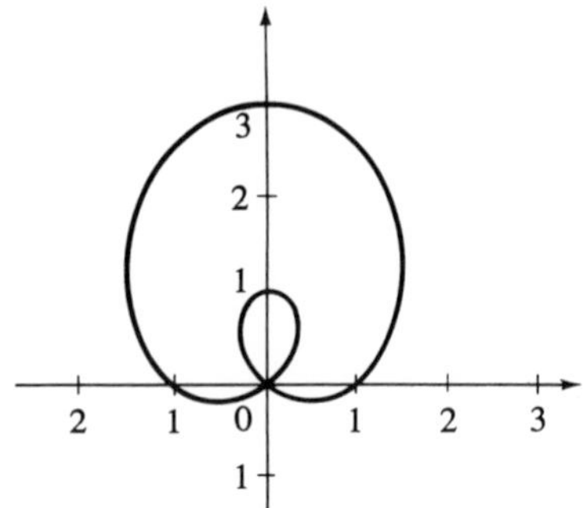

19.

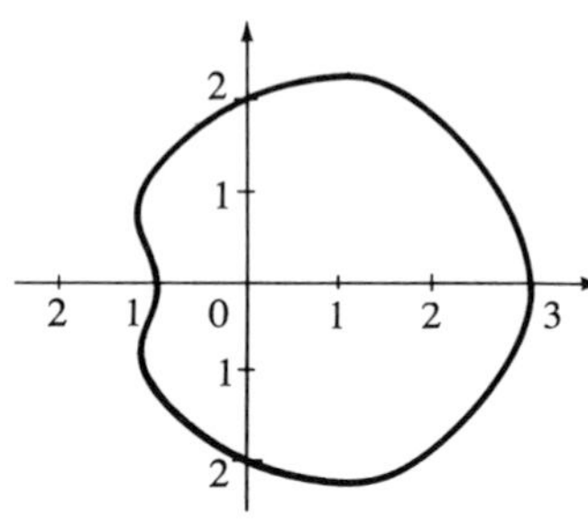

21.

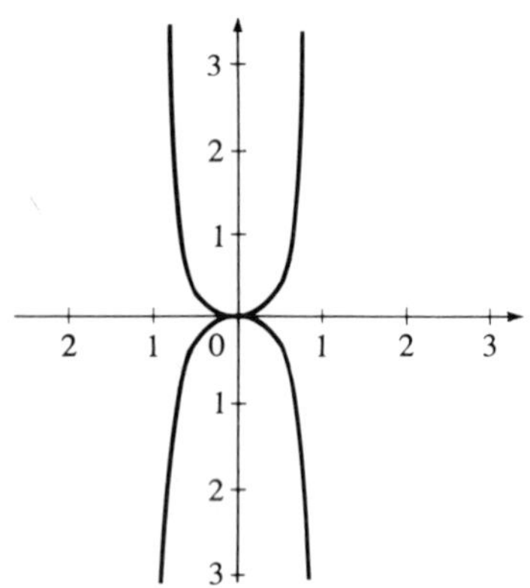

23.

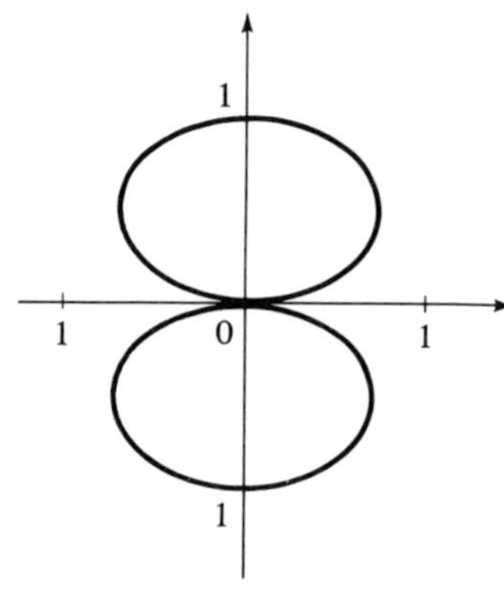

25.

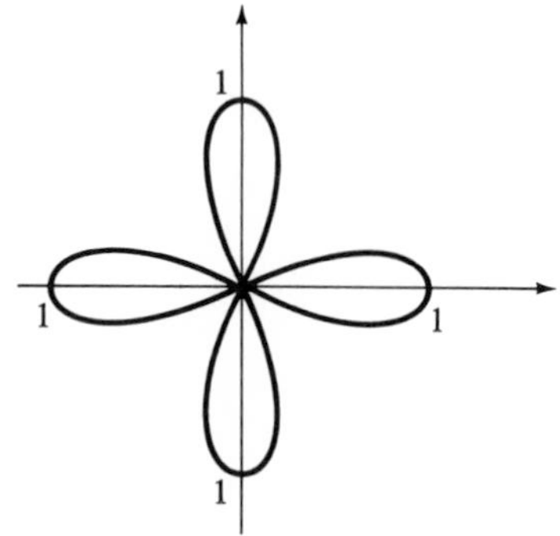

27.

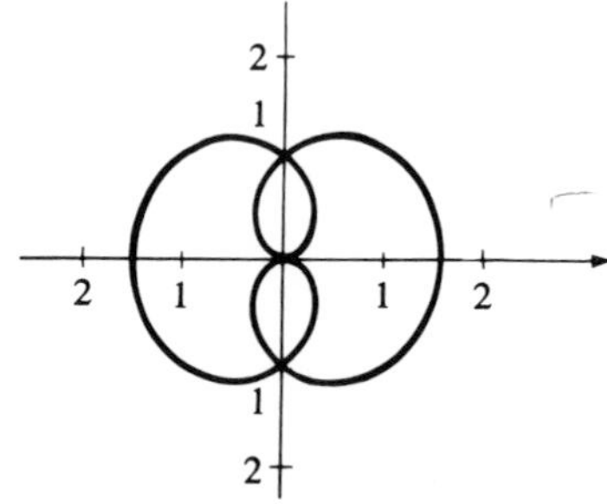

29.

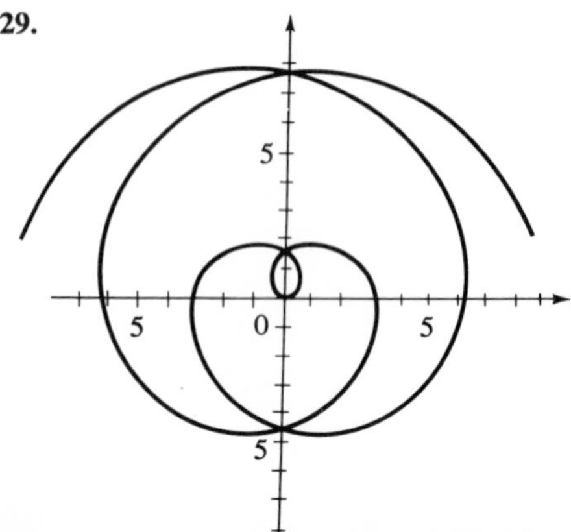

31.

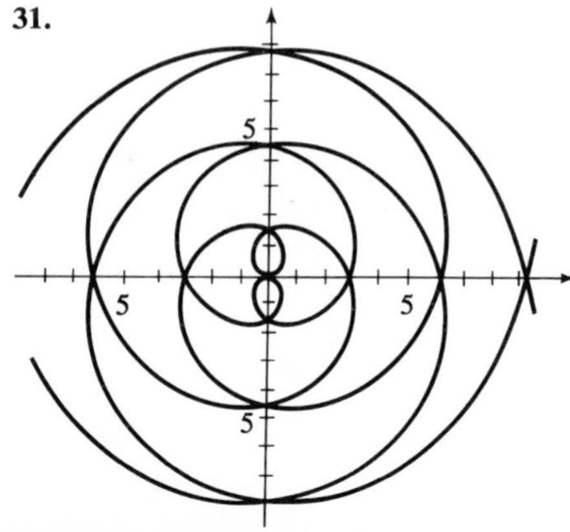

33.

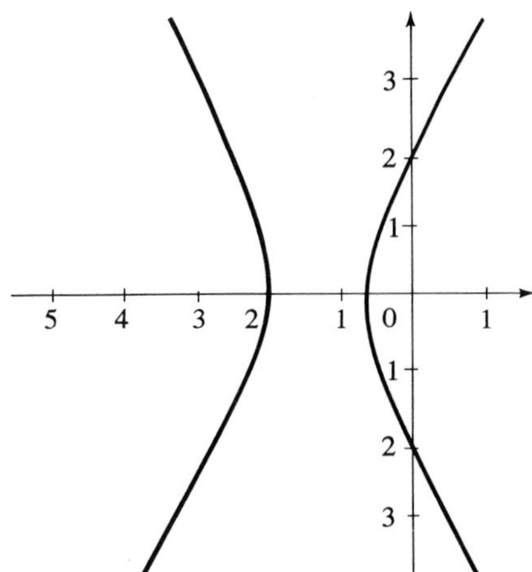

Section 14.3, page 305

1. $(\sqrt{2}, 45°)$, $(\sqrt{2}, 315°)$. **3.** $(2, 0°)$, $(2, 180°)$.

5. $(1/2, 60°)$, $(1/2, 300°)$, $(0, 90°) = (0, 0°)$. **7.** $(\sqrt{3}/2, 60°)$, $(-\sqrt{3}/2, 300°)$, $(0, 0°)$.

9. $(\sqrt{2}, 45°)$. **11.** $(3, 109.5°)$, $(3, 250.5°)$.

13. $(2 + \sqrt{2}, 45°)$, $(2 - \sqrt{2}, 135°)$, $(2 - \sqrt{2}, 225°)$, $(2 + \sqrt{2}, 315°)$.

15. $(1 - 1/\sqrt{2}, 45°)$, $(1 + 1/\sqrt{2}, 225°)$, $(0, 90°) = (0, 0°)$. **17.** $(1, 0°)$, $(-1, 0°)$.

19. $(0, 0°)$, $(1, 90°)$.

Section 14.4, page 307

1. $(-1, 0)$, $(\sqrt{3}/2, 3/2)$, $(1, 0)$, $(-1, 1)$.

2. $(2, 7\pi/4)$, $(2, 2\pi/3)$, $(4, 0)$, $(\sqrt{2}, 5\pi/4)$, $(2, 3\pi/2)$. **3.** $r = 2 \sec \theta$. **5.** $r = 1$.

7. $r = \sec \theta \tan \theta$. **9.** $r = (\cos \theta - \sin \theta)/(1 + 2 \sin \theta \cos \theta)$. **11.** $\tan \theta = 3$.

13. $r = 4/(2 \sin \theta + \cos \theta)$. **15.** $r^2 - 2r(\sin \theta + \cos \theta) + 1 = 0$.

17. $r^2 = \sec \theta \csc \theta$. **19.** $x^2 + y^2 = a^2$. **21.** $\sqrt{3}x - y = 0$.

23. $x^2 + y^2 - 4x = 0$. **25.** $(x^2 + y^2)^3 = (x^2 - y^2)^2$.

27. $x^2 + y^2 - 4y - 9 + 4y^2/(x^2 + y^2) = 0$ (note that the origin is not a point of the given curve).

29. $(x^2 + y^2)(x^2 + y^2 - 1)^2 = y^2$. **31.** $y^2 = 2x + 1$. **33.** $x^2 + y^2 = 3x + 2y$.

Section 14.5, page 310

1. hyperbola, $(0, 0)$, $x = 2$, 2.

3. ellipse, $(0, 0)$, $y = 2$, $2/3$.

5. parabola, $(0, 0)$, $y = 3$, 1.

7. ellipse, $(0, 0)$, $y = 3$, $2/3$.

9.

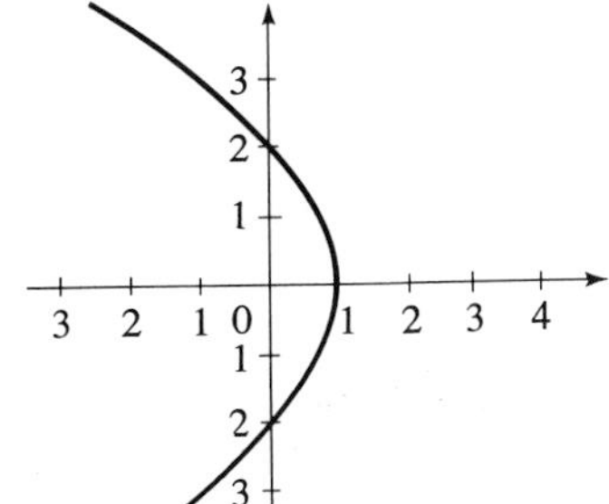

11.

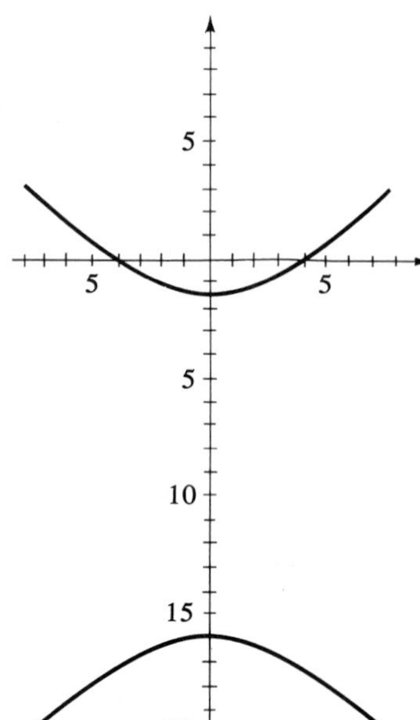

13.

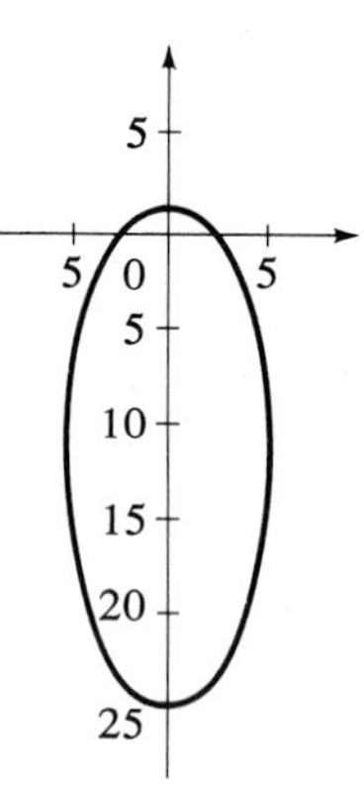

15. $r = 10/(3 + 2 \cos \theta)$.
17. $r = 2/(1 + \sin \theta)$.
19. $r = 25/(4 + 5 \cos \theta)$.

21.

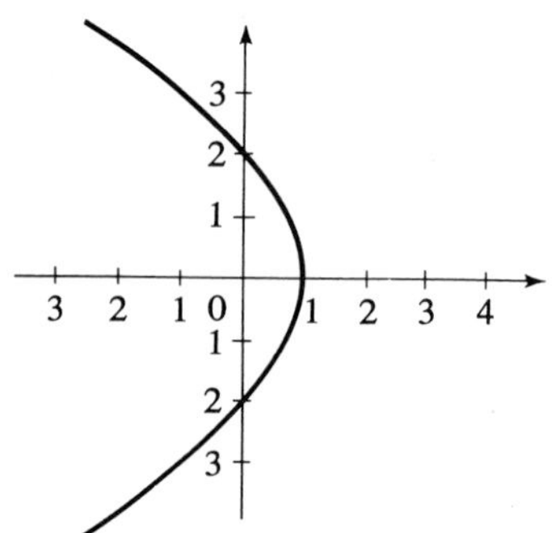

Section 14.6, page 314

1. $-(\cos \theta + \cos 2\theta)/(\sin \theta + \sin 2\theta)$. **3.** 0.
5. $(3 \sin \theta \cos 3\theta + \cos \theta \sin 3\theta)/(3 \cos \theta \cos 3\theta - \sin \theta \sin 3\theta)$.
7. $(\sin \theta + \theta \cos \theta)/(\cos \theta - \theta \sin \theta)$. **9.** $(\cos \theta)/(1 - \sin \theta)$. **11.** $-\sqrt{3}$.
13. $-1 - \sqrt{2}$. **15.** $-\sqrt{3}$. **17.** $x - y + 1 = 0$. **19.** $y + 1 = 0$.
21. $3\sqrt{3}x + 5y + 2 = 0$. **23.** $(3/2, 2\pi/3)$ max, $(3/2, 4\pi/3)$ min.
25. $(2\sqrt{2}/3, 54.8°)$, $(-2\sqrt{2}/3, 125.2)$, $(2\sqrt{2}/3, 234.8°)$, $(-2\sqrt{2}/3, 305.2°)$.
27. $[(3 + \sqrt{33})/4, 53.6°]$, $[(3 + \sqrt{33})/4, 306.4°]$, $[(3 - \sqrt{33})/4, 147.0°]$, $[(3 - \sqrt{33})/4, 213.0°]$.
31. $-\sqrt{3}$. **33.** 3/2. **35.** 1/2.

Chapter 15

Section 15.1, page 321

1. $x^2/2 + x - 3\ln|x| + C.$ **3.** $x^2 - 3x/2 + (5/4)\ln|2x+1| + C.$
5. $u^3/3 + u^2/2 + 2u + 2\ln|u-1| + C.$ **7.** $(1/3)(2x+1)^{3/2} + C.$
9. $(3/10)(x^2+2x)^{5/3} + C.$ **11.** $e^{x^2}/2 + C.$ **13.** $(\ln^2 x)/2 + C.$
15. $-\ln(1+\cos x) + C.$ **17.** $1/[6(1-2u)^3] + C.$ **19.** $\ln(e^x+1) + C.$
21. $\ln|1+\tan u| + C.$ **23.** $(\sin^2 x + 1)^2/2 + C.$ **25.** $-\ln|1-\cosh x| + C.$
27. $-\dfrac{1}{6}\ln\left|\dfrac{3+x}{3-x}\right| + C.$ **29.** $(1/2)\text{Arctan}\, x^2 + C.$ **31.** $2\tan\theta + 2\sec\theta - \theta + C.$
33. $\theta + 2\ln|\sec\theta + \tan\theta| + \tan\theta + C.$ **35.** $\text{Arctan}\sin\theta + C.$
37. $1/(1-\tan\theta) + C.$ **39.** $x - 4x^{3/2}/3 + x^2/2 + C.$ **41.** $-x + 2\ln(e^x+1) + C.$
45. $-\ln|\csc u + \cot u| + C.$ **47.** $2\,\text{Arctan}\, e^u + C.$

Section 15.2, page 327

1. $(2/15)(x+2)^{3/2}(3x-4) + C.$ **3.** $(2/105)(x+2)^{3/2}(15x^2 - 24x + 32) + C.$
5. $(1/15)(2x+1)^{3/2}(3x-1) + C.$ **7.** $(2/3)\sqrt{x-2}(x+4) + C.$
9. $(2/15)\sqrt{x-1}(3x^2+4x+8) + C.$ **11.** $(2/7)\sqrt{x-5}(x^3+6x^2+40x+400) + C.$
13. $(3/28)(x+1)^{4/3}(4x-3) + C.$ **15.** $(4/45)(x+1)^{5/4}(5x-4) + C.$
17. $(1/15)(2x+1)^{3/2}(6x+13) + C.$ **19.** $(2/3)\sqrt{x-3}(2x+15) + C.$ **21.** $12/5.$
23. $(550\sqrt{5} - 38)/35.$ **25.** $124/15.$ **27.** $2\sqrt{e^x+1} - \ln\left|\dfrac{1+\sqrt{e^x+1}}{1-\sqrt{e^x+1}}\right| + C.$

Section 15.3, page 329

1. $2\sqrt{x^2+1} + \ln(x + \sqrt{1+x^2}) + C.$ **3.** $\ln|x^2-2| - \dfrac{1}{\sqrt{2}}\ln\left|\dfrac{\sqrt{2}+x}{\sqrt{2}-x}\right| + C.$
5. $-4\sqrt{1-x^2} + \text{Arcsin}\, x + C.$ **7.** $(1/3)\ln(3x^2+4) - (\sqrt{3}/2)\text{Arctan}(\sqrt{3}x/2) + C.$
9. $-(1/2)\sqrt{3-2x^2} - (1/\sqrt{2})\text{Arcsin}(\sqrt{2}x/\sqrt{3}) + C.$ **11.** $x + \ln(x^2+1) + C.$
13. $x - \dfrac{3}{2}\ln\left|\dfrac{2+x}{2-x}\right| + C$ **15.** $\ln 2 - \pi/4.$ **17.** $4 - 2\sqrt{2} + 3\ln(\sqrt{2}+1).$
19. $-\ln\sqrt{3} - \dfrac{1}{2\sqrt{2}}\ln\dfrac{3+2\sqrt{2}}{3}.$ **21.** $\dfrac{\sqrt{3}+\pi}{3\sqrt{3}}.$

Section 15.4, page 331

1. $\text{Arctan}(x+1) + C.$ **3.** $\ln(x - 2 + \sqrt{x^2-4x+3}) + C.$
5. $\dfrac{1}{5}\text{Arctan}\dfrac{2x-2}{5} + C.$ **7.** $\dfrac{1}{8}\ln\left|\dfrac{x}{2-x}\right| + C.$
9. $4\ln(x - 1 + \sqrt{x^2-2x+5}) + C.$ **11.** $-(3/2)\ln(2x + 4 + \sqrt{4x^2+16x+7}) + C.$

13. $(2/3)\text{Arctan}(3x-2)+C.$ **15.** $-\frac{1}{12}\ln\left|\frac{2x-1}{2x-7}\right|+C.$

17. $(4/3)\ln(3x+2+\sqrt{9x^2+12x+8})+C.$ **19.** $-1/(25x-20)+C.$

Section 15.5, page 334

1. $\ln(x^2+2x+2)-\text{Arctan}(x+1)+C.$ **3.** $-2\sqrt{2x-x^2}+3\text{ Arcsin}(x-1)+C.$

5. $\frac{5}{8}\ln(4x^2-8x+13)+\frac{7}{6}\text{Arctan}\frac{2x-2}{3}+C.$

7. $-\frac{3}{8}\ln(4x^2+24x+41)+\frac{11}{2\sqrt{5}}\text{Arctan}\frac{2x+6}{\sqrt{5}}+C.$

9. $-\frac{4}{9}\sqrt{52+36x-9x^2}+3\text{ Arcsin}\frac{3x-6}{2\sqrt{22}}+C.$

11. $x+4\ln(x^2-4x+8)+8\text{ Arctan}\frac{x-2}{2}+C.$

13. $\frac{x^3}{3}+x^2+\frac{3x}{4}-\frac{5}{2}\ln(4x^2-8x+13)-\frac{119}{24}\text{Arctan}\frac{2x-2}{3}+C.$

15. $-(1/5)\sqrt{-5x^2+20x-13}+C.$

Section 15.6, page 337

1. $(1/3)\sin^3 x+C.$ **3.** $-(1/4)\cos^4\theta+C.$ **5.** $(1/5)\cos^5 x-(1/3)\cos^3 x+C.$
7. $(1/5)\cos^{5/2}2\theta-\sqrt{\cos 2\theta}+C.$ **9.** $\theta/16-(1/64)\sin 4\theta+(1/48)\sin^3 2\theta+C.$
11. $\theta/16-(1/64)\sin 4\theta-(1/48)\sin^3 2\theta+C.$ **13.** $3\theta/8+(1/8)\sin 4\theta+(1/64)\sin 8\theta+C.$
15. $\sec x+\cos x+C.$ **17.** $(2/5)\sin^{5/2}x-(2/9)\sin^{9/2}x+C.$
19. $(1/10)\cos^5 x^2-(1/6)\cos^3 x^2+C.$ **21.** $(1/4)\sec^4\theta+C.$
23. $(1/32)(4\theta-\sin 4\theta)+C.$ **25.** $(2/21)\cos^{3/2}t(3\cos^2 t-7)+C.$
27. $(1/2)\sin^2 x+C_1=-(1/2)\cos^2 x+C_2=(-1/4)\cos 2x+C_3.$

Section 15.7, page 341

1. $(1/3)\tan^3 x+C.$ **3.** $-(1/5)\cot^5 x-(1/7)\cot^7 x+C.$ **5.** $(1/3)\sec^3\theta-\sec\theta+C.$
7. $-(1/3)\csc^3 x+C.$ **9.** $\tan x+(2/3)\tan^3 x+(1/5)\tan^5 x+C.$
11. $(1/2)\sec^2\theta-\ln|\sec\theta|+C.$ **13.** $(1/8)\sec^4 2\theta-(1/2)\sec^2 2\theta+(1/2)\ln|\sec 2\theta|+C.$
15. $(1/3)\sec^3\theta-\sec\theta+C.$ **17.** $-(1/9)\cot^3 3x+(1/3)\cot 3x+x+C.$
19. $(1/6)\tan^3(2x+1)-(1/2)\tan(2x+1)+x+C.$ **21.** $-(1/4)\ln|\cos 2\theta|+C.$
23. $\theta+\sin\theta+C.$ **25.** $(1/4)\ln|\cos 2\theta|+C.$ **27.** $\tan\theta-\cot\theta+C.$
29. $(1/3)\sin^3 x+C.$ **31.** $(1/2)\tan^2 x+C_1=(1/2)\sec^2 x+C_2=1/(2\cos^2 x)+C_3.$

Section 15.8, page 347

1. $-\sqrt{1-x^2}/x-\text{Arcsin }x+C.$ **3.** $\ln|x+\sqrt{x^2+9}|+C.$

5. $-(1/3)\sqrt{4-x^2}(x^2+8)+C.$ **7.** $-x/5\sqrt{x^2-5}+C.$

9. $(9/4)\text{Arcsin}(2x/3)+(x/2)\sqrt{9-4x^2}+C.$ **11.** $-(1/12)(4-3x^2)^{3/2}/x^3+C.$

13. $\frac{(2x^2-9)\sqrt{4x^2+9}}{24}+C.$

15. $(1/2)(x+2)\sqrt{x^2+4x+13}+(9/2)\ln|x+2+\sqrt{x^2+4x+13}|+C.$

17. $-(x+1)/\sqrt{x^2+2x}+C.$ **19.** $1/\sqrt{2}.$ **21.** $81\pi/128.$

Section 15.9, page 353

1. $x \sin x + \cos x + C.$ **3.** $xe^x - e^x + C.$ **5.** $x \ln x^2 - 2x + C.$

7. $-\ln x/x - 1/x + C.$ **9.** $x \operatorname{Arcsin} x + \sqrt{1 - x^2} + C.$

11. $x \operatorname{Arctan} x - (1/2)\ln(1 + x^2) + C.$ **13.** $-\cos\theta \ln\cos\theta + \cos\theta + C.$

15. $x \cosh^{-1} x - \sqrt{x^2 - 1} + C.$ **17.** $-(1/3)x^2(4 - x^2)^{3/2} - (2/15)(4 - x^2)^{5/2} + C.$

19. $(2/9)x^3(x^3 + 1)^{3/2} - (4/45)(x^3 + 1)^{5/2} + C.$ **21.** $(x/2)(\sin\ln x - \cos\ln x) + C.$

23. $\ln\left|\dfrac{x-1}{x}\right| - \dfrac{\ln x}{x-1} + C.$

25. $x^4 \sin x + 4x^3 \cos x - 12x^2 \sin x - 24x \cos x + 24 \sin x + C.$

27. $e^x(x^3 - 3x^2 + 6x - 6) + C.$ **29.** $(1/32)x^4(8 \ln^2 x - 4 \ln x + 1) + C.$

31. $(1/2)e^x(\sin x + \cos x) + C.$

33. $(1/8)(2 \sec^3\theta \tan\theta + 3 \sec\theta \tan\theta + 3 \ln|\sec\theta + \tan\theta|) + C.$

35. $(1/5)e^x(\sin 2x - 2 \cos 2x) + C.$ **37.** $(1/8)(\cos x \sin 3x - 3 \sin x \cos 3x) + C.$

39. $(1/2)(\theta - \sin\theta\cos\theta) + C.$ **41.** $(1/8)(2 \sin 2x - \sin 4x) + C.$

Section 15.10, page 358

1. $\ln\left|\dfrac{x}{x+1}\right| + C.$ **3.** $\ln\dfrac{(x+2)^2}{|x+1|} + C.$ **5.** $x + \ln\left|\dfrac{x}{(x+2)^3}\right| + C.$

7. $\ln\dfrac{\sqrt{x^2-1}}{|x|} + C.$ **9.** $x + \ln\left|\dfrac{x(x-2)^5}{(x-1)^3}\right| + C.$ **11.** $\dfrac{-4}{x-4} + \ln|x-4| + C.$

13. $x - \dfrac{1}{x+1} - 2\ln|x+1| + C.$ **15.** $\dfrac{1}{x} + \ln\left|\dfrac{x-1}{x}\right| + C.$

17. $(2/3x) - (7/9)\ln|x| + (1/36)\ln|x+3| + (3/4)\ln|x-1| + C.$

19. $-\dfrac{1}{2}\left[\ln\dfrac{|x^2-1|}{x^2} + \dfrac{1}{x^2-1}\right] + C.$ **21.** $\ln\left|\dfrac{1+\sin x}{\sin x}\right| - \csc x + C.$

Section 15.11, page 362

1. $\ln\dfrac{|x|}{\sqrt{x^2+1}} + C.$ **3.** $\dfrac{1}{3}\left[\ln|x-1| - \dfrac{1}{2}\ln(x^2+x+1) + \sqrt{3}\operatorname{Arctan}\dfrac{2x+1}{\sqrt{3}}\right] + C.$

5. $\dfrac{3}{4}\left(\ln\dfrac{(x+1)^2}{x^2+1} + 2\operatorname{Arctan} x\right) + C.$ **7.** $\dfrac{1}{32}\ln\dfrac{(x+2)^2}{x^2+4} - \dfrac{1}{8}\dfrac{1}{x+2} + C.$

9. $\dfrac{1}{4}\ln\dfrac{x^2+1}{(x+1)^2} + \dfrac{1}{2}\operatorname{Arctan} x + C.$ **11.** $\dfrac{1}{2}\left(\operatorname{Arctan} x - \dfrac{x}{x^2+1}\right) + C.$

13. $\dfrac{1}{32}\ln\dfrac{x^2}{x^2+4} + \dfrac{1}{8(x^2+4)} + C.$

15. $-\dfrac{1}{3}\dfrac{1}{x-2} + \dfrac{2}{3\sqrt{3}}\operatorname{Arctan}\dfrac{x+1}{\sqrt{3}} + C.$

17. $\dfrac{5}{36}\operatorname{Arctan}\dfrac{x}{2} - \dfrac{1}{9}\operatorname{Arctan} x + \dfrac{1}{6}\dfrac{x}{x^2+4} + C.$

19. $\dfrac{1}{4}\ln\dfrac{x^2}{x^2+2x+2} - \dfrac{1}{2}\operatorname{Arctan}(x+1) + C.$

Section 15.12, page 365

1. $x + 1 - 2\sqrt{x+1} + C.$ **3.** $\sqrt{x} - (1/2)\ln(1 + 2\sqrt{x}) + C.$

5. $2\sqrt{x}+3\sqrt[3]{x}+6\sqrt[6]{x}+6\ln|\sqrt[6]{x}-1|+C.$ **7.** $3\sqrt[3]{x}-6\sqrt[6]{x}+6\ln(1+\sqrt[6]{x})+C.$

9. $x+4\sqrt{x}+4\ln|\sqrt{x}-1|+C.$ **11.** $2\sqrt{3x+1}+\sqrt{7}\ln\left|\dfrac{\sqrt{3x+1}-\sqrt{7}}{\sqrt{3x+1}+\sqrt{7}}\right|+C.$

13. $\sqrt{2}\,\text{Arctan}\,\dfrac{3\tan(\theta/2)+1}{\sqrt{2}}+C.$ **15.** $\dfrac{-2}{\sqrt{71}}\,\text{Arctan}\,\dfrac{10\tan(x/2)+3}{\sqrt{71}}+C.$

17. $\dfrac{1}{\sqrt{2}}\ln\dfrac{(\tan(\theta/2)-1+\sqrt{2})^2}{|-\tan^2(\theta/2)+2\tan(\theta/2)+1|}+C.$ **19.** $\sqrt{1-x^2}-\ln\dfrac{1+\sqrt{1-x^2}}{|x|}+C.$

21. $\dfrac{1}{15}(x^2-4)^{3/2}(3x^2+8)+C.$

Chapter 16

Section 16.1, page 372

1. 1/8. **3.** 1/2. **5.** $+\infty$. **7.** $+\infty$. **9.** 2. **11.** $+\infty$. **13.** $1+\sqrt[3]{5}$.
15. $+\infty$. **17.** $+\infty$. **19.** π. **21.** 1. **23.** 1/2. **25.** 3.

Section 16.2, page 376

1. π. **3.** $3\pi/2$. **5.** 1. **7.** $\pi/2$. **9.** $19\pi/2$. **11.** 4. **13.** $5\pi/4-2$.
15. $3\pi/2-2\sqrt{2}$. **17.** $(8+\pi)/4$. **19.** $\pi/4-3\sqrt{3}/16$.

Section 16.3, page 379

1. $\pi/7$. **3.** $\pi/30$. **5.** $\pi^2/2$. **7.** $(e-2)\pi$. **9.** $2\pi/15$. **11.** $3\pi/5$.
13. $\pi(\pi-2)$. **15.** $\pi/6$. **17.** $\pi/2$. **19.** $\pi/6$. **21.** $\pi/10$. **23.** $5\pi/14$.
25. $(2+\pi)\pi$. **27.** $2\pi^2$. **29.** $\pi/6$. **31.** $4\pi r^3/3$. **33.** $+\infty, \pi$.

Section 16.4, page 383

1. $4\pi/5$. **3.** $2\pi/5$. **5.** $\pi/6$. **7.** $\pi(e^2+1)/2$. **9.** $16\pi/3$. **11.** $512\pi/15$.
13. $+\infty$. **15.** $512\pi/15$. **17.** $32\pi/15$. **19.** $16\pi/5$. **21.** $2\pi^2$.
23. $\pi(e^4-13)/4e^4$. **25.** $\pi/3$.

Section 16.5, page 388

1. π. **3.** 8/3. **5.** $2\pi/3$. **7.** 32. **9.** 64/3. **11.** 16. **13.** 4π.
15. 192. **17.** 48π. **19.** 96. **21.** 24π. **23.** $2/(3\sqrt{3})$. **25.** 128/3.

Section 16.6, page 392

1. $(115^{3/2}-79^{3/2})/216$. **3.** $\sqrt{17}+(1/4)\ln(4+\sqrt{17})$. **5.** $\ln(1+\sqrt{2})$.

7. $\ln\dfrac{\sqrt{2}+1}{\sqrt{2}-1}$. **9.** $-1+\ln(e^2+1)$. **11.** $\sinh 1$. **13.** $-\ln(e-\sqrt{e^2-1})$.

15. $2\sqrt{2}$. **17.** 3/2. **19.** $8(10\sqrt{10}-1)/27$. **21.** $(4-2\sqrt{2})a$. **23.** $4\sqrt{3}$.
27. $\sqrt{2}(e^2-1)$. **29.** $(2\pi-3\sqrt{3})/4$.

Section 16.7, page 397

1. $4\pi R^2$. **3.** $2\pi b^2 + \dfrac{2\pi a^2 b}{\sqrt{a^2 - b^2}} \text{Arcsin} \dfrac{\sqrt{a^2 - b^2}}{a}$. **5.** 4π.
7. 4π. **9.** $1505\pi/18$. **11.** $2\sqrt{2}\pi + 2\pi \ln(1 + \sqrt{2})$.
13. $2\pi(\sinh 1 \cosh 1 + 1)$. **15.** $32\pi(2\sqrt{2} - 1)/3$. **17.** 3π. **19.** $32\pi a^2/3$.
21. $128(125\sqrt{10} + 1)/1215$. **23.** $2\pi(1 + \sinh 1 - \cosh 1)$.
25. $\pi[e\sqrt{e^2 + 1} + \ln(e + \sqrt{e^2 + 1}) - \sqrt{2} - \ln(1 + \sqrt{2})]$. **27.** $\dfrac{2\pi}{1215}(247\sqrt{13} + 64)$.
29. $\dfrac{4\sqrt{2}\pi}{5}(e^{2\pi} + e^{\pi} - 1)$.

Section 16.8, page 400

1. $(1/4, 0)$. **3.** $(5, 0)$. **5.** $(11/10, 6/5)$. **7.** $(3/5, 17/10)$. **9.** $(7/4, -1/5)$.
11. $(-19/4, 0)$. **13.** $(8/3, 0)$. **15.** $(-1/2, -5)$. **17.** $(-5, -4)$.
19. 157/46 to the right and 83/46 above the lower left-hand corner.
21. Half-way between the two sides and a distance $(5 + 2\sqrt{3})/(4 + \sqrt{3})$ up from the bottom.
23. Half-way between the two sides and a distance $(3 + 2\sqrt{3})/(2 + \sqrt{3})$ up from the bottom.
25. Half-way between the two sides and a distance $(2 + 3\pi)/(2 + \pi)$ up from the bottom.

Section 16.9, page 404

1. $(3/2, 6/5)$. **3.** $(5/6, 5/18)$. **5.** $(3/8, 3/5)$. **7.** $(3/5, -2/35)$.
9. $(17/27, 5/9)$. **11.** $(\pi/2, \pi/8)$. **13.** $(0, 1/4)$. **15.** $(8/15, 8/21)$.
17. $(0, 6/5)$. **19.** $(4a/3\pi, 4b/3\pi)$. **21.** $(a/5, a/5)$. **23.** $(0, 8/3\pi)$.

Section 16.10, page 407

1. $\bar{x} = 7/8$. **3.** $\bar{y} = 1/5$. **5.** $\bar{y} = 1/2$. **7.** $\bar{x} = 3/8$. **9.** $\bar{x} = 3a/8$.
11. $\bar{x} = 27/16$. **13.** $\bar{x} = 2/\pi$. **15.** $\bar{y} = \pi/8$. **17.** $\bar{y} = (e^2 - 1)/2(e^2 + 1)$.
19. $\bar{x} = -8/5$.

Section 16.11, page 411

1. $(2a/5, 2a/5)$. **3.** $\left(0, \dfrac{2[3\sqrt{2} - \ln(\sqrt{2} + 1)]}{3[\sqrt{2} + \ln(\sqrt{2} + 1)]}\right)$.
5. $(0, (1 + \sinh 1 \cosh 1)/2 \sinh 1)$. **7.** $(4a/3, 4a/3)$.
9. $[(15/7) + (3/28)\ln 3, (52/21)]$. **11.** $\bar{x} = 0$. **13.** $\bar{x} = 0$.
15. $\bar{x} = 53{,}941/21{,}070$. **17.** $\bar{y} = (391\sqrt{17} + 1)/10(17\sqrt{17} - 1)$.
19. $\bar{y} = (2 \sinh 1 \cosh 1 - \sinh^2 1 + 1)/4(\sinh 1 - \cosh 1 + 1)$.

Section 16.12, page 414

1. $22, \sqrt{22/7}$. **3.** $44, \sqrt{22/3}$. **5.** $2/5, \sqrt{1/5}$. **7.** $1/3, \sqrt{2/15}$.
9. $1/20, \sqrt{3/10}$. **11.** $1/6, 1/4$. **13.** $\pi^2 - 4, \sqrt{\pi^2/2 - 2}$.
15. $9(2 - 5/e), \sqrt{\dfrac{2e - 5}{e - 1}}$. **17.** $12, \sqrt{3/2 \ln 2}$. **19.** $1/2, \sqrt{1/2\pi}$. **21.** $2\pi, 1$.

Section 16.13, page 418

1. 29,950 lb. **3.** 3931 lb. **5.** 24.5 lb.
7. $62.4\{[\text{Arcsin}(2h - 1)]/8 + \pi/16 - (8h^2 - 11h + 3)\sqrt{h - h^2}/12\}$. **9.** 12.0 lb.

11. 360 lb. **13.** 1872 lb. **15.** 15,160 lb. **17.** 13,300 lb.
19. 12 ft above the top of the gate. **21.** 31,350 lb. **23.** 28,500 lb.

Chapter 17

Section 17.1, page 422

1. Limit point. **3.** Limit point. **5.** Not a limit point. **7.** Limit point.
9. Limit point. **11.** $\delta = \min\{\epsilon/5, 3\}$. **13.** $\delta = \epsilon$. **15.** $\delta = \epsilon$. **17.** $\delta = \sqrt{\epsilon}$.
19. $\delta = \min\{\epsilon/3, 1\}$. **21.** $\delta = \min\{\epsilon/2, 1\}$. **23.** $\delta = \min\{\epsilon/7, 1\}$. **25.** $\delta = \sqrt[3]{\epsilon}$.
27. $\delta = \min\{3\epsilon, 1/2\}$. **29.** $\delta = \min\{\epsilon/2, 1/2\}$. **31.** $\delta = \min\{3\epsilon/2, 3/4\}$.

Section 17.2, page 427

1. Choose $\epsilon \leq 1$. **3.** Choose $\epsilon \leq 1$. **5.** Choose $\epsilon \leq 1$. **7.** Choose $\epsilon \leq 1$.
9. Choose any ϵ. **11.** Choose any ϵ. **13.** True. **15.** False. **17.** False.

Section 17.3, page 431

1. If $N > 0$, $\delta = 1/\sqrt[4]{N}$; if $N \leq 0$, $\delta =$ anything.
3. If $N < 0$, $\delta = 1/\sqrt{-N}$; if $N \geq 0$, $\delta =$ anything.
5. If $N > 0$, $\delta = 1/N$; if $N \leq 0$, $\delta =$ anything. **7.** $N = 1/\sqrt{\epsilon}$. **9.** $N = -1 - 1/\epsilon$.
11. $N = \ln \epsilon$. **13.** Choose any N. **15.** Choose $N > 0$. **17.** Choose any ϵ.
19. Choose any ϵ.

Section 17.4, page 434

1. $\delta = \epsilon$. **3.** $\delta = \epsilon/2$. **5.** $\delta = \epsilon$. **7.** $\delta = \min\{\epsilon/5, 1\}$. **9.** $\delta = \min\{\epsilon/7, 1\}$.
11. $\delta = \min\{2\epsilon, 1\}$. **13.** $\delta < 1$. **15.** Choose $\epsilon < 1$. **17.** Choose $\epsilon < 1$.
19. Choose $\epsilon < 1$. **21.** Choose $e < 1$.

Section 17.5, page 438

11. Yes, there is a number c between 0 and 1 such that $f'(c) = 0$.
13. No, there is no derivative at $x = 0$. **15.** No, there is no derivative at $x = 1$.
17. Yes, there is a number c between -1 and 1 such that $f'(c) = 0$.
19. No, f is not defined at $x = 0$; nor does $f'(0)$ exist.

Section 17.6, page 442

11. No, f is not defined at $x = 0$ nor does $f'(0)$ exist. **13.** No, $f'(0)$ does not exist.
15. No, f is not defined at $x = 0$ nor does $f'(0)$ exist.

Chapter 18

Section 18.1, page 450

1. 2. **3.** $1/2\sqrt{a}$. **5.** 1. **7.** 1. **9.** 0. **11.** 1/2. **13.** 0. **15.** 0.
17. $\ln a - \ln b$. **19.** 2. **21.** 1. **23.** $-1/6$. **25.** -2. **27.** 2.

Section 18.2, page 453

1. 0. **3.** 0. **5.** 1. **7.** 7/3. **9.** 0. **11.** -1. **13.** a. **15.** 1/2.
17. -2. **19.** 1/2. **21.** 1/3. **23.** 1/2.

Section 18.3, page 456

1. 1. **3.** 1. **5.** e. **7.** 1. **9.** 1. **11.** 1. **13.** e^2. **15.** $+\infty$.
17. $1/e$. **19.** 1. **21.** 1. **23.** $1/e$.

Chapter 19

Section 19.1, page 464

1. $1/3 + 1/9 + 1/27 + 1/81 + \cdots$. **3.** $1/2 + 1/6 + 1/12 + 1/20 + \cdots$.
5. $-1/2 + 1/5 - 1/10 + 1/17 - \cdots$. **7.** $\sum_{n=1}^{\infty} (3n-2)$. **9.** $\sum_{n=1}^{\infty} 2n(2n-1)$.
11. $\sum_{n=1}^{\infty} (-1)^{n+1} n \cdot 2^n$. **13.** Converges to 0. **15.** Converges to 0.
17. Converges to 1. **19.** Diverges. **21.** Converges to 1.
23. Converges to 1/2. **25.** Diverges. **27.** Converges to 3/2. **29.** Diverges.

Section 19.3, page 471

1. 1/9. **3.** 143/999 **5.** 1. **7.** 41/33. **9.** Converges. **11.** Converges.
13. Diverges. **15.** Converges. **17.** Converges. **19.** Converges.
21. Converges. **23.** Diverges. **25.** Converges. **27.** Diverges.
29. Diverges.

Section 19.4, page 476

1. Converges. **3.** Converges. **5.** Converges. **7.** Diverges. **9.** Diverges.
11. Converges. **13.** Diverges. **15.** Converges. **17.** Converges.
19. Diverges. **21.** Converges. **23.** Diverges. **25.** Converges.
27. Converges. **29.** Diverges.

Section 19.5, page 483

1. Converges conditionally. **3.** Converges absolutely.
5. Converges conditionally. **7.** Converges conditionally.
9. Converges absolutely. **11.** Diverges. **13.** Diverges.
15. Converges conditionally. **17.** Converges absolutely.
19. Converges conditionally. **23.** 0.6. **25.** 0.1.

Section 19.6, page 487

1. $-1 \le x < 1$. **3.** $-1 < x < 1$. **5.** $-2 < x < 2$. **7.** $-2 < x \le 2$.
9. $-5 < x < 5$. **11.** $1 < x < 3$. **13.** $-6 < x < -2$. **15.** $-6 \le x \le -2$.
17. $-1/2 < x < 3/2$. **19.** All x. **21.** $-5 \le x \le -3$.
23. $x > 1$ or $x \le -1$.

Section 19.7, page 490

1. $e + e(x-1) + (e/2!)(x-1)^2 + (e/3!)(x-1)^3 + \cdots$, converges for all x.
3. $1 - (x^2/2!) + (x^4/4!) - (x^6/6!) + \cdots$, converges for all x.
5. $\dfrac{\sqrt{3}}{2} - \dfrac{1}{2}\left(x - \dfrac{\pi}{6}\right) - \dfrac{\sqrt{3}}{2}\dfrac{(x-\pi/6)^2}{2!} + \dfrac{1}{2}\dfrac{(x-\pi/6)^3}{3!} - \cdots$, converges for all x.
7. $1 - x^2 + x^4 - x^6 + \cdots$, converges for $|x| < 1$.
9. $x + (x^3/3!) + (x^5/5!) + (x^7/7!) + \cdots$, converges for all x.
11. $1 + x + x^2 + x^3 + \cdots$, converges for $|x| < 1$.
13. $1 + 3(x-1) + 4(x-1)^2 + (x-1)^3$, converges for all x.
15. $x + (1/3)x^3 + (2/15)x^5 + (17/315)x^7 + \cdots$.
17. $(1/2) - (1/2)(x-1) + (1/4)(x-1)^2 - (1/8)(x-1)^4 + (49/384)(x-1)^5 + \cdots$.
19. $1 - \dfrac{1}{2}(x-1) + \dfrac{1 \cdot 3}{2^2 \cdot 2!}(x-1)^2 - \dfrac{1 \cdot 3 \cdot 5}{2^3 \cdot 3!}(x-1)^3 + \cdots$.
21. $1 - x + x^2 - x^3 + \cdots$, $1 + x + x^2 + x^3 + \cdots$.
23. $\sin x^2 = x^2 - (x^6/3!) + (x^{10}/5!) - (x^{14}/7!) + \cdots$.
27. $(1+x)^n = 1 + nx + \dfrac{n(n-1)}{2!}x^2 + \dfrac{n(n-1)(n-2)}{3!}x^3 + \cdots$.

$$(a+b)^n = a^n + na^{n-1}b + \frac{n(n-1)}{2!}a^{n-2}b^2 + \frac{n(n-1)(n-2)}{3!}a^{n-3}b^3 + \cdots.$$

Section 19.8, page 497

1. 1.22, 0.003. **3.** 0.08716, 0.0000001. **5.** 0.99620, 0.0000001. **7.** 1.17, 0.02.
9. 0.08749, 0.000001. **11.** 1.22140. **13.** 0.08716. **15.** 0.81915.
17. 0.57358. **19.** 0.8391. **21.** 0.6.

Section 19.9, page 499

1. $1 - 2x + 3x^2 - 4x^3 + \cdots$. **3.** $x - (x^3/3!) + (x^5/5!) - (x^7/7!) + \cdots$.
5. $x - (x^3/3) + (x^5/5) - (x^7/7) + \cdots$. **7.** $x + \dfrac{1}{2}\dfrac{x^3}{3} + \dfrac{1 \cdot 3}{2 \cdot 4}\dfrac{x^5}{5} + \dfrac{1 \cdot 3 \cdot 5}{2 \cdot 4 \cdot 6}\dfrac{x^7}{7} + \cdots$.

9. $-\dfrac{x^2}{2}-\dfrac{x^4}{12}-\dfrac{x^6}{45}-\dfrac{17x^8}{2520}-\cdots.$

11. $(2/2!)x^2-(2^3/4!)x^4+(2^5/6!)x^6-(2^7/7!)x^8+\cdots.$

13. $C+x-\dfrac{x^5}{5\cdot 2!}+\dfrac{x^9}{9\cdot 4!}-\dfrac{x^{13}}{13\cdot 6!}+\cdots.$

15. $C+\ln|x|-\dfrac{x^2}{2\cdot 2!}+\dfrac{x^4}{4\cdot 4!}-\dfrac{x^6}{6\cdot 6!}+\cdots.$

17. $C+x+\dfrac{1}{2}\dfrac{x^4}{4}-\dfrac{1}{2^2\cdot 2!}\dfrac{x^7}{7}+\dfrac{1\cdot 3}{2^3\cdot 3!}\dfrac{x^{10}}{10}-\dfrac{1\cdot 3\cdot 5}{2^4\cdot 4!}\dfrac{x^{13}}{13}+\cdots.$ **19.** 1. **21.** 1.

Chapter 20

Section 20.1, page 503

1. $5\sqrt{2}$. **3.** 5. **5.** $\sqrt{131}$. **7.** 5. **9.** 9. **11.** $(-2, 1, 2)$.
13. $(1, 2, 2)$. **15.** $(-9, 7, -1)$. **17.** $(1, 1, 5)$. **19.** $(1, 3, 3/2)$.
21. $(8, 4, -6)$. **23.** $(-2, 4, -3)$. **25.** $5, -3$. **27.** ± 5. **29.** $-11, -5$.

Section 20.3, page 509

1. 84°, 64°, 27°. **3.** 103°, 116°, 29°. **5.** 35°, 35°, 35°. **7.** $\{-4, 2, 4\}$.
9. $\{2, 2, -2\}$. **11.** $\{5, 1, -2\}$. **13.** $(3, 8, 1), (4, 13, 3)$. **15.** $(3, 4, 5), (5, 5, 7)$.
17. $(5, 3, -2), (9, 3, -3)$. **19.** x axis: $\{0°, 90°, 90°\}$, $\{1, 0, 0\}$. **21.** Parallel.
23. Perpendicular. **25.** Coincident. **27.** None. **29.** Perpendicular.

Section 20.4, page 514

1. $x=5+3t,\ y=1-2t,\ z=3+4t;\ \dfrac{x-5}{3}=\dfrac{y-1}{-2}=\dfrac{z-3}{4}.$

3. $x=5+4t,\ y=-2+t,\ z=1-2t;\ \dfrac{x-5}{4}=\dfrac{y+2}{1}=\dfrac{z-1}{-2}.$

5. $x=1+2t,\ y=1,\ z=1+t;\ \dfrac{x-1}{2}=\dfrac{z-1}{1},\ y=1.$

7. $x=4,\ y=4,\ z=1+t;\ x=4,\ y=4.$

9. $x=4+2t,\ y=-3t,\ z=5+4t;\ \dfrac{x-4}{2}=\dfrac{y}{-3}=\dfrac{z-5}{4}.$

11. $x = 8 + 5t,\ y = 4 + 2t,\ z = 1 - t;\ \dfrac{x-8}{5} = \dfrac{y-4}{2} = \dfrac{z-1}{-1}$.
13. $x = 5,\ y = 1 + t,\ z = 3 + t;\ x = 5,\ y - 1 = z - 3$.
15. $x = 1,\ y = -2 + t,\ z = 3;\ x = 1,\ z = 3$. **17.** Do not intersect.
19. Do not intersect. **21.** The lines are identical. **23.** $(2, 1, -1)$.
25. Perpendicular. **27.** None. **29.** Parallel.

Section 20.5, page 519

1. $6/\sqrt{14}$.

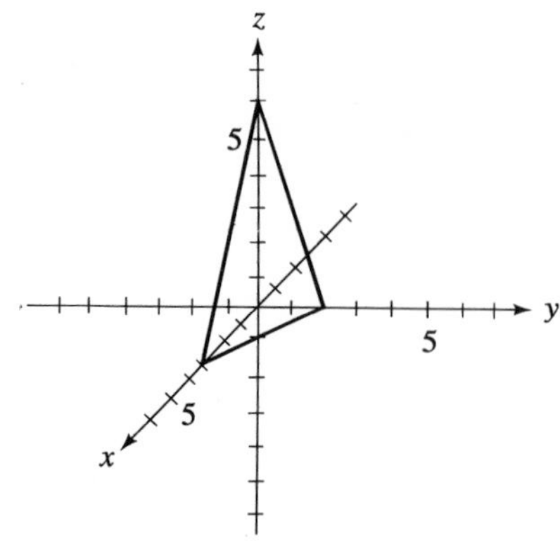

3. $4/\sqrt{21}$.

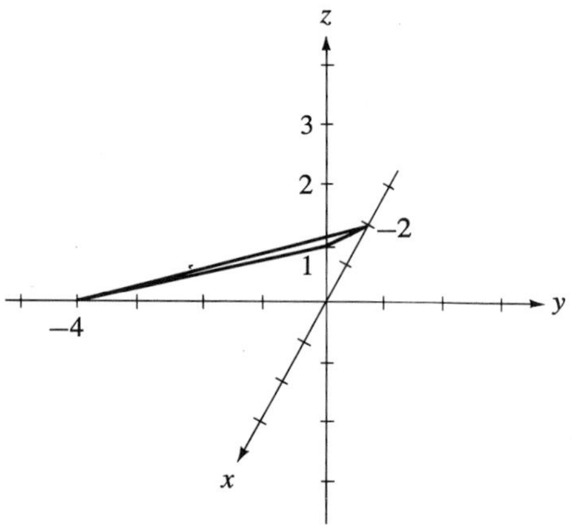

5. $3/\sqrt{5}$.

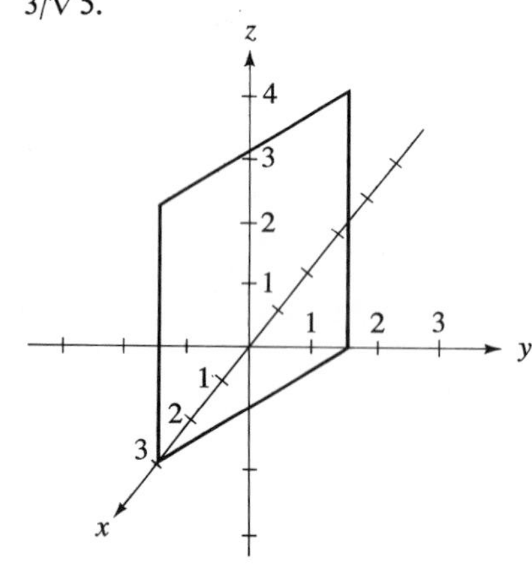

7. 7.
9. $11/2\sqrt{26}$.
11. $\sqrt{5}$.
13. $3x - y - 2z - 17 = 0$.
15. $3x - 4y + 2z + 9 = 0$.
17. $3x + y - 4z \pm 4 = 0$.
19. $2x + y - z - 4 \pm 2\sqrt{6} = 0$.
21. $x + y - 5 = 0$.
23. $3x + 5y + z - 23 = 0$.
25. $2x + y - 9 = 0$.
27. $x + 5y + 3z - 26 = 0$.
29. $3x - 7y - 5z + 22 = 0$.
31. $\sqrt{173}$.
33. $5\sqrt{2}$.
35. $8\sqrt{65}$.
37. $\sqrt{21}/3$.

Section 20.6, page 524

1. 5/2. **3.** 0. **5.** 0. **7.** $1/\sqrt{2}$. **9.** 2, −5/2. **11.** 52°. **13.** 80°.
15. 34°. **17.** 48°. **19.** None. **21.** Perpendicular. **23.** None.
25. Parallel. **27.** Perpendicular.

Section 20.7, page 528

1.

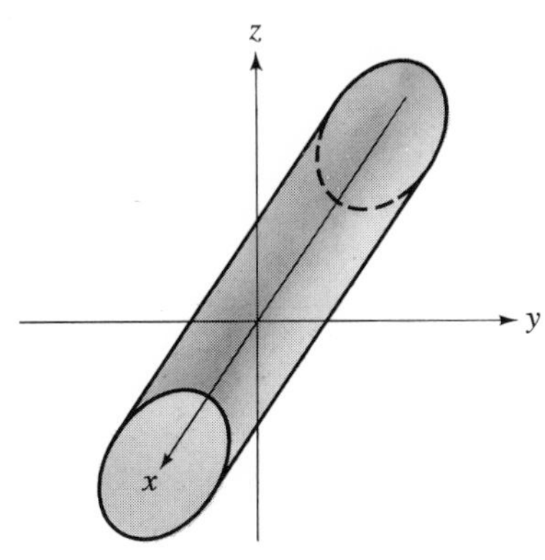

3.

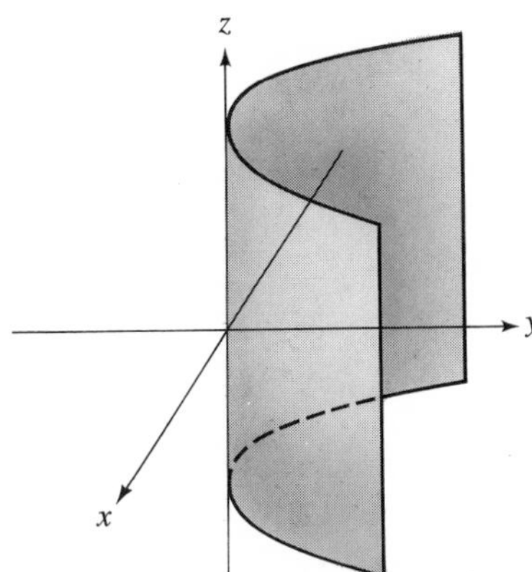

5.

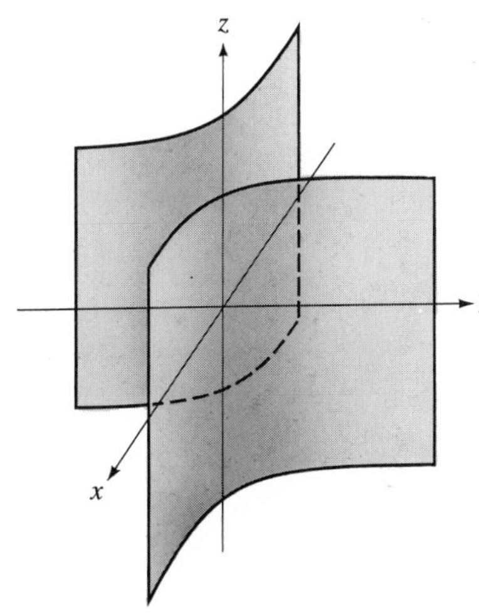

7.

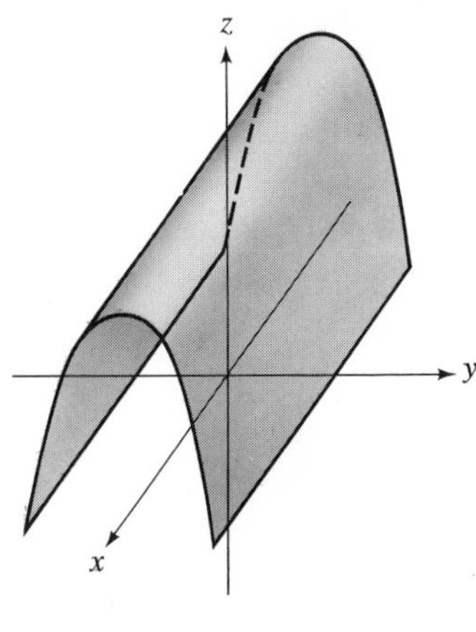

9.

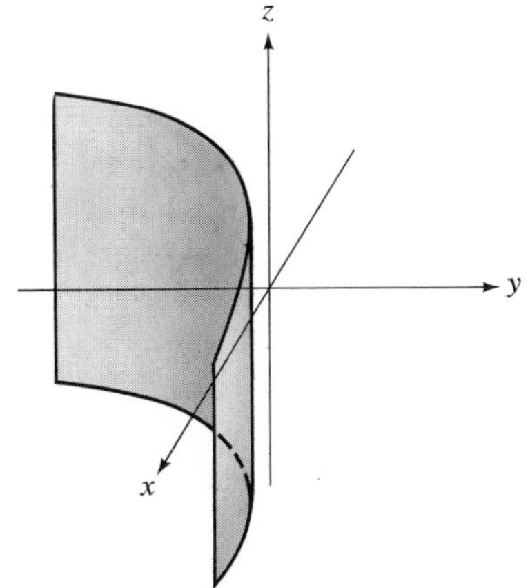

11. Sphere: (1, 0, −2), 3.

13. No locus.

15. Sphere: (−1/2, 3/2, 1), 2.

17. Sphere: (1/3, −1/3, −2/3), $2\sqrt{2}/3$.

19. Point: (1, 1/2, −2).

21. $x^2 + y^2 + z^2 - 8x - 2y + 4z + 12 = 0$.

23. $x^2 + y^2 + z^2 - 4x - 8y - 14z + 65 = 0$.

25. $x^2 + y^2 + z^2 + (-6k + 8l - 6)x - 2ky - 2lz + 10k^2 - 24kl + 17l^2 + 18k - 24l - 17 = 0$ (for any choice of k and l). **27.** $x^2 + y^2 + z^2 - 27x + 35y - 62z - 28 = 0$.

Section 20.8, page 532

1. Ellipsoid.

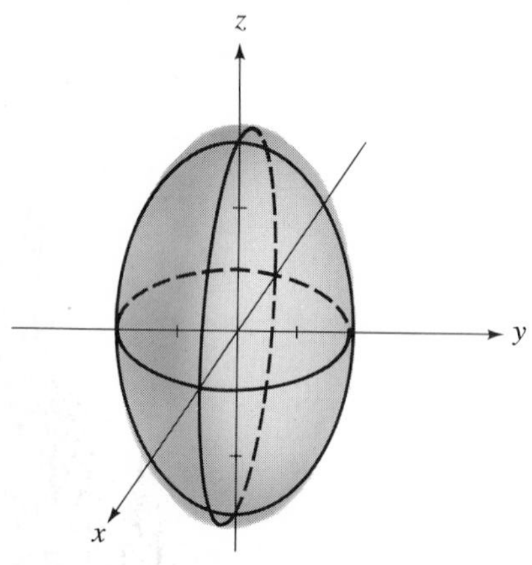

3. Circular paraboloid.

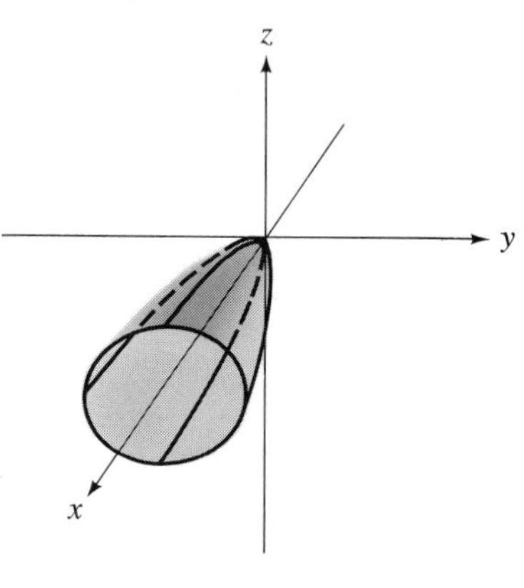

5. Circular cone.

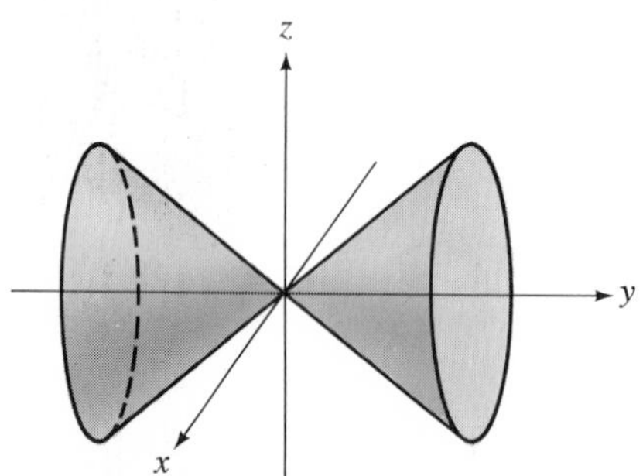

7. Circular paraboloid.

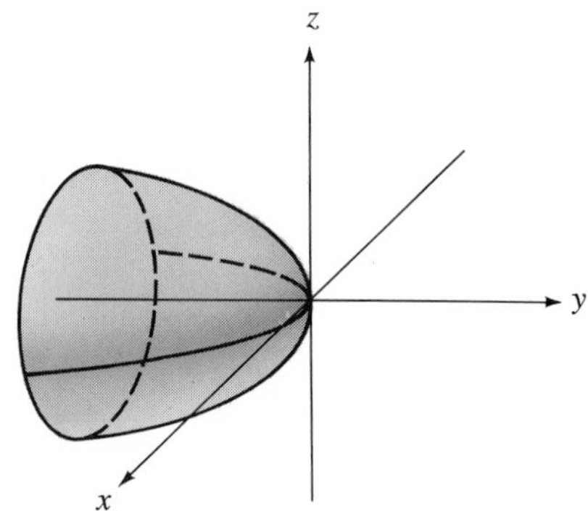

9. Hyperboloid of two sheets.

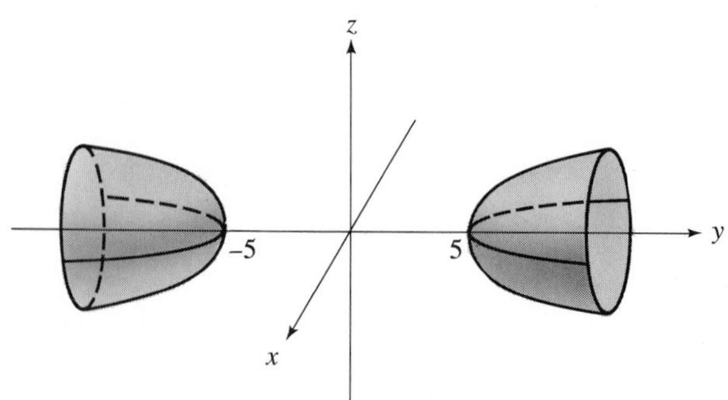

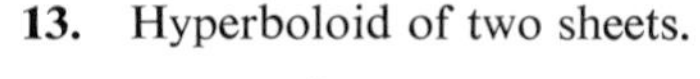

11. Hyperbolic paraboloid.

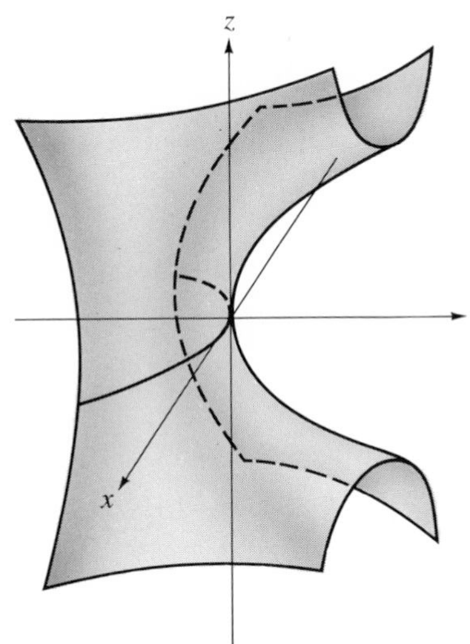

13. Hyperboloid of two sheets.

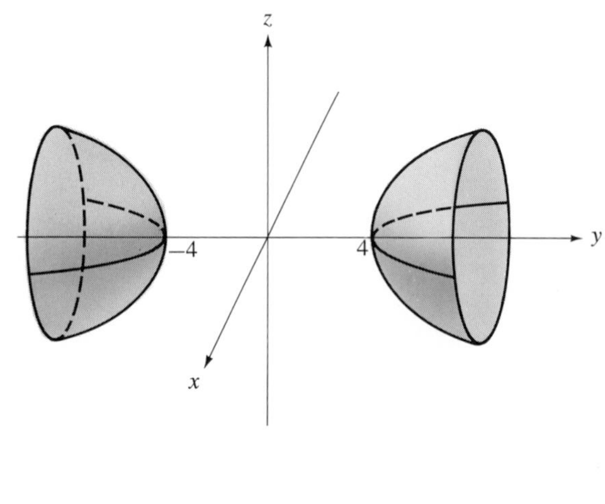

15. Circular cone.

17. Hyperboloid of two sheets.

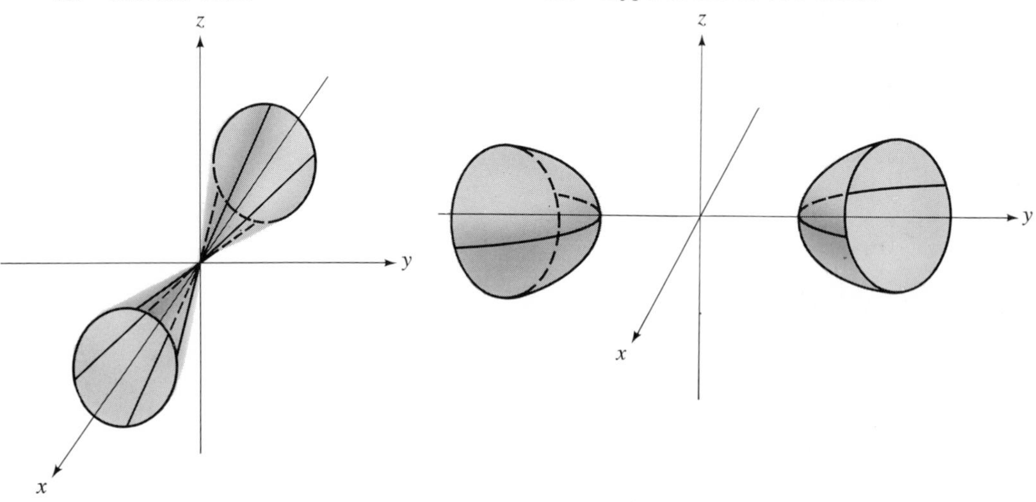

19. Hyperboloid of one sheet.

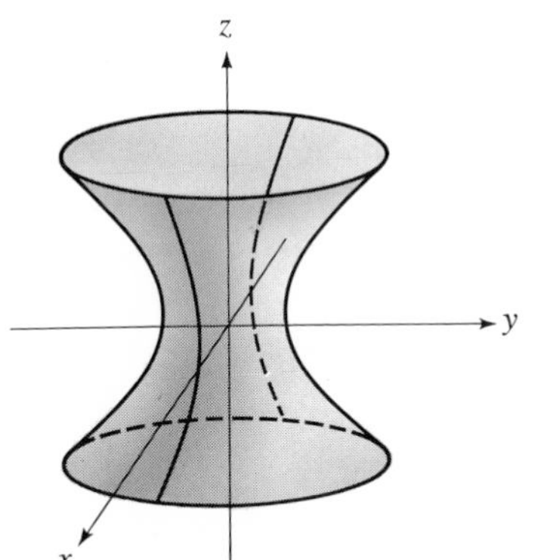

21. Hyperbolic paraboloid.

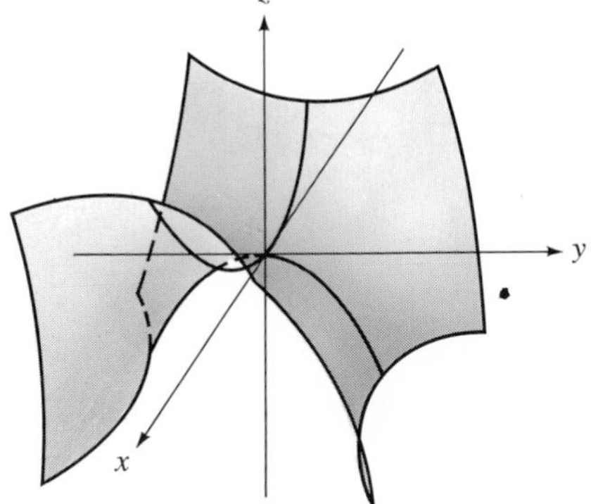

23. Circular cone. **25.** Hyperboloid of one sheet.

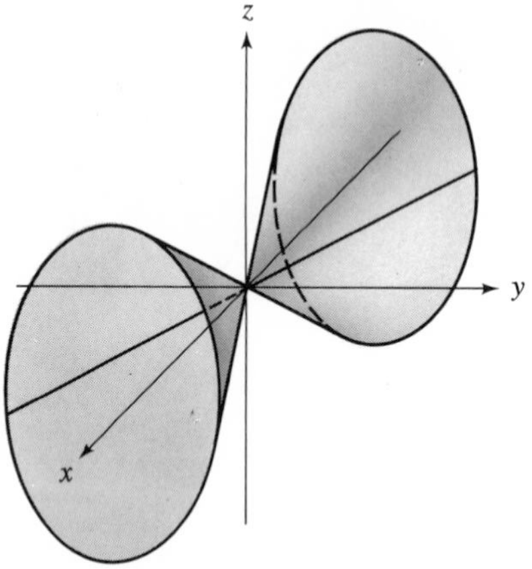

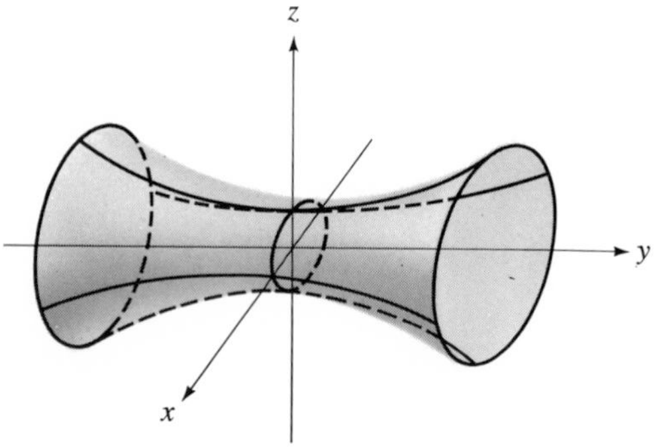

Section 20.9, page 535

1. **(a)** $(\sqrt{2}, \sqrt{2}, 1)$, **(b)** $(-3/2, 3\sqrt{3}/2, -2)$. **2.** **(a)** $(\sqrt{2}, 45°, 3)$, **(b)** $(2, 90°, -2)$.
3. **(a)** $(3/2\sqrt{2}, 3/2\sqrt{2}, 3\sqrt{3}/2)$, **(b)** $(0, 0, 1)$.
4. **(a)** $(2\sqrt{2}, 45°, 90°)$, **(b)** $(3, \text{Arccos}(2/\sqrt{5}), \text{Arccos}(-2/3))$.
5. **(a)** $(5, 30°, \text{Arccos}(4/5))$, **(b)** $(2\sqrt{2}, \pi/4, 3\pi/4)$.
6. **(a)** $(2, 45°, 2\sqrt{3})$, **(b)** $(2, 2\pi/3, 0)$. **7.** $r = 2, \rho \sin \varphi = 2$.
9. $r^2 = z, \rho = \csc \varphi \cot \varphi$. **11.** $r^2 \cos 2\theta - z^2 = 1, \rho^2(\sin^2 \varphi \cos 2\theta - \cos^2 \varphi) = 1$.
13. $r^2 - z^2 = 1, \rho^2 = -\sec 2\theta$. **15.** $z = 2xy$. **17.** $z = x^2 + y^2$. **19.** $xy = z$.
21. $x^2 + y^2 + z^2 - x = 0$.

Chapter 21

Section 21.1, page 542

1. $-6\mathbf{i} - 2\mathbf{j}$. **3.** $7\mathbf{i} + \mathbf{j}$. **5.** $-\mathbf{i} + 5\mathbf{j} - 4\mathbf{k}$. **7.** $4\mathbf{i} - 3\mathbf{j} - 2\mathbf{k}$.
9. $(1/\sqrt{10})\mathbf{i} - (1/\sqrt{10})\mathbf{j}$. **11.** $-(1/\sqrt{5})\mathbf{i} + (2/\sqrt{5})\mathbf{j}$.
13. $(1/\sqrt{6})\mathbf{i} + (2/\sqrt{6})\mathbf{j} - (1/\sqrt{6})\mathbf{k}$. **15.** $-(1/\sqrt{14})\mathbf{i} + (2/\sqrt{14})\mathbf{j} - (3/\sqrt{14})\mathbf{k}$.
17. $B = (4, 3)$. **19.** $A = (5, 0)$. **21.** $A = (5/2, -3/2), B = (11/2, 7/2)$.
23. $B = (6, 0, 4)$. **25.** $A = (1, 3, -3)$. **27.** $A = (3/2, -1/2, 5/2), B = (5/2, 1/2, 7/2)$.

29. 4**i** + **j**.

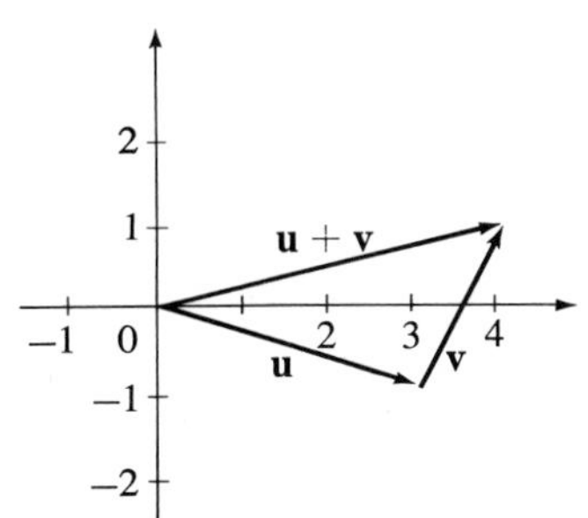

31. −**i** − 3**j**.

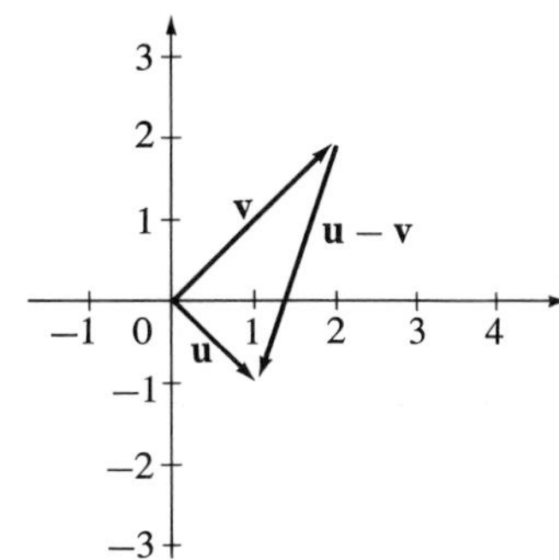

33. 4**i** − 2**j**.

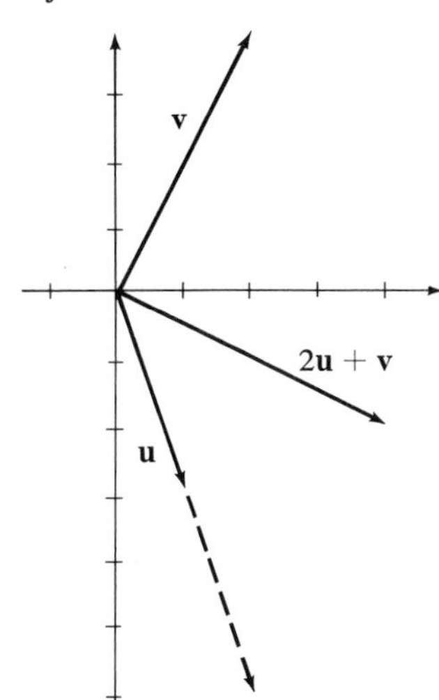

35. 5**i** − 3**j** + 3**k**, **i** + **j** + **k**.

37. 14**i** − 11**j** − **k**.

Section 21.2, page 547

1. Arccos $1/5\sqrt{2} = 82°$. **3.** 90°. **5.** 90°. **7.** Arccos $3/\sqrt{34} = 59°$.
9. 1, not orthogonal. **11.** 4, not orthogonal. **13.** 1, not orthogonal.
15. 0, orthogonal. **17.** (1/2)**i** + (1/2)**j**. **19.** −(6/5)**i** + (12/5)**j**.
21. **i** + (1/2)**j** + (1/2)**k**. **23.** (4/7)**i** − (2/7)**j** + (1/7)**k**. **25.** 3. **27.** −1/2.
29. $4 \pm 2\sqrt{3}$. **31.** −9. **33.** None. **35.** $-8 - \sqrt{70}$.
37. −(2/17)**i** − (8/17)**j**, −(19/17)**i** − (76/17)**j**.
39. (1/14)**i** + (1/7)**j** + (3/14)**k**, (15/14)**i** + (15/7)**j** + (45/14)**k**.

Section 21.3, page 551

1. −5**i** + 5**j** + 5**k**. **3.** 2**i** + **j** + 7**k**. **5.** −**i** − **j** + 3**k**. **7.** $x - y = 3$.
9. $x + y - z = 5$. **11.** $8x + 5y - 9z = 27$. **13.** $x - 3y - 5z + 8 = 0$.
15. $x + 3y - z = 1$. **17.** $y + z = 4$. **19.** $x - 4y + 11z = 13$.

21. $x = 3 - t, y = 1 + 5t, z = 4 + 3t$. **23.** $x = 2 + 4t, y = -2t, z = 5 - 7t$.
25. $24/\sqrt{30}$. **27.** $113/\sqrt{542}$. **29.** $|Ax_1 + By_1 + Cz_1 + D|/\sqrt{A^2 + B^2 + C^2}$.
31. $\sqrt{179}/2$. **33.** $\sqrt{341}/2$.

Section 21.4, page 553

1.

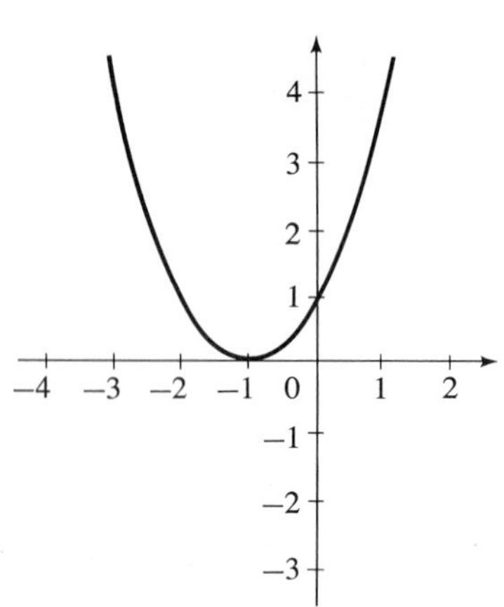

3.

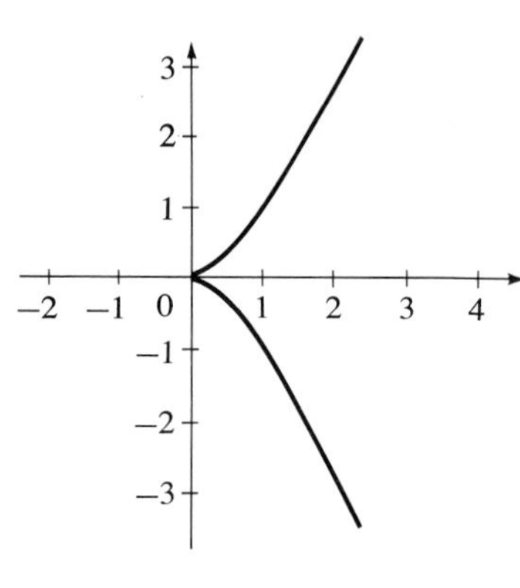

5.

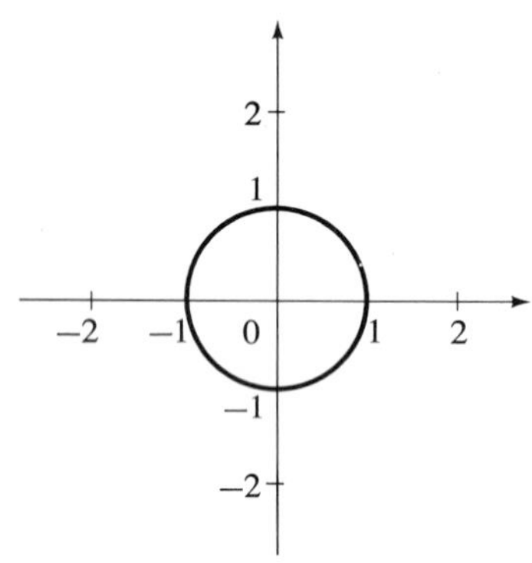

7.

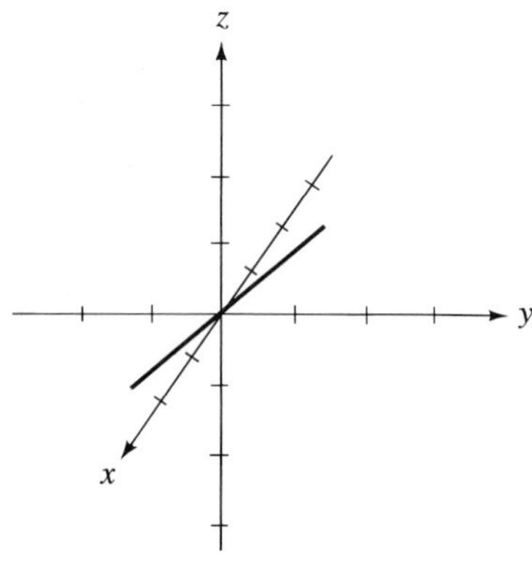

9.

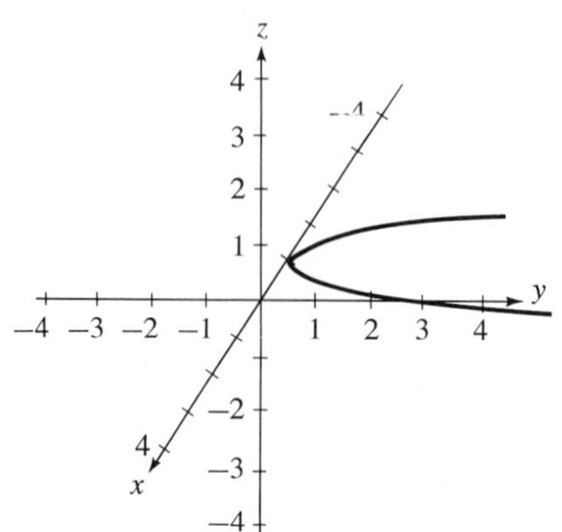

11. **i** + 3**j**.

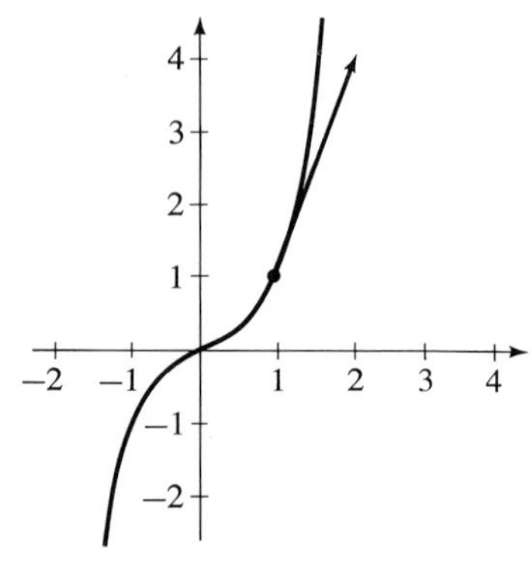

13. $\mathbf{i} + 4\mathbf{j}$.

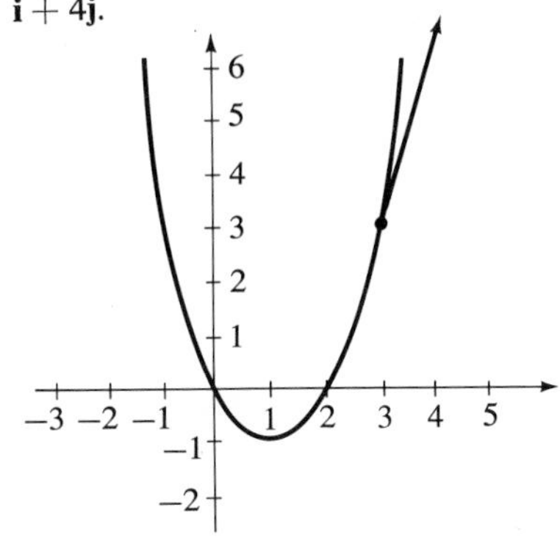

15. $\mathbf{i} + 2\mathbf{j} + 2\mathbf{k}$.

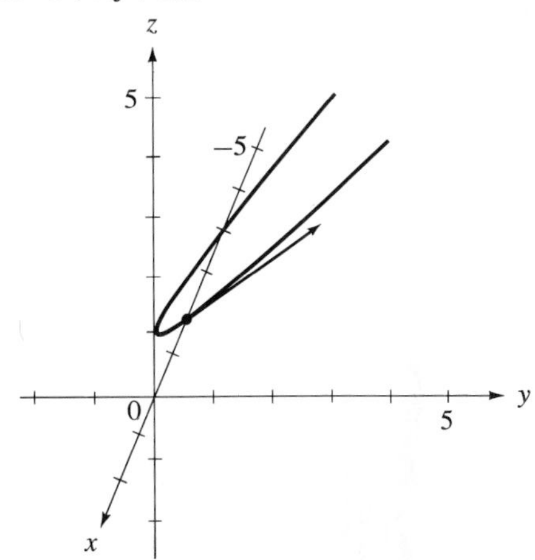

17. $\mathbf{i} + 2t\mathbf{j}$, $2\mathbf{j}$. **19.** $2t\mathbf{j} + 3t^2\mathbf{j}$, $2\mathbf{i} + 6t\mathbf{j}$. **21.** $-\sin t\,\mathbf{i} + \cos t\,\mathbf{j}$, $-\cos t\,\mathbf{i} - \sin t\,\mathbf{j}$.
23. $\mathbf{i} + 2t\mathbf{j} - 3t^2\mathbf{k}$, $2\mathbf{j} - 6t\mathbf{k}$. **25.** $2t\mathbf{i} + 3t^2\mathbf{j} + 4t^3\mathbf{k}$, $2\mathbf{i} + 6t\mathbf{j} + 12t^2\mathbf{k}$.
27. $1/t\,\mathbf{i} - 1/t^2\mathbf{j} - 2/t^3\mathbf{k}$, $-1/t^2\mathbf{i} + 2/t^3\mathbf{j} + 6/t^4\mathbf{k}$. **29.** $12t^2$. **31.** $(t + e^{2t})/\sqrt{t^2 + e^{2t}}$.

Section 21.5, page 557

1. $\mathbf{i} + 2\mathbf{j}$, $2\mathbf{j}$, $\sqrt{5}$, $4/\sqrt{5}$.

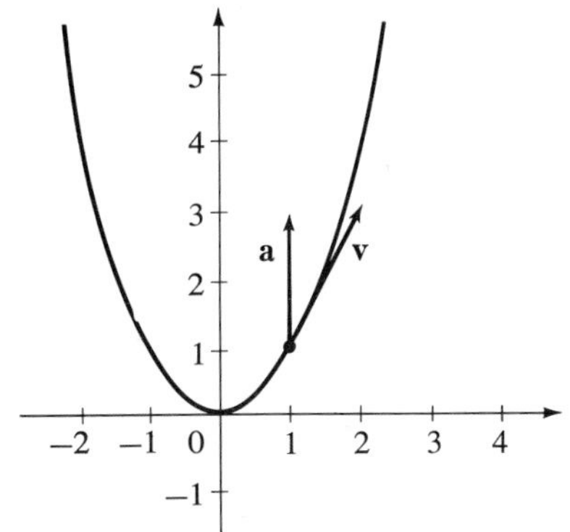

3. $2\mathbf{i} + 2\mathbf{j}$, $2\mathbf{i} + 2\mathbf{j}$, $2\sqrt{2}$, $2\sqrt{2}$.

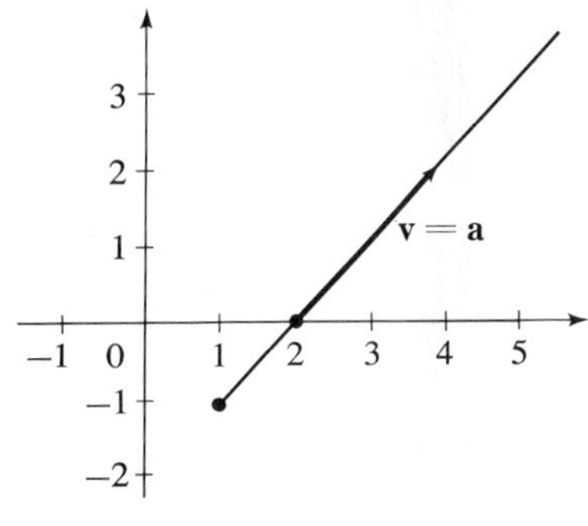

5. $\mathbf{i} + 3\mathbf{j}$, $6\mathbf{j}$, $\sqrt{10}$, $18/\sqrt{10}$.

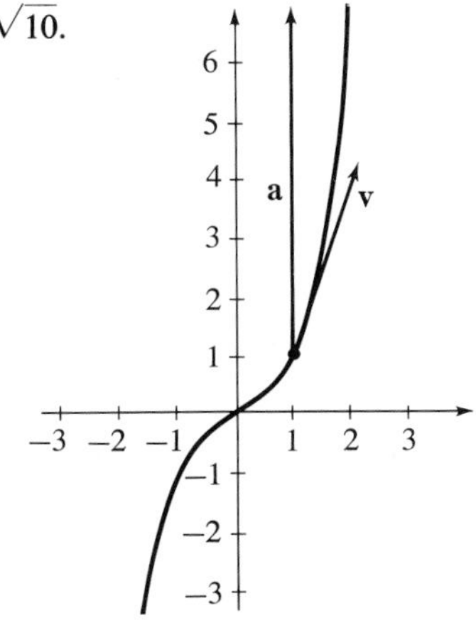

7. $-2\mathbf{i} - 4\mathbf{j}$, $2\mathbf{i} + 12\mathbf{j}$, $2\sqrt{5}$, $-26/\sqrt{5}$.

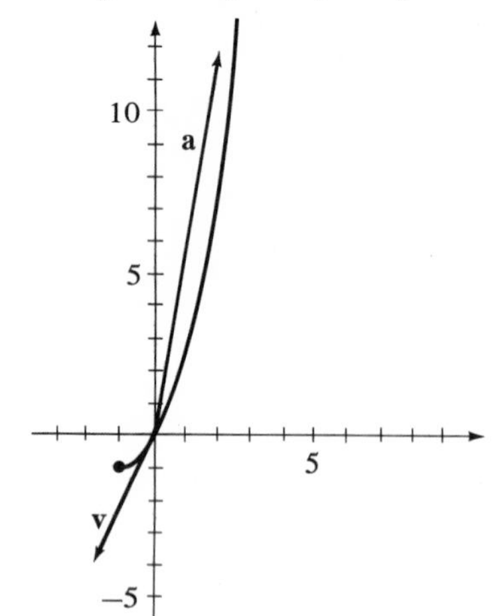

9. $\mathbf{i} - \mathbf{j}$, $2\mathbf{j}$, $\sqrt{2}$, $-\sqrt{2}$.

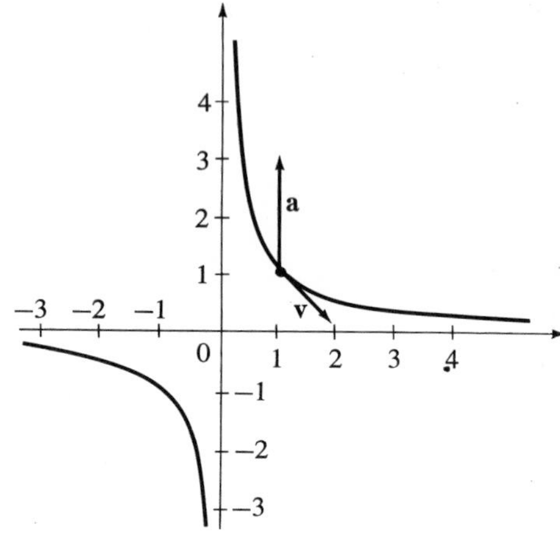

11. $-2\mathbf{j}$, $4\mathbf{i}$, 2, 0.

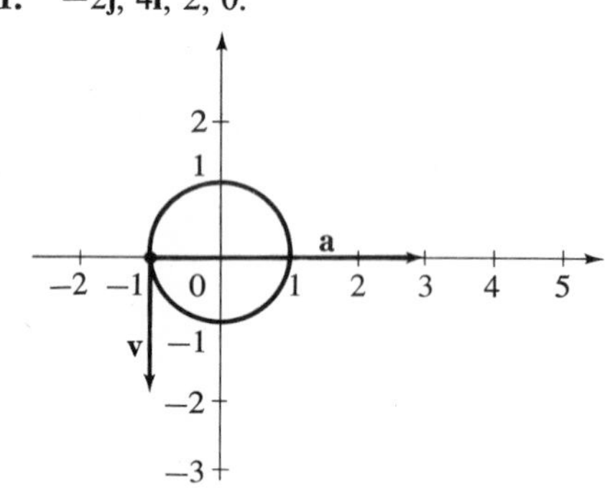

13. $\mathbf{i} + e\mathbf{j}$, $e\mathbf{j}$, $\sqrt{1+e^2}$, $e^2/\sqrt{1+e^2}$.

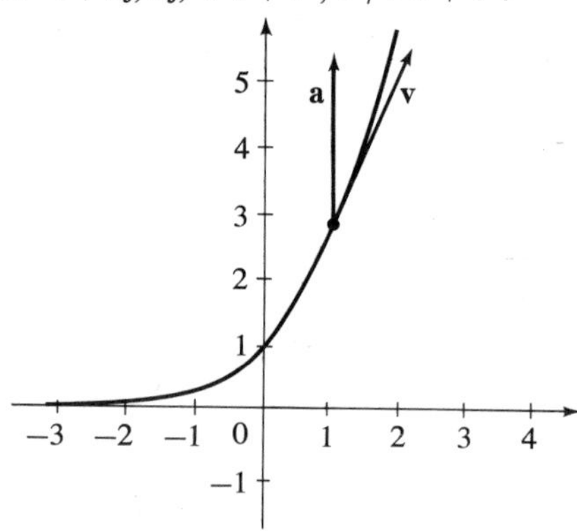

15. $\mathbf{i} - \mathbf{j} + 2t\mathbf{k}$, $2\mathbf{k}$, $\sqrt{2+4t^2}$, $4t/\sqrt{2+4t^2}$.
17. $2t\mathbf{i} - \mathbf{j} + \mathbf{k}$, $2\mathbf{i}$, $\sqrt{4t^2+2}$, $4t/\sqrt{4t^2+2}$.
19. $-\sin t\,\mathbf{i} + \cos t\,\mathbf{j} + \mathbf{k}$, $-\cos t\,\mathbf{i} - \sin t\,\mathbf{j}$, $\sqrt{2}$, 0.
21. $-1/t^2\mathbf{i} + \sqrt{2}\mathbf{j} + t^2\mathbf{k}$, $2/t^3\mathbf{i} + 2t\mathbf{k}$, $1/t^2 + t^2$, $-2/t^3 + 2t$.

Chapter 22

Section 22.2, page 563

1. $2x, 2y$. 3. $1/y, -x/y^2$. 5. $y/2\sqrt{xy}, x/2\sqrt{xy}$. 7. $3(x-2y)^2, -6(x-2y)^2$.
9. $-4xy^2/(x^2-y^2)^2, 4x^2y/(x^2-y^2)^2$. 11. $2x/(x^2+y^2), 2y/(x^2+y^2)$.
13. $\sin y e^{x \sin y}, x \cos y e^{x \sin y}$. 15. 2, −2. 17. −1, −1. 19. 1, 0.
21. $1, \pi$. 23. yz, xz, xy. 25. $2xy^2, 2x^2y + 3y^2 + 2yz^2, 2y^2z$.
27. $2x, 2y, 0$. 29. $6x - 6y, -6x, -6x, 6y$.
31. $6/(x+y)^4, 6/(x+y)^4, 6/(x+y)^4, 6(x+y)^4$.

33. $e^x \tan y,\ e^x \sec^2 y,\ e^x \sec^2 y,\ 2e^x \sec^2 y \tan y.$

35. $-\dfrac{\sin x}{y},\ -\dfrac{\cos x}{y^2},\ -\dfrac{\cos x}{y^2},\ \dfrac{2\sin x}{y^3}.$

Section 22.3, page 568

1. $2y + x\cos t.$ **3.** $(yt\cos t + y\sin t + x\sin t)/y^2.$ **5.** $2x + 2y + 2z.$
7. $(2xy + z^2)\cos t - (x^2 + 2yz)\sin t + (y^2 + 2zx)\sec^2 t.$ **9.** $4(x + y)u,\ 4(x - y)v.$
11. $2uy + (x/v),\ 2vy - (ux/v^2).$ **13.** $4xu + 4yu + 2zv,\ 4xv - 4yv + 2zu.$
15. $2\sin v + 3v\cos u - \cos u \sin v,\ 2u\cos v + 3\sin u - \sin u\cos v.$
17. $yzuv + (xz/u),\ yztv - (xzt/u^2) + (xy/v),\ yztu - (xyu/v^2).$
19. $yt + x + (w/t) + z,\ ys + x - (ws/t^2) - z.$ **21.** $2x + 2y(x\cos x + \sin x).$
23. $2 - xe^x - e^x.$ **25.** $(\partial z/\partial x)\cos\theta + (\partial z/\partial y)\sin\theta,\ -(\partial z/\partial x)r\sin\theta + (\partial z/\partial y)r\cos\theta.$
27. $(\partial w/\partial x)\sin\varphi\cos\theta + (\partial w/\partial y)\sin\varphi\sin\theta + (\partial w/\partial z)\cos\varphi,\ (\partial w/\partial x)\rho\cos\varphi\cos\theta$ $+ (\partial w/\partial y)\rho\cos\varphi\sin\theta - (\partial w/\partial z)\rho\sin\varphi,\ -(\partial w/\partial x)\rho\sin\varphi\sin\theta + (\partial w/\partial y)\rho\sin\varphi\cos\theta.$

Section 22.4, page 576

1. $\dfrac{x^2 - 2xy}{x^2 - y^2}.$ **3.** $-\dfrac{2\sqrt{xy} + y}{2\sqrt{xy} + x}.$ **5.** $-\dfrac{y\cos xy + 1}{x\cos xy}.$ **7.** $-x/y,\ -z/y.$

9. $-\dfrac{x + y}{y + z},\ -\dfrac{x + z}{y + z}.$ **11.** $-\dfrac{x\cos xy + z\cos yz}{y\cos xy},\ -\dfrac{\cos yz}{\cos xy}.$

13. $-x/2z.$ **15.** $2u,\ -2v.$ **17.** $\dfrac{x - z}{z - y}.$ **19.** $\dfrac{y - z}{-2z + x}.$ **21.** $2x.$ **23.** $-2z.$

25. $-\dfrac{y(xz^2 + w^2z + wx^2 - wz^2 - w^2x - x^2z)}{x(yz^2 + w^2z + wy^2 - wz^2 - w^2y - zy^2)}.$ **27.** 0. **29.** $\dfrac{1 + 2z}{5y}.$

Section 22.6, page 579

1. $3x^2\,dx - 3y^2\,dy.$ **3.** $(2xy + y^2)\,dx + (x^2 + 2xy)\,dy.$
5. $(1 + ye^{xy})\,dx + (1 + xe^{xy})\,dy.$ **7.** $-(1/x^2)\,dx - (1/y^2)\,dy.$
9. $2x\,dx + 2y\,dy + 2z\,dz.$ **11.** $\sin y\,dx + (x\cos y + \sin z)\,dy + y\cos z\,dz.$
13. $ye^{xy}\,dx + (xe^{xy} + z\cos yz)\,dy + y\cos yz\,dz.$ **15.** $2(x\,dx + z\,dy + y\,dz + w\,dw).$
17. $156.0 \pm 3.5.$ **19.** 0.54. **21.** $7.21 \pm 0.03.$ **23.** 0.81.

Section 22.7, page 585

1. $\dfrac{3x + y}{\sqrt{2}}.$ **3.** $-\dfrac{x + y}{\sqrt{2}y^2}.$ **5.** $\dfrac{3\sqrt{2}x^2 - 1}{\sqrt{3}}.$ **7.** $x + y - \sqrt{2}z.$

9. $\dfrac{2 + 2y - 3\sqrt{5}z^2}{\sqrt{10}}.$ **11.** $(1/2) + 2\sqrt{3}.$ **13.** $14/\sqrt{13}.$ **15.** $2 + 3\sqrt{3}.$

17. $12/\sqrt{14}.$ **19.** $1/\sqrt{3}.$ **21.** $\sqrt{4x^2 + 1},\ \dfrac{2x\mathbf{i} - \mathbf{j}}{\sqrt{4x^2 + 1}}.$

23. $\sqrt{9x^4 + 4y^2},\ \dfrac{3x^2\mathbf{i} - 2y\mathbf{j}}{\sqrt{9x^4 + 4y^2}}.$ **25.** $2\sqrt{w},\ \dfrac{x\mathbf{i} + y\mathbf{j} + z\mathbf{k}}{\sqrt{w}}.$ **27.** $4\sqrt{2},\ \dfrac{\mathbf{i} - \mathbf{j}}{\sqrt{2}}.$

29. $3,\ \mathbf{j}.$ **31.** $36°,\ -4\mathbf{i} - 9\mathbf{j}.$

Section 22.9, page 592

1. $4x - 2y - z - 3 = 0,\ \dfrac{x - 2}{4} = \dfrac{y - 1}{-2} = \dfrac{z - 3}{-1}.$

3. $x+4y-z-5=0, \dfrac{x-2}{1}=\dfrac{y-2}{4}=\dfrac{z-5}{-1}$.
5. $x+y+z-4=0, x-1=y-1=z-2$.
7. $3x-2y-z-1=0, \dfrac{x-1}{3}=\dfrac{y-1}{-2}=\dfrac{z}{-1}$.
9. $x+2y+2z-9=0, \dfrac{x-1}{1}=\dfrac{y-2}{2}=\dfrac{z-2}{2}$.
11. $2x+3y-3z-4=0, \dfrac{x-2}{2}=\dfrac{y-3}{3}=\dfrac{z-3}{-3}$.
13. $x+y+z-4=0, x-1=y-2=z-1$.
15. $x-2y-4z+5=0, \dfrac{x-5}{1}=\dfrac{y-1}{-2}=\dfrac{z-2}{-4}$.
17. $x=1, y=t, z=t$. 19. $x=0, y=1+t, z=-1+t$.
21. $x=1+3t, y=1+2t, z=1-t$. 23. $x=2\pi+1+2t, y=-t, z=-1$.

Section 22.10, page 595

1. (1, −2, −7) rel min. 3. (−1, 1, 0) neither. 5. (1, −2, 4) neither.
7. (0, 0, 0) neither; (−1, −1, 1) rel max.
9. (−1/3, −1, 32/27) neither, (1, −1, 0) rel min.
11. (0, 0, 0) neither, (0, 3, 0) neither, (3, 0, 0) neither, (1, 1, −1) rel min.
13. (0, 1, 0) rel min. 15. (1/2, 4, 6) rel min. 17. $x=10, y=10, z=5$.
19. $16/\sqrt{3}$. 21. (1/3, 10/3, 11/3). 23. 32/27.

Section 22.11, page 599

1. $2\sqrt{3}$. 3. $1/3\sqrt{3}$. 5. 2/41. 7. 1/27. 9. $2/3\sqrt{3}$. 11. 8.
13. 8/7. 15. 4. 17. (0, 0, 2). 19. $16/\sqrt{3}$. 21. 4/27.

Chapter 23

Section 23.1, page 606

1. 1/8. 3. 1/30. 5. 3/2.

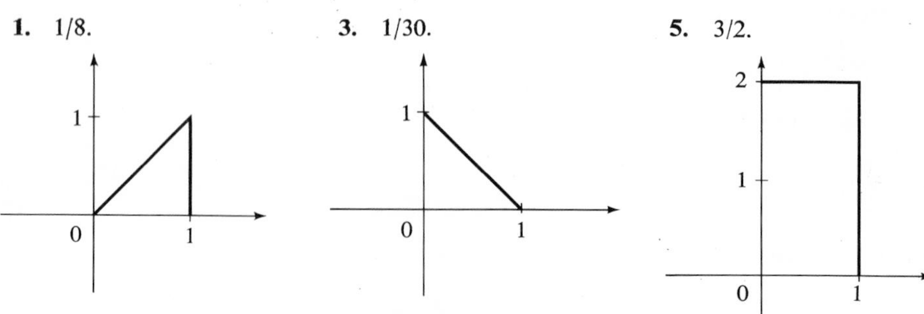

7. 9/8.

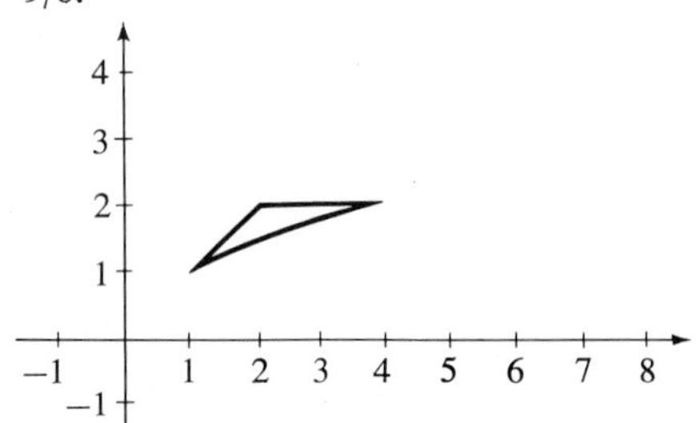

9. 4.

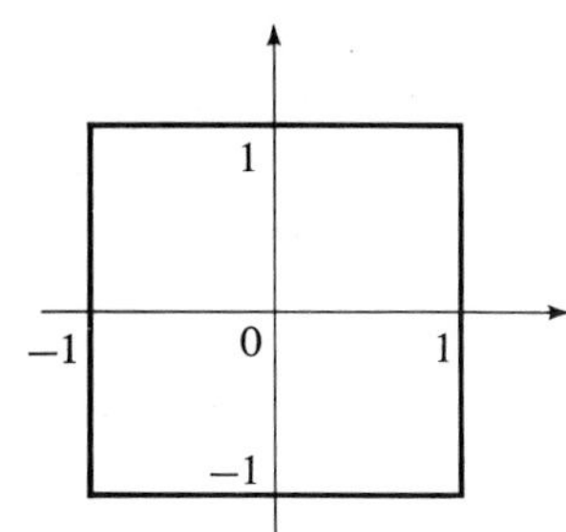

11. 88/105.

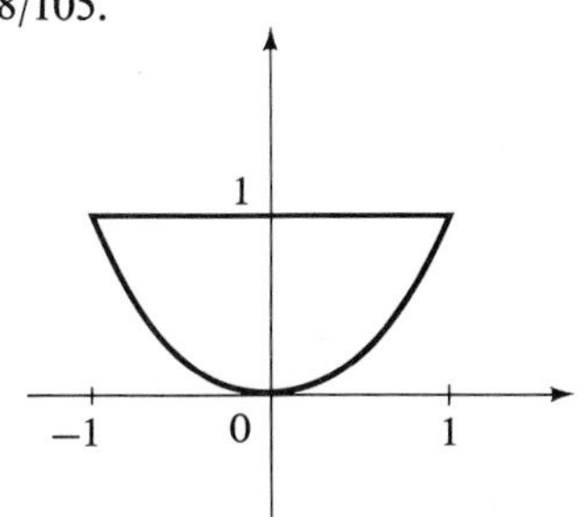

13. $(e^4 - 2e^3 + 2e - 1)/2e^2$.

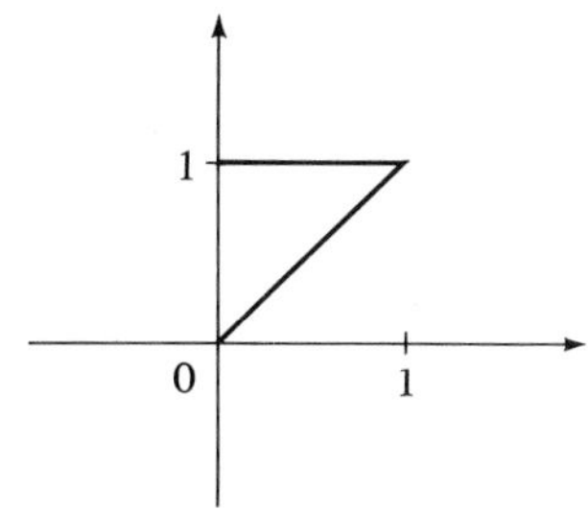

15. −1/6. **17.** −45/364. **19.** 45/8. **21.** 1/24 **23.** 488/3.

Section 23.2, page 611

1. $(4/3)\pi R^3$. **3.** 1/6. **5.** 16/3. **7.** 44/3. **9.** 1/90. **11.** $32\sqrt{2}/15$.
13. 16/3. **15.** 1/4. **17.** 1/6. **19.** 2. **21.** 1/16. **23.** 416/15.
25. 160/3. **27.** 1.

Section 23.3, page 614

1. $3\pi/4$. **3.** $5\pi/3$. **5.** $11\pi/16$. **7.** 8/9. **9.** $5\pi/3$. **11.** $\pi/16$.
13. 4/3. **15.** $7\pi/12$. **17.** 4π. **19.** $4\pi(27 - 16\sqrt{2})/3$. **21.** $\pi(2 - \sqrt{2})/3$.
23. 64/9.

Section 23.4, page 620

1. (6/7, 1/2). **3.** (6/13, 190/273). **5.** (287/384, 79/384).
7. (−1208/1071, 1903/765). **9.** 1/16, $\sqrt{3}/2$. **11.** 185/504, $5\sqrt{37}/3\sqrt{182}$.
13. 25/126, $5\sqrt{5}/3\sqrt{19}$. **15.** (0, 9/14, 23/28). **17.** (−1/8, −1/8, 35/32).
19. 1/30, $1\sqrt{5}$. **21.** 80/189, $5/3\sqrt{7}$.

Section 23.5, page 624

1. 6. **3.** 255/16. **5.** 1. **7.** 10. **9.** 6. **11.** 2π. **13.** $32\pi/3$.
15. 3/20. **17.** 1/8. **19.** 1/4. **21.** 2. **23.** 1/12.

Section 23.6, page 629

1. (2/3, 2/3, 2/3). **3.** (4/5, 4/5, 32/75). **5.** (0, 0, 2/3). **7.** (0, 0, 5/12).
9. 1/8, 1. **11.** 23/288, $\sqrt{23}/2\sqrt{3}$. **13.** 7/18, $\sqrt{7}/3\sqrt{2}$. **15.** 64/9, 4/3.

Appendix A

Section A.1, page 634

1. $x < -1$. **3.** $x < 3$. **5.** $x \leq -6$. **7.** $x > 5/2$. **9.** $x \geq 1$.
11. $-3 < x < 1$. **13.** $0 \leq x < 3/2$. **15.** $3 < x < 7$. **17.** $3/2 \leq x \leq 5$.
19. $2 < x < 3$. **21.** $-5 \leq x < 4$. **23.** $x > -1$.

Section A.2, page 635

1. 3, −7. **3.** 5/4, 3/4. **5.** 2. **7.** −4, 2/3. **9.** −5/2, −1/4. **11.** 1.
13. $-4 < x < -2$. **15.** $-3 < x < 0$. **17.** $1/2 \leq x \leq 9/2$. **19.** $x > 5$ or $x < 3$.
21. $x \geq 1$ or $x \leq -5/3$. **23.** $x = 2$. **25.** <1. **27.** $<2\delta$.

Section A.3, page 638

1. <5. **3.** <5. **5.** <629. **7.** <7. **9.** <28.

Index

Index

U

V

W

Z